ALOIS SENEFELDER

Portrait painted in 1829 by Professor Joseph Hauber.
The original painting is in the *Deutsches Museum*, Munich.
This illustration was reproduced in four-color lithography
by the Litho-Krome Company, Columbus, Georgia.

THE LITHOGRAPHERS MANUAL

Fourth Edition

THE

LITHOGRAPHERS

MANUAL

Fourth Edition

Edited by
CHARLES SHAPIRO

THE GRAPHIC ARTS TECHNICAL FOUNDATION, INC.

FORTY-SIX FIFTEEN FORBES AVENUE

PITTSBURGH, PENNSYLVANIA

Lithographed in the United States of America

Foreword

Printing has traced the progress of man since the dawn of written history. Whether the achievements of man were inscribed by wooden blocks as the Chinese did many centuries ago, or by web offset lithography as modern man does, it is sufficient to say that printing has travelled with man throughout the ages, recording for immortality his deeds, his thoughts, his discoveries and his hopes.

But much change has occurred. Where once lithographers laboriously handworked their process, today presses wind the recordings of man through its cylinders at 2,000 feet per minute. The jargon of our time contains words like *computerization, automatic film processing, flying paster, in-line* and others—each connoting a greater mechanization of the process; an improved ability to produce the recordings of man at less cost, with greater efficiency, and with finer quality than ever before.

While lithography is no "Johnny-come-lately" to the field of graphic processes, it can, I suppose, be considered a junior partner to wood-block printing, to copperplate etching, to woodcut engraving, or to letterpress. Nevertheless, lithography has been known since the late 18th century.

But, it is in the last five decades that lithography has taken its proper place with other commercial processes. Indeed, it is in the last decade that offset lithography has become the predominant process of our time.

In the midst of this drive to the forefront of graphic processes appeared the first edition of The Lithographers Manual, produced after nearly ten years of labor by Walter Soderstrom, that remarkable chronicler of the process.

The publication has, with this volume, undergone three revisions, each of these marking the ever-increasing technological change in the business of lithography. The date of these revisions alone evidences the rapidity with which change is occurring in lithography.

Mr. Soderstrom produced his first edition in 1937. The second edition occurred twenty years later—in 1957. The third edition was printed nine years later in 1966.

And now, only two years later, a fourth edition is being published. The tenor of our times is one of quick change, and this book reflects that fact. Several chapters of this edition have been revised to some extent—six considerably, and one completely—as a result of major changes which have occurred in just the last three years.

Further, these chapters have been authored by some of the most eminent and respected authorities in lithography. Their contributions reinforce the strength and validity of this publication.

The contents of this single volume comprise the most complete, up-to-date reference book on lithography which is available to the industry. Indeed, the material in the appendix includes several Research Progress Reports of the Graphic Arts Technical Foundation, which were published after the edition's revision was completed. But we included them in an effort to give the reader contemporary information.

As technology forces even more complex growth upon the business of lithography, there will continue a need for knowledge of the fundamentals of the process, a need to know the basic facts as well as up-to-date practices. This edition of *The Lithographers Manual* continues a strong and long tradition of providing both these elements—as much for the practiced craftsman as for the novice.

WILLIAM H. WEBBER
Executive Director
Graphic Arts Technical Foundation, Inc.

Editor's Preface

Fourth Edition

This edition carries forward Walter Soderstrom's and the Foundation's original pledge to keep The Lithographers Manual—a title of 30-odd years—as current as is physically and economically feasible.

Accomplishing a considerably revised Fourth Edition so soon after the third edition (1966) is due in large part to the unusual efforts on the part of many people. Special thanks are here expressed to: Jack Gerber, Education Department of GATF, for up-dating and interpolating the statistical data in Chapter One; John A. Burgess, Public Relations Director of GATF for bringing Chapter Two up to date; Frank M. Preucil, Radio Corporation of America and Zenon Elyjiw, Rochester Institute of Technology, both formerly with GATF, for the revisions of Chapters Six and Seven; Michael H. Bruno, International Paper Company, and also formerly with GATF, for the complete rewriting of Chapter Ten.

Practically all the staff members of the Foundation's Research, Technical and Education Departments were willingly at my beck and call as I constantly sought help and guidance. This was especially important with the revising of the Glossary, Bibliography, and List of Abstracted Periodicals. For his invaluable help with production problems, I am deeply grateful to William H. Smith, Assistant Director of GATF's Education Department.

A statement made in my preface to the Third Edition of this book bears repeating: "The reader is bound to find items which invoke critical comment. The author in question should not be blamed. The criticism should be first aimed at this editor because, in all likelihood, he chose the wrong point-in-view from among the many that may have been offered; or, he may have misinterpreted a suggestion."

Victor Strauss' editor's preface of the Twentieth Anniversary Edition of The Lithographers Manual has been included in this edition for its historical significance to this long-lived and vital publishing project.

CHARLES SHAPIRO
Publications Editor, GATF
August, 1968

Editor's Preface
to The Twentieth Anniversary Edition

When the LITHOGRAPHERS MANUAL was originally published twenty years ago, it represented the first attempt at a complete and unbiased presentation of modern lithography. A second edition—long out of print—added to the information contained in the first, and served many thousands all over the world as a source of reference. The publisher has been very often asked in the course of the last years to reprint this edition, but he decided that a complete revision of the LITHOGRAPHERS MANUAL was needed to do justice to the great changes that have occurred in the recent past.

The growth of lithography has been immense. During the last twenty years the number of wage earners has more than trebled, that of lithographic establishments has multiplied by six, and the dollar volume has increased approximately ten times! But the most significant aspect of this growth cannot be expressed in figures: it is the increased know-how in the industry and the eagerness for even more of it. This thirst for knowledge has propelled lithography into the front ranks of printing, this thirst for knowledge is the best guarantee for a continued future growth, this thirst for knowledge is the reason for the new LITHOGRAPHERS MANUAL.

EDITORIAL POLICY OF THE LITHOGRAPHERS MANUAL

The first step in the development of the new LITHOGRAPHERS MANUAL consisted in making a careful study and analysis of the field and its needs. Based on this study the editorial concept and policy were formulated for the Twentieth Anniversary Edition of The LITHOGRAPHERS MANUAL. This policy was published in the summer of 1956; it has remained unchanged throughout the development of the work.

It seems appropriate to summarize here the main points of this policy: (1) The new level of lithographic technology would be fully reflected in the new LITHOGRAPHERS MANUAL. (2) The LITHOGRAPHERS MANUAL would not duplicate existing books, but on the contrary attempt to fill the gap left in lithographic literature. (3) The LITHOGRAPHERS MANUAL would provide concise information on all phases of lithography as well as on related subjects. (4) the LITHOGRAPHERS MANUAL was planned for the convenience of the reader and therefore divided according to areas of activity. (5) Each area of activity was presented in two divisions. Editorial studies, written by recognized authorities in their field, discuss the theory and practice pertaining to each specialized area. Resources presentations, prepared by manufacturers of available equipment and supplies, inform the reader on the variety of means available in the industry. (6) All information is as complete as possible; it is to-the-point, easy to read and interesting. (7) Wherever possible the written word is supplemented by illustrations.

It is not for the editor to say how successfully these points were executed. But the size of the finished LITHOGRAPHERS MANUAL—the fact that it required two large volumes to put the material in print—proves that this plan was quite interesting to very many people and companies, that this plan provided a workable basis for industry wide cooperation.

The presentation of resources—equipment, materials, and supplies—available to lithographers is an innovation in our literature and needs therefore a few explanatory words. The basic thought is rather simple. Every day brings new developments, every day new products appear on the market. These products are of course publicized by their manufacturers and reported in the trade press. But most people cannot find the time necessary for a critical reading of this material, they have no way of storing and classifying this information for the time when they need it. When the time when they need it does come, and it comes sooner or later in every lithographic business, a considerable effort must be made by the individuals concerned to gather the required material.

The resources sections of the new LITHOGHAPHERS MANUAL attempt to solve this problem. These resources sections may be considered as information on all existing machinery, equipment, materials, and supplies.

The manner in which resources presentations were developed may be of interest to the reader. It was the intention of editor and publisher alike to make the resources presentations as complete as possible. The editor invited the manufacturers of lithographic resources by individual letters to participate in this project. In order to make the project known to manufacturers who might have been overlooked, an advertisement was placed in the trade press. Every effort, including follow-up letters and telephone calls, was made to include all available information. *All resources presentations were of course printed free of charge, as a service to the whole industry.*

Manufacturers were asked to cover the following points in their descriptions: (1) Exact designation of item. (Illustrations or photographs were desirable.)

(2) Its specific purpose. (3) Its most distinctive characteristics. (4) Specifications containing pertinent data (size, weight, space occupied, for example). (5) How the product operates or is used. (6) If special skills are needed, which, and how they could be acquired. (7) Name and address of manufacturer. They were further invited to keep their descriptions plain and factual so that the reader, presumably a busy person, might grasp the essentials of the items described as fast as possible.

Even though many manufacturers responded with great enthusiasm, others did not cooperate. It may be assumed that the novelty of the project and the absence of precedents is the reason why some companies did not submit product presentations. It may further be assumed that these companies will be interested in having their products included in subsequent editions of the LITHOGRAPHERS MANUAL.

METHOD OF PAGINATION

The pages of the new LITHOGRAPHERS MANUAL are not numbered in the traditional way. In the LITHOGRAPHERS MANUAL we use a system that has been adopted for several technical publications. Every page is numbered with the chapter number and the page number of this particular chapter. Both figures are separated by a colon. A few examples follow: Number 2:12 refers to the 12th page of chapter two, number 12:122 to the 122nd page of the 12th chapter.

This system is serviceable for the reader; it can even be contended that this numbering system is superior to the traditional, once the reader is used to it. That the numbering system selected for the LITHOGRAPHERS MANUAL has very considerable advantages for speedy production, every experienced lithographer can easily see. It is assumed that the reader is a progressive person and will accept this innovation.

TABLE OF CONTENTS

The LITHOGRAPHERS MANUAL has unfortunately no subject index. The subject grew and grew, the time in which the work had to be produced became shorter and shorter, until it became impossible to include an index of subject matter in this issue of the MANUAL. The editor is aware of this defect and hopes that it will be corrected in subsequent editions of the LITHOGRAPHERS MANUAL.

In discussing the index problem, which was by no means treated lightly, it was finally decided to assist the reader by expanding the table of contents to include a very detailed topical listing of subjects presented in the editorial section of the MANUAL. Even though this treatment was originally selected as a substitute for an index, the result has certain advantages of its own, not

offered by an index. The reader, and the educator in particular, will find it a very usable itemized review of the subject matter discussed in every editorial study.

❖ ❖ ❖ ❖

Writing a preface is melancholy business. For you, the reader, the preface is the beginning—for the editor it is the end. More than a year of planning, writing and editing has passed. The copy is set. Plates are made. The presses may even be running. The mind is still on the job, shivers run down the spine when one thinks of all the possible mistakes, of all that could have been done better, that should have been done better. But the past is irrevocable. Tomorrow will become today; another book is waiting.

Writing a preface is friendly business. The mind goes back to all the people who have helped, who have made the work possible. When one thinks of them, the end is only the beginning. New friendships were made; the new friendships will live. The end is far away. Writing a preface becomes giving of thanks. . . .

The first to be thanked is the publisher, *Mr. Walter E. Soderstrom.* Twenty years ago, he published the first edition of the LITHOGRAPHERS MANUAL and therewith gave the industry its first modern work on offset printing. In the new edition he not only gave fully and unreservedly from his wealth of experience accumulated in a life devoted to the lithographic industry, but he also bore the heavy financial burden of carrying through this new ambitious project. Throughout the whole project Mr. Soderstrom held steadfastly to his original aim: to put as much information as possible at the disposal of the lithographic industry. The editor wants to thank Mr. Soderstrom particularly for his graciousness and understanding, for his considerateness and good humour that made the work on the LITHOGRAPHERS MANUAL highly enjoyable.

Mr. Wade E. Griswold, Executive Director, Lithographic Technical Foundation, was exceptionally important in the planning of the new LITHOGRAPHERS MANUAL. He had many conferences with the editor, made many most valuable suggestions, and was always ready to assist. *Mr. Michael H. Bruno,* Research Manager of LTF, not only contributed one of the most important chapters of the MANUAL, but also often gave the editor the benefit of his long experience. *Mr. Charles Shapiro,* Educational Manager, LTF, contributed a most important chapter on presswork; beyond that he took a very active part in the whole project and advised the editor on many thorny problems. Thanks are due to *Mr. John F. Perrin,* 1956 and 1957 President of LTF, who graciously permitted the use of LTF's many publications.

Mr. Martin J. Weber, the noted photographic artist, contributed many illustrations as well as the cover design. *Mr. Thomas E. Dunwoody,* President, International Printing Pressmen and Assistant's Union, made it possible for the Technical Trade School to contribute the color printing of several sections and therewith to greatly enhance both appearance and instructive value of the MANUAL. *Mr. J. Tom Morgan,* President of Litho-Krome Company, Columbus, Georgia, produced a masterly reproduction of our frontispiece, Senefelder's portrait by Hauber. *Mr. Bernard J. Taymans,* General Manager, Printing Industry of America, took a very lively interest in the project and assisted in many ways.

For reading the original draft of chapter one, the History of Lithography, and commenting on the subject, thanks are due to the following people: *Mr. Fred W. Baker,* Public Relations Manager, Harris-Seybold Company; *Mr. Hamilton C. Carson,* Editor, Modern Lithography; *Mr. Maxwell R. Conclin,* Chief, Industry Division, Bureau of Census; *Mr. Clarence Dickinson,* Sales Manager, Lithographic Division, R. Hoe & Company (retired); *Mr. William C. Huebner; Mr. Douglas G. Manley,* Sales Manager, American Type Founders Co., Inc.; *Mr. Dante V. Mazzocco,* President, Eureka Photo Offset Engraving, Inc.; *Mr. John McMaster,* Manager, Graphic Reproduction Sales Division, Eastman Kodak Company; *Mr. R. J. Niederhauser,* Manager, Sales Engineering, Harris-Seybold Company; *Mr. Harry A. Porter,* Senior Vice-President, Harris-Seybold Company (retired); *Mr. Robert F. Reed,* Senior Consultant to the Lithographic Technical Foundation.

Chapters five, six, and seven, covering the camera department, color separation photography, and photographic masking and color correcting, owe very much to the generous cooperation of the Eastman Kodak Company and to LTF. Without the assistance of *Mr. John McMaster, Mr. Syl Hall, Mr. Earl Sundeen* and without the guidance of *Mr. J. A. C. Yule* and *Mr. Frank M. Preucil* these chapters could never have been as well developed as they finally were.

For reading the original draft of chapter twelve, Lithographic Presswork, and commenting on the subject we want to thank the following people: *Mr. Albert T. Kuehn,* Miehle Printing Press and Manufacturing Company; *Mr. Charles W. Latham,* Consultant; *Mr. Robert J. Niederhauser,* Manager, Sales Engineering, Harris-Seybold Company; *Mr. Robert F. Reed,* Senior Consultant, LTF; *Mr. August A. Saul,* Chairman of the Board, and *Mr. Carl Siebke,* Chief Engineer, Miller Printing Machinery Co.; *Mr. Roy P. Tyler,* Manager Installation and Service Department, Harris-Seybold

Company; and *Mr. Reginald F. Wardley,* Superintendent, Paper Division, National Blank Book Corporation.

The editor cannot hope to mention everyone by name who has helped in one way or another in the course of the project, but he wants to thank particularly the following people for their assistance and encouragement: *Mr. G. O. Baker,* Director, Technical Trade School; *Mr. Kenneth Burchard,* Assistant Dean, School of Printing Management, Carnegie Institute of Technology; *Mr. Walter F. Cornell,* President, International Printing Ink Corporation; *Mr. Byron G. Culver,* Head, Department of Printing, Rochester Institute of Technology; *Mr. John S. Dively,* President, Harris-Intertype Corporation; *Dr. Ellsworth Geist,* Vice-President, S. D. Warren Company; *Mr. John G. Gervase,* President, John F. Cuneo Company; *Mr. Rod Greig,* Advertising Manager, American Typefounders Company; *Mr. William F. Hall,* Director of Research, Folding Paper Box Association of America; *Mr. Anselm Inzinger,* Design Engineer, American Typefounders Company; *Mr. Leo H. Joachim,* Publisher of the Ninth Graphic Arts Production Yearbook; *Mr. A. F. Johnson,* President, Princeton Polychrome Company; *Mr. Edward E. Katz,* Vice-President, Crafton Graphic Company; *Mr. John L. Kronenberg,* S. D. Warren Company; *Mr. Joseph Mazzaferri,* President, Colorcraft Lithoplate Co.; *Mr. Carl Mellick,* Vice-President, Miehle Printing Press and Manufacturing Co.; *Mr. Walter E. Reed,* Vice-President, Dexter Folding Company; *Mr. Fred Roblin,* Associate Editor, The American Pressman; *Mr. Vincent Stafford,* Harris-Seybold Company; *Mr. Richard B. Tullis,* Vice-President, Harris-Intertype Company and *Dr. John Vinton,* E. I. du Pont de Nemours Company.

◈ ◈ ◈ ◈

The last word of thanks goes to my wife. It is the traditional lot of writers' and editors' spouses to share their husbands' labors. But the extent to which my wife participated in the LITHOGRAPHERS MANUAL exceeds the traditional by far. She travelled thousands of miles with me, attended many meetings and conferences, provided lunches for dozens of callers, smiled uncounted little conflicts out of the way, helped me to keep my not always so good senses in many cases, and even permitted her home to be turned into an office during the final stages of the project. All this she bore with charm and poise; she made and was the good atmosphere that kept the work alive.

VICTOR STRAUSS

New York, October 1957.

TABLE OF CONTENTS

TABLE OF CONTENTS

CHAPTER FIVE
THE CAMERA DEPARTMENT

CHAPTER SIX
COLOR-SEPARATION PHOTOGRAPHY
J. A. C. Yule

CHAPTER SEVEN
PHOTOGRAPHIC MASKING AND COLOR CORRECTING

CHAPTER EIGHT
THE LITHO ART DEPARTMENT
Bernard R. Halpern

TABLE OF CONTENTS

CHAPTER NINE
THE STRIPPING AND PHOTOCOMPOSING DEPARTMENTS

CHAPTER TEN
THE PLATEMAKING DEPARTMENT
Michael H. Bruno

CHAPTER ELEVEN
THE PROOFING DEPARTMENT

CHAPTER TWELVE
LITHOGRAPHIC PRESSWORK
Charles Shapiro

TABLE OF CONTENTS

CHAPTER THIRTEEN
INK AND PAPER FOR LITHOGRAPHY

CHAPTER FOURTEEN
BINDING

CHAPTER FIFTEEN
VARIOUS SUPPLEMENTARY PROCESSES

CHAPTER SIXTEEN
LITHOGRAPHIC TRADE CUSTOMS
Arthur A. Atha

THE LITHOGRAPHERS MANUAL

CHAPTER ONE

The History of Lithography_____

Section One: The Invention of Lithography

Lithography was invented in 1798 by Alois Senefelder. The story goes that Senefelder, who was interested in printing some of his own compositions, had at hand a freshly polished stone upon which he wrote down a laundry list for his mother using a greasy crayon. Being curious, he experimented with the stone and found that, when chemically treated and inked, impressions could be pulled from the stone; thus lithography was born.

FACTS, FICTION AND A LAUNDRY LIST

Actually, the Senefelder laundry list has been highly fictionized in the course of time. Almost every single item in the above told story is distorted. If we want to use contemporary expressions we can say that Senefelder had been working on a printing and engraving research project for quite some time before this famous incident.

In 1796, when this incident occurred, Senefelder was practicing for copperplate engraving on the cheaper Bavarian limestone rather than on the expensive copper. The stone was therefore not at hand by chance. Nor was the greasy crayon a crayon. Senefelder wrote on the stone with an ink specially developed by him. (Alois Senefelder, *The Invention of Lithography*, N. Y. 1911, p. 8.)

If the word compositions refers to *musical* composition, as one can often read, this is again misleading. Senefelder was no musician; he was bred for the law and had studied for three years at a Bavarian university. The so-called compositions were dramatic writings with which he tried to earn a living after his father died. *Finally, and most important, the result of the laundry list incident was not lithography but a relief etching process.* It is indeed surprising how many errors and halftruths can be packed in a few sentences!

This distortion of the origin of lithography is that much more unnecessary as Senefelder himself laid down the story for the record in his book "The Invention of Lithography" which was translated into English (the second time) by J. W. Muller and published by the Fuchs & Lang Manufacturing Company in 1911 in New York. There Sene-

felder states clearly that the 1796 process was "purely mechanical in its purpose" whereas lithography "may be called purely chemical" (op. cit., p. 7). In this book he also vigorously protests against the story that he invented lithography by chance: "I have told all these things fully in order to prove to the reader that I did not invent stoneprinting through lucky accident, but that I arrived at it by a way pointed out by industrious thought" (op cit., p. 6).

THE LITHOGRAPHIC PRINCIPLE

The principle on which lithography is based is the mutual repellence of water and greasy substances. The limestone used by Senefelder was porous and particularly well suited to lithography. But limestone is not essential for the process. Senefelder preferred the term *chemical printing* for his invention and used this term as a generic one; stone printing (in German *Steindruck*) or lithography was for him only one branch of many possible in chemical printing.

Terminology is neither generally accepted nor consistent throughout history. At certain times and in certain countries a distinction was made for example, between lithography and zincography (lithography from zinc plates). The term chemical printing was less used in the Anglo-American orbit than planography, and planography too has been used and is used by different people with differing connotations. In the course of this century the term lithography has lost its meaning as stone printing and is in our day more or less generally used in the same sense in which Senefelder used chemical printing.

LITHOGRAPHY AND COPPERPLATE ENGRAVING

The original method of stone printing was slow and cumbersome if compared with our contemporary lithographic techniques but it was very fast and simple in comparison to copperplate engraving, the art with which the new invention competed the most vigorously.

The superiority of lithography — at least costwise — is set forth in a cost comparison of lithography and copperplate engraving in the English translation (by C. Hullmandel) of Raucourt's treatise on lithography, published in London, 1821. There it is shown that "lithography is about seven times cheaper than copperplate engraving, if plate costs of both processes are compared. The printing costs show much less of a difference, but lithographic printing costs only a little more than half of the printing of copperplate engravings. (*A Manual of Lithography* translated from the French by C. Hullmandel, Second Edition, London, 1821, p. 128 ff)

LITHOGRAPHY AS A DUPLICATING PROCESS

The great popularity of lithography can be explained by these cost figures. Lithography is also ideal as a "duplicating process." Our illustration shows an "Autographic Press," if not the first, then certainly one of the first lithographic duplicators. Under the title "Every man his

The Autographic Press, possibly the first lithographic duplicating machine.

own printer, or lithography made easy" a book was published anonymously in 1854 in London, Manchester and Edinburgh. This book is obviously sales literature for the Autographic Press which enables "any person of ordinary intelligence to perform all the operations of this form of lithography without being compelled to seek the aid of a professional printer."

This "wonderful" press was at first intended merely to facilitate the production of a few copies of manuscripts of a private nature, for which the merchant or banker would ordinarily employ the more valuable services of confidential clerks to copy by hand. In a short time, however, the press came into use, not only in the counting houses of the merchant, but in the offices of the principal railway and insurance companies; proving a valuable accessory (op. cit., p. iv). Times have not changed so much, after all!

EARLY LITHOGRAPHY WAS COMPLETELY DO-IT-YOURSELF

The technical details of stone lithography are much too involved to be discussed in the frame of this study. At the beginning, the lithographer had to provide all equipment by his own efforts. There were neither lithographic presses nor inks or chemicals available for purchase. The art was primitive but it was very difficult to learn; a successful lithographer did not easily divulge his trade secrets.

Every step, every item had to be slowly and painfully developed. The preparation of the stone, the creation of the image, inking and dampening, preparing the paper, and finally taking the impression were all manually performed.

According to the craftsman's ability and training the results differed greatly.

But the intrinsic strength of the lithographic process was powerful enough to overcome all these hurdles. Lithography spread from Munich, its birthplace, to Vienna and Offenbach as well as to other German cities; then to France, England, Russia and over all of Europe. In 1818 it reached the shores of the New World. But before we proceed, a short biographical sketch on Alois Senefelder, the inventor of lithography, is in order.

THE INVENTOR OF LITHOGRAPHY

Alois Senefelder (1771-1834) was born in Prague, then belonging to Austria, as the son of a German actor in 1771. He received an excellent education by the standards of his time in Munich, where his father found permanent employment at the Electoral Court Theatre.

When his father died in 1792, Senefelder could not continue his studies for the law at the University of Ingolstadt, Bavaria, but had to earn a living. We know already that he invented lithography in 1798. In 1799 the *Churfuerst* (Prince-Elector) Max Joseph of Bavaria gave him an exclusive privilege lasting 15 years for the exploitation of his invention. In 1809 Senefelder was appointed, by the King of Bavaria, Royal Inspector of Lithography at the Lithographic Institute operated by the Crown. His salary was 1500 gulden and permitted a very comfortable living.

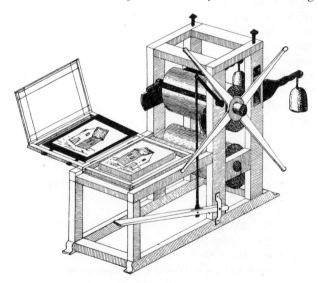

Senefelder's first lithographic press.

The life of Senefelder was devoted to lithography. In the interests of lithography he travelled to Vienna, Paris and London. He was engaged in various business enterprises, had legal and family trouble but kept on improving lithography as long as he lived. In 1817 he submitted a model of a lithographic press, with automatic inking and dampening, to the Royal (Bavarian) Academy which gave him a gold medal in recognition of this invention. At about the same time, he invented the first paper plates with which he wanted to replace the heavy lithographic stones (Senefelder, op. cit., p. 90).

Contrary to the widely spread story, Senefelder's merits were well recognized by his contemporaries. He received valuable presents and prizes as well as medals. Senefelder was two times married, seems to have been rather careless with money, was always thinking about new inventions and died after a very full and active life at the age of sixty three. It is deplorable that his biography by Carl Wagner is not translated into English. (Carl Wagner, *Alois Senefelder, His Life and Work*, Leipzig, 1914.)

LITHOGRAPHY AS A MEDIUM FOR ARTISTIC SELF-EXPRESSION

Alois Senefelder, though not an artist himself, gave to the world a new medium of artistic expression. From its very inception lithography has led a dual existence. It has been a commercial process for the reproduction of art, books, music and advertising material; at the same time it has been a medium for artists who work directly on stone with crayon, brush or pen, and produce fine limited editions. In this latter respect lithography is similar to the processes of etching or wood engraving; the final prints are multiplications of the artist's design without the intervention of a commercial engraver. It is the work of the artist-lithographer that is discussed in the following.

Of all the graphic arts none is so simple as the making of a lithograph by drawing on stone. The wood or steel engraver must learn to draw lines with a graver or burin, which is no easy task. The etcher must learn to bite in his lines with acid, a delicate and uncertain proceeding. Furthermore, the wood block or metal plate in no way resembles the finished print and the artist must wait until a proof is pulled to ascertain the result of his effort. In lithography the lines drawn by the artist are the lines that will print and he sees them before him all the time he works. With the possible exception of color, all the beauty of line and tone and texture that oils or pen and ink or any other media offer to the artist may be found in lithography; all effects from line to full tone, from black to lightest gray may be transposed to stone.

In nearly a century and a half, commercial lithography has made extraordinary technical advances. Photographic methods, halftone screens, metal plates, offset presses and other developments have revolutionized lithography without, however, altering the basic principles discovered by Senefelder. That the artist-lithographers of today use the same type of Bavarian limestone recommended by Senefelder and, with but few changes, employs the principles explained in Senefelder's book, *The Complete Course of Lithography,* is evidence of the basic soundness of the process. Modern commercial methods have increased production and lowered costs; photography has entirely changed the commercial methods of platemaking; but for the artist the original methods are still the best, and the archaic hand press still has its place in a world of high speed production.

Because lithography is an easy medium for the artist, its reputation has, throughout its existence, been hurt by the work of the unskillful. It has often been used by the lazy as a means of acquiring many pictures with the labor of doing one.

Following the discovery of lithography, came a wave of popularity which spread throughout Europe and resulted in the enduring work of Isabey, Raffet, and Daumier in France, Bonnington and Harding in England, Goya in Spain, and Menzel in Germany. Then less masterful artists brought the medium into disrepute, and for a long time it was considered principally as a commercial means of reproduction. Soon, however, the inherent value of the medium reasserted itself, and to the second great era belong such men as Manet, Fantin-Latour, Toulouse-Lautrec, and Whistler, followed by Sterner, Pennell, Davies and Bellows. Today lithography is in the hands of Kent and many other contemporaries in this country, who are sustaining the highest standards of the art.

Section Two: Stone Lithography in America

The first lithograph to be published in the United States is by Bass Otis and appeared in the Analectic Magazine of August, 1819. This magazine also published a comparatively detailed description of the process. It summarized the uses to which this art can be employed in the following eight points. (Analectic Magazine, August 1819, p. 72-3.)

1st. It is a perfect facsimile: there can be no mistake or miscopy.

2d. It supersedes all kinds of engraving: when the drawing is finished, it is now sent to the engravers, and no impression can be taken till the engraving is finished: in lithography, impressions can be taken the instant the drawing is dry, more perfect than any engraving can possibly produce.

3d. It can imitate not only drawings in crayon and Indian ink, but etching, mezzo-tinto, and aqua tinta.

The first American lithograph.

4th. The plate is never worn out as in copper-plate engraving. In France, 70,000 impressions of a circular letter were taken, before the engraving was finished of a similar letter written on paper.

5th. Maps, large prints, calico printing, &c. can be executed in this way on rollers of stone, turned and the design drawn, etched or aqua tinted, on the stone roller itself. For roller work in calico-printing, it would be inestimable.

6th. All works of science may now be freed from the prodigious expense attending numerous engravings.

7th. Any man who can draw, can take off any number of impressions of his own designs, without trusting to any other artist.

8th. The advantage of expedition in the process now recommended, is beyond all calculation.

The publication of Bass Otis' lithograph did not lead to an immediate spreading of lithography in the United States. Only a handful of people were active in this field during the twenties and thirties of the nineteenth century. Barnett and Doolittle opened shop in New York in 1821 and therewith became the first lithographers of the U.S.

The most important early American lithographers were two brothers, William S. and John B. Pendleton. Harry T. Peters, to whose admirable work we owe much of our knowledge of American lithography, says that "these two brothers may almost be spoken of as the founders of American lithography." (Harry T. Peters, *America on Stone*, N.Y. 1931, p. 312.) William S. Pendleton started the first lithographic business of Boston together with Abel Bowen in 1825. His brother John B. Pendleton became, together with Francis Kearny and Cephas G. Childs the first Philadelphian lithographer in 1829 or 1830.

In 1835 Duval, of whom you will later read more, produced the first American color lithograph "Grandpapa's Pet, drawn and lithotinted by John R. Richards, expressly for Miss Leslie's Magazine." (Peters, op. cit., p. 164.)

But the real spread and growth of lithography in the United States did not set in before the forties of the nineteenth century. In the following decade chromolithography, the making of lithographic prints in many colors, became established. In these chromos stone lithography reached its highest and in a sense final form. The next great changes, whereby modern lithography—lithography without stone—was created, did not take place before the beginning of the twentieth century.

THE PRODUCTS OF EARLY LITHOGRAPHY

Lithography became soon the most popular and the most economical picture and illustration reproduction process. The world was small a hundred years ago. In 1850 the population of the United States was a little over twenty-three millions. The majority of the American people lived outside of cities, and the cities themselves were far from big. In our age, when speed and mass production dominate everything, hand printing from stones looks hopelessly inadequate. But a hundred years ago, when everything was handmade, this was not the case. Lithography was a very efficient process if measured by the standards of its own time.

The products of lithography were highly diversified. Prints stood possibly in the first place. The American people could participate in politics, the exploration of their country, great and not so great political events, the achievements of science and technology, by looking at lithographic prints depicting the contemporary scene. Currier and Ives are the best known lithographic print-makers, but there was a host of others besides them. Other products of lithography were maps and sheet music. Illustrations of books and magazines, too, were often lithographed, and commercial lithography was of course not missing. Advertisements were often lithographed and so were business stationery and checks, not to forget the beautifully calligraphed stock and bond certificates or life insurance policies.

THE WORKINGS OF STONE LITHOGRAPHY

If you are interested in the technique of American stone lithography at the time of its flowering, in the seventies of the last century, you can find a full description in American Encyclopedia of Printing, edited by J. Luther Ringwalt (Philadelphia, 1871). Mr. Peter G. Duval, whose name is mentioned above, one of the outstanding American lithographers of the time, gives a very clear description of the subject.

A good lithographer was first and foremost a graphic artist; in some cases he was a creative artist himself, but in any case he had to be a good reproductive artist. No lithographic establishment could exist without good artists. In many cases a business man and an artist went into partnership. Currier & Ives are an example of this combination. Nathaniel Currier was the business man and J. Merrit Ives the artist.

The lithographer of the second half of the nineteenth century did not build his own press anymore. As the building of letterpress printing machines developed so did that of lithographic presses. Mr. Duval informs us that at about 1871 there were at least 450 hand- and about 30 steam-presses running in the United States (Ringwalt, op. cit., p. 278).

The same author tells us that: "the first steam-press was invented in Paris in 1850 by a Frenchman, named Eugues He sold the patent for England to Messrs. Hughes and Kimber, press builders of London, who made improvements on the first pattern and introduced it into the United States

A lithographic steam press built by R. Hoe & Co.

in 1866. It is the pattern most in use at the present time, although there was one manufactured in Massachusetts some time previous which is still in use in some establishments in New York and Boston. There are now several patterns imported from Germany and Mr. Hoe, the celebrated American press builder, has also lately introduced a steam-lithographic press. (Ringwalt, op. cit., p. 278/9.) (The designation steam-press refers of course to the steam engine that supplied the power for this press.)

The lithographer of the time under discussion was already assisted by a supply industry. He could purchase his ink and many lithographic supplies on the market. But many a lithographer had his own special formula for this or that item which he kept highly secret and considered essential for his work. Lithography as chemical printing provided a fruitful field for the experimentalist with more or less of a chemical background.

It is of course not possible in the frame of this sketch to discuss or even indicate the many techniques of stone lithography. Most of them are of historical interest only in our time. But the transfer process must be mentioned, if ever so briefly, because the transfer process expresses one of the most essential lithographic features: the ease and simplicity of making duplicates of a printing image. When lithography was outclassed by other printing processes in the last two decades of the nineteenth and the first decade of the twentieth century — to indicate the approximate time — the transfer process was one of its greatest assets.

TRANSFER PROCESSES

Transferring goes back to Senefelder who was inclined to consider it the most important of his inventions. (Senefelder, op. cit., p. 190.) Senefelder had in mind the unique feature of lithography, whereby drawing or writing made with a special ink on a special paper can be transferred to the lithographic stone where it becomes the printing image.

The same principle can be used for making transfers from copperplate engravings, woodcuts and, last but not

A transfer press.

least, engravings made on lithographic stones. The transfer process compensated for the slowness of stone lithography by making it possible to combine many units in a single printing image carrier. This feature became crucially important in label work where a great number of comparatively small units is needed.

The technique of transferring was rather involved. Inks and papers had to be just right; various kinds of inks and papers were used for particular purposes. The required number of transfers was pulled. These transfers were then placed on the stone and pressed onto its surface with great pressure. Thereafter the backs of the transfers were wetted, the paper was released and the inked image became the printing image of the stone after the proper treatments.

DIRECT ROTARY PRESSES

At the beginning of the twentieth century the position of lithography within the graphic arts was considerably weakened. The advance in photoengraving made quality picture reproduction by the letterpress method possible. The advances in printing press technology made it possible to print much more efficiently in letterpress than in lithography.

The flatbed stone press was well adapted to the necessities of stone lithography, but it was absolutely unsuitable for the use of photomechanically made printing image carriers. It did not require great ingenuity to aim at a replacement of the stone press by a press that would operate on the rotary principle, and where thin sheets of metal would replace the lithographic stone. The rotary principle had proved its soundness in newspaper press design, zinc was already suggested by Senefelder and had been successfully used for replacement of lithographic stones for quite some time, aluminum had also been introduced into lithography in the early nineties of the last century.

At this point it should be mentioned that the use of metals instead of stone was not only envisaged by Senefelder, but that he expressed also the thought that metals and other materials should be made capable of being used for chemical printing by treating them for this purpose and "thus change their natures," so to speak (Senefelder, op. cit., p. 97.) How far ahead the ingenious man was of the time is demonstrated by the fact that Cronak and Brunak, our effective plate-treatments for zinc and aluminum were developed more than 120 years later.

An additional and very important reason for the building of rotary lithographic presses was the scarcity and enormous cost of large size stones. Such stones were a necessity for the printing of large posters; their replacement by sheet metal which was available in the desired dimensions, was an economical necessity. In the nineties of the last century rotary lithographic presses began to be used. But they did not answer to the real needs of the lithographic industry.

Direct rotary presses fulfilled of course a function; they were valuable in the poster field and had other uses too, particularly in large sheet size applications. But direct rotaries brought the problem of the lithographic plate to the fore. Be it now that lithographers did not know enough about platemaking, be it that the available paper was not suitable, direct rotary presses were, as a rule, not successful.

The solution to the problems of the lithographic industry came from a completely unexpected development: the offset press. But before we turn to the offset press we must discuss the effect of photography on lithography.

Section Three: Photography and Lithography in the Nineteenth Century

Photography and lithography are closely related to each other. Contemporary lithography is unthinkable without photography. Photography supplies not only a considerable part of the subject matter to be reproduced lithographically but it is also responsible for essential steps of the lithographic reproduction process itself.

The scientific basis of photography lies in physics and chemistry. The same sciences are of great importance to lithography. Even though these sciences are essential for all phases of the lithographic process they are nowhere more needed in a lithographic plant than in the departments in which photography plays a dominant role. These departments are the camera department, the tone and color correcting department and the platemaking department.

It is of course way beyond the scope of this historical sketch to give a history of photography. Here we are not concerned with photography as a picture making process but only with such aspects of photography as are used in the lithographic reproduction of pictures. These two functions of photography cannot be sharply divided but are closely related to each other.

Historically, photography was first used in lithography for the making of the printing image, the stone or the plate. The next important contribution of photography to lithography had to do with the reproduction of tonal images. At this point photography became a decisive step in the conversion of the subject matter to be lithographed into a press plate. Process color printing depends of course completely on photography. It is the latest but not the last contribution of photography to lithographic reproduction.

For the purpose of this study we will first trace the influence of photography on the making of the printing image, next we will discuss the role of photography in the making of tonal reproductions and last we will review process color printing.

HELIOGRAPHY AND DAGUERREOTYPY

The first practical photographic process was announced in 1839. It was the result of the combined efforts of two Frenchmen, Louis Jacques Nandé Daguerre (1765–1833), and Joseph Nicéphore Niepce (1765–1833). Daguerreotypy produced photographic images in a camera obscura on silvered copper plates. The silver was made light sensitive with iodine. Exposure took originally 15 to 30 minutes, but was later considerably reduced. The silver image was developed with fumes of mercury.

But daguerreotypy was not nearly as important for lithography as heliography, which is by some considered the true invention of photography. This process was developed by Joseph Nicéphore Niepce, in 1822. In this year Niepce made a contact print of an engraving representing Pope Pius VII which he oiled and thereby made more or less transparent on a glass plate coated with a solution of bitumen. Exposure time was two to three hours, development was done with a solvent consisting of a mixture of lavender oil and petroleum. The exposed areas became insoluble, the unexposed remained soluble and were washed out during development. (*The History of Photography*, by Helmut Gernsheim in collaboration with Alison Gernsheim, London, N.Y., Toronto, 1955, p. 38.)

Heliography plays an important role in the history of graphic reproduction. In 1826 Niepce made the first experimental photoengraving by using metal instead of glass and by etching the photoprinted and developed plate. (Gernsheim, op. cit., p. 39.) The first successful photolithographic process was based on the same material, bitumen. This process was developed in Paris by the optician Lerebours and the lithographer Lemercier in 1852. A grained lithographic stone was coated with a solution of bitumen of Judea in ether, contact printed and developed with ether. In 1853, prints made by this process and published "under the title *Lithophotographie* showed good half-tone, but the process was later abandoned in favor of Poitevin's, because only a limited number of proofs could be pulled" (Gernsheim, op. cit., p. 365). Lemercier and Lerebours were not the only ones to use the bitumen process. Gernsheim's *History of Photography* lists several other people in addition, none though in the United States.

BICHROMATED COLLOIDS

Bitumen or, as they are also called, asphalt processes were considerably refined in the course of the nineteenth century, but they were completely superseded by a group of processes which are all based on bichromates and colloids.

Mungo Ponton, the Secretary of the Bank of Scotland and an amateur photographer discovered in the spring of 1839 "that bichromate of potassium spread on paper was light sensitive." (Gernsheim, op. cit., p. 272.) He thought that the much cheaper bichromate could replace the expensive silver salts used in daguerreotypy.

Ponton's discovery was published in The Edinburgh New Philosophical Journal, July 1839. The French physicist

Edmond Becquerel "experimented with variations of Ponton's process on different kinds of papers." In 1840 "he established that it was not the bichromate of potash as such which was very light sensitive, but that the size in the paper (starch) greatly increased the light sensitivity." (Gernsheim, op. cit., p. 273.) Becquerel's observations were published in 1840.

The effect of bichromates on various colloids was studied by several people. In 1852 the English inventor William Henry Fox Talbot (1800–77) discovered the light sensitivity of a mixture of potassium bichromate and gelatin. "He took out an English patent on Oct. 29, 1852 for the production of photographic etchings on steel by the aid of this chromate mixture. . . ." (Josef Maria Eder, *History of Photography*, N.Y. 1954, p. 553).

Another investigator was the French chemist and civil engineer Alphonse Louis Poitevin (1819–1882), one of the greatest contributors to photomechanical reproduction processes. Poitevin was the inventor of collotype and several carbon processes. To him we also owe the invention of the first successful photolithographic process. Our surface plates are still based on his work.

Poitevin invented photolithography based on bichromated albumin in August, 1855. He designated his process *photolithography* but was not necessarily the first to use this term. Poitevin's procedure is described in Eder's *History of Photography* (p. 611) as follows: "Poitevin coated the stone (grained for halftone pictures) with a solution of potassium bichromate and albumin, equalized the coating with a tampon, dried, exposed under a negative, washed with water, rolled up with greasy ink (or rolled up first and then washed) which only adhered to the parts which had become insoluble by exposure to light but did not adhere to the moist parts. The stone was then etched and printed by the usual lithographic method."

In 1855 Poitevin started his own lithographic business in Paris. He was able to print 300 impressions from a stone; but two years later he sold his process to the well known Parisian lithographer Lemercier who got up to 700 impressions from a stone. (Gernsheim, op. cit., p. 365.) If we compare these figures with the number of impressions produced by contemporary lithography, we realize the enormous strides made.

PHOTOLITHOGRAPHIC TRANSFER PROCESSES

Sensitizing a lithographic stone and photoprinting directly on it was of course not a practical procedure. It was all but impossible to obtain uniform coatings and it was equally difficult to provide flawless contact during exposure. In the hands of very skilled craftsmen, and under the most favorable conditions, direct sensitization of stones could possibly work. But photolithography needed a different technique if it was to be commonly used. This technique consisted in making photolithographic transfers.

According to Eder (op. cit., p. 612), "the photolithographic transfer process from chromated papers was invented by Eduard Isaak Asser (1809–94), in 1857, at Amsterdam. . . . He was the first to make photographic prints with greasy ink on paper coated with starch paste and sensitized with bichromate for transfer on stone. . . ."

Photolithographic transfer processes were improved in 1859 by J. W. Osborn, head of the Government Survey Office in Melbourne, Australia, and independently in the same year by Colonel Sir Henry James (1803–77), head of the Ordnance Survey, Southampton, England. Osborn's method "allowed a much greater number of impressions to be taken — an edition of 2000 to 3000 against Lemercier's 700 by the Poitevin process," (Gernsheim, op. cit., p. 366).

Osborn and James also made transfers to zinc. They both were, in consequence of their position, most interested in cartographic or map printing. Stephen H. Horgan informs us that "the rights for the United States of Osborn's process were secured by the American Photolithographic Company of New York, and thus began in the seventies the use of photolithography for reproducing government maps, Patent Office drawings, and the reproduction of steel engravings which were so popular for home decoration at that time." (Horgan's *Halftone and Photomechanical Processes,* by Stephen H. Horgan, Chicago, 1913, p. 12.)

THE DEVELOPMENT OF THE HALFTONE
PROCESS

Two problems dominate the history of picture reproduction. One is the rendering of tonal values, the other is the combination of reading matter and pictures for printing in one and the same press run. The halftone process is the first effective solution of both problems. It was developed for letterpress printing and made possible the reproduction of photographs and other tonal pictures together with reading matter.

It was not by chance that "this important invention was perfected at precisely the time that the technical revolution in photography was taking place. Dry plates, flexible film, anastigmat lenses and hand cameras made it possible to produce negatives more quickly, more easily, and of greater variety of subjects than ever before. The halftone enabled these photographs to be reproduced economically and in limitless quantity in books, magazines and newspapers." (*The History of Photography from 1839 to the Present Day,* by Beaumont Newhall, the Museum of Modern Art, N.Y., 1949, p. 221.)

The development of the halftone process took place outside of lithography. In the eighties of the nineteenth century, when the revolution in photography occurred, lithography was utterly unsuitable for mass production printing. Nothing illustrates this backwardness better than the story of the New York Daily Graphic. On March 4, 1873, the New York Daily Graphic published its first issue and therewith "the first illustrated daily newspaper in the world." (Horgan, op. cit., p. i.) "The Daily Graphic was an eight page paper, the pictorial four pages were printed first lithographically and the inside four pages were run off from type." (Horgan, op. cit., p. 13.)

The pictorial part of the Daily Graphic was produced by a photolithographic transfer process on stone presses. Production on these presses was between 700 and 800 sheets per hour, much too small to satisfy the demand. Lithographic stone presses were completely outdistanced by letterpress machinery. The halftone process was developed for letterpress. In photoengraving, letterpress found an excellent picture reproduction process.

As the development of the halftone process does not belong in the history of lithography, the subject is here treated very briefly. In 1851 Frederick Scott Archer, an Englishman (1813–1857), published the wet collodion process which was the basis of most graphic arts photography until the middle of the twentieth century (Gernsheim, op. cit., p. 153). In 1855 Archer made his second great contribution to graphic arts photography by inventing the stripping of collodion film. (Eder, op. cit., p. 346.) Many people worked on the problem of making tonal pictures reproducible by breaking them up into very small units. Fredrick Eugene Ives (1856–1937), of Philadelphia, solved the problem of tonal reproduction in 1886 by introducing the glass cross-line screen. Max Levy of Philadelphia succeeded in 1890 in developing a precision manufacturing process for these screens. (Eder, op. cit., p. 632/3.) These contributions were by no means the only ones that made photoengraving into the leading reproduction process. Lithography stagnated technically until it received its next great impulse through the offset press.

The offset press revived the interest in photolithography. But now conditions had vastly changed if compared to the seventies of the nineteenth century when photolithography had been a contact printing transfer process for line work. At the time of the broad new interest in photolithography, which may be arbitrarily placed at the period shortly after the First World War, graphic arts photography had immensely advanced. Now photolithography acquired a different meaning. It stood for offset lithographic printing in which the camera and, where necessary, the halftone screen was used for converting line and tone originals by means of photography into printable form. This new photolithography could and did draw on the storehouse of knowledge developed, since the nineties of the past century, by photoengraving.

PROCESS COLOR PRINTING

The thought of producing a wide gamut of color by printing with only three inks was first conceived and executed by James Christopher Le Blon (1667–1741), a painter and etcher. Le Blon based his process on Newton's theory of color. He made his color separation by eye, and his plates in the mezzo-tinto process, then a very popular gravure reproduction method. In 1704 he was ready for commercial exploitation of his three-color process (Color Printing and Color Printers, by R. N. Burch, New York, 1911, p. 53). The few prints still in existence attest to the beauty of Le Blon's process. But the process failed to establish itself permanently.

Three color printing in the modern sense is a product of the nineteenth and twentieth century, it is closely related to color photography. The development of color photography is outside the frame of this study. Here, just as in the history of the halftone process, we will merely mention some of the most outstanding events. The first of these took place on May 17, 1861 at the Royal Institution of Great Britain. On this day James Clerk Maxwell lectured on the theory of primary colors and demonstrated a photograph in color. (Principles of Color Photography, by Ralph N. Evans, W. T. Hanson, Jr. and Lyle Brewer, New York, 1953, p. 271.) The next impulse to color photography and to color printing came from two Frenchmen, Louis Ducos du Hauron and Charles Cros who: "Independently of each other and without either one knowing anything of the other's work outlined, in 1868 and 1869, the idea of producing objects in their natural colors by the superimposition of three photographically produced pictures (blue, yellow and red)." (Eder, op. cit., p. 642.)

Du Hauron is not only important in the history of color photography because "he forecast, in fact, almost all the color processes which have since been invented" (Evans, Hanson, and Brewer, op. cit., p. 273), but also in the history of graphic arts reproduction. From a lithographic stone print made in three colors, we know that he experimented with three-color lithography. One such print was presented by him to Stephen H. Horgan and dated 1870 by Horgan. This early process-color stone lithograph is in the possession of the American Museum of Photography in Philadelphia. A reproduction of this picture is included in "A Half Century of Color" by Louis Walton Sipley, Director of American Museum of Photography, New York, 1951, opposite page 10.

A further contribution to graphic arts color process work made in 1869 by Du Hauron must not be omitted. In this year he described not only full-color printing but also pointed to the importance of color-balance. "It must be emphasized that Du Hauron was the first to describe the screen color-plate process. He also pointed out the necessity of adjusting the screen by such an arrangement of color elements that it would appear gray and show no excess of any color whatsoever" (Eder, op. cit., p. 645).

One other basic contribution to photography and process-color reproduction must be mentioned. It is the discovery of photographic color sensitizers made by Dr. Herman Wilhelm Vogel (1834–1898) and published by him in 1873. "Vogel's discovery was another milestone in the history of photography, for it not only paved the way for correct reproduction of colors in paintings, landscapes and portraiture, obviating a lot of retouching, but also proved an essential step in color photography" (Gernsheim, op. cit., p. 269).

Much more work was necessary than the few above mentioned contributions before process color printing became practical. But at the end of the nineteenth century this result had been achieved. The lead was with letterpress printing; gravure followed second. Collotype was the only branch of Senefelder's chemical printing that counted in process color reproduction. Lithography lay dormant; color process work was plainly beyond the scope of stone lithography.

Section Four: The Offset Press

There can be no doubt that the offset press and photo-mechanics are the foundation of contemporary lithography. Of these two, the offset press is the more important contribution because the application of photomechanics would not have been nearly as successful without the offset press than it was with it. This statement is of course debatable. But it should be remembered that direct rotary presses had the field for themselves before the offset press appeared on the scene; it should further be considered that direct rotary presses did not establish themselves for general use but died out once the offset press had found acceptance. Nor should it be disregarded that our contemporary surface plates which permit long run quality reproductions are no radical innovations; their basic elements existed, on the contrary, at the time of direct printing. But direct printing put a much too heavy burden on photomechanical plates. Only indirect printing made modern long run lithography from photomechanical plates possible.

THE ORIGIN OF THE OFFSET PRESS

The origin of the offset press is one of the least discussed subjects in the literature on printing. It is agreed that the basic principle of this press was known for a long time before the paper offset press was introduced. It is also agreed that offset presses were used for metal lithography long before they were adapted to paper use.

The first metal decorating presses were lithographic stone presses equipped with an intermediate cylinder. In 1875 an English patent was granted to R. Barclay, of Barclay & Fry, for such a press. The intermediate cylinder had a surface of specially treated cardboard for transferring the inked design to the sheet metal. (Frank Heywood in "Photo-Litho and Offset Printing" by F. T. Crocket FRPS, London 1923, p. 60 and 61.) The same author informs us that shortly thereafter a rubber blanket was substituted for the cardboard and that such presses were successfully made in England at about 1880.

It is interesting to note that there were also made offset presses that could be used for either paper or metal in case a lithographer wanted to use the same press for both materials. But strangely enough the offset method was never used for paper lithographing by the owners of these machines. One can only agree with Mr. Heywood's melancholy comment: "When one realized that for offset printing on paper it was only necessary to use this machine . . . it is really astonishing that offset was not discovered twenty five years earlier." (Frank Heywood in op. cit., p. 63.)

The history of lithography and of the offset press is not yet written. The best account of the beginnings of offset lithography known to the present writer was given by Mr. Harry A. Porter, retired Senior Vice-President of the Harris-Seybold Company. Mr. Porter not only participated in the early days of offset printing but also collected much valuable historical data. He discussed the early days of offset printing at a meeting of the Detroit Litho Club on December 14, 1950, and has graciously permitted the use of his notes for the following presentation.

IRA W. RUBEL DEVELOPS THE FIRST PAPER OFFSET PRESS

It is generally agreed that Ira W. Rubel was the first to develop an offset-lithographic press for the printing of paper. According to Mr. Porter, Ira Rubel operated a small paper mill in Nutley, N.J. There he made sulphite bond and converted this paper lithographically into bank deposit slips.

At the time when Mr. Rubel developed his offset press, assumedly 1904 and 1905, lithographic stone presses had a rubber blanket on the surface of their impression cylinder. Whenever the feeder, then not a machine but a person, missed feeding a sheet when the press was operating, the inked image was transferred to the rubber blanket from the stone. The following sheet would then be printed on both sides because the rubber blanket transferred the inked image to the back of the sheet. It was generally known that this unintentionally made transfer produced a print superior to that made directly from stone. Mr. Rubel noticed this fact and decided to utilize it as the basis of a printing press.

Like many other inventors Ira Rubel had not enough capital. He joined forces with a Chicago lithographer, A. B. Sherwood and formed together with him the Sherbel Syndicate. The policy of the syndicate was to admit only one lithographer in a territory and therewith to monopolize the new invention. Approximately twelve presses were placed in this manner. These presses were built by the Potter Printing Press Co., of Plainfield, N.J. The Potter Printing Press Company was merged in 1927 with the Harris and the company name was changed to Harris-Sey-bold-Potter Co. The engineer who redesigned the original Rubel Press at Potter was Mr. Irving F. Niles, later Chief Engineer of the Harris Automatic Press Company.

We are not informed about the internal trouble in the Sherbel Syndicates, but we may assume that there was plenty of it. In 1906, Mr. Rubel went to England and took an offset press along, the first ever installed in this country. "The manufacture of this machine was undertaken by a firm of Lancashire engineers, and although for various reasons — the principal being Rubel's somewhat untimely death in 1908 — it failed to make good, his efforts must be recognized as beneficent and a distinct contribution to lithographic offset printing." (Heywood, in op. cit., p. 73.)

The plan to monopolize the offset press proved unworkable. Competition was keen; those who had offset presses took advantage of them and made their competitors who were outside the syndicate look for an independent source of supply. They found it in the Harris Automatic Press Company.

HARRIS ENTERS THE PICTURE

According to Mr. Porter, who was then working for the Harris Automatic Press Company, things took place as follows. Some time prior to June 1906 a Harris salesman tried to sell a rotary stone press, developed by Harris, to the Goes Lithograph Company in Chicago. "Mr. Charles B. Goes was not at all interested in this type of machine but apparently had been needled by Sherwood and told our representative that, if we could make him a machine which he described, he would be interested.

"The salesman returned with Charles G. Harris who was the inventive genius of the Harris Company at that time. They then returned to Niles, the seat of the Harris Company, and I know from personal experience (although Goes did not get the first press) that, from the ideas developed, work was immediately started on an offset press designed and built around the sheetfed letterpress machine which

The first Harris offset press.

was known as the S4, the same size as the S4L 22 x 30. Different frames were designed and three cylinders instead of two were used." (Quoted from Mr. Porter's notes for his Detroit lecture.)

At this point it should be mentioned that Mr. A. F. Harris had witnessed the offset-effect in 1898 while installing a Harris Envelope Press in the plant of the Enterprise Printing Company in Cleveland, Ohio. This press was installed right along the side of a lithographic stone press. The feed girl missed a sheet and Mr. Harris, who was at that time not conversant with lithography, got a demonstration of offset printing then and there. He remembered this incident when his company was asked to build an offset press. It should also be kept in mind that the Harris brothers were builders of rotary letterpress equipment and therewith experienced in the design of rotary printing machinery. Starting with October 1906, four presses were shipped by Harris during the year of 1906; the remaining six presses in the first lot of ten were shipped in 1907.

THE IMPACT OF THE OFFSET PRESS

The offset press was the talk of lithography, as can be seen from the trade press. The National Lithographer discussed "The Rubber Blanket Puzzle" in its September, 1906 issue (p. 11). The confusion that was caused by various rumors on the offset press is well reflected in this item.

In November, 1906, The National Lithographer discusses the offset press again (p. 13). This time the tone is changed. The offset press is clearly considered a very important topic, as can be seen from the following quotation: "There is nothing in the lithographic trade which is attracting so much interest today as is the offset, rubber blanket, commercial lithographic press. That these presses will be a success nobody doubts, and just why some of the manufacturers do not get them on the market is a question. . . ."

Next month, in December, 1906, The National Lithographer reports again on the rubber blanket offset press. "Quite a number of letters have been received this month on the subject of the rubber blanket offset press. From Chicago comes the information that in that city the Sherwood Litho Co., and the Goes Company are successfully using them. The largest size in use being 22 x 32 inches. One correspondent writes that the work done on them is far better than on stone and that they are an unqualified success, and then he wonders why the manufacturers are keeping so quiet about them." (p. 10.)

In April, 1907, The National Lithographer headlines a story: "Off-set Press a Success." Part of this story follows:

"The rubber blanket off-set press is no longer a mystery. We have finally been able to get a practical demonstration of its workings. . . . The job being run was a fine clouded letter heading, on a good quality bond paper. It had been engraved for a stone press, and therefore had to be re-transferred to the zinc plate of the offset press."

"An attempt had previously been made to print this job from the stone on dry paper, but the attempt was unsuccessful. It was then put on the off-set press and run at the rate of more than 4000 sheets per hour. The finished product was as good as could possibly be done from stone with dampened paper. In fact it was as satisfactory a piece of work as the writer ever saw turned out of a lithographic establishment. . . .

"This settles the question of the practicability of the offset press for commercial work — at least as far as the Harris Automatic model is concerned."

"The writer closed his report with the following sentence: 'The Harris Automatic Rubber Blanket Off-Set Press has revolutionized commercial lithography.'"

The offset press was of course not welcomed with the same enthusiasm by everybody in the lithographic industry. The subject was quite controversial, and, as is so often the case, also emotional. In December 1907, it reached the editorial page of The National Lithographer. The magazine had been attacked for booming the offset press even though its "columns do not contain the advertisement of such a press, but, on the other hand, do contain advertisements of other styles of presses." The editor emphasized that "the editorial pages of this paper are not controlled by the advertisers." The reason for booming the off-set press was stated in one sentence: "We believe it to be the salvation of the commercial lithographer." The energetic and well written articles in The National Lithographer contributed much to the acceptance of the offset press. The history of lithography cannot overlook the important service rendered to the industry by Mr. Warren C. Browne (1856-1935), the editor of this magazine.

COMMERCIAL AND COLOR LITHOGRAPHY

The offset press was originally intended for commercial lithography but not for color lithography. Mr. Porter informs us of the then accepted definitions: "Commercial lithography is when the original is engraved on stone or sheet," whereas color lithography was the appropriate designation "when the original is drawn on stone, zinc, or aluminum."

Commercial lithography produced business and bank stationery, mainly in black and white; color lithography, greeting cards, labels, posters and so on. But it took not very long until the offset press was very successfully used for color work. Its advantages over stone and direct rotary

presses were thereby established in both branches of lithography; as time went on the offset press became the dominant lithographic printing machine.

THE GROWTH OF THE OFFSET PRESS

The success of the offset press was a strong stimulus for many manufacturers to enter this field. Mr. Harry Porter informs us that at the end of 1912, 560 offset presses were in operation. These presses had been built by eight different concerns and were of at least ten different sizes. Another source (The Lithographers Journal, Vol. II, June 1916, p. 9) states that 847 off-set presses were in operation in the United States and Canada at the middle of 1916.

The detailed progress of the offset press cannot be told in this sketch. Every element of the press has been further and further developed in the sixty years of its existence. The first offset presses were hand fed; mechanical feeders followed several years later; then came proof presses. In 1914 Walter Scott & Co. installed perfecting offset presses for the printing of newspaper supplements in New York (*The American Manual of Presswork,* second ed.; N. Y. 1916, p. 166) Web offset presses and multicolor presses followed. Now the offset lithographic press is a marvel of efficiency and perfection, second to no other printing machine.

Section Five: Lithography in the Twentieth Century

The lithographic offset press made modern lithography possible; photomechanics made it practical and accounts, together with the offset press, for much of its success. It took some time until modern offset lithography became generally accepted. Approximately 25 years after the introduction of the offset press it dominated the field almost completely. Stone lithography had ceased to exist as a commercial printing process and had become a medium for artistic self expression. Direct lithography from metal plates, never too successful as an all-round method, was more and more replaced by the offset press until it finally lost much of its importance. The offset press grew and developed at an increasing speed; press sizes became larger and running speed faster; two, three and more color presses as well as perfectors became available.

THE NATURE OF LITHOGRAPHIC PROGRESS

It must be understood that progress in lithography — like in other industries — depends on progress in each component element. The continued growth of lithography is not the result of one single advance; it is due to many improvements in every element and phase of the process. Many people and many companies played and continue to play important roles in this process. Constant improvements in plates and presses, but also in photographic materials and techniques, papers, inks, rollers and blankets have made lithography what it is now.

Most of these improvements are made outside the lithographic shop or plant and are therefore too easily overlooked. But it should be understood that it takes a long time and a sizeable investment before an improvement of lasting value is created. It is unfortunately not possible to go into the wide variety of improvements in all different fields that have contributed so much to lithographic technology. Our historical remarks are here restricted to problems of the lithographic plate, and the founding of the Lithographic Technical Foundation. But not even a sketch of lithographic history can omit William C. Huebner, the most prolific inventor of the graphic arts in the first half of this century.

WILLIAM C. HUEBNER AND THE PHOTOCOMPOSING MACHINE

William C. Huebner, an American lithographer, was the first who grasped the full potentialities of offset lithography combined with photomechanics. From 1906 to 1912 Mr. Huebner invented many machines and processes that have since become commonly used in lithography.

The invention of the photocomposing machine is one of Mr. Huebner's major contributions to lithography. This invention made it possible to produce press plates bearing multiple images in a precision until then never considered possible. The first photocomposing machine, together with the equipment and materials needed for its operation, was shipped in 1912 to the plant of Stone Ltd., at Toronto, Ontario, Canada. The cost of this equipment was (as Mr. Huebner informed the present writer by letter of Dec. 3, 1956) over $50,000.

The photocomposing machine was only one of the very many inventions made by Mr. Huebner. Here, it is merely mentioned that Mr. Huebner was also one of the pioneers of lithographic process color reproduction. "In 1910 Huebner reproduced in four colors, by offset lithography, a full-color photograph of orchids, in which the separations were made direct from the object. A set of press sheet progressives of this historically interesting work was presented by Mr. Huebner to the American Museum of Photography as part of its historical collection. Six reproductions appeared on a sheet — all being identical. . . ." (Louis Walton Sipley, Director of American Museum of Photography, *A Half Century of Color*, N. Y., 1951, p. 55.)

THE LITHOGRAPHIC PLATE AND THE FOUNDING OF LTF

At a first glance it may look odd that the problem of the lithographic plate and the founding of LTF are to be discussed under the same heading. But they are not only the two points singled out for our brief historical discussion of the technical side of modern lithography, but these two subjects are also very related to each other.

The plate was the most important single problem in lithography during the first half of this century. The plate was also the problem closest to the individual lithographer. All other elements combined in lithography were either not at all or only to a very small degree subject to change by the individual average lithographer. Presses, paper, ink, photographic materials, rollers and blankets are all manufactured by specialized industries. But the plate was made in the lithographic shop; it was the only major item that was produced by the individual lithographer. (It was, of course, possible to purchase plates from firms specializing in their making. But these firms were not better equipped to cope with the problems of the lithographic plate than many a lithographic shop.)

The quality of the plate is important in many respects. For one, it is decisive for the quality of the final lithographic print. Another point is plate life which has a great influence on length of run and costs. Photomechanical platemaking is a complex process. The effort necessary to control this process could never be made by an individual lithographic shop of average size. The solution of the plate problem had to wait until the industry had learned to do cooperative research — until LTF was in existence.

Two kinds of photomechanically made plates were used in lithography up to the end of the Second World War: albumin plates and deep-etch plates. Albumin was first used by Poitevin as already mentioned; deep-etch plates have a long history in which many inventors participated. Mr. J. S. Mertle credits the Reverend Hannibal Goodwin for having made "one of the first attempts toward the reversal of photomechanical images on metal plates" which he patented in 1881. (J. S. Mertle, *Photolithography and Offset Printing*, Chicago, 1937, p. 193.) Many other inventors worked

on lithographic deep-etch plates. Their contributions can be found in chapter XIII of the quoted work by Mr. Mertle.

But the real change in platemaking techniques had to wait for LTF, which was founded in the early twenties. This is not the place to discuss the work of LTF; this subject is treated in the following chapter. Nor is it intended to say that all plate problems are eliminated for lithography. But the plate has ceased to be the problem child of lithography, due to the efforts of LTF. In the middle of the twentieth century lithographic platemaking became a field of activity for the supply industry. Chronologically, bimetallic plates preceded pre-sensitized plates which appeared in the nineteen-hundred-fifties. In the sixties there came into commercial use the "wipe-on" plates.

THE NEW LITHOGRAPHER

As the lithographic process changed, so changed the lithographers. During the dominance of stone lithography artistic ability was an essential personality trait of a good lithographer. With the disappearance of stone lithography and the ascendance of photomechanics, artisic ability in the traditional lithographic sense became unnecessary.

The modern offset lithographer needs a thorough understanding of photography and photomechanics much more than the ability to draw or paint. He also should have a good scientific background because science, chemistry and physics play an ever-increasing role in lithography. Nor must managerial ability be forgotten. Lithography sheds more and more of its craft characteristics and becomes more and more an industry. Here too, as in every other industry, management becomes a decisive factor.

THE ECONOMIC IMPORTANCE OF THE LITHO-GRAPHIC INDUSTRY

The question is often asked, "How many lithographic plants are there in the United States?" Those who ask this question sometimes want to know the number of plants whose chief item of production is lithography. Others want to know the total volume of lithography produced, while still others want to know the approximate number of firms who have lithographic equipment, even though it may be but a small part of their productive equipment.

The number of lithographers operating in this country depends on the definition of "lithographer." Obviously firms specializing in operating lithographic presses are lithographic firms. Then there are those firms who operate a number of small duplicating presses, such as the Multilith or the Davidson. These small firms operate their equipment on the same principles and utilize, in a large part, the same supplies and materials as the owner of a larger lithographic plant; finally, they produce a lithographed product. Some of these small duplicating press owners do a volume running into six figures and therefore can be considered as lithographers. However, if such a firm has only one or two small duplicating presses, should it be considered a lithographic plant? If the answer to this question is in the affirmative, then the number of lithographers is much higher than otherwise.

TABLE I
Census of Lithography **

Year	Number of Establishments	Wage Earners	Value of Receipts
1899	263	12,994	$ 22,240,679
1904	248	12,614	25,245,266
1909	318	15,073	34,109,233
1914	336	15,171	39,135,973
1919	331	15,618	73,151,115
1921	296	13,971	79,472,260
1923	328	16,317	91,670,752
1925	331	16,957	98,721,268
1927	309	16,348	97,050,124
1929	376	18,979	121,014,321
1931	364	16,215	87,164,000
1933	346	14,579	68,447,000
1935	387	17,688	92,046,916
1937	516	22,533	129,244,000
1939	789	26,000	159,527,000
1947	1413	52,408	485,081,000
1954	2924	77,037	853,571,000
1958	3746	89,678	1,290,412,000
1959	* NA	94,472	1,496,383,000
1960	* NA	102,462	1,662,437,000
1961	* NA	102,273	1,685,760,000
1963	6822	121,072	2,150,000,000

* NA . . . Not Available
** Does not include *lithographic production* of greeting cards, books, lithographic plates made for others.

TABLE II
Value of Shipments ($1,000)

Products	1954	1963	% Change
Newspapers, ready prints, etc.	2,481	9,165	+87
Magazines and Periodicals .	34,195	138,547	+72
Maps, Atlas, and Globe Covers	4,082	11,996	+65
Cards other than Greeting Cards	4,507	4,717	+ 4
Labels and Wrappers	98,019	147,343	+33
Business Forms	112,000	300,000	+63
Tickets and Coupons	1,702	6,883	+75
Calendars and Pads	32,222	24,457	−25
Catalogs and Directories . .	50,452	165,269	+70
Other General Commercial Printing	469,484	99,528	−76
Decals	11,339	10,559	− 1
Book Printing	72,940	230,796	+70
Litho Plates Made for Others	40,952	129,502	+68
TOTALS	934,375	1,288,762	+27

*Source: Census of Manufactures, Bureau of Census

It is very difficult, therefore, to give an incontestable figure, because there is no one source of figures that covers all phases of lithography. The best source of information is the Census of Manufactures of the U. S. Department of Commerce. For companies primarily engaged in lithographing in 1958 the following figures were released by that agency.

Number of establishments: 6,822; wage earners: 121,072; value of receipts: $2,150,000,000. The last figure, however, excludes lithographic printing done by letterpress establishments (although it includes any receipts for any other printing processes performed in the primarily lithographic plants). Table I, Census of Lithography, was especially prepared for this study and reflects the growth of lithography from 1899 to 1963.

Table II, Lithographic Commercial Printing By-Products, provides a more comprehensive picture of the lithographic industry for the year 1954 and the year 1963. A study of the percentage change shows which branches of lithography have grown fastest.

An examination of the figures also shows that the number of lithographic plants in 1963 was almost 43% more than the 3,746 reported in 1958 and the value of receipts in 1963 was about 40% more than the value of receipts in 1958.

The effort to determine the number of lithographic plants is further complicated by the fact that there are many "cap-tive" plants which produce both paper and metal lithography in business concerns doing printing solely for their own use; and further, that there are some who utilize lithographic equipment for research purposes. It is estimated that, including all firms who own presses 17 x 22" or two or more duplicating presses or larger equipment, there are no less than 7,000 lithographic firms.

Because of different methods of collecting and assembling information, in Table II 1954 and 1963 Census of Manufactures, this data is not strictly comparable in all cases. For complete information, reference should be made to the detailed census reports available through the Printing and Publishing Division of the Department of Commerce.

THE WIDE RANGE OF LITHOGRAPHED PRODUCTS

What types of products does the lithographic industry turn out each year to amass such impressive figures? In its earliest days litho stones were usually employed to produce drawings and paintings by well-known fine and commercial artists. Years later, with the advent of photolithography, many lithographers made their living turning out comparatively short runs of such inartistic items as office forms, cards, mailing pieces, etc. In more recent years, however, and particularly since World War II, color has come into great demand, and offset has been ready to supply it. The process is used for such high quality jobs as direct mail advertising, business reports, point-of-purchase material, posters, display cards, packaging materials, bank stationery, books and book jackets, magazines, maps, menus, cards, calendars, decalcomanias, metal products, (such as beer and oil cans, trays, etc.) and (as history repeats itself) art prints.

The rapid expansion of lithography, the figures indicate, has not altogether been at the expense of other processes— all processes have made marked gains in recent years—but, it is interesting to note that lithography's gains have outdistanced all others. During the past thirty years the dollar volume of lithography has increased from about 10 percent to about 25 percent of the total printing dollar volume.

THE BEST IS YET TO COME

Prophesying is always risky, but even a conservative person will agree that the future of lithography seems assured. If the past permits conclusions for the future, the growth of lithography will continue for many years to come. The lithographic industry has many modern well-equipped shops and commands a large number of highly skilled craftsmen; the product of lithography is in demand wherever printing is bought; new developments are in process in every phase of lithography. Last but not least important, the amount of knowledge residing in the industry is most impressive as reflected in the fact that so large a volume as this edition of the Lithographers Manual is considered as only a survey of the industry. *The best is yet to come.*

CHAPTER TWO

LTF Now GATF—The Keystone of Modern Lithography

Section One: GATF—The Trail Blazer of Graphic Arts Research

Every industry has its own problems, its own peculiar conditions and its own laws of inertia that cause it to pursue scientific developments. This would seem to be particularly true in the case of such a complex printing process as lithography.

When the Lithographic Technical Foundation (now Graphic Arts Technical Foundation) came into existence in 1924, few people in the printing industry could foresee the far reaching consequences this institution would have for one branch of the printing industry. And yet, a small group of men recognized the necessity for the systematic development of scientific and educational knowledge essential for successful lithographic reproduction.

Who were these founders and what were their reasons for founding LTF? They were Alfred B. Rode of Rode & Brand; William H. Merten of Strobridge Lithographing Company (now a division of H. S. Crocker Co. Inc.); R. V. Mitchell of Harris Automatic Press Co. (now Harris-Intertype Corp.); Joseph Deutsch of Edwards & Deutsch Lithographing Co.; and Maurice Saunders, first Executive Director of the National Association of Employing Printers (now the Lithographers and Printers National Association).

The first LTF Board of Directors consisted of William S. Forbes of Forbes Lithograph Mfg. Co., Boston (now a division of Diamond-National Corp.); Albert J. Ford of Fuchs & Lang Mfg. Co., New York (now Sun Chemical Corp.); Charles W. Frazier of Brett Lithographing Co., New York (now a division of Diamond-National Corp.); John J. Gleason of Gleason Printing Co., St. Paul, Minn.; Leroy Latham of Latham Litho. Co., New York; A. B. Lewis of George D. Barnard Co., St. Louis, Mo.; David L. Luke of West Virginia Pulp & Paper Co., New York; Earl H. Macoy of National Printing & Engraving Co., Chicago; R. V. Mitchell of Harris-Seybold Co., Cleveland (now a division of Harris-Intertype Corp.); Alfred B. Rode of Rode and Brand, New York (now a division of Stecher-Traung Litho. Corp.); Charles F. Traung of Stecher-Traung Litho. Corp., San Francisco; Sidney L. Willson of American Writing Paper Corp., Holyoke, Mass.

Why did William H. Merten suggest setting up the Foundation at the 1921 Convention of the National Association of Employing Lithographers? And why did the Association decide to create the suggested cooperative research and educational institute at its 1923 convention?

The above questions are best answered with the words of Alfred B. Rode who served as LTF's president for many years:

1. The remarkable phenomenon of the increasing rate of obsolescence
—products, processes, established enterprises and even whole industries being superseded as a result of scientific and engineering progress;

2. Increasing evidence that no enterprise or industry can hope to maintain the status quo in a world that has discovered scientific research as a practical tool;

3. Advancement in industrial methods requiring a more and more highly trained personnel.

Read these sentences over again! Then decide whether or not they are still valid for our times. Revolutionary changes had taken place in the graphic arts and had resulted in a realignment of forces and in an entirely new outlook. The offset process had revived lithography and had given it new life. A new competitor, gravure, had entered the field. The result was a race in which still newer competitors might enter and in which honors and profit would go to the most resourceful. In short, the time was ripe for lithographers to get together and support a program of systematic research and education effort for the industry.

A LOOK AT THE TWENTIES

When the founders of LTF became conscious of the need for lithographic research, they were not under the impact of the atomic age. In 1923, Hiroshima was twenty-two years in the future and atomic physics was not even a recognized branch of science. It was the year that Dr. Millikan of the University of Chicago received the Nobel Prize "for his work on the elementary electric charge and on the photo-electric effect."

Television was unheard of, radio was in its infancy—WEAF in New York broadcast the first commercially sponsored program in 1923—the age of plastics began with the manufacture of cellophane by Dupont. Ford cars without self starters cost $290 in 1924. A Zeppelin crossed the ocean and RCA demonstrated wireless transmission of photographs!

And what about lithography—where did it stand? In 1923, there were 328 lithographic establishments in the United States, employing 16,303 people, producing a product valued at less than 92 million dollars. Forty years later, there were almost 7,000 establishments, employing approximately 121,000 people with a product value of over $2,000,000,000.*

---

* These figures are based on the U.S. Census. They do not reflect the total size of the industry because many of the uses of lithography—metal decorating, etc.—are not included in the census data. The total figures exceed the census figures by far.

The Early Days at the University of Cincinnati

HOW LTF WAS FOUNDED

After consultation with many people in 1924, it was decided (to quote Mr. Rode again): "to organize the Lithographic Technical Foundation as a non-profit corporation with a dual program—research and education. To finance this program, the founders chose the method of endowment—the establishment of a perpetual trust only the income of which was to be used."

The purpose of the Foundation as stated in the original Certificate of Incorporation, dated April 21, 1924 was as follows: "The particular objects for which the corporation is to be formed are exclusively charitable, scientific and educational; but limited to the following purposes and objects, that is to say—the promotion and encouragement of the training and education of lithographic workmen, the promotion and maintenance of lithographic trade schools; the investigation, research and discovery of subjects, principles, laws and processes of a scientific or technical character which relate to lithographic processes; and the application of such knowledge to the improvement of those interested in the lithographic trade."

In this declaration of purposes are the principles that have made LTF what it is—a unique organization that combines education, scientific research, practical development, the dissemination of newly gained knowledge, and the application of it to the whole industry. This combination of activities, this search for new horizons and the enlargement of the scope of people in the industry, have made the Foundation the living, moving force of the lithographic industry.

LTF'S FIRST TWENTY YEARS

An endowment fund of approximately $750,000 was raised, and at the same time research was started. Working at the University of Cincinnati, Robert F. Reed became the first research director for the new organization on March 1, 1925. He worked under very moderate conditions for many years, his assistants being mainly physics and chemistry graduate students who worked part time. If we consider that the research budget never exceeded $25,000, until 1945, it is hard to understand how Mr. Reed managed to produce the significant results that emerged from that modest laboratory.

In the same year that Mr. Reed started lithographic research Layton S. Hawkins, an outstanding figure in industrial education, established educational activities in New York. How the Foundation operated during the next twenty years, how the depression and World War II affected this organization, cannot be told here. But the second World War contributed greatly to the transformation of lithography from a handcraft to a full-

The GATF Library in Glessner House

fledged graphic reproduction process. There were also disruptive effects from the war and the depression years on the Foundation. The original endowment had shrunk to $448,000 and the annual income was down to approximately $29,000. It became obvious that a thorough readjustment to the changed times was needed and, in 1944, a group of energetic business men headed by E. H. Wadewitz, President of Western Printing & Lithographing Co., took the initiative in a reorganization.

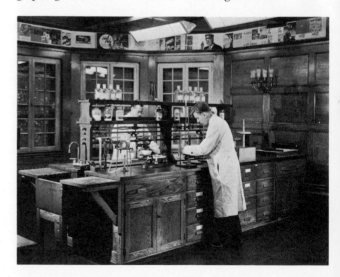

A Laboratory in Glessner House

REORGANIZATION

The most important single step taken was to introduce professional management. The man chosen to head LTF's new management group was Wade E. Griswold who served as Executive Director from 1944 to 1958. LTF was transformed into an effective and generally respected model of graphic arts research and education. In 1959, William H. Webber succeeded Mr. Griswold as Executive Director and he has been responsible for further reorganizational measures. The membership had grown to more than 1,000 companies in 1963. In addition to the United States and Canada, there were member firms in 33 countries. The research and educational programs were considerably broadened and improved to meet the industry's needs.

LONG RANGE PLANNING

In 1963, after an intensive study of the research and educational needs of the industry in an era of increasing technological change, a Long Range Plans Committee recommended that the Foundation broaden the scope to include all areas of the graphic arts. LTF's name was changed to the Graphic Arts Technical

The E. H. Wadewitz Memorial Library

Foundation, and the Board of Directors also approved the Committee's recommendation that the Foundation consolidate its educational, research, and administrative operations in Pittsburgh.

THE TECHNICAL CENTER

In November, 1965, the Foundation formally dedicated its new, four-story Technical Center in Pittsburgh, Pa. These contemporarily designed administrative and educational headquarters, as well as research laboratories contain expanded quarters for GATF's growing programs, including a technical library, seminar rooms, laboratories, and a large research pressroom.

Exterior View of GATF

The Center was built by the gifts of nearly 800 industry donors who pledged a total of $1,272,000 in cash and securities to underwrite the costs of the building. An additional $367,000 was contributed in equipment, making the Technical Center one of the finest equipped research institutes in the graphic communications industries.

Section Two: Planning and Management for Progress in Lithography

GATF takes pride in being a member-supported and member-directed institution. It is governed by a Board of Directors composed of industry representatives. These directors are elected by the membership of the Foundation. Both the membership and the Board of Directors represent a cross-section of the graphic communications industries.

The Board of Directors elects the members of the Executive Committee and the officers of the Foundation. The Executive Committee acts for the Board in matters of policy and the development of the Foundations' annual budget. The Board also elects the members of the Finance Committee which oversees the investment portfolio of the Foundation.

The President of the Foundation appoints the chairmen of standing Board committees, such as Long-Range and Public Relations and *ad hoc* Board Committees. He also appoints the chairmen and steering committees of various departmental functions, such as research, education, special programs, and technical services.

All of these committees are composed of industry representatives or such allied industry groups as graphic arts education, unions, trade associations, research institutes, etc.

Professional management is in the hands of an Executive Director. The staff directors of the four operating departments —education, research, special programs, and technical services, and the two service departments—administration and public relations—report to the Executive Director.

THE BUDGET

GATF's programs and activities have undergone an extensive expansion over the last five years. In large part, this is because of industry's increasing demands for Foundation services and programs. It is also because of the Foundation's expansion into graphic communication processes other than lithography. Finally, it is because of the growing requirements for more sophisticated research and education programs and the consequent increase in the cost of maintaining such programs.

In 1958, the Foundation's annual budget was $347,000. By 1963, it had increased to $570,000. The budget for 1968 totals $1,068,000—a three-fold increase in ten years. Compare the 1968 budget with the highest annual budget prior to the reorganization of 1944–45—$41,000!

The Foundation receives its annual support from (1) membership dues; (2) other member contributions; (3) income from investments; (4) income from departmental activities and programs; and (5) federal grants.

In 1967, earned income totaled $430,000, an increase of 26 per cent over 1966. Most of this increase was the result of GATF's receipt of a Special Merit Grant under the State Technical Services Act of 1965. This was the second year in which the Foundation was given such a grant. The grant is designed to enable the Foundation to accelerate its technical education and information dissemination programs.

Investment income, too, increased in 1967 over the previous year. Up 14 per cent, it totaled $102,000.

Net assets of the Foundation have increased from $2,000,000 to $4,000,000 over the last ten years, largely as a result of industry's generous financial support of GATF's Technical Center.

MEMBERSHIP

The Foundation was initially organized as an endowed institution. It was intended that it would operate on the income from the endowment. However, the depressions of the 1930's depreciated the endowment, and budgets exceeded annual income (which meant that the Foundation was depreciating its endowment).

During the 1944–45 re-organization, a method of yearly support was devised and applied. In effect, the Foundation had established two forms of membership: endowment and yearly.

Endowment Membership had started with the beginning of the Foundation. It is divided into four classifications: Founder Member, $25,000 and over; Benefactor Member, $10,000 to $25,000; Life Member, $5,000 to $10,000; and Associate Member, $1,000 to $5,000.

A member earns an Endowment classification, an honorary category of membership only, according to the amount of contributions over and above yearly support which the member has given the Foundation since his enrollment in GATF. These contributions may be in cash or securities or they may be in the giving of services, equipment, supplies, etc.

As of 1967, some 381 GATF members held an Endowment Membership.

Yearly Membership, which began in 1945, consists of three categories: Annual, Sustaining and Contributing.

Glessner House

On January 1, 1968, the Board of Directors voted a new dues structure. While GATF membership has been increasing at a stable rate in recent years, the percentage of income derived from membership dues has been dropping. Of all income received, membership dues represented only 32 per cent in 1967 while it represented 59 per cent in 1958.

In addition, GATF had not had a dues increase in ten years; mergers and consolidations tended to inhibit membership growth; inflation was causing a decline in the purchasing power of the dollar; and GATF's programs had been vigorously expanding.

For these reasons, the directors voted to change the membership dues structure.

Annual Membership now costs $300 per year. Any company may join the Foundation at this rate.

Sustaining Membership now ranges from $400 to $2,000 per year, dependent upon a guideline formula of graphic arts sales volume or total graphic arts payroll. This is a voluntary membership which companies may take upon their own choice. About 40 per cent of GATF's membership hold a Sustaining Membership.

Contributing Membership, costing $25.00 per year, is open to any employee of a member firm. It was initially designed so that member firms could add additional key personnel to the Foundation's mailing listing to directly receive its various publications, reports, textbooks, etc.

Full-time teachers and students of graphic arts and related fields may also take a Contributing Membership in the Foundation. GATF offers a Special Education Discount of 40 per cent to these persons. This GATF subsidy allows full-time teachers and students to gain the benefits of GATF membership at $15.00 per year.

MEMBERSHIP BENEFITS

The graphic communications industries benefit from the work of the Foundation in a variety of ways.

Indirectly, all companies in these industries receive some benefit from GATF programs. There can be little doubt that GATF's work in education has played a major role in the up-grading of all industry craftsmen over the years, whether or not they have been employees of a representative firm. GATF's work in research, and in the establishment and up-grading of industry's technical standards, has assisted all in the industry and not merely the membership.

Directly, each member of the Foundation has available a number of special benefits. They include:

Research Progress Reports: six to eight yearly bulletins describing GATF research developments and how they may be practically used.

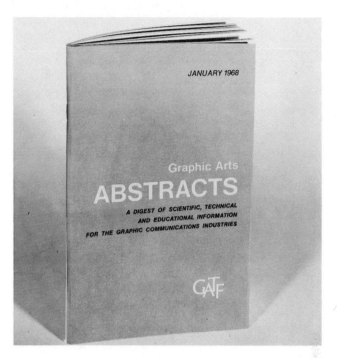

Graphic Arts Abstracts

Education Reports: a new series of bulletins giving information on graphic arts education and designed primarily for teachers in schools or in-plant training programs.

Special Reports and Proceedings: occasionally issued reports on unique research, surveys, or conference proceedings.

Special Programs: The Foundation conducts a wide variety of programs designed to keep those in graphic communications abreast of the latest technology. These programs take a variety of forms—seminars, held at GATF's Technical Center in Pittsburgh, Pa.; workshops, forums, and conferences held in cities throughout the U.S. and in other countries; specially designed programs for the specific needs of GATF members or sectors of the graphic communications industries.

SEMINARS. The Seminar is an intensive education program by research and technical staff. Attendance is limited to groups of 10 to 20 persons. The Seminars usually run for three days. They have been a most effective means of disseminating techni-

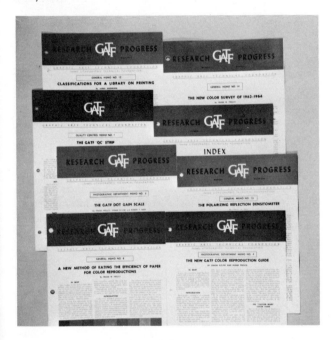

Research Progress

Graphic Arts Abstracts: a monthly digest of important technical articles in nearly 400 foreign language and English periodicals.

Information Services: photocopies of technical articles, literature searches, and bibliographies, available at special member rates.

Technical Services: expert and experienced staff capable of solving plant and supplier technical problems through in-plant or laboratory evaluation and analysis. GATF members receive these services at special member rates.

Education Services: helpful counseling on in-plant and school programs, or consultation on other training and education problems. Special member rates are available to GATF members.

Educational Aids: Textbooks, audio-visuals, instructor and student materials plus other training aids for in-plant programs, graphic arts schools, and self-study.

Technical Service Reports: a quarterly publication containing helpful technical information for production and other personnel.

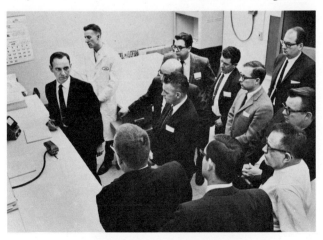

Seminar Session in the Color Lab

cal information, because of the limited size of the audience, the fact that facilities of the Foundation are available throughout the program, and staff can be fully utilized. For this reason major attention has been focused on the seminar program since its inception in 1957 and the program has been expanded considerably. More members of the research and technical staff of the Foundation are being brought into the seminar program, and even more attention is being given to discussion of specific problems of plants of participating people.

Seminars are now presented in the following areas:
1. Plate & Press Problems
2. Web Offset
3. Paper & Ink Problems
4. Color & Color Reproduction
5. Process Quality Controls
6. Paper & Ink Testing
7. Packaging
8. Offset Techniques
9. Halftone & Process Photography

TECHNICAL FORUMS. The GATF Technical Forum is a day and a half program covering all of the major aspects of the lithographic process. The program is designed for large audiences who can attend a Friday evening session and all day Saturday sessions. In this way, the Foundation is able to take an expansive technical program to a large member of industry personnel. Over 80 Technical Forums have been presented to audiences ranging in size from 150 to over 1,000 production, supervisory, sales, and technical management personnel. Forums are conducted primarily by members of the technical and research staff.

Group Attending a Workshop

The program presents technical information during the Friday evening session that is generally useful to all in attendance. During most of the program on Saturday, participants are divided into separate concurrent sessions consisting of platemaking, press operations, color reproduction, and paper and ink problems. During these sessions, specialized technical instruction is provided for the specific needs of those in each group.

WORKSHOPS. The Workshop is an adaptation of a seminar-type program to a format which permits its presentation in various industry centers around the country and abroad. The Workshop is of shorter duration than the seminars, being conducted in one or two days, and the program is open to larger audiences than the seminar (50–150 registrants compared to 12–20 registrants). Thus, the Workshop, unlike Seminar, is presented to a much larger number of participants, and unlike the Forum, presents technical information in a specialized area of knowledge. Because of these advantages, great attention is being focused on expansion of the Workshop program.

Workshops are currently conducted in the seminar subject areas of Color Reproduction, Plate & Press Problems, and Paper & Ink Problems.

Group Attending a Technical Forum

CONFERENCES. A Conference is a one- or two-day technical program directed more to engineering, research, technical-management and other professional personnel. The program is directed at a fairly specialized area of technical information, with the program devoted to new technology and research accomplishments and progress. The Conference utilizes not only staff of the Foundation but industry specialists and leading research men throughout the industry.

Section Three: Research and Development for The Graphic Arts

Through a series of meetings during 1965, members of the Research Steering Committee of the Foundation examined and re-evaluated the research objectives, practices, and policies of the Foundation. As a result of this study, the committee submitted to the Board of Directors and they, in turn, after discussion, subsequently accepted the following statement of research objectives. In addition to the following statement of objectives, a detailed statement of research policy to govern research practices was also developed.

The general research objective of the foundation is the conduct of research on the nature and the relationships of processes and materials involved in the total processing of graphic images, including all phases of production from initial preparation through final finishing as related to commercial graphic arts operations.

The specific research objectives are:
1. Study and understand the present and future technological needs of the graphic arts industry.
2. Accomplish studies to aid in the realization of continuing efficiency in the use and relationships of materials, supplies,

facilities and personnel making up the complete production system.

3. Review and understand work carried on outside the Graphic Arts Technical Foundation with relation to the GATF research objectives.

4. Accumulate readily retrievable information on work at GATF and on related research or technical work done elsewhere.

5. Do, and have done, specific laboratory work to develop desired information not available elsewhere.

6. Develop and assist in the development of uniform standards of measurement and necessary standard instruments and procedures to aid in the overall control of processes.

7. Develop specifications and, when necessary, develop evaluation instruments and procedures for better performance.

8. Interpret and disseminate information on all pertinent research results to assist in improved economic performance of the industry.

9. Communicate progress and results of GATF research in useful form to the membership and the industry.

THE EQUIPMENT OF THE RESEARCH DEPARTMENT

The Research Department occupies a specially designed underground level at the Graphic Arts Technical Center. Because of the critical limits of relative humidity and temperature needed in a research atmosphere, the underground laboratory allows extremely fine controls for relative humidity, temperature, and even air pressure. For example, in one research laboratory (the TAPPI Laboratory) tolerances of ±2% in RH and 1° in temperature can be maintained at a predetermined level. The photographic-process camera rooms have greater air pressure in the room than in the surrounding corridors. Therefore, dust and other airborne particles are forced out of the room, rather than circulating in the same air current which feeds the room.

The research level is actually a pilot graphic reproductions plant. There are two process cameras, and a full complement of processing equipment, a special color evaluation room, paper and ink problems lab, chemistry lab, instrumentation lab for designing and constructing needed research devices or prototype

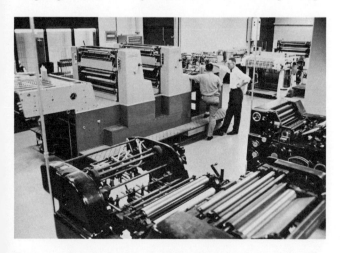

Research and Reduction-to-Practice Pressroom

quality control devices, a complete platemaking room, and a pressroom with equipment ranging from single-color small offset to two color 35″ perfector, and a web press capable of printing letterpress, gravure, and flexography simultaneously. The equipment on the research floor is valued at nearly a half-million dollars.

ORGANIZATION OF THE RESEARCH DEPARTMENT

The Research Director administers, reviews, evaluates, and guides the activities of the Research Department. The department contains seven divisions, each under the direction of a technical expert. The divisions are: (1) Paper, Ink & Chemistry; (2) Engineering; (3) Color & Photography; (4) Reduction to Practice; (5) Physics; (6) Instrumentation; and (7) Technical Information.

The Tappi Laboratory

NEW DEVELOPMENTS

Usually, new developments involve at least two and frequently more research divisions. Work is planned by the heads of these divisions under the direction of the Research Director. The staff then does the necessary scientific research with the participation of division supervisors. If the experiments are satisfactory, the Reducation to Practice Division enters the project.

This Division handles the new project in the same manner as a lithographic plant. In this way, many of the bugs or kinks inherent in every new development become obvious. After they are discovered, there is more lab testing and experimentation. Changes and adaptations are made until the Reduction to Practice Division is satisfied that the new development is practical and of real value.

At this point, the new development is again evaluated by the Research Steering Committee which then selects or approves a number of plants in different regions of the country for additional practical testing.

If minor technical problems still occur, the development is brought back to the lab for further study, modification, lab, and plant testing. Every comment, and every observation stemming from plant testing, is studied and considered before the new item is presented to the industry.

ACHIEVEMENTS OF FOUNDATION RESEARCH

Some of the contributions made by the Research Department in the areas of photomechanics, stripping, platemaking, paper, ink, presswork and quality control are reviewed below.

Photography and Color Reproduction. This subject was of interest to LTF as early as 1935 when it started work on contact screens, which have since attained great importance in photomechanical reproduction. This has been due in part to the work done by LTF in developing and publishing methods for the making of contact screens during the decade between 1935 and 1944, and again in 1951. (GATF Txb. 216—Designing and Making Contact Screens)

In 1937, the Research Department made a thorough study of camera positives versus contact positives. In the same year, it standardized the procedures for dot etching and developed two very important methods, one for producing stain-free positives, and another for controlling the work.

The problems of tone reproduction had been under study for a long time. The first results of a thorough study of dot area, dot density, and tone value in lithography using densitometric measurements were published in 1945. Later (1954), the LTF Contact Printing Lamp was developed to eliminate undercutting of contacts due to the light source.

Methods of producing shaped vignettes photographically were developed in 1954 and in 1956. The Research Department developed the LTF Color Test Strip and designed the LTF Color Chart for use by individual plants. This was the first practical and accurate chart to help control the uniformity and quality of process color work under individual plant conditions.

The first industry wide study of color reproduction was conducted in 1957. Techniques were devised to measure, plot, and evaluate process ink colors. When the relationships between the capabilities and limitations of color separation photography and process ink colors became better understood, work was started that eventually produced Balanced Process Ink colors. A second color survey was conducted in 1963–64 to again evaluate and compare various properties of process inks, and how they printed as combinations with each other. The principles of hue and grayness of a process ink were combined graphically in the

color circles. The various process inks in the 1957 survey are plotted on circle 1, while the inks of the second survey are plotted on circle 2. The two circles will indicate the greatly improved printing color of the various process inks, and the improved quality of the actual printed product which resulted from the study stated in 1957.

In 1957, glass screen halftone techniques were improved, and new methods for the measurement and analysis of photographic problems were introduced.

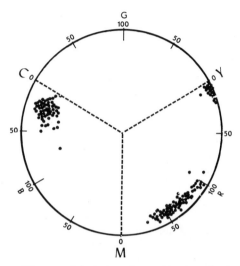

Range of Process Ink Colors Being Used in the Industry

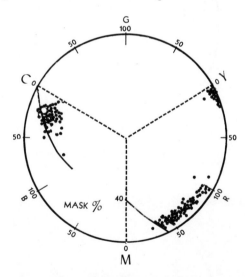

Lines Show Which Pairs of Cyan and Magenta Inks Could Be Corrected with a Single 40% Mask

Photographic masking was simplified and color separation methods were improved. In 1963, methods for color separating line copy appeared in Research Progress Number 63, and in 1964 Research Progress Number 67 reported the development of the color reproduction guide. The color reproduction guide combined solids and tints of the process colors as single prints, two-color overlaps, three-color overlaps, and a four-color overlap. The guide facilitated masking and screening procedures which would take into account the individual plant's paper, ink,

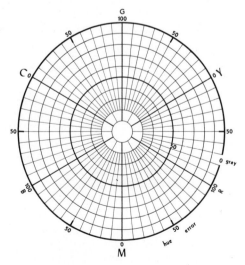

The GATF Ink Hue and Purity Chart

and printing variables in process color reproduction.

In addition to purely photographic research, the Foundation explored the proofing techniques for such new areas as four-color magazine web-offset printing on coated papers. After extensive evaluation and investigation of the requirements of four-color wet-offset proofing, and in cooperation with other associations, the Foundation developed (1968) a standard offset color control bar. The proofing bar consists of solids and tints of process colors and their overprints for densitometric measurement and evaluation. The bar also includes several quality control devices created by GATF for visual evaluation of dot gain (checked with the GATF dot gain scale), slur (checked with the GATF Slur Gauge), doubling (checked with the GATF Star Target), and other factors which affect printing quality.

Stripping. This is an area that does not lend itself easily to formal research. The Foundation has, however, contributed much, particularly in combating stripping faults that could lead to plate-making troubles.

One example of this kind of technical advance resulted from the cooperation of the Foundation with manufacturers of pres-

sure sensitive tape to produce tapes of proper optical characteristics and working qualities that would prevent reactions on the plate coatings from the adhesive. Also, the opacity of masking materials were made of different weights and colors to determine those best suited for lithographic requirements.

Platemaking. Not too many years ago, this was the most troublesome element in lithographic printing. Today, because of research, the plate is the least difficult factor in lithographic production, and it is generally acknowledged that the Foundation deserves major credit. Here are some of the major developments of plate research.

The years between 1928 and 1948 saw the development of the Bichromated-Gum Desensitizing Treatment for zinc, and new formulas for etches as well as the testing of well-studied etching techniques to permit every etch to perform its best. In 1932, LTF pioneered pH control and the use of the Baumé Hydrometer. The now classic 3:1 colloid-bichromate ratio was established at the time, and data on the effect of relative humidity on plate coatings was first released. Comprehensive data on the proper procedure for making albumin plates was published in 1932.

To reduce the danger of occupational dermatitis, Lithotine, a non-toxic substitute for turpentine, was developed in 1933. Shortly after this the first complete data on deep-etch platemaking using the gum process was compiled and published, followed in 1944 by information on an improved method of making deep-etch plates.

The Cronak plate surface treatment to prevent the oxidation of zinc plates was improved and announced in 1946, and the Brunak process for aluminum plates followed a year later. Other surface treatments included Post-Cronak and Post-Brunak in 1949, the Post-Phosphate Treatment in 1952, the Post-Nital Treatment in 1954, and the Nicohol Treatment for deep-etch plates in 1958. The concept of surface treatments to prevent undesirable reactions between plate metal and coating was picked up by supplier manufacturers leading to the development and widespread use of presensitized and wipe-on plates.

Other research highlights include intensive and fundamental scientific studies on the sensitivity of bichromated coatings which produced the LTF Sensitivity Guide in 1948, and recommendations for improved plate etching techniques. Recommendations for standardized graining procedures were published in 1949.

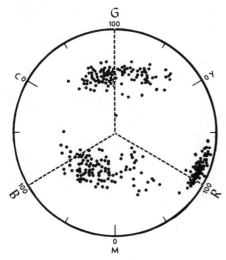

Typical Reds, Greens, and Blues Produced by
Two Color Overprints

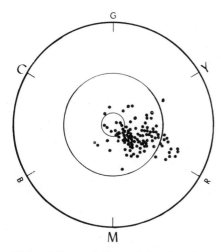

Typical Hues of Three Color Overlaps

The Sensitivity Guide

In 1952, the Research Department announced its grainless deep-etch zinc and aluminum plates, a dramatic demonstration that a grain was not necessary for a plate to print on the press. It started the trend to finer and finer grains which improved tremendously the overall quality of lithographic printing. In addition, LTF developed the copper-aluminum bimetal plate, now marketed as Lithengrave.

Non-blinding lacquers for both surface and deep-etch plates were introduced in 1953 and improvements in chemically copperized deep-etch images came in 1955. The ultra-fine brush graining technique was announced a year later. Again, these were tremendous improvements to assure the life of plates and the quality of the printing.

Another major contribution was the publication of simple and practical methods for comparing and evaluating different platemaking methods and materials. This enables a plant to select those best suited for their individual requirements.

An investigation into the reasons for the corrosion of aluminum plate images was made in 1959 and a solution found for the problem. Research in 1960 to produce an ultra-fine tub grain for zinc made possible the development of a zinc wipe-on plate. A time saving Ink-Developer which develops the plate, inks the image and desensitizes the background in one operation, was part of this new plate process.

There is no doubt that all this work has revolutionized lithographic platemaking. Lithographers now have a choice of plates to fit a particular job—plates that not only stand up in performance but are capable of producing the finest quality of printing available.

Paper Research. LTF started, encouraged or sponsored much of the research done on offset paper. Since 1925, considerable technical data on lithographic paper problems has been gathered and published. Simple methods for testing paper in a lithographic plant have also been published.

During this continuing work, the Paper Hygroscope was developed, in 1931. This instrument measures the relative humidity of the pile of paper. It is possible with this instrument to foresee trouble during the run due to a wrong moisture balance between the paper and the air in the pressroom. In 1936, the Register Rule, which makes systematic register control possible was designed.

The idea of pre-conditioning paper at the mill to match conditions in the buyer's pressroom was pioneered in 1937. The first control system for conditioning the relative humidity and temperature of paper in the plant was introduced in 1940.

The LTF Pick Tester was developed in 1952 to measure the pick strength of paper. This instrument also makes it possible to predict how paper will perform when the job goes to press.

Data was published in 1955 on how to identify hickies and spots to determine whether press troubles were caused by paper or by other problems.

Previous studies were reviewed and new work involving the relationship between paper, relative humidity, and color register were again discussed in Research Progress Number 54, published in 1962. In 1963, the affect of paper gloss and paper absorption on the resulting color of a standardized ink where combined in the Paper Surface Efficiency Factor for evaluating and comparing the predicted color of an ink on a specific printing surface. Continuing studies have explored the mysterious phenomena of chalking, gloss ghosting, and other strange ink drying factors. By extensive use of the elaborate scientific instrumentation available at the nearby Mellon Research Institute, University of Pittsburgh, and Carnegie-Mellon University, studies have been conducted on the highest possible scientific levels.

Ink Problems. Research on ink parallels the scope of that done on paper. The Foundation has concentrated on the use and handling of paper and ink—the relationships between paper and ink—rather than on the actual formulation or manufacture of these two products.

The LTF Inkometer, developed in 1939, is a practical instrument for measuring ink tack and testing inks under operating conditions. With this instrument ink manufacturers have been able to conduct more effective research resulting in litho inks of better quality and uniformity. Additional work on the Inkometer, aimed at making it the industry's standard tack testing device, has been in progress since 1953.

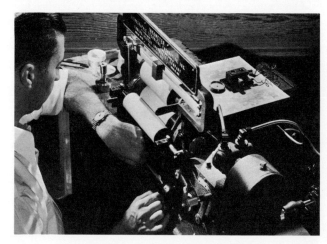

Testing Ink Tack on the Inkometer

Basic scientific information for lithographers on the drying of lithographic ink was published in 1944 dealing with the effects of moisture, paper pH, and fountain solution pH on ink drying.

In 1954, the first working model of the Press Inkometer was developed to measure the ink-water balance on a press in operation, and the first plant tests were made in 1961.

Current studies with especially built equipment are concerned with ink transfer to establish what the differences are—and the "why" of the differences—in the way various types of inks print on different papers or other surfaces.

The work on ink and paper makes it possible for the industry to standardize techniques, to adjust inks for different papers, improve trapping and thereby avoid troubles and delays in production.

Presswork Research. The work that is done in this area relates to methods and materials used on the press rather than to the design and building of press equipment. Of the many contributions made to presswork by the Foundation, the following are particularly significant.

In 1927, basic information on the electrolytic effect of brass rollers in the water fountain on the plate was patented.

Starting in 1929, four comprehensive surveys that followed through to 1948 were made to evaluate lithographic blankets. These studies for the manufacturers have enabled them to progressively improve their products. It is reported that the life of a blanket has increased on an average of from one hundred thousand impressions to well over a million.

The Litho-Kleen blanket and roller cleaner was developed in 1939 and the first Blanket Packing Gauge was designed in 1945. Four years later, a study on the cause and remedy for dot slurring on coated paper was published. The Blanket Thickness Gauge was developed in 1951.

In the same year, press roller wash-up materials were studied, tested and greatly improved, and non-foaming solutions for washing dampeners were developed in 1951. Later, LTF started its testing, evaluation, and encouragement of research on throwaway paper dampeners. In this same year, the Foundation brought out the method—and the materials for it—to copperplate steel rollers during the wash-up. This technique can eliminate stripped ink rollers on the press.

Since 1953, the Research Division has been working on and experimenting with dampening systems and has patented two with electrostatic and pneumatic controls. Considerable work on methods to eliminate dry-scuffing was done in 1956. In 1958, the Foundation cooperated with F. C. Wildeman in the testing and evaluating of the work done to produce the Magnetic Packing Gauge. Similar testing and evaluating for manufacturer's has been conducted on various types of plates, plate surfaces, blankets, papers, inks, and other materials. All this contributed to make the lithographic process the success it is today.

Quality Control. Obviously, all the knowledge, methods, materials and instruments that GATF has been developing are related to quality control. But in addition to what has been mentioned here, there are many other contributions by the Research Department which are specifically aimed at the measurement and control of printing quality.

The designing and the construction of the LTF Recording Densitometer took place during 1949–51. This instrument made it practical to collect the large amount of statistical data necessary to conduct research on print quality. In 1957, announcement was made of a method for measuring graininess in printing. This device quickly and accurately measures the important factors which constitute quality in the printed image. The LTF Star Target, a device for measuring ink spread and resolution was developed in 1960. In the same year, an instrument for measuring print sharpness and resolution was announced. Future work with the Print Quality Instrument can lead to whatever true press automation there will be in the future.

A CASE HISTORY OF RESEARCH

The foregoing illustrates how long lithographic research takes and how many people may be involved. For example, the GATF Print Quality Instrument was developed after years of print quality studies by many people. It is of particular interest, too, to note by-products that result from research work—the tools, instruments and knowledge that can be put to work quickly and which progressively improve technology and quality control.

Although it probably was not recognized as such at the time, it can now be said that work on the Print Quality Instrument was started in 1932 when studies were made of the tone reproduction characteristics of glass halftone screens. Later on, further extensive research was conducted through 1944 to acquire more scientific data in the broad area of tone reproduction. Publications were issued as knowledge accumulated.

The first step in the print quality project was to define what is meant when we say quality. This called for a statistical study of comments made by many people on samples of good, bad, and indifferent printing.

Three principal factors emerged that appear to govern the impression of quality: (1) interference patterns such as graininess and mottle; (2) image definition or the sharpness and resolution of fine detail; and (3) tone and color reproduction—the relationship of the hue, saturation, and lightness of corresponding areas in the original and the lithographic print. The accumulation of the required quantity of data by the manual operation of a standard densitometer would have been a staggering and impossible task.

So, in the period of 1949–51, LTF designed and built its Recording Densitometer. This device mounts a micro-densitometer head on a moveable carriage above a plate-glass table. The head was designed and built by LTF staff. Held to the table by vacuum are test press sheets, over which the carriage is moved slowly. As it does so, the electrical signals generated by the different ink densities on the printed sheet are amplified and used to operate a device that draws a graph. The required data is then taken from the graph.

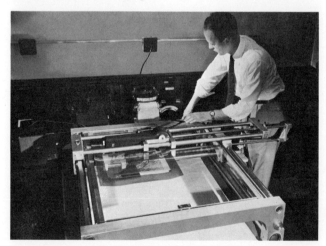

The Recording Densitometer

Using the recording densitometer, studies were made on graininess and mottle, and their effect on print quality during 1952–1955. A number of people looked at printed samples and graded them for graininess. Different ways of measuring these sheets were tried with the recording densitometer until a method was found that graded the samples in the same order that the observers did.

The first work was done with only a few samples of light, moderate and severe graininess. The differences were so great that everyone agreed on the order of the rating. Later, samples were added in which the differences in graininess were not as obvious. This, in turn, required improvements in the measuring method so that the ratings of the recording densitometer continued to be in agreement with the human judgments.

Then there followed similar studies on sharpness and resolution of halftones in 1956–1957.

As the basic research project progressed, a number of simplifications and improvements were made in the measuring techniques and equipment. It was found, for example, that all the information necessary for the measurements could be taken from a 150 line, seventy percent line-tint control strip only 1/16 inch wide.

EQUIPMENT DEVELOPMENT FROM RESEARCH

At one point in the print quality studies an effort was made to

The Contact Printing Lamp

improve the light source on the recording densitometer. A wide variety of miniature low voltage electric lamps were obtained and studied. One of these had a heavy filament in the tip of a glass envelope about 3/8 inch in diameter and about an inch long. While this particular bulb did not work on the densitometer, it was thought that it might be very suitable as a near point-source light in photographic operations. Further work resulted in the development of the GATF Contact Printing Lamp for photographers. Such a light source eliminates undercutting due to the light source, and is now widely used in the industry.

Quality Control Devices from Research. The studies of sharpness and resolution in printing quality included an investigation of targets or test shapes that could be printed on the press sheet and measured to produce the required data. And here again, an important by-product was developed—the GATF Star Target. This is a half-inch diameter circle with thirty-six black and white wedges of equal size. When printed on a sheet, the shape and size of the center, where the lines converge, was found to be a very sensitive measurement of the ink spread and slur that occurs on the press. Thus another valuable tool for achieving high quality in printing was gained. Platemakers can use it also to measure dot sharpening or spread in platemaking.

Though the Recording Densitometer works well as a research tool, it has disadvantages as an instrument for plant use. The speed of the machine is limited to the speed that the electrically operated pen can be moved over the record paper to draw an accurate graph. Secondly, it is necessary to take the information from the graph, and use it in a number of rather involved mathematical equations to obtain the rank numbers.

The important thing in the operation of the Recording Densitometer is that the basic information comes from the photocell in the form of a varying electric current. In this case, the current is amplified and used to operate a pen. So, the next logical step was to do the computations electronically in the measurement of the different quality factors. This investigation produced the first model of an actual and practical Print Quality Instrument.

The Print Quality Instrument

This was accomplished by developing a number of analog electronic computer circuits. The same basic electric current from the photocell fed into the different computers gives a direct measurement of the different quality factors as a reading on a meter. The current can also be put into an oscilloscope. The picture on the face of the cathode ray tube shows the various quality factors as differently shaped traces. The characteristics of the traces on the picture tube and the meter readings permit fast corrections of the press adjustments to bring the printing back to within the limits established from the OK sheet.

The first prototype of the Print Quality Instrument was completed in 1961. In its use, a line test strip is cut from the OK sheet and taped around a drum. The drum is revolved, the scan is made, and the measurements of the various quality factors are given ... all this in less than a minute. Test strips from sheets pulled during the run are measured and compared with the original OK sheet strip.

Information given by the instrument includes (1) The distribution of the ink film across the press sheet; (2) Reflection densities (or tone reproduction) of the halftones and solids; (3) The sharpness of the halftones; and (4) The graininess and mottle of the halftones and solids.

While the print quality instrument has been a research tool, the special test strip has now been developed into a simple, visual control device for the pressman. This strip is now called the "QC" Strip.

GATF can now foresee using the electric current generated by the Recording Densitometer's photoelectric cell to operate servo-mechanisms on the press that automatically adjust ink feed or water feed, for example. In other words, press automation to maintain the acceptable quality of the OK sheet throughout a run is now feasible and likely to come.

As mentioned, the Print Quality Instrument represents years of work by many people. Outstanding among the early contributors on tone reproduction studies were Robert F. Reed and Paul W. Dorst of the GATF staff. Their work was extended by George W. Jorgensen, who later was assisted by William B. Lyon, to include other factors in the development of the instrument.

FUTURE TRENDS OF LITHOGRAPHIC DEVELOPMENT

The Graphic Arts Technical Foundation will continue to develop the many areas that comprise lithography as in the past. In the decade following 1947, research was centered on the lithographic plate. Now that plate problems are minor, attention is focused on the problems of reproduction quality, process color work and basic problems in the relationships between paper and ink.

Process color printing, which is scientifically the most advanced branch of printing, has become more and more important in lithography. At the same time, and precisely because it requires a good basis of knowledge of physics and optics, it is a difficult subject for many lithographic craftsmen.

Largely, through the Foundation's work, the lithographic process is now capable of producing fine quality printing. But, it is not yet possible to produce this high quality consistently in every job. Continuous research is bound to shed more light on the remaining variables in the process and help to develop methods and tools with which to measure and control these variables.

There is a vast and thorny field waiting to be tilled. It is not easy to develop the needed communication between the men of science and lithographic craftsmen. But the Foundation has almost forty years of experience in doing this. If past work is used as a yardstick, there will undoubtedly be many notable achievements in the future.

Section Four: The Role of Education in Graphic Arts

There are good reasons why a technical education program in lithography was recognized as a vital necessity as early as the 1920's. Offset lithography is fundamentally a chemical printing process and it requires of lithographic craftsmen a knowledge of chemistry, physics, and mathematics, along with the craft skills of the process. Since lithography is not a mechanical process, it is necessary to understand the science of the process to be a top craftsman and technician.

There was another important reason why the lithographic industry, over 40 years ago, decided upon industry-owned facilities, both in research and in craft and technical training. Since lithography is a variable process, and has the potential for good and inferior quality, the high quality potential is what excited the interest of the group who founded the Lithographic Technical Foundation (Graphic Arts Technical Foundation). If through research, the process could be improved and, if through better craft and technical education, the potentials of the process could be realized, lithography had a bright future. This early investment in the Foundation—in research and education—has certainly "paid off" in the growth of lithography.

One other factor that makes lithographic education essential is the multiplicity of small lithographic plants. Most company members of the Foundation do not have regular training departments. They do not have specialists to handle training programs or provide instruction. This makes it essential that educational training materials be provided, and that they be designed to meet the needs of the small and medium sized plants as well as the large ones.

EDUCATION DEPARTMENT

In 1967 the GATF Education Department was organized into three main areas of activity: (1) The Education Council of the Graphic Arts Industry; (2) The National Scholarship Trust Fund; and (3) Graphic Arts Technical Foundation programs. The various activities of the department are listed under one of the three areas; however, these projects, programs and activities are complementary to each other and are administered under the GATF Education Department.

Purpose. The GATF Education Department provides educational assistance to industry and the graphic arts education field. Its activities include the publication of textbooks, instructor materials, and self-study booklets; the development of audio-visuals; administration of scholarships and fellowships; providing educational consulting service to industrial plants, schools, and various institutions and graphic arts training centers; the conducting of training workshops for personnel responsible for training programs in their organizations; providing of aptitude testing services; and the conducting of special programs such as careers, awards, film library, and educational exhibits.

The Education Department represents the Foundation at various educational meetings and conferences; promotes special educational activities with other graphic arts organizations and groups; and maintains liaison with government educational agencies and educational associations.

Statement of Objectives. In previous years the main purposes of the Education Department were to assist in setting up craft and technical education programs, and publish and disseminate technical information. With the affiliation of the Education Council of the Graphic Arts Industry and The National Scholarship Trust Fund with GATF, there has been an expansion of the educational activities. The general objectives are to:

1. Study and evaluate the present education needs and determine the future direction of educational programs;

2. Provide information to teachers, guidance counselors, and students about the graphic communications industry.

3. Maintain a leadership role in assisting the graphic communications industry in selecting and training personnel for the industry.

4. Maintain liaison and develop programs with industrial, educational, and governmental organizations and agencies.

5. Provide opportunities for teachers of graphic communications to upgrade themselves in industrial processes and procedures.

6. Increase an international leadership role in the development of publications and audio-visuals;

7. Carry on educational research related to graphic communications;

8. Develop various types of publications and audio-visuals related to general and technical graphic communications infor-

mation, and serve as an authority on the usefulness of educational and training materials for the industry;

9. Provide financial assistance to young men and women interested in a career in graphic communications.

Committees. There are four committees in the educational structure directed to guide the various activities. They are: (1) GATF Education Steering Committee; (2) GATF Education Committee; (3) Education Council Executive Committee; and (4) National Scholarship Trust Fund Trustees. The general purposes of each committee are to:

1. Provide direction for the specific projects and activities of the Education Department.

2. Render assistance in evaluating educational materials.

The GATF Steering Committee is that arm of the GATF Education Committee charged with the responsibility for acting on behalf of the entire committee during intervals between Annual Meetings. It exercises authority in making emergency decisions between Annual Meetings and reports such action to the Education Committee.

Educational Committee Meeting

The Education Council Executive Committee acts on behalf of the members of the Education Council of the Graphic Arts Industry. It, too, exercises authority in making decisions between Annual Meetings. When GATF and the Education Council affiliated, a decision was made to have the Education Council Executive Committee and the GATF Education Steering Committee meet as a joint committee for the purpose of planning programs and activities.

The National Scholarship Trust Fund Trustees are directly concerned with the administering of funds for the scholarship and fellowship programs. The NSTF Trustees meet during the Annual Meeting. NSTF Officers also attend meetings of the GATF Education Steering Committee and Education Council Executive Committee.

TEXTBOOKS

The textbooks published by the Foundation cover nearly every phase of lithographic production. Within this range,

Courtesy Eureka Specialty Printing Company
Division of Litton Industries

An In-plant Training Program

Some Books Published by GATF

there is a wide variety of treatments, from the broad appeal of the "Lithographers Manual" to the advanced technical information found in "Tone and Color Correcting." Some books assume only an apprentice's understanding; others require a craftsman's experience. All (with the exception of The Lithographers Manual) are in paperback or loose-leaf form, written in an easily read style, and complete with charts, diagrams and illustrations.

TRAINING MATERIALS

The second principal category of the GATF education program is training materials. For many years, GATF has been publishing training courses for use in in-plant and appentice school training programs. These instructional materials, which are based largely on GATF textbooks, are professionally written and validated in plant and school programs.

GATF's comprehensive training materials present the knowledge necessary for satisfactory performance in each of the craft classifications. They are designed for students and trainees in lithography. The aids include plans for instructors, self-study workbooks, and programmed lessons for trainees.

Instructor Materials. The Instructor Materials are designed for in-plant instructors, supervisors, foremen, or experienced craftsmen who are selected as instructors, mainly for their technical experience. These materials are also suitable for schools with graphic arts courses. All information is outlined into workable lesson units explaining the specific subjects, the order of presentation, sample job sheets, and the teaching aids required for each lesson.

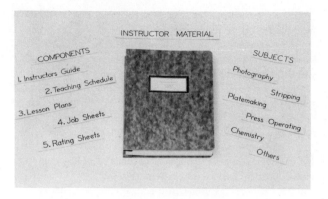

Instructor's Material

Self-Study Materials. The Self-Study Workbooks contain the lesson materials for students and trainees. These workbooks are conveniently organized into short reading assignments, self-check lessons which reinforce the new knowledge, and review examinations. Both the Instructor Materials and Self-Study Workbooks are based on GATF's technical publications.

Individualized instruction, which includes self-study, has already made a major contribution in the technical education of students and trainees in the graphic communications industries. Individualized instruction allows the learner to become an integral part of the learning process; his involvement with educational materials is first-hand. Extensive technical depth can be more easily conveyed through the individualized approach, also allowing the student to progress at his own speed.

Self Study Workbook Material

In addition to the self-study series, the Education Department has also developed programmed instruction courses. Programmed instruction, which is one form of individualized instruction, is based on four educational principles:

1. The learner works individually at his own pace;

2. A relatively small amount of technical information is presented to the learner at one time;

3. The learner becomes actively involved as he is required to make some type of response.

4. The learner is immediately informed whether his response is correct or not, as the correct answer is made available for review and reinforcement.

The educational implications of programmed instruction are many. A few of these are:

1. The learner can work at his own pace, on his own time, and with a minimal amount of supervision;

2. The instructor can devote more time to developing materials that will supplement the learner material, and devote more time in special consultation with the learner;

3. The learner is assured that the material is necessary to satisfactory performance, and that all technical material and procedures have been reviewed and approved by the most authoritative technical experts.

Audio Visual Components

Audio-Visuals. GATF Audio-Visuals demonstrate the latest methods and procedures used in lithography and will result in better craftsmanship, improved quality, and greater profits. They are designed for individual use or in technical sessions, and for in-plant or school educational programs.

The slide format may be used with either a script or a sound tape, providing maximum flexibility for use with a group or for individual instruction. One script is automatically provided with each purchase of slides. Additional scripts are available at extra cost. The cost of sound tapes is in addition to the cost of slides.

IN-PLANT CONSULTING

One of the essential educational services GATF offers is a consultation service to plants to assist them in setting up training programs tailored to particular needs. When plants get together to establish a training center in an area, the Foundation provides advice on the overall program, content of courses, curricula and training material.

In recent years, the Education Department has cooperated with numerous medium to large printing firms in the states. Also, education departments in South America; apprentice groups in South Africa and Europe have availed themselves of this consultation service by means of correspondence.

COOPERATIVE PROGRAMS

GATF cooperates with other industry organizations on many projects. Of particular importance is a joint GATF-PIA Foreman's-Management Program. This is an organized course of leadership training designed to assist foremen in perfecting the three basic skills of a supervisor: (1) Leadership, (2) Instruction, and (3) Work methods improvement.

Trainer conferences are organized as the first step of the program. These are conducted by professional trainers and attended by industry people selected with a view to their becoming leaders in the foreman's management training program in their home areas.

NATIONAL SCHOLARSHIP TRUST FUND

In order to assure that the industry will have a continuing supply of well qualified and trained managers, designers, scientists, engineers, economists, accountants, and other professional personnel, various members of the Education Council have established the National Scholarship Trust Fund. NSTF was organized in 1956 by the executive committee of the Education Council, with the assistance of industry leaders. The purpose of the Trust Fund is to provide scholarships to qualified and interested students who want to prepare themselves for careers in this growing, dynamic industry.

Each year's competition provides approximately a dozen four-year scholarships to students who have demonstrated their interest in pursuing graphic communications careers. The grants range in value from $100 to $1000 per academic year for each of the four years. The Education Council is in the process of increasing the number of awards through an active program based on the theme that "Education Is Your Company's Economic Security."

The first annual National Scholarship Program of the Printing and Publishing Industry was established for the 1958–1959 academic year.

In 1963, NSTF broadened its program by establishing a fellowship competition to aid students interested in furthering their education through graduate studies in the graphic communications field. Seven firms now provide funds through the Technical Association of the Graphic Arts which, with NSTF, administers the awards.

The fellowships are awarded for research and study in mathematics, chemistry, physics, industrial education, engineering, and business, as a means of promoting the study of the basic sciences and their application to the graphic communications industries.

EDUCATION COUNCIL OF THE GRAPHIC ARTS INDUSTRY, INC.

The Education Council carries the programs of the GATF Education Department into the public school systems, community colleges, trade and technical institutes, and four year colleges and universities. The Education Council represents an expanding GATF philosophy by promoting education at all educational levels and in all areas of study appropriate to the graphic communications industries. As an example of the total concept of graphic arts education, the major programs of the Education Council are given below.

Career and Recruitment. The need for competent men and women who will enter the industry is strongly suggested by the estimated sales volume growth of the industry from $20 billion in 1968 to $35 billion in 1975, a 50% increase in the volume of printed material by 1975, and 80% by 1980. Career and recruitment programs are, therefore, an absolute necessity. The Education Council also provides career and recruitment brochures which represent the entire industry, and a career "kit" for counselors, graphic communications instructors, and speakers. The kit contains an approved script, an audio-visual presentation, brochures and other descriptive material, and general information for the speaker. Long range career and recruitment programs have been developed with the assistance of national guidance counselor associations, other printing and publishing associations, and teacher groups.

Aptitude Testing. The Education Council directly provides an aptitude testing service for the following positions; Printing Salesman Trainee, Printing Estimator Trainee, Printing Management Trainee, Tape Perforating Machine Operator Trainee, Business Forms Salesman Trainee, and Clerical Trainee. These test batteries have been specifically researched and validated for printing occupations. The Education Council also cooperates with the United States Bureau of Employment Security in validating aptitude tests for prospective craft trainees. Over thirty-five job classifications have been studied by the U.S.E.S. The tests are administered directly by the local state employment service office.

Film Lending Library. The Education Council is the only national organization which provides a film lending service on graphic communications topics. Such a service has proven invaluable to schools with limited access to certain types of printing operations; to apprentices or students who would benefit by a visual presentation of a subject; to management personnel conducting orientation courses; or to those who just want to see what is going on in other parts of the industry. The Council has approximately a dozen titles on their current listing.

Cooperative Industry Exhibits. To maintain maximum personal contact with many large groups in the educational community, various Education Council members sponsor a cooperative industry exhibit. The exhibit is displayed at five major educational conventions each year. In this way, the programs and services of the Education Council are presented to these groups. At the same time, the exhibit is one of the most valuable ways in which Education Council personnel can "feel

out" the needs of educators, and thereby plan programs which will satisfy their ever-changing needs.

Curriculum Development. In cooperation with the Education Department of the Graphic Arts Technical Foundation, the Education Council is able to provide a wide range of curriculum development services to schools and the industry. The Foundation has an educational staff which is fully qualified to analyze, evaluate, and structure a complete school graphic arts curriculum. This service may also be extended to suggesting possible shop laboratory layouts, and contacting various manufacturers who can assist the school or plant in selecting equipment and supplies. The department is also experienced in constructing instructor guides, organizing course outlines, publishing textbooks, and designing other teaching aids.

Awards Program. The Council actively supports the philosophy that individual and group recognition is a positive factor in the success of any program. To this end, the Council annually awards the Elmer G. Voigt Award for outstanding work in the field of graphic arts industry education in the service of the national association with which an individual is affiliated. The James J. Rudisill Award is presented each year to local graphic arts associations chosen for conducting an outstanding program of cooperation with their local school system toward the development of improved programs in graphic communications education and training. The Horace Hart Award is presented annually to an individual employed in Federal, State, or Local Government who has encouraged, sponsored, or personally directed a notable advancement in education for the printing and publishing industries.

Special Projects. From time to time the Education Council is called upon to perform or negotiate a special program which has either immediate or far reaching consequences. A few of the recent projects are described below, many of which have been completed, with many in the planning stage.

In response to the growing use of small offset equipment in public school systems, in government training programs, and in the industry, the Council cooperated with the Department of Labor in constructing a small offset-press operating course. The material is designed largely for the MDTA programs, and for school use. It is also useful for industrial training.

To get to the heart of the manpower situation of the industry, the Council has investigated existing statistical data gathered by various government agencies and reviewed gathering procedures used at the various national agencies. To date, various trade associations and companies have been brought together for evaluating the manpower status of the industry.

FUTURE ACTIVITIES OF THE EDUCATION DEPARTMENT

The changeover from Lithographic Technical Foundation to Graphic Arts Technical Foundation involves broadening the scope of the Education Department to cover other printing processes. This will come about as membership and support come from graphic arts areas other than lithography. The aim in looking ahead to expanded coverage is to equip GATF to do the best possible job, through research and technical education for the graphic arts as a whole—now and in the future.

When consideration is given to the fact that a young man in his twenties entering the graphic arts industry has forty working years ahead of him, and that much of the equipment he is now using may become obsolete in the course of that time, it is obvious that it is not enough for a man to learn only to *operate* a piece of equipment. It is necessary that he know not only what he is doing but the whys and wherefores. He must know the chemistry, the physics and the underlying principles of his craft if he is going to be responsive and adjust to a rapidly changing technology.

As printing by all processes continues to grow and prosper, it will require more highly trained technicians to match the advancing graphic arts technologies.

CHAPTER THREE . .

The Flow of Lithographic Production_____

Section One: General Exposition of Lithography

In this section we are not concerned with the detail of lithography but only with its essentials. For the purpose of our presentation the subject is divided into the following units: (1) Alphabetic printing and picture printing, (2) Lithography and photography, (3) Water and oil do not mix, (4) The offset method, (5) The principle of Rotary printing, and (6) Lithography as an integrated industry. Each of them is presented in the following.

ALPHABETIC PRINTING AND PICTURE PRINTING

Printing in its original form (and that means letterpress or typographic printing) was marvellously suited for the mechanical reproduction of the written word. But it was sorely lacking when it came to picture reproductions. The nature of relief printing explains this limitation. For this reason a variety of picture reproduction methods such as etching, engraving and last but not least, lithographing developed side by side with printing. They are the forebears of our contemporary gravure and lithographic processes.

Stone Lithography was Not Suited for Printing Reading Matter in Bulk. Letterpress and stone lithography were in almost exactly opposite positions. Letterpress was badly limited in picture reproduction, but excellent in

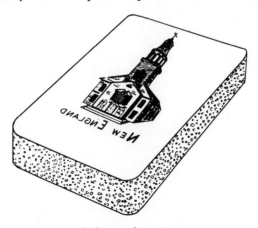

A lithographic stone.

the printing of the written word; stone lithography excelled in picture reproduction, but was badly limited in its ability to duplicate the written word. Many books were produced by combining two processes, the verbal message was printed in letterpress and the pictures in engraving or lithography. The term "plate" that you still find used in books for full-page color illustrations reminds us of this condition.

Stone lithography was originally and for many decades primarily a picture printing process. It enriched the graphic arts in its own way, but did not change the existing division between printing of verbal and of pictorial matter by reproduction processes.

The Challenge of Photography to All Reproduction Processes. Things went on about the same way until the advent of photography. Photography brought a revolution to the graphic arts: Photography was responsible for an entirely new kind of picture that was in universal demand; a picture tied to the fleeting hour and impossible to reproduce by manual skills. All processes of printing were stymied. When it came to reproducing photographs, all were equally impotent.

The Equalizing Effect of Photography on Printing. But photography was not only a challenege to printing, it was also its great benefactor. Photography achieved what had seemed impossible for centuries: the combining of pictures — including photographs — with reading matter into a single printing plate. Even more! Photography achieved this result not for one or another graphic arts method but for the whole lot. Photography has become the greatest equalizer in the printing industry. This revolution has been going on for about a hundred years; it is still going strongly even though the first signs of a change, electronic devices, have already appeared. It is a sad proof of human inertia that many printers have not yet grasped the immense consequences of this photographic revolution. But ideas move fast; people are slow.

LITHOGRAPHY AND PHOTOGRAPHY

The relationship between lithography and photography is a very old one. Lithography actually stood at the cradle of photography. Joseph Nicéphore Niepce, to whom photography owes so much, began his experiments in 1813 with lithography. The two arts have been related to each other ever since. Nobody can hope to understand lithography without a good basis in photography.

Lithographic Printing Plates are Made Photomechanically. Lithography was the first printing process that learned to make its whole printing plate, pictures and reading matter as well, photographically and photomechanically. But platemaking is not the only field of application for photography. Photography makes possible the conversion of pictures into printing plates and provides the lithographer with a variety of fast and economical processes for this purpose.

The Role of Photography in Color Printing. Last, but not least, photography spearheads the drive for economical and true color reproduction. No other topic can compare in interest for lithographers to this one. No other market for lithography is as bullish, as wide open as the color market; no other field is wider, more rewarding. Here too photography, including the related science of color, holds the key to success. No word is strong enough, no sign sufficiently arresting to emphasize how much a knowledge of photography, photomechanics and the science of color means for a modern lithographer.

WATER AND OIL DO NOT MIX

Our discussion of photography and its paramount role in modern lithographic production might lead the reader to the question whether there is anything left of the original invention, whether we have any right but that of custom and tradition to speak of lithography at all. This question can be simply answered without any if's and but's. Yes, there is something left of the original invention; yes, we have a right to call our process by its original name.

Lithography Has Retained Its Basic Principle. In spite of all developments, in spite of all metamorphoses that lithography has experienced, in spite of the fact that we neither use stones, nor write on them as the word lithography suggests, our process has still retained its basic principle. It is the proverbial truism that water and oil do not mix. Like all such simple statements it has its limitations when we get to the finer points. But for a basic explanation it may be taken at face value.

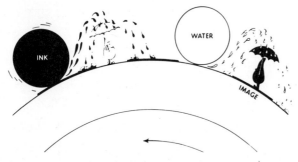

Oil and water resist each other.

The Printing Image Carrier Is the Most Characteristic Element of Every Printing Process. What bearing does the fact that water and oil do not mix have on lithography? To answer this question we must turn to the printing plate of lithography. The printing plate or, as their variety is called by a collective noun, the printing image carrier is the most characteristic element of every printing process. By comparing different printing image carriers we can learn a great deal about different printing processes.

The Essential Features of Lithographic, Letterpress, Gravure and Silk Screen Printing Image Carriers. If we look at a lithographic printing plate, we find that here the printing and non-printing areas have almost the same level. In letterpress, things are radically different; there, only the raised areas of the printing image carrier are inked and thereby also print. In gravure, on the other hand, things are exactly the reverse because there only the intaglio or sunken areas of the plate print. In silk screen, finally, the printing image carrier consists of a porous fabic through which the ink is pressed according to a pattern for printing.

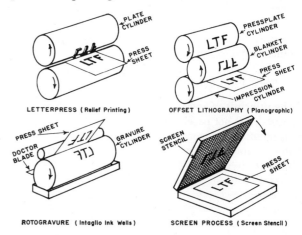

The four principal printing processes.

Chemical Plate Treatment Is the Key to Lithographic Printing. In lithography, the printing and non-printing areas are at approximately the same level in the printing image carrier. In spite of this fact, ink adheres only to the printing areas of the plate and does not adhere to the rest. This unique result is based on the principle that oil and water don't mix, or — if we may re-phrase this statement — that ink is water-shy. (Ink consists to a large proportion of oils or other greasy substances.) *In lithography, the printing areas and the non-printing areas lie at the same level of the printing image carrier but they are differently treated chemically.* The non-printing areas are chemically treated for the contrary effect, namely, to be ink-repellent. A solution containing primarily water plays the key role in this process.

THE OFFSET METHOD

The overwhelming majority of contemporary lithographic presses use the offset method of indirect printing. This method is not restricted to lithography, but it is nowhere in the graphic arts used to the same extent as in lithography. For this reason lithographic printing has become widely known as offset printing.

The Blanket Is Essential for the Offset Method. In offset or indirect lithography, the inked plate image is not directly impressed on the paper or other printing stock but transferred to an intermediate member, the blanket, which in turn makes the impression on the paper. Offset or indirect printing is a very essential feature of modern lithography. Old-style lithography was printed directly on the paper, either from stones or from metal plates; modern lithography prints indirectly and is therefore known as offset lithography, or abbreviated in colloquial speech, as offset printing.

The Consequences of Offset Printing. Indirect or offset printing has many consequences. One of them is the reversal of the plate image before it is transferred to the paper. Offset lithographic plates can therefore be made to *"read right"* as the printer says. The other result of the offset method is its ability to print finer detail on coarser or structured papers than is possible in direct printing. The blanket is comparatively soft and elastic, it snuggles itself onto the surface of the paper without squashing it. Still other consequences of the blanket will occupy our attention in other chapters when we discuss the process in its detail.

THE PRINCIPLE OF ROTARY PRINTING

The principle of rotary printing is used in many printing processes; it is not peculiar to lithography. But rotary printing is important for contemporary lithography, photography, photomechanics and indirect or offset printing.

The Principle of Rotary Printing Accounts for a Faster and More Economical Kind of Printing. All modern lithographic printing is done on rotary presses.

The consequences of rotary printing are difficult to exaggerate. Rotary printing is, other conditions equal, the fastest and most economic type of printing. The speed of offset printing as well as its comparatively simple makeready are intimately connected with rotary printing.

LITHOGRAPHY IS AN INTEGRATED INDUSTRY

The lithographic business is, as a rule, operated as an integrated business. The term integrated means in this context that a printing plant handles and controls a job in all its phases from the prepared copy to the completion of running.

Integrated Plants Have Their Own Platemaking Departments. Integrated lithographic plants have their own platemaking departments. But there are also plants that prefer to buy their plates from outside sources specializing in platemaking. This is particularly true for process-color printing. Many lithographic plants that make their own plates for all other jobs, buy plates for process-color work from specialized platemaking houses.

Integrated Operation Has Benefited the Lithographic Industry in General But May Not be Advisable in Specific Cases. The ways of American lithographers are not uniform; making plates inside of a plant is not necessarily preferable to buying them. But there is a school of thought that attributes the general growth of lithography to lithographic research directed towards all phases of lithography. The fact that so many lithographic businesses are operated as integrated plants is responsible for this all-embracing approach to lithographic research. Even though the author of this study is partial to this school of thought, he *wants to emphasize that the advantages and disadvantages of operating a platemaking department cannot be determined by generalizing, but only by detailed analyses of specific cases.*

Section Two: The Main Steps of Lithographic Production

In this section we present a brief survey of the main steps, and therewith the main production departments commonly found in a lithographic plant. The purpose of this presentation is two-fold: We want to survey the field for those who are not too well acquainted with it, and at the same time we want to provide a guide to and through The Lithographers Manual.

The subject is divided into three units: (1) The main steps of all graphic reproduction processes, (2) The flow of lithographic production, and (3) The lithographic industry. Each of these is presented in the following.

THE MAIN STEPS OF ALL GRAPHIC REPRODUCTION PROCESSES

All printing processes provide mechanical reproduction of graphically expressed statements or messages. These can be divided into two groups: reading matter and pictures. Reading matter does not need further explanation; under

pictures we subsume the great variety of drawings, paintings and photographs. As was pointed out in the preceding section, the efficient combination of both kinds of graphically expressed statements — *reading matter and pictures* — into one printing image carrier is a comparatively recent achievement that is due primarily to the progress of photography.

The Common Steps of All Graphic Reproduction Processes. All reproduction processes must take several steps in order to fulfill their tasks. If we want to bring these steps to some common denominators we can do that by distinguishing five phases of graphic arts production. These five phases are: (1) Art and copy preparation, (2) Conversion of art and copy into printable form, (3) Assembling the converted elements into a printing image carrier, (4) Printing itself or making the impression, and (5) Binding or finishing. Every graphic reproduction process takes these steps, but every one takes them in a different manner and also to a certain extent in a different order.

General Discussion of the Five Phases Common to All Reproduction Processes. Some of our five phases are self-evident, others need a few explanatory words. Art and copy preparation belongs to the first kind. It is the phase that provides the subject matter of printing. Two other more or less self-evident phases are printing itself, or making the impression and binding or other finishing.

Conversion of Art and Copy into Printable Form and Assembling the Material into a Printing Image Carrier. The two phases that need explanation are conversion of art and copy into printable form and assembling the converted material into a printing image carrier. These two phases are — if you permit a little sensationalism — the secret phases of printing, its real inside story. The first three mentioned phases are known to most people who have even a remote interest in printing: Everybody has seen art and copy, presses and the finished printed product. Not so the other two phases. They are highly technical and vary for every process and even for different applications and methods within a process. Both phases are necessary steps in the making of the printing image carrier, the most characteristic element of every process.

The Four Elements Necessary for All Printing Processes. All printing processes require a combination of four elements: (1) The printing press, (2) The printing image carrier, (3) The printing ink, and (4) The paper or other printing stock. The act of printing or making the impression takes place in the printing press. The printing image contained in the printing image carrier is transferred during this act by means of the printing ink to the paper. In this process the *printing* image becomes the *printed* image. All contemporary industrial printing requires a most careful combination of these four elements.

Printing Without Ink. It might be mentioned that there are also ways of printing without ink. People who have lost their eyesight use their fingers for reading. Braille, the printing process for the blind, does not employ ink. Other processes, at the time of this writing in the development stage, use colored powders instead of ink. In spite of these exceptions, we may nevertheless say that ink is one of the four essentials of all — or practically all — printing for people in possession of their eyesight, and that is fortunately the overwhelming majority of our population.

The Role of Planning. Planning is one of the most essential steps in all printing. Planning coordinates the five main phases of printing; it is an absolutely necessary prerequisite of successful operation. As printing is done on all economic levels, from the one-man shop to the industrial giant plant, planning varies accordingly. But even the very small shop needs planning, possibly more so than larger organizations. Printing is an intrinsically hazardous business where a small undertaking can cause a big damage. The role of careful planning, therefore, can hardly be exaggerated.

How Lithography Copes with the Problems and Executes the Tasks Common to All Graphic Reproduction Processes. The following unit explains how lithography works. This unit is also a guide to the chapters

of The Lithographers Manual. Planning for a lithographic plant is the subject matter of the third section of this chapter.

THE FLOW OF LITHOGRAPHIC PRODUCTION

In this unit we will present how lithography copes with the five phases of all graphic arts production and how these phases are treated in The Lithographers Manual. We will also discuss the specific characteristics of the four main elements of all printing for the lithographic process.

Our discussion follows the departmental structure of a lithographic plant which is also the basic plan of organization for The Lithographers Manual. We begin with the inception of a lithographic job, the creation of its subject matter, and end with the printed and finished product.

But before you begin your round trip through a lithographic plant you will be interested in background information on the lithographic industry. The following paragraphs give you a brief resume of each chapter of the Lithographers Manual.

Chapter One: The History of Lithography. In this chapter you find a discussion of the most important events in the fascinating history of lithography. You will read about the change wrought by the introduction of the offset principle and follow the course of all major developments as they took place in the growth of our industry.

Chapter Two: LTF now GATF—The Keystone of Modern Lithography. In this chapter you will be introduced to GATF and its method of operation. You will learn how research is planned, executed and how the results of these activities are disseminated in the industry.

Chapter Three: The Flow of Lithographic Production. You are in the middle of this chapter when you read these lines. Following our section you find a presentation of estimating and production control in a lithographic plant. The next chapter takes you to the inception of a lithographic job, the place where art and copy is prepared.

Chapter Four: The Creative Art Department. The extent to which a lithographic job requires art and copy preparation depends entirely on the job. Nor is art and copy preparation necessarily a part of the lithographer's services. Many jobs are prepared by advertising agencies or the advertising departments of business organizations. Art services and free-lance commercial artists, photographers and typographers, are very often commissioned by the buyers of lithographic printing to prepare art and copy.

In The Lithographers Manual art and copy preparation is treated very extensively. Art and copy preparation influences many phases of production as well as cost, quality, and delivery of a lithographic job. Further, many people prepare art and copy for lithography but know very little about lithographic production. There are, of course, highly qualified commercial artists and art directors in the field. But they will be the first to confirm the fact that the overwhelming majority of those who prepare art and copy for lithography are not overburdened with knowledge on the subject.

The Lithographers Manual provides the reader with very

Copy preparation.

copy into printable form for lithographic reproduction. The camera department is a key department of integrated lithographic plants. Its function and equipment vary with the size and specialization of a plant.

Generally speaking, the camera department produces transparent photographic film replicas of the copy in which the printing and the non-printing areas are sharply distinguished.

Our presentation of the camera department is especially broad. It covers basic scientific subjects, layout and equipment, line photography and three halftone processes, and also includes a discussion of the job habits and attitudes of the cameraman.

Chapter Six: Color Separation Photography. In this chapter you find a detailed discussion of color separation photography. The most advanced methods are here set forth, including exact instructions for their practical execution. The emphasis put on color separation photography is in keeping with the general policy of The Lithographers Manual that color printing is one of the most topical subjects of contemporary lithography. This policy finds its most striking expression in the next chapter "Photographic Masking and Color Correcting."

Chapter Seven: Photographic Masking and Color Correcting. No other chapter in The Lithographers Manual is as indicative of the great impact exerted by science on contemporary lithography. Masking for color correcting is beyond doubt the most intriguing topic for the progressive graphic arts color reproduction specialist, the photographer in particular.

The subject is new and old, depending on your way of looking at it. Old in the sense that some of the basic work dates back almost half a century, new in the sense that photographic masking and color correcting has achieved

detailed information on art and copy preparation. The progressive and sales-minded lithographer will find many hints on economical and effective art preparation. The lithographic salesman who bears the brunt of trouble in the struggle for the right kind of art preparation can learn from the Manual how art and copy must be prepared and why. He will be better equipped to explain these necessities to the customer or his art department and therewith increase his own prestige as well.

Finally a word on type and copy preparation. Lithographers are more and more learning that the printing of books and other jobs containing large amounts of reading matter is just as much within the province of lithography as the reproduction of pictorial subjects. For this reason and also because of the new developments in the field of photographic and other non-metallic type-setting, The Lithographers Manual contains a very detailed presentation of typography.

Chapter Five: The Camera Department. In the camera department begins the conversion process of art and

Preparing to shoot the copy.

A litho artist at work.

industry-wide attention only recently. In this chapter The Lithographers Manual presents a unique collection of the most advanced work and the most important methods for process color reproduction.

Chapter Eight: The Litho-Art Department. The product of the camera department needs very often further treatment before it can be assembled for platemaking. The litho-art department is the place where highly skilled craftsmen improve the quality of negatives and positives, correct their flaws, and exercise special lithographic techniques for color reproduction. Once the material has passed the litho-art department it is ready for assembly.

Chapter Nine: The Stripping and Photocomposing Department. The stripping and photocomposing department is very characteristic for lithographic production. It provides the platemaking department with a complete and precise assembly suitable for making the final press plate.

Platemaking.

the great achievements of the Lithographic Technical Foundation and is prepared by the man who directed this work during the last decade.

Chapter Eleven: The Proofing Department. The proofing department has a variety of functions. It is one department that is bound to increase in importance with the growth of process-color work.

Lithography has developed a great variety of proofing techniques. These were developed in the course of years according to the needs of different plants. In The Lithographers Manual you find a systematical discussion and comprehensive presentation of the whole subject.

Layout and stripping.

But stripping consists not only in assembling, it includes many highly technical operations besides. Very often stripping combines various elements into one, or converts negatives into positives before they can be finally assembled. In The Lithographers Manual photocomposing is discussed as part of the "Stripping and Photocomposing Department" chapter.

Chapter Ten: The Platemaking Department. In the platemaking department the conversion of art and copy into printable form is completed. The product of the platemaking department is the assembled printing image carrier, ready for the press.

Platemaking was for a long time the problem child of lithographic production. It was also the first part of lithography which was subjected to scientific study and improvement. The results of this process are known to the industry. The Lithographers Manual presents a comprehensive description of the whole subject, including the scientific basis of the work. This chapter of the Manual bears witness to

Proofing.

Chapter Twelve: Lithographic Presswork. The pressroom is the department where the product of lithography is brought about. It is beyond doubt the most important department in a lithographic plant. Preparatory steps up to and including platemaking may be taken outside a lithographic plant, not so presswork. A pressroom is an absolute essential for every lithographic business.

In The Lithographers Manual this subject is treated with particular care and in a broad sweep. Here too you find discussions of the most modern equipment and techniques, from the single-color sheet-fed press to the complex multicolor web-press installation. Presswork is intimately related to ink and paper. They are the subject matter of the following chapter.

The lithographic press.

Chapter Thirteen: Ink and Paper. These two are essential in all printing production. They are also very important cost factors. In The Lithographers Manual ink and paper are accorded a treatment commensurate with the importance of the subject and the vast amount of research devoted to it. All points of interest to the lithographer and to his supplier are extensively discussed, together with a great deal of background information.

Chapter Fourteen: Binding. The product of the pressroom is a lithographed sheet. This sheet must in most cases be further processed before it becomes the finished product ready for final use. Binding is one of these subsidiary processes. Binding, too, is not a static industry, but in constant flux. In The Lithographers Manual you find a presentation of the subject including modern techniques of bookbinding and binding for advertising specialties.

Chapter Fifteen: Various Supplementary Processes. In many cases the lithographed sheet is not bound, but subjected to some other supplementary processes. Labels, for example, are bronzed and varnished; posters and displays may be silk screened before they are finished; or, they may be mounted and diecut directly after lithographing. In this chapter, The Lithographers Manual presents information on bronzing, varnishing, silk screen printing, mounting, die-cutting, display finishing and folding box making.

THE LITHOGRAPHIC INDUSTRY

Lithographers are not only interested in the detail of production, but also in their industry in general. They know that the well-being of an individual plant is closely related to the life of the whole industry. The closing chapters of The Lithographer's Manual are devoted to this subject.

Chapter Sixteen: Trade customs. Trade customs are very important, particularly in case of disagreement between customer and lithographer. In the Manual you find a discussion of trade customs including the citation of court cases and court decisions on a variety of points.

Chapter Seventeen: Glossary of Terms. As lithography develops so does its language. In this chapter you find a short dictionary of lithographic and many other related technical terms.

Bibliography. The literature on lithography and related fields keeps growing. The Manual presents a selected list of books as well as a list of periodicals regularly abstracted by GATF. Both lists were prepared by the Research Department of GATF.

Section Three: Estimating and Production Control*

In this section you find a description of the estimating and production control system used at the Spaulding-Moss Company in Boston. Our presentation of the system includes all forms used in its practical execution. The subject is divided into the following five units: (1) The Production Control Supervisor, (2) Estimating, (3) Processing the Order, (4) Production Control, and (5) Various Tie-in Functions. Each of them is presented in the following.

THE PRODUCTION CONTROL SUPERVISOR

The moment a lithographic sales department accepts an order it places the company under obligation to produce work:

1. When the customer expects it.
2. At the proper price.
3. Of satisfactory quality.

---

* Illustrations in this section are by courtesy of Marshall L. Russell.

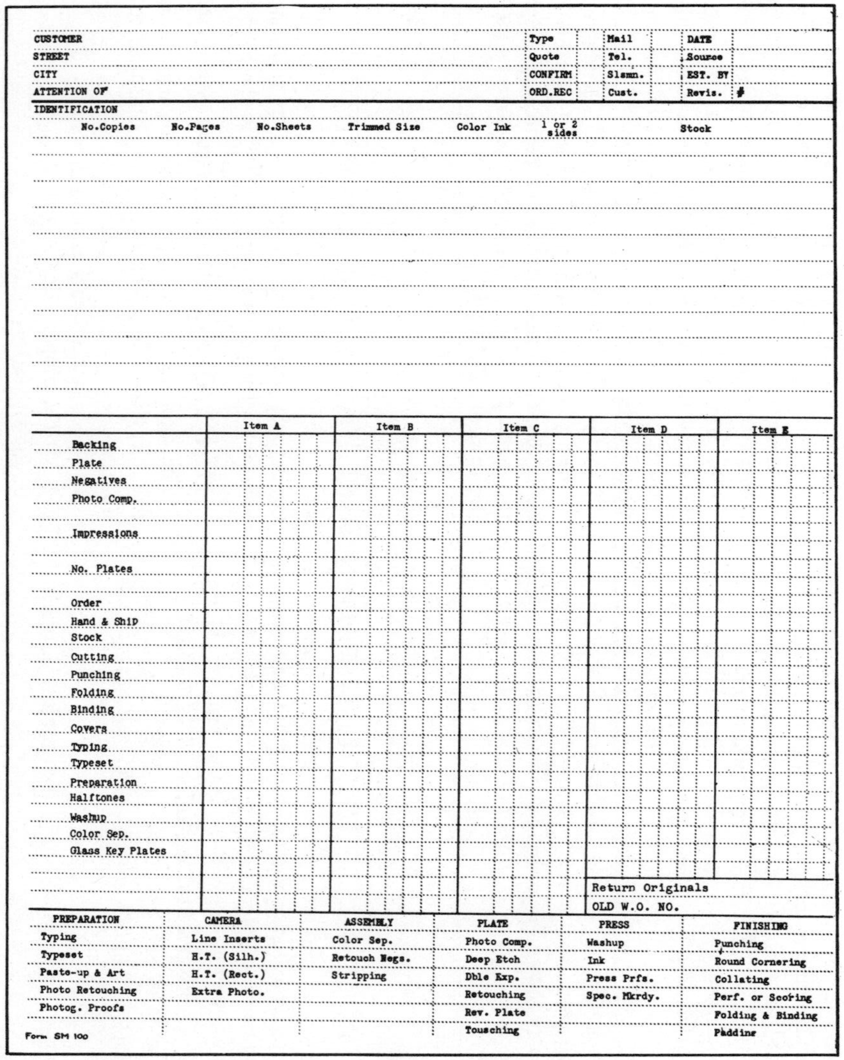

BACK

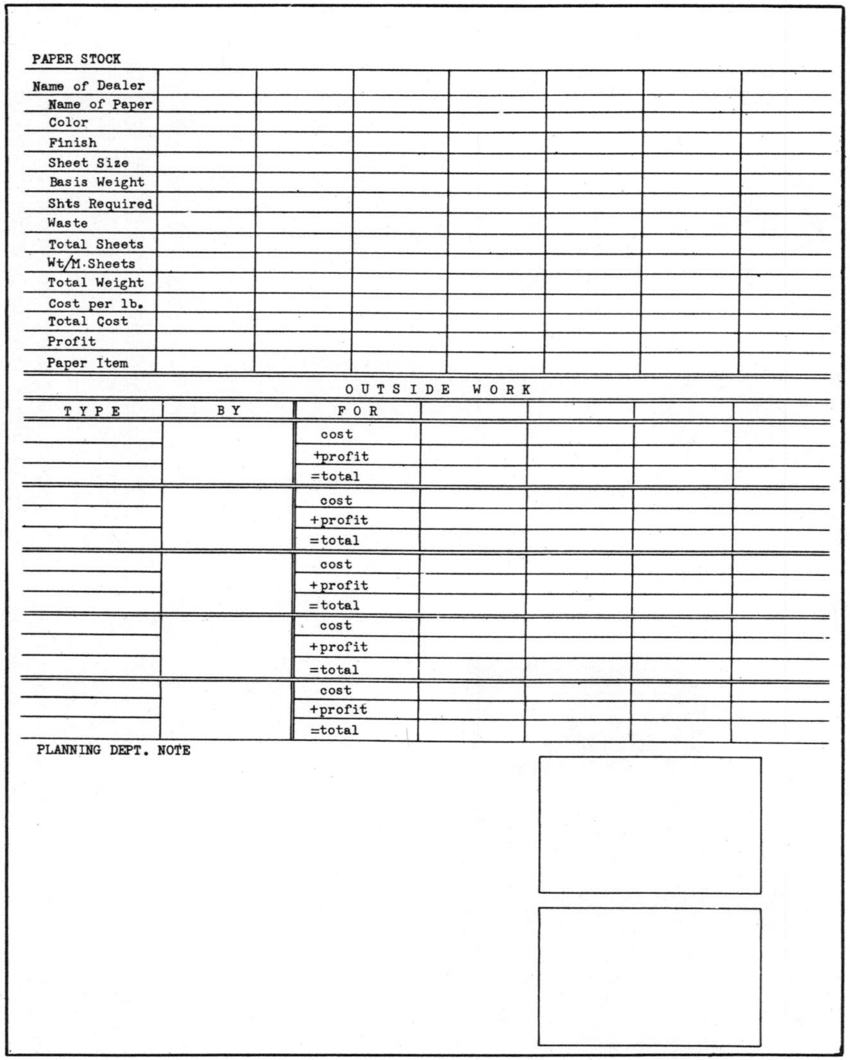

PAPER STOCK								
Name of Dealer								
Name of Paper								
Color								
Finish								
Sheet Size								
Basis Weight								
Shts Required								
Waste								
Total Sheets								
Wt/M.Sheets								
Total Weight								
Cost per lb.								
Total Cost								
Profit								
Paper Item								

OUTSIDE WORK

TYPE	BY	FOR
		cost
		+profit
		=total
		cost
		+profit
		=total
		cost
		+profit
		=total
		cost
		+profit
		=total
		cost
		+profit
		=total

PLANNING DEPT. NOTE

FRONT

CUSTOMER
STREET
CITY
ATTENTION OF
IDENTIFICATION

Type	Mail	DATE
Quote	Tel.	Source
CONFIRM	Simm.	EST. BY
ORD.REC	Cust.	Revis. #

No.Copies No.Pages No.Sheets Trimmed Size Color Ink 1 or 2 sides Stock

	Item A	Item B	Item C	Item D	Item E
Masking					
Plate					
Negatives					
Photo.Comp.					
Impressions					
No. Plates					
Order					
Hand & Ship					
Stock					
Cutting					
Punching					
Folding					
Binding					
Covers					
Drying					
Typeset.					
Preparation					
Halftones					
Washup					
Color Sep.					
Glass Key Plates					

Return Originals
OLD W.O. NO.

PREPARATION	CAMERA	ASSEMBLY	PLATE	PRESS	FINISHING
Typing	Line Inserts	Color Sep.	Photo Comp.	Washup	Punching
Typeset	H.T. (Silh.)	Retouch Negs.	Deep Etch	Ink	Round Cornering
Paste-up & Art	H.T. (Rect.)	Stripping	Dble Exp.	Press Prfs.	Collating
Photo Retouching	Extra Photo.		Retouching	Spec. Mkrdy.	Perf. or Scoring
Photog. Proofs			Rev. Plate		Folding & Binding
			Touching		Padding

Form SM 100

Front and back sides of the estimator's calculating sheet.

To carry out this obligation, the lithographer should have Production Control, Cost Control, and Quality Control.

In this study we will graphically show and explain a Production Control System in action.

A System is Never Better Than the People Who Operate It. The first thing we should recognize is the importance of the Production Control Supervisor and other workers who play a part in planning, scheduling, and loading. A system is necessary, but it is worthless without competent people to operate it.

The Necessary Qualifications for a Production/Control Supervisor. When one selects an individual to head up Production Control it would be well to bear these qualifications in mind:

1. He should have a "sales" attitude — a real desire to serve the customer and meet deadlines.

2. He should be a clear thinker — one who can exercise good judgment and make proper decisions.

3. He should possess the ability to get along with other people — more especially the salesmen and production supervisors.

4. He should have a capacity for detail and a rigid adherence to complete follow-through.

ESTIMATING

Estimating normally is not considered as a part of Production Control. It does start the ball rolling in that direction, however, since delivery schedules and other factors affecting Production Control come into the picture and are determined and settled here.

Estimating Is Part of Selling. The job has not been sold at this point, so estimating is a part of the selling function in the sense of preparation and presentation of an estimate to the customer or prospect. The Estimating Department expense is charged to the plant. Organizationally this department comes under the Works Manager.

We try to develop a "selling" attitude in our Estimators, a real desire to "get the order" through intelligent thinking and planning as well as fair and proper pricing. The Estimators work from a complete list of standard prices for different types of work. These standards have been built from engineering studies of time against which the departmental hourly rates are applied. Although adjustments are many times necessary to care for a given estimating problem, our feeling is that this method affords greater uniformity of pricing.

Estimate Requests are Cleared Through the Sales Department. In our plant all estimate requests clear through the Sales Department first, mainly to check them for completeness of information, clarity, a chance to note selling ideas and immediate follow-up on new prospects. In addition, the Sales Department will also establish the date the estimate is needed by the customer. When the salesman enters a request for an estimate, he is required to write down the job specifications on the "Request for Estimate" sheet. Verbal requests are not accepted.

The Calculation Sheet. The Estimator does his figuring on the calculation sheet. At the top he writes name, address, and specifications. The body provides space for listing figures on one or more items and the pre-printed increments at the left save writing time and serve as a check list. Paper is computed in the right-hand section at the top. Below this area, figuring is done for clarification and future reference. Estimates from outside suppliers are also recorded within this same area. A form size 11" x 17" printed on one side is used here. The reverse side can be used if added space is required.

The Formal Estimate. Upon completion this form goes to the typist who prepares the formal Estimate for the customer. This is a 4-part form 8½" x 11". The original goes to the customer; one copy is attached to the calculation sheet and retained by the Estimating Department; a copy is given the salesman for follow-up and the final copy is kept by the sales office for analysis and diary follow-up with the salesman.

The Salesman Reports the Reasons Why Jobs are Received or Lost. When orders are received or lost, the salesman turns in his copy to the Sales Department. Space is provided wherein he can report reasons why job was received or lost as well as other available competitive information. This data is analyzed by an estimator and serves as a guide for future competitive pricing. When an order is received the estimating department's copy and the attached calculation sheet are pulled from the file and used to check specifications against the actual copy received. Variations, if any, are noted at this time, re-estimated, and discussed with the customer.

PROCESSING THE ORDER

In this unit we discuss first the work order and then the camera slip. The accompanying illustrations show the forms used in the work.

The Work Order. Orders are written, planned, and scheduled in one operation. Dates are set for each department, paper or ink is ordered, press time is set aside and any special need is acted upon. The Work Order is an 11" x 17" form printed on one side of a 13# translucent paper. When this is completed we have a master copy from which Ozalid whiteprint copies are made and used as follows:

The Traveling Work Order. This copy becomes the traveling Work Order. It is folded in half and pasted around a blank kraft envelope.

The Invoice Set. The invoice typist receives a copy and from this prepares the invoice set. This multiple part snap-out form contains customer invoice, file copy, accounting copy, salesman's copy, acknowledgment, packing and shipping slips. After typing, the acknowledgment goes to the customer, the packing and shipping copies are sent to the shipping office and the salesman's copy forwarded to the sales office for distribution. The file copy is detached and held in the order department for reference. Invoice and accounting copies are kept intact for billing. Price is typed on later after the job has been shipped and cost has been computed by the billing clerk.

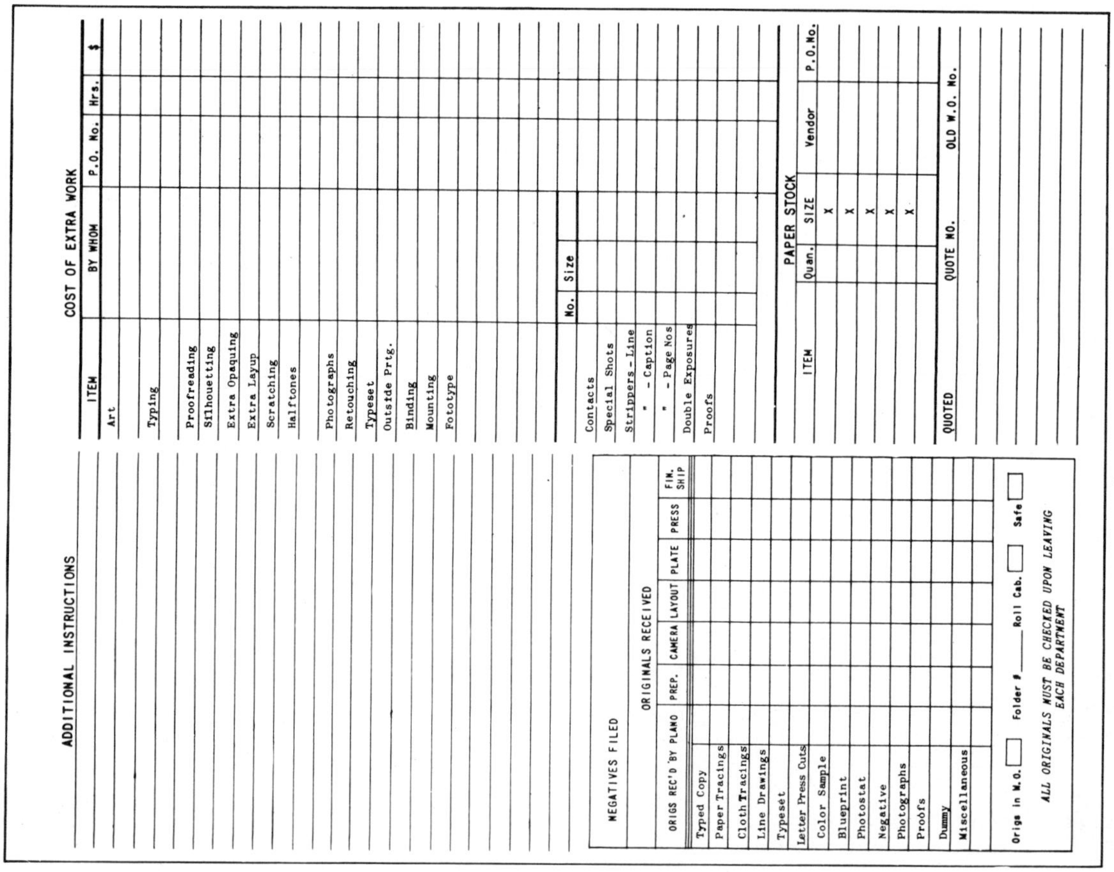
ADDITIONAL INSTRUCTIONS

COST OF EXTRA WORK

ITEM	BY WHOM	P.O. No.	Hrs.	$
Art				
Typing				
Proofreading				
Silhouetting				
Extra Opaquing				
Extra Layup				
Scratching				
Halftones				
Photographs				
Retouching				
Typeset				
Outside Prtg.				
Binding				
Mounting				
Fototype				

	No.	Size
Contacts		
Special Shots		
Strippers - Line		
" - Caption		
" - Page Nos		
Double Exposures		
Proofs		

PAPER STOCK

ITEM	Quan.	SIZE	Vendor	P.O.No.
		X		
		X		
		X		
		X		
		X		

QUOTED QUOTE NO. OLD W.O. No.

NEGATIVES FILED

ORIGINALS RECEIVED

ORIGS REC'D BY PLANO	PREP.	CAMERA	LAYOUT	PLATE	PRESS	FIN. SHIP
Typed Copy						
Paper Tracings						
Cloth Tracings						
Line Drawings						
Typeset						
Letter Press Cuts						
Color Sample						
Blueprint						
Photostat						
Negative						
Photographs						
Proofs						
Dummy						
Miscellaneous						

Origs in W.O. ☐ Folder # ____ Roll Cab. ☐ Safe ☐

ALL ORIGINALS MUST BE CHECKED UPON LEAVING EACH DEPARTMENT

BACK

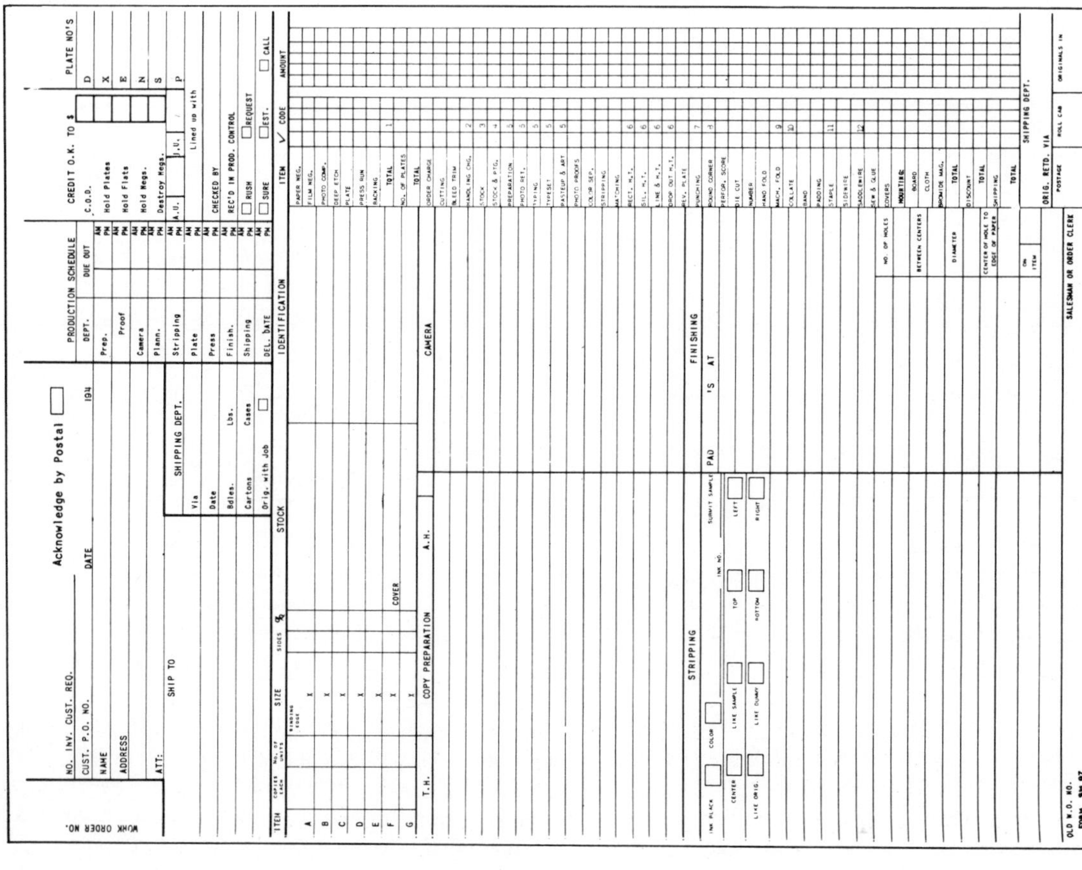
WORK ORDER NO.

Acknowledge by Postal ☐

NO. INV. CUST. REQ.

CUST. P.O. NO.

NAME

ADDRESS

ATT:

SHIP TO

DATE 194

PRODUCTION SCHEDULE

DEPT.	DUE OUT	
Prep.		AM PM
Proof		AM PM
Camera		AM PM
Plann.		AM PM
Stripping		AM PM
Plate		AM PM
Press		AM PM
Finish.		AM PM
Shipping		AM PM
DEL. DATE		AM PM

CREDIT O.K. TO $

C.O.D. — Hold Plates — Hold Flats — Hold Negs. — Destroy Negs. — A.U. — I.U. — Lined up with — CHECKED BY — REC'D IN PROD. CONTROL — ☐ RUSH ☐ REQUEST — ☐ SURE ☐ EST. ☐ CALL

PLATE NO'S: D X E N S P

SHIPPING DEPT.: Via — Date — Bdles. Lbs. — Cartons Cases — Orig. with Job ☐

ITEM	COPIES EACH	NO. OF UNITS	SIZE	BINDING EDGE	SIDES	%	STOCK
A				X			
B				X			
C				X			
D				X			
E				X			
F				X			COVER
G				X			

IDENTIFICATION

T.H. — COPY PREPARATION — A.H. — CAMERA

STRIPPING: INK PLACK ☐ COLOR ☐ — CENTER ☐ LIKE SAMPLE ☐ TOP ☐ LEFT ☐ — LIKE ORIG. ☐ LIKE DUMMY ☐ BOTTOM ☐ RIGHT ☐ — INK NO. — SUBMIT SAMPLE

FINISHING: PAD 'S AT

NO. OF HOLES — BETWEEN CENTERS — DIAMETER — CENTER OF HOLE TO EDGE OF PAPER — ON ITEM

ITEM	✓	CODE	AMOUNT
PAPER NEG.			
FILM NEG.			
PHOTO COMP.			
DEEP ETCH			
PLATE			
PRESS RUN			
BACKING			
TOTAL		1	
NO. OF PLATES			
TOTAL			
ORDER CHARGE			
CUTTING		2	
BLEED TRIM		3	
HANDLING CHG.		4	
STOCK		5	
STOCK & PTG.		5	
PREPARATION		5	
PHOTO RET.		5	
TYPING		5	
TYPESET		5	
PASTEUP & ART		5	
PHOTO PROOFS			
COLOR SEP.			
STRIPPING			
MATCHING			
RECT. H.T.		6	
SIL. H.T.		6	
LINE & H.T.		6	
DROP OUT H.T.		6	
REV. PLATE			
PUNCHING		7	
ROUND CORNER		8	
PERFOR. SCORE			
DIE CUT			
NUMBER			
HAND FOLD		9	
MACH. FOLD		10	
COLLATE			
BAND			
PADDING		11	
STAPLE			
SIDEWIRE			
SADDLEWIRE		12	
SEW & GLUE			
COVERS			
MOUNTING: BOARD			
CLOTH			
BROMIDE NEG.			
TOTAL			
DISCOUNT			
TOTAL			
SHIPPING			
TOTAL			

ORIG. RETD. VIA — SHIPPING DEPT. — POSTAGE — ROLL CAB — ORIGINALS IN

SALESMAN OR ORDER CLERK

OLD W.O. NO.

FORM 9H 07

FRONT

Front and back sides of the work order.

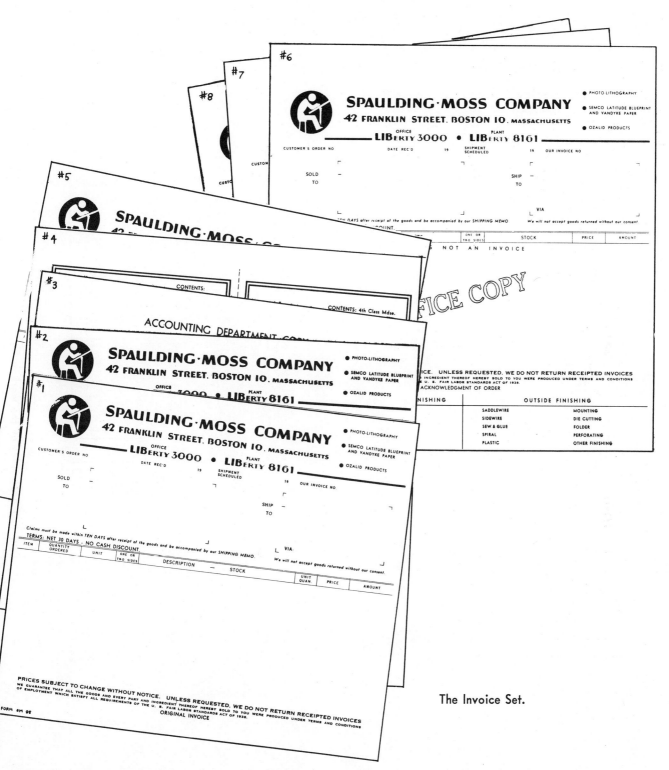

The Invoice Set.

The Copy for the Stock Department. One copy is sent to the stock department — stock is placed at the press according to schedule.

The Copy for the Purchasing Department. One copy goes to Purchasing so that necessary outside materials or services can be ordered and coordinated to the schedule.

The Copy for the Press Supervisor. When ink matches or outside purchases of ink are called for, a copy of the Work Order goes to the press supervisor. He will compute the ink requirement and order by using the Material Requisition.

Additional Functions of the Work Order. In addition to providing space for basic job information such as quantity, size, stock, etc., the Work Order contains the complete production schedule and serves as a planning and layout sheet for stripping, press, and finishing.

Supplementary Records. We also record the following: (1) Outside purchases, (2) Location and description of customer's original copy, (3) Shipments made.

The Master of the Work Order is Preserved. The translucent master is kept in the order department for ready reference until the job is completed. When the work clears the plant, it is discarded.

The Camera Slip. If an order is complicated, or for some reason cannot be put into production quickly, the original copy is sent to camera so that work can get under way. The Order Writer fills out the camera slip and sends it to the camera department. The art department also uses the form to order negatives, contacts, etc. They are returned to the camera department to be accumulated in the Work Order Jacket. Later they are used by the billing clerk to price the job.

PRODUCTION CONTROL

We now arrive at the heart of the Control System. Here we use the Master Control Board and the Press Loading Board.

Control Board and Job Status Cards. The purpose of these cards is to show the location of each order in the plant as they move between departments. They provide a constant check on progress against the set delivery schedule. Cards are initiated when the order is written. Hung on the board in numerical order, they carry the Work Order number which eventually becomes the customer invoice number. White cards indicate black-and-white printing. Pink cards are used for color work.

The Board Card and Follow-Up Cards. A board card is the master of the set and contains customer name along with the complete production schedule. This is immediately hung on the control board and the remaining cards are handled in the following manner: Preparation and Camera cards are clipped to the Work Order; Stripping, Plate, Press and Finishing cards are sent directly to each department supervisor as advance notice of work to come. Each card shows in-and-out dates for a particular department.

Information on flats, plates, presswork and binding is also listed on the card for each supervisor so that he knows

The Production Control Board.

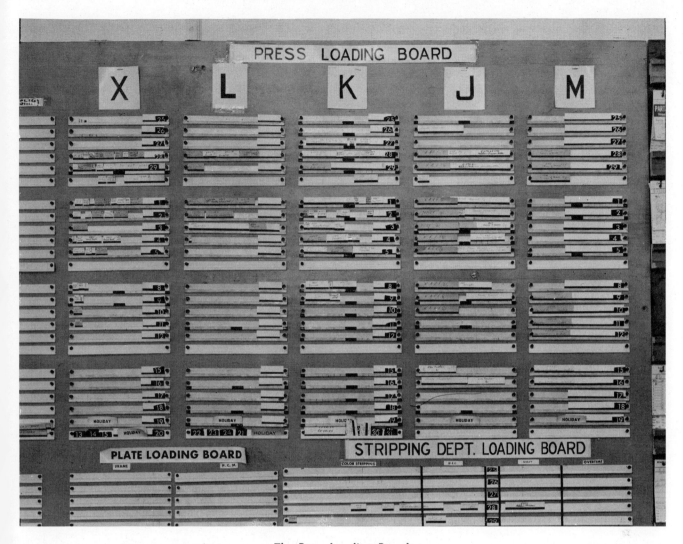

The Press Loading Board.

exactly what to expect. Every department has its own control board and cards are hung on them until the work clears.

Job Schedules and Their Changes on the Control Board. With few exceptions, a complete schedule is set for every job. Occasionally we find it is not possible to establish a complete schedule on a job. Schedules do change, however, and it then becomes necessary to revise dates. This is the responsibility of the man in charge of the scheduling board.

The Flow of Follow-Up Cards. As jobs flow from department to department the cards are stamped with the time cleared and are returned to Production Control to be hung on the control board with the board card. At a glance we then know the location of each job and can communicate with the department for specific information when needed.

Quick Reference Cards. Production Control has an assortment of quick reference cards which are hung to cover certain circumstances. Among these are "Proof Out," "No Stock," "Report of Delay," etc. Being printed with large type and colored ink they stand out on the board as reminders for necessary follow-up.

Handling of Delays. Whenever a job falls behind schedule and time cannot be made up, the new production schedule is sent to the Sales Department. Here it is decided how the customer should be informed in order to maintain good relations. As soon as the job is shipped, the cards are discarded.

The Press Loading Board. In setting up the Control System we found press loading critical to the Production Control problem. Actually we couldn't accurately schedule without proper knowledge of what work load was ahead for the presses. For this reason, press loading was incorporated into our Production Control function.

The Press Loading Board is Set Up for a Four-Week Period. The presses are indicated across the top. Each strip represents a work day. It is divided into two parts, day and night shift. Each shift is divided into seven one-hour periods.

The Operation of Press Loading Board. When the job ticket is written up, planned and scheduled, press time is estimated and a paper tab is cut to proper length in hours. This tab is then loaded under the press assigned

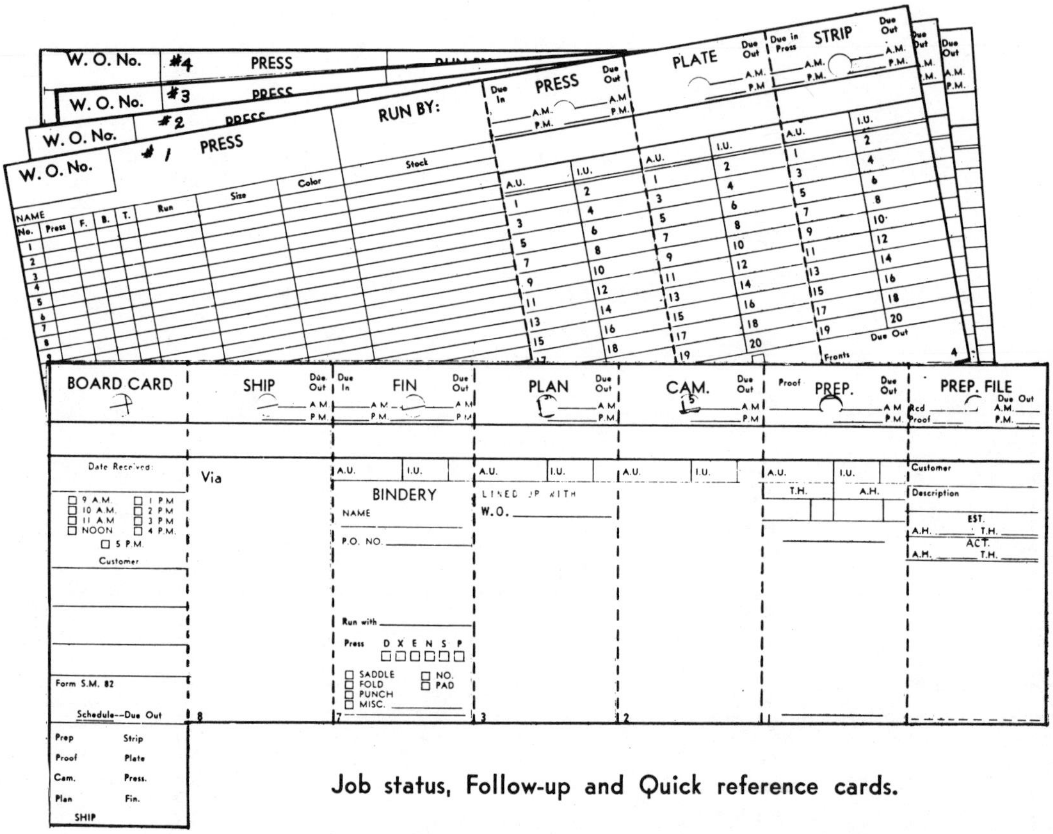

Job status, Follow-up and Quick reference cards.

Form S-M MC #1

MATERIAL & SUPPLY REQUISITION
SPAULDING-MOSS COMPANY

DEPT.

DATE_____194__
REQ'N NO.

P. O. NO.

W. O. NO.

SUGGESTED SUPPLIER _____

PLEASE PLACE ORDER, _____ DELIVER FROM STORES OR FROM ANOTHER DEPARTMENT. _____
WANTED ON_____194__
ORDERED & PRICED ON _____194__ AT_____ A P M   SCHEDULED DELIVERY_____194__

ITEM	QUANTITY	DESCRIPTION	TLWC	TERMS - DISCOUNT	UNIT $	AGREED - TOTAL $

APPROVED BY

AUTHORIZED BY

DR. DEPT.	DR. ACCT.	CR. DEPT.	CR. ACCT.

PER _____

Materials and supply requisition form.

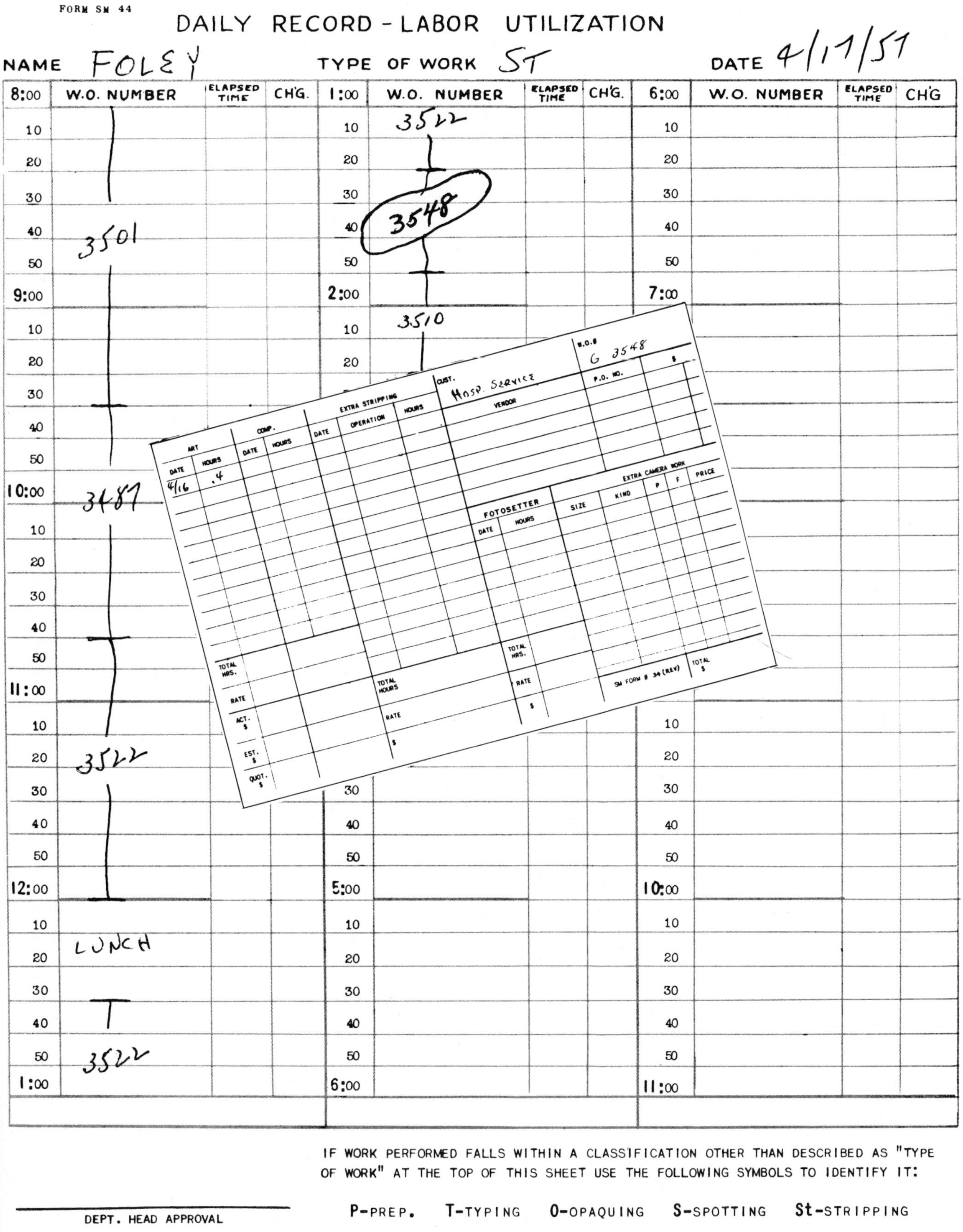

FORM SM 44

DAILY RECORD - LABOR UTILIZATION

NAME *FOLEY* TYPE OF WORK *ST* DATE *4/17/51*

8:00	W.O. NUMBER	ELAPSED TIME	CH'G.	1:00	W.O. NUMBER	ELAPSED TIME	CH'G.	6:00	W.O. NUMBER	ELAPSED TIME	CH'G
10				10	3522			10			
20				20				20			
30				30				30			
40	3501			40	3548			40			
50				50				50			
9:00				2:00				7:00			
10				10	3510						
20				20							
30											
40											
50											
10:00	3487										
10											
20											
30											
40											
50											
11:00											
10								10			
20	3522							20			
30				30				30			
40				40				40			
50				50				50			
12:00				5:00				10:00			
10				10				10			
20	LUNCH			20				20			
30				30				30			
40				40				40			
50	3522			50				50			
1:00				6:00				11:00			

IF WORK PERFORMED FALLS WITHIN A CLASSIFICATION OTHER THAN DESCRIBED AS "TYPE OF WORK" AT THE TOP OF THIS SHEET USE THE FOLLOWING SYMBOLS TO IDENTIFY IT:

P-PREP. T-TYPING O-OPAQUING S-SPOTTING St-STRIPPING

DEPT. HEAD APPROVAL

W.O.# *G 3548* CUST. *Hosp. Service* P.O. NO. $ VENDOR

ART		COMP.		EXTRA STRIPPING		
DATE	HOURS	DATE	HOURS	DATE	OPERATION	HOURS
4/16	*.4*					
TOTAL HRS.				TOTAL HOURS		
RATE				RATE		
ACT. $				$		
EST. $						
QUOT. $						

FOTOSETTER		EXTRA CAMERA WORK				
DATE	HOURS	SIZE	KIND	P	F	PRICE
TOTAL HRS.						TOTAL $
RATE		SM FORM # 34 (REV)				
$						

Job cost card and daily record of labor utilization forms.

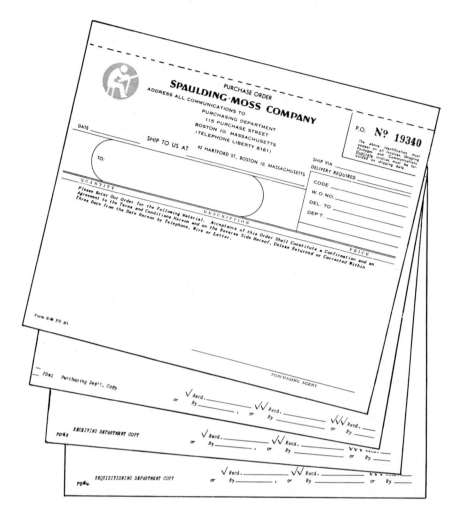

Purchase order set (materials other than type).

and on the day or days shown in the schedule. White tabs are used for black ink; colored tabs for color jobs. In loading ahead we try not to load shifts completely. An allowance is made to take care of down-time and special delivery needs which we recognize as bound to arise.

VARIOUS TIE-IN FUNCTIONS

Our presentation of the production control system would be incomplete without a discussion of several important tie-in functions. These as well as the forms used in their execution are now presented.

Material Requisition. The Material Requisition form is used to obtain material from the warehouse and request purchase through the purchasing department. Three copies are made out and sent along. The original is retained by the warehouse or purchasing. After pricing by the warehouse, or receipt of vendor's invoice, one is sent to accounting and the other is returned to the ordering department.

Purchase Orders. Our purchase orders are a four-part form. The original is sent to the vendor. One copy retained by purchasing for follow-up and file. One goes to the receiving department for check on incoming material and one goes to accounting with the vendor's invoice.

Special Purchase Order for Composition. The special purchase order form for composition is designed to speed up purchase of composition by the art department. This is a three-part form made out by the artist. The original goes to the vendor; one is retained in the art department for follow-up; one goes to Purchasing where it is checked against the vendor's invoice before being sent to accounting with the invoice for payment.

Job Cost Card. The job cost card form is used to record chargeable time in preparation and art departments, also for other operations not covered by predetermined standards. For example, color separation time in stripping department. It is originated by the cost control clerk and posted from the Daily Record of Labor Utilization. Prices of outside materials and services are also posted. Cards are kept on file until called for by the billing clerk. After billing they are filed in the Work Order.

Daily Record of Labor Utilization. The daily record of utilization form is used by the operator to record time spent on operations not covered by predetermined standards — operations which must be charged out on a time basis. Sheets are turned over to cost control clerk daily and chargeable time is recorded on the Job Cost Cards. They can also be used to check operating efficiency.

CHAPTER FOUR   .   .

The Creative Art Department_____

Section One: Introduction to Typesetting and Typography*

Typesetting and typography are highly specialized crafts and arts that play a very important role in the preparation of art and copy for lithographic reproduction. For this reason the subject is presented rather extensively in this Manual. It is, of course, not our purpose to teach anybody how to perform any part of typesetting. Our purpose is merely to inform everybody interested in the subject, the commercial artist primarily, but also sales personnel and people working in the lithographic shop, on some aspects of typography.

In this, our first section we present some of the most basic facts of this vast field. Our introduction to typesetting and typography is divided into the following three subjects: (1) The main kinds of composition; (2) The sequence of operations in composition; and (3) Type fundamentals. Each of these is presented in the following.

THE MAIN KINDS OF COMPOSITION

Contemporary composition is characterized by a great variety of materials and processes. The industry is in a process of development and change. Such a state is always expressed in great diversification and variety, making exact classification impossible. Too many things are the only ones of their kind, too many new developments cross traditionally established groupings and divisions. The reader should keep this general condition in mind during the following discussion of the subject.

MATERIALS AND PROCESSES FOR TYPESETTING

Type can be set in a variety of materials and processes. The traditional material, out of which type is made, used to be metal and to a very small extent wood. Paper, plastics

* Illustrations in this section are from the PIA Composition Manual, with permission.

and photographic films have been added to these two in the recent past. The processes in which type is set are customarily divided into two, hand typesetting and machine typesetting. This division is still valid, but the variety of materials is also expressed in a variety of hand and machine composition.

Hot Metal and Cold Type Composition. Contemporary typesetting is often divided into two main kinds; hot metal composition is one and cold type composition the other. Hot metal composition comprises in this division all typesetting methods using metallic type, in particular linecasting machines such as the Linotype and Intertype, and the Monotype. Cold type composition is a catch-all name for the more recent developments in the field of composition. These include photographic methods of different kinds as well as non-photographic ones. Our discussion of typesetting is divided into the following five points: (1) Hand composition of metallic type; (2) Hand composition of non-metallic type; (3) Machine composition of metallic type; (4) Machine composition of photographic type; and (5) Machine composition of typed type. Each of these is now individually discussed if ever so briefly.

Hand Composition of Metallic Type. We distinguish two kinds of hand composition. One kind is the traditional method of typesetting using *foundry type* in the main, and the other kind is based on the *Ludlow system*.

Hand-set type uses mainly—but not exclusively—*foundry type* consisting of individual type characters. These characters are selected one at a time from their storage trays which are called type cases. Hand-set type is assembled into lines in a composing stick which the compositor holds above the case in his left hand. In it he spaces and justifies each line of type to an exact degree of firmness, or tightness. The stick, as the printer calls it, is the compositor's most important tool.

Hand composition is not used in our times for the setting of type in quantity as needed for books or newspapers. Hand composition is primarily used for display work.

The *Ludlow Typograph* is a machine used for hand composition of metallic type. Here the compositor assembles not the individual type characters, but their matrices.

Special matrix sticks are used for the assembling of matrices on the Ludlow. The typeface matrices are assembled by hand into the stick, the line is justified, and then the stick with the matrices is inserted in the machine for casting. The result of casting is a slug of type that is used in much the same way as other metallic type. The matrices are returned to their cases for further use.

Hand Composition of Non-Metallic Type. Here we have a variety of processes and equipment; some are photographic, others are not. Some methods use individual characters on paper or plastic that are assembled in a tool similar in purpose to the composing stick and then either photographed or directly incorporated into the paste-up for offset lithography.

Several machines use a photographic matrix. Character for character is individually selected by the operator and immediately exposed to a photographic material. This material is then developed and finally incorporated into the paste-up.

Machine Composition of Metallic Type. Almost all typesetting in quantity is done on two kinds of composing machines. Technically speaking, the Linotype and Intertype are one kind and the Monotype is the other.

The *Linotype* and *Intertype* are line or slug casting machines. The operator actuates the machine by fingering a keyboard. Matrices and spacebands are assembled into lines and automatically *justified*. (Justification of type lines means that they are brought to their predetermined length.) Then a slug of type is cast, the matrices and spacebands are returned to their correct places for further use. All this takes place automatically. The product of either machine is a line or slug of type.

The *Monotype* produces justified lines of individual types. In the Monotype system two machines are used; the *keyboarding machine* is one, the *caster* the other. The operator actuates again a keyboard but this time for a different purpose. The keyboard machine produces a punched paper ribbon that directs the *caster*. The caster produces the final product of the Monotype, a justified line of individual type. Here too, most of the operations—apart from fingering the keyboard—are automatically performed by the machines.

The preceding description is most elementary, but a detailed presentation of these machines is outside the place of our Manual. They are very complex and a study in themselves.

Machine Composition of Photographic Type. The last decade has seen machine composition of photographic type just beginning to come of age. The Harris-Intertype *Fotosetter* was the first of such machines to establish itself in everyday use. It operates on the same recirculating matrix system of hot-metal line-casting machines

but substitutes a photographic component for the casting mechanism. The *Photon* and the *Linofilm* are two distinct departures in basic techniques for meeting a wide variety of type composition needs, and both have found their place in the setting of advertisements, directories, encyclopedia, etc.

In general, the machines are operated from a keyboard. However, there has been adapted to their use, several systems using punched tape. Work is going on to adapt magnetic tape signals to operate them.

To all this, should be added the work being done to virtually automate the entire typesetting process from the time a final manuscript is prepared to the point of a finished page on film, or, perhaps, a printing plate ready for press. However, some of these developments are also being applied to hot-metal machines. An example of this is the simultaneous setting of type for a publication produced in several locations at the same time. Here we have telegraphic or radio transmission from a central point producing tape which will operate widely separated photographic or hot-metal typesetting machines. It is not too visionary to expect direct operation to eliminate the production of tape-recorded signals.

This brief treatment cannot be complete without mention of Lanston's *Monophoto*. This is, essentially, the conventional Monotype keyboard and caster. The caster, however, is equipped with a photographic unit which operates through a photographic matrix case instead of the punch matrix case and lead-casting device.

Machine Composition of Type by Typing. The typewriter is the prototype for these machines. They aim at the production of type in quantity by office personnel. The high cost of typesetting, the growth of lithography and the constantly increasing social need for more specialized literature are three impulses for the growth of this field of composition.

Production of type by typing is possible in many ways. A variety of typewriters and typewriter-composing machines is available. Some of these machines have exchangeable type characters, others do not. Some use the same width for all characters, others differentiate character width in various ways. This field, too, is in flux. At this time it can merely be stated that all these machines require two operations for justification. The resources section of our chapter presents several of the more important machines for type composition by typing.

THE SEQUENCE OF OPERATIONS IN COMPOSITION

In this unit we are primarily concerned with the general procedures of machine typesetting. For purposes of this book, the specific steps and operations applicable only to hot-metal or photographic typesetting cannot be dealt with separately.

The Main Steps in Machine Composition of Type. It is most important, especially to best utilize the advantages of the modern hot-metal and photographic type-setting machines, that manuscript be clean and final. As a matter of fact, one of the principal reasons why photographic typesetting has advanced so slowly is the difficulties of handling corrections, whether they result from author's alterations or mechanical malfunctions.

After type has been set it must be proofed for reading. Hot metal is proofed by taking a print from the assembled galleys. Photographic composition is proofed by any one of a variety of inexpensive contact print techniques such as blueprinting, diazo, etc. After corrections have been made the material is assembled, grouped, and spaced into specified units of pages. In the case of hot-metal, the made-up pages may be assembled into forms for printing, may be used for making duplicate relief plates, or may be repro-proofed for photographing. Photographic composition may be assembled, grouped, and spaced while in negative or positive form. In many cases, high quality photographic contact prints may be made from the strips of film, and these prints assembled, grouped and spaced into pages or complete flats ready for platemaking. In some cases the product of the photographic type-setting machine is a paper print ready for camera. This technique is not in widespread use.

Hot metal pages or forms may be stored for reprinting or re-melted. With photographic type, the original films or flats may be stored for re-use or are simply discarded.

TERMS USED IN CONJUNCTION WITH COMPOSITION JOBS

At this time terminology in the field of composition (setting type) is in a state of flux. This is due to the fact that new techniques are bringing about considerable change in the way manuscript is transformed into a printing image. Personnel operating hot-metal or photographic typesetting machines are still called *operators*. But the increased use of tape is bringing in a new classification which may or may not be filled by the traditional *compositor* or operator. The compositors who specialize in the grouping, arranging and spacing of hot-metal are called *make-up men*. But those who handle photographic type are *paste-up men* or *strippers*. While the make-up man used a *bank* and the *stone-hand* used a *stone* (steel-topped table) for *imposing* printing forms, a stripper arranges photographic material into a flat, for making a lithographic plate, on a light-table or stripping table.

TYPE FUNDAMENTALS

Everybody concerned with copy preparation must know some fundamental facts on type. Our discussion of the subject is divided into the following twelve points: (1) The parts of type; (2) Elements of letter forms; (3) Roman and italics; (4) Type series; (5) Type families; (6) The American Point System; (7) Points and Picas; (8) Measuring body sizes; (9) Measuring paper sizes and type forms; (10) Leads and slugs; (11) Quads and spaces; (12) Line gages and galleys. Each of these points is briefly discussed in the following.

The Parts of Type. Our illustration shows the main parts of type. The *face* of a type is the image which stands out in relief on the upper end of the body. It is the surface which comes in contact with ink and paper. The *shoulder* is the lower, non-printing surface on the top of the body

at the base of the type character or image. The *counter* is the lower non-printing surface of a type between the ele-

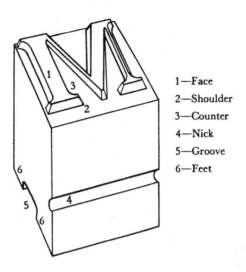

1—Face
2—Shoulder
3—Counter
4—Nick
5—Groove
6—Feet

The parts of type.

ments of the face. The *nick* is a groove cast on foundry type and monotypes for identification purposes. The *feet* and the *groove* are at the base of the type body.

Elements of Letter Forms. Identification and description of type faces is impossible without some reference to the elements of letter forms. The first element to consider is the *serif* and its formation. The serifs are the finishing strokes at the end or the beginning of a letter element. Our illustration shows examples of different serifs. Other points to consider are the *weight* of strokes, the *shape* of rounded characters, *ascenders*—or letter elements rising over the center area, in the letters *f* and *t* for example—and *descenders* — or letter elements descending under the center area, in the letters *j* and *g* for example. Of the very many characteristic points we merely mention the formation of terminals, on the letters *f* and *j* for example and the formation of *ears,* on the letter *r* for example. Our illustration shows these different points.

Roman and Italic. Most type faces, particularly those for body composition are made in roman and *italic*. In book composition, both faces are a necessity because our rules of style demand the use of *italics* in certain cases. In this paragraph you find the word *italic* always in *italics,* the rest is in roman. The paragraph *lead* is in bold face.

Type Series. An ordinary series of foundry type consists of sizes 6 to 72 points. Some series of type include additional sizes of 84-, 96-, 120-, and some even 144-point. Odd sizes of type, such as 7-, 9-, 11-, and 16-point, are sometimes used in book work.

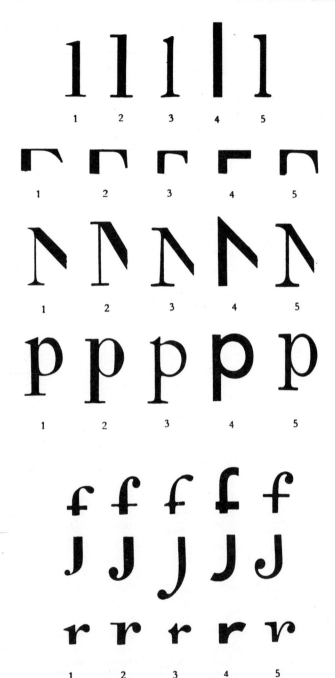

This composite shows characteristic elements of letter forms. First row shows serifs; second row, termination of top strokes; third row, weight of strokes; fourth row, shape of rounded characters; fifth and sixth rows, terminals on *j* and *f;* seventh row, formation of ears in letter *r*. The faces in these examples are: (1) Caslon Oldstyle; (2) Bodoni; (3) Garamond; (4) Futura; (5) Century Expanded.

Type Families. Types of a basic design are often made in a number of variations. These variations are most useful in many typographic tasks. Our illustration demonstrates a type *family* for Bodoni type.

Bodoni

Bodoni Italic

Bodoni Bold

Bodoni Bold Italic

Bodoni Bold Condensed

Bodoni Campanile

Bodoni Book

Bodoni Book Italic

Ultra Bodoni

Ultra Bodoni Italic

Some members of the Bodoni type family.

The American Point System. At the outset of any understanding of composing-room materials and procedures, one must acquaint oneself with the system of linear measurement which is used in the composing room. It is known as the Point System, and *its unit is the point,* which, in America *is .013837,* or approximately $\frac{1}{72}$ inch.

Instead of using feet and inches, with their common or decimal fractions, the calculations in the measuring of type and spacing materials, dimensions of type forms, and measurements on the printed page, are made in terms of the point system.

Points and Picas. Two new terms are involved: points and picas. The simple table is as follows: 12 points = 1 pica (pī'ca), 6 picas = 1 inch (i.e., .996 of an inch). To be exact, 6 picas are .004 less than an inch, and 72 picas are about 3 points shorter than 12 inches, but for nearly all calculations this slight difference may be overlooked.

Measuring Body Sizes. The sizes of type bodies are always given in points. The smallest size of type in common use in commercial plants is 6 point, i.e. all its characters are cast on a 6-point body. (However, a majority of newspapers use 5- and 5½-point sizes for the classified advertising pages, and these sizes are also used in some catalog and directory printing.)

Measuring Paper Sizes and Type Forms. Sizes of paper and paper-page or sheet sizes, however, are always designated in inches. Accordingly, it is correct to say: "A type form of 24 x 40 picas, printed on a 6 x 9-inch sheet, may carry top and side margins of 6 picas, and a foot margin of 8 picas." The paper-page or sheet size is of course determined in terms of pica width and length for the purpose of calculating the margins, but it is always expressed in inches. With the exception of bookbinding, the first dimension in the size of a sheet of paper or of a type form is always considered the width and the second is the length.

Leads and Slugs. Leads and slugs are strips of line spacing materials. If these strips are less than six points thick they are known as *leads;* if they are 6 point or more they are called *slugs.* The term lead alone, without a point thickness, indicates a two-point lead, the term slug alone a six-point slug.

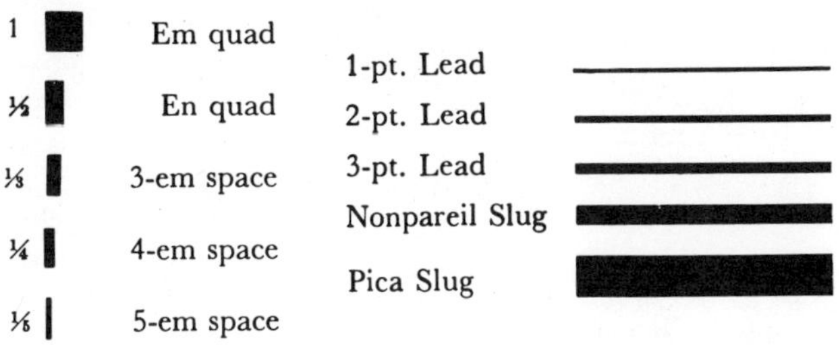

1	■	Em quad		
½	▮	En quad	1-pt. Lead	
⅓	▮	3-em space	2-pt. Lead	
			3-pt. Lead	
¼	▮	4-em space	Nonpareil Slug	
⅕	▮	5-em space	Pica Slug	

Quads, spaces, leads and slugs.

Quads and Spaces. Quads and spaces are spacing material to be used between letters and words. The *em* quad is the square of a given body size, the *en* quad is half the square of a body size; our illustration shows a series of such material.

Line Gages and Galleys. The line gage is the printer's "ruler." One of the common styles is shown in our illustration. Other recognized names for this tool are "type gage" and "type rule." A slang term used in some shops is the "pica stick."

The shallow metal trays in which the printer assembles his type forms are called *galleys.* Some, known as *makeup galleys,* are of very rigid and precise construction, so that

Oldstyle

Modern-Face

Transitional

Square-Serif

Sans-Serif

Script

𝕿𝖊𝖝𝖙=𝕷𝖊𝖙𝖙𝖊𝖗

DECORATIVE

Type specimens showing the eight main kinds of type faces.

forms may be made up in them to an exactness of size and alignment.

Note: Our presentation is restricted to the barest essentials of this broad and important subject. The reader who wants further information is advised to consult "A Composition Manual," PIA Tools of Industry, Printing Industry of America, Inc., Washington, D. C., 1953. This work is the standard book of the industry. He should also contact the manufacturers of photographic type-setting equipment and accessories.

Section Two: Converting Letterpress Images for Lithography

For this presentation the subject is divided into the following eleven units: (1) Reproduction proofs; (2) Transparent proofs; (3) One-sided dusted proofs; (4) Translucent proofs; (5) Double-offset transfer; (6) The Brightype method; (7) The direct image method; (8) Inked acid resists; (9) Photoelectronic engravers; (10) other techniques; and (11) Summary. Each of these subjects is presented in the following.

With the growth of offset and gravure, and the increasing interest in these methods among commercial printers and publishers, the problems of composition and conversion deserve more attention and careful analysis.

In its broadest sense, conversion is any transition or change in an image or composition — this embraces photographic, photomechanical and simple mechanical or physical transfer of type or image from one stage to another.

The purpose of this article is an objective discussion of common, practical, new and novel methods of conversion from letterpress composition to offset and gravure.

The majority of composition for all methods of reproduction originates in metal for letterpress or direct printing. The reasons for this are many. Letterpress was the first major method of mass reproduction. In the era of development of various typesetting machines, all printing images were purely mechanical — reaching a high degree of development before the advent of photography to composition as we know it today.

Composition for letterpress offers the greatest variety of type and sizes. It is understandable, with its earlier development, that letterpress composition possesses the greatest inventory of equipment and available services.

REPRODUCTION PROOFS

The most common conversion is made from a reproduction proof, via a camera and photomechanical steps of plate-making for offset or gravure.

Reproduction proofing by trade composition houses is practiced as a fine art. All too often, however, this starting point is subpar. By maintaining accepted standards and rigidly following sound practices, quality can be improved.

Checking the Type. The ultimate quality in all methods of conversion starts with the composition. A good printing face and a smooth level surface are essential. All elements in a form should be as nearly the same height as possible — 0.918 in. Type should be checked frequently on a Hacker style of type or slug gauge or a micrometer. Engravings and large elements can be checked on a Vandercook plate gauge or similar device. The reasons, of course, are two-fold: Variations in the height affect both inking roller pressure and printing pressure. It should be realized that type higher than the surrounding area will ink unevenly, or heavier, and also receive more squeeze in proofing.

Certain type should be surfaced before proofing. The larger sizes of type cast from linecasting machines using die-stamped matrices, have a hollow or lower center than the outside edges. When sufficient inking roller and transfer pressure are used to produce solid coverage, these outside edges of the characters are embossed into the surface of the paper. This frequent and serious error is not commonly understood.

In copying a reproduction in a process camera, the lights used to illuminate the copy are placed at a 45 deg. angle. Any aberration in the surface reflects the camera lights at an unsafe angle to the camera lens — which, if direct, records on the film as many times more powerful than the surrounding area, causing ragged edges about the offending elements.

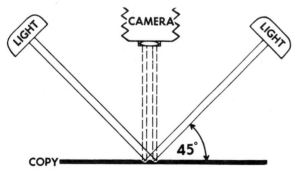

Lighting the reproduction for shooting.

Surfacing Type. Type may be surfaced by using a Ludlow surfacer which mills off high spots on line cast composition, or, an electrotyper's eraser or engraver's charcoal block may be used as an abrasive to level the surface. These latter two methods may be employed on the locked-up form if care is exercised in removing the resulting dust, either through brushing or compressed air.

Remove the Resist. It is desirable to proof from the base metal of engravings rather than the purple or brown acid resist coating which has less affinity for ink. Engravings may be ordered free of resist.

Only *stiff* inks which dry readily should ever be used for reproduction proofing. The ink should be as stiff as possible for the class of work, yet should not pick the surface coating of the proof paper.

Cylinder Packing. The cylinder packing should be as hard as practical. The harder the packing, the less embossing and sharper the print. This requires great care in leveling and exceptional composition. A happy medium is an all-tympan packing adjusted for minimum squeeze. By using two sheets of proofing paper or a temporary sheet of hard stock between the draw sheet and the proof, to absorb impression, the packing will give longer service.

Ink Acceptance. To properly accept ink, the printing face must be free of dirt and oil. Composition cast from certain machines where oil is used in the molds frequently carries a film on the surface of the type and rule. Oil transferred from human skin when handling will cause trouble. Just before proofing, an oil-free solvent should be applied from a lintless cloth or clean type brush. Type cleaner, white gasoline or acetone are suitable solvents.

Press Rollers. The press rollers must be perfectly smooth and true and not too hard. Rollers should be set

Showing recommended arrangement of all elements required for good proofing.
1. Sixty watt incandescent lamp for checking ink coverage and impression.
2. Large magnifier.
3. Fluorescent light source for inspecting transparent and translucent proofs.
4. Five pound lead weight to hold roller carriage at pre-set and constant pressure.
5. Form roller bearers one-half inch wide positioned to extend beyond each end of form.
6. Tint bar extending beyond width of form. One-half of width consisting of solid; the remaining half ($\frac{1}{4}$ inch) a 70% halftone tint in a ruling suitable for paper being proofed.

to stripe a $\frac{3}{16}$″ band. The inking system, as well as the ink, must be free of lint, dust, dried ink particles, and other foreign matter. It is important that no trace of kerosene or oily solvents remain on the roller surfaces before inking.

Bearers. It is desirable to use bearers on each side of the form, running in the direction of cylinder travel, to minimize the wiping action of rollers against the type face. These type high bars also help bear off excessive roller pressure. Bearers should be approx. $\frac{1}{2}$ in. wide and positioned to proof on the paper together with the form, thus acting as a control to the sheet.

Tint Bar. As a control to indicate the amount of ink carried on the form, a halftone tint bar of approx. 70 percent tone value should also be proofed with the form and bearers. This bar is positioned across the foot of the form and parallel with the inking rollers. If an excess of ink is used to make up for insufficient impression, or roller pressure, the dot pattern will fill and print solid.

Many publishers now require a tint bar, and also demand of the engraver that the same stock and ink used in the publication be employed in proofing.

Proof Stock. Choice of stock should be limited to 80 lb. or 100 lb. No. 1 enamel; Kromekote by Champion Paper Mills, Lusterkote by S. D. Warren Paper Co., or a stock made especially for proofing. This is sold under the name of Relyon Reproduction Paper, manufactured by Ludlow Papers, Inc., Ware, Mass.

Ink Film Thickness. Ink film thickness is influenced markedly by the relationship of the area of the form to type height and impression, speed of inking, rate of transfer, and the direct relation of ink to transfer pressure.

Maximum ink film thickness is obtained from stiff ink, slow inking, slow transfer and maximum pressure possible without embossing. Also, paper surface coatings differ widely in the amount of ink they will take from the surface of the type.

The importance of judging the proof under magnification cannot be overemphasized. Weak areas in the ink that may appear black or solid to the unaided eye, may be penetrated by the camera lights and ultimately result in ragged or broken letters.

Quality requires standards of press settings, ink, paper, bearers, tint bar, etc., and control through the use of pressure-loaded gauges to measure the height of all elements in the form, and a micrometer to check packing and paper thickness. We cannot compensate for poor adjustments and preparation of the form by heavy inking and excessive squeeze.

TRANSPARENT PROOFS

Transparent proofs have gained limited acceptance in conversions. Under ideal conditions it is possible to use these positives in place of camera work for platemaking. A photographic contact negative may be made from them, or they may be used as acetate overlays in copy preparation.

Transparent proofs present additional problems not found in reflection copy — namely, complete opacity and front-to-back register of the images. These proofs are usually printed on both sides of the sheet to gain sufficient ink film thickness or density for complete opacity.

A special thin offset blanket is substituted for the normal proof press cylinder packing, and a proof is made directly onto this blanket; the form is reinked and a transparent plastic film (between $1\frac{1}{2}$ and 3 mills) is positioned to the guides and fed through the press, simultaneously printing direct and offsetting on the reverse side.

Blankets used as packing are of two general types: A plastic coated tag board 0.022 in. thick, and the more popular two-ply offset type blanket 0.037 in. thick of approx. 80-82 Shore A Durometer hardness.

Sheet Thickness. The thickness of transparent sheeting changes the cylinder diameter, the resulting surface travel causes a longer print direct from the type than the backside (offset) image. The thicker the transparent member, the greater this error in register. Conversely, the thinner the sheet, the more difficult to control during proofing.

It is surprising to note the progressive error in images starting a few inches from the gripper edge on a large form. In a halftone proof it can be seen that the highlight dots on one side are printing between the dots on the reverse side, causing a single line effect. This condition thickens type and destroys definition.

ONE-SIDE DUSTED PROOFS

An alternative is to print only one side of the sheet and strengthen the image by dusting with powdered iron oxide or lampblack. This method leaves much to be desired. The plastic material develops considerable static during proofing which attracts powder overall, requiring great care in removal from the non-image areas.

As a general rule, the lights used to copy an image have a less penetrating effect on the image or ink used in reflection copy (repros) than transparent proofs. Hence, absolute opacity is required. This problem is the more difficult since paper will generally accept more ink from the type face than plastic films.

This suggests that transparent proofs be limited in size or restricted to work falling in a definite class, or to coarse halftone rulings and line work.

TRANSLUCENT PROOFS

Translucent proofs may be of excellent quality. For work to be produced same size, a minimum of equipment is needed to produce a negative for platemaking. Technique and requirements are identical to reproduction proofs.

Image opacity is most important, as in transparent proofs. We may ask why a single impression on one side of an acetate sheet would not serve as well: The reason is that greater ink film thickness is possible on the recommended stock than on most transparent materials.

Translucent proofs should be pulled on a special lightweight baryta-coated paper. This stock is made for the photographic industry as the starting point in the manufacture of photographic paper.

The base stock is a special type of alpha cellulose, of wood origin, often containing 25 to 50 percent pure rag pulp added for strength. This paper exhibits a marked freedom from fiber structure. The single or double emulsion coating is gelatin and pure precipitated barium sulphate. It is this unique surface that takes substantially more ink than most plastic surfaces, resulting in a more opaque image.

Only a few mills produce this special sheet — it is not normally available from a paper supply house.

All domestically manufactured baryta coated stock is converted into photographic paper; therefore only imported paper is available from Harte Litho Company, 118 Fenway, Rockville Centre, N. Y.

Light scattering can be minimized and the proof made more translucent by wiping the back of the dried proof with mineral oil. In practice, a photographic contact negative is made from the translucent proof by contact printing in a vacuum frame, using a point source light.

The photographic film is placed emulsion down in contact with black paper on the vacuum frame blanket; this arrangement prevents possible transfer of an oily film from our proof to the photographic emulsion. Or, the inked side of the proof and the film emulsion may face one another if separated by a sheet of thin plastic — if oil was used on the proof.

A practical variation of the described technique consists of proofing onto a rubber blanket as in transparent proofing.

Next, the form is substituted for a smooth impression base, larger in size than the form, and somewhat over type high. The baryta-coated sheet is then positioned coated side down on the feed board and fed through the press. As the cylinder traverses the impression base, squeeze offsets the image onto the surface of the paper. The resulting print from this approach is laterally reversed, requiring proper positioning to produce a right reading negative for offset.

It is possible to pull two or more images in perfect register onto the cylinder blanket to build greater than normal ink film density.

Presses without grippers — capable of being properly packed, are suitable for use with this technique. With such equipment, the sheet is Scotch taped to the surface of the impression base. This is equivalent to taping the stock onto the cylinder to eliminate slur.

By using Autopositive film or chemical reversal, negatives or positives may be produced in the photographic step of all methods of conversion not entirely mechanical, such as the direct image process.

DOUBLE-OFFSET TRANSFER

This method of conversion was developed from a research project on conversions in the Graphic Arts Research Dept. of Rochester Institute of Technology.

Double-offset transfer is an indirect method of proofing onto an offset plate. Conversion is made by proofing directly onto the surface of a rubber blanket-covered proof press cylinder; substituting the form with another rubber-covered type high impression base and transferring the cylinder image onto this second blanket. Next, the offset plate is positioned to the guides and this second (laterally reversed) image offset onto the plate.

There are two obvious advantages in this method. Debossing is unnecessary, and like the direct image process a minimum of makeready is required because of the resilient blanket, and its tendency to cushion and level small errors in the form. Unlike the direct image process, however, little more than a kiss impression is used on the initial form-to-cylinder transfer.

The key to this method lies in the special ink developed for the process (Conversion Black No. 20) by Homer W. Palmer and Co., 515 N. Halsted St., Chicago 22, Ill. This ink is high in fatty acids and silicones to repel the gum or coating used to form a protective stencil over the non-printing areas.

Satisfactory blankets for use on both the cylinder and impression base are Goodyear Red, 2 ply, No. 6482, pumiced surface.

This method has been tested on a large Miehle No. 3 flatbed cylinder press to produce plates for our 35 in. ATF web offset press. On this large size, some blanket creep, initially experienced in this 0.040 in. thick blanket, was overcome by laminating the rubber blanket to an offset plate. On heavy forms, it is desirable to pull two impressions in register onto the cylinder blanket in order to build sufficient ink film thickness.

The preferred plate for use with this method is a pumiced

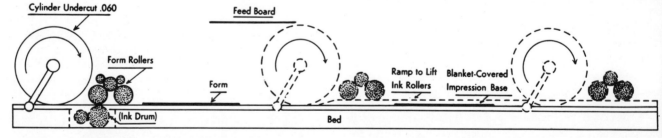

Suggested design for a special proof (double transfer) press to facilitate this conversion method; however, any type of press may be used by following the prescribed procedure.

When taking a double-transfer proof, the press cylinder makes two complete revolutions; the same cylinder printing area covering first the form, then the impression base. The impression base serves to laterally reverse the image. Next the cylinder is tripped at the delivery end of the bed and returned to a position midway between form and impression base. The offset plate is next positioned to grippers, and fed to the delivery end of the press.

surface on a new, ungrained aluminum plate. Other grains, as well as zinc, may be used.

As mentioned, a blanket-covered impression base is substituted for the letterpress form; a single impression is offset onto this base to laterally reverse the image. Next, the plate is fed through and this impression base image is in turn offset onto the plate. The affinity for press ink exhibited by this thin image is not reliable for actual production. It is necessary to replace this proofing ink with a conventional lacquer. Then the plate is gummed up, dried down, and washed out with turpentine, followed with a brief second application of chloroform (any oil-free solvent) to remove the oily turpentine film. Next, lacquer is applied, followed with a heavy developing ink, and clearing under water, after which the plate is given a conventional desensitizing etch and finally gummed.

In processing a deep etch plate, a less permeable stencil is required before washing out the proof press image. Dichromated gum, or any light sensitive coating may be applied in the same manner as gumming up a plate, followed by exposure to insolubilize the protective stencil, and washing out with turpentine, etching, and identical steps as outlined for a surface plate.

THE BRIGHTYPE PROCESS

This method of conversion, announced in 1956 by Ludlow Typographic Company, is based on direct photography of the letterpress form. Proofing is eliminated.

The form is prepared by removing the enamel from all original engravings through chemical cleaning or the use of a rubber erasure. The form, which may have both type and halftone elements, is next sprayed with a special non-reflecting black lacquer which dries immediately, after which the printing surfaces are gently polished with a soft, rubber erasure to remove the lacquer from the printing face.

Type worn beyond use for direct printing can be copied by Brightype with remarkable fidelity. To explain this more fully, in direct printing there occurs an ink build-up at the perimeter of each minute element in the form. Together with the pressure required to effect complete transfer of the ink, the sidewalls of type and dots are pressed into the paper surface. In photographing only the topmost surface, the ragged, thickening or spread characteristic of poor printing or worn type is eliminated. Too, since the depth of field in the camera lens is in sharp focus 2 pts. above and below the surface of type height (± 0.028 in.) a superior copy results from a form too unlevel to print direct.

Damaged type or scratches may be obliterated by carefully removing the black coating from the damaged area before photographing.

Since the form is not subjected to the rigors of printing, only a minimum amount of justification to insure lifting is required. After the form is prepared, it is slid onto the Brightype camera board, the chase is clamped, and the unit is raised to a vertical position.

A unique system of lighting is employed in this *same size* camera, consisting of an array of incandescent bulbs rotating *around the camera lens*. This light source produces direct (specular) reflection from the brightly polished surfaces. Rounded, worn edges are not photographed because the light is not reflected back to the lens from the sides of the type. Since the light originated very close to the lens, it is reflected straight back from the topmost surfaces only.

This light would not reflect highlights from glossy surfaces or embossed copy and the paste-up edges of mechanicals would not cast their usual shadows.

Another advantage would be uniformity or absence of light falling off in the corners, hot spots and other faults characteristic of conventional side lighting.

Considerable flexibility and economy seem to be possible in Brightype, since wrong reading reverse prints or veloxes may be combined with type and plates.

Rather than original engravings, halftone negatives may be prepared by a special Brightype method for inclusion with the form. A less expensive photographic halftone print may be used in place of an engraving. Reversed (white type on a black background) display type can be combined as well.

THE DIRECT IMAGE METHOD

Standard Rate & Data Service, Inc. is licensor of a direct-image method called d-i-Offset. This is based on proofing directly onto a special plate of paper-backed aluminum foil.

The press cylinder is packed using a rubber blanket of 80 durom. hardness. A special transfer ink is then applied to the press, the form is inked, and the impression is made directly onto the plate. The impression is so adjusted as to cause the image to become intaglio approx. 0.003 in., thus assuring complete transfer with a minimum of makeready. After the transfer, the plate is given a conventional desensitizing etch, and gummed.

The plate is next debossed to restore the image areas to the printing plane. A plastic sheet is first clamped to the cylinder of the debosser, and the bottom of the d-i plate is inserted, foil side out, between the cylinder and the plastic sheet. Static electricity on the plastic sheet which overlaps the plate causes both to hug the cylinder without further clamps or tape. As the drum revolves, the plate is scanned by small wheels which exert pressure in a series of overlapping lines, restoring all areas to an even plane. Three minutes is required for debossing, after which the plate is ready for printing.

If long runs are required, or the plate contains fine detail, it is desirable to replace the ink image with a more durable lacquer. To apply the lacquer after gum, the plate is washed with naphtha, dried and coated with a conventional plate-making lacquer. The gum serves as a protective stencil against the solvent and lacquer.

Any flat bed cylinder press in good condition, with proper packing, is suitable for making d-i plates and all other proofed conversions described in this article.

The characteristic grain of the d-i plate, the rubber blanket, necessary transfer pressure and debossing suggest this process as best suited to tabular, text, or directory composition.

Still another process usually limited to inter-office work is the xerographic process by Xerox, Inc. This electrostatic

TABLE I — PROCESS ELEMENTS

	Proof	Photography	Plate Exposure	Processing Plate
Double Transfer	X			X
Reproduction Proof	X	X	X	X
Brightype	*	X	X	X
Translucent Proof	X	X	X	X
Direct-Image	X			X

* Time to prepare form roughly equals time to proof.

means of image formation is very rapid. The image formed in a camera attracts charged resin particles. After a dry development step, these resins are transferred to the offset plate surface and form the image areas.

Also suitable for conversions is a variation of Xerography, known as the Electrofax process. At the time of this publication, the method is under further development by RCA.*

Other methods of conversion evaluated, consisted of proofing onto light sensitive photographic paper, film or presensitized offset plates.

In one method, proofing ink served as an opaque mask to a light source in exposing the non-image areas, after which the material was processed to form an image on a presensitized plate. In another approach, using plates, transparent proof press ink served to repel the presensitized plate developer, after which the plate was exposed and further processed. to form an image on a presensitized plate. In another approach, using plates, transparent proof press ink served to repel the presensitized plate developer, after which the plate was exposed and further processed.

Proofs were also made on the emulsion of previously exposed, developed and fixed photographic film or paper, the ink serving as a resist in a final bleaching solution to clear the background, thus producing a positive.

A variation tested under darkroom illumination, consisted of proofing on the emulsion of light sensitive film, hypoing to dissolve out the silver halides, rinsing to remove hypo and proof press ink stencil, exposure to light, and finally

Penrose Annual, 1956; page 133
* ibid.; page 128

TABLE II — EQUIPMENT

	Double Transfer	Translucent Proof	Reproduction Proof	Brightype	Direct Image
Proof Press	$8,500	$8,500	$8,500	$	$8,500
Camera			8,000	11,000	
Vacuum Frame		450	450	450	
Arc Lamp	500	500	500	500	
Darkroom		2,500	2,500	2,500	
Plate Processing	1,000	1,000	1,000	1,000	1,000
Whirler		1,000	1,000	1,000	
Extras				1,000	*
Total	$10,000	$13,950	$21,950	$17,450	$9,500

* $1,000 initial installation fee required for debosser; this includes first month's rent, and adequate licensee training.

TABLE III — MATERIALS

	Plate and Chemicals	Paper	Film and Chemicals
Double-Offset Transfer	$3.00	$	$
Brightype	3.00		2.50
Reproduction Proof	3.00	.25	2.50
Translucent Proof	3.00	.40	2.50
Direct Image	1.90		

developing the image to produce a negative.

Photographic film or paper may be proofed under room level lighting—the inked image serving as a stencil to repel the subsequent processing solutions. If the film is first developed, a negative is produced; if the background is first cleared in hypo, then transferred to the developer and the ink swabbed off, a positive results.

These latter methods have not been productive of good images but are basically sound and further experiments should produce better results.

In Table I, are shown the elements required in each method, according to quality in this order:

Brightype
Translucent Proof
Reproduction Proof
Double-Offset Transfer
Direct-Image

There are three cost factors to be considered: Equipment (Table II), materials (Table III), and labor (Table IV). Since these costs vary from plant to plant (some equipment is already available), they must be figured in the plant where the process will be used. Tables II, III, and IV are submitted as a basis for estimating.

Considering all three factors, it is apparent that double-offset transfer and direct-image are the most economical.

Table II should not be used without correcting for equipment already available in the plant. Before comparing net capital outlay for any system, the cost of equipment already available should be substracted from the various totals. For instance, if you already have camera equipment, the extra expense of equipment for the reproduction proof method over the translucent proof method is not particularly significant.

It is also evident that the basic Brightype equipment (including darkroom) would amount to approximately $14,500.

TABLE IV — LABOR

	Make-ready	Proofing	Photography	Conventional Plate-making	Presensitized Plate-making	Special Plate-making
Double-Offset Transfer	5 min.	5 min.			*	30 min.
Reproduction Proof	5 min.	3 min.	4 min.	1 hour	20 min.	
Translucent Proof	5 min.	3 min.	4 min.	1 hour	20 min.	
Brightype	7 min.		4 min.	1 hour	20 min.	
Direct Image	5 min.	5 min.				15 min.

* Presensitized plates have not been fully evaluated.

| 1. Reproduction Proof | 2. Press Sheet Reproduction Proof | 3. Press Sheet Translucent Proof | 4. Press Sheet Brightype | 5. Press Sheet Double-Offset Transfer |

With the exception of No. I above, showing approx. 30X enlargement from a reproduction proof, other examples were photographed from press sheets printed from four methods of conversion. It is interesting to note that there is a tendency to sharpen (thin) the copy in the double-offset transfer. Other conversions are approximately equal, with loss of detail attributed to offset blanket surface and fibre structure of paper.

Photoengravings and duplicate plates can be converted directly in the camera to form film images by filling the relief areas with powdered magnesium carbonate, briefly inverting the plate over steaming water to pack and secure this chalk, inking the surface to improve contrast, and making a simple camera line exposure.

EXPLANATION OF COMPARATIVE TABLES

In Table I are shown the elements required in each method.

In Table III is summarized the materials required in the five methods. Figures are approximate for a single 26¼ inch by 35½ inch plate.

Labor costs are difficult for us to estimate, but the summary shown in Table IV provides information from which costs could be determined. Approximate times shown are for production of single plates as described in Table III.

Most trade composition houses now offer reproduction proofs and transparent proofs. Technical aid in considering other methods can be had from manufacturers, consultants, or RIT's Research Department.

INKED ACID RESISTS

It is interesting to note that the nameplate industry has used conversions from offset to etched relief surfaces for many years; this method is also employed in the production of printed circuits.

In this branch of platemaking, offset proof presses are used to transfer an acid resistant inked image to stainless steel, brass or aluminum surfaces. The wet, greasy ink is dusted with powdered asphaltum or resins to improve its acid resistance and to set the ink. After dusting, the plate is heated which causes the ink to absorb the powder. Next, plate is cooled and etched in an appropriate mordant.

The products of the nameplate industry are right reading, or course, and more shallow than a letterpress printing plate. A practical variation of this process can be used, however, for the production of duplicate photoengravings and allied products.

Acid resistant ink can be transferred from the relief images of type or letterpress plates by a single offset transfer according to the instructions outlined under *translucent proofs*. The special ink required for Double Offset Transfer is recommended for this application. After printing, the inked image is dusted as outlined above.

The single offset transfer laterally reverses the image, resulting in a duplication of the original.

PHOTOELECTRONIC ENGRAVERS

First introduced in 1946 to automate the production of photoengravings, these machines are now serving as a means of conversion.

The operating principle of all scanners (which, in effect, electronic engravers really are), is much the same as wire-photo or facsimile and color scanners for producing separations.

A light source mirrors the tone values of the copy, thus causing varying amounts of light to reach a photoelectric cell, where visible differences in tone are transferred into electrical impulses. These impulses are amplified by circuitry much like that used in our phonograph between the pick-up and loud speaker. These electrical impulses actuate a cutting stylus which is embedded or cuts itself into the plate surface in direct proportion to the strength of the signal.

The white portions of the copy reflecting maximum light causes a large current to flow and maximum movement in the cutting tool . . . gray areas are represented by less energy to the cutting tool and dense blacks, reflecting little light do not generate power for the cutter, thus, the plate surface remains smooth or 100% tone.

The products of the several different machines now in use are employed as any relief printing surface. Special coated plates serve also as line or halftone positives for direct exposure in offset platemaking, thus by-passing all steps of process photography.

These special plates used in conversion are coated with an opaque or non-actinic color which is penetrated in the process of relief cutting, thereby producing a positive photo image. Relief plates produced in this manner can be contact printed to film and stripped conventionally.

OTHER TECHNIQUES

The continued growth of lithography into fields of products heretofore traditionally letterpress, has caused continued and vigorous pressure for development of better techniques for converting metal type and engravings to lithographic images. Lanston-Monotype is preparing to enter this market with a new photographic system of conversion. duPont has demonstrated a completely new device for converting, directly, letterpress plates into film images. Underway, by duPont is development of parallel equipment which will produce films directly from type forms. 3M has made available another conversion system based on proofing techniques. All these offer promise of filling, at least specific needs if not completely solving the problems of converting letterpress forms for lithographic use. All these, plus many still to come, should be watched closely.

SUMMARY

Work of satisfactory quality can be produced with any of these conversion methods, depending on requirements and on the craftsmanship applied. Only rough comparison of methods is possible because of the differing equipment and circumstances in various plants. The tables show some of the information that is needed to size up the applicability of the methods in a particular shop.

If we assume that conventional surface plates are to be used, then there seems to be no significant difference in the speed of operation of the four methods. Under average shop conditions the double-offset transfer and direct-image methods would probably be the fastest. If presensitized plates were used, then double-offset transfer might be the slowest method. Presensitized plates cannot be used in the direct-image method.

Section Three: Planning Art and Copy Preparation

Art and Copy Preparation for offset lithography provides the subject matter of lithographing; it embraces all activities necessary for this purpose from the inception of a job to the time when the job is ready for production and actually enters the lithographic shop for this purpose.

The Crucial Importance of Planning. Many people neglect planning because they are under the pressure of doing various chores such as pasting-down type proofs, retouching photographs and preparing overlays. But planning is nevertheless the most important part of art and copy preparation. Both the planning of a job and the subsequent manual and artistic operation require a sound, fundamental understanding of the lithographic process. Everybody active in art preparation for commercial purposes must also be thoroughly familiar with the attitudes, requirements, and customs of the business or industry for which a specific artwork is prepared.

Poor Planning Is Very Expensive. Unfortunately, all too few people recognize this importance of being familiar both with the lithographic process and with the segment of industry for which they are working. Or, said differently, because all too few people take the trouble to equip themselves properly for doing art and copy preparation, far too many lithographic jobs are poorly planned, incorrectly and incompletely prepared, and subject to many corrections while in process. That the same proportionate number of jobs is not poorly produced too is a tribute to the skill and patience of the executives and craftsmen of the lithographic industry.

Proper Planning Benefits All Concerned. Proper job planning and good copy preparation, then, benefits everyone concerned: art preparation services, lithographers and their customers as well as the ultimate consumer. It makes for better work, faster delivery, lower costs and greater volume.

Art and Copy Preparation Needs Experience and Good Judgment. There are very few cardinal rules which can be absolutely stipulated for art and copy preparation. This activity is largely a matter of common sense; and, since common sense is nothing more than the application of good judgment in an atmosphere of experience and knowledge, we are right back at the importance of one's knowing what he is doing before he undertakes the planning and preparation of lithographic printing.

There are No Generally Accepted Hard and Fast Rules for Art and Copy Preparation. The ways of American printers and lithographers are not uniform and standardized. Every lithographic shop has its own methods, its own preferences and requirements. Every job is different. Art and copy preparation for every specific job will be the more efficient the better it is adapted to the specific conditions under which a job is finally produced.

The Purpose of Our Presentation of Art and Copy Preparation for Lithography. Our presentation of the subject is not intended as a collection of laws to be observed but as an aid to the intelligent practitioner. In this Manual we want to provide *information* on some of the more commonly used methods and techniques. But the *decision* on the selection of a particular method or technique is left to the reader, and to him alone. It is left to his judgment which of the presented techniques is most suited to his particular needs and requirements.

The Assumed Audience of Our Presentation. The Lithographers Manual is destined for the practicing lithographer and his staff. It is not planned for independent artists, advertising agencies, or generally speaking, the customers served by the lithographic industry. Consequently we assume that the reader of this chapter is either an artist within a lithographic organization, or a person belonging to a lithographic organization in some other capacity. The reader might presumably be the plant owner, production man, contact man or salesman. He may want to study our presentation with a view to explaining one or the other aspects of the subject to customers or their printing buyers and artists. Our presentation should make this possible because the technical aspects of art and copy preparation remain the same regardless of where the job is prepared. Both the artist working inside a lithographic plant and an outside artist must cope with the identical problems when it comes to art and copy preparation.

The Scope of Our Presentation of Art and Copy Preparation. In the following section you find a check list for pre-planning a lithographic job. Thereafter, in Section 4, layouts and dummies are discussed. Section 5 is devoted to line copy, and Section 6 to continuous-tone copy and the halftone process. The fundamentals of tone control and retouching are set forth in Section 7, followed by a discussion on black-and-white photography for lithographic reproduction in Section 8.

The airbrush and its use in lithographic art preparation is the subject matter of Section 9. Section 10 discusses the handling and scaling of art, Section 11 the paste-up, and Section 12 the keying of separate art elements to the paste-up. Overlays for line, halftone and color combinations are treated in Section 13, and in Section 14 you will find a presentation of the Weber techniques.

In Section 15 fake-color processes are discussed, with the Bourges Process following in Section 16. In Section 17 you find a discussion on art presentation of reflection copy for process color reproduction, Section 18 is devoted to color photography.

Section Four: A Check List for Planning

Every printing job, depending on its purpose, is subject to several limiting factors. You will save yourself work and disappointment, and you will increase the efficiency of all those whose work must follow your efforts if you will take the time to discover these limiting factors. Intelligently followed, they will practically pre-plan the job for you. In analyzing a printing job you should ask the following three questions: (1) What is the purpose of the piece? (2) Who will receive it and how will it get there? and (3) How important is the piece to the accomplishment of the main purpose? Each of these questions is now discussed.

What Is the Purpose of the Piece? Answers to this question will aid in the determination of format, size, shape, and appearance. If it is to be a mailing piece, the postal regulations will have some influence; if an enclosure, the envelope or larger piece in which it is to be enclosed will help determine both size and bulk, or weight; if it is intended to be filed, standard file sizes will influence. If the piece is expected to sell, explain, instruct, or inform in detail, it must be large enough (in size or in number of pages) to accomplish its purpose effectively; if it is intended only to remind, announce, introduce or repeat, it is possible that brevity might be a virtue.

Who Will Receive It, and How Will It Get There? Answers here will further aid in determination of quantity, format and size insofar as the known habits of its intended recipients may affect these restrictions, as well as to the extent to which packing, shipping, transportation, mailing, and handling are involved. The method of packing and distributing frequently influences the size of a lithographed piece, but its total bulk too needs consideration.

Imagine, for example, the plight of a customer accustomed to thinking of 5000 quantities as small quantities, who ordered 5000 12-sheet calendars and 5000 2″ x 12″ mailing tubes shipped to his rather small office for inserting, addressing, and mailing. After delivery of the job he finds himself knee-deep in 60,000 calendar pages, and 140 cubic feet of mailing tubes!

How Important Is the Piece to the Accomplishment of the Purpose? Format, size, and quantity again come up for review as you consider the importance of the individual job in relation to the main effort it serves. Additionally, quality of design, printing, paper, and editorial content are involved. Perhaps, having considered the number of colors necessary for minimum accomplishment, you will review the piece again but this time in terms of how many additional colors are needed to derive maximum impact, result or effectiveness.

SEVEN CHECK POINTS

Application of these three broad limiting factors inevitably begins to narrow down the possible variations of a job into specifications which can now be detailed in a positive check list. The following seven points will specifically characterize a job: (1) Format, (2) Style, (3) Size, (4) Quantity, (5) Colors, (6) Paper and (7) Binding and Finishing. Each of them is now individually discussed.

Format. The limiting factors ought to have determined the suitability of a folder, a booklet, a mailing piece, a display, a poster and so on for the case in hand. *The form which will do the job best is the form to be adopted, regardless of any preconceived notions on the part of anyone concerned.*

Style. Whether the style will be strictly textual, or photographic; a period design, or excitingly modern with large, colorful areas of original art. The style, too, will be determined by the job to be done and by the audience to be influenced.

Size. Size, too, ought to have been fairly well-established by the limiting factors. However, if the customer or an art-service is taking care of art and copy preparation, they should be informed that it will pay them to consult the lithographer before proceeding. By adapting a job to the available equipment and standard paper sizes, the lithographer might save considerable time and money. Sometimes such savings are possible by a simple size reduction of $\frac{1}{8}''$ or by suggesting that an 8-page stuffer be folded as two parallel folds rather than as two right-angle folds.

Quantity. Although the nature of a job will generally determine the required quantity, quantity too should be discussed with the lithographer; he may be able to suggest some real savings, for example in suggesting the most economical quantity on items which probably will have to be reprinted several times in a short period. Conversely, he might be able to suggest a minimum advance run, thereby providing an economical means of testing the printed material and of finding out what changes are required in order to make subsequent runs up-to-date.

Colors. Once the needs of a job and the artistic sensibilities of all concerned have been satisfied, the planning in color too should be done in cooperation with the lithographer. In some cases, the addition of another color may save much costly stripping and tint laying and thereby cost; in other cases, the use of screened tints might obviate the use of an extra color and save cost this way.

Paper. The esthetic and utility aspects of the paper ought to have been determined by the already mentioned limiting factors. Availability, printability, and ultimate utility of the paper must be carefully investigated. Artists should not be too hasty to specify brands and grades. Rather they should inform the lithographer what purpose must be satisfied, and they should then let him find the fastest, cheapest, and most effective way of satisfying these needs. He has great experience in paper procurement and he has the right sources at his disposal.

Another point is frequently neglected by artists, but is of greatest importance in production; that is grain direction. The lithographic process has certain definite requirements on grain direction; folding too has its grain requirements. Job planning must take account of both as well as other factors such as press size and stock paper sizes.

Binding and Finishing. The format and importance of the job ought to specify quite clearly whether the job is to be folded, stitched, mounted, tinned, mechanically bound or strung. Of supreme importance to the ultimate success of the job is the determination, *before any further work is done,* of the method of binding and finishing, packing and distributing.

Much valuable work has ended up costing far more than it is worth or has suffered severe losses in effectiveness or still worse has been destroyed because of changes in mind concerning the finishing during the course of the job. Finishing too is a matter of planning carefully with all limiting factors in mind before the job begins. Then, barring unforeseen situations (and it can be said that very often so-called "unforeseen situations" too could have been anticipated) no changes should be made in the basic plan once it is adopted.

The lithographer should make clear to his client that he must always be consulted on binding and finishing because finishing has a bearing on his work too. Extra trim allowances, head margin uniformity between text signatures and covers or binders, and many other technical necessities of finishing must be provided for in the original planning and in the art and copy itself. If the lithographer is kept in ignorance of the finishing operations, he cannot guide the customer and prevent either unexpected high costs or total failure of the job when it becomes impossible to tin, stitch, fold insert, mount, punch or to do whatever other finishing may be required.

Avoid the Hackneyed. A final word on planning art and copy preparation in general: *Don't play follow-the-leader!* The man whom you copy may not know his business any better than you! He may have made grievous mistakes in size, format, art treatment, number of colors, quantity, distribution, etc., of which you may never know. The finished piece can tell the story of its origin!

It is appalling to see the number of jobs which are forced into a hackneyed mold of size, shape, color and format because "that's what the rest of the trade is doing." If the piece you are supposed to copy is a good piece, it is good because it is designed to satisfy the specific needs and limiting factors of the problem in hand. Such a piece is not automatically useful to you, but only if your own limiting factors are the same and they never really are!

Section Five: Layouts and Dummies

The term 'copy' is used to describe all elements of the prepared artwork that must be combined by the lithographer in order to produce the final printed piece.

The Handling of Manuscript Copy. Section one of this chapter very briefly sketched the operation of typesetting. Space did not permit discussion of such aspects of manuscript handling as copyfitting. There are available excellent texts and handbooks in this field. Here we are concerned

with manuscript as it effects planning. By *handling of manuscript copy* we mean the work to be done with this part of our copy so that the heading, general style and format will suit the purpose of the printed piece.

Approval of the Text. Since it is the task of the designer or artist to interpret the prose or verbal message, and the task of the lithographer to reproduce this interpretation in printed form, it is considered mandatory by many people that the manuscript copy be completed and approved *before* planning and art preparation begins.

Making Changes and Corrections. Good practice requires that everyone in a position to make suggestions or changes be compelled to read the entire manuscript copy, and to note in writing all changes to be made in consequence of his suggestions. He should further initial each sheet of the manuscript as a record of his approval. *This must be done before the designer is asked for a layout, and before the manuscript is sent to the typographer for typesetting.*

Numbering Manuscript Pages. It is also good practice to number each sheet of manuscript copy and to indicate at the same time the total number of sheets; for example, if there are 14 pages of manuscript, the third sheet would be marked "page 3 of 14." This method of numbering prevents the erroneous adding or omitting of manuscript sheets and planning the job on a wrong basis.

Rough Sketches. With the format established and the manuscript copy furnished, the job is ready for final planning. A layout is required of the complete job.

If the job is a booklet, it is generally speaking, best to prepare several rough sketches of representative spreads and of the cover before proceeding further. Once approval has been received for the style of the preliminary sketches, it is possible to complete the layouts for the finished piece, following the agreed style.

Various Kinds of Layouts. The layout may be a very rough visual, a semi-comprehensive, or a tightly rendered comprehensive drawing, looking quite like the finished job in all details. The technique with which the layout is rendered is never as important as the accuracy with which it is prepared.

The Final Layout Must be of Correct Size. The final layout may be rather crudely and hastily drawn, but it must be precise in one respect. It is only usable if it is to the correct size; if all elements are sketched in their proper relative positions, to the right scale, and in the proper colors. Above all, the final layout must provide the best possible interpretation of the manuscript copy — the theme, or meaning, of the piece.

A Layout Should be Either Very Accurately Drawn or Very Accurately Marked. As mentioned before, the ways of American lithographers are not uniform and standardized. Some plants prefer layouts of correct size, others do not. But there seems to be all-around agreement on one point: A layout must be either very accurately drawn or very accurately marked.

Why Layouts May Fail. Many labored and highly rendered layouts, while things of beauty in themselves, totally fail in their purposes. Either the headlines do not break suitably for maximum impact, or the illustrations — which may be arranged very artistically — are not sufficiently related to the story to dramatize its message. It also happens that some of the elements are useless in spite of the fact that they are so neatly sketched in by the designer — because they bear no relation to the purpose of the finished job. Other reasons for trouble can be that the type

consumes more space — or less space — than allotted to it in the sketch; that the illustrations crop to different shapes or proportions; that some of the several copy elements finally turn out differently in some manner or other from the way they are sketched and intended on the layout.

The Layout Is the Blueprint of Art and Copy Preparation. Since the layout is the blueprint from which all people who handle the job will take their specifications and instruction, it cannot serve its purpose unless it is a precise preview of what the final job is to look like.

Revising the Layout. Very often the designer will indicate on the layout photos and original art which are to be created from these indications and the layout in general; occasionally the finished art for some such elements will necessarily result in slightly different shapes, sizes, or appearance from those originally planned. Such cases do not pose great problems as long as the layout is promptly revised to accommodate the new situation.

Folding Dummies. Concurrently with the preparation and approval of the layouts it is indicated to secure several folding dummies. They may be supplied by a paper merchant in many cases. These consist of blank dummies of the job, on the actual stock to be used, carefully cut, folded and stitched, or otherwise finished, in accordance with the job specifications.

The blank dummy will help the designer to visualize the appearance of the job, enabling him to provide properly for bleeds, margins, drilling, and binding.

The Problem of Creep. In the case of saddle-stitched booklets where creep may be a consideration, the blank dummy will enable the designer to avoid serious difficulties with the outside margins in the center sections. Creep is the result of the build-up of paper thickness at the backbone of a saddle-stitched book — the thickness of one sheet for every four pages. This causes the front edge of the booklet to project out beyond the cover by the amount of build-up which occurs at the backbone; when the front edge of the book is trimmed flush in the final front trim, it leaves the horizontal dimension of the center pages shorter than the balance of the book by the amount of paper build-up at the backbone.

Adjusting a Layout for Creep. Alerted to the fact that creep will influence the critical page dimensions in the center of the book, the designer will instruct his artists to reduce the gutter margins on the paste-ups gradually as they approach the center of the book. Where all-over page designs are involved, the designer himself must adapt his designs and page content to allow for creep.

Pasting the Final Layout into a Blank Dummy. Once the final layouts are checked for completeness and accuracy they should be pasted down to one of the blank dummies and submitted for final approval. A carefully done layout, mounted into an accurate blank dummy, should provide a sufficient preview of the finished job to enable even the least experienced customer to approve it, or if necessary to correct it.

Section Six: Line Copy

Art and copy for lithographic reproduction normally falls into one of three general categories: *line, continuous-tone,* or *full-color.* In this section we are concerned with the first mentioned one, line copy. Line copy, as the name implies is composed of black-and-white lines and masses which have no gradation in tone. Line drawings and type proofs are without tonal gradations and are therefore the same thing, as far as the lithographer is concerned.

Line Copy Is the Simplest Type of Copy. Line copy, generally speaking, is the simplest and easiest type of copy to handle. The lithographic process is excellently suited for imprinting patterns of individual bars, lines, shapes or specks, in a single solid color of ink, on a sheet of paper. Continuous-tone copy needs further preparation before it attains printable form as we will see further down.

Line Copy Should be Prepared in Black. Line copy should be prepared always in black (regardless of the color of ink subsequently to be used in printing). Since the line negative, which is made photographically, is capable of extremely high fidelity, all lines and edges should be as clean and sharp as possible. Any fuzziness in the artwork will reproduce equally fuzzy in the negative, and consequently on the plate and finished job.

Dangerous Imperfection in Line Copy. However, since the photographic negative (and the plate as well) is designed to distinguish only between jet black and pure white, any color values less positive will confuse it and will result in distorted reproductions. Poor execution of art preparation includes such things as fuzzy edges on type proofs; dirt, rubber cement, and fingerprints on or adjacent to art; weak pen lines or brush strokes where the ink or paint has become diluted or where the pen started to run dry; grayed or yellowed paper surfaces; bleeding lines where ink or paint has been ruled on a soft, fibrous paper or board.

The rule for line art is simple: keep the blacks uniformly black, the whites white, and the edges clean and sharp.

Type Proofs for Reproduction. Because type proofs constitute a major part of many lithographed jobs it will pay the customer and his artists to consult the lithographer selected for a job on the kind of type proofs required by the lithographer for best results.

Basically, the lithographer will be looking for a proof having crisp, sharp letters, intensely and uniformly black, on a smooth, hard, white sheet. A good typographer will be able to comply with these requirements by making uniformly good proofs.

Adding to Already Existing Type Proofs. However, when adding new type proofs to already existing copy, or to proofs previously pulled, you should take the time to compare the new proof with the old. One proof may have more or less pressure or ink, or be pulled on a different paper stock, resulting in a different color of the mass of type. The camera will certainly record this difference if your eye can notice it. (The proofing of type for offset reproduction is discussed in detail in section two of this chapter.)

Techniques for Preparing Line Art. Line art is prepared by means of a number of techniques, all resulting in deposits of uniform masses of black on a white surface: line drawings, using pen, brush, pencil or crayon; lettering, using any of the same tools; scratchboard (a combination removal and additive technique where the artist may paint on a smooth, clay-coated removable surface, later to scratch away part of the surface containing the black, creating delicate, knife-sharp lines and edges which appear white on black); croquille board, or ross board, which is a rough textured board permitting a soft crayon to create apparent variations in tone depending upon the amount of crayon deposited around each of the microscopic peaks; dry brush which — as the name implies — is applied with a brush (often aided by a pen in detailed areas) with a heavy, almost dry paint. In dry-brush techniques solids are created basically, but where the artist trails off his brush stroke, a pleasant feathered edge results, giving the illusion of a lighter tone.

Line Art is Often Prepared Larger than Finished Size. It is customary, because of convenience to the artist, to draw original line art one-third or one-half larger than the final reproduction size. The reduction of the original art by the camera to its reproduction size normally tends to minimize slight imperfections and crudeness in the art; conversely, enlargements will tend to accent imperfections. However, imperfections ought not to be present in professionally executed art; often, it is quite practical to prepare line art reproduction-size.

Pencil Drawings and Fine-Line Pen Art Should be Prepared in Final Size. This is particularly true of pencil drawings and fine-line pen drawings. Too great a reduction (sometimes any reduction at all) will cause the delicate lines to crowd so close together that the photographic film used to make the line negative will have difficulty in separating them. The lines will fill in, thereby appearing blacker and showing less sharpness of detail than desired. Pencil drawings can cause various complications and produce mirror effects that make their reproduction sometimes rather difficult. They should be discussed with the lithographer selected for the job.

Original Art Must Always be Prepared with the Final Size in Mind. The finished reproduction-size will determine the size to which the artist works in many cases. Where it is most sensible to work larger (for example, where the reproduction is to be postage stamp size), the artist should be alert to the fact that lines tend to fill in if they are too *heavy* in the original or that lines may vanish, if they are too *thin* in the original. Always prepare the original, not as an end in itself, but with the final in mind. In determining the reduction rate the limitations of the camera should not be overlooked. Copy should not be too big for the copyboard, nor should it exceed 20 to 30 percent reduction or enlargement. (The exact figures should be ascertained in each case beforehand.)

Section Seven: Continuous-Tone Copy

The most easily recognizable form of continuous-tone copy is the black-and-white photograph. Even a brief study of a photo reveals that it contains an infinite number of tones, varying from the pure white of the photographic paper (generally the white border) to the densest black in the deepest shadow.

The Lithographic Process Lays Down Ink Films of Uniform Thickness. As outlined earlier, the lithographic plate and press does not select the amount of ink necessary to create each of these variations in tone — variations in grayness — because it lays down an equal ink film in all areas. This condition is not peculiar to lithography but applies to other printing processes too.

Tonal Values are Converted into Printable Form by the Halftone Process. The halftone process is used for the printing of tonal values, permitting high-fidelity reproductions of photographs and other continuous-tone subjects such as wash drawings and watercolor paintings, charcoal, pencil, and crayon renderings where the drawing and modeling are enhanced by many values of gray in addition to the pure blacks and whites. (Wash drawings are made in varying tones of black and gray by painting with transparent watercolors; charcoal, pencil and crayon renderings are made by drawing with these materials.)

How the Halftone Process Converts Continuous-Tone Images Into Reproducible Form. In order to evaluate and prepare continuous-tone copy most effectively for reproduction, it should be kept in mind that the halftone process creates the illusion of continuous tone by converting the tonal image into a large number of very small areas known as dots. These dots are not recognized from a certain distance by the human eye but blend with the paper on which they are printed into different tones.

The Halftone Screen. By the introduction of a halftone screen between the lens and the film in the camera when making the negative, a continuous-tone subject is converted into a finely dispersed pattern of dots, varying in size according to the tonal value of the original. To give the reader an idea how small these dots can be it is mentioned that a very frequently used screen produces 17,600 dots per square inch; other screens go even much higher. It is easy to understand that individual halftone dots are not visible to the human eye at normal reading distance.

Halftone Dots Vary in Size. The important thing about these dots is the fact that, while they are always uniformly spaced, center to center, they vary in size in proportion to the intensity of the tonal value they are intended to reproduce.

Highlight Areas. The effect of tonal difference, then, is created by the amount of black ink (in the case of a black-and-white halftone) which is seen by the eye in proportion to the amount of white paper which surrounds it. The pure white areas of the subject (known as the highlights) may contain no dots at all. Here the eye sees white paper only, and the highlight area appears therefore brightest.

Shadow Areas. The pure black areas of the subject (known as the shadows) may be represented by dots so large that they blend together with their neighbors and totally fill an area with a solid film of black ink. Since no white paper can be seen in these areas, the shadows will appear the darkest area on the printed sheet.

Middletones. A middletone gray will be reproduced with what are known as connected dots, or 50% dots: They will form a perfect checkerboard pattern in which the eye will see exactly the same amount of black ink (50% of the area) as it will see of white paper (50% of the area). We perceive the image created by this dot pattern as middletone or middle gray.

Summary of Halftone Dots and Their Tonal Effects. In this manner the amount of light intensity reflected by the various areas of the subject through the screen to the halftone negative will record dot sizes proportionate to the intensity of grayness. The result is a dot pattern that creates a wide range of tonal images. *Each dot, seen separately, can also be considered a piece of line art in itself in that it will reproduce as a single, solid black speck of ink.* Regardless of the tonal value involved, each dot within an area will be a tiny island of black with a sharp outline. The size of the dot in any one area determines how much ink in relation to the white paper background the eye will see. The dot sizes, therefore, determine how dark or how light that area appears to the eye in relationship to the other areas, which may be lighter or darker, that surround it.

Section Eight: Fundamentals of Tone Control

There appears to be an infinite number of different values of grays between the purest white and the deepest black on a good continuous-tone subject such as a photograph, for example. This infinite range of tones is not suitable for a discussion and control of continuous-tone image. We cannot hope to achieve precision in an atmosphere of vagueness. Before continuous-tone images can be discussed, we

must find a way of identifying their various tones in a precise manner.

The Gray Scale or Step Tablet. For practical purposes we divide the gamut of tones into a series of measurable and numbered steps. The number of steps is arbitrary; gray scales used in photography often have ten divisions. The steps on a gray scale or step tablet represent uniformly increasing tone densities, from white to black. The gray scale provides with a basis for discussion and comparison of tonal values.

The Limitations of Graphic Reproduction Processes. It is a generally accepted fact that *all* reproduction processes have their limitations, particularly in tone and color work. The commercial artist who is concerned with art and copy preparation is not so much interested in the reasons for these limitations as in their nature and the manner in which they express themselves. The reasons are very technical and often not clearly understood by many advanced printing research people themselves. But the nature of these limitations is very well known and easy to comprehend, as you can see for yourself in the following discussion of tonal reproduction.

Comparing a Photographic and a Printed Gray Scale. If we compare a photographic and a printed gray scale we see that the printed gray scale produces fewer steps than the photographic gray scale. Fortunately the number of steps on the gray scale is not as important for good tonal reproduction as is the degree of tonal difference between adjacent steps in a reproduction.

The Reproduction of Tonal Values. In the preparation and selection of tonal subjects — and these include all black-and-white photographs — the artist must understand the workings of the lithographic reproduction process. In particular, he must be able to evaluate a tonal subject for its final appearance on the printed sheet. This evaluation is not too difficult, if the basic problem is clearly understood. In discussions of this subject, artists often hear that the necessities of printing reproduction require "compressing the scale" of continuous-tone pictures. This statement is very often either not at all understood or misunderstood and therefore explained here.

Compressing the Scale and Its Meaning. You remember that a printed gray scale has fewer steps than a photographic gray scale. If the gamut of tones from white to black is divided into ten steps in a photographic scale, it may take only seven steps on a printed scale. In this case, all tonal values must be compressed into the smaller scale. The result is that the differences between individual grays is less strongly pronounced in the printed scale than in the photographic continuous-tone original. If such an original has important detail expressed in subtle tones of gray, this detail may be more or less lost in the printed reproduction because the tones of gray are not sufficiently different after they are compressed in the printing scale.

Contrast Is a Requirement for Well-Prepared Reproduction Artwork. Art for reproduction must have maximum definition between various tones of gray. Sharp separation of gray tones makes a picture interesting and shows its detail. This condition is known as contrast. *But it is possible to be fooled by a photo with too much apparent contrast;* here, much of the detail which should have been rendered in several distinct shades of deep gray loses its identity and becomes all black, whereas detail which ought to have been rendered in several distinct shades of light gray succumbs on the opposite end of the scale by disappearing completely. Even though the whites are bright

and the blacks dense, detail is lacking in such a picture, and will be still more lacking on the printed sheet as the lithographer cannot put in his plates what does not exist in the copy.

Flat Copy Is the Opposite of Contrasty Copy. In flat copy, much of the shadow detail which should have been expressed in deeper tones of black in the shadows, and much of the highlight detail which should have been expressed in lighter values of gray, fuses with adjacent areas of medium-dark gray and medium-light gray. The result is, of course, a serious loss of detail. This detail can again not be produced by the lithographer, because it exists just as little in the copy as the detail in the over-contrasty picture discussed in the preceding paragraph.

Increasing the Contrast by Retouching. In addition to the normal routine chores of correction, such as silhouetting, vignetting, squaring-up, and so on, the big function of the retoucher is to locate the significant tonal areas and to increase their contrast. The retoucher will either accent the area to be emphasized or its outlines; he may subdue or he may intensify the surrounding areas to increase the contrast of the picture.

Changing Contrast by the Bourges Process. Retouching is not the only technique by which contrast can be influenced. The Bourges process offers a different and very interesting approach. These techniques are discussed in Section 17 of our chapter.

Over Retouching Is Undesirable. If the retoucher knows his business he will select only the critical areas, and he will treat them with a minimum effort. A good retoucher knows from experience just how much emphasis is wanted to obtain the right amount of contrast. But it is also possible to over-retouch a picture. Beware of the artist who does not concentrate on a few crucial spots but who works over the entire subject. His handiwork may be a beautiful specimen of his craft but more often than not, the result will be poorer copy for reproduction than the original un-retouched photo was.

There is a limit beyond which no retoucher can simulate photography. The skilled craftsman knows this and avoids excessive retouching. An unskilled or inexperienced man spends hours in a misguided effort that produces a false, artificial-looking rendering. *Such a rendering is completely unattractive; it has neither the realism of a photo nor the charm and individuality of an original creation.* Retouching is an art in itself. You find a discussion of this subject in Section 10 of this chapter.

Paper Has a Strong Influence on Tonal Reproduction. Paper is one of the most important items in tonal reproduction. It is also one item that can be influenced in a very simple manner merely by making the right choice among the great available variety of papers. Paper influences highlights as well as shadow areas.

How Paper Influences Highlight Appearance. Obviously the less white, or the grayer the paper, the less bright will be the highlights. And, in this sense, colored or tinted papers may be considered graying influences to the extent that they are not white. Even among bright white papers there is a difference in maximum brightness in the highlights. Hard, glossy, coated paper is the best for high-light reproduction. Even in white sheets the highlights print less bright as the paper surface becomes duller, and as its texture becomes coarser.

Coarser papers disperse the reflected light and thereby reduce the sensation of brightness in our eyes.

How Paper Affects the Appearance of the Shadows. Similarly, there is a maximum blackness for every reproduction system. Many factors influence maximum printing blackness; ink is one of them and the paper another. Again, even though a maximum film of ink is laid down, *the coarser the paper the grayer the black,* because of the dispersion of light rays.

Section Nine: Black-and-White Photography

It takes Artistry with a camera to illustrate a fact, create an impression or tell a story photographically. But however skilled, the genius for staging and taking good pictures will suffer if it is not assisted by craftsmanship. It requires craftsmanship to make allowances for the changes that inevitably take place in each step from the original film, to a photographic print, to the lithographer's negative — and finally to dots of ink on a sheet of paper. The ideal photographs for reproduction are those planned from the beginning with one eye on the final reproduced form.

Planning for Good Reproduction Begins Before a Picture is Taken. In the normal rush of producing material for publication, there is often little opportunity to think about the reproduction qualities of a photograph until prints are seen. If it is possible, at the time a photograph is taken, by all means plan for good reproduction before the shutter is opened. A little extra spent for good photography can save a great deal of costly and unsatisfactory retouching.

Photographs for Reproduction Should be Taken by Professional Photographers. The photographer has a number of matters to control in the making of a negative: arrangement, lighting, choice of film, exposure, filters and developing. Such things are beyond the scope of this Manual. The best insurance against photographic headaches is the service of a man who knows his business. Ask him to use his skill to produce a negative which is very sharp and brightly lighted to produce detail.

Lighting Effects. Softness, fuzziness, very dark shadows, and eccentric lighting may be desired in special cases. But for normal, commercial purposes, the negative which is sharply in focus, clear and distinct is best for lithography. These things the photographer can supply if he knows they are required.

The Influence of the Halftone Process on Reproduction Quality. The halftone process rarely improves the quality of any original photograph. The white dots of the screen in the dark shadows of a picture tend to make the shadows lighter; fine dark dots in the light areas dull the whiteness of highlights. Thus the range from dark to light in the original photograph is compressed and the printed picture appears grayer. At the same time, a certain amount of detail is lost.

High Contrast and Low Contrast Pictures. The term for this range of tonal values is contrast. A picture with a great range between its deepest black and brightest white has high contrast. Pictures in which the darkest and lightest tones are not greatly separated have low contrast.

Contrast and Detail. Some popular misunderstanding about photography for offset lithography has centered around the term, "contrast." Contrary to a common belief, a so-called "contrasty" photograph is not necessarily a good one for lithography. Obviously, a photograph may have high contrast and yet have little detail.

Rather, a photograph with well-distributed spots of strong accents that define detail is the more desirable. Over-all contrast can be increased in succeeding steps of the lithographic process but nothing can be done to provide detail which was never caught by the camera.

The Three Broad Categories of Photographic Lighting. The difference can perhaps be better understood by comparing three broad categories of photographic lighting. There is, first, the case of flat, front lighting such as is common in flash bulb photography. This may produce high contrast but it also gives large masses of tone values that are either very dark or very light. Details are lost. Notice some newspaper portraits in which the face becomes a white oval with no modeling.

Side lighting from a single source may be better because it perks up the illusion of depth, but here, too, the tones are usually in larger masses. Shadow edges merge with backgrounds and are lost; the light side is often too light to show any detail. Look at many outdoor snapshots in, say, a company house organ.

The alternative to these is a picture with the lighting balanced to show a full range of tonal values that give attention to all the desired details. It is contrasty, true, but it also has the interesting pictorial clarity which is most often desired in lithographed pieces.

Distinction between the Subject and Its Background. If the subject of the photograph is to be outlined or must be otherwise retouched, the photographer can provide for a firm distinction between subject and background. This eliminates guesswork on the part of the retoucher. Large sheets of cardboard are useful as background for dark machinery and the like to keep edges from being lost in the shadows. Light objects, of course, require dark backgrounds.

Prints for Reproduction Should be Carefully Made. Even though it is not always possible to direct the taking of the picture, the photographic negative is very often available to the person responsible for preparing

The appearance and the mood of a photograph can change with the lighting. The illustration above shows a portion of the New York skyline taken in daylight at normal exposure. Below is the same view taken during the evening. *Photo by A. Devaney.*

High-key photo. *Photo by A. Devaney.*

Low-key photo. *Courtesy Eastman Kodak.*

This illustration was taken at the same time as the daylight picture illustrated at top of facing page. It was exposed on infrared film with a red filter. You can see the slight time differential by the position of the ferryboat and cloud movement. The blue sky goes dark while the green foliage at the shore line turns to a light tone.

Normal Photo. Good film negative; well-exposed print on normal grade paper. Full tonal scale — light areas adjacent to shaded areas with each properly separated to give excellent reproduction. *Photo by A. Devaney.*

Print Too Flat. Light areas are veiled with a grayish cast. Deep tones and shadow areas do not carry full density. An attempt by lithographer to increase contrast will not duplicate result of that obtainable from properly exposed print.

Print Too Contrasty. A client may prefer this higher contrast. Certainly it is preferable to the too-flat picture. Yet with an attempt to come as close as possible to a facsimile reproduction it does not hold true to the original.

The above experimental print shows the importance of adjacent tones. The dense background adjacent to the distinct gray panel gives the illusion of a lighter gray tone in the upper portion of the gray panel. Actually the gray is of the same intensity over-all. It is exactly the same as the panel on the right. Covering the dark background will erase this illusion. Prepare or adjust your illustrations to give the proper tonal separations.

lithographic copy. A little care in making a good print will go a long way toward getting better reproductions at no extra cost.

Reproduction Qualities of Photographic Prints. The many manufacturers of photographic films produce dozens of different grades of photographic papers that vary by contrast, color, texture and weight. With these, any negative can be made to produce a wide variety of prints. Generally, the photographer will select the grade of paper which suits the contrast of the negative and produces a print of normal contrast. Unless told otherwise, the photographer is likely to be interested in a print that looks good. For the best reproduction, however, a print must have qualities that photograph well. Remember that the print is going to be re-photographed in the reproduction process.

Off-White Papers Should be Avoided. Glossy, white prints which get all the detail out of the negative are generally considered to be the best for lithography. It should be pointed out, however, that there are glossy photo papers that are off-white — ivory, cream, india and other papers used for exhibition prints. These should be avoided because they tend to dull the highlights in the lithographic camera. The film used by lithographers for halftones is partially color blind; that is, light reflected from the warm background affects the film less than light from pure white stock.

Similarly, various photographic papers produce images that differ somewhat in color. Those that produce a neutral or brown-black image will provide better shadow detail for the lithographic camera.

Paper Texture and Toning Affect Reproduction Quality of Photographic Prints. The character of photographic paper surfaces also influences the brilliance and detail of a print. The more textured and the duller the surface, the less detail and brilliance will be obtained from the negative. Some smooth semi-matte prints are acceptable, but in general, toned prints such as sepia, matte surface prints and hand-colored prints make poor copy for any reproduction process.

Size of Reproduction Photos. Usually, 8″ x 10″ photo prints are the most convenient to handle and give ample opportunity for retouching. Photographs with an exceptional amount of fine detail to retouch must, of course, for best results be larger.

In any case, plan to have the lithographer reduce your photograph rather than enlarge. This helps to reduce any imperfections in retouching. Naturally, too great a reduc-

tion is undesirable because detail becomes lost. The rough rule of thumb is: Make prints approximately one-half again as large as they will appear when reproduced.

Photographs Can be Made Same-Size as Finished Reproduction. Prints may be made the size of the intended reproduction. This is desirable in some cases because it affords a more accurate view of the detail which will actually be retained when the picture is lithographed. If prints are of uniform quality, it also permits the lithographer to group a number of photographs for a single "shot" and thereby save the cost of making individual halftones.

Techniques for Improving Quality of Photographic Prints. A photographic print cannot be much better than the negative from which it is made, but the skilled photographer can get a great deal more out of a negative than the unskilled photographer. There are certain procedures during the developing of the film which will intensify or reduce the tonal values of an inferior negative. Occasionally some areas of a negative may not be dense enough and cause areas of the print to be too dark. Or, other portions may require additional exposure. To vary the strength in different portions of the print, the photographer uses his hand or a paddle to shade these areas during the printing. This is called "dodging."

When there are fine lines or highlight detail which do not print distinctly, the photographer may strenthen them by turning and tilting the printing frame during the printing operation. This allows the light to undercut the image on the negative and produce a heavier, darker-appearing finished protographic print.

Photographers in general are familiar with these tricks of their trade and know a great many more. An explanation of the use and purpose of the photograph will go a long way toward obtaining a print which has the contrast, detail and brilliance that you require. If you think the print should be better, ask your photographer if he can improve it for reproduction.

Care and Protection of Photographic Negatives and Prints. Remember, too, that improper photographic handling can produce imperfect prints from good negatives; spots, cracks in the emulsion, blurred images, flatness, stains and discolorations may be the fault of the print. If this is suspected to be the case, check the negative rather than run the risk of an unnecessarily poor reproduction.

Certainly it is much less costly to have the photographer take extra pains to get all the detail out of the negative than to have an artist retouch detail on a poor print.

Section Ten: The Airbrush and Its Use*

The airbrush is an instrument used to apply paint to a surface. Watercolor, either transparent or opaque, a dye, a lacquer, or other liquid is placed in a color cup attached to the airbrush, and pressure for spraying is provided by a small air compressor or carbon dioxide tank. One of the

most characteristic and important functions of the airbrush is its ability to apply color in soft, subtle tonal gradation which may range from the lightest discernible tint to a completely opaque coverage. With the proper type of airbrush, any amount of control can be obtained, so that the

This is the original photo supplied. Insufficient attention was paid to the preparation of this photo. Too much work was left to the retoucher. White backdrops should have been hung from the balcony to help silhouette the illustration, with additional light focused into the dark fittings. This still would have left much retouching. The final illustration shows the creditable job the retoucher did. *Photo retouched by A. S. Van Eerde.*

paint can be applied in any pattern, ranging from a thin pencil line to a broad spray. It can also be adjusted to give a stipple or spatter effect. Since the brush does not come into contact with the surface, successive coats of pigment can be applied without disturbing the previous ones. Also, pigment or dye can be applied to film or glossy surfaces in flat, even washes or in graded tones.

An example of the tone range possible with the airbrush.

The airbrush is used in practically every phase of the commercial art field — in Illustration, such as figure, mechanical, advertising, architectural, and technical illustration; in Photo Retouching, both black-and-white and color on positives or negatives; and in Design, such as textile, plastic, product, greeting card, and poster. It can also be applied to many phases of the graphic arts field; for preseparation art of multiple color printing, either solid or halftone; to lighten or darken areas of art or copy for our printing, and for many special effects.

EQUIPMENT

Several manufacturers make airbrushes of various types and models. The two basic types used by artists are the "single-action" type and the "double-action" type.

---

* Illustrations from *The Complete Airbrush Book* by S. Ralph Maurello; Wm. Penn Publishing Co., N. Y.

Single-Action Airbrush. In the single-action airbrush, the paint flow is secured by one action — pressing down on the finger lever. This brush is the simplest in design with the least number of parts. It has a color adjustor which can be regulated for fine or coarse effects, but the spray pattern cannot be varied during a stroke, except by varying the distance from the paper. While this is good for background work and simple airbrush art, it does not permit the precise control that the double-action airbrush does. Watercolors, lacquers, and oil paints can be used in the single action brush.

Double-Action Airbrush. The spray pattern from the double-action airbrush is controlled by two actions — pressing down on the finger lever and pulling back — the further back, the larger the pattern. This makes for easier control and variation of the pattern. The distance from the airbrush to the paper must be varied accordingly. The three major all-around studio brushes of this type are the Paasche V and V Jr., the Thayer and Chandler Model A, and the Wold Model A1. These are capable of producing fine work or fairly broad work. A more specialized airbrush is the fine arts Paasche AB airbrush. This is used for the finest detail work in photo-retouching and air-painting, giving the artist absolute color control and enabling him to draw in freehand manner with pencil accuracy a wide range of patterns. It is a slower-acting brush than the VI, an asset in directing the pattern. The VL Paasche is a large double-action brush capable of doing fairly fine work, covering large areas quickly, and giving a good heavy stipple or spatter when required. It is useful for poster, display and architectural rendering. It can be used for spraying lacquers or varnishes as well as watercolors.

Sources of Air Supply. Pressure for the airbrush can be supplied in the form of carbon dioxide, the same compound which makes the fizz for ice cream sodas. It is available in various size cylinders, the one containing 20 pounds of gas being the most practical.

A unit for compressing air can be used as an alternative to the carbon dioxide cylinder. This consists essentially of an air compressor and a motor to operate it. It may or may not have a storage tank.

Other Materials. Aside from the airbrush and source of air supply, the usual drawing materials and equipment employed by any commercial artist are used. Opaque watercolors in various standard shades of gray tones, known as "retouch grays" are very useful for rendering "retouching."

PROCEDURES

In air painting, any one, or a combination, of several methods may be used, depending upon the effect desired, the medium used and the surface worked on. The airbrush may be used freehand, with masks or friskets, or with a combination of all three.

Freehand Use of the Airbrush. If the airbrush is held about two inches from a sheet of paper and the spray

Using the airbrush freehand.

directed across the paper in a straight line, the pattern shown in our illustration will result. It is a tonal area which blends out rather abruptly at its top and bottom edges. (A pencil guideline is visible along its center.) If the airbrush were held further away from the paper and the finger lever pulled back further, a wider band with edges fading more gradually would result. If the airbrush were held closer to the paper and the finger lever pulled back very slightly, a thin, almost sharp, line would result. (Naturally, if the hand were moved in an arc when airbrushing, a curved band or line would occur.) If the broad strokes were allowed to overlap each other slightly, a flat even wash or tone of color would be obtained. Values are controlled by building up the tones by continued application, and by using darker or lighter pigment.

Masks. If instead of a "soft" or fading edge, a sharp edge of color is required, either in a regular or irregular shape, a blotter or a sheet of acetate can be cut to the desired shape and placed in position on the surface being airbrushed. The spray is then directed along the edge of this mask which when removed will leave the airbrush pattern shown. If this mask were raised slightly off the surface when directing the spray, the sharp edge would be softened slightly. If one wished to airbrush the background of a portrait photograph, this method could be used by moving an oval-shaped raised mask around the head while spraying.

Friskets. If the area to be airbrushed is too complicated or large for the use of masks, a sheet of thin tracing paper or frisket paper is covered with rubber cement and laid over the surface. The frisket is cut away and removed from the area to be airbrushed, and the area sprayed. When the desired effect is obtained, the frisket is removed. If necessary, another frisket can be placed over the painted area without harm. Liquid friskets are also available and are merely painted on the surface with a handbrush and peeled off after use. A rubber-base maskoid is used on paper and a plastic-base maskoid used on photographs or film. Masking tape can also be used.

PHOTO RETOUCHING

Photographs are retouched for various reasons. In the majority of cases, it is done in order to secure good reproduction qualities when the photograph is to be reproduced

Before airbrushing.

After airbrushing.

Using a frisket for a shaped area.

of the types mentioned is done with the airbrush and hand-brush (sable) on the positive print. This retouched photo is either directly used for reproduction or it is photographed

Using a frisket for a large background area.

in a publication. Next in importance is the necessity to present the product or subject photographed to best advantage, especially for advertising purposes. Again, the limitations of the camera or the circumstances under which the photograph was taken may have to be compensated for by retouching.

Special effects such as fading out the image around the edge (vignetting) or elimination of the background, combining part of one photograph with another, emphasizing only certain portions of a photograph, all of these are achieved through retouching. For the most part, retouching

and a print is submitted to the lithographer. Additional copies can be filed for future use. Naturally the retouching that was on the original print will appear in the copies.

Section Eleven: Handling and Scaling of Art

All art and copy must be photographed for lithographic reproduction and therefore must be kept clean. Since most jobs require more than one piece of art, and since most users of lithography tend to file art for future use, it is advisable to establish standard sizes for artwork. Standard sizes greatly contribute to ease of handling, classifying, storage and use. Further, since all artwork has a value of some sort or other, it will pay to protect it during handling, storage and use.

Mounting and Flapping of Artwork. Photographs and all other art on paper or lightweight board should be well mounted — (*and that means securely and also perfectly flat*) — to artist's mounting board or to illustration board. Where special instructions are required, these should be made on a tissue overlay which in turn should be flapped over the subject. In all cases, art should be flapped with a protective covering of kraft paper or lightweight coverstock.

Using Identifying Colors for Flaps. It is common practice for agencies, studios and advertisers to select a distinctive color of flap paper for all or certain classes of their work. These colors serve either for classification or for identification of their own art and for distinguishing it from other artwork.

Margins for Notations. Sufficient margins should be left on all four sides of the mounting board for notations

and instructions pertaining to cropping, scaling, identification, possible multiple use, and so on.

Marking of Artwork. Regardless of the extent of information recorded on the identifying flap of each subject, all pertinent information must be repeated on the margins of the subject. The reason for this rule is easy to understand! When the art is photographed, the photographer either removes the flap or folds it back. All information on the flap is thereby either lost or hidden whereas all information on the margins of the art is reproduced together with it on the negative. Information recorded on the negative will identify the subject and will carry all specific instructions with itself throughout its travels in the course of production.

Markings Must Always be Made in the Margins. All necessary markings must be made in the margins and never in the subject area itself. (It sounds rather superfluous to discuss the apparently obvious, but experience teaches that the obvious is very often not so obvious to everybody.) Special care must be taken with continuous-tone subjects. One must never write on their flaps or on any other surface when the subject itself lies directly beneath; pen or pencil pressure will make marks which the eye may miss but which the camera is sure to reproduce. Photographs must not be marked on their backs either.

Improperly Marked for Cropping . . . . . . Trimming lines should not be marked across the surface of the photo. This type of marking makes the re-use of the photo more difficult. If the markings are not perfectly square the lithographer must cut further into the actual picture. After making the halftone negative to desired size it may be necessary to use a little more of the picture to fit the layout or change in layout.

Properly Marked for Cropping . . . . All trim marks and instructions should be indicated on the outside of photo. Photo should be mounted to avoid rolling or cracking of photo. Cover all art with an acetate or tissue overlay. Do not write on overlay after it has been affixed to artwork, to avoid indentations on surface of original art. *Photo by A. Devaney.*

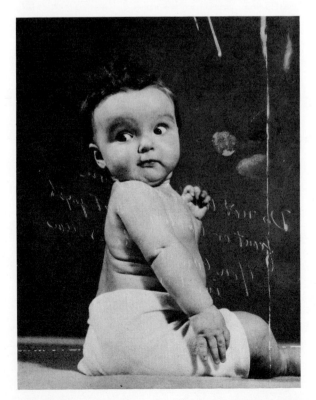

The picture at the left was badly mishandled. Most likely you will never get a single photograph having all of these injuries, but many pictures are mutilated at one time. Avoid the use of paper clips on photos. The paper clip eventually imbeds itself creating an embossing difficult to eliminate. Writing on the back of photo also tends to create an embossed effect. Thumb prints, especially on retouched copy, will show up in the halftone negative. To avoid cracks, mount the photo on double-weight mount board. Do not mount photo with any of the adhesive tapes. Attempts to remove the tape may catch the edge of photo and rip the thin emulsion layer. To help remove surface stains of unretouched photos, clean surface with absorbent cottom lightly moistened in benzol, naphtha or diluted ammonia.

THE CREATIVE ART DEPARTMENT

The Percentage Scale System. Most graphic arts cameramen or photographers enlarge and reduce copy by percentage scale or by the ratio of the reproduction to the original. It is therefore sensible and practical to mark copy in the same manner.

Courtesy Dorval Publishing Co.

Selecting the desired area before scaling and cropping.

Many artists resist using the percentage scale; the reasons for this resistance are difficult to understand. All that is needed is the figuring of proportions, something that every schoolboy must learn. Not to use the percentage system means to forego a valuable technique for speed and accuracy in job planning.

Scaling Tools. Through the simple use of one of the many proportional scales on the market, or with a conventional slide rule or old-fashioned arithmetical long division as a last resort, the artist can discover at a glance what the new dimensions are. If, for example, he reduces an 8″ x 10″ subject to 4½ inches on the short dimension, the long dimension will be 5⅝ inches and the scale will be 56½%. The reproduction will be 56½% of the size of the original.

Combining Scaling and Cropping. It may be the case that reducing the 8-inch dimension to a 4½ inch repro-duction depth fits the layout but that the height cannot be 5⅝ inches but only 5⅜ inches according to the layout. The slide rule helps again; without altering its setting, the artist can find out that he can maintain the same reduction scale and also obtain the correct reproduction height of 5⅜ inches if he crops the original to 9½ inches.

The Slide Rule Indicates Many Choices of Re-arranging Size and Crop. Cropping may or may not be a satisfactory solution, as the case may be, but the slide rule technique quickly provides a number of multiple choices, one of which will be the best. Such a system is ten times as fast, and much more reliable than drawing rectangles and diagonals which must be re-drawn each time a better solution comes to mind. It should also be considered that the rectangles and diagonals were possibly not too accurate in the first place whereas the slide rule is.

Preparing Art in the Same Reduction Scale Throughout. On a job containing a number of pieces of copy, the artist can record the number of reductions and enlargements called for, and simplify the cameraman's job (thereby reducing the time and cost involved) by altering some of the scales and croppings slightly to keep the number of different scales to a minimum. This is of great importance as each different enlargement or reduction scale requires interruption of work and makes necessary a change in camera setting. Otherwise — assuming that density ranges and tonal values are similar — the cameraman can group several subjects of one scale and photograph them all in one exposure.

An Example of Adjusting the Scale. For example, if a group of similar subjects call for reductions of 54, 54½, 55½, and 56%, they could all be re-scaled to 55% achieving 4 negatives in the time it would otherwise take to make one. A good graphic arts photographer would probably perform this work simplification without discussing it with the artist. Therefore, it makes sense to plan the cropping and scaling of artwork for economy in general but to insist on exact scaling in the rare situations where scaling and cropping is really critical.

Section Twelve: The Paste-up

In preparing artwork for lithography, it is customary to assemble as much line copy as possible into a single-master arrangement ready for the camera. This assembly is known as the paste-up or the key. All type proofs, lettering and line art that can be photographed in the same size is mounted in position onto one assembly, or, in the case of large units and books, onto a series of such assemblies.

The Convenience of Preparing Art Same Size as Final Reproduction. As mentioned previously, in the section on line art, it is most convenient if line art is done in the same size as final reproduction and if it is pasted-up together with reproduction proofs of type. The main reason why "same-size" paste-ups are so economical is that type is

— as a rule — set in the "same-size" too. It is — again as a rule — expensive and difficult to set body type in a larger size — often live illustrations are directly drawn on the board used for paste-ups.

The Use of Photostats in the Preparation of the Paste-Up. To achieve the accuracy, work simplification and orderliness necessary for reproducing the bulk of the job in one piece on a single line negative, photostats are often used. Photostats are a practical means for reducing or enlarging separately prepared line art which was not originally prepared to the same size. Such photostats are generally glossy for maximum sharpness and are pasted in position on the paste-up. This procedure makes it possible to check their relationship to the rest of the job and to eliminate the otherwise necessary stripping of separate line negatives by the lithographic stripper.

But it must not be assumed that photostats are in all cases the best solution. In complex cases where various operations can be combined, the lithographic stripper may be able to do a better and more economical job than the paste-up artist. Nor must it be overlooked that photostats are not always of the necessary dimensional stability. This remark pertains not only to changes in size but also to irregular distortions. Care is therefore needed in all work requiring very high accuracy.

Negative and Positive Stats. Photostats (or high-contrast photographic prints) are a great convenience to the artist who prefers to work to a different scale; a negative stat is required by the photostat process in order to make the final positive stat. Negatives are often very useful as it can be convenient to add, delete, or correct detail on the negative, particularly where several drawings are to be combined with lettering or type. The positive stat made from the negative can have most of the corrections incorporated before it is further improved and pasted in its proper position. But it must again be mentioned that photostating, though a cheap and practical method, is not a high precision one. Photostats are not nearly as dimensionally stable as the material used by the litho stripper. Nor is their general quality of the very best.

Photostats for Reversing of Art Elements. Where reverses of lettering, type, or drawings are required, the negative stat is also handy; it provides the needed reverse image that can be incorporated into the complete paste-up for the camera and eliminates the separate "shots" and

Courtesy Dorval Publishing Co.

Blackening the cut edges.

stripping that are necessary when the cameraman and the stripper must make reverses from positive copy. But here too it must be said that many quality houses prefer to make reverses in the camera.

Accuracy and Cleanliness. Accuracy and cleanliness are among the important factors in preparing paste-ups. Good care must be taken when using T-square and triangles; first, that the tools are square and accurate, and secondly that they are carefully handled. A combination of inaccurate tools (damaged by careless handling) and sloppy working habits is in most cases responsible for inaccuracies in the prepared art. Corners, bleeds, centers, and construc-

tion marks on paste-ups may be out of square, thereby causing lines of type and other art and copy elements to be also out of alignment.

Joining of Several Line Negatives Should be Considered. It should be considered that the necessities of lithographic production often require the joining of several line negatives made from different paste-ups and their combining into a single press plate. It should also be remembered that several press sheets may be required for the finished job. If all these facts are appreciated, it will be evident that quality work cannot be produced from paste-ups that are inaccurately prepared.

Center Marks. Putting center marks on each paste-up is the best way to assure accuracy. All other marks and copy elements should be squared-up with relation to the centers and rechecked frequently with the base center marks.

Illumination at Photographing of Artwork Must be Considered. Because the copy is illuminated from two sides by powerful carbon arc lamps during photography, all cut lines where one element has been pasted over another will cast shadows resulting in thin, unwanted lines in the negative which must be opaqued by hand on the negative. For this reason, *all type proofs and other separate copy elements that are assembled in the paste-up should be trimmed so as to leave plenty of blank paper around the work — as much as possible but never less than $\frac{1}{8}$".* Thereby the opaquer will have sufficient room for his work on the negative.

The shadow line will still appear on the negative, but the opaquer can work much faster if his brush is not too close to critical work, and the risk of inadvertently damaging the copy by painting out the serif from a type character or the dot from an "i" does not exist.

Do Not Paste in Single Letters, Words or Lines of Body Type. Similarly, the practice of correcting a character, a word, or a line of type by pasting a new proof of the correction over the old proof should be avoided; even though it is a nuisance to secure a corrected proof of the entire paragraph or column, it is easier and safer to do so than to assume that every opaquer has the ability to flawlessly paint out the shadow lines between type lines and words.

On the other hand, there are some very highly skilled craftsmen with almost acrobatic skills; it is therefore advisable to make sure which kind of correction a particular shop wants before deciding on the technique to be used in a specific case.

Rubber Cement Too Can Cause Trouble. It seems needless to say that rubber cement picks up dirt, but too many people forget that. Therefore, all excess cement should be removed completely with a rubber cement pickup. Removing excess rubber cement not only makes a more presentable job, but it also spares the opaquer needless work.

The Particular Artist Should Work Particularly Clean. Doing a perfect job has another aspect too, especially for the very particular creative artist who wants everything he designs to be just so. Such persons should keep in mind that they are inviting another person to give their creation the final touch whenever a litho artist must make good for their own carelessness.

Paste-Up for Book Work. In book work it is a generally accepted rule to treat facing pages as one design unit. Every typographer and book designer knows and observes this rule. It depends on the nature of the case whether individual pages or facing pages are pasted-up in a job, but the beginner should always keep the rule of facing pages in mind when he evalautes a book paste-up. This rule is especially important in book work having a considerable number of illustrations.

The Binder's Imposition. A glance at a binder's imposition (which you should secure when you request the blank dummies) will indicate that facing pages are not necessarily located adjacent to each other on the press sheeet as it is imposed for folding. The position of pages on the sheet depends entirely on the specific imposition. The imposition on its part depends first on the folding equipment selected for a specific job, but also on several other considerations that are rarely of interest for the layout artist.

If you combine pages that are not imposed together in one paste-up either the cameraman or another lithographic craftsman will slice them apart because he must separate them for correct imposing. It is certainly better to arrange the pages on the paste-up in the sequence in which they must be imposed and thereby to save time and effort all around.

Spreads. On spreads where complicated art runs right across the fold in such a way that the entire spread is actually one, you may have to render the artwork in one piece. But you should be aware of the fact that the stripper will still have to slice through the negative to place each page where it belongs. Many people prefer to have spreads rendered as if they were facing pages. On bleed jobs they should have individual matching bleeds where they must be joined.

The practice of arranging pages to suit the sheet layout is known as *"Binder's Spreads, Imposition Spreads, or Folio Pages* — as opposed to the term *Facing Pages.*

Section Thirteen: Keying Separate Art Elements

The space allowed on the paste-up for photos and other separate art which is to be combined later by the lithographic stripper must be clearly and accurately indicated. Several techniques are used for this purpose, as you can see from the following discussion.

Cross-Referencing Separate Art Elements. It is essential that the key notations used to indicate the proper space for separate art elements in the paste-up are also noted on the flap and on the margin of each separate art element. Sloppiness in cross-referencing is sure to cause trouble later on.

The Outline Method of Keying Separate Art Elements. A common method, although not the best, for keying strip-ins (as separate art to be combined in a paste-up is known by the trade) is to outline the area involved in black or in red. Red is sometimes used to clearly separate guide lines from actual copy such as rules, although both red and black photograph the same on the negative. In the case of square halftones, a simple rectangle is sufficient.

The Tracing Method of Keying Separate Art Elements. Where odd shapes are involved, a *camera lucida,* or "luci" is very practical. This optical device permits the artist to trace the outline of the subject to whatever size he chooses in its proper position on the paste-up.

The Photostat Method of Keying Separate Art Elements. Another technique uses photostats of all separate copy, reduced or enlarged to their correct size. The photostats are pasted in their proper position on the paste-up. These pasted-up photostats are, of course, carefully related to the art element which they represent. Often the notation *for position only* is added to indicate that the photostats are not the real artwork but only stand-ins for it.

In jobs requiring highest accuracy it should never be forgotten that photostats may be dimensionally incorrect or distorted.

How Paste-Ups and Keyed Art Elements are Used by the Cameraman. When using any of the methods described above, the cameraman can make a single line negative for each paste-up, where the outlines or photostats clearly indicate the position of all strip-ins. The stripper must then cut out the film in each area where a separate piece of film bearing the separately photographed art elements is stripped in.

The Transparent Window Method of Preparing Paste-Ups. Many lithographers prefer to simplify this phase of the stripping operation by requesting the artist to prepare the paste-up with transparent "windows" on the key-line negative, drawn to the proper size and shape of the strip-ins.

The areas to be occupied by the strip-ins are painted in solidly by the artist. Because india ink often does not lie smooth, flat and uniform, and therefore often photographs in streaks which impair the transparency of the window on the negative, india ink is not suitable for painting in. Lightweight black paper is sometimes pasted down and cut to the correct silhouette of the window. As red photographs the same as black, red construction paper can also be used.

Why the Transparent Window Method is Preferred by Some Plants. The purpose of applying opaque shapes to the areas designated for separate strip-in art is to provide transparent windows in the negative. Now, instead of cutting and removing the film from the key negative, the stripper simply tapes the halftone negative to the back of the key negative, using the sharp outlines of the window as a mask. Because the window is transparent, it does not interfere with the passage of light during the plate exposure.

Selecting a Particular Keying Technique. As already stated in this chapter the ways of American lithographers are not uniform and standardized. Our presentation of art preparation provides information but does not lay down any rules to be slavishly followed. The selection of a particular technique must be made considering the job on hand as well as the plant chosen for its production. Such comments as "for best quality" or "for highest accuracy" are merely directional indications. We have no rules for measuring these attributes. Judgment is still a personal function that must be exercised as the case demands it. One man's bread can be the other man's poison!

Several Drawbacks of the Transparent Window Method. One of the objections to this method is the fact that the stripper has no guide to tell him which strip-in goes where. Some people attempt to help him in this respect by painting a key number or initial, in white, on the black or red shape on the paste-up. This is contrary to the whole purpose of the method because the white lettering on the paste-up will appear as black lettering across the window, making it necessary to remove the film anyway.

Some people overcome these difficulties by putting identifying numbers in the margins or gutters of a piece. But this technique, too, is not liked by everybody.

Another objection to the transparent window method is the fact that dust, lint, etc., may adhere to the opaque copy windows, making dark specks on the transparent film window — again rendering it useless. But as so often, everything depends on the case and the people involved. The transparent method is in spite of its limitations widely used.

Ruby Red Proprietary Films. Perhaps the best solution is the use of a ruby red proprietary film material which can be mounted in position on the paste-up. Because it is of transparent red, it provides an ideal transparent window in the negative; because it is of shiny film, it remains clean during handling, permitting the photographer to make it ready for use by wiping it quickly before shooting, if necessary at all. Because of its color, finally, a ruby red film photographs in the desired manner.

Actually this material, available from several suppliers, consists of a sheet of clear film, covered with a thin pigment which may be removed with a knife or stylus; this makes it possible to draw or cut any shape, achieving very sharp, precise lines.

Keying Separate Art Elements with Proprietary Ruby Red Films. Because this material is transparent, it is possible to clearly identify each strip-in. This is done by placing a photostat of the subject or a simple code number in its proper position on the paste-up, and by then covering it with a piece of red film of the proper size and shape. The red color provides, as already mentioned, the window. Visual identification is possible as the photostat or code number can be seen through the red window because it is transparent. Of course, the key negative will show only a transparent opening, but with the paste-up nearby as a

guide, the stripper can readily determine where each strip-in should go.

Crop Marks and Register Marks. Where windows, or other forms of guides are used, the crop marks originally placed on the separate art (and therefore still showing on the halftone negative) will serve as the final guide for positioning onto the key negative. This applies to single-color halftones only. In the case of duotones and process subjects, register marks must be placed, *on centers,* in the original artwork.

Normally this will mean that one or more marks will fall inside the page; as long as the marks do not conflict with other work, that is perfectly all right — the stripper will remove the offending marks after he has achieved position for the strip-ins in all colors.

Screened Prints or Veloxes. The use of screened velox prints provides an even simpler solution in many cases. Screened prints which may be obtained from lithographers, photoengravers, and in larger cities from specialists in the process, consist of a halftone printed on glossy photographic paper.

Because the velox (as such screened prints are commonly known) is a rendition of all values of the subject in a pattern of tiny solid black dots, it may be construed to be line copy — that is, the photographer will reproduce it, dot-for-dot, on his key-line negative.

By ordering veloxes of all continuous-tone strip-ins, the artist can paste them into final position on the paste-up, eliminating the need for keys or windows, and saving considerable stripping time by the lithographer. An additional advantage of the velox lies in the fact that the artist can do further work on it: silhouetting, dropping-out highlights, adding line work and so on.

The Advantages of Veloxes. The velox is particularly useful for yearbooks, catalogs of small parts, and any work where there is a large number of identically sized halftones. The responsibility for properly locating the illustrations with regard to captions or model numbers can be kept away from the lithographer and left with those who prepare art and copy; checking by various departments in a company is easy in this case.

The Limitations and Disadvantages of Veloxes. But it should not be overlooked that veloxes are not suitable for highest quality reproduction. Very often, a velox print is made with much less care than a halftone negative would be made in the lithographic plant. Another reason is that the velox has two more intermediate steps if compared with a halftone negative: the print on photographic paper and the re-photographing together with other line copy. The quality of a velox can therefore never be the same as the best quality obtainable by halftone photography in the lithographic plant.

Line and Halftone Combination with Kodalith Autoscreen Ortho Film. Kodak Autoscreen film makes it possible to photograph line and tone elements together. Wherever Kodak Autoscreen film is practical it is possible to make paste-ups containing both line elements and photographs or other tonal elements in one assembly. But Autoscreen film cannot be used without previous investigation into its suitability for a specific job.

Section Fourteen: Overlays

Where the layout calls for combinations of two or more elements in the same color, or overprinting of one or more colors over another, it is not possible to place all of them on one and the same paste-up. In these cases, a different technique must be employed.

Overlays for Line and Halftone Combination Jobs. Conventionally all art elements appearing in the key color (generally but not necessarily black) are assembled as the paste-up. In cases where several elements must be combined that cannot be pasted next to each other they must be arranged over each other. Such an arrangement is known as an overlay. Examples for cases requiring overlays are line and halftone elements and line and tint combinations as the combination between line and flat screened areas are called. In overlays one group of elements is drawn or pasted on board whereas the other group of elements is drawn or pasted on a sheet of frosted acetate which is placed in register over the paste-up.

Many plants prefer the following arrangement for line and halftone combination art. *The tonal elements should be put on the board and the line elements on the overlay.* This arrangement is more conducive to quality reproduction than the opposite of having line copy on the board and tonal copy on the overlay.

Register Marks on Overlays. Register marks and center marks are traced from the paste-up to the overlay. In production, the cameraman will make a separate negative of the overlay, and the stripper will combine it with the key negative from the paste-up. In very complex (regular-type) cases where several steps are needed in the combining of art elements, it may be necessary to prepare more than a single overlay. When in doubt, the artist should furnish positive copy for all elements, and provide separate overlays for each area. (A detailed discussion of lithographic stripping techniques can be found in "The Stripping and Photocomposing Department" chapter of this Manual.)

Overlays for Color Work. The same basic principle of making overlays is used in preparing art for additional flat color jobs. The area to be reproduced in color is drawn or painted on the acetate, in black, tracing over the key art on the paste-up to achieve register.

Overlaps. For tight fitting colors, or where a design in one color is to be eliminated (or, to say it in trade language, "knocked out") of another color, a slight overlap is required to assure fit on the press — the width of this overlap should be as small as practical; its actual size depends on the job and the standards of a particular shop. It is often about five to ten one-thousandths of an inch.

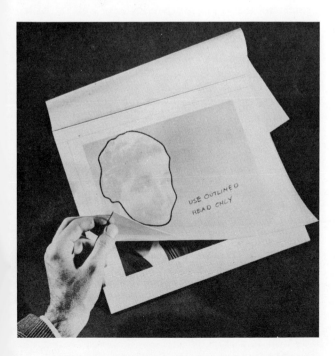

Indicating silhouetting by use of an overlay.

Courtesy Dorval Publishing Co.

Indicating silhouetting by outlining the copy.

Intricate Line Color Art. Where intricate color plates are required, for example, those involving the removal of lettering, type, or intricate design elements from one color to another color, it is best to rely on lithographic camera and stripping techniques. Through a series of photographic steps the lithographic craftsman can make the necessary negatives from a single piece of copy. He can also provide the required "line width" overlap in the process.

The same suggestion, namely to leave such jobs to the lithographic craftsmen, also applies to large solid areas of color, particularly where fit to design elements of another color is involved. The lithographic craftsman may have to use manual techniques for part of the job, but he has the skills and facilities and, not the least, the experience necessary for such complicated tasks.

Tissue Overlays for Line Color Artwork. In any event, whether the artist provides the complete color separation on overlays, or whether separation is completely left to the lithographer, the artist must provide a tissue overlay as a color guide for each paste-up overlay assembly. Such a tissue overlay color guide consists simply of a colored pencil or crayon tracing of the paste-up, indicating carefully which elements are to appear in what color.

Various Techniques of Making Color Tissue Overlays. Often it is not necessary to cover the entire tissue overlay with color; if the design and color break-up are fairly the same throughout, you may be able to draw a two- or three-inch diagonal strip down through the work, coloring only that part of the layout appearing within the strip. This works only if the strip, or strips, includes at least one each of all representative elements in the layout. If in doubt, spend another few minutes and color in the entire spread.

Here too, methods are not uniform. Some lithographic plants want every area indicated in color on the tissue overlay. In booklet work every page should have its own independent overlay. It often happens that one page is colored as a guide for the whole job. If the coloring on this page is changed during production the whole job follows automatically even if other pages are not intended to be changed. Making color tissues for each page is an added safety measure.

The Key-Line Method of Color Break-Up. Least effective in offset lithography is the key-line or painting-up method of color break-up. Used chiefly for photoengravings, this method consists of outlining all islands of color, then painting in solid wherever color appears, up to within a sixteenth of an inch of the outline, leaving a ragged edge.

The Safest Method Is the Best. The safest method for indicating color break-up is either to provide positive color overlays for each additional color, or to key the color break-up on the paste-up and on a tissue overlay. The lithographic production department should be left in charge of making color separations; it has the know-how and experience for this kind of work.

Section Fifteen: The Weber Techniques

Few words occur as frequently in a discussion of art and copy preparation as the word photography. Many times photographs are an essential part of the artwork; if they are not present in the artwork itself photography enters the picture when the conversion process of art into press plates begins. In this section of our chapter we will present a very different application of photography. Here we want to discuss how photography can be utilized in the making of creative artwork for lithographic reproduction.

To make the subject matter of this section absolutely clear we do not want to discuss the photographing of people or objects or even the techniques of combining various photographs into a photo-montage. Here we are interested in the use of photography for the purpose of commercial art preparation. In a sense our subject is similarly related to the art of taking photographic pictures as the making of non-photographic commercial art is related to such visual arts as painting or drawing.

The art of utilizing the camera and photographic methods for the making of commercial artwork is still in its first development stages. Several people have been interested in this subject and have contributed to its developments. But in the opinion of this writer as well as many other people, one name stands out before all others; it is the name of Martin J. Weber. During a quarter of a century he has devoted himself single-mindedly to the application of photography for the creation of commercial artwork. His processes and techniques have become firmly established in the field of advertising art. Like all genuine contributions, they have attracted the interest of other people and are utilized by them to an ever increasing extent.

That is as it should be; the arts belong to everyone. No single contribution, no matter how important, can count when compared to the combined efforts of those before us. In this spirit, Mr. Weber has contributed a number of pictures and illustrations that demonstrate what the Weber techniques can achieve.

The purpose of this presentation is stimulation and inspiration of the reader, in particular the creative artist or cameraman in a lithographic plant. Our discussion is not a technical one in the sense of making step-by-step explanations. What we intend is to demonstrate the almost unbelievable variety of possibilities that this medium offers. Readers who love photography and who have a sense of the artistic will find their own ways and develop their own procedure to express their personalities.

The great variety of the Weber Techniques makes a complete showing almost impossible. But even a sampling is better than none at all. Therefore it has been decided, not without hesitation, to discuss the Weber Techniques under the following six main headings: (1) Polymorphic letterforms, (2) Thematic photo-combinations, (3) Photographic pattern designs, (4) Photographic line drawings, (5) Photographic tone translations and, (6) Photographic silhouetting. Each of these is described in the following.

POLYMORPHIC LETTERFORMS

Polymorphic letterforms were the first major achievements of Mr. Weber. He had spent many years in the

Pictures do tell a story. The theme in this picture is so direct that it does not need a caption. Its preparation is uninvolved and its result uncomplicated. The small globe was enlarged and the figure mounted into position. The tonal definition is good. *Photo by A. Devaney.*

GRAPHIC GRAPHIC
GRAPHIC GRAPHIC
GRAPHIC GRAPHIC
GRAPHIC GRAPHIC

Polymorphic letterforms.

Many types of line renderings can be produced from continuous-tone originals. The specimens illustrate mezzotint, photo-line, circle line and wavy line. *Courtesy of Martin J. Weber Studio.*

experimentation for this new medium. Almost 20 years ago, many articles appeared in the trade press that reported on this new development. "Publishers' Weekly," "Art Instruction," "The American Printer," "The Inland Printer," as well as other magazines, all devoted enthusiastic articles to this new Weber Process, as it was called, of making handlettering out of regular type.

"Publishers' Weekly"—(Vol. CXXXV, No. 14, pp. 1364-67) stated that the Weber Process "given a certain piece of artwork, whether type, handlettering, or design" can do the following nine things with it: (1) Condense or expand it in either direction, (2) Thicken or thin the lines, (3) Add shading of all kinds, (4) Add shadows of any sort, (5) Add outlines, (6) Angle the copy in any direction, (7) Add perspective, (8) Add color, and (9) Repeat patterns. These techniques have become well established in the past 20 years. They have been refined and further developed ever since. Our illustrations show examples of Weber's polymorphic letterforms.

THEMATIC PHOTO-COMBINATIONS

Under the heading of thematic photo-combinations we group a variety of photographic artwork creations. Here various elements are combined by photographic means into a harmonious piece of artwork that expresses a given theme. We present two examples of thematic photo-combinations executed by Weber techniques. One example illustrates the use of these techniques for titling in television; the other shows how a very difficult problem of institutional advertising was solved.

In the early years of television, thematic combination was a most important technique in the development of titles, trademarks and station symbols for television. The industry was young and had neither experience nor precedents to follow. Reading matter of the proper shape and tonal values did not exist nor were guiding principles for their renderings known. Our illustrations demonstrate some of the results that thematic photo-combining achieved in this new industry.

The Bethlehem Steel panorama that you see in our full-page illustration is another case in point. It shows not just a lot of ships as someone might think. It shows every single one of the 1124 ships built by Bethlehem Steel during World War II. In the full-page illustration you see a number of ringed capital letters. The legend tells you what ships the particular area shows. (Pages 2:38-2:39)

Aircraft carriers, cruisers, destroyers, mine layers, LST's — from the giant battleships to the smallest trawler — they are all here represented. This panorama was made from true proportioned models; some of them had to be specially built from blueprints! Thematic photo-combination was the only practical solution for this enormous task.

PHOTOGRAPHIC PATTERN DESIGNS

Continuous decorative patterns have many peculiar design requirements. The Weber techniques have proved very successful in some of the most exacting pattern design prob-

lems. Take, for example, the pattern for Formica "Moon-glo." This pattern must be continuous, it must also be completely disoriented or without any linear direction — otherwise waste in cutting of Formica material would be very high — it must furthermore have several tonal grades because tonal grades will subdue possible imperfections in production. Last, but not least, it must be neutral in design, suitable for many purposes and of course pleasing to the eye. Photographic pattern design uses step-and-repeat machines, but the techniques by which each new problem is worked out are developed for or adapted to the needs of the particular case.

PHOTOGRAPHIC LINE DRAWINGS

Is it correct to speak of photographic line drawings? Look at some of the examples and decide for yourself. If you would not see the continuous-tone photograph and the line drawing next to each other, you — or someone less conversant with graphic arts techniques — would certainly believe that the line picture is an artist's rendering. And so it is indeed, but it is a photographic rendering by a photographic artist.

Why, you may ask, make line drawings out of photographs? Because they are different. They have a charm and an attraction, a power all their own. Line drawings from photographs are a particularly powerful medium. They combine the convincing naturalness of the photograph with the controlled emphasis of the drawing.

PHOTOGRAPHIC TONE TRANSLATIONS

A continuous-tone image is converted into an image of clearly defined areas of different intensity. The photographic picture retains its fidelity but it becomes an image that expresses also an artist's interpretation of the subject.

Photographic tone translations can be prepared either for monochrome or for polychrome reproductions. In monochrome reproductions the color of the paper is carefully blended with the tonal areas into which the continuous-tone image is now integrated. The steps, or percentage values, of these tones must be selected with a view to the desired distribution of accents in the picture. The translated monochrome picture can finally be reproduced as a conventional halftone print.

Photographic tone translation utilizes a variety of techniques; all of them are selected according to the effect desired by the "translator," if this term be permitted. The artistic intuition of the artist making the conversion of the continuous-tone photo to the converted tonal monochrome is a most important part of the conversion process.

The same principles and techniques also hold true for conversion of continuous-tone photographs into polychrome translations. These processes are often designated as photographic posterizing. But they lend themselves not only to poster and advertising display art preparation, but also to many other purposes.

Even though these techniques were devised with a view to their artistic possibilities they also have some rather in-

Silhouetting the picture into a story-telling shape is simple and effective. To handle this silhouetting in the most efficient manner do not hand paint the shape on the original photo. Supply the photo in its original square (or oblong) shape. With the photo, supply a solid black-and-white shape, easily prepared. Indicate the position of the silhouetting on a tissue overlay.

teresting cost aspects. It is much less expensive to develop an interesting monochrome or polychrome translation than to make new artwork of comparable quality. It must never be overlooked that a polychrome translation automatically includes color-separation negatives. These separation negatives are a necessary stage in the making of a polychrome translation.

Finally it should not be forgotten that it is possible to make finished art in color translation techniques. Mr. Weber uses either a dye transfer or some other method whereby he can show a colored image of the separated negatives and their appearance in the final reproduction.

PHOTOGRAPHIC SILHOUETTING

Photographic drop-outs and photographic silhouetting techniques are very popular in lithography. These tech-

niques contribute very desirable improvements to the reproduction of photographs. They permit increased contrast and snap, eliminate undesirable gray backgrounds and insure proper reproduction quality.

The Weber techniques obtain these results without hand retouching by photographic means exclusively. The effectiveness of photographic silhouetting can be seen on our accompanying illustrations.

In conclusion it is repeated that these techniques show what can be done if artistic training and photographic techniques are wedded together. Many a lithographic artist or photographer will be inspired to try his own mettle when he studies the results obtained by this pioneer and innovator of creative photography in the field of commercial art preparation.

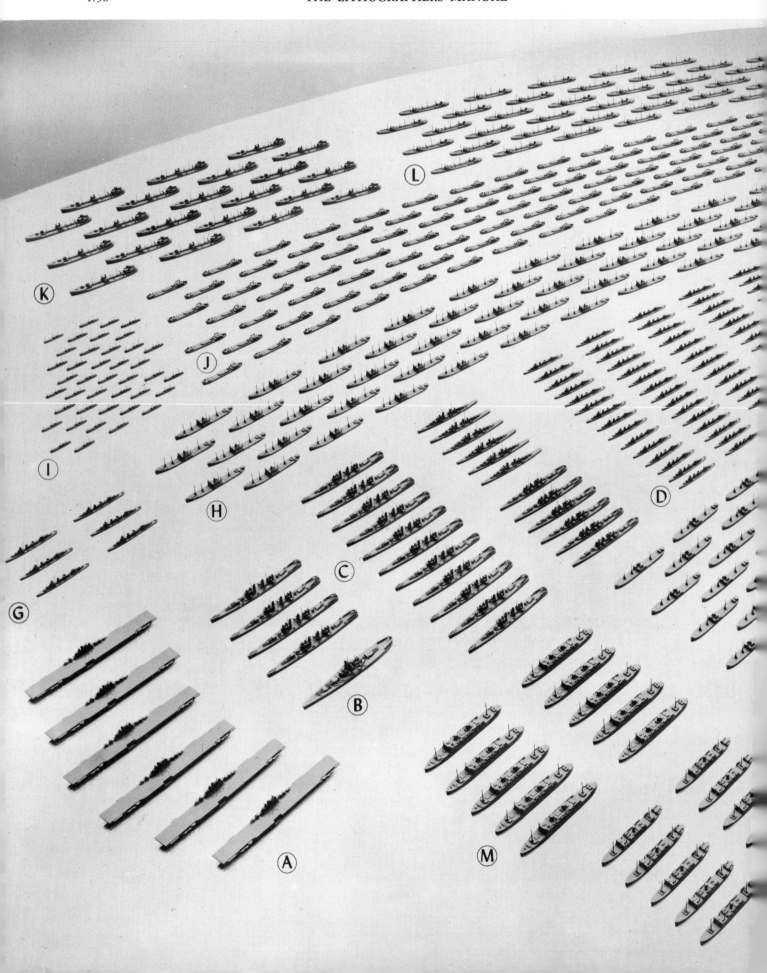

This shows one single photo in a complete panorama of 1124 ships in 20 classes built by Bethlehem Steel Company. The model ships were carefully positioned in their respective arcs on a flat platform. The entire panorama was artificially illuminated from above to avoid base shadows. The sky and edge shading was added to heighten the illusion of the globe.

This illustration of one cruiser shows the actual size and detail. Courtesy Martin J. Weber Studio.

Section Sixteen: Fake Process Art Preparation

There are several methods of achieving pleasing many-color effects at the disposal of the artist. They are distinguished from full-color process work by the not too complimentary name of fake-color process. Some of the most commonly used fake-color processes are here presented.

The Key-Line Tint Sheet Technique. The simplest fake color process involves the preparation of key-line drawings which are to print in black outline, filled in with a number of values of flat colors — similar to the techniques used in comic books.

The artist can advise the lithographic craftsman of his intentions by using as his guide a color chart where the results of the mixture of various percentage tints of the three process-color inks are shown. Color charts indicate what percentage of flat tints should be laid in every area in order to achieve the desired colors. If, for example, within a certain area a special shade of blue is desired, the instructions may call for 30% yellow, 60% blue, and 10% red. Fire engine red would require 100% yellow and 100% red; kelly green might call for solid yellow and solid blue, with perhaps 10% or 15% of black to gray in it.

This technique is limited, generally, to large flat areas of color. It becomes prohibitively expensive when tiny, fussy or critical areas are involved.

The Blueboard or Blueline Technique. The blueboard or blueline technique makes it possible for the artist to handle fake-color work in a more detailed manner than in the tint sheet technique discussed above.

The artist prepares the job as an open line drawing; this drawing is photographed in the camera department. Thereafter a plate is made and printed in non-photo blue on a proof press or on a production press. These prints are known as blueboards or blueline prints. For every color to be finally printed a separate blueboard is needed. In a four-color job a set of four blueboards is prepared for the artist.

The blueboards might be sheets of frosted vinyl or kid-finished bristol mounted on zinc sheets for dimensional stability. In either case, each board would carry an identical reproduction of the original art in pale, non-photographic blue.

Making Blueboard Color Separations. Armed with his color chart and a set of retouchers' grays (calibrated in percentages of black, generally 15%, 30%, 40%, 60% and 80%) plus pure retouchers' white and solid retouchers' black, the artist proceeds to render the pre-separated art for each color plate, all in values of black.

If, for example, in the yellow separation the area of a subject requires 30% of yellow, this color value would be rendered in gray from the jar marked "30%"; the area which will appear in fire engine red would be painted in solid black; the kelly green areas would be painted in solid also; but cold pink areas, or deep purples, where the ink chart indicates no yellow is wanted, would remain untouched on the yellow plate.

Values are Expressed As Tonal Values. Each area of each of the four pieces of copy would be rendered in the proper value of gray (representing that color's proportionate contribution to the final color mixture). It is even possible for the experienced artist to model the color areas for added richness, being careful that the drawing and blending are handled similarly for each of the colors involved in a given area.

How Blueboard Drawings are Processed in the Lithographic Plant. The lithographer makes halftones of each of the four pieces of copy, and, on the press, inks up each separate plate in its own color. The result is a rich, pleasing colorful subject, that can be as suitable to a given purpose as the more difficult and far more costly full-color process. But it must be emphasized that all depends on the skill and artistic ability of the artist and the craftsmen who do this kind of work.

Limitations and Hazards of Fake-Color Processes. As already mentioned, everything depends on the skill and artistic intuition of artists and craftsmen in fake-color process work. One of the most troublesome points is the problem of communication.

The customer cannot see finished art before the job goes into production. If the job is not proofed, the customer sees it only after the first sheets are off the press. Then it is, of course, impossible to change anything! *Colors cannot be communicated by word of mouth* (disregarding, of course, scientific color descriptions that are generally speaking, not within the scope of artists and advertisers) *but must be seen, particularly in case of artwork where the personal reaction is completely unpredictable.*

The same general technique can be applied to simpler drawings by means of acetate overlays; by passing the blueboards (which are recommended for control in tight areas), each color copy can be prepared by superimposing frosted acetate over the key drawing and painting each value of each color directly on the acetate.

Section Seventeen: The Bourges Process

Albert R. Bourges was the inventor of the Bourges Process. He has been a photoengraver and color reproduction consultant for more than fifty years and has developed a number of techniques for art and copy preparation that have found constantly increasing use in lithography.

If we want to find a common denominator for the great

variety of Bourges techniques, we might say that they all aim at a better coordination of art preparation and processes needed for platemaking. The detail of the lithographic camerawork, shipping and platemaking is very intricate. Our commercial artists are, understandably enough, much more concerned with the appearance of their work than with lithographic reproduction techniques. This lack of common knowledge leads to work and friction. The basic philosophy of the Bourges Process is simple and straightforward: Artists and lithographic craftsmen should each play that part for which they are best equipped. They should work hand in hand, and they can do so in the Bourges Process.

As the Bourges Process is based on the necessities of lithographic production, the creative art department in a lithographic plant is the ideal place for its execution. There the creative artist is in constant touch with production and has the best opportunity for taking full advantage of the inherent possibilities of this process.

Bourges Process Crosses Many Lines and Serves A Variety of Departments. It is only natural that the Bourges Process must cross many lines if it wants to connect unrelated activities and departments, if it wants to fulfill its function as a medium of art communication. It also is rather natural that many people who are used to seeing their particular job and nothing else, do not immediately understand what this process offers. Our presentation is divided into the following five subjects: (1) Black-and-white photographs, (2) Line and halftone combinations, (3) Two-color jobs and duotones, (4) Pre-separated color art and (5) Full-color process transparencies. Each of these is now presented.

BLACK-AND-WHITE PHOTOGRAPHS

Under this heading we discuss the following three points: (1) Adding backgrounds on black-and-white photographs, (2) Changing emphasis on black-and-white photographs, and (3) Drop-outs. Each of them is individually taken up in the following.

Adding Backgrounds to Black-and-White Photographs. Although this sounds like a very simple thing to do, it can be both difficult and exasperating. It is very difficult to apply an area of tone absolutely smooth with a brush, and the camera has a disconcerting way of picking up the slightest unevenness in the tone. This risk to the drawing itself must also be considered.

The artist will therefore often ask the platemaker to add the background. This is not difficult if the copy has a

The unretouched photograph. They wanted to subdue the background in order to make the figure stand out in the foreground.

Photographer: Zolton Farkas

The photograph with a white "Solotone" overlay. Note the coating being removed over the figure. The white "Solotone" not only lightens the background, but also slightly fogs the detail, creating a phantom effect.

definite outline that can be followed. However, backgrounds must be added on wash drawings or pencil sketches where there is no definite outline; you will often get a harsh, cut-out effect. A simple solution for the artist is to use a gray "Solotone" overlay sheet of the desired value over the drawing, removing the gray coating for the highlight areas. This gives a transparent, precision smooth tone for the background, and if necessary, can be easily changed or corrected without risk to the illustration. The cameraman reproduces the drawing with the overlay-background as a single composite copy for halftone reproductions.

Changing Emphasis on Black-and-White Photographs. In many cases it is desirable to change emphasis on photographs; some parts should stand out, others be rather inconspicuous. The adding of "phantom" backgrounds is one example of such tasks and therefore here discussed.

Phantom backgrounds are often added by covering the area that is not to be affected with a frisket, and airbrushing the background with white opaque. There are, however, several disadvantages. First, the artist may not have an airbrush. Second, it is difficult, while you are applying the tone, to evaluate the density of white that is being sprayed. Third, the results are often deceiving because white airbrushing has a way of not reproducing in the camera the same way it appears visually to the artist. Also, there is always the inherent risk to the original copy. Since the airbrushing is applied direct to the photograph, which may have other retouching, it will be difficult or impossible to make any corrections.

To accomplish phantom effect with better control, there are special white sheets called Bourges "Solotone" that can be used as an overlay over the photograph. These "Solotone" sheets come in 5 different values of white, so that you can select the particular tone that will give you the desired effect for the particular photograph. These smooth, white overlays reproduce far more accurately than airbrushing, and give you a uniform white.

They are also very simple to use. You attach the sheet with tape, as an overlay, to the photograph. The coating is made so that you can remove the white tone in any area that is not to be "phantomed." This is done with a special wedge-shaped stylus. (There is also a liquid "Coloremover" which softens the coating so that large areas can be quickly removed.)

Changing emphasis by making objects lighter. There are similar "Solotone" Sheets in transparent grays, which can be used in the same manner to retouch photographic copy. These, too, come in 5 different values. They are very helpful when you want to make an object appear lighter. Instead of retouching the object with white paint (where you would also have to redraw the detail covered by the white paint), it is far better and easier to add a transparent gray tone to the rest of the copy with one of these sheets. Attach the sheet to the photograph as an overlay, and remove the coating over the light object. This increases the contrast, making the object appear whiter.

The method is particularly effective for photographs of silverware, or other metallic objects, and white clothing, for example, where loss of detail is very critical.

Drop-Outs. The following demonstrates a use of the Bourges Process in a production department of a lithographic plant. Very often a platemaker will receive tonal copy that contains too little contrast to be able to get the drop-out in the camera. This may be a wash drawing or a pencil sketch, for example. Rather than opaquing on the

The original photo, unretouched. The client wanted to emphasize the gloves, and also make them appear whiter.

The 30% gray "Solotone," with the coating removed over the gloves.

Photographer: Stephen Michael

The desired contrast was obtained by deepening the rest of the photograph with a transparent 30% gray "Solotone" overlay. The coating was removed over the gloves.

Matern and York, Architects

The original pencil sketch. The problem was to add a gray background to the sketch, and at the same time give an added boost to drop out the highlight areas.

A 30% gray "Solotone" overlay was added over the illustration. Note where the coating was removed for the highlights.

The resulting pencil drawing with the "Solotone" overlay. Note how the background has been added without any hard edges, or loss of detail in the drawing — and how the highlights have been cleanly dropped out.

negative, the platemaker will find it very helpful to add a 10 percent gray "Solotone" Sheet as an overlay over the art, removing the coating in the highlight areas.

This light transparent gray over the tonal copy gives a uniform boost to the tones, which provides the added contrast required to drop-out the highlights. As the overlay would be used merely as an assist in the halftone reproduction, it can then be removed, and the art returned in its original form to the client.

NOTE: Be sure to use the overlay type of "Solotone" Sheet for this purpose. Bourges also makes a similar Sheet with an adhesive backing, but these are for layouts, and dummies, not for tonal finished art. All that is required with the overlay type is to attach it one side of the copy with tape — it is not necessary to adhere it to the whole copy.

LINE AND HALFTONE COMBINATIONS

Certain illustrations require a halftone negative and a separate line negative in order to do justice to both the line and tonal qualities. The artist, in this case, will give the platemaker much better copy if he will keep his line art separate from his tonal art. The artist prepares a wash drawing, which would be reproduced as a regular illustration, but he puts his accents of brush or pen line detail on a separate transparent overlay, rather than right on the drawing itself.

He can very easily do this by using a special treated acetate called Bourges "Kleerkote." This is a crystal-clear acetate that has an invisible coating that gives it an excellent working surface. The artist can use the same inks or paints he would use on paper — with complete ease — and no problem that the color will chip or peel as it does on regular acetate.

TWO-COLOR JOBS AND DUOTONES

Photographs are in many cases combined with background colors. The use of Bourges "Colotone" makes the decision on the most desirable color and the preparation of the final art a very simple operation. Colotones come in many hues and intensities that can be well matched in lithographic production.

Selecting the Second Color. As Colotones are transparent, they are merely placed on the photograph; the effect of a particular color is immediately apparent. The adding and elimination techniques possible with Colotones make changes easy and expedient.

Improving of Duotones. This application of Bourges techniques leads us again into a lithographic production department; this time Bourges is used in the camera department. As generally known, altering the density of the original black-and-white-photograph when the negatives for the black plate and color plate are being made will often greatly improve the conventional duotone. This can also be done by skillful retouching after the duotone-angled negatives are made. However, it is more difficult to work on the negative, and there is less visual control.

As a standardized means of making these tonal alterations from the original photograph, the cameraman will find it helpful to utilize the Bourges "Solotone" Sheets which come in whites and grays. The coating of these sheets can be easily removed over areas that are to remain the same.

For example, with a photograph of an outdoor scene, it might help by making a house in the foreground lighter on the black plate, and the sky deeper on the blue plate. For the black negative, a white "Solotone" Sheet, of whatever value is desired, can be attached as an overlay over the photograph, and the white coating left over the house. The white coating also serves to slightly fog detail, which is not a disadvantage, because the exact photographic detail appears in sharp focus on the other plate.

When making the negative for the blue plate, at the conventional screen angle for the second color, this overlay can be removed, and a 50 percent gray may be added to deepen the sky, removing the coating over the areas that are to remain the same. The gray "Solotone" coating is highly transparent, and steps up the tonal value without affecting the photographic detail underneath. Although the photographic image remains the same, the varied densities on each plate add far more interest to the resulting duotone.

In addition to being able to lighten or deepen areas with the Sheets, you can also add modeled tones to the overlays with black and white "Solotone" liquids or pencils which are made to work on the coating of the sheets. This gives you still further opportunities to add tonal variations to the black or the blue plate.

PRE-SEPARATED COLOR ART

A comparatively new and totally different technique applicable to many types of art has become possible with the Bourges Colotone Overlays.

The overlay sheets, like the Bourges Solotone and Transopaque, are sheets of dimensionally stable acetate coated with removable color films. In the case of the Colotone, the Bourges sheets are available in the standard process colors, process-red, process-yellow and process-blue, or, as we prefer to designate these colors more correctly in magenta, yellow and cyan.

How Colotone Sheets are Manipulated. Provided with a stylus, removal fluid, additive fluid and additive pencil, the artist can manipulate each of the three colored overlays, over a key or black-and-white drawing, much in the same way as he would with any separation overlays, and provide the correct value for each color in each area.

In the Bourges Method the Artist Works with Colors and Not with Tones of Gray. However, the big advantage in working with the Bourges Colotone lies in the fact that the artist is not working in values of gray, but in the actual printing color itself. He no longer has to visualize how a 50 percent value of yellow must be translated into grays. Now he actually renders the 50 percent value of yellow in the yellow color.

Color Changes are Immediately Apparent. By superimposing the three overlays, at stages throughout the job, the artist has an immediate visual check: Since the overlays are colored corresponding to the printing ink colors, and since they are transparent, the superimposition of the three overlays gives a value and is more or less similar to the final print. By using the Bourges Colotone, the artist can tell what color he is making: If by laying the three overlays one over the other, he is not satisfied, say, with the resulting shade of blue, he can correct one or several of the colors until the combined effect is to his liking.

The Bourges Method Produces Communicable Results. At the discussion of fake-color processes in a preceding section of this chapter, it is pointed out that there the resulting artwork cannot be communicated in its color values to customer and other people not versed in the interpretation of such art. In the Bourges method it is possible to show the customer pre-separated art in color and thereby to eliminate a source of friction and misunderstanding.

Pre-Separated Line Art. As an improvement over the standard black-opaque acetate overlays, there is now a transparent, red-orange overlay material called Bourges "Transopaque." This has the same photographic quality as black, but gives the artist the advantage of being able to see through the overlay as he is working.

The Artist Can Work More Accurately and Take Greater Advantage of the Second Color. Not only does this enable him to work more accurately, but it also allows him to take greater advantage of the effect he gets with his color. Although he works in separation, he can make the color a more integral part of the black-and-white key drawing. This particular Sheet has an unusual working surface — the artist can remove it to a sharp, clean edge with a stylus, or to a rough, free edge. He can remove it with scratchboard tools for extremely fine line effects, or with steel wool or stiff brushes for interesting textures.

An illustration with a "Transopaque" separation overlay. A gray tint has been used to indicate the transparent red-orange color. A feature of this separation material is the removable color coating, which allows the artist to create a wide variety of line techniques.

Pre-Coated Overlay Sheets and Adhesive Sheets for Spotting. "Transopaque" comes in two types of Sheets. One a pre-coated overlay sheet, that the artist will use for large areas of color; the other an adhesive sheet, which he uses when he needs just small areas, or spot color. (The artist would use a clear acetate as the overlay base — Bourges recommends their "Kleerbase" for this — and adds the "Transopaque" color areas to this with the adhesive-backed sheet.)

Transopaque Accessories. There is also a Transopaque Liquid which can be used in brush or pen to add fine line detail to either type of Transopaque separation copy. "Transopaque" can be used for any line separation copy as the red-orange color is merely for the camera, and the resulting line plate can be run in any color. It is also excellent to use for copy for the platemaker which is to be used as a mask for a gray tint block.

FULL-COLOR PROCESS TRANSPARENCIES

When a transparency is correct in detail, but not exactly the desired colors, there is a very simple, safe way you can alter the colors — either locally or the overall tone — with a transparent colored sheet attached behind the transparency.

Colotones and Their Composition. These transparent color sheets are called Bourges "Colotone." They come in a complete range of colors, and in different strengths of each color. The color is not dyed into the sheet, but made as a coating which can be removed. This makes it an extremely flexible material, as you can use the "Colotone" as an overlay behind the transparency to correct the entire area, or you can remove the coating so as to leave the color only over a particular area you want to change. Two or more overlays may be used behind the same transparency. For example, one to correct the overall color; another to improve the color of a product or a dress.

Accessories to Colotones. As a further corrective measure, there are matching Liquid Colors and Pencils which can be used right on the "Colotone" overlays, so that you can further improve the color correction made by the overlay. For example, if a transparency needs the 30 percent Process-Red to make the desired basic change, but one area becomes too red, you can neutralize it by adding a green tone with the Liquid or Pencil to the overlay. In another area, you might also want to add a touch of yellow, or even more red.

Colotone Techniques Do Not Harm the Transparency. This method of correcting color transparencies is not only very simple to do, but completely safe as far as the original is concerned. The work is done on the overlay, rather than on the transparency itself.

Suggestions for the Use of Colotones with Transparencies. Here are some of the things you can do with these overlays: (1) Correct a local color by making it warmer, brighter, cooler. (2) Increase the contrast between a product in the foreground, and the incidental background detail. This is done by selecting the complementary color of the predominating color of the product. If the object you want to accent is orange, a blue over the background will give it more contrast. Bourges also has transparent gray Sheets which may be used, too, to key back the background color, and give the main subject more emphasis. (3) Correct the overall color balance. If a transparency looks too yellow, too green, too warm, you can add an overlay of the deficient color to improve the hue. If it is too green, it lacks red, etc. There are many colors to select from — not only are there different strengths of each color, but also a warm red, a cool red, a warm blue, a cool blue, etc. Bourges has a Color Guide which has individual 3" x 5" sheets of all the colors that you can lay over the transparency to see which one will give you the best effect.

The Use of Colotones by the Cameraman. It should also be noted that these "Colotone" overlays are also very helpful to cameramen who want to group a number of transparencies together to make the reproduction. The overlays can be used to bring all of the transparencies into the same color balance. They are also very helpful when the cameraman is using the Three-Color Process, where the reproduction is made photomechanically from mass separations, with no allowance for correction on the plates, and it is important to start with the correct transparency.

Section Eighteen: Full-Color Reflection Copy

Full-color process reproduction is the most difficult of all reproduction tasks. It is also the most scientific branch of color lithography. Here we try to produce a very wide gamut of colors by printing only a few different inks. If we distinguish between inexpensive and economical, we may say that full-color process lithography is the most economical kind of color reproduction though not the least expensive one. This statement may look questionable to those who never had an opportunity to analyze the subject. But if you consider the enormous variety of color that is produced by not more than three, four, or five press runs, you will agree that full-color printing is very economical indeed.

Reflection and Transmission Copy. We distinguish two kinds of copy in full-color printing: Reflection copy and transmission copy. This distinction was made by technical people; it is based on the manner in which we view photographic full-color material. All copy that is painted or otherwise put on paper or other opaque material is classified as reflection copy. Color prints of various kinds are examples of non-painted reflection copy. Transmission copy comprises all copy of a transparent nature, especially color transparencies such as Kodachromes or Ektachromes, for example. In reflection copy the light is reflected by the copy, in transmission copy the light passes through it.

Reflection Copy and Transmission Copy Are Differently Made and Differently Reproduced. Full-color reflection copy is in most cases produced by painting; full-color transmission copy is as a rule a color transparency. Reproduction techniques and color correcting are very different in either case. In this section we are concerned with reflection copy exclusively; transmission copy is discussed in the following section under the heading of color photography.

Art Preparation for Reflection Copy. Art preparation for reflection copy hardly needs any discussion. In full-color reflection copy preparation the artist is very little restricted; color separation and color correction are left to the camera and to the color-correcting techniques practiced in a lithographic plant.

Fine Art and Commercial Art Preparation. In the case of fine art reproductions which are outside of our frame of presentation, the artist creates in utter disregard of any reproduction process. But the commercial artist who paints for lithographic reproduction should know something about reproduction problems and methods if he is interested in the final appearance of his work.

The Gamut of Color. One of the main trouble spots in process color reproduction is the gamut of color and the exactitude of color matches. Many artists and advertising production men do not understand the limitations of the color gamut in process color work. It has been said too often by well-meaning but, alas, ignorant people that every color can be reproduced in process work. This is a serious mistake. The color gamut is unfortunately rather limited in full-color reproduction. Everybody interested in this subject is advised to study chapters six, seven and eight of our Manual where various aspects of process color work are presented.

The GATF Color Chart. The most effective practical tool available is a color chart made according to the system developed by the Graphic Arts Technical Foundation. This subject is discussed in chapter seven of this Manual. A color chart will convince artists and production men of the limitations in process work better than all verbal arguments.

Spot Colors. A study of the available color gamut in

a specific reproduction system also explains *why certain critical colors that must be very well matched should be printed by themselves.* Advertisers invest huge amounts of money in some colors which become characteristic for them and in a sense almost proprietary items. These colors, but also others that are essential to the composition carefully devised by a commercial artist, are in many cases obtainable only by separate runs.

The Creative Artist and His Work. Every piece of artwork has its own reproduction problems; every artist has his own preferences and dislikes. Every artist loves certain aspects of his creation more than others — they may be specific colors, relation of elements in a composition, or still more vague, the general "atmosphere" of a picture. All of us are rather prone to loving the products of our labor in an uncritical way, and the artist is just as human as the next person.

Communication Between the Creative Artist and a Lithographic Plant. Very often artists are not conscious of their preferences and dislikes. Still more often they fail to communicate them to the lithographer. Every experienced lithographic salesman who has worked with artists knows that. Such a salesman will try in every case to find out where the artist has his touchy spots. (And a salesman needs plenty of intuition in this endeavor.) But it happens nevertheless that all preliminary discussions fail to disclose exactly what an artist wants. We must never forget that the visual arts must be judged by seeing, because they manifest themselves only in the seeing process. We must never assume that words can replace shapes and colors.

The Proof is the Most Important Medium of Communication Between Artist and Lithographer in Full-Color Printing. The proof brings out the true reaction of the artist. There he can see the form his work takes on, there he can see how so-called minor changes manifest themselves. Showing a proof to the artist is always dramatic. The atmosphere can become very tense. Some artists react rather emotionally and criticize many things in a proof, others are more pleasant. Everything depends on the case and the people involved. But even the strongest temperaments — and we should remember that salesmen too can be very temperamental — can find common ground if they want to. Kindness and good-will are essential; knowing one's business and talking to the point has been found helpful, too, in such situations.

Section Nineteen: Color Photography

The following paragraphs describe some of the basic practical problems which to a greater or lesser degree are peculiar to color photography. They are intended not only for experienced black-and-white photographers who are just entering the field of color photography, but also for the increasing number of photographers who are making color pictures without extensive experience in black-and-white

work. Our presentation is divided into the following four subjects: (1) Color quality of illumination, (2) Subject contrast, (3) Exposure accuracy, and (4) Color perception and color harmony. Of necessity our treatment of color photography is most elementary. Readers interested in the subject are advised to consult the literature, in particular the *Kodak Color Handbook*.

COLOR QUALITY OF ILLUMINATION

Though virtually negligible in black-and-white photography, the color quality of the light source is an all-important consideration in color photography. Essentially, the problem in color work arises from the fact that a color film does not always "see" colors as human beings see them. For example, if the cover of a book appears green in daylight, that is, in illumination which is a combination of sunlight and skylight, we think of it as having the same color in tungsten light. Although the difference in the quality of the illumination actually affects the quality of the light reaching the eye, our vision automatically compensates for the change. A color film, having no such automatic compensation, *reproduces color approximately as the eye sees it only when the illumination is the same as that for which the film is balanced.*

It must be emphasized that, *except for special effects, light sources which are appreciably different in spectral-energy distribution cannot be mixed for any one exposure.* In viewing an original scene lighted by two different light sources, the eye adapts to an intermediate color quality, thus tending to minimize the visual effects of the color differences between the two sources. The film, however, has no power of adaptation and will show the full color difference in parts of the subject illuminated by a light source differing in quality from that for which the film is balanced.

Color Temperature. For visual purposes, the color quality of a light source is evaluated in terms of the color of a perfect radiator, or "black body," heated to a certain temperature. This temperature is expressed in degrees Kelvin (K), obtained by adding 273 to the temperature in degrees Centigrade. When the light source matches the black body in color, it is said to have a *color temperature* equal to the actual temperature of the black body in the Kelvin scale.

Color Temperature Does Not Describe the Photographic Effects of Light. The color of light is bluer with higher and yellower with lower color temperatures. *Note that color temperature refers only to the visual appearance of a light source and does not necessarily describe its photographic effect.* For example, one type of "white" fluorescent lamp is rated at 3500 K, but the spectral distribution of the light it emits produces photographic results quite different from those produced by a tungsten lamp operated at the same color temperature. *Color-temperature values for various daylight conditions also tend to be misleading when they are applied to color photography.* Tungsten lamps, however, have spectral qualities closely resembling those of black-body radiators, and in this case, color temperature is a reliable indication of photographic effect.

SUBJECT CONTRAST

At first glance, subject contrast might be considered as a property of the physical subject matter before the camera lens. Suppose, for example, that we are photographing a man wearing a white shirt and a dark suit. If the shirt reflects eight times as much light as the suit, and these are the lightest and darkest objects in which detail must be reproduced, we might assume that the subject contrast ratio is 8 to 1. Actually, 8 to 1 is the reflectance ratio. From the point of view of the film, subject contrast involves an additional and very important factor, the *lighting contrast.*

Main Lights and Fill-In Lights. Lighting contrast can be defined as the ratio between the highest and lowest amounts of illumination falling on the principal subject. Continuing with our example, let us assume that we are going to make a portrait with the simplest type of portrait lighting, involving the use of only two lamps. One might be placed at the same distance from the subject as the camera, but on a line forming an angle of about 45° with the camera axis. This light would be the *main light,* and would cast shadows which, seen from the camera position, would delineate the contours of the subject's face. But the shadows cast by this single light would be very dark and would obscure some of the important detail of the face. To soften them, we might place another light of equal strength close to the camera. This would be a *fill-in light,* because it would partially fill in with light the shadows caused by the main light.

With this particular lighting arrangement, involving two lamps of equal strength used at the same distance from the subject, the areas illuminated by both lamps would receive two units of illumination, while the areas illuminated by the fill-in light alone would receive one unit. Thus the lighting ratio would be 2 to 1. If the main light were replaced by another light twice as strong as the fill-in light, the areas illuminated by the fill-in light would still receive only one unit of illumination, but the areas illuminated by both lamps would now receive three units, and the lighting ratio would become 3 to 1.

Brightness Range. We can describe subject contrast in terms of the brightness range which the film must reproduce. With a lighting ratio of 3 to 1, an area of our subject's white shirt which is illuminated by both lamps will be eight times as bright as a corresponding area of his suit and twenty-four times as bright as an area of his suit that is illuminated only by the fill-in light. The overall subject contrast is the product of the reflectance ratio of the subject (8 to 1) and the lighting contrast ratio (3 to 1). In this case, the product is 24 to 1. Since the reflectance ratio is established by the nature of the subject itself, it is apparent that the lighting offers the only practical method of contrast control.

Soft Lighting. Even in black-and-white work, the skilled photographer knows that he must exercise special care in lighting if he is to reproduce detail in both black-and-white objects in the same picture. Since reversal color materials like Kodachrome Film and Kodak Ektachrome Film are processed to positives by standardized techniques which do not allow the selective control possible in the case of printing black-and-white negatives, softer basic lighting is necessary. Light-colored and dark-colored objects cannot be reproduced successfully in the same transparency unless the lighting is adjusted to offset the more extreme differences in tone. Otherwise, dark areas will be much too dark and off-color, while light areas will be "burnt out," lacking color and detail. In general, the lighting ratio should not be greater than about 3 to 1. The use of higher lighting ratios for special effects should be undertaken only after the photographer has gained considerable experience with relatively soft lighting.

Indoor and Outdoor Work. In this discussion, we have been speaking principally in terms of indoor work, which allows control of lighting contrast by variation in the placement of the lights. In outdoor work, the sun can be considered as the main light and the sky as the fill-in light.

EXPOSURE ACCURACY

Compared to black-and-white negative materials, reversal color films have much less exposure latitude. In other words, there is a much smaller difference between the greatest and least amounts of exposure which will produce satisfactory results. Lens settings must therefore be determined with a correspondingly greater degree of accuracy.

The Reason for the Limited Latitude of Color Materials. The reason for the limited latitude of reversal color films is clear if it is borne in mind that to insure proper color balance, the films must be processed by standardized techniques. There is no separate printing stage, as in the case of a negative-positive process, at which compensation for over or underexposure in the camera can be introduced.

Color negative materials have somewhat more latitude than reversal films, particularly on the over-exposure side. For best results, however, they must be exposed with considerably more care than black-and-white films. Color printing materials, too, have limited exposure latitude, and as previously mentioned, a color print tends to be judged more critically than a black-and-white print. All in all, it is a fair statement to say that every phase of color photography requires careful determination of exposure, and that attention to this factor is a prerequisite for success with any color process.

The Use of Exposure Meters. In the determination of camera settings, a photoelectric exposure meter can be of real assistance, especially under unusual lighting conditions and with complex studio lighting arrangements. However, the meter must be properly calibrated, and it should be used in accordance with instructions. Furthermore, the photographer must be fully aware of the characteristics and limitations of his meter if he is to obtain consistently reliable exposure indications. For the most critical work, an actual photographic exposure test is recommended.

Daylight lighting conditions such as clear sun, hazy sun, etc., are constant enough so that it is practical to give fixed exposure recommendations in the form of tables, guides, and built-in camera computers. These recommendations give excellent results under the specified conditions. Similar exposure aids are supplied for use with simple arrangements of artificial lights.

COLOR PERCEPTION AND COLOR HARMONY

Color pictures occasionally show colors which appear faulty to an observer inexperienced in color photography, but which were actually present, unnoticed, in the original scene. In judging results, the photographer is frequently unable to compare the picture directly with the subject. Instead, he compares it with his mental image of how the subject appeared when photographed. If he has not learned to observe color, that is, to recognize subtle tints, mixtures, and reflections, he may find colors in the transparency or print which he did not notice in the original subject.

Unnoticed Colors. Unnoticed colors are due largely to the effects of the lighting conditions and the surroundings. An example is a snow scene, photographed in bright sunlight under a clear blue sky. Although it might be thought that shadows on white should be colorless, the picture shows bluish shadows. Actually, the shadows are blue, and appear so in the picture, because the light that does reach them comes largely from the blue sky.

Influence of Time of Day. A second example is a color picture exposed early in the morning or late in the afternoon. The color of sunlight during these hours is quite orange, and as a result the picture comes out too orange. Although the warmth of color and shadow effects obtained early or late in the day may occasionally be desirable with architectural and scenic subjects, they seldom result in satisfactory rendering of skin tones.

Influence of Other Reflecting Surfaces. Still a third example is a portrait of a girl posed near a strongly colored reflecting surface. Her face and arms may look perfectly natural at the time the picture is taken, but the colored light reflected on them may produce an unnatural effect in the finished picture. It is interesting to note that if colored surroundings are actually included in the scene area, the resulting picture will seem more natural because the reason for the unexpected color in the subject is evident.

Two Reasons Make It Difficult to Recognize How Colors Will Appear in Photographs. There are two reasons why such color effects are more difficult to recognize in viewing the original scene than in viewing a reproduction of the scene in the form of a color photograph: First, we commonly think of the color of a real subject as characteristic of it under all circumstances, and therefore do not expect any change. Second, in viewing the original scene, the eye tends to reduce disturbing illumination color by adapting to it in a way quite beyond the powers of the film. The photographer can train himself to detect color effects in the original scene and take steps to prevent their appearance in the color picture. In this way he will attain a better appreciation of color and will improve his ability to remember colors and to judge his results in color photography. The experienced worker avoids unnatural effects and achieves beautifully realistic colors by exposing his film in the most favorable lighting and surroundings.

Color Differences in Objects and Color Photographs. The foregoing should not be interpreted as indicating that Kodak color films will provide a perfect reproduction of the colors of the light which is reflected from a subject into the camera lens. If we make critical measurements on the very best color photographs, we find considerable differences between their colors and those of the original subjects. Actually, there is no available process of color photography which can be said to give entirely accurate and repeatable reproduction of color. Kodak color films, properly used, give satisfactory color rendering for their intended purposes, but in the present state of technical knowledge it is not possible to design materials suitable for making precise color records, or for matching or measuring colors. Further, since the reproduction of a physical subject by means of a color transparency or print involves psychological factors in the response of the observer, it can never be "perfect" in any simple sense.

Color Harmony. Color harmony may be defined as the systematic arrangement of colors to give a pleasing effect. The subject of color harmony is complex and very largely a matter of personal taste; nevertheless, a few general suggestions can be offered as a starting point.

The Habits of the Mind Decide What is Pleasing. Most outdoor scenes display good color harmony, probably because the mind has grown to accept the color combinations of nature as pleasing. Indoors, the colors of the background, clothing, and other properties are usually within the control of the photographer, and therein lies the danger that it is easy for the beginner in color work to become obsessed with the fact that a wide gamut of colors is at his disposal. It will be found, however, that the most pleasing photographs, as pictures, are generally those in which only a limited range of colors is used. The use of relatively unsaturated colors will frequently add to the naturalness of the color picture. In any case, care in the selection of those which are subject to control will pay dividends in more pleasing results.

Point to be Considered in Portraiture. In portraiture, the face of the subject before the camera should be the center of interest in the picture. Since conspicuous patterns or contrasting brilliant colors in either clothing or background tend to distract attention from the face, they should be avoided. Clothing colors should harmonize with the complexion and hair color of the subject. Medium or light colors are usually more effective than dark colors or black, and do not require so much care in lighting to insure satisfactory detail in the shadow areas.

Background Treatment in Color Photographs. Unlike black-and-white pictures, color pictures do not require the use of a background lighter or darker than the subject, because color differences help separate the planes of the scene. In general, the background color in a portrait should be related to the dominant color of the clothing, that is, one which lies near it on a color wheel. Touches of color complementary to the clothing color, that is, opposite it on the color wheel, are suitable for small areas or accessories. While these suggestions refer to hue, the photographer should never lose sight of the possibility, indeed desirability, of variations in brightness and saturation as well. All three characteristics of color play their parts in the success of the picture as a color composition.

The Main Subject Can be Made to Appear More Dramatic by the Use of Complementary Colors. In commercial and illustrative work, where the principal subject will frequently dominate the picture simply because of its size or shape, regardless of the color scheme, more dramatic effects can be obtained by surrounding the subject with complementary color. Small touches of related colors will soften the severity of the bolder contrasts. Large areas of harsh, brilliant colors should be avoided, because they are seldom pleasing, either in the original scene or in a color photograph.

Color Photography as a Means for Expressing Originality and Personality. Color photography allows full scope to originality and individual taste. An observant eye can find endless ideas for effective color schemes in paintings, printed and woven fabrics, interior decoration, and in the purely accidental combinations that occur in everyday life. The effectiveness of a given color scheme depends not only upon the colors themselves, but also upon their comparative areas and their distribution in the scene area. The textures of the colored surfaces are also important, because they lead to different color rendering under different lighting arrangements. Ease in composing with color is to a great extent the result of experience and observation, but no color scheme can be entirely preconceived. There is always some adjustment, some shifting of the elements, until the scene looks right to the photographer.

CHAPTER FIVE . .

The Camera Department_____

Section One: Light and Illumination

Light is a form of *radiant energy* that can illuminate objects. When light comes from or is reflected from an object, it enters the eye and permits the object to be seen. For practical purposes, light can be thought of as traveling in a straight line known as a *ray*. Because of this, it is impossible to see in back of an opaque object. As these rays do not — to any great degree — bend around the opaque object, a shadow is created behind it.

Light Source. There are many sources of light — some natural and some artificial. Our most important source of natural light is the sun, and an electric light bulb is probably our most common artificial source. In the electric light bulb, the wire filament is heated electrically causing it to send out light radiations.

We can also create light indirectly by means of certain chemical substances. The inside of the glass tube of fluorescent lamps is coated with chemicals called "phosphors" that fluoresce (glow) when struck by the invisible ultraviolet rays generated within the tube.

The Passage of Light. Light may pass through or be stopped by an object. If all the light hitting an object is kept from passing through it, the object is called *opaque*.

When some light passes through an object in such a way that we cannot see other objects clearly through it, it is known as *translucent*. An example of translucent material is ordinary waxed paper.

A transparent object, however, allows light to pass through it in such a way that we can clearly see objects through it. A window pane is such a *transparent* object.

The Speed of Light. Many people have tried at one time or another to measure the speed of light. As far back as 1675, a Danish astronomer noticed that when the Earth was closest to Jupiter, an eclipse of one of Jupiter's moons occurred 1,000 seconds sooner than when the Earth was farthest away. He figured that the 1,000-second delay was due to the time it took for the light to travel across the earth's orbit. As this orbit was 186,000,000 miles, the light, therefore, traveled at 186,000 miles per second.

Later on, during the 1920's, Michaelson found a way to measure the speed of light over a distance on the earth's surface. From this method, Michaelson figured the speed of light to be 186,285 miles per second.

One other factor about the speed of light should be mentioned. When a ray of light travels through a substance (known as a "*medium*"), the denser the substance the more the ray is slowed down.

For example, as water is a denser medium than air, light travels slower in water. Diamonds, as another example, slow down light rays to about 40 percent of what their speed would be in air.

Shadows. If we take a very small light source (known as a *point source* of light) and let its rays strike an opaque object, a sharply outlined shadow will be projected on it.

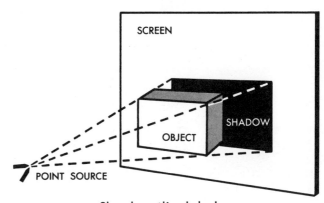

Sharply outlined shadow.

Using a large light source, the projected shadow has two areas — one of total darkness which is called the *umbra*, and one of partial darkness which is called the *penumbra*.

The eclipses of the sun and moon show how areas of umbra and penumbra are formed by natural bodies.

Illumination. Light is used in the litho plant so that the men can see what they are working on, or to examine the materials and equipment they are working with. In other words, light, both natural and artificial, is used to make it possible for them to see.

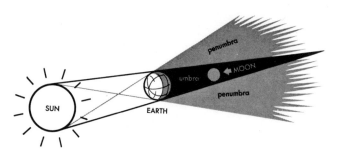

Formation of umbra and penumbra.

Light of a particular spectral quality is also used for photography. Here the light is used to enable the camera to "see." Another use of light is to tan or harden the light-sensitive plate coatings in order to make them less soluble in water. In other instances, light is used to actuate meters and timing devices.

The amount of light that strikes a surface is called the *illumination*. We use the term *candle-power* to measure the brightness of a light source. Originally, there was a special candle made of a certain type of oil that burned at a given rate, and this candle was used as a standard. Two such candles would produce a candle-power of two. The term candle-power is often abbreviated to "C.P."

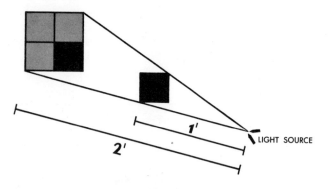

Law of inverse squares.

Intensity of Illumination. To measure how much *intensity* we have on an illuminated surface, we use the term *foot-candle*. This is the amount of light falling on a surface that is one foot away from the standard candle described previously.

The amount of light that falls on an object depends upon two factors: the candle-power of the original source, and the distance from the source to the object. Over this distance (from light source to object), light obeys a rule known as the *Law of Inverse Squares*. This states that:

The amount of light of a given source falling on an object varies inversely as the square of the distance from the source to the object.

The Law of Inverse Squares can also be written as:

$$\text{Amount of Illumination (in foot-candles)} = \frac{\text{Candle-Power of Source}}{\text{Sq. of Distance from Object to Source (in feet)}}$$

Example for Applying the Law of Inverse Squares. A negative is placed in a printing frame that is 3 feet away from a double-arc lamp. Each of these arcs gives off 27,000 candle-power of light. Find the total amount of illumination falling on the printing frame. If the arcs were moved back to 5 feet, what would be the total amount of illumination on the frame? If an exposure of 100 seconds made a good positive when the arcs were 3 feet away, what would the equivalent exposure be now that the arcs are 5 feet away?

For each arc (3-foot distance to frame)

$$\text{Amt. of Illumination} = \frac{\text{C.P.}}{(\text{Distance})^2}$$

$$\text{Amt. of Illumination} = \frac{27,000}{(3)^2}$$

$$\text{Amt. of Illumination} = \frac{27,000}{9}$$

$$\text{Amt. of Illumination} = 3000 \text{ foot-candles}$$

As there are 2 equal sources, the total illumination on the printing frame would be $2 \times 3,000$ foot-candles or 6,000 foot-candles when the lights are 3 feet away.

For each arc (5-foot distance to frame)

$$\text{Amt. of Illumination} = \frac{\text{C.P.}}{(\text{Distance})^2}$$

$$\text{Amt. of Illumination} = \frac{27,000}{(5)^2}$$

$$\text{Amt. of Illumination} = \frac{27,000}{25}$$

$$\text{Amt. of Illumination} = 1,080 \text{ foot-candles}$$

Total illumination when lights are 5 feet away would be 2 x 1,080 or 2,160 foot-candles.

To determine the new exposure we can substitute our values in this relationship:

$$\frac{\text{Original Foot-Candles on Frame}}{\text{New Foot-Candles on Frame}} = \frac{\text{New Exposure}}{\text{Original Exposure}}$$

Let "X" equal our new exposure, and then—

$$\frac{6,000}{2,160} = \frac{X}{100}$$

$$2,160X = 600,000$$

$$X = 277.8 \text{ seconds for new exposure.}$$

The Photometer. When we must determine the strength of an unknown light source, we can use an instrument known as the photometer. It is a simple instrument consisting of a graduated bar having a known light source clamped to one end, and a movable socket for the unknown light source.

To use this, you adjust the positions of the unknown light source and card until the grease spot apparently disappears. If you then substitute the distances from the lights

A photoelectric exposure meter.

to the card in the following formula, you can obtain the candle-power of the unknown source.

$$\frac{\text{Known C.P.}}{\text{Distance}^2 \text{ Between Grease Spot and Known C.P.}} =$$

$$\frac{\text{Unknown C.P.}}{\text{Distance}^2 \text{ Between Grease Spot and Unknown C.P.}}$$

Example for finding candle-power of a bulb. A known C.P. bulb of 10-C.P. is used in a photometer. When the grease spot apparently disappears, the known bulb is 2 feet away, and the unknown bulb is 6 feet away. What is the candle-power of the unknown bulb?

$$\frac{\text{Known C.P.}}{\text{Dist.}^2} = \frac{\text{Unknown C.P.}}{\text{Dist.}^2}$$

$$\frac{10}{(2)^2} = \frac{\text{Unknown}}{(6)^2}$$

$$\frac{10}{4} = \frac{\text{Unknown}}{36}$$

$$\text{Unknown} = \frac{360}{4} = 90 \text{ candle-power}$$

Foot-Candle Meter. This instrument measures the amount of illumination falling on it from any and all sources of light.

Usually, this type of meter uses a photoelectric cell connected to a meter that is marked in foot-candles. When light strikes the sensitive cell it generates a current that registers directly on the meter giving a reading in foot-candles.

Exposure Meters. The photoelectric exposure meter used to determine the correct exposure for negatives, positives, and color transparencies, is essentially a foot-candle meter as described above. It has, in addition, a number of scales on it. One is set for the speed of the emulsion used, and the second is set to the meter reading.

Then, from another portion of these scales, the correct exposure (in seconds or fractions of a second) can be read opposite the various apertures (lens openings) that can be used.

Integrating Light Meters. These instruments are a combination of light meter and timer. The light falling on a photoelectric cell generates the current that registers units on a timing device. When the pre-set time has been reached, the instrument turns off the device that has been connected to it (usually the shutter and arc lights).

REFLECTION

The *Law of Reflection* states that:
The angle of incidence is equal to the angle of reflection and that the incident ray, the reflected ray, and the normal all lie in the same plane.

The word "plane" is used here to mean a flat area like a level surface. The angle of incidence (i) is the angle that the incident ray makes with the normal. The normal is that line perpendicular to the surface.

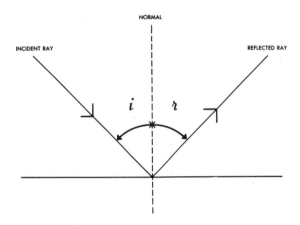

Angles of incidence and reflection.

Regular Reflection. When a ray of light is reflected from a smooth surface, it is known as *regular reflection*.

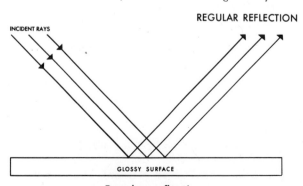

Regular reflection.

The ordinary mirror that we look into when we comb our hair produces regular reflection. With this type of reflection, a parallel beam of incident light produces a parallel beam of reflected light and this explains why we get an undistorted image from our mirror.

Diffuse Reflection. When a beam of incident light strikes a rough surface, such as a grained lithographic plate, each ray within that beam strikes a surface that has a slightly different angle. For this reason a parallel beam of incident light becomes a group of reflected rays that are reflected at many different angles and produce diffuse reflection. Reflection from uncoated papers is diffused, making the printed image appear to lack contrast. Some people term this "softness." Some jobs look better as a soft reproduction. Others require the "snappier" reproduction given by coated paper. This snappier appearance is due to the fact that the smooth-coated surface produces much more regular reflection and less diffused reflection than an uncoated paper.

Reflection and the Copyboard. When a cameraman puts a piece of copy on his copyboard, he arranges his arc lights in such a way that they will give him no glare. Since the glass surfaces of copyboards produce regular reflection, he will be most free of glare when his lights are at a 45°-angle to the board. As this angle decreases, there is more and more chance for unwanted reflections shining into the lens, especially if the area of the copyboard being covered is large. In other words, the direct reflection of the light must not be seen by the lens. When copying an oil painting, it is sometimes necessary to pick up the texture of the brush strokes. By reducing the angle between copyboard and lights, this added texture can be picked up.

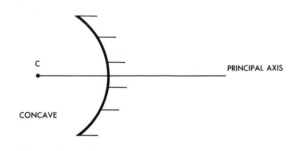

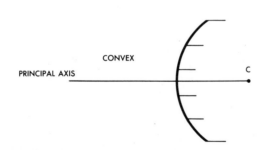

Concave and convex mirrors.

Reflection and Curved Mirrors. There are two types of curved mirrors in general use: the *concave and convex*.

These mirrors are actually parts of a sphere whose center (known as the *center of curvature*) is shown at the point marked "c" in our illustration. The *principal axis* of the mirror is the line connecting the center of curvature to the midpoint of the mirror.

When a beam of incident light that is parallel to the principal axis strikes the surface of a concave mirror, the reflected rays cross the axis at a single point known as the *focus*. In the case of the concave mirror, this is a "real focus" as the rays of light actually meet at this point. This distance from the focus to the midpoint of the mirror is known at the *focal length*.

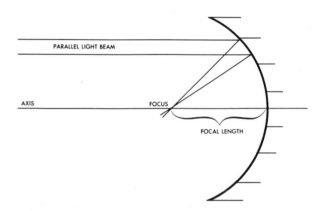

Reflection by a concave mirror.

With a convex mirror, the results are slightly different. The parallel incident rays are spread out after being reflected from the mirror surface, and do not cross the axis as in the case of the concave mirror. However, if we could extend these reflected rays *backwards* through the mirror, they too would cross at a common point. This point is called a *virtual focus* because the reflected rays seem to come from this point although they do not really do so.

The Use of Curved Mirrors. If we wanted to send out a parallel beam of light to cover a copyboard evenly, we could obtain a sufficiently large concave mirror, and

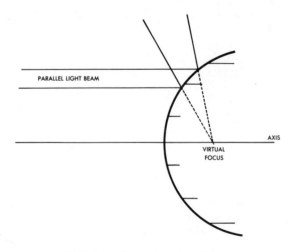

Reflection by a convex mirror.

place an arc light at its focus. This would reverse the process described above and produce our parallel beam. One type of arc lamp uses this method.

Reflectors in automobile headlights, flashlights, and shaving mirrors are also the concave type because they are able to magnify an image.

On the other hand, the convex mirror makes objects seem smaller. So we use this mirror for the rear view mirror of an automobile in order to get a broad view of the highway behind our car in a mirror of small size.

REFRACTION AND LENSES

Refraction occurs when a ray of light is bent as it passes at an angle from one medium to another of a different density.

If you happen to drop a piece of soap in your bathtub, you sometimes find it difficult to pick up because it is not where it seems to be. This is due to the light being refracted as it passes from the medium of water to the medium of air.

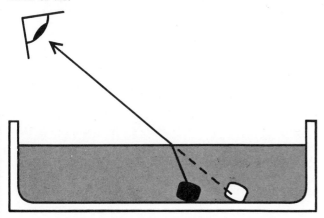

Refraction of light.

The Law of Refraction. All light rays obey the law of refraction. This law states that:

A ray entering a less dense medium, at an angle other than perpendicular, will bend away from the normal. A ray entering a denser medium at an angle other than perpendicular will bend toward the normal.

In addition, a ray passing from one medium to another parallel to the normal (perpendicular to the surface) will not be bent or refracted at all.

The Index of Refraction. Light travels at different speeds in different mediums. The *index of refraction* (n) is the ratio of the speed of light from the medium it is leaving to the speed of light in the medium it is entering. This can be written as a formula as follows:

$$n = \frac{\text{Speed of Light in Medium it is Leaving}}{\text{Speed of Light in Medium it is Entering}}$$

The Effect of Refraction. Refraction makes an object appear to be in a different position than it really is.

To show this, let's take two examples: the parallel plate, and the prism.

If we look at a can of developing ink obliquely, measuring at an angle through a piece of plate glass having sides parallel to each other, we will see the can in a slightly different position than it actually is in.

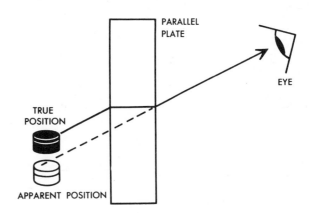

Effect of refraction through plate glass.

What has happened is this. A ray of light leaving the can strikes the plate glass. Because glass is a heavier medium than air, the ray is bent toward the normal as it continues in the glass. However, within the glass, its rate of speed and angle of travel are different than when it traveled in air.

When the ray finally exits from the glass, it is again bent — this time away from the normal because it is entering a lighter medium (air). After having been refracted twice, the ray leaves the glass at the same angle it entered because the glass sides are parallel. In actual use, this glass only slightly displaces our can of ink.

A prism also makes a light ray go through two refractions, but because the entering and exit sides are not parallel, the displacement is greater. The diagram shows the path of a ray of light through a prism.

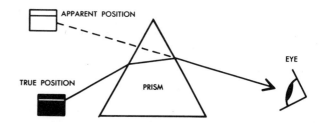

Effect of refraction through prism.

Critical Angle. Our illustration shows four rays of light striking the surface of water at different angles. Rays 1 and 2 are refracted into the water, and at a certain point (ray 3) the angle is such that the ray, after striking the surface, continues along the surface of the water. Ray 4 is totally reflected after striking the water surface.

The angle that ray 3 makes with the normal to the surface is called the *critical angle*. Light at larger than the critical angle will be reflected, while light at smaller angles will be refracted.

Suppose we have two different materials bonded together. When the angle of incidence of light in the first medium, at the time it strikes the surface between the two mediums, is greater than the critical angle of the first medium, the ray becomes internally reflected within the first medium. This

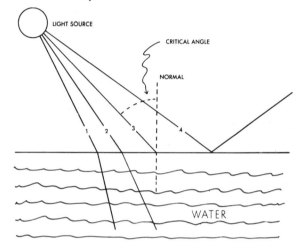

Critical angle.

fact is used in the design of many optical instruments such as the prism binocular or the prism periscope where the prism is used to change the direction of light.

The Lens. At present, we have yet to devise a lithographic camera that will work without a lens. Because of their vital importance in photolithography, it's essential that we know more about them, so that we can more easily use them to our purposes.

Basically, a lens consists of one or more pieces of curved glass having polished surfaces and mounted in such a way that we can easily handle it. There are two basic types of lenses: concave and convex. In this, and in many other respects, lenses are very similar to the mirrors we have already described.

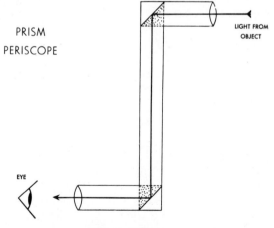

Prism periscope.

The convex lens is one whose center is thicker than its edges. If parallel light rays shine directly on this lens, the

emerging rays will all come together at a point known as the focus. The focus is a definite distance from any given convex lens. This focus is real because the rays actually meet at this point.

The concave lens has edges thicker than its center, and parallel rays falling on its surface will be diverged. How-

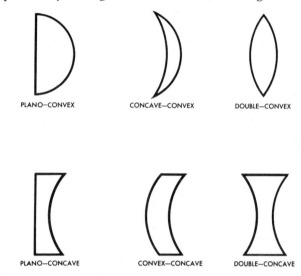

Various lens shapes.

ever, extending these diverging rays backward, they will seem to come from one point — the focus of this lens. This focal point is virtual rather than real because the rays do not actually meet there.

The imaginary line drawn through the focus and the center of the lens is called the *axis*. The distance from the focus to the center of the lens is called the focal length of the lens.

Lenses do not always have both their sides curved in the same way, and, because of that, the name of the lens depends upon the curvature of the sides. Our diagram shows examples of various lenses.

Images and Ray Tracing. Perhaps we'd like to know what will happen to the image of an object as it passes through the lens system. To aid us in finding out various

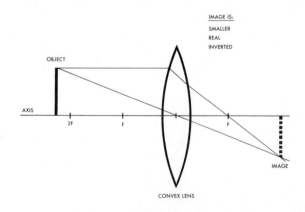

Object at distance greater than twice the focal length of lens.

facts, we use a method known as *ray tracing*. Using this method, we can take advantage of certain laws:

1. All light rays entering the lens parallel to the axis will emerge and pass through the focus of the lens.

2. All the light rays passing through the center of the lens (the point within the lens on the axis and halfway between both surfaces) and parallel to its axis will continue in a straight line.

These two facts can be used regardless of which side of the lens is toward the light source. Thus, each lens has two foci (focal points), one on each side of the lens.

Image Formation by Convex Lenses. With the convex lens, we will assume the object to be in three different positions, and show what happens at each. The object distance can be:

1. At a distance greater than twice the focal length of the lens.

2. At the focus.

3. At a distance less than the focal length of the lens.

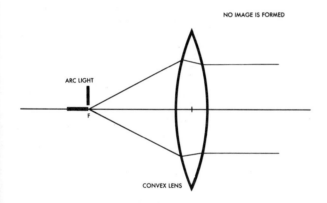

Object at focal point of lens.

In each of these cases it will be shown what the magnification is, whether the image is real or virtual, and its position.

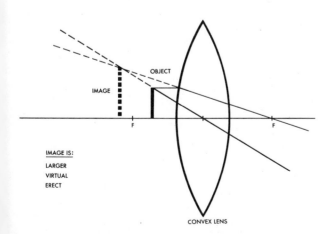

Object at distance less than the focal length of lens.

When the object is at a distance greater than twice the focal length of the lens, the created image is smaller than the object, real and inverted. As it nears the point that is twice the focal length, the image grows in size until at the point twice the focal length it becomes same size as the object. All this time the image remains real and inverted.

Between the distance of one and two focal lengths, the image size becomes larger than the object while still remaining real and inverted. Finally, at the focal point, no image is formed.

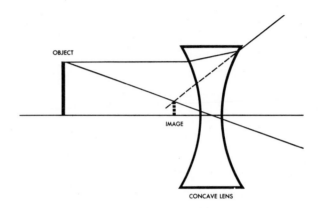

Image formation by concave lens.

Now, as the object gets between the focus and the lens, the image gets larger, and changes to virtual and erect.

Image Formation by Concave Lenses. Because the light rays diverge after striking a concave lens, we can only get virtual images. In all cases, these images are smaller than the object and erect. Our diagram shows an example of image formation by a concave lens.

Once more we must take advantage of the "rules" of ray tracing we previously mentioned. A ray through the lens center continues in a straight line, and an entering ray parallel to the axis will pass through the focus. With the concave lens, however, the emerging ray formed by the parallel ray will seem to come from the front focus of the lens rather than actually passing through the back focus as in the case of convex lenses.

Lens Aberrations. Lenses can have a number of faults that will not permit them to create a perfect image. However, most of these faults can be partially or completely corrected. They are called *spherical aberration, astigmatism, and chromatic aberration*.

Spherical aberration is the aberration that occurs when the lens surfaces are spherical (curved). In this case the rays entering the lens near its edges are brought to a focus closer to the lens than are the rays entering near the center of the lens. This produces a blurred image. This fault can be corrected in two ways. We can use a smaller diaphragm opening which would allow the light to pass through the central part of the lens alone. However, this would mean we would have to have longer exposures to allow the same amount of light to fall on our film.

A second method of correction for this aberration is the use of other lenses combined with the faulty one. The compound lens (as the combination of two or more lenses is called) is especially designed to reduce spherical aberration to a minimum.

Astigmatism is another form of lens aberration. It is a defect that causes horizontal and vertical lines in an object to be brought to a focus on different planes. When the lens is sharply focused on the horizontal lines, the vertical lines are out of focus. When focused on the vertical lines, the horizontal lines are blurred. This fault is also corrected by a combination of lenses of different kinds of optical glass.

Chromatic aberration is a third form of lens aberration. In this case, the white light passing through the lens is split up into various colored beams. Each of these colors comes to a focus at different points. When this fault exists in a lens, the blue beam of light comes to a focus nearest to the lens and the red beam focuses farthest away. This again results in a blurred image and can be corrected by making the component parts of the lens of various types of glass to neutralize this effect.

When a lens is corrected for these three types of aberration — spherical, astigmatic and chromatic — we call it an *anastigmat* lens.

LIGHTING COPY FOR REPRODUCTION

Light is the essence of the photographic process. Light is the cause, and illumination is the effect. When photomechanical reproduction of color originals is attempted, this effect must be consistent in even coverage of the subject, consistent in light output (intensity) and color temperature. All of these things are necessary in the illumination of the camera copyboard.

There are different light sources which can be used for this purpose: carbon arcs, which have been a mainstay for many years; and pulse xenon arcs, which were introduced more recently to the industry. Other light sources are available, such as photoflood and quartz lamps. These latter sources emit light more toward the infrared end of the spectrum than arc lights, having a color temperature of approximately 3200° K. Such light sources are more suitably used for monochromatic work. Color temperature is defined as the temperature at which a black body emits radiant energy, sufficient to evoke a color of the same hue and saturation as that evoked by radiant energy from a given source, such as lamp. This means that a lamp rated at a color temperature of 3200° K. will have the same spectral distribution as a black body at a temperature of 3200° K. An illustration of color temperature from two light sources would be: sunlight at noon, 5400° K.; a standard candle, 1900° K.

High intensity carbon arc lights are probably the most widely used for illuminating copyboards. They do an adequate job. The light emitted from high intensity carbons is given forth because the carbons are cored with metallic salts. This light intensity is greater than it would be if pure carbon rods were used. The color temperature of high intensity carbon arc lights is 5400° K. This temperature is excellent when using filters and panchromatic emulsions in reproducing color originals, and black and whites.

Carbon arc lights need a sixty-second warm-up period to reach peak intensity. Constant intensity of the arcs is governed by the burning rate of the carbons, compensated for by motor-driven feeds. It is important to trim the carbons equally on all lamps, thus keeping the carbons proportional in all lamps. This will eliminate the need to stop production periodically and to retrim each lamp at a different time, especially where two double banks of lights are used.

Five years ago a new type of lighting was introduced to the graphic arts industry. It was claimed to be superior to other types of lighting equipment in use. This is the pulse xenon arc light system. The light is emitted from xenon gas-filled tubes that are pulsed 120 times a second, but appears as a continuous emission of light. Peak intensity is reached instantly upon starting, and color temperature remains constant throughout an exposure. The color temperature is in the daylight spectral energy range of approximately 5400° K. The cleanliness of this system is very definitely an asset to the cameraman.

As mentioned before, there are other light sources that can be used for color reproduction, but they are not as desirable as high intensity carbon arcs or xenon lamps. High intensity incandescent lights are available, but are more suitable for black and white reproduction.

Various problems will be encountered in the illumination of the copy, some of which are discussed in the following paragraphs. The accepted angle of lamp direction for eliminating reflection copy is forty-five degrees from the center of the copyboard. This angle of the lights may be varied, according to the size and nature of the copy. An example is reproduction of a textured original, where it may be necessary to retain or accentuate the textured appearance in the reproduction. This can be done by placing one light or both lights (using two single camera lamps) at unusual angles, to arrive at the desired effect. Also, in black and white, when reproducing large pencilled drawings, a reflection from an area of pencil lines may reflect light at the forty-five degree angle. To eliminate this problem, it is necessary to change the angle of the lights to a more desirable position.

The evenness of the light coverage at the copyboard should and can be checked by reading the light falling upon each corner of the copyboard with an exposure meter. The use of a high intensity light source which will emit a certain amount of ultraviolet light, may cause a problem in making masks and color separations. Unusual density readings may be encountered in masks and/or separations from a particular piece of art. This can be accounted for by the fact that some art board and pigments will absorb, reflect, or fluoresce the ultraviolet light. An ultraviolet absorbing filter, used in front of the light source, may reduce this effect.

It is very important, in both color and black and white reproduction, that maximum contrast for the process is obtained. The tonal contrast may be lost in camera negatives or positives (half-tones and continuous tone) because of flare. Flare will have more effect on the shadow contrast than on the highlight contrast. It can be caused by a dirty optical system. One cause of flare is the "stray" illumination from a light left turned on over the copy-

board while making an exposure. An ideal setup to al-
leviate this is an electrical connection between the camera
lamps and the overhead working lights. When the camera
lamps are switched on, the overhead and working lights

near the copy and lens are automatically switched off, and
vice-versa. Another factor that can contribute to flare, and
result in poor image contrast, is the reflection from light-
colored or gloss walls in the camera area.

Section Two: Densitometry

The densitometer is one of the most valuable control devices available to the photographer. With it you can measure numerically the density of a tone area, on black-and-
white, or color; transparent or opaque materials. These
density measurements can be used as a guide in determining
exposure conditions for simple black-and-white copying, or
for setting up masking procedures. However before trying
to use a densitometer you should have an understanding of
what is meant by the term density.

OPTICAL DENSITY

Density simply called, meaning in our context always
optical density, is a standard means of expressing the value
of a tone area — its light-stopping ability. *The darker a
tone, the higher its density.* The highlights on a photographic print will have a low density and the shadows a
high density. On the negative the same highlights will
appear dark and therefore will have a high density.

Transmission Density. The ability of a silver layer
on film to absorb or pass light may be expressed in terms of
transmission density. The term *transmission* refers to the
light passing ability of the silver layer. The term density
refers to the light-absorbing ability of the layer.

The transmission of any tone area is the fraction of incident light transmitted through the area without being absorbed or scattered.

$$T = \frac{I_t}{I_i}$$

T = transmission
I_t = intensity of transmitted light
I_i = intensity of incident light

Density is equal to the logarithm of $\frac{I}{T}$

$$D = \log \frac{I}{T} = \log \frac{I_i}{I_t}$$

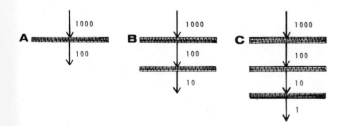

Transmission and density relationship.

The relationship between the two terms can be illustrated
in our table. In our illustration, the light intensity on the
first layer is the same for A, B, and C. However the light

intensity leaving the silver layer decreases as we increase
the number of layers.

TABLE: Transmission and Density Relationship

	A	B	C
layers	1,	2	3
transmission	$\frac{1}{10}$	$\frac{1}{100}$	$\frac{1}{1000}$
density	1	2	3

The transmission has decreased by a factor of 10 for
each additional layer, while the density has increased by 1.
When working with density units we add to obtain combinations of different tones. When working with transmission units we have to multiply. It is easier to handle density

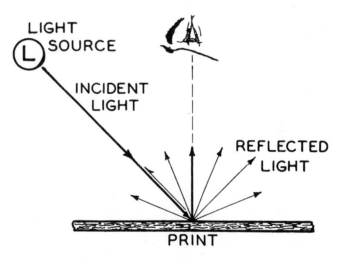

Reflection.

units in calculations. The use of the logarithmic scale, density units, permits us to express large quantities by small
numbers, which in turn permits us to plot a large range of
numbers on a reasonably sized graph. Another reason for
using a logarithmic scale is that the response of the eye is
logarithmic. For example in our next illustration we have
a transparency with four different tones W, X, Y, and Z.
The intensity of the light transmitted through each tone is
indicated by the lower arrows. The numerical values of the
light intensity is shown beside the arrows. The length of
the arrow is proportional to the light intensity it represents.
The value of these tones as the eye sees them are indicated
by the solid blocks, and the optical density of each tone is
beneath the block.

Arrow X is only half as long as W, Y is half as long as
X, and Z is half as long as Y. As the light intensities are

cut in half, the apparent tone values increase equally from W to Z, and the measured density increases by steps of .3. The eye sees as equal tone steps equal changes of density units.

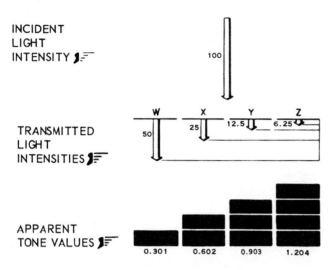

INCIDENT LIGHT INTENSITY

TRANSMITTED LIGHT INTENSITIES

APPARENT TONE VALUES

Incident light, transmitted light, and apparent tone values.

Reflection Density. Reflection density is very much like transmission density. When light falls on an image, for example a paper print, part of the light is absorbed, while the remainder is reflected in various directions. How much light is reflected in each direction depends on the tone density and the surface of the paper.

In measuring reflection densities it is standard practice to illuminate the area at an angle of 45 degrees and measure the amount of light reflected at 90 degrees to the surface.

Just as transmission density is based upon the transmittance of a tone area, so reflection density is based upon reflectance from a tone area. However reflectance does not involve the incident light at all. Reflectance is expressed as the ratio between the amount of light reflected from a given tone area and the amount reflected from a white area on the same paper, or a standard surface.

$$R = \frac{I_r}{I_{rw}}$$

R = reflectance
I_r = intensity of light reflected from tone
I_{rw} = intensity of light reflected from white paper

Reflection density has the same relationship to reflectance that transmission density has to transmittance.

$$D_T = \log 1/T \qquad D_T = \text{transmission density}$$
$$D_R = \log 1/R \qquad D_R = \text{reflection density}$$

Reflection density readings express the values of tones in an image, like a paper print, in exactly the same way that transmission density readings express the values of tones in a transparency. Reflection density values, like transmission density values, are proportional under most viewing conditions to visual tone values. Like transmission density readings, reflection density readings are relative. They are not affected by changes in intensity of illumination. They do not express the value of a tone in terms of light intensity. Instead, they tell how much darker a tone is than some other tone. The most extreme highlight on the print — a white area — is chosen as the zero point, and all of the other readings on the print are expressed in relation to this value.

CHOOSING A DENSITOMETER

There are various types of densitometers. They differ in what they will do, how they do it, and what they cost. The choice of a particular densitometer depends on what it is to be used for, and on how much is expected of it. The best instrument for a particular purpose will be the one which does everything required of it with the greatest accuracy, in the shortest time, and which changes least in accuracy with age and use.

Some densitometers are designed to measure only transmission densities. Others will measure only reflection densities. Combination instruments will measure both. If all the readings in the plant are to be made on one densitometer, the instrument should be equipped to measure both reflection and transmission densities. If a number of in-

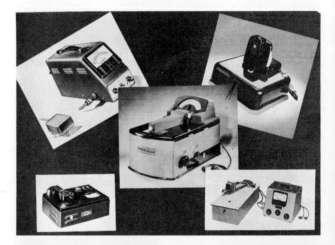

Various kinds of densitometers.

struments are required then it might be more economical to supply the pressroom with only the reflection type. The photographic, and art departments should have combination instruments, since they handle transparent negatives and positives as well as opaque original copy.

Both reflection and transmission densitometers should cover a range from 0 to 3.0. The scale should be calibrated so that it can register a density difference of .02 over its entire scale. In practical plant operations, an accuracy of 0.02 units will be satisfactory. A calibrated reflection and transparent gray scale should be set aside as a standard against which the densitometer could be checked frequently. When an error of more than plus or minus .03 is detected the instrument should be adjusted.

OPERATION OF A DENSITOMETER

Densitometers are of two general types; visual and photo-electric. In visual instruments, an arrangement of lenses and mirrors bring together the tone being measured and a control tone, for visual comparison. By making an adjustment the operator increases or decreases the density of the control tone until he sees, judging by eye, that the two tones match. He then reads the density on a calibrated scale.

Photoelectric Densitometers. There are several types of photoelectric densitometers. One variety uses a barrier-layer cell similar to that employed in photoelectric exposure meters, with a microammeter and a dial, reading directly in density values. This variety gives fast readings, but the accuracy falls off for densities over 2. Another type employs a vacuum photoelectric cell and an electronic amplifying circuit. This type can measure densities above 3. Another type employs a photomultiplier tube which is more sensitive than a photo cell. It can measure densities above 4.

Comparison of Visual and Photoelectric Units. Generally visual units are much less expensive than the photoelectric units. Because there are no electronic parts or sensitive meters involved, visual units are generally more rugged. The accuracy obtained with visual units is generally adequate for most lithographic work. Most people will feel eyestrain when making 20 or 30 readings with a visual unit. With visual units it is sometimes difficult to make comparisons if there is a slight color difference between the tone being measured and the control tone. Electronic units can be used rapidly and easily. Measurements made with electronic units are generally more reproducible than those made with visual units. The physical condition of the operator does not effect the measurements made with electronic units. They can also be used as sensitive light meters, to measure the illumination level and evenness at the focal plane of the camera or in similar applications.

THE CHARACTERISTIC CURVE

The characteristic curve, also known as the H & D curve, or D log E curve, is a graph which shows how the film or plate material can be expected to perform under certain conditions of use.

The negative density is plotted against the logarithm of the exposure as in our first graph. The film manufacturers use elaborate equipment to expose and develop the test strips used to make these curves. A more practical method

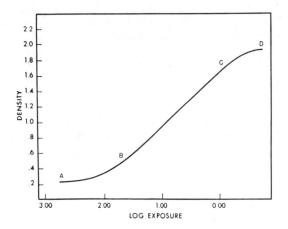

A characteristic curve.

of obtaining these curves can be used by the photographer. A gray scale can be photographed or contacted and the density of the contact positive or camera negative can be plotted against the density of the original as in our second graph.

The curve you obtain is for a given set of conditions; therefore, when you make these curves, indicate the materials and equipment used. Use fresh developer every

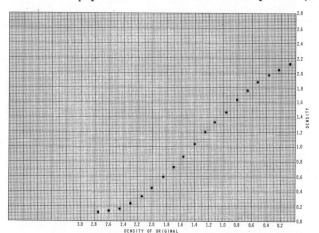

Plotting a characteristic curve.

time and try to develop the same way every time. After the negative or positive has been made, make a table of the scale step numbers, density of the original and the negative or positive as in our table. Using regular graph paper, set up a scale of density values along the vertical and horizontal axis as shown in our illustration. The horizontal

Density of Step No.	Original Density	Density of Test
1	0.08	2.20
2	0.27	2.13
3	0.41	2.03
4	0.57	1.94
5	0.74	1.84
6	0.86	1.74
		and so on.

Tabulating density measurements.

axis will represent density values of the original, while the vertical axis will represent density values of the negative or positive. For point #1 we would locate .08 along the horizontal (D_o) axis, and then locate 2.2 along the vertical axis (D_n) axis. Where these two values intersect make a cross. Repeat for the other points. When all the points have been plotted, draw a smooth curve through the average of these points. It is seldom that all the points line up perfectly to produce a smooth curve. This is the characteristic curve.

The curve has three general regions, the toe, the straight line portion and the shoulder. If we represent the curve as being cut by a series of lines at equally spaced horizontal distances, in the toe and shoulder regions there is an unequal increase in vertical distance for equal horizontal distances. This means that there is an unequal density increase for equal amounts of exposure. However in the straight line portion of the curve, the density rises an equal amount for equal increases in exposure. Working with photographic materials we generally use the straight line portion of the characteristic curve. If we use the toe or shoulder regions we will get tone distortions.

From a series of curves we can determine the contrast of an emulsion, filter ratios, and relative speed. While this information is generally given on the film data sheets, the results you obtain under your shop conditions may differ from those of the film manufacturers. You may also want to try combinations of emulsions and developers not specifically suggested by the manufacturer, and therefore there may not be any data available on these combinations.

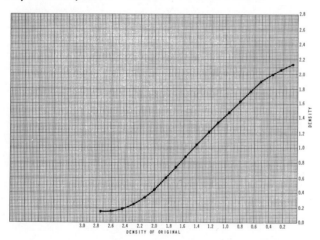

Making the final curve.

Contrast. *Contrast* is a term which may have a different meaning for different people. Some people may use the term to describe the separation of tones in a picture. The words soft or hard may be used in describing the contrast of an image. When comparing a reproduction with the original, we might say that the reproduction has a higher or lower contrast. When examining a reproduction we might speak of the contrast in different parts of the tone scale, such as the shadow contrast or the highlight contrast. When comparing a negative with the original we again use the term contrast.

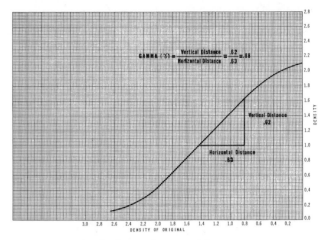

Analyzing a characteristic curve.

Gamma. In photography the Greek letter, *Gamma,* is defined as "a numerical designation for the contrast of a photographic material is represented by the slope of the *straight line portion* of the characteristic curve. Gamma is numerically equal to the tangent of the angle which the straight line portion makes with the base line."

Generally, the longer you develop any film in any developer, the higher the gamma will be until it finally reaches a limit. We can say this another way: The higher the gamma, the greater the contrast of the negative, *due to development.* That italicized phrase is important. The total contrast is due to quite a few factors; subject contrast, development contrast, flare in the optical system of camera, etc. So when we talk about gamma we are referring to development contrast only.

In our illustration we see how gamma is determined. Vertical and horizontal lines are drawn which intersect each other and the straight line portion of the curve. The numerical value of gamma is equal to:

$$\gamma = \frac{\text{vertical distance}}{\text{horizontal distance}}$$

OTHER USES OF THE DENSITOMETER

At the Camera. The densitometer is an instrument of many practical uses, in a photographic department. For example the photoelectric cell of some instruments can be detached and placed on the ground glass of the camera. Here it can serve as a very sensitive light meter to measure the amount of light coming through the lens. Once a test negative has been made and the proper exposure determined, the ground glass reading will permit you to determine the correct exposure for other camera positions.

Densitometers with detachable heads also permit a simple and accurate method of positioning the arc lamps for proper illumination. "Proper illumination" means even illumination on the *ground glass of the camera.* Many process photographers make the mistake of thinking that if the copy is illuminated evenly, the exposure of the emulsion in the camera will also be even.

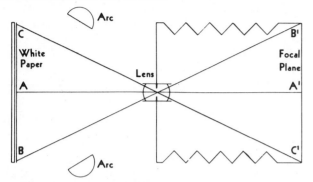

If the intensity of the light from A which strikes the emulsion at A' is taken as 100%, the intensity of the light which strikes the emulsion of C' from C, and at B' from B (25° off the axis) is only about 67% due to the factors discussed in this article.

Our diagram shows why this is wrong. Light rays from the outer edges of the copy have to travel farther than those which are on or closer to the optical axis of the lens. These same light rays also strike the emulsion at an angle and since they cover a greater area than those close to or on the axis, their intensity is further diminished. Furthermore, lenses tend to vignette the light rays from the edges of the copy due to the barrel length, lens thickness or both.

So, if the illumination at the focal plane (ground glass) is to be even, the edges of the copy must receive more light than the center of the copy. The procedure for checking illumination using a densitometer with a detachable head is as follows:

Adjust the camera and lens for same-size reproduction. Replace the ground glass in the camera with a pane of clear glass. Cover the copyboard with a sheet of white paper. Cover the window of the photometer search-head with opal glass and place the opal glass against the clear glass in the camera. Open the shutter of the camera, warm up the arcs, and then slide the search-head over the clear glass noting the variations in light intensity on the meter dial. Move the arc lights to different positions until the meter readings show that the intensity of the light at the film plane is as uniform as possible. A record should be made of these final arc light positions and used whenever you are shooting at same-size.

This same procedure should be followed to determine the best positions of the arcs at other camera settings. Once the positions have been determined for each of the most commonly used camera settings, they should be recorded for reference on future jobs.

If only two arcs illuminate the copyboard, it probably will be possible to get fairly even illumination in a band across the focal plane but not vertically. In such cases, oblong copy should always be placed on the copyboard with its longest dimension horizontal.

Color Control of Pre-Separated Artwork. In some areas of color printing, such as greeting cards, children's books, etc., the artwork is prepared with copy for each color prepared as a separate piece of art. This may be either in a black medium (ink, paint, etc.) on opaque board; or as colored films (Bourges, etc.). A reflection densitometer makes it possible to establish an exact relationship between the tone values of the art and the size of the halftone dots required on each color-printer to produce the desired end result.

Color Control of Color Separations of Full-Color Copy. Most color separation of full-color art — opaque or transparent — is accomplished by the indirect method. The first step is to shoot a set of continuous-tone separation negatives. A transmission densitometer can be used to standardize the operation of producing the desired halftone positives. This same type of densitometer is also useful to check the densities of the halftone positive to determine that the desired printed result will be produced. Here the densitometer can be used before and after any color correction is done. It will guide the dot etcher in planning his work, and will indicate accurately when he has accomplished the desired end result.

Planning and Control of Black-and-White Photography. The use of a reflection densitometer to measure the densities of black-and-white continuous-tone copy makes it possible to plan the proper photographic technique for a desired result. Following this with density measurements of the halftone negative (or positive) will produce almost complete control. Such techniques make it possible to better group pieces of copy when a large number and variety are to be reproduced in such a way as to produce a final printed piece whose overall appearance will be reasonably uniform.

And Still Other Uses. Densitometry as a control technique is finding greater and greater use in the industry. Their uses will be discussed at appropriate places in this volume.

Section Three: The Chemistry of Photography

The chemistry of photography is a vast subject; in this Manual, we can merely present some of its fundamental aspects. Our presentation is divided into the following four points: (1) The photographic emulsion, (2) Developing, (3) Fixation, and (4) Reduction. Each of these subjects is discussed in the following.

THE PHOTOGRAPHIC EMULSION

The silver emulsion used on sensitized materials consists of a colloid such as gelatin, silver halides, and other additives producing certain effects. It is odd that this term emulsion is used for the description of the sensitized coating, for according to the technical definition, an emulsion is a heterogeneous liquid mixture of two or more liquids. The photographic emulsion does not consist of this liquid mixture but of a colloid and solids held in a colloidal dispersion. However, in the coating of the film or glass plate, the sensitizer is in liquid form and the origin of this term can probably be traced back to the colloquial designation of this liquid as an emulsion.

Gelatin. About 1871, the first successful dry plate using gelatin was made, and since that time the use of gelatin has been indispensable to the progress of emulsion technology. The unique properties of gelatin are responsible for this acceptance and years of research have not to date yielded an equal or improved substitute.

Gelatin is a protein obtained from the tissues, hides, cartilage and bones of animals. Since it is of animal origin, its composition is extremely varied and consequently complicates the process of standardization. The important specifications for photo use of gelatin are jelly strength, pH, moisture content, metal contents of iron, lead, copper, alumina, together with limits of ash and sulfur dioxide.

Silver Halides. The important salts of silver chloride, silver bromide and silver iodide, which are formed by precipation in the emulsion, are extensively used in emulsion manufacture. Silver fluoride is not used to any extent because of its fog action in combination with other silver halides.

Silver bromide (AgBr) is the most widely used of the silver salts for paper, glass and film products. It is usually the major portion of the halide salts in film and is characterized by the effect of its high speed and low fog action on the emulsion.

Silver iodide (AgI) is used generally in combination with other halides. In speed it is approximately one-third that of silver bromide.

Silver chloride (AgCl) is a pure white powder, which is used primarily on paper-type emulsions for amateur use. Its speed is approximately one-eighth that of silver bromide.

Although the halides of silver are widely used, the oxalates, nitrates, tartrates and citrates of silver have been and still are used to a lesser degree for sensitization.

Additives to Emulsions. The silver salts are color sensitive inherently to the blue portions of the spectrum only and to increase this sensitivity to red and green, color sensitizing dyes are added to the photographic emulsion. These sensitizing dyes are absorbed by the silver halide and the increase in color sensitivity by this process is referred to as optical sensitization.

To obtain special effects such as an increase in speed, prevention of fog, control of gamma etc., all emulsions contain certain additions to achieve these desired effects. The specific chemical reaction and function of these additives are complex and the subject of widespread patent literature.

Preparation of the Photographic Emulsion. The technique of manufacture for photographic emulsions has long been considered as a "trade secret," but the basic procedure is well-known and consists essentially of the following:

1. Soaking and dissolving a portion of the gelatin.
2. Addition of bromides and iodides used in precipitation of the silver halide.
3. Addition of silver salts, causing the precipitation of the silver halide. This process is called emulsification.
4. Recrystallization of emulsion by heating. This is commonly referred to as the "first ripening."
4. Addition of the remaining gelatin, and chilling.
6. Formation of "noodles" by forcing the chilled gelatin through a wire screen.
7. Washing, to rid the emulsion of unwanted salts.
8. Reheating, which is referred to as after-ripening or second-ripening, to recrystallize the silver salts.
9. Addition of special chemicals, such as sensitizing dyes, preservatives, anti-foggants, stabilizers, etc.

Although the preceding list of operations is considered a basic procedure, there are endless variations which will affect the finished product. Purity of gelatin, agitation, salt concentration, degree of heat, and procedure of addition of silver salts are just a very few of the factors that make emulsion manufacture a complex procedure.

DEVELOPERS SOLUTIONS

Light affects the photographic emulsion by the formation of a latent image. This image has to be converted to a visible image, which is accomplished by reduction of the silver halide to black metallic silver with the use of a solution referred to as a developer.

The developing solution consists of:
1. A solvent, such as water.
2. A developing or reducing agent, such at Metol.
3. A preservative, such as sodium sulfite.
4. A restrainer, such as potassium bromide.
5. An accelerator or alkali, such as sodium hydroxide.
6. Miscellaneous additives.

Chemicals in a developer function according to the above grouping; the difference among developers is caused by the different types or proportions of these chemicals to achieve the desired developing action.

Constituents of a Developer. Almost all developers use water as their solvent, although some color coupling developers use other solvents in combination with water as their solvent. The water used for developers should be of fairly high purity and should not contain large amounts of calcium or chloride salts. The fluoridation of water, recently installed in many communities throughout the country, can possibly cause difficulties in its use for photographic purposes. There has not been any comprehensive study on this problem published to date; however, the writer has been advised that technical publications on this subject will soon be made public.

The Developing Agent. Organic chemicals are widely used as developing agents and are characterized as strong reducing agents containing the hydroxyl (OH) and amino (NH$_2$) radicals in varying proportions. The most important of this group is paradihydroxybenzene or *hydroquinone* and monomethyl paraminophenol or *Metol.* Hydroquinone is a slow but powerful developer, taking longer to show a visible image on the film, but gaining density much more rapidly over a prolonged period of time. Metol is a much more energetic agent, showing an image rapidly but building density slowly. The combination of Metol and Hydroquinone in developers is excellent, for each chemical helps correct the shortcomings of the other. Varying combinations of these two agents are used in the most popular types of paper and film developers.

The Preservative. Due to the high reducing action of the developing agent, a preservative (or antioxidant) is necessary to prevent or control developer oxidation. Sodium sulfite is the most common chemical in this group. The sulfite, in addition to acting as an antioxidant, also prevents the formation of staining developer products, acts as a silver solvent and in some cases serves as a weak alkali increasing the rate of development.

Accelerator. In order to increase the pH of the developing solutions, thereby increasing the ionization of the developing agent, the addition of an alkali or accelerator as it is commonly referred to, is important in developing formulae. The alkali also has the dual function of absorbing the bromine ions formed by the action of the developing agent on the silver salts. The more important types of alkalis include the carbonates and hydroxides of sodium and potassium. Paraformaldehyde is the common type of alkali control used in "lith" type developers due to its ability to produce extreme contrast.

Restrainer. The action of potassium bromide in a developing solution is such that it reduces the ionization of the silver salt thereby restraining development. This action, however, is greater on the fog image than on the denser image. According to Lobel, in the Bulletin of the French Photographic Society (1928), the citrates, tartrates and boro-tartrates act similar to potassium bromide.

Miscellaneous Additives. There are a number of additives to developing solutions each designed to achieve some desired effect. The most common in use today are the following:

1. Wetting agents . . . to permit the rapid penetration of developer into the gelatin.

2. Densitizers . . . to reduce the color sensitivity of the emulsion without affecting its speed. Phenosafranine and the pinakryptols belong in this group of chemicals.

3. Silver solvents . . . used for reduction of grain size, include sodium thiocyanate, ammonium chloride, etc.

4. Other chemicals . . . used to increase gamma, control water impurities and permit use of developers in extremes of temperature.

The Action of Development. The action of the developer on the photographic emulsion has been the subject of debate for some time, and to date, there is not a complete understanding available on this complex reaction. However, in the case of a hydroquinone developer, the reactions have been thoroughly investigated and reported by Roebuck and Staehle (1), to proceed as follows:

1. The alkali produces dissociation of the hydroquinone with the liberation of ions of the developing agent in solution.

2. The hydroquinone ion reacts with the silver bromide yielding Quinone and ions of silver and bromine.

3. The quinone then reacts with sodium sulfite to form sodium hydroquinone monosulfonate and sodium hydroxide.

4. The sodium hydroquinone monosulfonate is oxidized to quinone monosulfonate which in turn reacts with sulfite to form sodium hydroquinone disulfonate. The latter chemical is practically inert as a developer.

5. As the development proceeds, hydroquinone ionizes and at the same time hydrogen ions are formed, hydroquinone is used up and is replaced by the weaker hydroquinone monosulfonate, bromine ions are released into the solution and this is equivalent to adding potassium bromide to the developer.

Basically this reaction may be simplified by saying that the developing agent is gradually used up, and during this process it forms complex developing agents salts, which act on the image to a lesser degree. The solution then reaches a point when the developing agent is completely exhausted and the bromine ions formed by the silver bromide restrains development and will not produce sufficient density in the negative or positive.

FIXATION

When development is completed those areas not affected by exposure or developing have to be removed to make the image on the film permanent. These unexposed and undeveloped areas are removed from the film by the use of a fixing bath.

In addition to its reaction of dissolving the unexposed and undeveloped silver salts the fixing bath also serves two other basic purposes: it neutralizes developer alkali, thereby stopping developer action and eliminating oxidation staining; and it sufficiently hardens the emulsion preventing scratches, and washing away of the gelatin image.

Composition and Reactions of the Fixing Bath. The fixing bath contains a number of chemicals each acting on the silver image in some manner. The formulation of a typical bath used for general purposes on lith films would consist of the following:

1. A *solvent* . . . such as water.

2. A *silver halide solvent* . . . such as sodium thiosulfate (hypo) which is used to dissolve the silver halides. Generally emulsions with large grain size will clear much faster if ammonium thiosulfate is used. This is the common ingredient of the liquid type fixers.

3. A *stabilizer* . . . such as sodium sulfite. In this reaction the sodium sulfite combines with the ionized sulfur of the sodium thiosulfate, to form a complex sulfite salt thereby stabilizing the bath and preventing formation of a sulfur precipitate.

4. An *acid* . . . such as acetic acid to bring the bath to the required pH necessary to neutralize the alkalinity of the film caused during development.

5. A *buffer* . . . such as boric acid to limit the change of pH of the fixing bath solution, thereby preventing formation of aluminum precipitates.

6. A *hardener* . . . such as potassium alum. In this reaction the hardener toughens the emulsion so that the

resulting physical hardness is such that it will not be affected by washing or normal handling when the film is dried. The hardening action of chrome alum is greater than the potassium salt but since it has a tendency to form a sludge more rapidly, it is not used too widely.

REDUCERS

The action of a reducer is essentially that of an oxidizing agent; oxidizing the metallic silver to form a soluble silver salt. In some cases, the silver salt is insoluble in water, and the solution must contain another chemical which converts the silver salt into a soluble silver compound.

The most common type of reducer used today is Farmer's reducer, and contains a mixture of potassium ferricyanide and sodium thiosulfate. The silver acts with the potassium salt to form silver ferrocyanide. At the same time the iron in the ferricyanide ion is reduced to form ferrocyanide ions. Then the sodium thiosulfate reacts with the insoluble silver ferrocyanide, converting it into soluble complex ions.

Another reducer is a mixture of iodine and sodium or potassium cyanide. The potassium iodide reacts with the iodine forming potassium iodate. The latter is the substance which oxidizes the silver. Silver iodide is very insoluble in water, but is soluble in a potassium cyanide solution. The silver iodide is thus converted into a silver cyanide complex ion which is soluble in water. This type of reducer is sometimes used for flat etching of halftone positives.

CONCLUSION

The chemistry of photography is an extremely broad and complex subject. However, an understanding of the basic points are helpful for a complete understanding of the photolithographic process.

Readers interested in further study of the subject will find several books listed in the bibliographical appendix of the Manual.

Section Four: Photo-Materials and Their Properties*

Our presentation of photographic materials and their properties is divided into the following thirteen subjects: (1) Dimensional stability of photographic films, (2) Cellulose ester base films, (3) Polystyrene base films, (4) Film handling suggestions to minimize size changes, (5) Dimensional stability of Du Pont "Cronar" based films, (6) Photographic properties, (7) Color sensitivity and types of sensitizing, (8) Filters, (9) Safelight color and safety, (10) Emulsion contrast and the characteristic curve, (11) Effect of development on contrast, (12) Exposure, and (13) The use of the exposure index for graphic arts photography. Each of them is presented in the following.

DIMENSIONAL STABILITY OF PHOTOGRAPHIC FILM

The dimensional stability of film is of critical importance in a number of applications such as the reproduction of mechanical drawings, typographic maps, color separations, and various other graphic arts and industrial products. This discussion is intended: to explain why photographic films change size; and to provide dimensional stability data for both cellulose ester- and polystyrene-base sheet films.

Theory. Photographic film is comprised of a plastic base coated with a light-sensitive emulsion usually made of gelatin. It is essentially a laminate of two chemically different materials, each of which is affected by environment and age. As a result, the dimensional behavior of film is extremely complex.

Classification of Dimensional Changes. To understand why films change size the way they do, it is helpful to classify the various types of dimensional changes into two groups: (1) Temporary or reversible dimensional changes; and (2) Permanent changes. Temporary or reversible dimensional changes may be due to: (1) Humidity expansion or contraction; (2) Thermal expansion or contraction. Permanent shrinkage may be due to: (1) Loss of residual solvent or plasticizer from the base; (2) Plastic flow of the base caused by contraction of the emulsion; (3) Release of mechanical strain (recovery of stretch introduced in manufacture).

Factors Influencing Dimensional Changes. The magnitude of each of these types of dimensional change in a given film depends on the chemical composition and thickness of the base and emulsion, the treatment received in manufacture, and the conditions under which the film is stored. There are also other complex phenomena such as hysteresis and elastic memory. These account for small dimensional changes in photographic film.

Humidity Expansion. Humidity expansion or contraction of film is caused by gain or loss of moisture from the air to which it is exposed. The magnitude of this type of size change depends on the chemical nature of the film. Polystyrene-base film, for example, changes much less with humidity than acetate-base film. For any one film it is the relative humidity of the air (not the absolute humidity) which determines the film's moisture content and corresponding size. After a change in the relative humidity of the air, the dimensions of a piece of polystyrene-base film change gradually for about five minutes; acetate-base film changes gradually for about an hour. In both cases, the change continues until equilibrium between film and atmosphere is re-established.

Thermal Expansion. Film, like other materials, also expands and contracts with changes in temperature. Thermal size changes occur rapidly, sometimes in a minute or two. Frequently, an increase in air temperature is accompanied by a decrease in relative humidity or vice versa. Therefore, these two effects may partially cancel each other. Under other conditions the effect of temperature and relative humidity may be additive.

Processing Shrinkage. Film swells during processing and contracts again during drying. If brought to equilibrium with the same relative humidity after processing as existed before, a small net change called the "processing shrinkage" is usually experienced. If the film is not brought back to the same moisture content after processing, the apparent processing shrinkage may be increased by humidity contraction or reduced by humidity expansion, sometimes resulting in a small swell.

Aging Shrinkage. Permanent shrinkage during storage, prior to exposure, is generally very low and unimportant for sheet film because there is no image on it at the time. After processing, film continues to shrink at a rate which gradually decreases with time in any given storage condition. Where negatives are used within a week or two after processing, shrinkage caused by aging is of little practical importance unless subjected to extremes of climatic conditions. Over longer periods of time, the amount of shrinkage depends on the composition of the particular film; for example, the residual solvent content of the base. Heat accelerates all three types of permanent shrinkage listed above, so that elevated storage temperatures (over 90°F) should be avoided. Both extremes of relative humidity may result in permanent film shrinkage. Low relative humidity causes greater contraction of the emulsion, increasing plastic flow shrinkage. On the other hand, high relative humidity facilitates escape of any residual solvent which may be present. For these reasons, film should be stored at approximately 70° to 80°F and 40% to 50% R.H. This will minimize shrinkage due to aging.

CELLULOSE-ESTER BASE FILMS

The term "acetate" base is commonly used to designate film base made of cellulose acetate butyrate or cellulose triacetate. The film base is cast from solutions of the materials in a solvent. A small amount of this solvent remains in the base. The gradual escape of the solvent during aging is one possible cause of shrinkage.

Domestic production of cellulose-ester film bases is confined primarily to casting techniques; however, the resins can be extruded to produce satisfactory films for emulsion coating.

Dimensional-Change Properties of Cellulose-Ester Base Films. The dimensional-change properties of these films are given in the accompanying table. The values for the different acetate films vary somewhat depending on the thickness of the base, the particular emulsion used, and other factors. The reversible size-changes of acetate-base films are more likely to be caused by humidity than by temperature. This is partly because of the magnitude of the coefficients involved, and partly because the relative humidity of most shops and laboratories is more apt to vary widely than the temperature.

Portrait and commercial films on heavy base exhibit only moderate shrinkage on aging as long as the storage relative humidity does not exceed 60% for an extended period of time. Long storage at high relative humidities can result in shrinkage up to 1%.

Lith-type films on standard thickness acetate base have quite low aging shrinkage properties under moderate storage conditions. If stored for a year or more at relative humidities above 60%, a shrinkage of .5% to .7% can result. These films have good uniaxialism, that is, their properties are nearly the same in both length and width directions of the sheet. This is a desirable characteristic for map reproduction work. The dimensional stability of thin base films is not quite as good as that of standard thickness acetate base.

POLYSTYRENE-BASE FILM

Polystyrene base (P.B.) films offer unusual advantage where size holding is of critical importance. This is shown in the accompanying table. Polystyrene is well known for its low moisture absorption. This gives these films a humidity expansion coefficient only one-third that of similar films on acetate base. However, its thermal coefficient is approximately the same as that of acetate film, so that temperature control is relatively more important than humidity control when using polystyrene film.

Dimensional Change Properties of Polystyrene-Base Films. Polystyrene base contains no solvent or plasticizer. This eliminates one of the three types of permanent shrinkage in film, mentioned earlier. Polystyrene base itself shows no change in size when put through photographic processing. However, polystyrene-base films do undergo small size changes in processing due to the complex effects of the photographic gelatin coating. If the room air is constant at some low relative humidity, the size change in processing is usually a swell of up to about .03%; if the room air is constant at some high relative humidity, the size change on processing is usually a shrinkage of up to about .03%. In a laboratory air conditioned at 70°F and 50% R.H., the processing shrinkage of P.B. film is nil, as indicated in the table. Polystyrene has a lower softening temperature than cellulose-ester film supports. As a result, its shrinkage may be excessive above about 120°F, although its actual softening temperature is around 200°F. Storage at 70°F to 80°F and 40% to 50% R.H. is recommended.

Additional Information on Polystyrene Base. Polystyrene base is made by melt extrusion. For plastics manufactured in this way, its physical and optical quality is excellent. It is clear and transparent, and has relatively few defects. However, it should not be expected to be the equal of cast acetate-base in optical perfection or thickness uniformity. It is comparable to acetate base in strength and flexibility, but has less resistance to tearing.

FILM HANDLING SUGGESTIONS TO MINIMIZE ITS SIZE CHANGES

Where the film user cannot prevent large variations in atmospheric conditions, size changes can be greatly minimized by attention to handling details. Some change in moisture content of the unexposed film may occur depending on the storage conditions, manufacturer's packing specifications, etc. It is unlikely that the film will be in equilibrium with the workroom air. Where the utmost in dimensional stability is required, the film should be conditioned to the air of the workroom by hanging up individual sheets in the dark for approximately one hour before exposure. Gentle circulation of air is beneficial. If the film is reconditioned in the same atmosphere after processing, dimensional changes caused by changing humidity will be reduced.

Dimensional-Change Requirements in Color Work. In color work, a moderate amount of dimensional change is often permissible provided that all color separations change exactly the same amount. In such cases, it is important that each sheet of film be treated in exactly the same manner from the moment the original package is opened. It is desirable for the conditions in the workroom to be similar to those in the storage room. If the relative humidity of the workroom is either low or high, the films should each be conditioned to room air before exposure, as described above.

Well-Controlled Air-Conditioning is Recommended. Well-controlled air-conditioning for laboratories and workrooms is highly recommended. A temperature of 70° to 75°F and a relative humidity of 40% to 50% are most satisfactory. Too-low humidity should be avoided as it increases the possibility of static. If the film becomes electrified, dust will adhere and spots will appear after the film is exposed and developed. Too-high humidity (over 60%) is to be avoided because of the danger of mold and other moisture defects, as well as higher shrinkage of acetate film.

Film	Dimensional Change in Percent							
	Portrait and Commercial Films		Lithographic Films					
Type of base	Cellulose Acetate Butyrate		Cellulose Acetate Butyrate		Cellulose Triacetate		Polystyrene	
Nominal base thickness, in.	0.0083		0.0053		0.0033		0.005	
Coating Directions**	Length	Width	Length	Width	Length	Width	Length	Width
Humidity Expansion per 10% R.H. (Measured between 20% and 70% R.H. at 70 F.)	0.06	0.08	0.06	0.07	0.07	0.09	0.02	0.02
Thermal Expansion per 10 F. (Measured between 0 F. and 100 F. at 50% R.H.)	0.035	0.045	0.035	0.04	0.03	0.04	0.035	0.035
Processing Shrinkage (Measured at 70 F and 50% R.H.)	0.10	0.12	0.02	0.03	0.05	0.03	0.01	0.01
Aging Shrinkage*** 1 year at 78 F., 60% R.H. 1 month at 90 F., 90% R.H.	0.15 0.20	0.20 0.30	0.03 0.18	0.04 0.20	0.07 0.25	0.05 0.30	0.07 0.03	0.07 0.03

*These values were obtained under carefully standardized laboratory conditions and may vary slightly depending on the departure from these test conditions.
**Sheet film is sometimes cut along and sometimes across the roll, but all sheets in the same box are cut the same way.
***The figures for aging shrinkage include processing shrinkage and are for film freely exposed to circulating air.

Average dimensional change values for cellulose ester and polystyrene film.

DIMENSIONAL STABILITY OF DU PONT "CRONAR" BASED FILMS

"Cronar" ® polyester photographic film-based films have excellent size holding properties, and are only slightly affected by changes in relative humidity and temperature.

While not offered as an unqualified replacement for glass, "Cronar" based films may be used instead of glass for many applications where atmospheric conditions would rule out ordinary flexible bases.

Since the "Cronar" base contains neither solvents nor plasticizers, aging changes in the base itself will be negligible, and "Cronar" based films have excellent long term storage characteristics. In normal shop operations no particular handling precautions will be necessary. But when extremely accurate film registration is required the following suggestions may be found useful:

1. Maintain storage, exposing, stripping and plate exposure areas at the same relative humidity and temperature insofar as possible.

2. Break the seal on fresh boxes of film 24-48 hours before use and store in the working area to allow films to seek the room relative humidity and temperature equilibrium.

3. Allow individual sheets to condition in the darkroom for at least twenty minutes before exposure in order to come to room equilibrium.

4. Handle all films of a set together.

5. Dry processed films quickly for most accurate register. Squeegee film surface and dry in circulating warm air at 100°-125° F. for optimum results.

6. Allow processed films to condition at room temperature for at least two hours before further use. This permits all films in a set to become thoroughly dry and avoids usage of films before equilibrium is reached.

7. Store processed film sets together.

8. Note that season to season relative humidity changes are substantial in unconditioned shops. Return of stored processed films to original size can be obtained in such cases by conditioning them back to the relative humidity and temperature under which they were first used.

PHOTOGRAPHIC PROPERTIES

The photographic properties of a film or plate determine the type of image we get after exposure and processing. If we know what type of image is needed for a particular purpose, we can select the proper film or plate to do the job. Specifying such properties as speed, contrast, and color sensitivity usually narrows the choice of material to a very few possibilities. The first consideration in the choice of a photographic film or plate is usually the color sensitivity needed. In most cases, this is primarily a choice between the materials for use in black-and-white reproduction, on the one hand, and those for use in color reproduction, on the other. The former have sensitivity to a few colors of light, while many of the latter are sensitive to all colors.

COLOR SENSITIVITY AND TYPES OF SENSITIZING

All photographic emulsions are sensitive to blue, violet, and the invisible ultraviolet light. For many applications, this sensitivity is not enough. The photographic emulsions used in photomechanical color reproduction must be capable of recording densities for the broader range of colors which the human eye can see — that is, the greens, yellows, oranges, and reds. During manufacture, dyes are added which make the emulsions sensitive to these other colors.

Wedge Spectrograms and Their Interpretation. The color sensitivity of each film or plate is indicated by the "wedge spectrogram." These are positive prints made from the original spectrograms. In these diagrams, the height of the white patch indicates the relative sensitivity of the film or plate to the various colors. The diagrams would be more spectacular if we printed the actual colors in the background. Our spectrograms would then look like a slice from a rainbow with the violet, at the left, grading into blue, the blue into green, the green into yellow, orange, and finally, red at the right end. We could then see at a glance the height of each color. This is rather difficult, so we have compromised by labeling the general areas of the spectrum so that we can interpret the diagrams more easily. The lens system used in making wedge spectrograms will not transmit ultraviolet light. For this reason, all of these

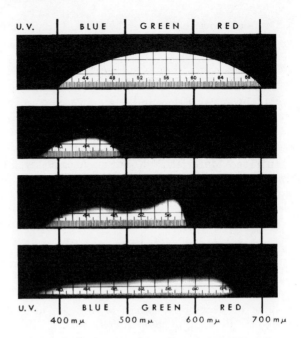

Wedge spectrograms showing: Top—sensitivity of the human eye; Second—Sensitivity range of colorblind materials; Third—Sensitivity of orthochromatic materials; Bottom—Sensitivity range of panchromatic materials.

spectrograms show a low sensitivity in this area. This causes little difficulty, because this light is not transmitted by process lenses either and can be ignored in all ordinary work. We also show wedge spectrograms of four types of film sensitizing, and, for comparison, the sensitivity of the human eye approximately as it would appear if we would make a similar wedge spectrogram of it.

The Role of the Light Used in Making Wedge Spectrograms. Wedge spectrograms depend on the composition of the light used in making the exposure. For example, if the light source gave off no blue light, the spectrogram could not indicate any sensitivity in the blue region, even though the film was sensitive to blue light. The spectrogram, then, shows the response of a particular photographic material to a particular light source — the one used in making the spectrogram. A general picture of the overall sensitivity of the film or plate can be obtained by making a spectrogram with a light source which contains all or most of the visible colors of light. The white-flame arc is such a light source commonly used in the graphic arts industry, and for this reason most spectrograms are made with such light. Spectrograms are made with tungsten light for those films with which tungsten light is commonly used. It should be noted that wedge spectrograms give no indication of film speed — only relative color sensitivity.

Blue-Sensitive Photographic Materials. Blue-sensitive photographic materials record high negative densities for blue areas of the original and, in the final reproduction, render blues very light and reds, yellows, and greens very dark. They are very useful in such specialized work as copying black-and-white photographs.

Orthochromatic Films and Plates. Orthochromatic films and plates are not sensitive to red light and therefore render reds as very dark when reproduced. These materials are normally faster than blue-sensitive materials because they are sensitive to a wider range of colors.

Panchromatic Films and Plates. Panchromatic films and plates are sensitive to all visible colors, as well as ultraviolet. They, therefore, give excellent monochromatic rendering of colored copy.

Infrared Materials. Infrared materials possess a particularly high sensitivity to infrared radiation. Their principal use in photomechanical reproduction is for making black-printer negatives.

FILTERS

A filter is a device which transmits light of certain colors while it absorbs light of other colors. The most common types are thin sheets or disks of gelatin or glass placed in front of the lens of the camera or in a slot in the lens mounting. By using the proper filters, we can "filter out" or reduce selected colors of light from a multicolored object. Our photograph will then record only the colors transmitted by the filter. Kodak Wratten filters in the form of dyed gelatin sheets are used extensively in graphic arts photography because of their consistently high quality.

Filters Do Not Change the Color of Light. A filter never "changes" the color of light. It can only allow a part of some colors to pass through and stop other colors. A "red" filter appears to be red because it transmits red light to the eye and absorbs most other colors. This is shown in the accompanying illustration. All filters absorb some of the light which strikes them, making necessary longer exposures than when no filter is used under the same conditions of illumination.

Filter Factors and Filter Ratios. There are two basic uses of filters in photomechanical work. In one, filters are used to emphasize tonal areas in making black-and-white reproductions from colored or soiled copy. In the other use, filters are used in making color reproductions from color copy.

Color Separation Filters. In the latter case, the original is photographed successively through each of three "color-separation" filters. The three black-and-white negatives obtained are called "color-separation negatives" and are used in making the three printing plates which print the respective colors on the paper. (A fourth plate is usually added — the black-printer — to add density to the dark areas of the picture.)

Filter Factors and Filter Ratios Require Different Exposure Calculation Methods. Each of the above two uses of filters requires a separate method of calculating the correct exposure when using a filter. The first is based on filter factors and the second on filter ratios.

The Filter Factor. The filter factor, expressed in a number, such as 1.5 or 2, indicates the number of times the exposure must be increased when the filter is used, compared to the exposure under the same conditions with no filter.

The Filter Ratio. The filter ratio is more useful for color-separation work. The correct exposure for the red filter (Kodak Wratten No. 25) is first determined by trial or by the use of the exposure index and a meter. The correct exposures for the other separation filters can then be calculated directly by multiplying this red filter exposure by the appropriate filter ratio for each of the other filters. For color-separation work, filter ratios are determined for negatives developed to equal contrast and are corrected for reciprocity effects.

Specially selected Wratten gelatin filters are now available for critical photomechanical work. These filters are designated "Kodak Wratten Photomechanical Filters, PM8, PM23A, PM25, PM29, PM33, PM47, PM47B, PM58, PM61, PM85B, and PM96, (.60 and 1.00 densities only)." They are particularly useful in cases where partial exposures are to be made through each of several filters, as in the split-filter method of making a black printer.

SAFELIGHT COLOR AND SAFETY

Any photographic material will fog if left long enough under safelight illumination. This is not necessarily because the safelight transmits any light that it should not, but because even blue-sensitive materials have some sensitivity to green, yellow, and red light. This sensitivity is not sufficient to be useful in picture taking, but it is enough to cause fog, or veiling, with prolonged exposure under a safelight.

Darkroom Illumination. Darkrooms used for photomechanical work should have as high a degree of illumination as is consistent with the type of materials being processed in them. It is the function of a safelight to transmit a maximum of the visible light to which the negative material is the least sensitive. If the safelight is chosen carefully and used wisely, this total illumination level can often be sufficiently high for very comfortable vision. For example, a negative material, such as ortho litho film,

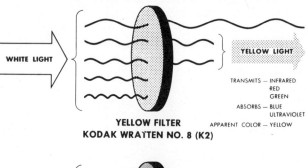

WHITE LIGHT

YELLOW LIGHT

TRANSMITS — INFRARED
RED
GREEN
ABSORBS — BLUE
ULTRAVIOLET
APPARENT COLOR — YELLOW

**YELLOW FILTER
KODAK WRATTEN NO. 8 (K2)**

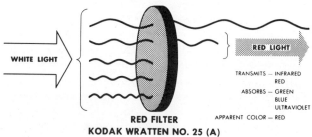

WHITE LIGHT

RED LIGHT

TRANSMITS — INFRARED
RED
ABSORBS — GREEN
BLUE
ULTRAVIOLET
APPARENT COLOR — RED

**RED FILTER
KODAK WRATTEN NO. 25 (A)**

The action of a yellow and a red filter.

which is sensitive only to blue and green, can be handled briefly under a Kodak Safelight Filter, Wratten Series 1A (light red), without danger of fogging. *Caution:* Ruby bulbs should not be used, because many of them transmit some green light to which orthochromatic films and plates are sensitive.

Panchromatic Materials Must be Handled with Greatest Care. With panchromatic materials, which are sensitive to all colors of light, the safelight, if any, must be of a color to which the eye is most sensitive. It is preferable to work in complete darkness where at all possible, but a dark-green safelight, such as the Kodak Safelight

Filter, Wratten Series 3, can be used if the printed precautions furnished with each package of panchromatic material are observed.

Bulbs to be Used for Direct and for Indirect Illumination. With direct illumination, where the light from the bulb shines directly through the safelight to the working space, a 15-watt bulb should be used in the safelight lamp at a distance of no less than 4 feet. With indirect illumination, where the light is reflected from a matte white surface inside or outside the safelight, a 25-watt bulb can be used at 4 feet. Note that, even with lights used as described, a safelight is "safe" for only a limited time.

A gray scale and the corresponding tones in a picture.

Overexposure to Safelight Can Cause Fogging. Under these conditions, materials can be handled for 30 seconds while dry, and for longer when in the developer. The absence of any fog in clear areas of the film does not prove that a safelight is safe, since overexposure to a safelight has an effect on halftone dots which is not readily noticeable. A safelight exposure which is insufficient to produce fog in clear areas of the film will frequently cause damage to halftone dots when added to the halftone-image exposure. The size of a halftone dot is determined by the amount of exposure it receives, and the slight addition of an excessive safelight exposure can increase the size of the dots markedly and cause a fog in the areas between.

EMULSION CONTRAST AND THE CHARACTERISTIC CURVE

"Contrast" is a photographic term which refers to the separation of the tones in a picture or a negative. We are discussing contrast when we say that a negative looks "flat" or "soft," or that it looks "contrasty" or "hard." In photomechanical work, where some loss in tones must be accepted because of the limitations of the printing process, we frequently refer to the contrast in particular portions of the scale of a picture as the "shadow contrast," "middletone contrast," and "highlight contrast." (Contrast should not be confused with "density range," which is the difference between the maximum and minimum densities of a picture or negative.)

Indicating Contrast of Photographic Materials. The contrast of film or plates — that is, their tendency to produce pictures of high or low contrast — can best be indicated by their characteristic curves. The curve for each film and plate commonly used in photomechanical work is furnished by the film manufacturer and available through film dealers.

The characteristic curve is a curve or line which shows how the film can be expected to react when it is used as recommended. Actually, it shows how much density will be recorded (how much blackening will take place) for the exposure corresponding to each tone in the original subject or picture being photographed. The shape of the characteristic curve is the key to the type of image obtainable from the film or plate. The curve indicates whether or not a particular material will do the job at hand. Examining curves is easier than making trial exposures.

Comparing Film Characteristics by Comparing Pictures. One way to compare the characteristics of films would be to photograph the same picture with each film and compare the effect, on the films, of each tone in the picture. We could select a typical picture like the one in our illustration and select a series of tones from the picture to use in the comparison.

The Gray Scale. Here, then, is a series of tones which can represent a picture and which has a uniform series of density steps of a size that can be easily seen and measured.

Comparing Films by the Use of Gray Scales. If we use this gray scale as our copy and photograph it with a separation negative film, for example, we will get, after proper processing, a negative which looks much like the original in reverse — that is, each of the steps of the original will be recorded as a distinct density. By measuring with a densitometer the density of each step of the negative, recording it on a graph, and then drawing a line through the points, we get our curve as shown below.

The Numbering of Gray Scale Steps. Since we started with a gray scale, of which each step represents a uniform density increase, we can merely number the steps and record their densities above the evenly spaced numbers on the horizontal scale (let's say, one every half-inch).

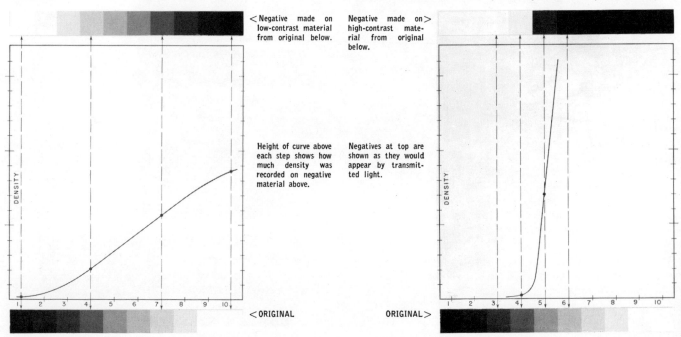

Characteristic curves of low and high contrast materials.

Above each of these points on the horizontal scale, we place a point at a height which corresponds to the density on the negative exposed from that particular step. A scale of densities is marked on the vertical edge to help us place these points.

The Characteristic Curve of High Contrast Material. We now get a characteristic curve of a typical high-contrast "line and halftone" material, so called because of the steep curve indicating a sharp jump from low to high density as a result of a slight increase in exposure. We need that sharp jump in density to give clean edges on lines and halftone dots. When this type of film or plate is used behind a halftone screen, little or no density is recorded in the areas shielded by the opaque areas of the screen, while a maximum density is recorded behind the center of the screen opening, if at least the critical amount of light is passing through. More light passing through the screen opening causes the jump in density to take place farther from the center of the opening in all directions, and a larger dot results. The size of each dot therefore depends on the amount of light coming through each screen opening, and a pattern of dots of varying size is formed. This is the halftone pattern.

The Gamma. In order to have a numerical value to represent contrast, the steepness of the curve — at least the straight-line portion of it — is measured and is known as "gamma." Thus a material developed to a high contrast can be represented by a steep curve and will be said to have a "high gamma."

EFFECT OF DEVELOPMENT ON CONTRAST

The contrast of continuous-tone materials increases with an increase in development time and can be controlled satisfactorily to give great flexibility to photographic processes and techniques. The increase of the contrast with development time of continuous-tone films and plates in the recommended developers is shown by the "time-gamma" curves in the data sheets available from dealers. Strictly speaking, gamma is the slope of the straight-line part of the characteristic curve.

The Effect of Temperature and Agitation on Contrast. Contrast for a given development time increases with increasing temperature up to the point where fogging begins to reduce contrast, particularly in the low-density areas of a negative. The contrast for a given development time is also increased by agitation during development which increases the rate of development.

The Effect of Developers on Contrast. Highly concentrated and active developers develop more rapidly and produce an image of higher contrast than developers of the softer and slower-working types. A fresh developer solution works faster and, for a given development time, will produce images of somewhat higher contrast than a partly exhausted solution.

The Development Characteristics of Different Materials Are Different. The development characteristics of litho materials are rather different from those of the continuous-tone products. Litho materials are nearly al-

ways developed to their maximum contrast. With litho materials, an increase in effective emulsion speed with an increase in development time can often be used to advantage; for example, minor errors in exposure can be compensated for by varying the development time. This is referred to as "development latitude." Beyond a development time of about 2½ minutes, however, there is less change in effective speed. Film exposed to non-critical line copy so that it develops in about 2½ minutes can be developed for a period of time after this and still produce a good negative. This characteristic is advantageous when several line negatives are processed together or whenever exact timing of development is difficult.

Time-Temperature Development Procedure Is Recommended. For the sake of consistent negative quality and shop efficiency, the use of the time-temperature development procedure is recommended except for materials of the litho type, for which development by inspection is usually desirable. In "time-temperature" development, adjust the temperature of the developer to the value recommended in the appropriate data sheet and develop for the recommended time. If it is necessary or desirable to work at some other temperature, the corresponding time is shown on the time-temperature development chart.

EXPOSURE

An underexposed continuous-tone negative is lower in both contrast and density than a fully exposed negative, and lacks shadow detail. A negative which is greatly overexposed is also lower than normal in contrast, but is high in density and lacks highlight detail. High-contrast line negatives lose sharpness and detail when overexposed. When underexposed, the backgrounds of line negatives are not sufficiently opaque. When printed, fine detail has a tendency to spread; thus, sharpness is lost.

Film Speeds and Exposure Indexes. The many types of photographic films and plates require different but quite definite amounts of exposure. Films and plates which require very little exposure are loosely termed "fast" and, conversely, those which require more exposure are called "slow." Since these terms are relative and by themselves, quite meaningless, films are assigned an "exposure index" — a number related to their "speed" and to aid in exposure calculations. The higher the number, the "faster" the material, and the less exposure it requires. These exposure indexes can be used with standard photoelectric exposure meters calibrated for their use.

Exposure Meters. There are two common types of photoelectric exposure meters in use. The "incident-light" type, which is held in the position of the subject being photographed, measures the light falling on the subject. With this instrument, the exposure indexes can be used directly according to directions supplied by the manufacturers of the meter. The "reflected-light" type, on the other hand, measures the amount of light reflected by the subject toward the camera.

Using the Kodak Neutral Test Card. Since these readings otherwise vary from subject to subject and with

Proper Exposure.　　　　　　　　Underexposure.　　　　　　　　Overexposure.

The effects of varying exposures when making continuous-tone positives. Notice the loss of highlight detail due to underexposure and the loss of shadow detail due to overexposure.

the operator's method of using the meter, and since the variations are difficult to interpret, a Kodak Neutral Test Card (18 percent gray side) should be placed at the copy-board position and the reflected-light measurement taken from this card. A matte white card can also be used, in which case the exposure should be five times the calculated exposure time. This procedure, in effect, converts the re-flected-light meter to incident-light use. The slight variations from this exposure, which are needed for different subjects, are small and can best be learned by experience. All the above calculations refer to continuous-tone work, and linework.

THE USE OF THE EXPOSURE INDEX FOR GRAPHIC ARTS PHOTOGRAPHY

Standard exposure indexes are calculated for lenses fo-cused at infinity. However, in photomechanical work, where the lens is usually focused for same-size copying or for some reduction or enlargement in that vicinity, the quantity of light falling on the film or plate varies greatly with change in image size and is considerably less than when the lens is focused at infinity. For this reason, the exposure calcu-lated by use of the exposure meter and the exposure index must be adjusted for the percentage of enlargement or re-duction. This adjustment can be calculated quickly and easily by use of the Kodak Copying Dataguide. The fol-lowing table indicates the amount by which the calculated exposure must be multiplied for a few typical situations.

For example, an exposure-meter reading taken from an 18 percent gray card at the copy position indicates an exposure of 5 seconds. If the reproduction is to be same size, the correct exposure is 5 x 4, or 20, seconds.

Screen Exposures. When a halftone screen is used in the camera, the light reaching the film is greatly reduced. For contact screens, the correct exposure time will be about 10 times the exposure calculated from the meter reading. For glass crossline screens, the factor is much higher, and variations in method of use make advisable a calculation of the factor by the user. This can be done by finding the ratio between a typically good screen-exposure time and a good line-exposure time.

Reproduction Size (% of original Size)	25%	50%	100% same size	150%	200%	300%
Multiply calculated exposure by	1.6	2.2	4.0	6.5	9.0	16.0

Section Five: Selecting Photo-Materials

The fundamental requirement in a film or plate for pho-tomechanical line work and screened halftone work is high contrast. In negatives of line work, dark lines will then be rendered as clear areas, and background areas as ex-tremely dense areas, even if the original copy has light or weak lines. In halftone work, the high contrast of the emulsion will produce sharp, crisp halftone dots. A fine-grain emulsion is also necessary so that the edges of lines and dots will not be ragged. Halftone dots must be of such quality that they can be altered in size by chemical means after development and still retain their opacity.

Our presentation is divided into the following four subjects: (1) Color-sensitized materials, (2) Stripping materials, (3) Direct positive materials, and (4) Storage and care of films and plates. Each of these is presented in the following.

COLOR-SENSITIZED MATERIALS

For color copy, it is necessary to use a color-sensitized material which can record colors in their relative black-and-white tone values. Although emulsions with extreme contrast are lower in speed than continuous-tone materials, high film and plate speed is important in reducing costs by saving time. Of equal importance, the films and plates must be physically stable to withstand handling and rapid drying. They must dry flat for ease in handling under production conditions.

Each of the many photographic materials has characteristics which meet specific needs. In order to select the material best suited to a particular job, the information sheets provided by the manufacturers of photographic materials should be consulted.

STRIPPING MATERIALS

Kodak stripping films are unlike other photographic materials. Their construction allows the image-bearing layer to be readily removed, or "stripped," from the support layer, or base, as indicated in our diagram. This "stripping" procedure permits a lateral reversal of the image on the metal printing surface in letterpress printing, necessary for obtaining a right-reading image in the final reproduction.

The thin membrane of stripping film.

The Construction of Stripping Films. As can be seen from the diagram, stripping films contain more layers than do ordinary films. A thin adhesive layer, which softens in water, allows the image-bearing layer to be removed. The very thin support layer, or "skin," serves as a stable support for the emulsion layer while it is being stripped. After stripping (which usually includes lateral reversal), this tough thin layer serves as protection for the emulsion. It is so thin that it does not degrade the definition of the image when printing on metal. The procedures recommended for applying the stripping-film membrane to glass or acetate are given in the instructions supplied with the film.

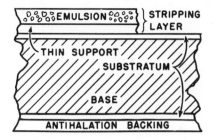

Diagrammatic cross section of stripping film.

Use of Hardener in Fixing Stripping Film. Proper handling of stripping film is quite important for the craftsman doing complicated insert work. Improperly hardened stripping film causes such difficulties as poor adhesion and curling of the edges. Fresh baths of rapid liquid fixer with hardener are quite satisfactory when used in accordance with instructions. The use of an acetic acid stop bath materially prolongs the useful life of a fixing bath. A 10-second rinse in 3 to 5 percent acetic acid just prior to wet stripping usually aids in producing better adhesion between the film and glass plate.

Causes of Stripping Troubles and Their Remedies. During periods of high relative humidity or when the temperature of tap water is increased, stripping troubles usually increase, especially if the fixing bath is not fresh. It is sometimes desirable to add extra hardener to the bath, particularly in the summer, when the relative humidity is high. In the winter, it may be desirable to reduce the quantity of hardener in the bath. The two solution rapid liquid fixer with hardener is ideal because it is rapid in action and the amount of hardener can be easily controlled. The addition of one to two extra ounces of hardener solution to one gallon of fixing-bath solution will normally overcome any problems caused by insufficient hardening action. Too much hardening is to be avoided because this causes difficulties in laying the stripping skin down flat.

Use of Stripping Film Cement. When stripping film is used in the normal manner for lateral reversal, the emulsion acts as an adhesive to hold the film negative in place. When the support side of the stripping film is to be in contact with the glass, however, stripping film cement should be applied to the glass, the film fitted into place, and a little of the cement spread in a thin coat around the edges of the cut film. As an extra precaution, some operators prefer to place an extra "skin" of the clear stripping layer over the negative when working in this manner. The use of stripping film cement is quite advantageous in assuring position holding in all complex stripping and inserting jobs. By simply spreading a thin coat of this material around the edges of all the pieces of film after they have been fitted into place, a craftsman can be sure the film will stay flat.

Stripping Films in Photolithography. Stripping films were originally manufactured for the photoengraving trade, but have been found to be quite useful and adaptable in photolithography. Many photolithographers use stripping techniques similar to those employed by photoengravers. Production can often be facilitated by stripping negatives or positives of complicated combination work into glass, heavy sheet acetate, vinylite, or regular film base. The use of stripping film cement is recommended for these procedures. Easy lateral image reversal is obtained simply by "flopping" the negatives, and "normal" prints are made on metal printing plates without image reversal. Either method produces high-quality results, the film staying firmly in place with either emulsion or base side down on the glass or acetate.

DIRECT POSITIVE MATERIALS

With direct positive materials, a negative can be made directly from a negative — or a positive from a positive. This immediately makes practical a large number of operations in multiple-negative work and step-and-repeat operations.

Direct positive materials can be used to make outline effects on lettering and line work in a few simple steps.

With direct positive materials, portions of a single negative can be reversed so that positive and negative combinations and effects can be combined on the same sheet of film without stripping.

Direct positive materials make possible such effects as solid, clear or tint lettering on halftone backgrounds, halftone tint joined to halftone tint with clean division between the two, clear or solid areas set in halftone-tint backgrounds, and many more — all without stripping.

With direct positive materials, reflex copies can be made of drawings, and printed matter without the use of a camera or intermediate negative.

Direct positive materials make it a simple matter to produce blue-key positives instead of the usual blue-key negatives. Stripping to positive keys is easier and more accurate than stripping to negative keys.

Working with Direct Positive Materials. If direct positive materials are developed without exposure, a high even density will result. If however, the material is exposed to strong yellow light before development, this density will be removed. Furthermore, the density removed by the yellow light can be restored by re-exposing to strong white light, and again removed by strong yellow light. All these exposures must, of course, be made before the film is developed.

Remember, the basic principle in using direct positive material is: Yellow light removes density; White light adds density.

Making a Laterally Reversed Duplicate. To make a laterally reversed duplicate which can be either a negative or a positive on direct positive film (thin base), the following steps are necessary:

Step One. Working in subdued room illumination, place a sheet of direct positive in a printing frame with the negative to be reproduced just as is done when making any normal photographic contact print.

Step Two. Between the printing frame and the light source, hang a piece of yellow sheeting. For convenience in handling, the sheeting can be mounted on a light wooden frame equipped with hooks for suspending it in position. If the yellow sheeting is hung an inch or more from the glass of the printing frame, accumulated dirt specks or scratches will not image on the film.

Step Three. Expose for about 2 minutes to white-flame carbon arc light (3000 foot-candles), such as that from a 35-ampere arc at about 3 feet. The exposure can be made to tungsten light of about 6000 foot-candles for 1 minute. Four No. 2 reflector-type photofloods mounted so that their bases are at the corners of a 6-inch square will give adequate exposure at a distance of about 2 feet. If only one lamp is used, the exposure will be about 4 minutes. Evenness can be improved by having the lamp suspended above the printing frame and allowing it to swing slightly during exposure.

Step Four. Develop the film for 2 minutes with continuous agitation in litho developer (undiluted) at 68°F. (When making halftone duplicates, where it is necessary to reproduce the complete tone range, use fine line developer.)

Step Five. Rinse in a stop bath at 65° to 70°F (18° to 21°C) for 15 seconds. These baths check development instantly, provided the acid has not been neutralized. They also tend to prevent stains and streaks in the film when it is immersed in the fixing bath.

Step Six. Fix at 65° to 70°F (18° to 21°C) for 3 to 5 minutes.

Step Seven. Wash about 10 minutes in an adequate supply of running water. Wipe the surface carefully with a chamois or a viscose sponge before drying.

Making Uniform Halftone Tints on Direct Positive Film. Since direct positive will develop to a uniform high density (about 6.0) before exposure, it can be used in making tints with high-density sharp dots which are free from pinholes. Use a gray contact screen or a magenta contact screen. (The exposure is more critical on the latter.) Place the screen in contact with the emulsion-side of the film in a vacuum printing frame and expose through yellow sheeting. The percent dot size of the tint will, of course, vary with the exposure; as the exposure is increased, the dots will become smaller. The following will serve as a guide: Using a gray contact screen and a 35-ampere arc at 3 feet:

4-minute exposure — 80 percent dot
6-minute exposure — 50 percent dot
12-minute exposure — 20 percent dot

Normal Positive-Negative Work. Direct positive materials are the right choice when it is desired to use a film or plate that can be handled in normal room illumination for making a negative from a positive, or a positive from a negative. The following procedure can be used: first, flash the direct positive with an all-over yellow-light exposure for 2 minutes with a 35 ampere arc at 3 feet and then give a white-light image exposure for 5 seconds using contact-printing methods.

The laterally reversed duplicating technique and the normal positive-negative procedure can both be used when exposing from the same original to give a combination result.

Negative and Positive on the Same Film. By a simple masking operation, part of a negative can be printed as a negative and other parts as a positive. For example:

(1) Place an opaque paper or film mask over those parts of the image which are to be printed as a positive. (2) Print the remainder of the negative with yellow light. (3) Remove the negative, cover the areas just exposed, and uncover the area to be printed as a positive. (4) Give this "positive area" a 2-minute flash exposure to yellow light. (5) Replace the negative and expose this same area for 5 seconds to white light. (6) Process as usual.

This entire operation can be carried out easily if the Autopositive Film is fastened to a base, such as a piece of pressboard or acetate sheet, by means of a few pieces of cellulose tape. Each mask is then placed in register and taped on one edge to serve as a hinge. By hinging these masks and the negative along different edges of the direct positive film, any of them can positioned immediately. A register frame can be used to maintain register between the various masks and negatives.

The masks may, of course, be lettering or line images on a litho film. By this means, clear or black lettering or other line work, can be superimposed on a previously exposed area. Just remember that a 2-minute yellow-light exposure will remove density and a 5-second white-light exposure will restore the density if a single 35-ampere arc is used at 3 feet. *Note:* When a white-light exposure has been added to the original density, an increased amount of yellow exposure is necessary to remove the density.

Outline Effects. From a line negative containing lettering, for example, a negative can be made on Autopositive Film which has a fine clear line or a dark line at the edges of the letters. A line negative will produce lines on the outside of the edges, and a line positive will produce lines on the inside of the edges. Negatives with clear lines can be produced as follows: (1) Yellow-light exposure through the line negative; (2) White-light exposure through the line negative.

A dark outline on a clear background can be made as follows: (1) Uniform yellow-light flash exposure; (2) White-light exposure through the negative; (3) Yellow-light exposure through the negative.

The proportion of white and yellow light must be adjusted to retain the lines and maintain the proper background density. Wider lines can be produced if a spacer (a piece of clear, fixed-out film or a piece of sheet acetate) is placed between the negative and the film.

Intermediates for Making Positive Blue Keys. Usual practice in making blue-key plates for stripping guides in color work is to make a positive from the black-printer negative, and from this print, three blue-key negatives.

Stripping negatives to a blue-key positive is much easier and more accurate. By using direct positive film or plates, a laterally reversed duplicate negative can be made from black-printer negative. From this, the three blue-key positives are made.

Reflex Copying. Line work or typematter on paper can be copied by the reflex method. Place the direct positive film face down on the image side of the original and give a yellow-light exposure through the base of the film.

A piece of clear glass can be used to maintain contact between the film and the original. Expose through yellow sheeting, for 90 seconds with one 35-ampere arc at 3 feet or for 45 seconds with four No. 2 reflector-type photofloods at 2 feet.

Eliminating Newton's Rings. Newton's rings are irregular curved lines which frequently appear in contact-printing operations, particularly when film base comes in contact with the glass of the printing frame. These are caused by interference between light rays reflected from the two surfaces which are touching each other. The best remedy for this difficulty is to use some anti-offset spray in a small polyethylene "squeeze bottle" with a short tube projecting. The end of the tube should have a minute opening, only a few thousandths of an inch in diameter. In the bottle is placed about ½ inch of some powder used for preventing offset on the delivery end of printing presses. When applying the powder, the bottle is first shaken and then squeezed. The resulting spray of powder should be hardly visible. It is usually effective if applied to any one of the surfaces involved.

STORAGE AND CARE OF FILMS AND PLATES

To assure the maintenance of consistent processing results, all photographic materials should be stored under fairly constant conditions. Temperatures from 70° to 75°F and relative humidities between 40 and 50 percent are recommended. Moderate temperature with low relative humidity is preferred to low temperature with high relative humidity. Films and plates should always be stored away from chemical mixing rooms, industrial gases, x-rays, and radioactive materials.

Heat Protection of Photographic Materials. The packages in which sensitized photographic materials for the graphic arts are supplied provide adequate protection to withstand normal handling and the relative humidities commonly encountered in temperate climates. In general, they are not intended to withstand long periods of high relative humidities. The packages are not heatproof and should not be placed near steampipes or other sources of heat, or be left on top floors of uninsulated buildings or in other places where they might be subjected to excessive heat.

Refrigerated Storage and Care of Refrigerated Photographic Materials. During summer heat in temperate or tropical zones, refrigerated storage is recommended for unopened packages of films or plates, particularly infrared and very fast film and plates. To avoid condensation on the cold surfaces of these materials, packages which have been kept in cold storage should be removed to a warmer location several hours (preferably 24 hours) before they are to be opened for use. Packages of films or plates which have been opened should not be placed in refrigerators, because the high humidity will damage photographic materials in open packages.

Storage of Processed Films and Plates. Processed films and plates are best stored in dry, dust-free places away from harmful gases and chemicals. *They should not be stored, after processing, for long periods at high relative* *humidities* (*over 60 percent*). Film negatives should be filed in durable envelopes, plainly marked, in case further use of them is to be made. The envelope should be chemically inert, and the seam should be located along one side.

Plates can be stored conveniently in their original boxes placed on edge, rather than flat, so that any box can be removed from a shelf without first having to move plates piled on top.

Section Six: The Darkroom*

All darkrooms have somewhat the same layout and equipment within their walls. Processing of photographic materials requires the steps of development, stopping, fixing, and washing. Equipment such as ventilators, safelights, electrical fixtures, and entrances can be very nearly identical in darkrooms for professional, industrial, and photomechanical photography.

The greatest changes in darkrooms are necessitated primarily by the size of the materials handled and the required flow of work. The general physical requirements of a satisfactory darkroom are as follows: (1) The room must be lightproof. (2) Both "safe" and white-light illumination must be provided. (3) Trays or tanks must be available for holding processing solutions. (4) Running hot-and-cold water is needed. (5) An accurate thermometer and timer or clock are necessary. (6) A bench-top or wall viewing light should be available. (7) Storage space of the proper type is necessary for photographic materials and supplementary equipment. (8) A drying rack or cabinet will be found useful.

LAYOUT OF A PHOTOMECHANICAL DARKROOM

The essential characteristic of any good darkroom layout is usability. It is true that the existing structural members of a plant or building may restrict the usability of a proposed design. But in unrestricted situations, darkrooms of simple and useful design should be considered.

A well-planned and equipped darkroom.

Arrangements of Tanks and Trays. The necessary trays or tanks can be arranged along a wall, in a corner, or down the center of a room. However, the best arrangement is a straight line of trays or tanks along a wall. Suf-

* © Eastman Kodak, 1951.

ficient working space should be allowed, with aisles at least three feet wide. When planning the area to be used, two factors should be considered: (1) the amount of work to be done each day, and (2) the possibility of a future increase in the production load.

Layout For a Modern Combination Darkroom. Our illustration shows a modern combination darkroom of a simple, workable design. This has been laid out for movement of work from left to right, ending with the densi-

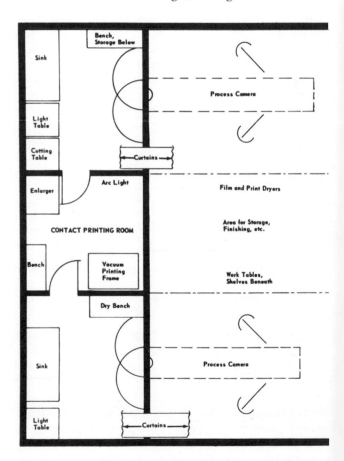

This layout was designed for two process cameras and darkrooms, with space for the possible addition of a third camera later. The contact-printing darkroom was placed between the process camera darkrooms so that it could be entered from either one.

tometer (for photomechanical work) on the bench at the far right. This plan can be reversed easily for those workers who prefer to work from right to left.

SIZE OF DARKROOMS

The size of the darkroom is directly dependent on the use to which that room is to be put. It is often found best to have two specialized darkrooms rather than one large universal room. For example, extra rooms may be feasible if a shop will do such work as contact printing and masking in its usual run of work.

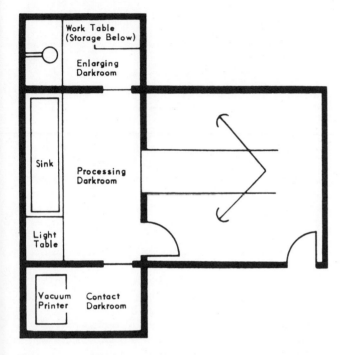

Layout for setting up a single 18-inch process camera and darkroom combination. The number of darkrooms depends on the space available. Process camera manufacturers can supply data on the space required for other camera sizes. The wall facing the easel, and the ceiling above the tracks, should be painted flat black to avoid "hot-spot" reflections on the copy.

Minimum Size. The minimum size for any photochemical darkroom is usually considered to be 6 feet by 8 feet. If equipment such as a darkroom-type camera is installed, this minimum should be increased to about 8 feet by 10 feet. If you want to do contact printing and to handle large plates, your darkroom area should be approximately 10 feet by 20 feet.

Planning of Proper Size. Rooms must be large enough to accommodate conveniently the maximum size film or plate likely to be handled and to enable adequate ventilation to be maintained. On the other hand, large rooms with unusable space serve only to waste time and effort of the operator. The important thing is, again, pre-planning.

DARKROOM EQUIPMENT

It is desirable to be able to enter and leave the darkroom without admitting any light. This is possible by the con-

struction of double doors or light locks. The walls of entrances and passageways should be painted with a dark, matte finish to prevent reflection of light around the baffle. Oftentimes two darkrooms can open into one light-locked passage.

The Open-Passage Entrance. The open-passage type of entrance is considered best because it provides both good ventilation and easy access. The latter is especially important when workers are carrying large films and plates. Like darkrooms themselves, the exact size of these entrances must depend somewhat on the size of the photographic materials used.

Double-Door Light Lock. When floor is space is at a premium, it may be necessary to use a double-door light lock. With this arrangement, one or both of the doors can be replaced by heavy single or double curtains. If two solid doors are used, it will be necessary to place a light-trapped vent in the wall of the passageway in order to relieve the changes in air pressure caused by opening and closing the doors. If several persons are to use a light lock, it is a good plan to install a warning light or buzzer which will operate when either door is open, thus reducing the possibility of both doors being opened at once.

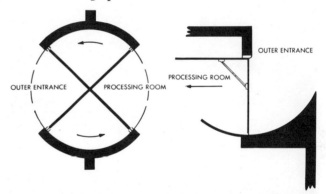

A revolving door can also be used as a light lock. The unit on the left is quite convenient, while the one on the right is a bit more cumbersome in use but takes up little floor space.

Darkroom Equipment. The selection of equipment is naturally a matter for each shop to consider in the light of other requirements. Well-built equipment will usually cost less in the long run, and all equipment should be selected with consideration of the maximum plate or film size to be handled.

Processing Sinks. Careful consideration must be given to the materials and construction of processing sinks. Improper choice of materials may result in corrosion of the material itself, and faulty fabrication may cause leaks and shorten the useful life of a sink. Many factors must be considered in selecting materials for the construction of processing sinks. These include resistance to the corrosive action of the solutions, mechanical durability, adaptability to fabrication, ease of cleaning, and appearance.

Processing sinks can be made of fiberglass, stainless steel, lead- or plastic-lined wood, stone, stoneware and cypress wood. In the Resources Section of this chapter, you find several makes of sinks presented. If you want to construct you own sink you should consult the Eastman Kodak booklet *Darkroom Construction*. There you find (on pages 10 to 12) diagrams and instructions for the making of various kinds of sinks.

Drainage Systems. Drainage systems can be fabricated by normal plumbing methods. However, for continued trouble-free service, it is best to use pipe, valves, and flanges made of stainless steel or Duriron. Stainless steel materials are available from several sources and Duriron materials are manufactured by the Duriron Company of Dayton, Ohio.

Care of Processing Sinks. The care of processing sinks consists largely of keeping them clean and repairing minor leaks. The type of material from which the sinks are constructed determines in many instances the best methods for cleaning and repairing.

Scouring powders can be used for cleaning lead, stone, wood, and stainless steel sinks. Citric acid can also be used for removing hard scale. A 10 percent solution is usually satisfactory, and can be prepared by dissolving one pound of citric acid crystals in approximately five quarts of water. This method should be followed by thorough rinsing with water.

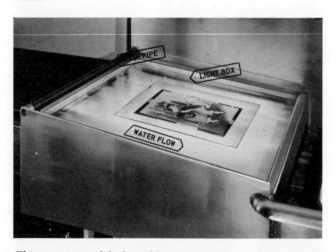

This waterproof light table incorporates a foot treadle by which the operator controls the flow of washing water.

Sink-Top Light Table. Extra sink-top space can usually be used to build-in a combination light table and dot-etching bench. It is most convenient to have this placed at the end of the sink so that the glass top, set in waterproof cement, can be sloped to drain into the sink. As shown in the illustration, frosted glass is installed below the clear glass to diffuse the light source. It is usually desirable to install a perforated waterpipe at the upper edge to supply washing and flushing water for negatives during reduction or etching and inspection. A foot-treadle type of valve for the wash water makes this arrangement even more convenient.

Tray Storage. General experience has shown that a vertical arrangement as illustrated is most convenient for tray storage. It permits easy access and at the same time allows wet trays to drain. Some workers prefer to have the

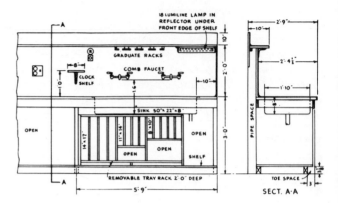

Particularly suitable plan for small and medium-sized darkroom.

lower portions of the vertical separators cut off so as to provide easier access and cleaning of the storage areas.

Water Temperature Controls. Accurate and consistent control of the conditions under which photographic materials are processed, particularly control of the temperature of the processing solutions, is desirable in all cases and is a necessity in photomechanical work and in work with color materials.

When only small quantities of photographic materials are to be processed, it is possible to get along with manual adjustment of temperature. For example, the drain of the darkroom sink can be fitted with a standpipe, and water from an ordinary mixing faucet can be allowed to overflow from the washing tank and surround processing tanks to the level of the standpipe. With such an arrangement, a thermometer placed in the water flow must be watched constantly to make sure that varying loads on the water-supply lines are not allowed to change the temperature of the mixture.

When appreciable quantities of sensitized materials must be handled on a production basis, however, a more accurate and dependable temperature-control system is almost a necessity. With such a system, mistakes and delays can be avoided, and savings in time and materials will quickly repay a reasonable investment in equipment.

Mixing Valves. Automatic, thermostatically controlled mixing valves provide the most compact and least expensive of the systems available for the control of water temperatures.

These valves operate by mixing warm and cold water to obtain the desired temperature. Therefore, the temperature of the cold water supply must, of course, be at least as low as and preferably lower than the temperature required for the mixture. In areas where the cold water during the summer months is warmer than the desired temperature, an auxiliary cooling system is necessary. This, in turn, necessitates a few additional fittings to permit switching the unit from the normal use of existing hot-and-cold water supplies to the use of cold and artificially cooled water. In winter months there will seldom be any necessity for a refrigerated water supply.

Temperature-Controlled Sinks. Several very satisfactory temperature-controlled processing sinks are now manufactured by graphic arts equipment concerns. There are two basic types. One type has a built-in refrigeration unit with cooling coils under the sink. This type maintains a shallow level of water at a constant temperature. The other type has no coils directly under the sink, but continuously circulates water through a built-in mechanical cooler at the required temperature. In the Resources Section of this chapter, you find several temperature-controlled sinks presented by their manufacturers.

Dry Bench. The dry bench is where sensitized goods are handled and stored. It should be located away from wet areas, such as sinks and chemical mixing benches. To provide storage space for supplies and accessories, a combination of drawers similar to the unit illustrated is recommended. A lightproof drawer in which to store opened packages of photographic materials can be built according to our diagram.

An integral wiring system might be desirable for such a unit. Three separate circuits are found in the bench. The convenience outlet with a switch above the bench provides an outlet for the various electrical devices, such as timers, clocks, and printing lamps. The other convenience outlet is controlled by the right-hand switch in the front center space. On the bench itself, a snap switch to control the

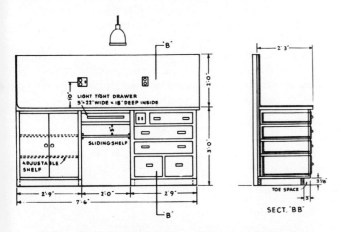

Suggested dimensions of a dry or work bench.

safelights is especially useful if a photographic enlarger is used, because it is easier to focus an enlarger without a safelight shining down on the easel.

Chemical Storage and Mixing. Chemicals and chemical solutions can be stored wherever it is relatively cool and dry. It is very necessary to keep powders away from open film and plate boxes. Space for bottled chemicals can be built into a sink unit.

Covering Bench-Tops. A linoleum covering is quite satisfactory for some sink and bench units. It is quite suitable for dry-bench work. If possible, it is desirable to carry the linoleum up on the back of the bench or sink to form a splash shield. A curved junction can be achieved by using 1½-inch cove molding under the linoleum where the bench joins the back of the bench or sink. This arrangement forms surfaces which are free of "dust catchers" and therefore easy to clean.

FLOOR COVERING

The choice of floor covering in a photographic darkroom presents several unusual problems. The ideal floor should have these qualities: resistance to corrosive substances, resistance to staining, watertight installation, durability, freedom from slipperiness, resiliency for foot comfort, and a suitable color. It is impossible to obtain all of these qualities in one material, but a compromise can be achieved by selecting a flooring that combines the most essential properties for your use. Of the various floor coverings available, the following two types stand out as highly desirable:

Ceramic Tiles. Ceramic tiles are available in several colors and types. The degree of vitrification and body density are important factors in the choice of ceramic tiles. A fully vitreous tile will absorb practically no moisture and is therefore easily cleaned. Most porcelain and natural clay tiles are impervious to dirt and liquids, and are non-staining, easily cleaned, and available in non-skid types. Semi-vitreous and non-vitreous tiles are not usually satisfactory because of their greater absorptivity for photographic solutions and chemicals.

Composition Tiles. Composition tiles are of many types and some are quite inexpensive. They are made of plastic, hard-rubber, asphalt, or synthetic resin and can be laid down over existing flooring, including wood. The asphalt tiles are usually the best for most installations because they are quite stain-resistant and have long-wearing properties. Hard-rubber and plastic tiles are usually satisfactory, but some types stain easily, so a certain amount of caution must be used in the selection of these materials. Synthetic-resin tiles are undesirable because they tend to absorb chemicals and therefore stain easily.

SAFELIGHTS

Darkrooms for efficient work should have as high a degree of illumination as is consistent with the safety of the types of materials being processed in those darkrooms. It is the function of a safelight to transmit a maximum of the visible light to which the negative material is the least sensitive. Safelights must be chosen carefully and used wisely. In this way, the total illumination level of the darkroom can often be sufficiently high for very comfortable vision. For example, a negative material such as Kodalith Ortha Film, Type 2, which is sensitive only to blue and green, can be handled in a relatively high illumination of red light without danger of fogging. For this particular example, a Kodak Safelight Filter, Wratten Series 1A, is recommended. *Caution: Ruby red bulbs should never be used, because, even though they look red, they often transmit light to which orthochromatic films and plates are sensitive.*

Working with Panchromatic Materials. With panchromatic materials, which are sensitive to all colors of light, it is preferable to work in complete darkness where at all possible. If a safelight is used, it must be of the color to which the eye is most sensitive, namely, green. A dark-green safelight such as the Kodak Safelight Filter, Wratten Series 3, is usable with panchromatic materials if the printed precautions furnished with each package of sensitized material are observed.

Safelight Colors. It is usually necessary to have several safelights and safelight filters for the different classes

KODAK SAFELIGHT FILTERS

Wratten Series No.	Color	For Use With:
OA	Greenish Yellow	Contact printing and enlarging papers.
OC	Light Amber	High-speed enlarging papers, including Kodak Polycontrast Papers.
1	Red	Blue-sensitive films and plates, such as Kodak Commercial Film and Kodak Lantern Slide Plates; Kodagraph Projection Paper.
1A	Light Red	Kodalith Ortho materials and Kodagraph Contact Papers.
2	Dark Red	Orthochromatic films and plates, Kodagraph Fast Projection Paper, and green-sensitive film for photoradiography.
3	Dark Green	Panchromatic films and plates
6B	Amber	X-ray film and blue-sensitive film for photoradiography.
7	Green	Infrared-sensitive films and plates. Not safe for orthochromatic materials.
8	Dark Yellow	Eastman Color Print Film, Type 5382.
10	Dark Amber	Kodak Ektacolor Paper; Kodak Ektacolor Print Film; Kodak Panalure Paper.

of photographic materials being used. The correct safelight filters are recommended in the manufacturers' direction or data sheets packed in each film package or box.

Kodak Safelight Filters have been specifically prepared and tested for exacting photographic use. Other materials may appear to have the same color as the tested safelight filter, but they may have a much greater photographic effect. The use of makeshift darkroom illumination is one of the surest ways of getting poor dot quality of halftones and poor tone rendition in continuous-tone images.

Safelight lamps are so constructed that it is a simple matter to change the safelight filters to suit the material being handled. As indicated in the table, a set of six different safelight filters for each lamp is sufficient to provide the optimum illumination for any type of sensitive material which might be used. When the safelight filters are not in use they can be stored in slotted racks located in a convenient position.

In the case of indirect-light boxes which are mounted near the ceiling for general illumination, however, it usually will be difficult to reach them to change the filters. In this case it is desirable to have two safelights, each fitted with one of the two most commonly used safelight filters, and each controlled by a separate switch.

Safety of Safelights. Any photographic material will fog if left long under safelight illumination. This is not because the safelight transmits any light which it should not, but because even non-color-sensitive materials have

some sensitivity to green, yellow, and red light. This sensitivity is not sufficient to be useful in picture taking, but it is enough to cause fog or veiling with prolonged exposure under a safelight. All Kodak Safelight Filters, when used with the recommended bulb and at the recommended distance, are safe for at least 30 seconds with the dry materials for which they are recommended, and for a longer time when the material is in the developer.

Testing Safety of Darkroom Lights. Since safelight exposure can decrease quality even without producing fog, a more sensitive test of the safelights must be used. When it is suspected that safelights are causing trouble, a simple but sensitive test can be made as follows:

a. Make a print from a typical negative on a whole sheet of the film or paper in question, using the printing method commonly employed. Use a border mask to produce an unexposed area around the image. No safelight should be used during this part of the test.

b. Now expose parts of the same sheet of film or paper to the safelight by covering successive areas of the film or paper for different lengths of time and keeping one area covered at all times. The test should be made where the material will be handled and developed, and with the safelight located where it is commonly used.

c. Process the film or print and notice the amount of safelight exposure which can be given without noticeable change in quality of the image or highlight dots.

In general, it will be found that an amount of safelight exposure which does not produce any fog in the border will show appreciable veiling of highlight dots and highlight areas in the print.

DRYING FACILITIES

In planning drying facilities, there are two general types of graphic arts films and plates which must be considered. Each dries at a different rate, and therefore the amount of drying equipment depends on the type of materials used. Films with thin emulsions, such as Ortho Litho Film, dry very quickly under almost any condition. Films and plates with thicker emulsions, such as Commercial Film and Separation Negative Plates and Films dry more slowly under normal darkroom conditions.

Electric Fans. For small-volume plants which process films with thin emulsions, the installation of a hot-air dryer is not usually justified. In this case, when drying is to be accelerated, a flow of air from an ordinary electric fan can be directed toward the film or plate. Large-volume plants using all types of photographic materials can, however, easily justify the expense of a hot-air dryer.

Prevention of Overheating. The most important consideration in planning facilities for drying films and plates is to preclude all possibility of overheating. Slightly warmed, freely circulating, dust-free air will dry photographic materials quickly enough for most purposes.

Hot-Air Dryers. The component parts of a hot-air dryer consist of one or more compartments for holding the films or plates, a fan, an air filter, and electric heating coils. These complete units are commercially available, but they

A film and plate drying cabinet of ample capacity. The drying air is cleaned by the filter on the left, heated by the lamps in the center, and circulated by the fan on the right.

can also be made by a woodworking shop. The drying unit illustrated is a home-made unit which is in daily satisfactory use. A less expensive unit can be made by assembling an electric fan and heating coils in a small cabinet through which clean air can be passed.

VENTILATION

Satisfactory ventilation of any darkroom is more complex than the ventilation of a room for comfort only. Naturally, the health and efficiency of the cameraman must be considered, but certain other elements directly affect the air in these rooms. For example, uncovered solutions increase the humidity in the room, processing solutions create slight odors, and drying cabinets give off heat.

Effects of Temperature and Humidity. When improperly controlled, the temperature and humidity of the air have adverse physiological effects on the worker as well as physical effects on photographic materials during handling and storage. For example, excessive humidity causes the body to perspire, and damp fingers will readily leave marks on dry films or plates. If the air is too dry, film is susceptible to static accumulations. In addition, lack of proper humidity causes the mucous membranes in the nasal passages of workers to become dry and the skin to become chapped.

Cleansing the Air. The incoming air should pass through suitable filters to remove dust particles. The air flow should be in sufficient volume to change the air in the darkroom six to ten times an hour. It is advisable to have the air in the processing room maintained at a positive pressure, that is, the air should be pumped *in* rather than *out*. This will prevent dust entering through windows and doors.

Exhausting the Darkroom Air. The drying cabinet must never exhaust *into* the processing room. If an air-conditioning system is installed in the building, the use of the air from the processing room for the drying cabinet may be undesirable as it might overload the ventilating

system and upset the balance of the pressure and circulation. In such instances, the dryer should have separate ducts not connected with the air-conditioning system. However, in other ventilating systems, the drying cabinet may be useful as a method of exhausting the air from the room.

To insure air of proper quantity and quality, a competent heating and ventilating engineer should be consulted.

ELECTRIC WIRING

Although high-voltage circuits do not extend into the darkroom, low-voltage electric outlets and fixtures may present a hazard under certain circumstances. Voltages of 110 volts or less can prove fatal if electric contacts with the body are made on moist skin. Care should be taken to avoid a situation in which the body becomes part of an electric circuit.

Electric Wiring Must Conform to Regulations. The electric wiring and equipment in the darkroom must conform to the regulations of the National Board of Fire Underwriters in order to safeguard the worker and the plant. These recommendations are based on the regulations of the underwriters, but they are also subject to the approval of municipal or state authorities. They are applicable not only to existing darkrooms but also to those in which new equipment is to be installed.

All exposed non-current-carrying metal parts of both fixed and portable equipment, such as the metal frame and exterior of each illuminator, safelight lamp, electric timer, and foot switch, must be grounded unless they are beyond normal reach of the worker.

Insulation of Accessible Fixtures. As a safeguard, all outlets, switches, sockets, and the like should be composed of insulating materials. Chain pull-switches should have an insulating link in the chain or a section of cord.

Foot-switches eliminate the need for the use of hands in operating electric fixtures. However, the precautions which apply to the grounding of other fixtures are even more imperative when foot-switches are installed, because the floor may be damp or, on occasion, even wet.

Planning the Wiring. The placement and circuit wiring of the various outlets should be planned for the convenience of the worker. All processing-room circuits, white lights, safelight lamps, and outlets should be controlled by a master switch located above head height on or near the inside door frame. A red signal light should be located near the door outside the processing room. This should be controlled by the safelight-lamp switch so that, when it is on, the red light will glow and thus indicate that the darkroom is in use. This will prevent accidental opening of the door while films are being processed.

Placement of Switches. Below the master switch, another switch should be placed above shoulder level to control the white ceiling light of the processing room. Both the master switch and the white-light switch are placed high in this manner so they will not be accidentally turned on. It is also well to have a switch lock in the form of a flat plate placed on the white-light switch so that the white light cannot be turned on unless the switch is unlocked.

Below these two switches, another switch is placed at waist level to control the safelight lamps.

Painting the Darkroom. It is no longer necessary to paint darkrooms jet black. Light leaks should be plugged, and the walls painted light green, light gray, or white. These colors add pleasantness to the working surroundings, simplify keeping the darkroom clean, and at the same time increase the effectiveness of safe darkroom illumination.

Section Seven: The Process Camera

In view of the many different kinds of copy submitted for reproduction, the camera in a lithographic plant must be extremely versatile, particularly if the plant has only one such unit. A camera may be small and compact with a maximum film size of 16 x 20 inches. Or, it may be extremely large, capable of producing film negatives up to four by six feet. If intended for ordinary line and halftone work the camera may be of simple design. But for color separation, multiple exposures, photocomposing and other intricate camera operations, a fully-equipped precision model is needed. Camera equipment should be chosen not only for the immediate needs but also with future requirements in mind. A process camera is a long-term investment and it must have enough flexibility to keep pace with plant expansion and changes in the type of work handled.

Our presentation of the process camera is divided into the following five points: (1) Camera elements and camera types; (2) The lens and its mounting; (3) The rear assembly of the process camera; (4) Various types of copyholders; and (5) Operational accessories. Each of these points is discussed in detail in the following.

CAMERA ELEMENTS AND CAMERA TYPES

Knowledge of a few basic factors in selecting camera equipment may be repaid many times over in terms of immediate and future utility. It is the purpose of this article to discuss the design, function and features of modern process cameras so that the data may help in making the initial decisions when selecting camera equipment. A camera of limited utility imposes serious restrictions on the nature and quality of the output of the shop, for, with inadequate camera equipment, many jobs are handled disadvantageously while others cannot be handled at all. In addition, the speed and economy with which the camera operations can be performed have considerable influence on the competitive position of the plant.

In this unit we concentrate on five fundamental items: (1) The basic parts of a process camera; (2) Gallery and darkroom cameras; (3) Overhead and floor-type cameras; (4) Vertical darkroom cameras; (5) Cameras for color work; and (6) Size and capacity of cameras. Each of these six items is individually presented in the following.

The Basic Parts of a Process Camera. In order to clarify some of the camera terms to be used in the following discussion, it might be well to begin by analyzing the basic parts of a process camera. Negative-making for photomechanical purposes is essentially "copying" and generally calls for no more than the production of an image of a flat surface. This is accomplished by means of an image-forming lens which projects the image of the copy to the focal plane.

In its simplest form, the process camera is merely two parallel planes at right angles to the optical axis of the lens which lies between them. In practice, the focal plane

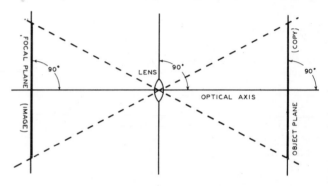

The basic requirements of a process camera.

is encased in a housing to which are attached all the necessary devices — the focusing screen (ground glass), the holder for the sensitive material, and the mechanism for supporting halftone screens. The copy is held in place by means of an easel or suction device or under glass in a pressure frame. The lens is maintained in proper relation to the other two planes on its own independent support.

The three units are mounted on a chassis, or main bed, which, in addition to providing the means for adjusting the relationship between lens, film and copy for reducing or enlarging the image, also functions as the means for maintaining the parallelism between the three essential planes.

Gallery and Darkroom Cameras. There are two general types of process cameras, namely — gallery and darkroom. The gallery camera is independent of the darkroom except for the bulky, lightproof holder for the sensitive material which must be transported between camera and darkroom for loading, exposing and unloading. The darkroom camera derives its name from the fact that the rear of the camera extends into, and is operated from, the darkroom.

With a camera so designed and operated, it is possible to perform both darkroom and camera operations at one and the same time. For example, while exposing a negative, the film or plate of a previous exposure can be processed. Although a gallery camera can be installed within a darkroom, only one operation can be performed at a time — exposing or processing, not both. The efficiency and convenience of the darkroom camera over the gallery type is

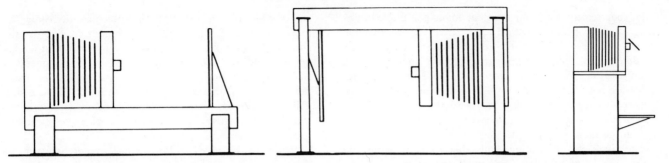

The three possible structural forms of darkroom cameras — floor type, overhead and vertical.

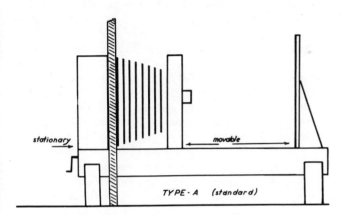

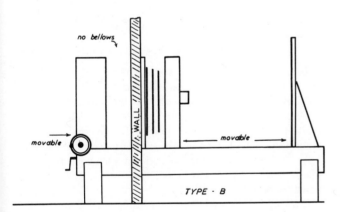

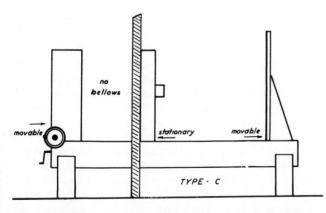

Three variations in the distribution of the horizontal darkroom camera within the darkroom and outside.

an established fact. The true darkroom camera is the main subject of consideration of this article.

Overhead and Floor-Type Cameras. Structurally, three differing principles are employed in assembling the essential camera planes to form the complete darkroom camera. Our diagram illustrates the essential construction differences of the vertical, floor-type and overhead cameras. The vertical camera is discussed further down; here we are concerned with overhead and floor-type cameras. The horizontal, floor-type camera main bed is raised anywhere from six inches to three feet from the floor and can be serviced from the side only. The elevation of the main bed on the overhead camera permits easy and unobstructed accessibility to lens, copy and lamps which may be, for certain classes of work (template, projection and handling very large copy), a desirable advantage.

The horizontal darkroom camera (overhead or floor-type) permits of three variations in regard to how much of the camera will protrude into the darkroom. Types B and C apportion the overall length of the camera between the darkroom and the area outside. In addition, both types require no bellows between camera-back and darkroom wall. This is an advantage when it is desirable that the operator have access to the front side of the sensitive material for purposes of dodging and masking during exposure. Design A is, however, the most popular arrangement.

Vertical Darkroom Cameras. The vertical darkroom camera has, as its outstanding advantage, the conservation of space. The camera proper is horizontal and within the darkroom. The supporting structure for the copyboard is vertical, parallel to and closely hugging the outside of the darkroom wall. Since the focal plane and copy plane are at right angles to each other, the use of a reversing mirror or prism is mandatory. Laterally reversed images are therefore standard with this design.

The chief limitation of vertical cameras is in size (film and copy capacity) and in range of enlargement and reduction. The latter is due mainly to the fact that the camera-back must be kept at a convenient working height which limits the extent of the copyboard movement. Nevertheless, within its capacity and range, the vertical camera is fully as functional as equivalent horizontal models.

Cameras for Color Work. So far we have made no distinction between operating features for black-and-white and color. Actually no clear-cut distinction can be made for the requirements of many types of monotone photography are as diversified and critical as those for color-separation work. Color work does require the utmost operating precision, hence color cameras are generally more rigid in construction. In addition, color work often requires features that are not essential for most black-and-white photography, as for example, the ability to rotate the positive holder around the optical axis for "squaring-up" the image.

Since color copy includes such varied subjects as color transparencies, oil paintings and other color drawings and photographs of both large and small dimensions, the copy-holding facilities must be extremely versatile. A combination including a large wooden copyboard, a positive holder, and for further convenience and utility, a glass-covered copyframe may be considered a satisfactory arrangement. The darkroom end of a color camera must also provide suitable and rigid support for the different sensitized materials likely to be employed.

The need for returning to a previous focus in the event that additional negatives or positives (makeovers) must be made to match the rest of a color set makes a scale focusing system mandatory on a color precision camera.

Although scale focusing systems are accurate enough for most camera operations, re-setting a camera to a previous focus requires a high degree of accuracy. To eliminate any errors in re-setting the focus, such as might occur from parallax in reading scale indicators or from backlash in the gear train of revolution counters, certain cameras are equipped with an additional re-set control. This usually takes the form of a dial micrometer gage which measures, to within 1/1000 of an inch accuracy, the physical location of lensboard and copyboard. In use, the dial micrometer is placed on the center-drive rack to correspond with a pre-recorded number from the original focus. With the dial in position the copyboard, or lensboard, is moved until the dial reading duplicates the original reading. By this means the copyboard and lensboard are precisely re-located in relation to their original position on the camera bed.

Size and Capacity of Cameras. The size of the camera, i.e. capacity of film holder, length of bed, and maximum and minimum bellows extension must be determined by consideration of a number of independent but interrelated factors. For example — the design, size and

construction of the camera-back influences not only the maximum area of film or plate accommodated, but also the size of the halftone screen that may be employed. As a general rule, the construction of most modern cameras is such that both line and halftone negatives can be made practically equal in area to the maximum film or plate size. This is true in the majority of cases only when applied to rectangular screens. The specifications of a representative group of cameras illustrates this.

When we consider circular halftone screens however, we must anticipate considerable reduction in the size of rectangular halftone image area. For example, although all of the 24″ cameras listed in the chart are capable of producing 20″ x 24″ halftone images from rectangular screens, all but two of them are limited to the use of 23½″ circular screens. The maximum image area (other than circular) obtainable from a 23½″ screen is approximately 15″ x 18″. If we should want a 20″ x 24″ halftone negative from a circular screen it would require a circular screen of at least 31½″ diameter. Since the capacity of the screen mechanism generally increases with increased film size we would have to choose a 31″ camera or larger.

For use with circular screens, then, the selection of camera size must be resolved by first ascertaining the diameter of the screen required to embrace the largest rectangular image desired. The next step is to determine the total area occupied by the screen including the holder. Obviously, only a camera whose screen mechanism capacity, as well as film (or plate) capacity, meets the requirements, is suitable.

THE LENS AND ITS MOUNTING

In this section we are not concerned with optics. In this, the process camera section of the manual, we are neither concerned with optics nor with lens properties in general; these are discussed in Section One of this chapter. Here we are restricted to the following five points: (1) The mounting of the lens; (2) The covering power of the lens; (3) The range of reduction and enlargement; (4) Auxiliary lenses; (5) Various lens requirements. Each of these points is now briefly discussed.

The Mounting of the Process Lens. A process lens consists of several glass elements that are most carefully made and joined together in the lens-barrel. A lens-barrel is usually filled with an iris diaphragm and may also have a slot for the inserting of other lens stops or of color filters. Lenses for color work are often equipped with special metal holders for the speedy handling of color filters. The lens-barrel is attached to the camera on the lensboard. The mounting permits simple and fast exchanging of various lenses or lens-barrels.

The Covering Power of the Lens. In order to determine the needed length of the camera bed, as well as the maximum and minimum positions of lensboard and copyboard, the focal length of the lens must be established. The covering power of a process lens is a fixed function of the lens. It is dependent upon the inherent image angle and the focal length. The diameter of the image area, with lenses of the same type and angle, becomes greater as the focal length increases.

SCREEN CAPACITY

CAMERA	A	B	C	D	E	F	G	H	I
RATED SIZE	24″	24″	24″	24″	24″	24″	31″	31″	31″
MAXIMUM FILM OR PLATE	24 x 24	25 x 28	24 x 24	24 x 24	24 x 24	26 x 26	28 x 36	31 x 31	31 x 31
MAXIMUM LINE IMAGE	24 x 24	25 x 28	24 x 24	24 x 24	24 x 24	26 x 26	28 x 36	31 x 31	31 x 31
MAXIMUM RECTANGULAR SCREEN	20 x 24	20 x 24	20 x 24	20 x 24	20 x 24	21 x 25	28 x 36	26 x 30	26 x 30
MAXIMUM CIRCULAR SCREEN	23½	23½	31½	23½	31½	23½	37½	30	31½

Relationship between maximum film (or plate) size and screen capacity of a representative group of process cameras.

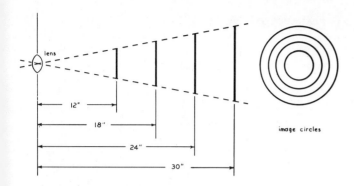

image circles

Covering power of a lens, i.e., size of image area covered without distortion or losses, increases with increased focal length.

When focused for same size, the image area and copy area are equal, as are the distances from lens to copy, and lens to film. As the copy is brought nearer to the lens, the size of the image area increases while the size of the copy area gets smaller. Just the opposite happens when the copy is moved further away from the lens. The size of the image area decreases while the copy area increases. Because of this, the focal length of the lens must be chosen on the basis of the image area desired, and the scale of reproduction.

The Range of Reduction and Enlargement. The next logical points for consideration are — the length of the camera bed, and the minimum and maximum bellows separation required to obtain the range of enlargements and reductions desired.

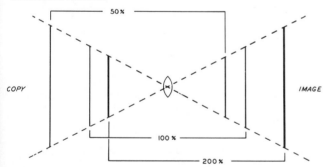

Diagram showing the diminishing diameter of the image circle as the lens moves near to the image (reduction), and, conversely, the increase in image size as the lens moves farther away (enlargement). Also shown is the image-copy relationship. As the image circle decreases the copy circle increases, and vice versa.

The distances separating the lens, film and copy are a function of the focal length of the lens and the scale of reproduction. The distance between lens and image, B, is directly related to the distance, A, separating the lens and copy. The distance between image and copy, C, is the total of A and B. Distances A and B are called conjugate foci and, except when the image and object are at same size, one is always greater than the other. The sum of conjugate foci, however, remains the same in all cases where the ratio between image and copy is the same. Assuming that the

required separation between copy and image can be achieved, the minimum bellows distance will limit the range of reduction, while the maximum bellows extension will govern the range of enlargement.

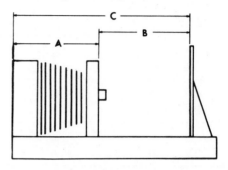

The minimum and maximum separation possible between lens and copy, B, and lens and film, A, will influence the reduction and enlargement range of a camera.

Auxiliary Lenses. The standard lens is often supplemented by one of shorter focal length in order to increase the range of enlargement and reduction. This practice will prove satisfactory only if the image-covering power is adequate and there are no mechanical limitations preventing the fulfillment of the required conjugate distances. For example, if the minimum distance between lens and image limits an 18″ lens at 20 percent (5-1 reduction) then a lens of lesser focal length could not be brought close enough to the image plane to affect further reduction.

RATIO BETWEEN IMAGE AND COPY SIZES									
Focal Length of lens	1-1	1-2		1-3		1-5		1-10	
	Same Size	Reduction	Enlargement	Reduction	Enlargement	Reduction	Enlargement	Reduction	Enlargement
10″	17	12	24	10½	31½	9½	47½	8½	85½
12″	21	15½	31	13½	40½	12	60	10½	105
18″	31½	23	46	20	60	17½	87½	16	160
24″	41	30	60	27	81	24	120	20	200
30″	49	37	74	31	93	28	140	25	250
36″	60	41	82	37	111	33	165	29	290

Approximate diameter, in inches, of the image circle sharply covered at $f/22$, at the various degrees of reproduction shown, for lenses of different focal length.

Various Lens Requirements. The optical considerations so far discussed are concerned with the lens characteristics that govern image size and camera range. The lens, more so than any other camera feature, is responsible for ultimate image quality and must be selected on the basis of all of its performance characteristics.

A good process lens must have excellent color correction, not only in the visible spectrum but, preferably, extending into the ultraviolet and infrared regions. The latter is necessary if color separation techniques are employed involving fluorescing and infrared absorbing copy. Image resolution should be high (this will vary with focal length and with sensitive material), and the lens should be free from flare. The latter condition is eliminated or minimized in modern process lenses by a special anti-flare coating.

SCALE OF FOCUS   FOCAL LENGTH OF LENS

(Ratio of image to copy size)		10"	12"	18"	24"	30"	36"	48"
1-1	b —	20	24	36	48	60	72	96
	a —	20	24	36	48	60	72	96
100%	c —	40	48	72	96	120	144	192
2-1r	b —	15	18	27	36	45	54	72
	a —	30	36	54	72	90	108	144
50%	c —	45	54	81	108	135	162	216
1-2E	b —	30	36	54	72	90	108	144
	a —	15	18	27	36	45	54	72
200%	c —	45	54	81	108	135	162	216
3-1r	b —	13.3	16	24	32	40	48	64
	a —	40	48	72	96	120	144	192
33%	c —	53.3	64	96	128	160	192	256
1-3E	b —	40	48	72	96	120	144	192
	a —	13.3	16	24	32	40	48	64
300%	c —	53.3	64	96	128	160	192	256
4-1r	b —	12.5	15	22.5	30	37.5	45	60
	a —	50	60	90	120	150	180	240
25%	c —	62.5	75	112.5	150	187.5	225	300
1-4E	b —	50	60	90	120	150	180	240
	a —	12.5	15	22.5	30	37.5	45	60
400%	c —	62.5	75	112.5	150	187.5	225	300
5-1r	b —	12	14.4	21.6	28.8	36	42.2	57.6
	a —	60	72	108	144	180	216	288
20%	c —	72	86.4	129.6	172.8	216	258.2	345.6
1-5E	b —	60	72	108	144	180	216	288
	a —	12	14.4	21.6	28.8	36	42.2	57.6
500%	c —	72	86.4	129.6	172.8	216	258.2	345.6
6-1r	b —	11.6	14	21	28	35	42	56
	a —	70	84	126	168	210	252	336
16%	c —	81.6	98	147	196	245	294	392
1-6E	b —	70	84	126	168	210	252	336
	a —	11.6	14	21	28	35	42	56
600%	c —	81.6	98	147	196	245	294	392
7-1r	b —	11.5	13.7	20.6	27.4	34.3	41.2	54.9
	a —	80	96	144	192	240	288	384
14%	c —	91.5	109.7	164.6	219.4	274.3	329.2	438.9
1-7E	b —	80	96	144	192	240	288	384
	a —	11.5	13.7	20.6	27.4	34.3	41.2	54.9
700%	c —	91.5	109.7	164.6	219.4	274.3	329.2	438.9

Table of approximate lensboard and copyboard distances for various focal length lenses. The table indicates the physical requirements of bellows extension and bed length for a particular focus setting and focal length lens.

Although the lithographer rightfully expects that the necessary lens qualities are built-in by the manufacturer, lens performance should be judged by practical tests made under the exact conditions of use.

THE REAR ASSEMBLY OF THE PROCESS CAMERA

Having established the overall dimensions of the camera on the basis of image size, image coverage, and range of enlargement and reduction, we now turn to the features of the main operating station camera — the camera-back or rear case. Located at this point are holding devices for the sensitive material, screen mechanisms and essential controls. These will be discussed in the following order: (1) The three types of negative supports; (2) Vacuum film-holders; (3) Various kinds of vacuum attachments; (4) Horizontal and vertical vacuum backs; (5) Plate-holder mechanisms; (6) Three-point register bars; (7) Hazards attending half-tone screen inserting and removing; (8) Screen elevating mechanisms; (9) Screen sliding mechanisms; and (10) Roll film camera-backs.

The Three Types of Negative Supports. Film and paper negative material may be supported by any one of three methods — stayflat, vacuum or sandwiched between two sheets of glass. This last method is rarely used except as an emergency measure. The stayflat method utilizes a sticky composition which is coated on a sheet of glass or metal. The back of the film or paper is pressed into contact with the stayflat surface by means of roller, squeegee or the palm of the hand after which the assembly is brought into the focal plane of the camera.

Vacuum Film-Holders. The vacuum film-holder usually consists of a metal supporting surface having small holes or shallow grooves through which air is drawn by means of a vacuum pump. A film placed upon the supporting surface seals the vents, sets up a vacuum, and atmospheric pressure against the face of the film holds it in place. Vacuum backs are basically of two types — the masking variety and the valve-cut-off type. The main difference is the manner in which the area not covered by film is sealed.

In the masking type, adjustable masks or individual metal shields corresponding to a particular film size are used. In the non-masking type, a valve, or a series of valves, confines the vacuum to a specific area depending upon the size of film being used.

Various Kinds of Vacuum-Holder Attachments. Vacuum-holders are attached to the camera housings by means of hinges on either the side or base of the holder. In the case of side attachment the holder is swung from the inoperative position (where the sensitive material is applied and removed) to the focal plane. This arrangement, in which the holder may be attached to either side, permitting a choice of left or right hand operation, makes possible the attachment, on the opposite side, of an additional unit such as a ground glass panel or a combination ground glass and plate-holder. When the base of the holder is hinged to the camera, the holder is lowered (tilted) to a horizontal position for applying or removing the sensitive material and is held in the horizontal plane by means of brackets or chains.

Horizontal and Vertical Vacuum Backs. Some cameras have both horizontal and vertical loading vacuum backs. In this case the vacuum holder is hinged, at the base, within a frame hinged to the rear case on the side. At the operator's option, either loading arrangement can be used.

Plate-Holder Mechanisms. Glass plates of the gelatin or collodion (wet plate) variety are supported by means of adjustable bars which provide means for positioning each plate in the required image area as well as assuring coincidence and parallelism of the emulsion surface with the focal plane regardless of the thickness of the glass. Plate-holder mechanisms are generally an integral part of the camera-back but are also available as independent units in which case the plate-bars are attached to a metal frame which is hinged to the camera in either the swinging or tilting arrangement. Such units provide multiple utility from one holder since they are readily converted to film-holders by installation of stayflat coated glass.

Three-Point Register Bars. The conventional plate-bars do not assure absolute accuracy in the placement of successive plates especially in regard to the coincidence of the vertical and horizontal plate centers with the image centers. For such operations as color composing, masking, and

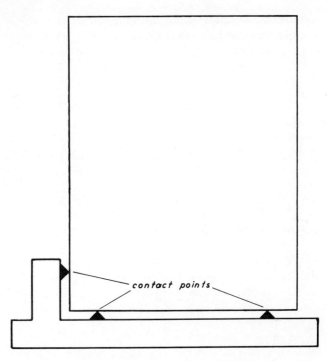

The principle of 3-point register bars and frames. The minimum contact area provides maximum accuracy in locating glass plates.

combining multiple images, it is necessary that all plates coincide in absolute register with each other, the optical axis and the holding device. Three-point register bars have three small hardened-steel pins for locating the plate — two on the base and one on the side. Since only a minute area of contact exists between holder and plate, a high degree of accuracy is obtained.

Hazards Attending Halftone Screen Inserting and Removing. The need for inserting or removing a halftone screen when alternating between line and halftone work promotes several serious hazards. First, the danger of breakage or other damage is naturally proportionate to the amount of handling the screen receives. Secondly, not only is it a time-consuming procedure but the more often a screen is moved, the more apt it is to disturb the screen distance setting. To re-set or check the screen distance in itself requires considerable time. Thirdly, excess handling of the screen will tend to promote an accumulation of dust and fingermarks, which will create blemishes in the halftone negatives. All of this annoyance may be eliminated by means of the screen-removal mechanism which may be had as optional equipment on most modern cameras. Such mechanism is available in either of two types — the elevating type in which the screen is raised out of position, and the sliding type in which the screen is moved to the left or right out of the image plane.

Screen Elevating Mechanisms. The screen elevating mechanism consists of a track in which the screen-holder bars ride. By a turn of a crank, the halftone screen and its holder moves upward out of the image field into a rack which is termed the screen storage housing. This type of mechanism, manual or motor driven, accomplishes a number of very important functions. In a matter of seconds, the halftone screen may be brought into position, or removed from the image plane, without disturbing the screen distance setting. When the screen is elevated out of position, it rests in its own storage compartment protected from dirt, dust and damage — a very noteworthy consideration. Furthermore, the movement of the screen does not require disturbing or moving the plate or film-holder.

Sliding Screen Mechanisms. The sliding screen mechanism consists essentially of a pair of tracks in which the screen holder is supported and which make it possible to slide the screen from the image plane either to the left or the right of the camera. With the sliding screen mechanism it is possible to provide for storage space on both sides of the camera thus making it possible to use two screens or one screen and a compensating glass of the panel type. The type in which the screen may be moved only in one direction also has provision for utilizing more than one screen. By means of a multiple track arrangement in the storage rack, a number of screens can be accommodated, any one of which may be transferred to its proper position within the camera. The sliding or elevating screen mechanism is an indispensable feature for any camera on which combination line and halftone work, and highlighting halftones by the fluorescence process, is contemplated. For these two applications, the ability to insert or remove the screen without disturbing the position of the plate or film is of utmost importance.

Roll Film Camera-Backs. A significant approach toward mechanizing the photographic operation is evident in cameras equipped with backs which can accommodate roll film. This eliminates the steps involved in the conventional procedure for loading a camera for each shot. In addition to this, roll film camera backs make it possible to have available in the camera, and ready for use, rolls of various widths. This allows the camera man to select the width as well as the length which will be most economical for the shot being made. Another advantage which can accrue by using such equipment is that of loading the camera with several types of film where the work requires this to a greater extent that it does size flexibilities.

A modern roll film camera will also have built into its back holders for contact and/or glass screens. One of the disadvantages of contact screens is their susceptibility to damage from handling. In the roll film camera, the screens are moved into place mechanically and need very seldom be handled. In additioned to this, the camera can be so equipped as to make possible complete operation from the gallery rather than the usual need for the cameraman to shuttle back and forth between gallery and darkroom several times for each shot.

On those occasions when it is necessary that sheet film or glass plates be used, the roll film backs are so designed as to make this feature also available. The roll film camera back does speed up the photographic operation considerably, as well as cut down on raw film costs as well as waste; all without any sacrifice of quality.

VARIOUS TYPES OF COPY-HOLDERS

Since the greatest variation in working procedure is created by reason of vast differences in the size, thickness and surface character of the copy submitted for reproduction, careful attention must be given the devices for holding copy. Unless the work is highly specialized and limited to a particular kind of copy, it is advisable to select a camera with some form of multiple copy-holder or one which by design and construction permits the installation of additional copy-holding units as needed. Here we discuss three types of copy-holders: (1) Wooden copy-holders for reflection copy; (2) Glass-covered copyboards for reflection copy, and (3) Holders for transmission copy. Each of these is briefly described in the following.

Wooden Copy-Holders for Reflection Copy. Copyboards of the open-face type are generally made of wood panels on which the copy is fastened by means of tacks, nails, or staples. Boards of metal or wood with special grooves and spring clips provide a means of attaching copy to open-face panels without the need for driving nails through the copy. The inability to achieve perfect flatness with wrinkled or very thin copy on the wooden panels has led to the development of the open-face vacuum copyboards which, by reason of suction and atmospheric pressure, hold the copy firmly in place without pins and with a minimum of effort in placing the copy in position.

Despite the inefficiency of the wooden copyboard, it nevertheless has a definite place in modern camera operations since it is the only practical means of supporting extremely large copy and of combining a number of copies of varying thicknesses. It is also desirable when it becomes necessary to position the arc lights at peculiar angles in order to minimize or retain surface characteristics of the copy which, if under glass, might give rise to unwanted reflections (hot spots) or distortions from the glass surface.

Glass-Covered Copyboards for Reflection Copy. The simplest design of glass-covered copyframe is a metal frame supporting the glass which is hinged to a wooden board with a layer of felt on which the copy is placed. Obviously, the "give" of the felt constitutes the limitation of the thickness of the copy placed thereon. To accommodate copy of greater thickness necessitates the use of other devices, notably the pressure back which consists of a cushioned panel supported on springs. By this arrangement, copy up to one inch in thickness (and more in some cases) can be accommodated. Both of the above designs, however, are efficacious only if the copy is of reasonably uniform thickness.

When such objects as books, or groupings with considerable variation in thickness must be placed under glass, the pneumatic cushion (air bag) device is desirable. The cushion is sandwiched between the glass and a stiff base. The copy is arranged on the surface of the cushion and when the frame is closed the air pressure within the cushion forces the copy surfaces against the glass. To overcome the difficulty often encountered with extremely thin or wrinkled copy may require the use of an enclosed vacuum copyboard similar in construction to the vacuum-printing frames which

THE CAMERA DEPARTMENT 5:41

permit attainment of optical contact between glass and copy surfaces.

All of the enclosed copy frames are of the titlting type and lower to a convenient horizontal position for inserting and removing copy. Glass-covered copyframes offer an additional advantage in that the surface of the copies, regardless of thickness, is always coincident with the object plane which is a necessary condition on cameras with focusing scales.

Holders for Transmission Copy. Negatives and positives are supported between the pairs of clamps on adjustable bars or in metal or wooden frames called positive-negative kits. These kits are generally a set of concentric interlocking frames of different sizes which make possible, in one unit, a range of openings corresponding to the standard plate sizes. Either of the two methods may be incorporated in the copyboard carriage, in which case the removal of the standard or glass-covered copyboard exposes the unit for use.

The convertible type consists of a set of kits which is inserted in a glass-covered copyframe after removal of the pressure back. Another arrangement utilizes a set of adjustable bars and lcamps attached to the back of a glass-covered copyframe with a removable pressure panel. An opal glass diffusing panel is generally provided when working with direct illumination — a curtain when operating by reflected light.

The bar and clamp-type holder usually includes a masking arrangement to exclude all light on all sides of the negative or positive. The kit type is self-masking since in each case the opening in the frame corresponds to the size of negative or positive used.

OPERATIONAL CAMERA ACCESSORIES

In addition to the basic camera elements there are numerous optional features and accessories which, although often overlooked, merit serious consideration. In many cases a certain appurtenance may be essential for one particular kind of work but a mere convenience for another. Regardless of the specific type of work done in a particular plant, the following items are here discussed as desirable accessories to the process camera: (1) Scale focusing; (2) Types of scale-focusing devices; (3) Methods of calibration of focusing mechanisms; (4) Calibrations made for specific lenses; (5) Aperture controls; (6) Fine adjustment of aperture control; (7) Single- and double-image reversers; (8) Lateral and "lens only" image reversal; (9) Single-reverser combined with special camera; (10) Lamp carriers; (11) The three basic types of lamp carriers; (12) Flashing lamps; (13) Hand-operated and automatic flashlamps; (14) Screen compensators; (15) Step-and-repeat backs; (16) Summary of operational camera accessories and conclusion.

Scale Focusing. In view of the fact that the distances separating the sensitive material, lens and copy are not determined arbitrarily by the operator, but by definite optical laws, it is possible to predetermine the precise position of

lensboard and copyboard for each degree of enlargement and reduction. Thus, by means of two factors — optical formulae governing the minor and major conjugate foci, and the exact focal length of the lens — it is possible to compute the required settings mathematically which are then correlated and mechanically applied to the camera.

Types of Scale-Focusing Devices. Scale focusing can be done by means of: (1) Rigid linear scales attached to the camera chassis with sliding indicators on the lensboard and copyboard carriages; (2) Sliding tapes made of flexible metal attached to the lensboard and copyboard which extend to the rear of the camera where they pass under indicators in a panel; (3) Revolution counters and/or vernier dials synchronized to the darkroom end of the driving mechanism of the lensboard and copyboard; and (4) Revolution counters and/or vernier dials attached to and synchronized with the movement of the lensboard and copyboard carriages. On some cameras, two focusing controls are provided, making it possible to focus the camera on scale from within the darkroom or on the outside.

Methods of Calibration of Focusing Mechanisms. Calibrations may be expressed in a number of ways all of which are correlated to the physical separation required. Thus, the linear scales and sliding tapes may be calibrated to read in inches, percentages or some arbitrary but correlated set of numbers. The revolution counters usually read directly in inches or are correlated to distance by arbitrary readings. All of these systems operate in conjunction with some form of proportional slide rule or dial and master chart. It is only necessary to determine, by means of the control device, the relationship between image and copy sizes and then adjust the camera settings according to the indicated distance, percentage or number.

Calibrations are Made for Specific Lenses. It is advisable to remember that focusing calibrations are usually made for the lens supplied with the camera or the lens furnished by the customer. If additional lenses are to be used on the same camera it will become necessary to have each lens calibrated. In the case of scales and tapes with graduations in inches and revolution counters, it is possible, after due allowance has been made for the difference in nodal position, to correlate all lenses to the focusing mechanism. Where the focusing device has been calibrated and so graduated that it functions exclusively with one lens, as in the case of perforated tapes and special linear scales, it is difficult if not impossible to correlate and apply such readings to other than the original lens in which case all other lenses will have to be focused visually.

Aperture Controls. The aperture indicator, as supplied on most process lenses, gives only broad divisions, forcing the photographer to set the diaphragm to the intermediate points by interpolation. With such arbitrary settings exposure can be subject to considerable variation due to lack of coordination between the diameter of the diaphragm and the distance between lens and film. For the same reasons, considerable deviation in the relationship between screen distance, diaphragm size, etc., will be encountered in halftone photography.

With each change in distance between lens and film, a coordinated change must be made in the diameter of the lens diaphragm in order to maintain the required light transmission factor (f:value). In halftone work, where more than one stop is used, it is not only necessary to maintain the required relationship between the lens opening, screen distance and bellows extension, but the relationship between the various stops must be accurately maintained. The minute changes required cannot be judged accurately by means of the lens diaphragm ring and scale.

Fine Adjustment of Aperture Control. Various devices are available which permit infinite accuracy in lens aperture settings. In general they consist of a finely graduated dial attached to the lens or lensboard, a pointer fastened to the lens diaphragm ring and, in some cases, a vernier movement for precision settings. The graduations on the scale are generally coordinated to some particular halftone theory although some scales are simply a fine graduation of the f:values. Whatever the scale may be, it will nevertheless permit lens settings exactly coordinated to the bellows extension. By means of such aperture control, the quality of halftone negatives will be improved, errors in exposure due to diaphragm variations will be eliminated and a uniform line and halftone technique evolved.

It is possible with several of these controls to operate them from the darkroom. This offers many advantages since the photographer need not leave the darkroom to change apertures during a halftone exposure or when making several negatives of different sizes from the same copy.

Single- and Double-Image Reversers. Many photographic operations require reversed negative or positives, i.e., transposition of image reading from left to right. The single-mirror or prism reverser usually employed for this purpose cannot be used on the conventional darkroom camera since the copy must be at right angles to the lens. Multiple-mirror reversers are designed to operate in a straight line and are thus applicable to darkroom type cameras.

The multiple-mirror reverser, however, because of distortion of the marginal rays, limits the usable picture area. When buying such equipment it is advisable to check with the respective manufacturers as to the proper combination of lens and reverser to adequately cover the maximum image area desired. As a general rule a lens of longer than normal focal length will be required.

Lateral and "Lens Only" Image Reversal. Double, multiple-mirror reversers are also available to provide both laterally reversed images and "lens only" type images. Two flat mirrors, or one mirror and one prism acting in unison, cancel out each other's reversal and thus produce the same type of image as when shooting through a lens alone. Three flat mirrors or one flat and one split mirror provide lateral, straight-in-line reversal. On cameras equipped with the double-reversing systems the changeover from one to the other is usually accomplished electrically. The reversed and regular images are of the same size and in register at the focal plane. Some cameras with double-reversing mirror systems provide, in addition, the ability to shoot through a lens directly.

Since the mirror systems displace the optical axis, cameras so equipped generally have special lensboards and special copyboards (raised or laterally shifted centers). Because of this requirement, it is generally impossible, or impractical, to install this type of equipment on a standard camera.

Courtesy Sidney R. Littlejohn & Co. Ltd., London.

Littlejohn Straight-Line Image Reverser.

Single Reverser Combined with Special Camera Design. The single-element reverser (mirror or prism) may be used in combination with a darkroom camera of special design. This camera has a separate bed for the copyboard set at right angles to the main camera bed. The two units are controlled from within the darkroom.

Lamp Carriers. In order to obtain uniformity of exposure, it is necessary that the desired distance and angle between the camera lamps and the copy remain constant. It is not always possible to judge, without actually measuring the distance and angle each time the camera is focused, whether or not the lamps are accurately positioned. Since the strength of light is inversely proportionate to the distance between light source and illuminated surface, any variation in lamp position will result in a variation of light strength reaching the copy. Such variation will induce underexposure, overexposure and uneven illumination. A simple solution to this problem is the lamp carrier which connects a pair of lights to each other and to the copyboard at a fixed distance and angle. Not only is the copy illumination standardized by this means but the movement of the lights is synchronized to that of the copyboard — effecting thereby a considerable saving in time and effort, for both lights and copyboard are positioned at one and the same time.

The Three Basic Types of Lamp Carriers. Of the many lamp carriers available, there are only three basic types. The simplest arrangement is the bracket type which, by means of a set of adjustable rods, ties up the lights on their original stand to each other and the copyboard. An elaboration of this type consists of a separate carriage hooked up to the copyboard which supports the lamps. Both of these devices ride on the floor.

The second type consists of a pair of adjustable arms emanating from the copyboard carriage to which the lamps are attached. The third type utilizes a rail mounted under the camera bed and running the full length, to which are attached separate carriages with adjustable arms supporting the lamps.

The latter two types have advantages in that there is no connection between floor and lamps to impede the travel of the lamps or for transference of vibration to the camera bed. Overhead carriers, for use with both overhead and floor-type cameras are also available.

Flashing Lamps. In most cases, halftone negatives require an auxiliary exposure to build up the proper opacity in the shadow dots. The old procedure of exposing to a white sheet of paper or cardboard placed over the copy is not only wasteful of time but eventually the flash sheet becomes dirty and wrinkled which gives rise to an uneven or mottled flash exposure — particularly noticeable when making tints.

To obtain a more uniform flash exposure it is advisable to use a flashing lamp. This consists of an incandescent light source in a housing with a suitable optical arrangement (condensers) which produces a uniform and concentrated light source. A flashing lamp is operated at a very short distance from the front of the lens and insures a short but uniform flash exposure.

Hand-Operated and Automatic Flashlamps. Flashing lamps are available in several models. The least expensive is entirely hand-operated. The photographer brings it into position in front of the lens, holds it securely during the exposure and then sets it aside. Lamps which are permanently attached to the camera can easily be swung in or out of position. One such lamp is supported by a swinging bracket attached to the front or side of the lensboard panel. Another model is pivoted on a shaft protruding from the lensboard.

Another type is completely automatic in operation, being controlled entirely from the darkroom. By pushbutton control the lamp is brought in or out of position and, by means of a synchronized electric timer, an accurate exposure interval is obtained. Obviously, this automatic flashing lamp, in conjunction with a darkroom diaphragm control, offers the most advantages since it eliminates the need for the photographer to leave the darkroom.

Screen Compensators. When a camera has been focused with an engraved halftone screen in place and the screen is then removed, the size and sharpness of the image is no longer the same as when the screen was in place. The influence of the glass of which an engraved screen is composed causes the light rays passing through it to be bent or refracted and thereby alters the distance between lens and film. If it is desired to obtain a line image of the same size and sharpness as a halftone image, two different camera settings would be required. This would prove an ambiguous situation on cameras with precision focusing systems for, unless adequate provision is made, the focusing system would be valid for either line or halftone use but not both.

The variants between line and halftone focal points are easily reconciled by means of screen compensators which are either disks or sheets of glass which possess the same refractive index as the halftone screen. By intentionally introducing an alteration or refraction of the light rays being projected to the film by means of the compensator device, we are able to produce line negatives which, at the same camera setting, will be equal in size and sharpness to halftone negatives. In use, the compensating device is brought into position when shooting line negatives and removed for halftone work.

Step-and-Repeat Backs. The step-and-repeat camera-back is essentially a plate-back with a special mechanism which permits shifting the negative material vertically and horizontally in relation to the image axis. By this means a single image may be multiplied or "stepped-up" on a plate in absolute register in monotone or color process. The movement of the plate may be actuated by vertical and horizontal micrometer screws or by quick acting micro-set stops and slide bars. As a general rule cameras so equipped may also be used for all other camera operations.

Summary of Operational Camera Accessories and Conclusion. Individually, each of the devices under this discussion has a function which it can fulfill by itself. However, utmost utility, or efficiency can sometimes be obtained only by means of a companion device. It might be well, therefore, to summarize some of the remarks made about these devices throughout this study.

Scale Focusing is based on optical laws governing the function of lenses. Introduction of other optical equipment either in front or in back of the lens can and will alter the conditions on which a focusing scale is based. The halftone screen alters the focus sufficiently to require a different distance between lens and film, at a specific degree of enlargement or reduction, than a line setting. Thus, to avoid the need and annoyance for differentiating (in focus) between line and halftone settings, scale focusing and screen *compensators* should be considered inseparable.

A Flashing Lamp operated electrically from within the darkroom serves no useful purpose unless the lens aperture can also be controlled inside the darkroom. An electronic exposure control, for greatest efficiency and advantage, should be complemented by *a diaphragm control* and *synchronized arc-light carrier*. The screen compensator should also be considered a companion device to an elevating or sliding screen mechanism.

Mention might also be made of the *rotating filter-holders* operated from the darkroom, which are desirable additions to cameras possessing darkroom-operated diaphragm controls and flashing lamps.

Most camera operations, with the exception of inserting or removing copy, can be performed or controlled within the darkroom. A fully electrified camera possesses many operating advantages if a definite need for such control exists. In the absence of a definite need many automatic devices become mere gadgets.

Consideration must also be given to the fact that many camera features are avaiable only when factory-installed or may be exclusive features of particular models. This may preclude installation, at a later date, of critically needed accessories.

Obviously, a camera with limited features will not keep pace with plant expansion and will soon prove inadequate. It is sound practice to fully determine the immediate camera requirements and also anticipate the future needs. The camera's features should meet both conditions.

Section Eight: Practical Problems of the Cameraman

One of the biggest bugaboos that haunt the average photographer is the problem of correct tone reproduction. In attempting to reproduce an original by converting it into a halftone image, many faults occur. For example, with a normal copy, a highlight negative will reproduce the shadows with a reasonable degree of correctness. However, the light areas of the image will appear too light and there will be poor separation between the various tones in these areas.

The main problem of correct reproduction is the halftone dot. It is not, however, a question of dot size alone; other aspects, such as dot density and tone density too, must be considered. Tone reproduction is an important and complicated subject; it is extensively treated in other sections of the Lithographers Manual. Here, I merely want to acquaint you with some aspects of tone reproduction and some methods of improving tonal quality.

DOT AREA, DOT DENSITY AND TONE DENSITY

As an introduction to this problem, let us consider for a moment the question of dot size, or dot area as it is commonly called. The size of the halftone dot is determined by certain factors over which the halftone photographer has some control. These factors include such items as exposure, the size of the lens aperture, and the screen distance. By varying each, or all, of these factors, the size of the dot can be changed. However, the tone of an image area is not dependent upon the dot size alone. In addition, there are the factors of dot density and tone density. To be certain that we are thinking in the same terms, let me define these three terms using the Graphic Arts Technical Foundation's definitions as found in Bulletin #305, *Dot Area, Dot Density and Tone Value.*

". . . The most convenient way of describing the size of halftone dots is by stating how large they are in relation to the white or transparent spaces between them . . . dot size is measured in terms of DOT AREA . . . the dot area of any tone region is the fraction of the total area of the region which is covered with black dots."

"The term TONE DENSITY means the optical density of a tone area — the overall density which takes into account both the dots within the tone area and the spaces between them."

"The term DOT DENSITY means the optical density of the dots themselves."

HOW DOT SIZE AFFECTS TONE DENSITY

Now, in terms of practical results, here is a major point that has been learned from the study of tone reproduction.

The dot size and the tone density within an area are not proportional. This means that if the dot size is changed by equal amounts, there will not be equal differences in the tone density. If dot sizes were changed an equal amount, it would be more noticeable in the shadow tones than in the highlight tones. If, for example, you wanted to show a tonal difference in a light-toned area, you would have to increase your dot size a greater amount than if you wanted to show the same tonal differences in a darker-toned area.

Remember that at this point we have been discussing only effect of dot size on tone density. Other important factors that we have not discussed will also vary the appearance of the final print. They include items such as the blackness of the ink, the whiteness of the paper, and the evenness of the dot, to mention only a few.

IMPROVING TONE REPRODUCTION

Having touched only ever so briefly upon one of the technical considerations of this problem, let us turn to some of the means available for improving tone reproduction.

Hand Retouching. This method can be used on both the screened negatives and positives. Possibly the most common form of hand retouching is normally done on a screen positive and is known as dot-etching. Here, the dot sizes are changed by etching in a mixture of Ferricyanide and Hypo. The solution is applied locally with the aid of a brush or cottonwad, or as an all-over bath in a tray of the solution. Staging is done with an asphaltum mixture to protect the areas on which no etch is to be done.

On either screen positives or negatives, blocking-out can be done with the use of opaque. When opaque is applied to a negative it will result in a perfectly clear white area on the final positive.

Stains or dyes can also be used in varying amounts to retard the passage of light through the screen negative or positive, and in this way, change the value of the tones in the following step of the process.

Combination Line and Halftone Exposure. This type of negative will do the most for copy where there is a distinct difference in tone values between the whites and the lighter gray tones. The halftone exposure is made first in order to faithfully record the shadow and middletone areas; then, the halftone screen is removed, a screen compensator is placed behind the lens, and the line exposure is shot on the same emulsion in register with the halftone image. The ratio of halftone to line-exposure time is very important, and must be carefully worked out for the most satisfactory results. In order for the images to be the same size and in register, the screen compensator must have the same refractive index and the same thickness as the glass screen that it replaces.

Halftone Negative with Continuous-Tone Mask.
This is another method to improve the tonal quality of the image in the highlight area. At the same time that the screen negative is shot, a weak-image continuous-tone negative is also shot. These two images are superimposed to make the halftone positive, or they can be utilized directly in order to print an albumin plate. The continuous-tone image adds a bit more density to the highlight area of the screen negative, and the highlights are thus more correctly represented.

Filters and the Contact Screen. When the contact screen is used rather than the glass crossline screen, the magenta color of the contact screen lends itself to certain general corrections through the use of the proper filters when making the exposure. Using a yellow filter (Wratten #4) will lower the contrast of the entire negative. With a rose filter (Wratten #30) the contrast is tremendously increased. In addition to a complete exposure through one of these filters, a partial exposure can be made through one of them for intermediary results.

The Controlled-Flash and Highlighting Methods with the Contact Screen. These two methods proposed by Eastman Kodak will help to increase the tonal range when used with the Magenta Contact screen. The Controlled-Flash method utilizes a flash exposure that is calculated to extend the shadow range of the image. It is simple and easy to use. The Highlighting method consists of a special flash exposure combined with still development and a partial exposure made without the contact screen. The resultant negative is increased in contrast, especially in the highlight area, and can produce very excellent results. This method is, of course, a particular variation of the Combination line and halftone method described earlier.

These, then, are only a few of the means available to the lithographic photographer to alter the tonal characteristics of his negatives and positives in order to get better reproduction.

THE PROBLEM OF ACHIEVING EFFICIENT OPERATION

The chances are that the layout of equipment and materials in your department were made before you ever came to work there. It is a little difficult, and in some cases impossible, to do very much about changing the position of heavy photographic equipment in order to operate more efficiently. You will therefore, in most cases, be limited to minor changes in your department. Do not, however, give up in disgust, for even small changes, if carefully worked out, can produce worthwhile improvements in efficient operation.

Let us see, then, what can be done in planning a department so that it can operate efficiently. In the first place, the equipment should be accessible. By careful and proper placement, walking distances and waste motions will be tremendously reduced. Proper placement of equipment is one of the most important factors in increased productivity.

With the equipment go the tools. It is necessary that the proper tools be on hand at the place where they will be needed. This not only saves time, but takes some of the pressure off a cameraman who has the problem of seeking the location of the needed tool before he can correct the fault that exists.

Just as you follow a planned step-by-step sequence of procedure in your operation, it is logical to have your equipment, tools and supplies arranged in such a way that they will be readily available in the same order in which they will be utilized.

A check will immediately tell you if tools are missing or if new ones should be purchased. All tools should be checked to see that they are in operating order and suitable for the purpose. A reasonable amount of thought will be required to make certain that the way you are doing things is the best possible way to do them. Look at each step of your operation. Are you performing it efficiently? Does it logically follow the step that preceded it? Is the operation you are doing in its logical place of procedure when you consider the step that will follow?

All of these are questions that you will have to ask yourself, and more important, questions that you will have to answer truthfully in order to determine how well and efficiently you operate. You must stand mentally aloof and try to look at the situation with a detached eye. Try, if possible, to picture that you are watching someone else performing the operations that are being done. Is there a constant walking around from one side of the room to the other? If the answer to this question and to others like this are in the positive, it is time that you stopped in your tracks and reviewed your operations.

When you have seen that certain changes are desirable and have made them, operate under the new conditions for a period. Give yourself enough time to be at ease with the new order of operation, or the new positioning of supplies, and then, once again, stand back, and look over the whole situation. Were the changes that you made good? Do they seem to have made a noticeable improvement? If they have helped, try to look into the procedure a bit more closely, and see if there are other details that you skipped that can be corrected at this time. In this manner, you should make a periodic recheck of the operations that you are performing. In some cases, once every year might be ample. In other cases, once every two weeks wouldn't be enough.

In all the photographic work that you do, there are certain things that remain constant and other things that are variable. For the most efficient working conditions, it is necessary that you control the variables as much as possible. In many cases the easiest and best method of control is to eliminate the human factor and substitute a mechanical one to do the work. So, from this point of view, let us discuss a few of the photographic variables and show how they can be controlled.

LIGHT AND INTEGRATING LIGHT METERS

One of the primary problems of the photographer is lighting. In order to calculate exposure properly, the photographer must know how much light he is getting, what quality the light is, and for how long a period of time he is getting it. Unless these factors are consistent, there will be a constantly changing exposure factor brought into the work.

To be able to measure how much light you are getting in a given situation is important. It is true that with the proper formulae the photographer can calculate how the light will change in quantity as he moves his light sources closer to, or further away from, the copyboard. But there is the factor of variability in the light sources themselves. With carbon arcs the light will change in intensity as air drafts cause the arcs to flicker. So for fractions of a second you would be getting little or no light on the copy. In addition, the line voltage that supplies the arc lamps with power can vary from second to second as additional heavy equipment on the same power line is put into operation. This will cause the same effect as the draft. It is true that the new motor-driven arc lamps available today are a boon for the photographer for they eliminate some of this problem, but they do not solve it completely.

The measurement of the strength of the light source can be made with an exposure meter of which there are many types available, but this leaves much to be desired. As soon as a measurement is made, conditions may change and another reading would be necessary. In a situation such as this, it would be impossible to make a constantly accurate measurement of the light source.

The actual time of exposure can be measured with one of the many photographic timers that are on the market. Almost all of them will give a very accurate measurement of the passing time, but with a varying light source, this is of no particular use. It is, therefore, necessary to either keep the light source from changing in the slightest degree or to be constantly measuring its variation.

There is an instrument available that will continually measure the strength of the light source, and simultaneously time the exposure. Such an instrument is known as an integrating light meter and it is available under a wide variety of trade names. It is what I believe to be one of the really basic instruments for photographic operation. This is especially true when accuracy and consistency of result are of paramount importance. True, it is still possible to produce faulty results in spite of an integrating light meter, but if I were allowed only one instrument with the camera to maintain consistent results, this is the instrument I would choose.

The instrument is extremely simple in its use. It is set by the use of some type of calibrated dial or by a push-button board on which the exposure values are designated. This value is in light units (which can be adjusted by the cameraman to approximate one second per unit). The light from the source falls upon a photo-electric cell which is hooked up electronically to a timer mechanism. If the light falling upon the cell fluctuates, it will either slow down or speed up the timer mechanism, depending upon the type of fluctuation. The end result is that twenty units of light today will be the same as twenty units of light tomorrow, and, even though the exposure time may be longer on one day than another, the total amount of light that is reaching the sensitive emulsion will be the same with the same set-

ting of the dial. This will help to eliminate one of the most important variables in the photographic operation.

The integrating light meter can help to eliminate *some* of the variables. There are, however, other variables that are almost impossible to eliminate. Three of these are the differences of working techniques between two cameramen in the same department, the variability of equipment, and the possibility of malfunctioning equipment. Still another variable is the change in performance in equipment over a period of years as the equipment is used more and more and parts become worn.

Because it is not possible to completely eliminate this type of variation, the next best thing that can be done is to measure it. For, once you can measure your errors or variables, you have the foundation for an intelligent modification in order to make the end results what you want them to be. In this category comes the next important instrument that is of great importance. Depending upon the type of work that you do, it may well be the instrument of primary value.

THE DENSITOMETER AND ITS FUNCTIONS

The densitometer performs one operation. It measures density. However, it can do it in a number of ways, and density measurements can be used for a wide variety of controls. But, before we go any further, let us define the term "density" so that we all will understand the same thing as we continue the discussion.

Density is a standard means of expressing the value of a tone area in the form of a number (definition from GATF Technical Bulletin #304, *Optical Density as a Measure of Tone Values in Lithography*).

This means that with the densitometer we can take any two or more tonal values (from either reflection or transmission copies) measure them, and make a comparison between the two. From density values we can determine:

1. The relative speed of a plate or a film.
2. The contrast of a particular emulsion.
3. Correct exposure values.
4. Correct development times.
5. Correct filter factors.
6. The correct balance between a set of separation negatives.

All these and many other factors can be determined with the help of this instrument. It therefore becomes one of the prime tools in the hands of the photographer. It will enable him to standardize his method of operation and permit him to duplicate the results that he wants. Used properly, it will eliminate a great deal of guesswork with a corresponding increase in production. Waste time and materials can be kept to a minimum, and the photographer can be confident of obtaining the results that he desires.

TROUBLE SHOOTING FOR THE CAMERAMAN

What exactly is meant by trouble shooting? It is the process, once a trouble is apparent, of locating the source of the trouble, and remedying it so that the operation can proceed in a normal manner without an undue waste of time. The process of locating a trouble is based upon two general factors. One of these factors is a logical approach to solving the problem, and the other is a background of experience in the operation. The experience that a photographer needs cannot be given in a short article of this nature. It is something that must be acquired over a period of time after having worked many types of jobs. However, one thing that can be done by the photographer is to learn the use of the equipment that he is working with. You, as a photographer, should become familiar with the camera that you are using. Learn what each part of it will do by experimenting when you have the available time. Once your general knowledge of the equipment is reasonably complete, you can devise a logical approach to the question of problem solving. The basic idea behind such an approach is this. If your vacuum back does not hold your film snugly against it, it would seem foolish to look for the reason for this fault in the developer that you used. It would seem more logical to look for the trouble in the camera itself. Either the vacuum pump is not operating well, or holes in the vacuum back might be plugged up. These would be the most likely places to look for the faults. If, in addition to noticing that the vacuum back is not holding the film, you noticed that the pump did not seem to be operating, the pump, then, would seem the best place to start your check of the faulty operation. This general procedure requires just a moment's time to mentally go over what seems to be the trouble and then to try to locate the fault. Toward this end, the following list of five common faults are supplied. They will give you a starting point on which to build your experience.

Poor Dot Structure. Dots may be fuzzy and will not stand up under the etching operation.

Most probably the fault will lie in camera operation. First, check for improper screen distance, then for correct exposure; finally, check to see if the flash exposure was omitted.

If none of these things reveal the source of the difficulty, check development. Was there excessive development time? Was developer temperature too low? Was the developer mixed improperly?

Multiple Dots. This is usually noticed as a small cluster of dots where a single dot should be. This pattern is especially noticeable in highlight areas. It is almost exclusively a camera fault. Check first for camera vibration, then possible film slippage on your vacuum back. It can also occasionally occur when there is movement of the screen with respect to the vacuum back while the exposure is going on, so check for this in old cameras that have seen much wear.

Poor Duplication of Tonal Range. Negatives will be either more contrasty or softer than the original art would indicate.

First check the copy. Is its tonal range too great for your normal method of exposure? Then check exposure. Did you use a one-stop method of exposure when a two- or a three-stop method was necessary to cover the tonal range? Did you forget to flash? Was your screen distance incorrect?

If these camera items check, then go to the development operation. Was the developing temperature correct? Has the developer deteriorated due to too much use?

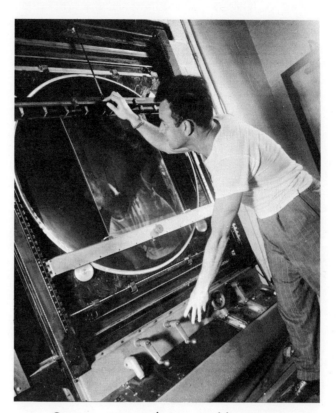

Cameraman at work on a precision camera.

Pin Spots. These are small little clear spots on the negatives. They are usually caused by dust or dirt on the copyboard, or on the halftone screen. In this case, a second shot would show the spot in the identical place on the picture area.

Check the developer. Pin spots can be caused by air bubbles clinging to the surface of the film. Try a more careful development technique to eliminate this.

A third possibility lies in the emulsion of the film or plate. Tiny air-bells on the emulsion formed during the coating operation cause these spots. They are readily recognized as being due to air-bells by a thin dark ring around the clear center.

Blotches and Streaks. These are uneven tone areas that are found on the emulsion after fixing. They are due almost exclusively to faulty development technique. The first cause is uneven immersion in the development solution at the start of development. Poor agitation is a second cause.

Still another possibility is that a magnifier was placed against the emulsion surface during development in order to watch the progress of the development. This contact can cause a blotch.

A final cause is lack of sufficient developer in the tray to cover the film.

NECESSARY CHARACTERISTICS OF THE CAMERAMAN

As a conclusion, I would like to mention the characteristics that I believe every photographer should possess. In the event he does not have them, I most certainly believe he should try to acquire them. One of these qualities is an ability and the second an attitude. The ability is the toleration of ideas and suggestions from all sources, and the attitude is one of active curiosity and experimentation.

Sooner or later we all have someone try to tell us how to do a certain job, or hear critical comments from another person. True, in many cases we feel they are wasting our time. Being a normal human being, we occasionally resent having someone tell us "what he would have done to do the job properly." But we must listen and try to comprehend what is being said, for, surprisingly enough, there are other people who have had experiences also, and they just might know the answer to our problem. So, as much as it in within your power, be tolerant. Listen to the other person and try to sift the valuable ideas from the chaff. You will be surprised at the amount of worthwhile information that you can receive that way.

The attitude of active curiosity and experimentation is another quality that is important to the photographer. Do not feel that there is no possibility for any worthwhile change to occur in your part of the lithographic process. Look carefully at the new equipment that comes on the market. Try to evaluate it in terms of your own use rather than to reject it on the basis of "They're trying to put something else over on the public." Read also about the new methods that are suggested, and try to see how they could apply to your plant. And then, when something seems reasonable, try it out. At first, try the process or equipment in the way that was suggested without any innovations of your own. Then evaluate the results, and if they seem reasonably valuable, look them over carefully for improvements that would be helpful in your own operation. In effect, I'm suggesting that you be your own research man. It is not necessary to know the technical reason behind a process or a piece of equipment to be able to determine if it will work for you. True, with a good technical background you will be able to do more with the information, but you can get a reasonable amount of technical background by reading the trade periodicals and trying to keep with what is going on. If you haven't already done so, start a reference file. When something interests you and you haven't the time to look into it immediately, put it someplace where you can get to it at a later date. Clip articles that are of interest, and file them. You will be surprised how well you will remember the basic facts in them, and you will be able to search out more detailed information in the event that the situation arises where you need it. Approach your job with the willingness to try something, if on the basis of your considered judgment, you feel it may be of some value. Notice that I said "considered judgment," and I mean just that. You must consider the facts and evaluate them and not make a snap judgment.

You must keep both an open and an active mind; open in the sense that you will listen; and active, in the sense that you will give new ideas serious consideration, and if they seem worthwhile, act upon them. In this way, you will help to make your photographic operations more efficient and you will develop greater assurance in the soundness of your working techniques.

Section Nine: Line Photography

Line photography is the most simple of the three groups in which all graphic arts photography is customarily divided. Line photography is used for black-and-white copy that does not require tonal reproduction or the use of a halftone screen. This copy may be single or multicolor, it may be a part of a job that is completely done in line, or it may be part of a line and halftone combination job.

Operational Steps. The operational steps of line photography can be considered under eight headings. (1) Inspecting and scaling the copy, (2) Placing the copy on the copyboard of the camera, (3) Setting the camera, (4) Loading the camera with the light-sensitive material, (5) Exposing the light-sensitive material, (6) Removing the exposed light-sensitive material, (7) Processing the exposed light-sensitive material, and finally (8) Inspecting and passing on the processed light-sensitive material for further use. All of these eight steps are individually discussed in the following. Although paper, film and glass photo products fall in the category of light-sensitive materials, the general term film will be used for this discussion since it is the most commonly used of these materials.

INSPECTING AND SCALING THE COPY

In inspecting the copy for reproduction, the cameraman usually divides his work into groups depending on (1) the quality of the copy received and (2) the reproduction size or scale required for the copy. All copy should be in perfect shape when it is turned over to the camera department, but more than often this is not the case. Poor repro proofs, faded typematter, grayed or yellowed backgrounds, contrasty stickups on fine pencil drawings, and an occasional group of good letterpress repro proofs is usually the type of copy the average cameraman receives. This wide assortment the cameraman will divide first into groups of the required reproduction size, for scaling. For this purpose he uses a proportionate scale to obtain the desired percentage of enlargement or reduction. Then the cameraman will segregate copy into several groups depending on its quality. This organization is necessary, for it allows the photographer to group the copy according to reproduction size and copy quality, thereby improving work efficiency.

Quality of Copy. The quality of copy is determined by considering: Color, Background, and Line quality. The color of the copy is an important consideration, for ortho film will not photograph all colors as black and consequently certain types of colored copy will require the use of filters. The background of the copy is another factor which will determine the use of a filter. For example in fine line pencil drawings on paper or vellum, the contrast range of this type of copy may not be sufficient to produce good background density on the finished negative and the use of contrast filters will greatly improve negative quality. The actual line work itself should be inspected, in particular the fineness and blackness of letter characters.

Scaling the Copy. The use of a proportionate scale for calculating enlargement or reduction percentages is common to the modern types of process cameras although some of the old type galley cameras require focusing on the ground glass to obtain the reproduction scale. The reduction percentage can also be calculated by dividing the original copy size into the reproduction (or negative) size and multiplying by 100 to obtain the percentage.

PLACING THE COPY ON THE COPYBOARD

To facilitate placement of copy on the copyboard, a diagram should be drawn having diagonals from corner to corner thus establishing the center of the diagram, and rectangles, drawn from the center, in the conventional film sizes, starting with 5 inches by 7 inches and going up to the maximum size of the copyboard. This diagram is placed on the copyboard and is used for positioning copy. With this diagram, the photographer can immediately figure the required film size to cover the copy, and also have the copy in proper position relative to the film.

SETTING THE CAMERA

The lens aperture, use of filters, lighting angle and camera setting for proper reproduction size are the main considerations involved in setting the camera.

For line work the most common openings used at same size are f/22 and f/32, as process lenses have their best definition and resolution at these apertures; f/16 is also used to compensate for low light intensity of arcs or for speeding up production with average arc illumination. Our chart illustrates the extension of these f openings for use at

Reproduction Percentage	f/16 at Same size	f/22 at Same size	f/32 at Same size
25%	f/27	f/35	f/51
30	25	33	49
33	23	32	48
40	22	31	45
50	21	29	42
75	19	25	36
Same Size	16	22	32
150	14	18	25
175	12	16	23
200	11	15	21
250	9	13	18
300	8	11	16

f opening chart.

different reproduction sizes. By using this procedure, the aperture is varied according to the enlargement or reduction while the exposure time remains constant. In modern types of process cameras, the lens is equipped with a diaphragm chart mounted on the lensboard. A pointer which is connected to the lens collar, extends from the lens to the diaphragm chart. For use the pointer is aligned to the proper reproduction size on the scale selected, and the f opening is automatically set. This diaphragm chart contains scales for all the f openings and allows for selection of any desired aperture.

Filters. Filters used for black-and-white photography serve two purposes: to increase the contrast of the original and to render certain colors monochromatic thereby holding or dropping them on the finished negative. The contrast filters are used extensively on poor copy, pencil drawings and grayed or yellowed background copy. They comprise the yellow and light orange series, namely Wratten K1, K2, K3 and G. These filters are characterized by increasing blue absorption of the spectrum thereby increasing contrast on ortho or pan film. In line photography it also common to photograph different colors in a monochromatic tone in relation to other colors; our chart which appears on the following pages illustrates the filter film combination for this purpose.

Lighting Angle. The lighting angle of 45 degrees of a distance of three feet from the copyboard is considered normal for process cameras. Reducing the angle gives much flatter lighting resulting in a reduction of light intensity on the copyboard. This may be advisable at times to increase the coverage of larger copy and also to eliminate "hot spots" or glare on the copyboard in the case of extreme enlargements. Increasing the light angle gives much greater intensity on the copyboard but should be done with discretion, for it usually results in copyboard glare and also in undercutting of weak or poor type characters in the copy.

Setting for Reproduction Percentage. The setting of the camera for reproduction percentage varies greatly according to the camera manufacturers. In some of the cameras, the actual reproduction percentage is also the setting of the camera; in others there are arbitrary systems in use. These require the use of a percentage scale (to obtain the reproduction percentage size) and reference to the camera scale for proper setting numbers.

We might consider another step in the camera setting, namely the focusing of the image on the ground glass. Here the photographer will check the sharpness of the image and adjust for positioning. In some types of process cameras the lensboard is equipped with vertical and horizontal movement; there, exact positioning of the copy on the ground glass is simply made by use of the handwheels for lensboard movement. The higher priced precision type cameras are equipped with electrically controlled movement of the copyboard, which greatly improves the ease of focusing and positioning on the ground glass.

LOADING THE CAMERA

After inspecting and setting the camera the next step is the actual insertion of film in the camera. The film back of

To Photograph	Pan Film Filter	Ortho Film Filter	Colorblind Film Filter
Blue as black	Red or orange	Yellow or orange	—
Blue as white	Blue	Blue	None or blue
Blue green as white	Blue or green	Blue or green	—
Blue green as black	Red	—	—
Green as white	Green	Green or yellow	—
Green as black	Red	—	—
Orange as black	Blue	Blue	None
Orange as white	Red or orange	—	—
Red as black	Green	Green	None
Red as white	Red or orange	—	—
Violet as white	Blue	Blue	None or blue
Violet as black	Green	Deep yellow	—
Yellow as black	Blue	Blue	None or blue
Yellow as white	Red or orange	Yellow or orange	—
Yellow green as white	Green	Green or yellow	—
Yellow green as black	Blue	Blue	None or blue

Film-filter chart.

cameras can be one of three types, vacuum, stayflat or pressure. The vacuum type back is the simplest and most productive of these types and consists of an opaque metal or plastic back, with channels for vacuum, which is supplied by a motor pump. Vacuum backs are usually marked in some manner for easy placement of the film. The channels for vacuum are so designed that they are adjustable for various sizes of films. Its glass plates cannot be used on this type of back. Cameras equipped with vacuum backs have also plate holders to be used specifically for glass plates. Stayflat backs consist of a glass with stayflat solution (either clear or matte) applied to the face of the glass. The film is placed on the stayflat with emulsion-side-up. Pressure type backs are used primarily on the smaller type galley cameras and consist of a clear glass for placement of the film with a pressure back.

EXPOSURE

During exposure the photographic film is subjected to the light reflected from the copy; the result of exposure is the formation of a latent image on the film. Exposure is actually equal to time multipled by intensity. ($E = i\,T$, where E is exposure, i intensity of light and T time.) Mechanical timers for exposure control only take care of the actual time portion of the equation and make no measurement of light intensity values. Consequently variations in line voltage causing arc fluctuation may effect the exposure equation, but these variations are not discernible by the mechanical timer. The commercial light integrator satisfies the measurement of intensity and time. It works in the following manner. Setting the integrator to a light value registers on a condenser a specific amount of electrical energy which is dissipated by the action of the light on a photoelectric cell.

The integrator measures not the time of exposure but the product of exposure, that is light intensity times exposure time.

Exposure by Variation of Aperture. Exposure can actually be standardized by varying the aperture and maintaining the same exposure time or by using a fixed aperture and varying time according to the enlargement or reduction. Variation of the aperture has already been considered above in the discussion on setting the camera. By using a fixed aperture, the exposure time is calculated according to the square of the proportional increase or decrease of the camera extension from same size.

Exposure Variation with Light Distance and Angle. Another variation of exposure by varying the light distance and light angle can be computed by the following formula:

$$\text{New Exposure} = \left(\frac{\text{new distance}}{\text{old distance}}\right)^2 \times \text{old exposure} \times \frac{\text{sine of old angle}}{\text{sine of new angle}}$$

The use of this formula simplifies the obtaining of a new exposure when making a radical change in lighting and/or light angle.

REMOVING THE EXPOSED FILM

After exposure the film is removed from the camera for further processing. Many cameraman doing mass production line photography have some procedure of storing this film in a film cabinet and then developing it all together. The deterioration of the latent image on high contrast films is small, but *prolonged storage* under varying temperatures and humidity conditions will affect the finished result.

PROCESSING THE EXPOSED NEGATIVE

During processing, the latent image is converted into a permanent visible image through the process of reduction in a solution called a developer. The developing agent reduces the exposed silver halides to black metallic silver, and the fixer dissolves those unexposed and undeveloped areas of the negative, thereby making the image permanent. Additional details on the chemistry of development and fixation are covered in the section "Chemistry of Photography" of this chapter.

Factors of Development. In line photography the two controlling factors of developing are agitation and temperature. The litho type developer used for high contrast film contains an alkali capable of extreme contrast; consequently, contrast can be greatly affected by agitation. Still development will reduce the development action and considerably reduce contrast, whereas increased agitation will greatly exaggerate contrast and may adversely affect the printing areas by filling in. The temperature of the developer effects contrast in much the same manner; that is, a cold developer will reduce contrast and a warm developer will increase it. Film manufacturers usually recommend development temperature at 68 degrees F.; developing time varies according to the make of films from $2\frac{1}{4}$ to $2\frac{1}{2}$ minutes.

Commercial Developers. There are a number of excellent commercially prepared developers available today. Some of these developers are designed for a specific type of work such as Kodak's Kodalith Fine Line Developer. Other developers such as those manufactured by Ansco, Phillip Hunt Co. and Kodak, have characteristics of long life, latitude and high density.

Liquid Concentrate-Type Developers and Fixer. In the past few years liquid-type developers and fixers have become quite popular because it is so easy to mix them. After dilution, the liquid concentrate developers exhibit working characteristics similar to those developers supplied in powder form. Before dilution for use, the concentrates should be stored at temperatures above 40°F to prevent the components from coming out of solution.

INSPECTING AND PASSING ON THE NEGATIVE FOR FURTHER USE

After development the negative is inspected as there are some measures that can be taken in the darkroom for corrective action. The most common of these corrective measures is the use of Farmer's reducer. By means of Farmer's reducer, silver is dissolved through a complicated chemical action, thereby improving an overexposed or overdeveloped negative. Intensifying is basically the addition of silver to an underexposed or undeveloped negative. This is a rather detailed procedure and not used to any extent in the graphic arts, but there are some types of direct intensifiers which are used by some with fair results. When inspection is completed, the negative is dried and passed on to the stripping department.

CONCLUSION

Line photography is considered by many cameramen as elementary and consequently not requiring much attention. But line work is on the contrary the basis of the photographic procedures and extremely important. With such new products as auto-positive films and the Kodak Autoscreen Ortho film, the work and knowledge of the line photographer is broadened. In the future you can look to many other new products which will greatly affect line photography.

Section Ten: Halftones with the Crossline Screen

The major requirement in reproducing continuous-tone copy by the lithographic process is that such copy be photographically translated into a discontinuous tone or gradation of dots.

CROSSLINE SCREEN

The crossline halftone screen, placed in front of the sensitive material, provides a means for creating the required pattern of dots. The size and shape of the dots on the negative vary according to the amount of light reflected by the copy and transmitted by the screen. Small opaque dots produce shades of gray and darker tones, while the larger, opaque dots produce the light tones of gray. This gradation of dots is illustrated in the example of enlarged dots in our illustration.

Transfer of Image. The photographic transfer of the image from the negative to the plate is possible because of the clearness of the transparent spaces between the opaque dots. The sensitized plate coatings require this clearness for the complete hardening of every dot, regardless of its size. Any other type of negative, i.e., continuous-tone, does not provide sufficient clearness, but progressively retards the light as its density increases; this produces a partially hardened, insecure plate image. Hence, a tone must be reproduced by a gradation of hardened dots whose size — in the final press plate — will carry ink according to the tone values of the copy. These dots must, of course, be small enough to be relatively invisible to the naked eye.

Appearance of Tones. The *highlight tones* in the original or copy appear in the screened negative as small transparent dots surrounded by large, round, opaque dots, whose edges overlap. These dots are the result of the greatest amount of light reflected by the copy. The *middletones* of the copy are represented in the negative by dots corresponding to the amounts of light reflected by such areas in the original, i.e., the light grays as small round transparent dots, and the dark grays as large transparent dots and smaller opaque dots. The *shadows* or darker areas in the copy appear in the negative as the most transparent portions. They take the form of small round, opaque dots, surrounded by large transparent areas. All of these dot formations are the result of correct screen distance, plus sufficient exposure with a suitable set of diaphragm apertures.

Classification of Screens. Halftone screens are classified according to the number of opaque lines ruled to the linear inch. For example, when there are 120 ruled lines to the linear inch, the screen is known as a 120-line screen. The 120- and 133-line screens are commonly used for black-and-white halftone reproductions. Finer screens, up to 300- and 400-lines, are used only for the higher grades of work. (Halftone screens used for black-and-white reproductions are generally rectangular in shape. Circular screens are also used.) Glass screens consist of two pieces of ruled glass cemented together so that the opaque rules (lines) on one piece of glass cross the lines of the other piece at an angle of 90 degrees.

Making a Glass Screen. The rulings (lines) are put on the glass with a high precision machine. These rulings are then etched into the glass, following which the depression is filled with a pigment. On the grating formed by the lines when the pieces of glass are placed face to face, the width of the aperture (opening) equals the width of the line in glass screens for photolithography. Finally the two ruled (lined) pieces of glass are cemented together with the lines at right angles to form the screen.

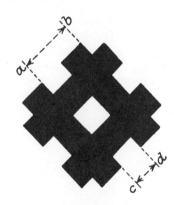

Enlarged unit of crossline screen.

Dot patterns.

Angle of Screen. In black-and-white reproduction work the screen is so positioned that the ruled lines form a 45-degree angle with the base of the camera. This angle is chosen because it is most conducive to the final appearance of the halftone picture. Each dot on the negative represents a minute area of the original. For our purposes it is inadequate to say that each opaque dot in the negative must be dense and sharp, and that each transparent area glass clear. If highly satisfactory reproduction is the goal then each dot must be of such size and shape that it is a true representation of the part of the original it is supposed to represent.

NATURE OF LIGHT

Before discussing the theories of dot formation by use of the glass screen, consideration should be given to the nature of light. We might therefore begin by asking the question "What is light?"

Definition of Light. Light may be considered as a form of radiant energy which acts upon the eye producing vision. According to the *corpuscular theory*, Newton considered light to be propagated as a stream of corpuscles or "LIGHT BULLETS," emitted by a shining or luminous body. This theory does not present a suitable explanation for a major portion of the actions and characteristics of light, although it has been proven that in some cases, light acts more as if made of particles than waves. The *Quantum Theory* states that light consists of bundles of light called quanta or Photons, the energy of which depends on the frequency of the radiation. The *wave theory* of light states that light, considered as radiant energy, is propagated in waves that vary in length from 400 mu in the violet to about 700 mu in the red portion of the spectrum. This theory has to date achieved the widest acceptance due to its ability to explain a major portion of the complexities of the phenomena of light.

THEORIES OF THE HALFTONE SCREEN

The nature of light has been used as the basis of several theories explaining the effects of the halftone screen. These theories base themselves respectively on *penumbra, pinhole* and *diffraction phenomena*. The *penumbra theory* of dot formation was worked out in 1908 by Clerc and Calmels, following the investigations of Tallent, Dolland and Deville. The *diffraction theory* of halftone images was investigated quite extensively by Fruwirth, Mertle and Yule, and explains dot formation by the phenomena of light diffraction of the screen ruling. The *pinhole theory,* also referred to as the Ives Theory, considers dot formation by the action of the diameter or pinhole affect of the lens on the halftone screen. Each of these theories has some merit towards an understanding of the theory of dot formation; consequently, each will be discussed here in some detail.

Penumbra Theory. When an opaque body is held in the light coming from a pinpoint source, all light is cut off from the space behind it, and a sharp edged shadow called an umbra is formed. When the light source is broad, some

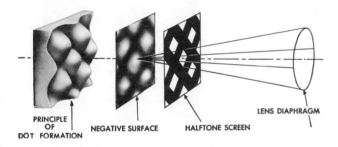

Dot formation with crossline screen.

of the light falls in regions from which other rays of light have been cut off, thus forming a penumbra (partial shadow) around the umbra, as shown in our illustration. If the opaque body is smaller than the luminuous body, the umbra tapers to a point and disappears.

We can see from this explanation of penumbra, that it actually consists of a continuous shadow varying in some degree of darkness, and the dot formation is caused by this vignetted effect of the halftone screen. The major critics of the penumbra theory state that it is based on the straight line propagation of light, and does not take into account the diffraction caused by the halftone screen. The detail of the penumbral theory is quite complicated; geometrical optics are used for explaining the depth of darkness or shadow at any point causing the dot formation.

Diffraction Theory. Diffraction may be defined as the bending of rays of light from a straight course when cut off by an obstacle, such as the ruling of a glass screen. According to this theory the halftone screen is considered as a double diffraction grating. The word diffraction as used in connection with grating, indicates a property of light of which the grating takes advantage to so separate, and recombine the light waves to produce spectra. Whenever light emerges from a narrow aperture, it spreads out much as a dense crowd of people spread upon emerging from a narrow gate.

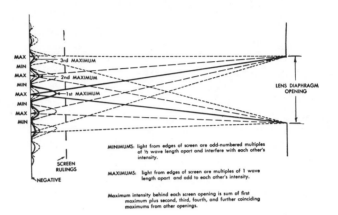

Diffraction theory of dot formation.

Laws of Diffraction Theory. The diffraction theory was extensively investigated by Fruwirth, and basically states that: (a) Each screen has a definite focal length, and consequently its distance to the sensitized film varies according to screen ruling; (b) Each screen has a speed ratio, the finer the screen ruling the faster the speed ratio; (c) The lack of color correction of the glass screen requires an adjustment in screen distance when various filters are used.

Acceptance of Theory. The opponents of this theory state that Fruwirth uses the general equation of the penumbra theory to calculate the stop size in terms of camera extension. Proponents of both the diffraction theory and penumbra theory have been partly wrong in maintaining exclusive explanation of dot formation. Diffraction plays the major role with fine screens while penumbra shadow patterns are less modified by diffraction with coarse screens. The whole range of dot formations may be more easily related to both effects as modifying each other.

Pinhole Theory. This theory was investigated by Ives in 1889, and considers the dot formation to be made by the diaphragm of the lens, projected through the transparent mesh of the screen to the sensitized film. This theory is strongly opposed by many with the argument that no consideration is given to the relationship of the lens diameter to the screen distance, to mention only one of the major points of dispute. The main result of the investigation into this theory was the information published on the results of various diaphragm shapes on dot formation.

RELATION OF LENS APERTURE TO DOT FORMATION

The formation of dots on the photographic sensitive material is dependent upon: (1) the size and, to some extent the shape of the lens apertures (stops), (2) the screen distance (measured from the screen ruling to the surface of the sensitized material or the ground glass), (3) the intensity of the reflected light, (4) the speed and contrast of the photographic sensitive material, and (5) the duration of the exposure.

Equation for Dot Formation. Correct dot formation on all halftone negatives is the result of adjusting the lens aperture and the screen distances, so that their ratios are balanced. This is shown in the following equation:

$$\frac{\text{Diameter of lens aperture}}{\text{Camera extension}} = \frac{\text{Screen aperture}}{\text{Screen distance}}$$

From this equation, you can note that there are two known factors, camera extension and screen aperture; with two variables, screen distance and lens aperture. The ratio 1:64

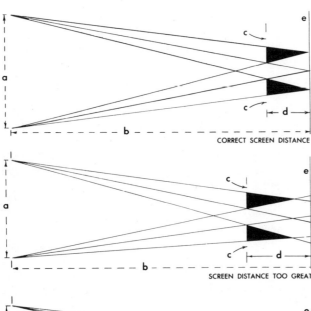

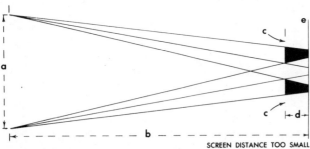

Correct and incorrect screen distances.

for this equation is widely used for average lighting conditions; however the 1:90 ratio (normally requiring twice the exposure of the 1:64 ratio) is convenient when the intensity of illumination is greater or the sensitive material is faster. When used for making projection positives from continuous-tone separations, the 1:45 or 1:32 ratios are best for overall performance.

Calculation of f Opening. The equation described above calculates the lens aperture in terms of a diameter and not an f stop. To calculate the f opening, let us illustrate just the left half of the equation and figure the lens di-

ameter. For the purpose of the illustration, we will use a 24-inch focal length lens and figure the f opening for same size on the 1:64 ratio. The camera extension is taken from our table. From this formula:

$$\frac{\text{Diameter of lens aperture}}{\text{Camera extension}} = \frac{1}{64}$$

then:

$$\frac{X}{48} = \frac{1}{64} \text{ or } X = \frac{1}{64} \times 48 = \tfrac{3}{4} \text{ inch}$$

The lens diameter of $\tfrac{3}{4}$ inch can be then computed to f stop as follows:

$$\frac{\text{Focal length of lens}}{\text{Diameter of lens aperture}} = f \text{ opening}$$

then:

$$\frac{24 \text{ inches}}{\tfrac{3}{4} \text{ inch}} = 24 \times \frac{4}{3} = 32 \text{ or } f/32$$

Calculations with the lens diameter is somewhat inconvenient and can be simplified by the use of the following equation:

$$f \text{ opening} = \tfrac{1}{64} \times \frac{\text{camera extension}}{\text{focal length of lens}}$$

substituting for this formula:

$$f \text{ opening} = \tfrac{1}{64} \times \frac{48}{24} = 1/32 \text{ or } f/32$$

Practical Calculations of f Opening. The use of this formula presented so far are of course too complicated for daily use. As a result there are numerous devices for stop or aperture calculations. In modern types of process cameras, the lens collar is equipped with an indicator to an enlarged ratio scale atop the lensboard. The operator just sets the pointer to the percentage of reproduction on the ratio scale and the lens aperture is automatically set.

Through the courtesy of Di Noc Chemical Arts, Inc., our chart illustrates a simplified straight line halftone calculator based on the 64 ratio. Instructions for use are contained below the chart.

Calculation of Screen Distance. The screen distance as previously stated is the distance from the ruling of the screen to the sensitized material. The importance of this screen distance is best explained by the diagrams contained in our illustration.

The screen distance is calculated by use of the right half of the general equation mentioned, using the same $\tfrac{1}{64}$ ratio viz:

$$\frac{\text{Screen aperture}}{\text{Screen distance}} = \frac{1}{64}$$

The screen aperture is obtained by multiplying the screen ruling by 2; in the case of a 133-line screen, the aperture would be 266. Substituting this in the formula above we would calculate for proper screen distance as follows:

$$\frac{\frac{1}{266}}{X} = \frac{1}{64}$$

then X equals $\frac{64}{266}$ of an inch (or $\tfrac{1}{4}$ of an inch).

Keep in mind that this calculated distance is to be measured from the ruling of the glass screen and not from the cover glass of the screen. In practice, measurement of the screen distance is made from the edge of the cover glass of the screen to the sensitized material; with this procedure the thickness of the cover glass should be subtracted from the screen distance calculated.

This portion of the general equation is of course constant, for the screen distance and aperture of the screen are not changed for a given screen. However, the camera extension varies according to the reproduction ratio and consequently the general equation will not be in balance unless compensation is made for f openings, thus keeping the same ratio throughout the entire equation.

HALFTONE STOPS

The spread of light around the rulings of the glass screen can be decreased or increased depending on the intensity of the light source, or the aperture of the lens. Consequently, exposure of a halftone to a large f opening will cause great spread and a small white dot (highlight dot) on the negative. Reducing the f opening in size will reduce this spread and dot size proportionately. As a result of this relationship of lens opening to dot size, the use of a multiple stop exposure for glass screen halftone work is generally accepted. The following three multiple stops are here described: (1) Highlight stops, (2) Middletone stops, and (3) Detail stops.

Highlight Stops. The highlight stop is the largest opening of the halftone exposure and is calculated on the basis of $\frac{1}{48}$th of the camera extension. At same size this is equal to $f/24$. This exposure effects primarily the highlights of the copy and if desired can be used for a complete drop-out of the highlight areas. Overexposure at this opening will result in enlarged middletones and fogged over or black highlights on the negative.

Middletone Stops. The middletone stop is approximately one full stop less than the highlight exposure and is calculated as $\frac{1}{64}$th of the camera extension. At same size this is equal to $f/32$, and the middletone stop requires twice the exposure of the highlight stop. This stop will properly record the intermediate tones of gray on the copy and extend slightly into the lighter shadows, and darker highlights of the original copy.

Detail Stops. The detail stop is approximately one full stop less than the middletone and is calculated on the basis of $\frac{1}{96}$th of the camera extension. At same size this is equal to $f/45$, and at this opening the exposure is twice the middletone exposure. This stop is used to record those fine details in the darkest or shadow areas of the original.

Exposure Ratios. Although different ratios are used for calculations of the f opening for the various stops, the average of the three e.g., $\frac{1}{48}$, $\frac{1}{64}$, $\frac{1}{96}$, closely approximates an average of $\frac{1}{64}$th, and consequently it is not necessary to balance the equation completely for a change of the screen distance. The exposure ratio of 1 for highlight, 2 for middletone and 4 for detail is considered normal for average copy.

Flash Exposure. Flashing is a supplementary exposure of the latent halftone image to the light which is reflected by a white sheet of paper of the bright evenly diffused light from a flashlamp. This exposure is made with a small lens aperture, and at same size is figured at $f/64$. The lens opening for this exposure should be at least one full stop smaller than the middletone opening. At same size the $f/64$ is equal to a ratio of 128th of the camera extension and $f/90$ at same size is equal to $\frac{1}{256}$th of the camera extension.

Purpose of Flash. The purpose of this flash exposure is to increase the opacity of each dot at its core without increasing the dot size or shape. Modern usage of flashing also has the purpose of extending the tonal scale and actually brings in latent shadow detail. Flashing is also used to improve overall tone reproduction of negatives by permitting greater highlight contrast, with fuller middletones and shadow detail retained. The range of tonal values of the average lithographic copy does not reflect enough light to produce a satisfactory gradation of dots over the entire negative image, especially if dot opacity is lacking in the shadow dots produced by the primary exposure. Thus, flash exposures increase the opacity of each dot at its center and help toward producing screened rather than solid shadows on the press plate.

Flash exposures, however, cannot overcome the loss of shadow detail when the main exposures are short. There must be a sizable dot produced in the shadows, in order to reproduce the detail.

Adjusting Flash for Copy. Copy with extreme contrast requires this additional concentration of light (the flash) on the cores of the weak shadow dots in order that the shadows of the negative will not print as solids. Flat copy does not require as long a flash because the light reflected by the shadows produces dots sufficiently dense to represent the tonal range and to transfer properly on the offset press plate.

Variations of Halftone Stops. Depending on the tonal range of the original copy, it may be advisable to vary the three-stop procedure of exposure. In some cases experienced operators prefer the use of a one-stop halftone, using the middletone exposure of the three-stop halftone. This single-stop exposure will produce acceptable results when the copy contains primarily grays and few highlights. The shadow portions can be adequately compensated for by use of the flash exposure.

A two-stop exposure, using any combination of the three-stop procedure outlined above, will produce satisfactory results when properly related to the tonal range of the original copy. The same ratios of exposure will apply to this system as well as to the three-stop procedure.

SPECIAL DIAPHRAGMS

There are numerous types of diaphragm shapes developed over the years, each of which will give varied dot formations. The most common in use today is the square diaphragm as shown in our illustration. The extended diagonals of these diaphragms will produce square dots throughout

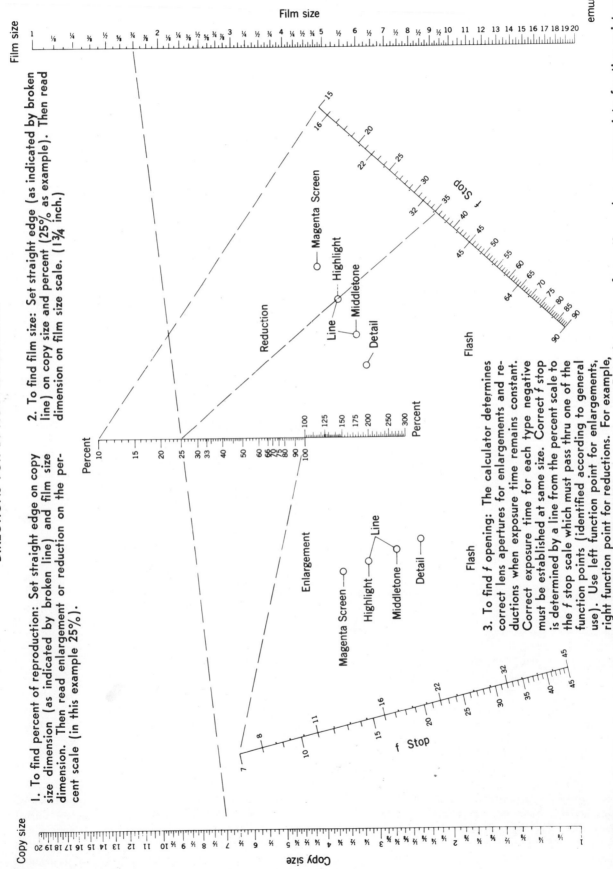

DIRECTIONS FOR DI NOC CALCULATOR

1. To find percent of reproduction: Set straight edge on copy size dimension (as indicated by broken line) and film size dimension. Then read enlargement or reduction on the percent scale (in this example 25%).

2. To find film size: Set straight edge (as indicated by broken line) on copy size and percent (25% as example). Then read dimension on film size scale. (1¾ inch.)

3. To find f opening: The calculator determines correct lens apertures for enlargements and reductions when exposure time remains constant. Correct exposure time for each type negative must be established at same size. Correct f stop is determined by a line from the percent scale to the f stop scale which must pass thru one of the function points (identified according to general use). Use left function point for enlargements, right function point for reductions. For example, for a 25% reduction align by use of a straight edge 25 on the percent scale to the circle for magenta screen, and read the f opening for this type of negative on the f stop scale in the right hand corner.

    For other types of negatives, choose appropriate function points and follow same procedure.

4. To find flash exposure: For glass screen halftones use a lens aperture at least one lens division smaller than used for the detail exposure.

the entire tonal range of the copy. This system was devised and patented in 1897 by Branfil and Gamble.

Square-shaped diaphragm.

Star-Shaped Diaphragm. The star-shaped diaphragm is intended to produce the effect of a two-stop exposure with only one stop. The center hole acts as the small stop, while the star rays are to give effect of shorter exposure to a large aperture.

Rectangular Opening. The elongated rectangular opening, advocated by Villemaire, is used for an extra exposure to the copy, eliminating the highlight dots. This stop causes a dot to be placed in the white highlights of the negative producing a drop-out or exaggerated highlight.

Elongated Slot. The use of a single elongated slot will produce an elongation or "chain link" of dots on the negative. This linking effect produces a better rendition of

tones in copy containing soft middletone to highlight gradations, because it eliminates the sharp break-off of dot formation normally attributed to dot formation by circular diaphragms.

Star-shaped diaphragm.

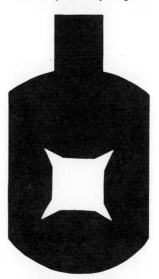

Dog-eared stop.

DEFECTIVE HALFTONE NEGATIVES, THEIR CAUSES AND REMEDIES

Any one of several factors involved may influence the final halftone negative. Because of this the photographer must thoroughly understand the factors contributing to the dot formation of the individual dots and the relation of each to the whole image.

The controlling factors in halftone reproduction are: (1) Illumination of copy; (2) Focus; (3) Setting of ruled screen; (4) Setting of lens aperture; (5) Exposure; (6) Development.

The following indicates the most common causes of defective halftone negatives with suggested remedies.

Elongated slot.

Incorrect Contrast. This defect can mean too high a contrast or too low a contrast range. *Causes:* Incorrect screen distance, overexposure at highlight stop, highlight stop too large, no flash exposure given, tonal range of copy too great. *Remedies:* Check screen calibration, decrease highlight exposure, reduce large highlight opening, give flash if necessary, make additional detail exposure for greater tonal range of copy.

Incorrect Contrast. Incorrect contrast caused by low contrast. *Cause:* Highlight stop too small, screen distance too short, insufficient highlight exposure, detail and flash exposure too long, or flash stop too large. *Remedies:* Use larger highlight stop, check screen distance, increase highlight exposure, decrease detail and flash exposure or reduce *f* stop of flash exposure.

Incorrect Dot Formation. Dots have soft edges, or are fuzzy or irregular. *Causes:* Screen distance too long, incorrect stop or stops, halftone screen and sensitive material are not in parallel, low temperature of developer. *Remedies:* Correct screen distance, check *f* ratio system used, check parallelism of planes of screen and sensitive material, de-velop according to manufacturer's directions, correct developer temperature to 68 degrees F.

Incorrect Dot Formation. Incorrect dot formation is indicated by square shadow dots and square transparent highlight dots. *Causes:* Screen distance too short, stops are too small or flash stop too large and exposure too long. *Remedies:* Correct screen distance, use larger set of *f* stops, use smaller stop for flashing or shorten flash exposure.

Variation in Dot Size and Shape. Dot size and shape sometimes varies from one side of negative to the other. *Causes:* Improper alignment of screen with camera back or uneven illumination. *Remedies:* Check parallel of planes, adjust for evenness of illumination.

Weak Soft Dots. Weak soft dots in the shadows sometimes occur with open highlights. *Causes:* Underdevelopment or underexposure. *Remedies:* Correct for proper exposure and development.

Weak Soft Dots. Weak soft dots in the shadows sometimes occur with correct highlight dots. *Causes:* Improper screen distance, or failure to flash. *Remedies:* Correct screen distance and use flash.

Section Eleven: Halftones with the Contact Screen

Our presentation of contact screens is divided into the following subjects: (1) General exposition of contact screens, and their calibration; (2) Single main exposure technique; (3) Shadow flash exposure technique; (4) Filters, equipment, and procedures for shadow flashing; (5) Highlight flash exposure technique; (6) Adjustment of screen range with CC filters; (7) Use of different development techniques; (8) Combining various techniques; (9) Highlight drop out technique; and (10) Choice of the right technique.

CONTACT SCREENS AND THEIR CALIBRATION

The development of contact halftone screens has greatly simplified the techniques of making black and white halftones and has made it possible for literally thousands of new plants to do their own halftone work. Basically, two types of contact screens are used. The illustration shows an enlarged view of a contact screen.

Gray and Magenta Contact Screens. Both the magenta and gray contact screens form halftone dots on sensitized films through the modulation of light by the optical action of the vignetted dot pattern of the screen acting on the film emulsion. This dot forming pattern is produced as a magenta dye image in magenta screens, and a developed silver pattern in gray screens. In use, the emulsion or image side of the contact screen is held in intimate contact with the sensitized litho film emulsion during the dot forming exposure.

The advantages of contact screens over glass screens are numerous and the major items can be listed as follows:

1. Easier and faster to use.

Contact Screen, highly magnified.

2. Better resolution.
3. No screen distance to consider or screen positioning mechanism needed.
4. Any camera can produce halftones if it is equipped with a vacuum back.
5. Contrast control is relatively simple and reproducible.
6. Initial screen cost is low.

Having listed the advantages, it is only fair that some of the disadvantages also be listed:

1. A contact screen is fragile and must be handled carefully to prevent kinking, finger marking, chemical stains, scratches, etc.

2. Density ranges and exposure factors may vary from screen to screen and from manufacturer to manufacturer.

3. The dye density of the dot forming pattern can change during the life of the magenta contact screen.

The magenta screen is undoubtedly the most popular contact screen available, and it is used extensively both in the black and white field and in making halftone positives from color separation negatives. Gray screens are used mainly for specialized direct color separation work, so the rest of this section will be confined to a discussion of the more important magenta screen techniques.

Halftone Screen Calibration. Before proceeding to an actual halftone exposure, it is necessary to first learn even more about the contact screen assuming, of course, that you are already familiar with routine camera operations on line copy work.

First, each magenta contact screen will handle a given type (or density range) of copy most effectively and, in order to make the best use of any particular screen, it is necessary to learn what its inherent working density range is under specific shop conditions.

Calibrating the halftone screen to establish its working range is a simple matter, if a reflection gray scale is used which has a density range of more than 2.0. The approximate density of each step of this original gray scale must be known for later use in the calibration procedure.

STEP ONE. The density-calibrated gray scale and an average piece of original art are placed in the camera copy holder. The figure shows a typical target set-up for calibration procedure.

Target setup for calibration procedure.

STEP TWO. The litho film is placed on the vacuum back with the emulsion side toward the lens and the contact screen emulsion is placed in contact with the litho film emulsion. To insure proper contact between the magenta screen and film, a soft rubber roller or a photo chamois should be used to smooth the film surfaces together.

STEP THREE. A series of test exposures is made until a 90% dot is obtained in step 1 (the highlight area) of the gray scale. Processing time should be in accordance with the halftone recommendations found in the direction sheet supplied with each box of film. The figure shows a typical halftone test result. The sole object of this test is to calibrate the screen with the gray scale; the photograph is used to simulate flare conditions and its faithful reproduction is not a function of this test.

Typical Halftone Test Result.

A close examination of the reproduction will show that the negative contained a 90%[1] dot in step 1 of the gray scale and a 10% dot in step 8.

Comparing the gray scale and halftone images, and matching the steps together, it is found that the negative from which this print was made had a 90% halftone dot which coincides with step 1 of the continuous-tone scale, and this step has a density of .11. The 10% negative halftone dot which printed 90% positive shadow dot corresponds to continuous tone step 8 which has a density value of 1.52. The effective density range of our screen can now be determined by simply subtracting the minimum density that produced a 90% dot in the negative (.11) from the maximum density step that produced a 10% dot in the negative (1.52). The effective density range of this screen according to this calculation is 1.52 minus 11 or 1.41. Remember this particular screen range value of 1.41 for it will be referred to frequently hereafter.

In terms of halftone practice it can therefore be assumed that when both the screen and the original art have equal

---

[1] Dot sizes of 10% and 90% are illustrative and are not to be taken as absolute values. Actual highlight and shadow dot value will vary with individual shop requirements for plates, presses and stocks.

ranges or approximately 1.40 it should be possible to reproduce the picture in halftone form (carrying a 90% dot in the highlights and a 10% dot in the shadows of the negative) using only a single exposure with the magenta screen.

The following discussion will show different halftone techniques that can be used with various types of copy and will illustrate the results that can be obtained with each.

SINGLE EXPOSURE TECHNIQUE

To further study the relationship of the halftone screen range and the copy density range, examine the halftone print that was made from copy which has a density range of 1.43 compared to the 1.40 density range of the contact screen. If the screen calibration procedure has been correct, it should be possible to make a magenta screen halftone negative of this photograph with one exposure and normal processing, and to hold a 90% dot in the highlights and a 10% dot in the shadows of the halftone negative. This halftone balance was achieved using a single main exposure.

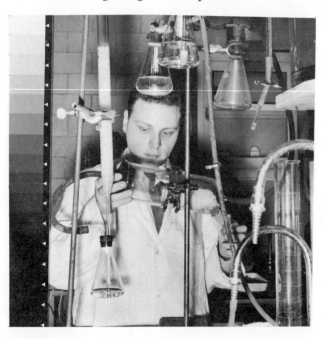

Halftone balance with single main exposure.

With the relationship of film-plate halftone values in mind, note that the printed shadows are carrying approximately the desired 90% dot and the printed highlights are holding a 10% dot. Since these printing-dot sizes are exact reciprocals of the desired negative halftone dot values, it may be assumed that our plate exposure and printing controls have essentially reproduced the dot character of our halftone negative.

SHADOW FLASH TECHNIQUE

The photograph shown is considered more or less average copy with a density range of 1.63. The density range of the portrait is therefore .23 higher than that of our calibrated screen which was 1.40. As a result if the same screen

Result when single exposure technique is used with copy whose density range is higher than that of screen.

exposure is given to this copy as that given to the laboratory copy, .23 density units of scene brightness will be lost somewhere within the density range of this picture. To show this loss, a halftone of this photograph was made using the same single exposure techniques. It is important to note that the halftone gray scales look very much alike, but the reproduced quality of the two pictures is in no way similar or satisfactory in this case.

The copy on 5:61 shows another halftone reproduction of the same photograph, but this time an additional shadow flash exposure has been added to extend the effective range of the magenta screen, thereby reproducing detail in the shadow area of the scene. This print now carries detail throughout the entire scale of the picture.

Digressing for just a moment, it should be pointed out that the inclusion of gray scales along with the copy is helpful in understanding and controlling camera halftone exposures *only when the critical highlight and shadow densities of each piece of copy are related to the corresponding density steps on the gray scale.*

When a shadow flash exposure is added, the halftone scale is extended to retain both the copy shadow detail and highlight detail as shown in the second illustration. Now look at the gray scale and observe that the halftone coverage has been increased (compared to first figure), so that a good highlight dot is produced on gray scale step 1, and a good shadow dot formed on gray scale step 9.

In other words, copy and gray scale areas having the same density will produce comparable halftone dots.

Turning this statement around, use of a gray scale (or a reflection densitometer) to learn the density range of the copy will permit pre-selection of halftone screen techniques that will fit all types of original copy to the relatively fixed range of the contact screen.

Result when density range of copy is considered and supplementary shadow flash exposure is used.

FILTER, EQUIPMENT AND PROCEDURES REQUIRED FOR SETTING UP A SHADOW FLASH TECHNIQUE

The shadow flash exposure can be made either with a yellow filtered flashing lamp on a process camera, or by means of an auxiliary safelight holder set up in a convenient spot near the camera back. Yellow filtered light should always be used when shadow flash exposing a magenta screen to insure the hardest, smallest dots possible, and use of a Wratten Series 00 safelight filter, a Wratten #4 gelatin filter (or equivalent) over the light source is recommended.

In practice, assemble the safelight holder with a 7½ watt frosted bulb and a suitable yellow filter and position it so that the opened camera back is uniformly illuminated. Under most conditions, the lamp will need to be at least 5 or 6 ft. from the camera back to insure even coverage, and average flash exposure should not be less than 10 seconds. (Use of a separate inexpensive exposure timer and a controlled voltage line for the light source is highly recommended to insure accuracy and reproducibility of flash results.)

To determine the average flash exposure that will be required with specific equipment, proceed with the following steps:

STEP ONE. Place an unexposed sheet of litho film on the camera vacuum back and cover with the magenta contact screen.

STEP TWO. Make a series of "stepped" exposures with the yellow filtered flash lamp. Usually a series of 5 second steps covering a range from 5 to 50 seconds will bracket the optimum exposure. If the optimum exposure is less than 10 seconds, reduce the light intensity level and run another set of test exposures.

STEP THREE. Process the test sheet in fresh litho developer; fixing, washing and drying the film normally. It is important that the development time, temperature and agitation be normal and consistent, so that this test is representative of average shop practice.

STEP FOUR. When the test sheet is dry, select the exposure time that produced the smallest shadow dot that will be successfully "held" by the printing press.

STEP FIVE. The full basic flash exposure value will rarely be used in practice because the litho film will usually have been given a preliminary threshold exposure by camera flare and a marginal amount of exposure from the copy shadows themselves.

Field experience has shown that with average copy and camera conditions only about 50 to 60% of the basic shadow flash exposure will be required to put a pin dot (10% dot) in the shadow area of average copy.

HIGHLIGHT FLASH EXPOSURES WHEN COPY DENSITY RANGE IS LESS THAN SCREEN RANGE

The serious printing quality problems that would be caused by use of a single main halftone exposure through our magenta screen are best shown by a close look at the first illustration which was made in this manner. Note how flat and gray the overall picture looks. The range of dots is only from about 10% to perhaps a 70% dot! It is small wonder then that this copy looks flat.

Looking back at how our halftone exposure was made, it will be found that the halftone negative was exposed to produce a good 90% highlight dot in the picture highlight area, but when this was done, the dot size in the picture shadow area was much too large — over 30% — and there was no way this could be prevented with a single exposure technique. The answer to this printing quality problem will be to produce a full range of halftone dots in the negative —but the question is how!

One very effective method for handling copy whose density range is shorter than screen range is to employ an auxiliary exposure technique arbitrarily called the *highlight bump exposure* which is given in the following manner.

Determine the main exposure that must be given to produce the proper shadow dot for the copy and give this exposure to the film. The camera back is then opened, the contact screen removed carefully to leave the litho film in exact position and the camera back again closed. Now with no contact screen covering the film, give extra unscreened exposure to the copy, by trial and error, until a 90% dot is produced in the highlight area. (A highlight bump exposure of 5 to 10% of the main screen exposure is about average for most camera-copy conditions.) A proper highlight bump exposure will not change the size of the shadow dots appreciably.

The short unscreened highlight bump exposure technique selectively superimposes most of the unscreened exposure light on the already heavily exposed negative highlight dot latent image, causing these relatively large (70%) dots to spread and become even larger, approaching the 90% level that is required. Less light falls on the middle tones so only a small change in dot size takes place, and almost no unscreened light falls on the shadow dot latent image from the dark areas of the copy, so these tiny 10% dots do not change size appreciably. A no-screen highlight bump exposure has thus produced a full range of halftone dots with this short range copy.

Now that the camera technique of making a highlight bump exposure has been illustrated, the actual procedure involved in this technique can best be understood by studying the printed halftones. The unsatisfactory print carries a normal 10% highlight dot but prints only 70 to 80% dots in the shadow region instead of the 90% dots that are needed to give depth. Obviously a single halftone screen exposure cannot successfully reproduce this kind of short density range copy, so the gray scale reproductions must be studied to reason out why and how the halftone bump flash exposure solves this common printing problem.

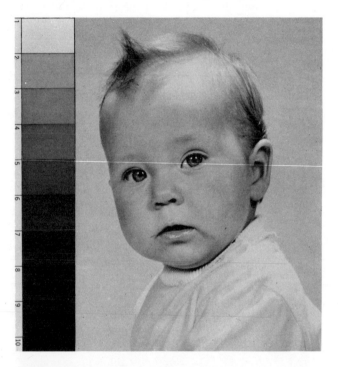

Result of single exposure technique when density range of copy is less than that of contact screen.

First, match the size of the shadow dot in the first print with the corresponding dot size in the printed gray scale reproduction. When this is done it will be found that the equal sized dot (80%) falls on the gray scale step 9 which had an original reflection density value of about 1.20.

By further examination of the printed halftone gray scale, it is also found that the shadow pin dot (90%) wanted is in step 10 which has an original density of 1.35. The first step in solving this quality problem therefore must be to reduce the basic negative halftone exposure so that in the printed sheet the 90% dot is produced on step 9 of the gray scale rather than on step 10 of the gray scale (density level 1.35). To do this it will be necessary to change the basic halftone screen exposure by a considerable amount and the following calculation from the gray scale can give an idea of the exposure change that will be required.

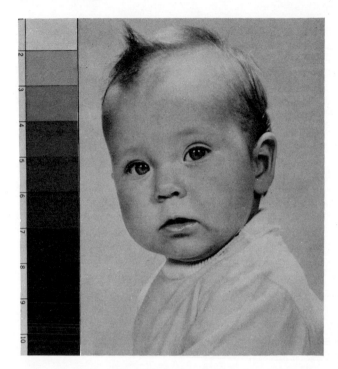

Result of adding highlight flash to basic main exposure.

Subtract the original density of the gray scale step 9 (1.20) which produced too large a pin dot (20%) in the negative from the gray scale step 10 (1.35) that produces the desired pin dot (10%) in the negative. The answer is a density difference of .15 between gray scale steps 9 and 10. Based on simple sensitometry it is known that changing exposure by a factor of 0.70 will produce an 0.15 density difference,

Result of combining highlight flash to shortened basic main exposure.

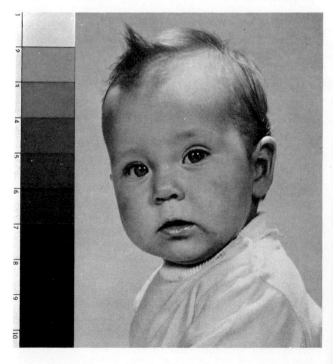

move the negative (pin) dot from step 8 to 7 will require that the basic exposure be reduced by a factor of just less than 2. When this done, it will also be noted that shortening the main halftone exposure by a factor of 2 times moves not only the 10% shadow dot into the proper position in the negative of both the gray scale and the picture, but it also shifts the highlight dot exposure a corresponding amount, thus producing highlight dots on the negative that are far too open to make a good quality printing plate.

Having reduced the basic screen halftone negative exposure so that the copy shadows will print correctly, sufficient auxiliary highlight bump exposure is given to produce the 90% dot that is required in the highlight area. Since this highlight bump exposure will not affect the tiny shadow dots, the desired full range of printing dots is now produced.

Comparison of the three figures shows that this highlight bump exposure procedure has greatly improved the printed reproduction of this particular copy, and this technique is widely used whenever copy with density range shorter than the range of the halftone screen is encountered.

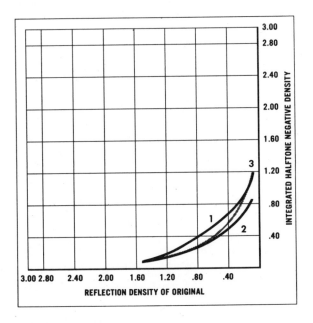

ADJUSTING THE MAGENTA SCREEN RANGE TO VARIOUS TYPES OF COPY WITH CC FILTERS

Magenta and yellow color-compensating filters (CC filters) can also be used to adjust the effective range of the magenta screen to different kinds of copy.

When the copy range is longer than the normal range of the screen, use the yellow CC series to lengthen effective screen range. The change in effective screen range is directly related to the depth of the color of the CC filter, so the very light yellow CC-10Y will make a very small range change, the darker CC-50Y will make a substantial change, and the true yellow #12 filter will produce the greatest possible change in screen range.

Exact figures on the amount of change produced by each filter will vary with individual magenta screens, light sources,

filters and films, but the following ranges were found with a laboratory camera set up and litho type emulsions:

	Effective Screen Range
No filter-white flame	
carbon arc	1.40
CC-10Y	1.45
CC-50Y	1.60

Comparable information can be quickly gathered for your screen through the use of gray scale.

When "copy range" is shorter than the "effective range" of the magenta screen use the magenta CC series of filters. Effective screen range is shortened as the color of the CC filter becomes darker, and the following range progression was found in tests.

	Effective Screen Range
No filter-white flame	
carbon arc	1.40
CC-10M	1.35
CC-50M*	1.15

The following three figures show the screen range change produced by 50Y and 50M filters.

No filter.

At first glance, the preceding tables of CC filter screen range control would indicate that the "best" halftone technique would be to use the proper CC filter for each piece of copy and exactly match screen and copy range. However,

---

* Heavy magenta filters like the CC-50M should be used with caution since this heavy magenta screen-magenta filter combination may tend to produce soft gradient halftone dots that will cause problems in dot etching or plate printing operations.

this approach is not necessarily correct for some types of pictures.

CC-50Y filter.

CC-50M filter.

It is important to note that highlight dots of somewhat different character are produced when the screen range is shortened by highlight bump exposure as compared to use of CC filters. The use of a no-screen highlight bump exposure principally affects the highlight and near highlight tones.

This effect can be observed with the aid of a magnifier as a subtle veil of density between the highlight dots which is lowest in the central "clear" area and reaches its highest value adjacent to the base of the dots. This veil result is the optical mechanism which enhances highlight detail and its full effectiveness often may not be realized when the halftone negative itself is viewed, but the effect becomes very apparent when a contact positive is made or when the printed sheet is examined.

Excessive highlight bumps exposure can cause complete veiling of the dots or a highlight drop-out effect. In most cases this exaggerated effect is undesirable and careful exposure control must be maintained. However, in some special cases it is desirable to fill or plug the highlight dot and this technique will be discussed later.

On the other hand, use of CC filters alters the effective screen range in quite a different manner and tends to keep the highlight areas of the halftone negative more open or unveiled.

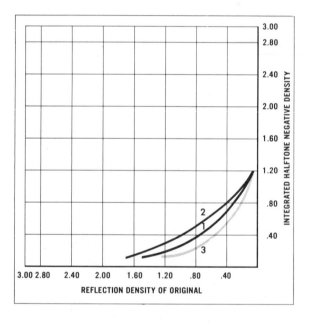

USE OF DIFFERENT DEVELOPMENT TECHNIQUES TO VARY THE REPRODUCTION QUALITY OF HALFTONE NEGATIVE

The discussion and illustrations thus far have all been based on use of constant development conditions, and only exposure procedures have been varied to change halftone quality.

The effect of different developer agitation techniques on halftone quality (and their tone reproduction curves) can be studied in the next series of four halftones of the same subject that were all given the same exposure.

The following four figures were made from a negative that was given: (1) normal agitation; (2) brisk agitation; (3) modified still development (the tray was rocked for 1¼ minutes, and still developed for 1¼ minutes; and (4) completely still development for 2½ minutes. Note carefully the differences in scale balance that are controlled by the rate of developer agitation. In general, still development techniques tend to produce longer scale halftones, while vigorous agitation tends to shorten the halftone scale, when exposure is altered to fit the development technique.

Brisk agitation

Normal agitation

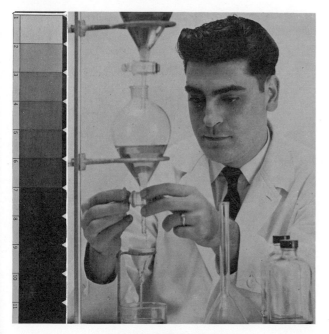

Modified still agitation

No agitation

In the last figure the scale appears to be shorter than in the first and third, which is due to the low rate of development, coupled with the fact that the exposure was not increased to compensate for this method of processing. Had the exposure been increased to bring the highlight areas up to normal density, the lengthening of the scale with very still development would have been quite apparent.

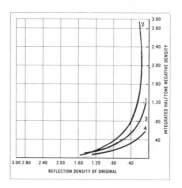

EFFECTS ON TONE REPRODUCTION QUALITY
WHEN DIFFERENT HALFTONE PROCEDURES
ARE USED TO MATCH COPY TO
SCREEN DENSITY RANGE

In all previous illustrations the exposure or development conditions have been separately varied to control the range of reproduction quality of a halftone negative. Now look at print quality changes that can be produced when both exposure and development procedures are varied.

The shop question that best sets the stage for illustration is the old one, "Where should the fifty percent dot fall in this copy?" A positive answer to this question is not possible because it depends on factors of copy, stock and personal preference. However, the next three figures illustrate the printing quality effects of differential placement of the 50% dot, both on the copy and on the gray scales. In this illustration the objective was to hold the same highlight and the shadow dot sizes in all three reproductions, and to shift the fifty percent dot placement by deliberate variation of exposure and developer agitation procedures.

Highlight	Basic	Shadow	Development
Exposure	Exposure	Flash	Technique
None	100 Units	3½ sec.	Normal Agitation

Highlight	Basic	Shadow	Development
Exposure	Exposure	Flash	Technique
None	300 Units	1 sec.	1 min.
			Normal Agitation
			1½ min.
			Still Development

* Light integrator units

The following tabulation shows how the negatives for these prints were made. This data of course is applicable only to a particular camera-screen-film condition, but this information can be useful as a starting point from which to begin to develop your own halftone controls.

The tone reproduction curves of the gray scales dramatically illustrate the print quality changes that can be caused by selective shifting of the middle tone of the picture.

Highlight	Basic	Shadow	Development
Exposure	Exposure	Flash	Technique
10% of basic	35 Units	5 sec.	Normal Agitation

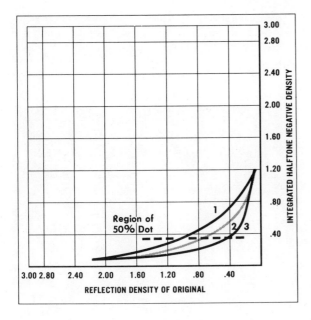

In usual shop practice, the original art is prepared with type matter stripped into position. The halftone exposure is made, the screen is then removed and the no screen image exposure or "highlight bump" is added to completely close the unwanted highlight dots. The results of such a technique can be seen in the figure.

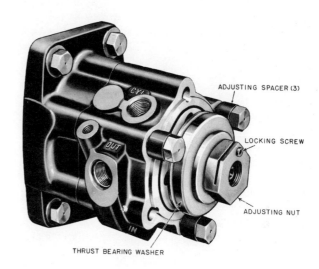

Highlight drop-out.

HIGHLIGHT DROP OUT TECHNIQUE

The highlight drop out technique is simply an extension of the highlight bump exposure procedures. This exposure method is a short cut procedure that can be used very effectively to drop out all dots in the background of an outlined photograph, thereby eliminating tedious opaquing or masking. It is also used by some shops to eliminate double printing when line type matter and halftones must be combined. Printed quality standards with this procedure cannot match a good stripping job, and the final choice of procedure must be based on the cost-quality requirements of the job.

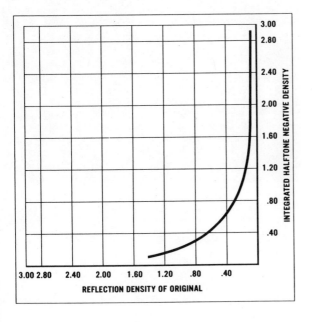

CHOICE OF THE RIGHT HALFTONE TECHNIQUE

Perhaps the choice of halftone technique will be clarified best by reviewing the overall effect of several halftone techniques on final "picture" quality.

1. HIGHLIGHT BUMP EXPOSURE — A proper highlight no-screen exposure tends to emphasize or "hold" highlight detail and to make the highlights more brilliant. High-key copy is especially benefited by this method.

2. SHADOW FLASH — The proper shadow flash insures the reproduction of the deepest shadow tones and does so by somewhat compressing the shadow scale of the print. This procedure also places additional density in the core of each dot which helps insure good plate printing and dot etching performance.

3. USE OF CC FILTERS — The CC filter method changes the overall working range of the halftone screen and affects the tonal gradation of highlights, mid-tones and shadow regions in a somewhat similar way. The overall visual response to this type of control is the impression that the highlights have been somewhat flattened or grayed, while better shadow detail has been retained Low-key copy is usually best handled with the CC filter technique.

4. USE OF COMBINATION HALFTONE TECHNIQUES — It now becomes obvious that combination halftone procedures

utilizing CC filter selection, highlight and shadow exposures, and even controlled agitation offer great flexibility for emphasizing highlight, shadow or mid-tone detail, depending on the nature of the original copy. The figures, therefore, have been re-shot to illustrate the quality improvements that can be achieved by careful use of combination halftone techniques, when compared to the moderate quality produced by the simplest and most straight-forward techniques. As a guide to this comparison, the original copy of the bathing beauty had a density range of 1.45 and was produced with a simple basic screen exposure. (pp. 5:63-5:64)

Copy for the man's portrait had a density range of 1.50, and a basic exposure plus shadow flash was used to make the halftone negative. (pp. 5:60-5:61)

Copy of the baby shot had a density range of 1.2 and a basic exposure plus highlight bump exposure was used to make this halftone negative. (p. 5:62)

For the following three photographs, a combination of all these techniques was used in different proportions depending on areas of importance in each of the illustrations. A five percent highlight no-screen exposure was used to compress the range and accentuate the highlight area, then the basic exposure was given followed by a shadow flash exposure to bring out shadow detail and add exposure to the core of each

dot. These combination halftone procedures were best for one particular camera, plate, and press relationship, and will undoubtedly vary for different shop conditions. Exposure and processing balance must be established in each individual shop to fit specific quality and equipment requirements.

CHAPTER SIX

Color-Separation Photography _____

Section One: Introduction to Color-Separation Photography

Color pictures frequently contain hundreds of small areas of distinctly different colors. It would be impractical or impossible to print each of these separately. Fortunately, most colors can be reproduced by printing in their place some mixture of three selected colors, sometimes with the addition of black. The four colors commonly used in printed color reproductions are: (1) Yellow, (2) Magenta, also known as process red, (3) Cyan, also known as process blue, and (4) Black. The terms magenta and cyan are used in place of blue and red, not only because they describe the colors of the actual inks more accurately, but because this avoids confusion with the blue and red of the color-separation filters, which mean something quite different. This confusion becomes serious in discussing masking methods.

Each color will be transferred to the paper by a separate printing plate. To make these printing plates, we first need four negatives, each recording densities for the varying amounts of color one of the plates will carry. Making these negatives is called "color" separation."

The negatives are exposed through color filters consisting of dyed sheets of gelatin. The filter used in making each negative is one which will make the color of the ink to be carried by that plate photograph as if it were black and the other colors as if they were white.

A good understanding of the nature of light is a prerequisite for every discussion of color separation and the very closely related subject of color correction. Some information on color —its use and controls—must therefore be included in every introduction to color separation.

Our discussion is divided into the following main points: (1) The nature of light, (2) The nature of color, (3) Combinations of color, (4) Color separations, (5) Printing inks and filters, and (6) The inter-relatedness of color separation and color correction. Each of these subjects is discussed in the following.

NATURE OF LIGHT

Light is that form of radiant electrical energy to which our eyes are sensitive. It is a very narrow region in the wide range of the electromagnetic spectrum. This range extends from cosmic rays through and beyond radio waves. The narrow region of visible wavelengths stimulates the full spectrum of color that our eyes see in a rainbow or through a prism. The spectrum shows a gradual color change that blends one color into another. For purposes of identification we can divide the spectrum into six groups. The narrow region of visible wavelengths stimulates the full spectrum of color that our eyes see in a rainbow or through a prism. The spectrum shows a gradual color change that blends one color into another. For purposes of identification we can divide the spectrum into six groups of colors which we call violet, blue, green, yellow, orange, and red.

Controlling Light. Light, as energy, can be directed, controlled, dissected, and re-combined. The instruments used to control light are classified as optical. The use of light to record an image of itself is called photography. When photography is further used to prepare a printing form, the process is described as being *photomechanical*.

THE NATURE OF COLOR

Color is a personal, mental experience. It is received as light that is reflected, transmitted, or radiated from an object to our eyes. The way this light stimulates the nerve cells in our eyes is used to identify the color. Color identification is a language taught to us in childhood. Being a personal experience, it varies between individuals, as well as with the state of our health, its physical surroundings, and other physiological and psychological factors.

Individual Variations in Color Vision. The personal relationship to color is noticeable by differences of opinion between individuals in color matching. This is pronounced when one of the colors is a prime or pure color and the other color that may appear to be identical is composed of a mixture of colors. The variation between individuals stresses the importance of good eyesight and freedom from any degree of color blindness for satisfactory color correction. A partially colorblind color etcher cannot be expected to reproduce colors that he cannot see.

How We See Color. Scientifically, color may be defined in terms of wavelengths of light, or as combinations of wavelengths and relative intensities. When light reaches us, it stimulates nerve responses in the retina of our eyes. The nerve responses are received by two types of cells. One, consisting of "rods," is colorblind yet is highly sensitive to blue-green light. The other group of cells, called "cones," have much less sensitivity to light.

The Color Response of the Cones. The cones consist of clusters of three types of cells that respond individually to the blue, green, and red color primaries. Consequently, if the light becomes dimmer, as may occur in the deep shadows or with low illumination intensities, these areas will appear grayer with incorrect brightness differences. The same color areas will become brightly colored under a more intense light.

Eye Fatigue and Color Vision. Fatigue of the nerve cells in our eyes also changes our judgment of color. Such fatigue can be to a particular color. When you look first at a bright color, and then immediately look at a second color of a different hue, the second color will temporarily seem to change its color as eye fatigue subtracts some of the first color from it.

The Color Composition of White Light. White light is made up of a balanced combination of all colors of the spectrum. This fact is demonstrated when a beam of white light is projected through a glass prism. If a colored filter is placed in the path of the white light, the light that passes through is changed in appearance. Some of the color is absorbed by the filter. The transmitted light is a combination of the remaining colors.

Pure Spectrum Colors. If the spectrum of light colors coming from a white light source is blocked off until only a single color, or a narrow band of wavelengths is transmitted, we see a "pure" spectrum color.

Reflection and Absorption of Light. If white light is directed against a sheet of paper, the reflected light will appear to be white if the sheet reflects all colors uniformly. When color inks are printed on this sheet, part of the white light will be absorbed by the ink. The remaining light that is reflected by the paper and through the ink is the ink color we see. When all light is blocked or absorbed, we define this absence of color as "black."

How We See Color In Things. The color sensation we get when viewing an object depends on the light reflected from the object to the observer. Colors can appear differently under different daylights as well as under different artificial lights. Fluorescent illumination is predominantly blue-green. It does not contain as much light in the red region as tungsten or daylight illumination. Therefore, red objects viewed under fluorescent lights will not appear as bright as when viewed under tungsten or daylight illumination. Tungsten light, having less blue than daylight, makes magenta appear redder and blues darker. When viewing colors, the observer must always keep in mind the light used to illuminate the object.

Color Identification. When describing a color, the following physical properties of the color should be given: hue, saturation, and brightness.

Hue. By hue we refer to the name of a color. Hue is the term that places the color in its correct position in the spectrum.

For example, if we describe a color whose hue is blue, we distinguish it from yellow, red orange, etc.

Saturation. Another attribute of color is saturation. Saturation is that quality which enables an observer to state how strongly colored it is; that is, how much it differs from a neutral gray. For example, a pure yellow can be distinguished from tan or brown. Or you might describe a tie as a dull green, bright green, or brilliant green. These distinctions are differences in saturation.

Brightness. Brightness is the term used to describe differences in the intensity of light reflected from or transmitted by the colored image. For example, we might describe a shirt as being dark blue or light blue. The hue or color of the shirt is blue, but the characteristic terms dark or light distinguish one shirt from the other.

In the trade, we more commonly use terms like "clean" or "dirty," instead of "saturation" or "brightness."

Color Notation. The use of such terms as hue, brightness, and saturation allows different observers viewing the same color to describe it in general terms. However, there are many times when this general description is not adequate. A paint or dye manufacturer trying to match a color described in this fashion would not be able to do it. To meet the demand of a more definite description, a number of color notation systems, complete with samples and charts, have been developed.

The most popular color notation system in this country is the Munsell System. "The Munsell Book of Color" contains opaque colored samples of stable pigments. These samples are made up in different hues, brightness, and saturation values. The Munsell System of notation has room for 100 different hues. However, The Munsell Color Tree contains 10 different hues spaced horizontally around the sphere. Each hue is given a number.

Radiating out from the center of the circle are series of samples with the same hue and value but different degrees of saturation, or chroma as it is called in this system. The different degrees are numbered from 0 at the center, which is a neutral gray, to steps as high as 14 or 16, whatever is the purest color possible with the given pigments. Some hues may only go as high as step 5 or step 6.

By matching a color with one of the samples, a numerical value can be given to each of the three attributes: hue, brightness or value, and saturation or chroma. Once the color match has been made and the numerical values given, other observers elsewhere can easily locate the designated color on the tree and know what color is being described.

The Ostwald System is another widely used color notation system. It was developed by Wilhelm Ostwald and improved by the Container Corporation of America. Their system is called the Color Harmony Manual. The Ostwald System is similar to the Munsell System in that it also has a central vertical gray tone scale which is surrounded by a color circle with complementary hues opposite each other. Instead of arranging the interior colors in horizontal and vertical rows, as in the Munsell System, Ostwald places them in angled rows. All colors between the basic hues, as well as the white and light grays, are arranged as tints made by the addition of white.

Shades are made by the addition of black, and tones by the addition of gray.

Both the Munsell and Ostwald Systems give orderly arrangement and are excellent reference standards. Munsell colors may be purchased separately as colored papers, while the Container Corporation's units are acetate hexagons with both a matte and glossy side.

COMBINATIONS OF COLOR

Colors can be combined to produce other colors. When light of one color is added to light of another color, such as by projection onto a white screen, the combination color is called "additive." When one or more colors is removed from white light (such as happens when white light passes through a filter or reflects from a colored surface) the colors that are not absorbed produce what is known as a "subtractive" color.

Additive Mixtures. The additive mixtures of colors is illustrated in the projection of the three primary colors of the spectrum. The additive primary colors of light are red, green, and blue. These colors cannot be produced by mixtures of other colors. Combinations of two of the primaries, red and blue for example, produce a third color called magenta. The combination of all three primaries produces white light. This is to be expected as we have already shown that white light is made up of all the colors of the spectrum from red to blue.

Another illustration of the additive process can be seen when a checkerboard pattern of two colors is viewed at a distance so that the eye can no longer distinguish the individual areas. The squares will fuse into one area of solid color. This new color will be the sum of the reflectance from the two color areas. If the two squares are colors such as red and blue, the resulting color sensation will be a magenta hue. Red and green squares will produce a yellow hue, while green and blue squares will produce a cyan hue. In this method, the color will appear darker than when using the projection method first described. This is due to the fact that in the checkerboard pattern the colors are side by side and not overlapping. As a result, you have only half the color intensity from a given area as compared to that produced by projecting the colors as light.

Another illustration of the additive process occurs when we view small elements of colors placed side by side without overlapping, such as halftone dots in the highlights and middletones of color reproductions. We see the combination of all the elements and not the individual dots. However, when the dots overlap, we see color combinations formed by the subtractive color mixture process if the colors are transparent.

Subtractive Primaries. These are the colors produced when the three colored beams overlap in pairs. When all three colored beams overlap, white is produced. When only red and blue overlap, the resulting color is magenta. Magenta is made up of red and blue, which is roughly two-thirds of the color spectrum. It can be described as white light minus green and, therefore, it is sometimes referred to as the minus-green color. When a magenta beam of light and a green beam of light are combined in the proper proportions, the result is white light. When the red and green light beams overlap, they form yellow. Yellow can be described as white light minus blue, or just minus-blue. When the green and blue beams overlap, they form cyan. If we subtract the red third of the spectrum from white light, the color obtained is cyan. Cyan is sometimes referred to as minus-red.

Subtractive Color Mixtures. In the additive-mixture process, we form new colors by projecting basic primary colors onto a screen. In the subtractive-mixture process we form new colors by subtracting parts of a white or colored light source. An example of subtractive color is seen whenever we place a filter in front of a light source. The filter subtracts certain colors and allows others to pass through it. The filter does not add anything to the light beam. It removes something from it.

Subtractive Color Mixtures With Additive Primaries. When a filter which has the same color as the additive primary colors such as red, green, or blue is placed in front of a white light beam, two-thirds of the light is absorbed and one-third is transmitted. For example, the red filter absorbs the blue and green portion of the spectrum, transmitting only the red portion. When another additive primary filter, for example blue, is placed over the beam of light transmitted by the red filter, no light is seen. The red filter transmits only red; however, the blue filter absorbs red. All three regions of the spectrum are absorbed by any combination of two additive primary filters.

Subtractive Color Mixtures With Subtractive Primaries. When a filter which has the same color as one of the subtractive primary colors such as cyan, magenta, or yellow is placed in front of a white light beam, one-third of the spectrum is absorbed and two-thirds transmitted. For example, the magenta filter absorbs the green third of the spectrum and transmits the red and blue portions. If another subtractive primary filter, for example the cyan, were placed over the beam of light transmitted by the magenta filter, we would see blue light. The magenta filter transmits the red and blue portions of the spectrum. The cyan filter absorbs the red portions, transmitting only the blue. In a similar fashion, the magenta and yellow filter combinations will produce red. The magenta filter absorbs green, and the yellow filter absorbs the blue portion of the spectrum leaving only the red to come through. The cyan absorbs the red portion of the spectrum, while the yellow absorbs the blue portion, leaving only the green of the spectrum to be transmitted. If all three filters were placed over a white light beam, we would not see any color.

We have seen that the additive primaries—red, green, and blue—cannot be used in the subtractive method of mixing colors because any combination of two would produce no color or black. When the subtractive primaries—yellow, magenta, and cyan—are used in the subtractive process of mixing colors, combinations of any two will produce a new color.

COLOR SEPARATION

To print a reproduction of a color original, it is necessary to prepare a set of press plates, one for each color to be printed. Each of these press plates will be used to print a specific color of ink, such as magenta (process red), cyan (process blue), or yellow. The printing design for each color must print the proportional amount of color in each area that is required to build up the complete color combinations in the reproduction. To prepare these individual color printing plates, it is necessary to separate the colors of the original into three or more photographic images. Each image represents the proportional amount of a printing ink color to be used.

PRINTING INKS AND FILTERS

We have been describing the additive and subtractive color primaries with light sources and filters. We cannot use lights and filters for printing purposes. However, we can use materials which behave in the same manner. A sheet of white paper which reflects all the wavelengths of light can be our light source. Transparent ink films which absorb or transmit different parts of the spectrum can act as our filters.

When we put a thin transparent ink film on a sheet of white paper, we are not adding any color to the paper. The purest and brightest color hues that can be produced on that particular paper are already reflecting from the paper before we put any ink film over it. Any thin reasonably transparent ink film transferred to paper can be no purer than the color already reflecting from the paper as part of the white light. This is very noticeable when the same ink is printed on a variety of papers such as cast-coated, coated offset stock, and yellowed newsprint.

Functions of Yellow Ink and Blue Filter. The best yellow inks available reflect almost as much red and green light as the paper they print on. However, this is only an auxiliary function. The prime characteristic of a yellow ink, for a subtractive printing process, is that it absorbs blue light. It thereby controls where blue reflects from the white paper. If the remaining two-thirds of the spectrum reflects fully, the ink will be a clean, pure yellow. A blue filter, transmitting only its own third of the spectrum is thus the proper filter to use to provide correct filter separation tone values for a yellow printer. The desired effect is to record only where the blue light comes from the copy. When a positive is made from this negative it will be a record of the minus-blue (yellow) of the copy.

Functions of Magenta Ink and Green Filter. The function of the magenta, or "process red," ink is to absorb green light only, without disturbing the reflectance of the red and blue light. Most magenta inks absorb some blue and red light. A green filter which transmits its own third of the spectrum will be the proper filter to use to make a record of the green areas of the copy.

Functions of Cyan Ink and Red Filter. The function of the cyan ink, or "process blue," is to absorb the red light without disturbing the reflectance of the green and blue light. Most cyan inks absorb some green and blue light. The red filter which transmits its own third of the spectrum should be used to control the red light reflected from the copy.

In the reproduction process we use the tri-color filters to separate the copy into its red, green, and blue components. We then combine these three components by controlling the red, green, and blue light reflected from the white paper. We use red-light absorbing ink (cyan), green-light absorbing ink (magenta), and blue-light absorbing ink (yellow).

Color Separation Filters. The color separation filters most commonly used are the Wratten Blue (47), Green (58), and Red (25). These divide the spectrum into approximately equal thirds which are complementary to the hues that printing inks should have. Unfortunately, with the exception of yellow, the best process inks are not close enough to the correct hue and purity. Because of the failure of the inks, color correction of the separation is necessary. It has been suggested that less correction would be needed if the filters were changed to be the exact complements of the printing inks which are actually used. In some cases other filters do give greater saturation, but shifting their hues from strict thirds always degrades part of their separation.

The Red (25), Green (58), and Blue (47) filters are called the broad-band set because they actually overlap a little in their transmission. This gives the most complete record of where red, green, and blue reflect from the copy. A narrower band set has been recommended for color transparencies because of the nature of their dyes. These are the Red (29), Green (61), and Blue (47B). These will give a little more saturation with reflected copy also. However, this is not recommended if masking corrections are to be used because two-color mixtures will be over-corrected.

The Limited Accuracy of Color Separations. The accuracy of these color separations is limited by two factors: (1) Each color filter cannot compensate for the ink and printing deficiencies; and (2) The photographic negatives do not record the exact ratios between color densities as they appear in the original.

THE INTER-RELATEDNESS OF COLOR SEPARATION AND COLOR CORRECTION

In all known methods of photomechanical color reproduction, there is a loss in color accuracy so that the colors of the reproduction do not match those of the original. This would be true even if a "perfect" set of separations could be made. The printing plates made from these separations would not produce the desired colors, because each of the commercially available inks act like a pure colored ink contaminated with small amounts of the other inks and therefore absorbs some of the light which it should reflect.

Magenta and Cyan Inks are Contaminated. The magenta ink absorbs some blue light in addition to green; that is to say, it is like a perfect magenta contaminated with yellow ink. In order to compensate for this absorption, less yellow ink must be printed wherever magenta is present. Similarly, the cyan ink absorbs some of the blue and green light which should be completely reflected; that is, it acts as if contaminated with yellow and magenta ink, and therefore the yellow and magenta ink must be reduced wherever cyan is to be printed.

Manual Color Correction. In lithography, this can be done by local dot-etching on halftone separation negatives or positives; in photoengraving, by local work on the plates; and in photogravure, by hand-retouching of continuous-tone negatives and positives.

Color Correction by Photographic Masking. A far better method, however, is to alter photographically the tone values of the separations from which the plates are made. Masks will do this job efficiently and without loss of detail. This is called "masking for color correction" and can result in changes in hue, brightness, and saturation of colors.

Undercolor Removal, and Tone Correction. Masks are also used for undercolor removal in four-color wet printing and for altering the tone scale of a reproduction, as in highlight masks and contrast-reducing masks.

Color Separation and Masking Are Siamese Twins. We mention the subject of masking advisedly at this point of our discussion. *The reader must accept the statement that color separation and color correction are most closely connected. It is not possible to discuss color separation as an independent operation.* Color-separation techniques depend on the kind of color correcting which is to be used more than on anything else.

Photographic Masking the Key to Color Reproduction. When we speak of color correcting we mean photographic rather than manual methods. These methods have become the most topical subject in lithographic color reproduction; they are extensively discussed in the "Photographic Masking and Color Correcting" chapter of the Manual. There you also find specific instructions for the making of color separations together with the masking process in which they are used.

In this chapter our discussion can therefore be limited to the most essential and most general points of color-separation photography.

Section Two: Color-Separation Essentials

Our discussion of color-separation essentials is divided into the following eight points: (1) The two main kinds of copy for color separation, (2) Camera essentials, (3) Lenses for color-separation work, (4) Filters, (5) Halftone screens for color separation, (6) Direct and indirect color-separation methods, (7) Arranging and illuminating of color copy, and (8) Gray scale and color patches. Each of these points is discussed in the following.

THE TWO MAIN KINDS OF COPY FOR COLOR SEPARATION

The two main kinds of copy for color separation are reflection copy and transmission copy.

Reflection Copy. Reflection copy is original material for reproduction which is normally viewed and must be photographed by reflected light. Examples include oil paintings, dye transfer and other photographic color prints, fabric swatches, watercolors, and pastels. It does not include transparencies, or color negatives.

Transmission Copy. Transmission copy is copy normally viewed and photographed by transmitted light. Transmission copy includes transparencies and color negatives.

CAMERA ESSENTIALS

Accurate register of images and correct transmission of colors are the underlying considerations in the selection and use of equipment for photomechanical color reproduction. The desired end result of the photographic steps is a set of balanced color-separation negatives or positives on which the images are exactly equal in size. Only by using good equipment properly can you be sure of accurate results on the printed page. This section of the Manual describes the precision equipment for photomechanical color reproduction and its proper use.

A discussion of process cameras for color separation can be found in Chapter Five of this Manual. In certain cases, particularly in that of the Kodak three-color process, specialized equipment may be needed. Such equipment is described as part of the specific method for which it is needed in the "Photographic Masking and Color Correcting" chapter of this Manual.

LENSES FOR COLOR SEPARATION WORK

No other single factor in color separation exceeds the lens in importance and for this reason we discuss the subject in great detail. Our presentation is divided into the following three points: (1) Lens requirements, (2) Testing a lens for color and separation work, and (3) Lens flare. Each of these points is now taken up in detail.

Lens Requirements. A good color-corrected or *apochromatic* lens must be used for all color work. Such a lens should produce separation negatives of equal size and sharpness regardless of the color of the filters used for exposing the separation negatives. An apochromatic lens for color separation work must be very highly color-corrected which involves two distinct characteristics: longitudinal color correction, which means that light of all colors must be brought to a sharp focus at the same focal plane; and lateral color correction, which means that light of all colors produces images of exactly the same size, suitable for registering in color printing.

Testing a Lens For Color-Separation Work. One of the simplest tests for lateral color correction of a lens can be made with a single exposure. The procedure is as follows:

1. Prepare an original with a white background and black lines: One method is to draw a series of india-ink lines on a

piece of white paper. Photograph this copy, using an 8 by 10-inch sheet of high contrast litho film, make a contact print of this negative to produce a positive image with black lines and a clear background.

2. Bind narrow strips of the color-separation filters over this positive, at right angles to the lines.

3. Place the above combination in the transparency holder of the process camera, but over to one side so that the image will be at the edge of the lens field and not on the lens axis. It should be placed so that the lines will be at right angles to a line drawn from the center of the test object to the center of the copyboard. Make a single exposure on a high contrast panchromatic litho film.

If there is any difference in size of the images, the sections of black lines masked off by the strips of filters will not be joined. They will appear out-of-line in proportion to the lateral color aberration of the lens. If there is only a slight departure from exact alignment, lateral color aberration may nevertheless be low enough for many types of work, and the lens should be tried on a typical subject.

If close-up work is contemplated, the performance of the lens should be checked at the greatest magnification expected in actual use.

Lens Flare. One of the notable causes of difficulty in color work is lens flare. This can be defined roughly as non-image light which reaches the film or plate through the lens. It can be caused by stray light entering the lens or by internal reflections from the lens-element surfaces or the lens mount. It is frequently unnoticed until a job is encountered that requires critical color reproduction or the reproduction of much fine detail. The effect of flare is to decrease markedly the contrast of the image especially in the shadows and lower the purity and saturation of shadow colors.

One of the most common causes of flare is dirt on the surfaces of the lens. This may be a thin, even film of dust and arc-lamp smoke. Front and back surfaces of the lens can be cleaned by careful polishing with a fresh piece of lens tissue. Avoid strong cleaners, abrasives, and ordinary wiping rags. One hard particle on a cloth can scratch the delicate lens surface. If the lens barrel has a slot for filters, keep a piece of tape over it when it is not being used. If the inner surfaces of the lens need cleaning, let the manufacturer do the job. The charge will be negligible compared to the cost of the lens. Modern lenses have their surfaces coated to eliminate reflections. Such lens coatings have a bluish-violet appearance which should not be confused with the hazy deposit of smoke and dust.

Stray light should be prevented from entering the lens during camera exposure. Bright room lights, windows, and reflections should be guarded against. Black paper over the outer edge of the copyboard will prevent direct reflection of the arc light into the lens.

FILTERS

In order to separate or divide the many colors of the original into the separate portions to be carried by each of the color printers, color-separation filters are required. These may be in the form of dyed gelatin sheets which are either unmounted or are mounted in glass. Unmounted Wratten filters are used ex-

tensively in the graphic arts. Most workers prefer them to glass filters.

Specially selected Wratten filters are now available for the critical requirements of the photomechanical reproduction of color. These are designated "Wratten Gelatin Filters for Use in Photomechanical Reproduction." They are particularly useful where partial exposures are to be made through each of several filters, as in the split-filter method of making a black printer. These selected filters are available in the following Wratten numbers: 8 (K2), 25, 29 (F), 33, 47, 47B, 58 (B), and 61 (N).

It is extremely important that the filters used for color-separation work have the proper transmission characteristics. The recommendations in this section are based on the use of Wratten filters, and the recommended filters for each exposure are stated in the following sections of this chapter. For further information on filters, see the Kodak Data Book "Graphic Arts Films and Plates."

HALFTONE SCREENS FOR COLOR SEPARATION

Our discussion of halftone screens* is concerned with various kinds of screens as well as their positioning for color separation. We present the subject under the following seven headings: (1) Glass crossline screens, (2) The magenta contact screen, (3) The gray contact screen, (4) The Moiré effect, (5) The purpose of different screen angles, (6) Using different screen rulings, and (7) Rotating contact and crossline screens. Each of these points is now discussed.

Enlarged contact screen pattern.   Enlarged cross-line screen pattern.

Two Principal Types of Halftone Screens

Glass Crossline Screens. Glass crossline screens are widely used for the photomechanical reproduction of color artwork, for making direct-screen separation negatives, and for making screen negatives or positives from continuous-tone images. For process color work, a conventional screen should be set in a round frame which can be rotated in guides in the camera back. For further information on glass crossline screens consult the section on halftone photography of the Camera Department Chapter.

The Magenta Contact Screen. The magenta contact screen provides a flexible and improved means of making screened color-separation negatives or positives by the indirect method.

_____

* A more detailed discussion of halftone screens is found in Section Eleven and Section Twelve of Chapter Five of this Manual.

That is, continuous-tone separations are made and, from these, screened images are made as required by the photomechanical processes. The magenta color of the screen makes possible the use of color filters to control contrast. It cannot be used for making direct separations because the magenta color interferes with the use of the separation filters. The magenta contact screen technique is applicable to surface and deep-etch plates, to photoengraving, and to some forms of gravure work.

Improved sharpness of highlight detail, simplified contrast control, and the elimination of the problem of screen-distance ratios encountered with conventional crossline screens are some of the advantages of magenta contact screens.

The Gray Contact Screen. The gray contact screen offers most of the advantages of the magenta contact screen and, in addition, the neutral color of the gray screen makes possible its use for the direct method of color separation. The chief difference is that color filters cannot be used for control of contrast. The three other methods of contrast control—controlled flash, controlled agitation, and supplementary highlighting exposures —make this a minor disadvantage, however. Complete directions are supplied with the screen.

The Moiré Effect. In all screened color-reproduction work, there is the possibility of a noticeable pattern, or "moiré" effect in the printed result. The most common causes of this pattern effect in color work are improper trapping of ink and improper screening. The latter possibility occurs whenever two halftone screen patterns are superimposed in printing. The moiré effect can be minimized by rotating, or "angling," the screen to a different position for each color separation. The angle between the vertical and one of the parallel lines or rows of dots of a screen is called the "screen angle." Certain combinations of screen angles can be selected to reduce or eliminate the moiré effect. The greater the angle between the rows of dots of the different color inks, the less chance there is for an undesirable moiré.

The Purpose of Different Angles. The purpose of selecting certain screen angles is to place the dots of the three strong colors—black, cyan ("blue"), and magenta ("red")—at angles

which will produce the minimum pattern. This condition is usually fulfilled when the screen angles of these colors are 30 degrees from each other. The screen angle of the black record in four-color printing remains the same as in a single-color job, that is, 45 degrees. Lines at the 45-degree screen angle are least noticeable to the eye. Therefore, the strongest color of a process set is usually screened at this angle. In color printing where each successive color is dried, or even when printing on two-color presses with drying after the first two colors, the black plate is often a weak image and should be screened at 105 degrees, with the cyan ("blue") then screened at 45 degrees. The usual screen angles for two-, three-, four-, and six-color reproduction work are discussed further down in this section.

Using Different Screen Rulings. Sometimes, to reduce the moiré pattern, it is desirable to use a different screen ruling for the yellow plate than for the other colors. For example, if a 133-line screen is used for the cyan ("blue"), magenta ("red"), and black, a 150-line screen yellow can be used to reduce the possibility of objectionable pattern.

Rotating Contact and Crossline Screens. In the case of contact screens, many cameramen find it convenient to mark the angles for rotation directly on the vacuum back of the process camera. A pair of reference marks should be placed on opposite edges of a contact screen which is to be used for color-separation work. These marks should be at the two ends of a line of dots running approximately through the middle of the screen.

To locate two opposite points, place a straight-edge on the screen over an illuminator. Using a magnifier, align the edge with a row of dots by sliding the magnifier along the straight-edge and observing whether or not the same line of dots follows the edge. When the correct position is found, scribe a mark on the margin of the screen at each end. This can be marked with a tab of white adhesive tape for better visibility in the darkroom.

A pair of corresponding tabs is placed on the vacuum back of the camera at each of the positions in which the screen is to be used. One of the tabs on the screen should be larger than the other or specially marked so that the screen can always be angled by reference to the same mark. This is also important with crossline screens, because a screen might have a slight departure from a perfect 90-degree relationship in its rulings, and a slight moiré pattern can appear if the same reference point is not used throughout in making a set of screened separations. (It is for this reason that we refer to a "105-degree screen angle" rather than a "15-degree screen angle" (105-90), as might be the case if we used two reference points 90 degrees apart on the screen.) *Under certain conditions in four-color work, an error of less than half a degree can produce a moiré pattern.*

DIRECT AND INDIRECT COLOR-SEPARATION METHODS

Color separation can be made by two methods: the direct and the indirect. In this section we present a general discussion of both methods; in the following sections you find detailed instructions for their execution.

Direct Method Color Separations. In this method, the

THREE-COLOR SCREEN ANGLES

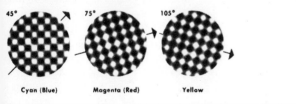

45° 75° 105°

Cyan (Blue)   Magenta (Red)   Yellow

FOUR-COLOR SCREEN ANGLES

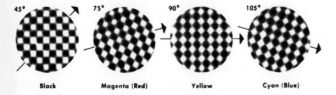

45° 75° 90° 105°

Black   Magenta (Red)   Yellow   Cyan (Blue)

Screen Angles for Three- and Four-Color Printing

color-separation exposures are made through the half-tone screen onto high-contrast films or plates so that half-tone separation negatives are obtained in the first step. A glass crossline screen or a gray contact screen should be used in this method, but not the magenta contact screen. Printing plates for photo-engraving or surface photolithography are made directly from these screen negatives after any necessary handwork has been accomplished. For deep-etch photolithography, screen positives are made by contact printing from the screen negatives.

Indirect Method Color Separations. In the indirect method the halftone negatives or positives are not made directly from the original copy, but from intermediate continuous-tone separations. The use of the continuous-tone negatives makes possible the broader use of masking procedures for tone control and color correction, and eliminates the very long exposures which are sometimes needed for direct halftone work.

Retouching for color correction can be done on the continuous-tone images either by using retouching pencils or by staining with a neutral dye or neococcine. When any one of several masking methods is used, much of the handwork can be eliminated.

The indirect method is capable of improving the general rendering of detail and color separation in separation negatives. It also makes possible an improvement in the dot structure of photoengraving plates because less handwork is necessary. Most masking techniques are more practical when used with the indirect method.

ARRANGING AND ILLUMINATING OF COLOR COPY

Copy arranging and illuminating differs for reflection and transmission copy. We discuss the subject under the following five headings: (1) Arranging reflection copy, (2) Arranging transmission copy, (3) Illuminating reflection copy, (4) Illuminating transmission copy, and (5) Tone and color controls.

Arranging of Reflection Copy. Copy should be mounted firmly in a central position of the copyboard, with register marks placed on all sides or at the ends of the longest dimension of the copy. On rectangular copy, it is customary to use register marks on the vertical and horizontal center lines. The register marks can take several forms, but one which appears sharply defined in both positive and negative images is the most satisfactory.

Arranging of Transmission Copy. Separations from transmission copy are often made by contact printing, which offers several advantages and is described elsewhere in this Manual. When they are to be made in the camera, the copy is placed in a copyholder, a transparency frame which is very often also equipped with registering devices.

Illuminating Reflection Copy. Good color separation depends upon proper copy illumination. The illumination must be of even intensity over the entire copy surface, the direction of the light must be correct, and the light output of the lamps must be constant in quality and quantity. To obtain the most even illumination with double-deck arc lamps, the copy should be mounted on the copyboard with the longer

dimension vertical. With single arcs, the copy, and particularly large copy, should be mounted with the longer dimension horizontal. The copy can be mounted under glass if desired.

The evenness of illumination can be checked by making incident-light readings with a photoelectric exposure meter in the four corners and the center of the copyboard. If a reflection measurement is made, a neutral gray or white card should be used for test readings, and care must be taken so that shadows are not cast on the reading area.

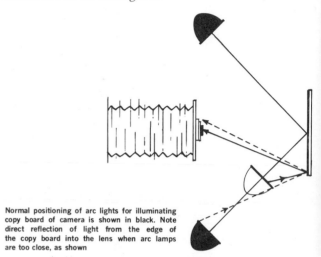

Normal positioning of arc lights for illuminating copy board of camera is shown in black. Note direct reflection of light from the edge of the copy board into the lens when arc lamps are too close, as shown

Proper and Improper Position of Arc Lights

Normally, the lights are placed at an angle of 45 degrees from the copyboard and back far enough to avoid reflection from the edge of the copyboard glass. This angle produces the maximum efficiency and is proper for all smooth-surfaced copy. In special cases, it is desirable to retain texture effects, such as the weave of cloth, brush marks in oil paintings, or chalk strokes. For this purpose, special or unequal lighting conditions will have to be set up by the cameraman. Texture effects and brush marks are usually best retained by evenly distributed lighting at unequal angles. One light can be placed at the normal 45-degree angle, while the other is placed at a more oblique angle to the copyboard. This second light produces the slight shadows under the brush and chalk marks which makes it possible to retain a greater feeling of relief or third dimension. The copy should be oriented so that its top is toward the light which produces the shadows.

High-intensity tungsten lamps (such as 3200-K lamps) are also satisfactorily used for illumination in continuous-tone color-separation work. Fluorescent light sources are also available. These can be used in making separations by the indirect method but require long exposures for direct color separation.

Illuminating Transmission Copy. This subject is discussed in the "Photographic Masking and Color Correcting" chapter of this Manual, in conjunction with the specific masking method.

Tone and Color Controls. Tone and color controls are essential elements in the arranging of copy for color separation. Their importance is sufficient to warrant a detailed discussion which you find in the following unit.

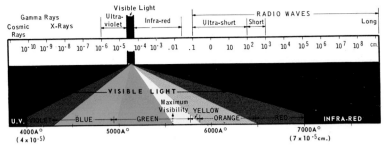

The Electromagnetic Spectrum

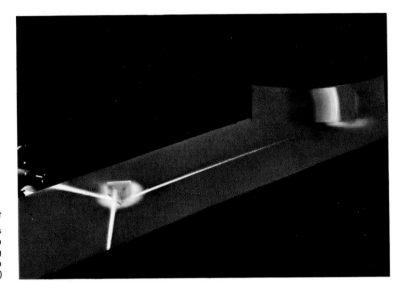

Prism Breaking Up White Light

The prism bends light of shorter wavelengths
more than light of longer wavelengths, spreading a beam
of white light out to a visible spectrum. (The beam extending
down is reflected from the surface of the prism
without entering it.)

Munsell Color Tree and Circle
Showing the Three Dimensional
Relationship of Hue, Value, and Chroma

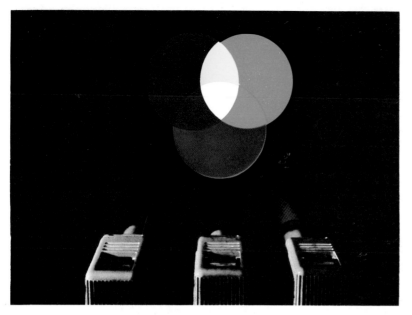

Color Combination by Addition

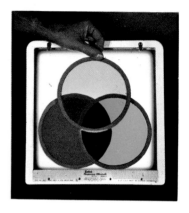

Color Combination by Subtraction

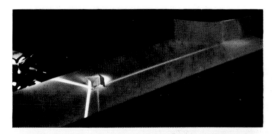

A yellow filter absorbs blue light, transmitting green and red light

A magenta filter absorbs green light, transmitting blue and red light

A cyan filter absorbs red light, transmitting blue and green light

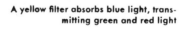

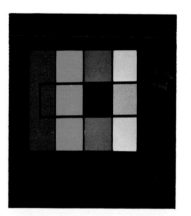

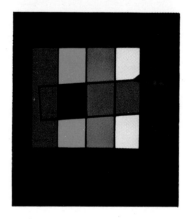

Transmission Range of Additive Primary Filters

Three Subtractive Primary Filters

FROM THE ORIGINAL TO THE FINAL REPRODUCTION
OF REFLECTION PROCESS COLOR COPY

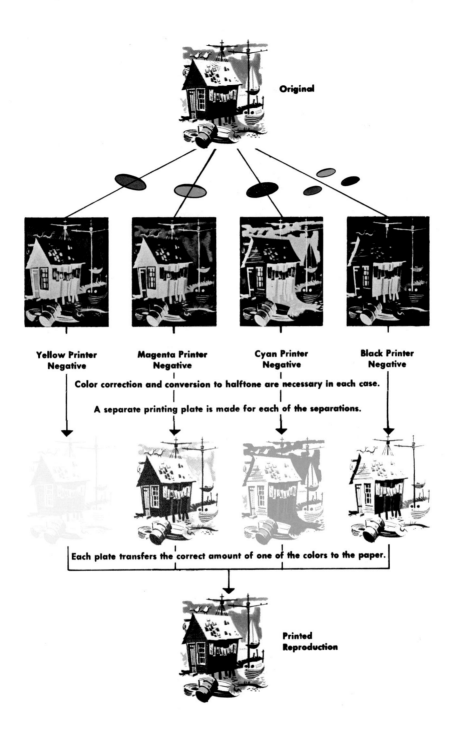

Original

Yellow Printer
Negative

Magenta Printer
Negative

Cyan Printer
Negative

Black Printer
Negative

Color correction and conversion to halftone are necessary in each case.

A separate printing plate is made for each of the separations.

Each plate transfers the correct amount of one of the colors to the paper.

Printed
Reproduction

KODAK GRAY SCALE

7 inch size

Red-Filter Negative
Cyan Printer

Green-Filter Negative
Magenta Printer

| black | 3-color | white | cyan | violet | magenta | primary red | yellow | green |

KODAK COLOR CONTROL PATCHES

These colors have been selected as representative of those inks commonly used in photomechanical reproduction.

Copy Ready for Camera

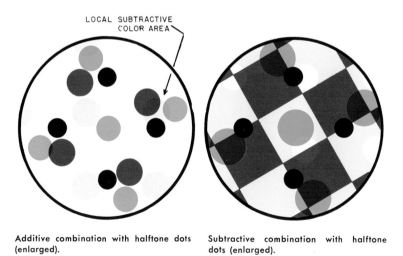

LOCAL SUBTRACTIVE
COLOR AREA

Additive combination with halftone dots
(enlarged).

Subtractive combination with halftone
dots (enlarged).

Enlarged Colored Halftones

GRAY SCALE AND COLOR PATCHES

The subject of tone and color controls is treated under the following thirteen headings: (1) The gray scale, (2) Balancing a set of separation negatives, (3) Contrast in different separation negatives, (4) Adjusting of contrast in direct method separations, (5) Adjusting of contrast for indirect method separations, (6) Selecting the proper inks, (7) Comparing inks and color control patches, (8) The color control patches, (9) Evaluating color-separation negatives by their control patches, (10) The wanted colors in the cyan printer, (11) The unwanted colors in the magenta printer, (12) The wanted colors in the magenta printer, and (13) The yellow printer and the black printer.

This unit transcends the subject of color separation in its most traditional sense by far. Here you can see how closely related color separation and color correction are! Study this unit and you will find the "Photographic Masking and Color Correcting" chapter much easier than you may fear. But back to business!

The Gray Scale. A photographic gray scale is a series of reflection densities, ranging from white to black, in a convenient strip on photographic paper. It is recommended that one of these scales be mounted along the edge of the original copy to be photographed. It must be placed so that it will receive the same amount of light as the subject, and so that there is no direct reflection from its semi-glossy surface into the camera lens.

Examination of the gray scale reproduced on each separation negative will give a visual indication of the tone separation in highlight, middletone, and shadow areas of each negative.

Balancing a Set of Separation Negatives. A "balanced" set of negatives is not necessarily one in which all the gray scales match, step for step. Such a set will not print a neutral gray scale with the commonly used process inks, but will result in a series of brown steps unless corrections are introduced at a later stage. Without further corrections, matching gray scales on the separations would reproduce as neutral gray only with a theoretically perfect set of process inks, not at present commercially available. *A "balanced" set of negatives is a set which will print a neutral scale of grays with a specific set of inks.* The gray scales on such a set will not match, but the differences between them will be much the same for every color job which is run with these same inks and printing conditions. The operator, then, instead of matching the separation gray scales to each other, matches the red-separation gray scale to other red-separation gray scales which he has found correct for his conditions, the blue to other good blues, and the green to other good greens.

Contrast in Different Separation Negatives. In general, the red-filter negative should be higher in contrast than the blue- and green-filter negatives, especially in the highlight end of the scale. Also, it may be found that the green-filter negative has too much contrast and the blue-filter negative not enough.

Adjusting of Contrast in Direct Method Separations. In the direct method of color separation, when using a glass screen, the contrast of the blue- and red-filter negatives can be increased by using a larger lens stop when using a one-stop exposing method or by giving a larger proportion of highlight exposure when using a two- or three-stop exposure. In the same way,

the contrast of the green-filter negative can be lowered by using a smaller lens stop for the one-stop exposing method or by giving a smaller proportion of highlight exposure when using a two- or three-stop exposure method. When using the gray contact screen, contrast can be controlled by flashing, still development, and supplementary highlight exposures, as described in the instructions supplied with the screen.

Adjusting of Contrast for Indirect Method Separations. In the indirect method of color separation, the contrast of the negatives can be controlled by varying the development times.

Selecting the Proper Inks. All masking procedures for photomechanical reproduction must be carried out for the specific set of inks which is to be used in the printing process. Since the need for color correction stems from the lack of color purity in all commercially available inks, it is important that the available inks be examined to select those which are best adapted for the method to be used for correction.

Comparing Inks and Color Control Patches. At the risk of being repetitious, it is again emphasized that ink and color control patches must match. If the inks used in a specific plant do not match the color control patches, patches made with these specific inks should be used. For further information on this subject consult the chapter "Photographic Masking and Color Correcting" of this Manual.

The Color Control Patches. These patches are supplied as part of color separation guides and kits available from graphic arts supply houses. The images of these patches on the negatives and positives provide measurable densities which indicate the effectiveness of the separation and color-correction methods being used. If the patches are correctly recorded, the balance of the copy will be also.

If the inks to be used do not match closely in hue, purity, and saturation, the inks of the color control patches, sample patches of the actual inks to be used should be substituted. If the reproduction is to be printed on other paper than glossy paper, these new ink patches should be printed on the paper being used. A four-color patch consisting of a three-color solid plus a 50-per-cent tint of black is also desirable and, of course, a more complete color chart will give additional useful information.

Evaluating Color-Separation Negatives by Their Control Patches. The appearance of the color patches in the masked negatives shows whether the color correction has been properly carried out. For a given color separation, the various patches may be divided into "wanted" and "unwanted" colors. For example, the unwanted colors in the cyan printer are yellow, magenta, and primary red. These require no cyan in their reproduction and, in order to achieve this result, they should match the white patch in density.

The Wanted Colors in the Cyan Printer. The "wanted" colors in the cyan printer—that is to say, the colors which should print solid—are cyan, blue, and green. These should all have equal densities, and, unless the original is so contrasty that its tone scale has to be compressed in the reproduction process, they should all print solid. Their color correction can be calculated by comparing them with each other and with a black area. In a three-color printing, the wanted colors should definitely match in density the three-color solid patch; in four-color printing, they should be intermediate in density between the three-color patch and the black patch, the exact value depending on the quantity of black which is to be printed.

The object of masking is to equalize these patches as described above, and its effects are most clearly seen in the magenta printer.

The Unwanted Colors in the Magenta Printer. The unwanted colors in the magenta printer are yellow, cyan, and green. These three colors are almost exactly equal to the white patch in a well-corrected magenta-printer negative. Without masking, the cyan and green patches would lack density; in an overcorrected negative, they would be too dark, a condition which is sometimes described as "whiter-than-white." (Remember that we are talking about negatives.) The mask has

little or no effect on the yellow patch which needs practically no correction.

The Wanted Colors in the Magenta Printer. The wanted colors in the magenta printer are magenta, primary red, and blue, and these should be a little lighter in the negative than the three-color solid patch, to allow for the addition of a black printer on the latter. Without masking, the magenta and primary red would be too dark in the negative and result in lack of color saturation in these areas. With masking, they are often too light (overcorrected) when the mask is strong enough to correct the cyan and green patches.

The Yellow Printer and the Black Printer. In the yellow printer, the unwanted colors are cyan, blue and magenta; the wanted colors are yellow, orange-red, and green. These can be evaluated as described above for the magenta printer.

In the black printer, all six colors are unwanted, but this is difficult to achieve by photographic means.

Section Three: Direct Method Color-Separation Procedure

Our description of direct method color-separation procedure is divided into the following twelve points: (1) Photographic materials for the direct method, (2) General discussion of making direct separation negatives, (3) Filters for direct separations, (4) Order of exposure, (5) Exposure, (6) Example of procedure with the gray contact screen, (7) Example of procedure with crossline screen, (8) Processing, (9) General discussion of black-printer negative for direct separations, (10) The split-filter method, (11) The single-filter method, and (12) The infra-red method. Each of these is now individually discussed.

PHOTOGRAPHIC MATERIALS FOR THE DIRECT METHOD

High-contrast panchromatic materials which produce clean, sharp halftone dots, suitable for dot-etching, should be used for the direct method. The following materials are recommended: For general lithography and photoengraving—high contrast litho pan film. For extreme dimensional stability—polyester-based high contrast pan litho. For lateral reversal, a prism or image reverser can be used on the camera with the polyester-based pan litho emulsions. For lateral reversal without using image reversers, negatives made on the materials listed immediately above can be contact printed to obtain a laterally reversed duplicate on direct positive material on polyester-type base.

General Discussion of Making Direct Separation Negatives. Direct halftone separation negatives are made in essentially the same manner as black-and-white halftone negatives, but each is exposed through an appropriate filter. With a ruled glass screen, use either a one-stop exposure plus a flash exposure, or a multi-stop exposure plus a flash exposure. As in black-and-white halftone photography, the flash exposure is given in order to produce a hard shadow dot and to prevent excessive shadow contrast. In color reproduction, the shadow detail is reinforced

by the black-printer plate which receives a minimum flash exposure. When using a gray contact screen, follow the directions supplied with the screen.

Filters for Direct Separations. The following Wratten filters are recommended for color separation by direct method: Cyan ("blue") printer—Wratten Filter No. 25(A) (red); Magenta ("red") printer—Wratten Filter No. 58(B) (green); Yellow printer—Wratten Filter No. 47B or 47 (blue)*; Black printer—Wratten Filter No. 8 (K2) (yellow).

Order of Exposure. The separations can be exposed in any order, but most operators make the red-filter (cyan-printer) exposure first. When the correct exposure for the red filter has been determined, the approximate exposure for the green and blue filters can be determined quickly by multiplying the red-filter exposure time by the filter *ratio*. Filter ratios for the recommended materials are presented in the direction sheets supplied by the film manufacturers.

Exposure. The exposure indexes given in the direction sheets for use with standard photoelectric exposure meters can be used in determining the correct exposure for the red filter negatives.

The white-flame carbon arc was once the most commonly used light source for photomechanical color reproduction. Pulsed Xenon and Quartz-Iodine tungsten lights have become more popular now. They provide high intensity lights with a nearly continuous spectrum which approximates the wide range of the spectrum of the sun. The index numbers are usable directly with an incident-light meter or with a reflected-light meter when used to take a reading of light reflected from a

---

* The No. 47B filter gives more complete color separation than the No. 47, but some operators prefer the latter because of its shorter exposure time.

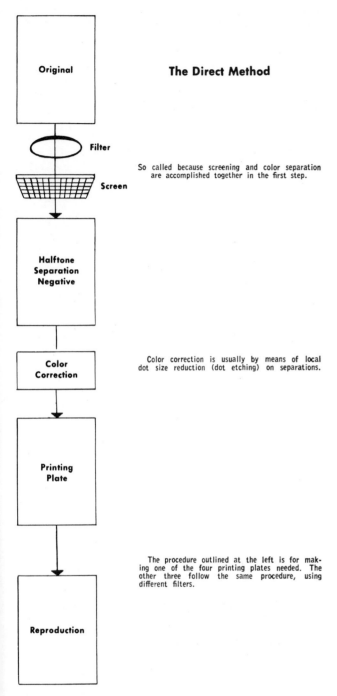

The Direct Method

So called because screening and color separation are accomplished together in the first step.

Color correction is usually by means of local dot size reduction (dot etching) on separations.

The procedure outlined at the left is for making one of the four printing plates needed. The other three follow the same procedure, using different filters.

Schematic Outline of the Direct Method*

neutral test card (18 percent gray side) placed in the position of the copy to be photographed. A matte white card may be used, in which case multiply the calculated exposure time by five. Remember, also, that the above exposure-meter calculation is for lenses set for infinity focus. When the camera is set for same-size (1:1), multiply the calculated exposure by four. For other camera settings, copying data-guides are available which will give the correct factors.

When a halftone screen is used in the camera, the light reach-

*By permission of Eastman Kodak

ing the film is greatly reduced. For the gray contact screen, the correct exposure time will be about 10 times the calculated exposure. For glass crossline screens, the factor is much higher and variations in method of use make a calculation of the factor really not worthwhile in most cases.

Example of Procedure with the Gray Contact Screen. For line negatives or halftone negatives made with the gray contact screen, the calculation of the correct exposure by means of an exposure meter can be summarized by the following typical procedure:

1. With the meter set for the correct exposure index, take a reading of the illumination at the copyboard if using an incident-light meter, or of the light reflected from a white or standard gray card at the copy position if using a reflected-light meter.

2. Read the meter as recommended by the manufacturer. The exposure time at any lens opening is given by the meter.

3. If a white card was used in taking the light measurement, multiply the exposure time indicated on the meter by five.

4. Adjust for image size. For example, if the reproduction is being made same size, then multiply the result by four.

5. If a gray contact screen is being used, then multiply the result by ten.

The result obtained from these calculations should be the correct exposure under average conditions. It should be noted that lights, lenses, and other equipment vary widely. If the operator finds that, under his conditions, the above procedure consistently yields underexposed or overexposed negatives, he can compensate by regularly exposing for a certain percentage more or less than the calculated amount. This percentage should remain the same as long as the same equipment is used.

Example of Exposure with Crossline Screen. With high contrast Pan litho film and Wratten Filter No. 25, the exposure for making a same-size direct-screen reproduction of colored copy with a crossline screen and a 1:64 aperture ratio will be approximately 4 minutes* at f/32 if two 35-ampere arc lamps are used about 48 inches from the copy.

If the 4-minute exposure through the No. 25 filter is satisfactory, the other exposures would be determined as follows: *Green-filter exposure:* the filter ratio for the Wratten Filter No. 58 will again arbitrarily be stated as 1.2. Therefore, the correct exposure through this filter would be 4 × 1.2 = 4.8 minutes, that is, 4 minutes and 48 seconds. *Blue-filter exposure:* The filter ratio for the Wratten Filter No. 47B is 2.5. Therefore, the correct exposure through this filter would be 4 × 2.5 = 10 minutes.

Processing. Recommendations for processing the materials for direct color-separation negatives are covered fully in the instruction sheet packaged with the material.

General Discussion of Black-Printer Negative for Direct Separations. A satisfactory black-printer negative is not easy to produce, and it is usually necessary to make a compromise

*This is an arbitrary figure used solely for illustration purposes. Actual exposure must be established under each shop condition.

between the rendering of the various colors. Further discussion of the black-printer problem will be found further down in connection with the indirect method. At this point, it is sufficient to remember that the chief difficulty is to record the grays without recording the pure colors too strongly.

The ideal black-printing plate is almost impossible to achieve photographically in the direct-screen method of color-separation work. There are, however, several methods of making black printers which need only moderate handwork and are used generally by the trade. We will here discuss the split-filter method, the single-filter method, and the infra-red method.

The Split-Filter Method. The split-filter method has some advantages. In this method, the black-printer negative is exposed successively through each of the three color-separation filters and on the same panchromatic material which was used for the other color-separation negatives. These partial exposures through each filter can be roughly proportional to the filter ratios and are usually between 30 and 50 percent of the exposures used in each case for the other three separation negatives. For example, if the exposure through the blue filter for making the yellow-printer-plate negative was 10 minutes, the blue-filter exposure for the black-printer negative would be 3 to 5 minutes.

High-Contrast Pan Litho Film	High-Contrast Pan Litho Film	Infrared Sensitive Plate
Split Filter Method	No. 8 Filter	No. 8 Filter

Black Printers for the Direct Method (positives from negatives made as indicated)*

Some operators prefer to give a full exposure through each of the three filters in making the black-printer negative. The advantage of the split-filter method over the single exposure

through a Wratten Filter No. 8 (K2), which is next described, is that it is possible to change the balance of exposures to suit the particular subject to be reproduced. For example, if the original subject contains no important red areas, use only the blue- and green-filter exposures to produce a better rendering of blues and greens. A red-filter exposure is not needed because there is no red to be recorded as white on the black printer.

The Single-Filter Method. Another method of making the black printer is to expose the same material through the Wratten Filter No. 8 (K2). This method records the various colors at about the same relative brightness as the human eye sees them. Thus, the neutrals are also rendered in normal brightness.

In both of these procedures, the neutrals are reproduced satisfactorily, but there will be too much black in the bright-colored areas. For certain types of copy, the method described below offers improvement in the rendering of dark-colored areas.

The Infra-Red Method. Infra-red sensitive films can be used for producing well-corrected black-printer continuous-tone negatives from suitable water-color or oil paintings. By using a somewhat special technique, these same films can also be used for making good black-printer negatives for the direct method of color reproduction. Briefly, the method consists in making a screen negative directly on an infra-red sensitive plate. The dots so produced are soft and ragged around the edges. However, by contact printing onto high contrast litho film, the dots can be sharpened to usable quality. A second negative is then made by contact printing from the screen positive.

The detailed procedure is as follows: Place an unexposed infra-red sensitive film in the plate-holder in the camera back. Exposure should be made through a Wratten Filter No. 8 (K2). The plate should be developed in a high contrast developer, full strength. This will produce a screened image with dots which have soft edges. The screen negative can then be printed by contact on a high contrast litho film. Contrast can be adjusted to some extent by controlling the agitation in the development of the screen positive. A contact negative is then made from the positive. The resulting halftone will have sharper dots than the original.

The chief advantage of this procedure is that, with suitable originals, the pure colors can be dropped out while the neutral or dark areas are recorded fully.

Section Four: Indirect Method Color-Separation Procedure

Our presentation of indirect color-separation procedure is divided into the following five units: (1) The color-separation negatives, (2) The black printers, (3) Continuous-tone positives, (4) The making of screened negatives and positives, and (5) Evaluating and changing various steps in the making of indirect color separations. Each of these subjects is treated in the following.

THE COLOR-SEPARATION NEGATIVES

Our description of color-separation negatives and their

making by the indirect method is divided into the following four points: (1) General discussion on the selection of photographic materials for the indirect method, (2) Exposure, (3) Example of exposure, and (4) Processing. Each of these is now individually discussed.

General Consideration on the Selection of Photographic Materials for the Indirect Method. Photographic materials should be selected to meet the requirements of the job at hand. The contrast of the original copy determines to a great extent the selection of the photographic materials. If the original copy is of high contrast, then a low-contrast, or "soft," negative material should be used. Similarly, if the original copy is of low

---

* By permission of Eastman Kodak

contrast, then a color-separation material of somewhat higher contrast should probably be selected. All of these materials are, of course, of considerably lower contrast than those used in the direct method. It should be pointed out that it is usually unsatisfactory to attempt to make low-contrast negatives on a basically high-contrast material by reducing the development time. This procedure usually makes the development critical and often produces a faulty tonal rendering, since it tends to flatten highlights.

LITHOGRAPHY*
Positive Processes (deep etch)

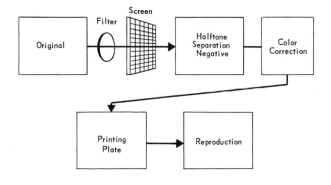

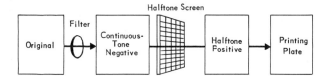

Schematic Outline of the Indirect Method

There are films and plates for each phase of photomechanical color-separation work. While no film manufactured can equal the dimensional stability of glass plates, more and more operators are finding that, when properly handled, film causes little or no difficulty in this respect. If, before use, film is conditioned for several hours in the same atmosphere in which it is to be used, and if all separations are treated in identical fashion according to recommended procedures, most register troubles disappear. Manufacturers who make both film and plates for color-separation photography list them. Their literature states which plates are comparable to each film emulsion. Although there are differences between each plate and its listed counterpart (such as in developing time, gamma, speed, etc.), the general photographic characteristics of the plate and film in each pair are quite similar.

Films with the new special bases are much more stable than

---

* Courtesy of Eastman Kodak

acetate-based film and require a great deal less special handling. However, even when using these stable-based films, it is desirable to make a set of separations with sheets taken from one package.

Exposure. Mount the copy and arrange the illumination as discussed later in this section. Select the proper material and expose the four separation negatives. The following filters are recommended: If the exposure for the red-filter (cyan-printer) negative is determined first by trial or by calculation or taken from the particular film or plate data sheet the exposures for the green and the blue-filter negatives can be calculated by multiplying the correct red-filter exposure by the ratios found in a table. The exposure indexes given in the table are for use with standard photoelectric exposure meters in determining the correct exposure for the red-filter negatives. The index numbers are usable directly with an incident-light meter when used to take a reading of light reflected from a neutral test card (18 percent gray side) placed in the position of the copy to be photographed.

Printer	Wratten Filter No.
Cyan ("blue")	25 or 29 (red)*
Magenta ("red")	58 or 61 (green)*
Yellow	47B (blue)
Black	2B, 8, or 88A‡ or by successive exposures through the red, green, and blue filters

*The No. 29 and 61 filters give more complete color separation and somewhat higher color saturation than the 25 and 58. This is useful when masking is not to be used for color correction, but the excessive color saturation causes trouble when masking methods are to be used.
‡For the special techniques involved in making the black-printer negative by infrared radiation, see page 6:12.

A matte white card may be used, in which case multiply the calculated exposure time by five. Remember, also, that the exposure-meter calculation is for lenses set for infinity focus. When the camera is set for same size (1:1); multiply the calculated exposure by four. For other camera settings, the copying data guide will give the correct factor.

Example of Exposure. Example of exposure with a continuous tone color-separation negative film and a Wratten Filter No. 25, for making a same-size continuous-tone negative of a color original with two single 35-ampere arc lamps 48 inches from the copy: about 15 to 30 seconds at f/32.

If a 20 second exposure through the No. 25 filter is satisfactory, the other exposures would be determined as follows: *Greenfilter exposure:* If the filter ratio for the Wratten Filter No. 58 is 1.2, the correct exposure through this filter would be 20 × 1.2 = 24 seconds. *Blue-filter exposure:* If the filter ratio for the Wratten Filter No. 47B is .3, the correct exposure through this filter is 20 × .3 = 6 seconds. *Black-printer negative exposure* is fully treated below.

Processing. Processing of the recommended materials for the indirect method of color separation is covered fully in the instruction sheet packaged with the material. Tables or charts show best development times in recommended developers.

At this point manual color correction, when it's required, is usually performed. (Photographic color correction is discussed in Chapter Seven.)

Two extra steps (a contact negative and then a contact positive) are frequently added at this point to obtain sharper half-tone dots and provide more flexibility for layout and composition purposes.

THE BLACK PRINTER*

Our discussion of the black printer for indirect color separation comprises the following seven points: (1) General discussion of black-printer negative for the indirect method, (2) Black plates for dry printing on single-color presses, (3) Black plates for high-speed wet printing, (4) The three methods of making a black printer, (5) The single-filter method, (6) The split-filter method, (7) The infra-red method. Each of these is now individually discussed.

General Discussion of Black-Printer Negative for the Indirect Method. Most craftsmen have come to agree that the black-printer negative is the most difficult of all the color-separation negatives to correct properly. However, by the selection of the proper photographic material for each of the various types of copy, it is possible to make the job of reproduction easier.

The object of a black printer is to make up for the lack of detail and contrast in the three color-printers. Since there is a great variation in the amount of color that can be carried by the three color-printers, the requirements of the black printer will vary correspondingly. The two extremes are represented by (1) glossy inks on coated paper, each color dried before the next is printed, for which the black plate, if used at all, can be very weak, and (2) four-color wet printing in which nearly all the blacks and dark grays must be carried by the black plate.

Black Plates for Dry Printing on Single-Color Presses. In the first case, where the black plate is required only to add a little density and contrast to the extreme shadow areas, and sometimes to cover up a lack of balance in the printing process, there is little difficulty in making a satisfactory black printer. By suitable choice of filters and by underexposing the black-printer positive, the pure colors can be dropped out of the black printer so that their brilliance will not be obscured by the addition of black. In many cases, a Wratten Filter No. 8 will be satisfactory for exposing the black printer. Where deep blues predominate, a Wratten Filter No. 2B may be used. For maximum control of a broad range of colors, the split-filter method should be used. In general, to lighten a color in reproduction, use a filter of the same color in making the black printer.

Black Plates for High-Speed Wet Printing. In letterpress high-speed wet printing, however, there is at present no alternative to carrying most of the dark tones in the black printer instead of in the three color plates. It is not practical to lay down enough of the three color inks to produce a dark gray or black. In this case, the three color plates must be reduced to quite a light tone by some color-correction method, and the primary object of the black printer is to replace the tones that have been removed from the other three plates. This is called "undercolor removal." This substitution of black can take place

only in dark or near-neutral areas; otherwise, the colors will be degraded. The ideal black printer for this purpose would carry a full range of tones in neutral areas, but the pure colors would be dropped out. In offset, wet colors trap much better, but some undercolor removal is sometimes used to minimize smudging and offsetting (setting off) with heavy forms.

The Three Methods of Making a Black Printer. There are three methods of making a black printer—the single-filter method, the split-filter method, and the infra-red method. All of these usually require considerable handwork. For more perfect correction, a photographic masking method is usually required, although the scanning machines now provide an excellent result.

The Single-Filter Method. In the single-filter method, the same panchromatic material that was used for the other three color-separation negatives is exposed through a suitable filter; usually the yellow Wratten Filter No. 8. This records the different colors at about the same brightness levels as they are seen by the human eye and provides a black printer which usually requires extensive hand correction unless the positive is made to have no more than a 50-percent dot (checkerboard pattern) in the shadows.

With some originals, a yellow filter may not be the best choice. For instance, if blues and greens are absent or unimportant, the red-filter (cyan-printer) negative often makes a good black printer. If warm colors are absent, a green-filter negative may be used.

The Split-Filter Method. The split-filter method offers somewhat greater flexibility than the single-filter method. Three exposures are made on the same film or plate—one through each of the three color-separation filters, with the exposure through each filter usually being between 30 and 100 percent of the exposure for each of the corresponding color-separation negatives. A lower proportion of blue than red exposure is usually required, but the proportions can be varied according to the predominant colors in the original. The black printer should be just as sharp as the other color-separation negatives.

A well-corrected black printer may be made by using different masks during the various exposures of the split-filter method. This is described under the Magenta Masking Method for Reflection Copy and the Two-Mask Method for Transmission Copy in Chapter Seven of our Manual.

The Infra-Red Method. The infra-red method can be used only with certain types of originals but when the original is suitable, it produces an excellent result. It consists in exposing an infra-red-sensitive film or plate through a filter which transmits infra-red (usually Wratten Filter No. 88A), and its success depends on the fact that most bright-colored pigments transmit or reflect infra-red and therefore reproduce as light when photographed by infra-red radiation.

A few bright-colored metallic pigments which require little or no black in their reproduction absorb infra-red strongly so that a good black printer cannot be made by this method if such pigments are present in the original. These include the paris and chrome greens and prussian or iron blues. The result will

---

* A new technique for making the black printer has been developed by GATF. Since it is involved with photographic masking, it is described in Chapter Seven.

also be unsatisfactory if the artist has obtained his dark colors by mixing complementary colors, in which case there will be no infra-red absorption. Moreover, the dyes of color photographs (including, of course, the black mixtures of these dyes) are mostly transparent to infra-red radiation, and they cannot be photographed by infra-red. In some cases, the cyan dye absorbs infra-red slightly so that a weak record will be obtained, but this is similar to the red-filter negative which usually is not satisfactory for a black printer.

The use of infra-red for the black printer is therefore restricted to paintings and pastel sketches from which certain pigments are excluded. However, when the original is suitable, the result is excellent.

The infra-red black printer is very different from that obtained by the other two methods. With these other methods, there is usually too much black in the pure colors. With the infra-red method, the pure colors are dropped out completely, even in their darkest tones, and this often does not provide enough "drawing" in the black plate for certain types of printing, particularly high-speed wet printing. By use of different filters, somewhat more detail may be obtained in the black plate. For example, detail can be obtained in blue and green areas by the use of a red filter. For detail in flesh tones, use a green filter.

CONTINUOUS-TONE POSITIVES

Our discussion of continuous-tone positives covers the following eight points: (1) General discussion of continuous-tone positives, (2) The two methods of making continuous-tone positives, (3) Evaluating continuous-tone positives, (4) Color-separation positives on paper, (5) Working instructions for making positives on paper, (6) Contrast requirements of reflection positives, (7) Advantages of reflection positives for the artist, and (8) Advantages of reflection prints for the cameraman. Each of these is now individually described.

General Discussion of Continuous-Tone Positives. After the four continuous-tone negatives have been given their final check for accuracy, continuous-tone positives are made if screen negatives are needed for making the printing plate. Preparation of the positives involves the recording of black-and-white values only, and therefore does not require the use of panchromatic materials.

In order to maintain the color correction achieved in the negatives, the positives must be handled with equally great care because any variation in the tonal quality at this point makes considerable difference in the appearance of the final color reproduction. The use of a densitometer is recommended as an aid in maintaining the tonal quality from step to step. In using the positive intermediate step, the color retoucher is able to build up tones corresponding to the color values he wishes to achieve in the final printed reproduction. This technique of building up positive tonal areas is easier for most artists than etching down the similar areas of heavy density in the negatives.

The Two Methods of Producing Continuous-Tone Positives. Continuous-tone positives can be produced by two methods: by contact printing and by use of the process camera. In contact printing, the emulsion of the negative is placed in contact with the emulsion of the unexposed material, and the

exposure is made in a printing frame. Stable-based commercial emulsions are especially recommended for this type of work. When the positives are made in the camera, the negatives are placed in the transparency holder and the illumination is directed from the back of the negative with the emulsion of the negative facing the camera lens for normal orientation of the image. As indicated in the diagram, the area between the transparency holder and the lens should be covered. This cuts out stray light, reduces lens flare, and aids in obtaining consistent results.

Evaluating Continuous-Tone Positives. The continuous-tone positives should exhibit full shadow detail and show as much highlight detail as possible to compensate for the typical loss of detail in this area on the tone scale of the reproduction. This improvement can be made by increasing the exposure slightly so that the minimum density is not below .4, and, if necessary, by decreasing the development time.

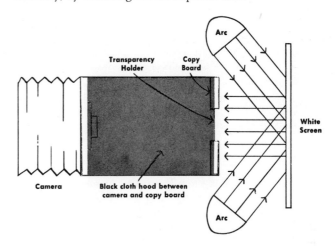

Set-up for Making Continuous-Tone Positives
Using the Process Camera

Color-Separation Positives on Waterproof Based Emulsion.* Good-color separation positives on paper or film can be made for, and used by, those retouchers in photomechanical shops who prefer to work on prints rather than on plates. Waterproof based emulsions are coated on a special water-repellent base to permit rapid washing and drying, which contribute to excellent size-holding qualities during processing. These paper materials are obtainable for both contact and projection printing.

Working Instructions for Making Positives on Waterproof Based Emulsion. A separation positive is made directly from each of the separation negatives by contact printing or enlarging on the suitable emulsion. A safe-light filter, Wratten Series OA (greenish-yellow) is recommended for handling this material in the darkroom. Develop for about one minute in one part of Dektol Developer or 53D diluted with two parts of water. Rinse the paper in a suitable stop bath, 3% acetic acid,

---

* Kodak Resisto Paper
Kodak Resisto Rapid Paper
DuPont Cunapaque on Cronar®

for 10 seconds and bathe in a fixing bath for two minutes with continuous agitation. Washing and drying should be carried out in the same manner as used with regular photographic papers except that the washing time is only about four minutes with good agitation.

The prints dry in a very short time—approximately two minutes with ordinary darkroom conditions.

To keep dimensional changes low, do not use heat. Do not ferrotype. Any processing step prolonged beyond the recommended time will allow the base to absorb moisture, with the result that dimensional changes may be increased and drying will not be so rapid.

Contrast Requirements of Reflection Positives. Separation negatives for this method of working should be rather low in contrast and have a density range no higher than 1.10. The print quality should be rather flat, with good detail in both highlights and shadows. The contrast of the negative and the exposure of the prints should be adjusted to produce these characteristics when the prints are developed for the recommended time. After corrective local adjustment of tone values by the artist, screen negatives are made in the camera.

Advantages of Reflection Positives for the Artist. To the artist, the most marked advantage of using this method of reproduction is the ease of working on a positive print. An experienced artist can judge easily the tone value on separation-positive prints, and this means rapid production and accurate results for the photomechanical shop.

Advantages of Reflection Prints for the Cameraman. To the camera operator, there are also advantages of working by this method. The copy for screening is of the reflection type and therefore does not require the use of a transparency holder in the camera as does the screening of positives on film or plates. The operator can produce the type of print needed to meet any particular photomechanical requirements of the job or shop.

On the other hand, there is a little more danger of dimensional changes with paper prints and the relative short scale of photographic papers, as compared with film, may cause a loss of highlight or shadow contrast, if the prints are too contrasty or are under- or over-exposed.

THE MAKING OF SCREENED NEGATIVES AND POSITIVES

The final screen negatives or positives can be made by contact in a vacuum printing frame with a contact screen or in a camera with either a contact screen or a conventional glass crossline screen.

The contact screens provide an efficient method of making screen images by contact printing without tying up the process camera. Either a Gray Contact Screen or a Magenta Contact Screen can be used, but the latter provides more facility in the control of contrast in this step.

When a conventional glass screen is used in the camera, the same screen separations and stop ratios should be used as for black-and-white work.

EVALUATING AND CHANGING VARIOUS STEPS IN THE MAKING OF INDIRECT COLOR SEPARATIONS

Under this heading we are concerned with the following seven points: (1) General discussion of exposure changes, (2) General discussion of development changes, (3) Judging results and making adjustments, (4) Establishing a color reproduction procedure, (5) Tone reproduction curves and their interpretation, (6) Changing the reproduction curve by means of flashing, and (7) Equipment for flashing.

General Discussion of Exposure Changes. The blackening (density) of a photographic image is controlled in two ways: by the amount of exposure to light, and by the degree of development in suitable chemical solutions. A certain minimum amount of exposure is necessary to produce an image under any condition of development. The amount of exposure necessary to produce a recognizable image on a photographic material is more than this minimum amount.

To see what happens you make a series of different exposures of the same subject. As the exposures are increased, the images become stronger until sufficient detail becomes visible in the extreme shadows. This can be called a "normal" negative. If the exposure is increased very much beyond this point, an excessively dense negative which often will lack detail in the highlights will result. Notice that as the exposure is increased the densities of all tones are increased in the negative, and the detail and contrast in areas corresponding to the shadow or dark tones of the subject are improved.

General Discussion of Development Changes. Change in development conditions or time has a somewhat different effect on the appearance of separation negatives from that with a change in exposure time. As development is increased the main effect is seen in the dense areas of the negative, which represent the highlights of the original copy. Notice that as development is increased, there is relatively little effect on the lighter or shadow portions of the separation negatives. At the same time, the highlights of the original, represented by the darker portions of the separation negatives, are progressively darkened. *In other words, the amount of exposure of the negative tends to control the rendition of shadow areas of the original whereas the amount of development controls the density of the highlights.* This can be put to very good use when processing negatives. If the shadow areas appear weak, and detail is not discernible, the exposure should be increased. However, if the shadows appear correct, and highlights appear too weak, the development time should be increased to help produce a correctly balanced separation negative.

Judging Results and Making Adjustments. The examples given above are merely a guide. They are based on separations of equal contrast and nearly straight reproduction curves to be used as a starting point. It has been pointed out, however, in the discussion of the gray scale, that equal contrast in the separation gray scales is usually not desirable and modifications should be introduced to meet particular printing conditions. This is also true of straight line reproduction curves.

Establishing a Color Reproduction Procedure. In establishing a procedure for color reproduction, start with the given example, study the results, and then alter the procedure to improve the reproduction. For example, if the reproduction appears brownish in tone when the highlights appear correctly balanced, insufficient contrast in the cyan printer is indicated; if the shadows are bluish when the rest of the scale is correctly balanced, the yellow-printer negative is too flat in the shadows and requires more exposure; if the middletones are too light, although the ends of the scale are correct, a more strongly bowed curve (produced by longer development and less exposure, preferably with the addition of a flash exposure as described below) is required for the separation negatives.

Tone Reproduction Curves and Their Interpretation. A bowed curve is illustrated in the accompanying diagram.

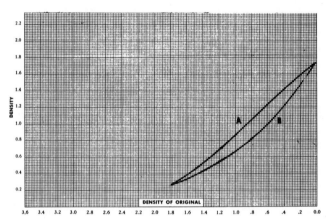

Diagram Illustrating a Bowed Curve

Shown there are the two separation negatives which correspond to the curves A and B. Although the desirability of straight line characteristic curves is often emphasized in photographic work, they are not necessarily the best choice for separation negatives.

A characteristic curve like B is often necessary to compensate for the flattening of highlights, the lack of color in the middletones, and the frequently excessive shadow contrast produced by most photomechanical processes. Even if the shadow contrast is not excessive, a slight loss in shadow detail is usually less noticeable than a loss in highlight detail. The best adjustment of exposure, development, and flash exposure depends on the characteristics of the whole process and must be determined by experience.

There can be no exact specification unless platemaking, inks, paper, and presswork are all under exact control. Since all of these factors vary widely from shop to shop, these recommendations can be given only as approximate guides.

Changing the Reproduction Curve by Means of Flashing. The best method of changing the reproduction curve from a straight line to bow shape so as to increase the highlight contrast and obtain more color in the middle-tones is by means of flashing. A separate light source mounted on the darkroom ceiling will be found most convenient for this purpose. By using this same light for all flashing, its effect on the film is quickly learned and thereafter predictable.

Equipment for Flashing. An arrangement which has been found satisfactory for making the flash exposure is a darkroom safelight lamp with a Wratten Series 2 filter, and a 7½-watt, 115-volt frosted bulb. One of these lamps can be either suspended from the ceiling or mounted at a suitable distance in front of the vacuum frame.

CHAPTER SEVEN

Photographic Masking and Color Correcting_____

Section One: The Principles and Techniques of Lithographic Process Color Reproduction

Lithography has always held important advantages over other printing processes in the reproduction of color. The first advantage was the straightforward simplicity whereby it was able to print from drawings, made by artists directly on stone or metal; another great advantage was its then unique ability of easily producing tints and tone values by crayon grain or stipple dots. The relative ease of producing large size printing images has always favored lithography for big pictures and posters, and the "offset" feature of transferring the ink from an intermediate rubber blanket surface has extended quality color printing to an important variety of surfaces which other processes could not handle as well.

Early lithographic color plates were drawn entirely by hand, and many more colors were used than are today. Ten to fourteen colors were commonly needed. These were selected to match important areas, and if the press run did not meet expectations, additional overprint color stones or plates were freely added. Photography has changed these procedures by radically reducing the number of colors required. To date, the importance of handwork and photography is almost completely reversed in color reproduction. The first help of photography to lithographic color work was to provide a more accurate detailed key image on stone, but the actual printing values were still created by hand art. This era, however, drew to a close when the halftone screen became practical, thereby providing an adequate substitute for hand-created tone values in color plates. The halftone screen broke lithography's virtual monopoly on picture reproduction by opening the door to photo-engraved letterpress color, but it also opened the era of photo-mechanical color for lithography which has steadily moved on towards always higher standards of perfection.

While letterpress was quick to take advantage of the fewer colors needed in process reproduction and soon did creditable work with only three colors or four, lithography continued the general use of at least six colors for many years. Recent times have seen the bulk of both lithography and letterpress standardized·in four-color process with lithography now taking the lead in expanding the use of three-color systems.

COLOR VISION AND COLOR REPRODUCTION

The use of only three color inks to seemingly reproduce thousands of colors is possible because our eyes do not need to receive exactly the same wavelengths from copy and print to simulate a match. In fact, our eyes are very poor in analyzing light mixtures and we are entirely unconscious of seeing all the colors of the rainbow in every white surface we look at. Our eyes are basically responsive to only three broad sections of the spectrum, and the many distinctly different colors we seem to see are simply our mental interpretations of varying proportions of red, green and blue signals transmitted to the brain through the optic nerves.

The manner in which we experience color is of greatest practical importance for our technique of color reproduction. This manner makes it possible to reproduce our many color sensations with three printing inks, provided that the ink mixture reflection matches the red, green and blue balance of the original colors. The brightest colors we will print are already reflecting from the white paper in equal balance; to create any particular color does not require that we print an ink that matches this particular color, but that we print some proportions of three inks which act like partial filters to properly influence the red, green, and blue balance to that of the wanted color. This condition makes color printing with overlapping process inks essentially a subtractive process.

Because all possible colors are already reflecting from the white paper surface we will print on, and because thin films of process inks are almost perfectly transparent, the press operation is—expressed in terms of color science—not one of putting color on the paper but one of controllably taking color away.

COLOR SEPARATION

The first step in any color reproduction system is to isolate the information as to the proportions of red, green and blue light reflected from each area of the copy. This step is called color separation and explains why we use red, green, and blue filters in their exposure. Many process workers think of color separation as trying to record the proper amounts of yellow, process-red, and process-blue inks which should print in each area of the reproduction. This is a practical thought but makes a misleading approach to the understanding of reproduction problems. *Color-separation negatives do not and cannot directly record the correct amounts of commercial process inks used to print.* This fact is often misinterpreted, leading to the false conclusions that the filters or plates are wrong and that color-correction steps must compensate for these separation errors.

Color separation is most generally accomplished in process cameras with arc-light illumination, although in recent years several new light sources have been developed to the point where they are practical as well as advantageous. The color separations are individual exposures through red, green and blue filters to panchromatic films or plates which are sensitive to all colors. Of course, color transparencies may also be separated in enlargers or by contact printing, and the light source may be a tungsten lamp. These two different light sources—arc light as well as tungsten light—are satisfactory for color separation because they both provide continuous radiation through the complete spectrum. Their difference in color temperature just changes the balance of exposure time through the different filters. The bluer arc light relatively shortens the blue-filter exposure while the yellower tungsten filament bulbs lower the red-filter exposure ratio.

The standard set of color filters, 25, 58, 47,* divide the spectrum into approximate thirds, each of them having a small overlap in the adjacent one. With modern panchromatic emulsions, these filters could give close to facsimile reproduction if we were able to carry out the following reproduction steps as efficiently as the step of color separation. This can be demonstrated by viewing positives of these separations by additive colored light either in a Chromoscope or on a screen by projection. Unfortunately, printing inks do not control light subtractively as well as filters do additively; in the process inks, as they transfer to paper, lie the sources of the most serious color reproduction errors which must be considered in correction methods.

REQUIREMENTS OF IDEAL PROCESS INKS

A simple statement of the requirements of process inks for subtractive color reproduction is, that they should each be complementary to the taking filters. More specifically, the ink which prints from the negative blue-filter record must be a positive image on white paper which locally shuts off the reflection of blue light to the same degree as it matches the blue reflectance of the copy. Black, red, green, or yellow all would perform this function equally well because they all absorb blue light. A most important second requirement, however, is that a process ink should completely reflect the other two thirds of

*These are Kodak filter designations. Other manufacturers of color separation film also have comparable color separation filters compatable with their film, and which carry their own designations. The manufacturers' published data should be referred to for this information since, normally, filters from different manufacturers are not likely to be interchangeable when used for full-color separation photography.

the spectrum while absorbing only one third. Only yellow—which reflects red and green while absorbing blue—meets these requirements.

The green-filter separation negative must print on white paper as a positive image which controls green light. Black, red, magenta and blue are equally efficient in absorbing green, but magenta alone meets the second requirement of reflecting blue and red. The red-filter separation negative record must be printed as a positive ink image which locally absorbs red light, and of course is transparent to the rest of the spectrum which is green and blue. This color is technically called cyan.

FAILURES OF COMMERCIAL INKS RELATED TO COLOR CORRECTION

Commercially-used process inks all fail to meet the described ideal of one-third spectral absorption and two-thirds reflection. This becomes obvious when we look at a reproduction printed from uncorrected separations, as all cold colors become warmer or grayer and warm colors lack full strength. These are failures of the process inks to fully reflect the colors that ideal inks would reflect.

While there has been some improvement in ink-hue purity in recent years, the best available cyan and magenta inks still absorb some blue light and the best cyans still absorb some green light. This means that more than one ink absorbs light in each third of the spectrum and that, consequently, the brightness of greens, blues and purples is limited to the reduced level that these ink mixtures can reflect. It also means that the purest colors these inks can reproduce will not be obtained without color correction of the separation negatives or positives.

COLOR CORRECTION

Color correction will be an important and critical step in lithographic color reproduction as long as we continue the use of inefficient process inks. Color correction will also remain an uncertain, time-delaying operation as long as the variables which create the necessity for it are not better understood and controlled. Color correction has the reputation of being one of the most misunderstood steps in graphic arts procedures. This is true because actually the whole process of color reproduction, too, is just as often misunderstood.

One of the clearest indications of this condition is in the names that most workers apply to process-ink colors. They speak of printing with yellow, red and blue. If we really printed with true yellow, red and blue inks, we would soon find that they are impossible to use as a set of process inks, as their overprints would produce no new colors. Yellow and spectral blue are complementary and subtractively produce black. Red and blue are spectrally exclusive colors and their overprints would also produce black, while red overprinting yellow would still be red. The subtractive primaries of ink which control the additive red, green and blue primaries of light, are called yellow, magenta and cyan. By tradition, we've used the terms "process red," and "process blue" because in most conventional inks these colors did look red and blue. As the whole process of color separation and correction became better known by more and more craftsmen, especially in the "integrated" litho plant, it became advisable to describe process red and process blue by their more technically correct names of magenta and cyan, respectively. This helped to avoid confusion with the terms used to describe the colors of filters used in color separation work.

The major problems in color correction stem from the use of magenta inks which in fact are too red, and the use of cyan inks which are too blue. We have used wrong-hued process inks so long that most process workers would probably not know how to recognize the correct, pure hues if these existed or were available. It wasn't until GATF started a systematic study of inks being used, that the industry recognized the full impact of the problems caused by inks not properly balanced for full-color reproduction from photographically separated and corrected color printers. Eastman-Kodak's introduction of a system for producing "pleasing" full-color reproduction in three color printing lent the whole movement great impetus. The development of color scanners, which could do a good job only under standardized conditions, also pushed the work to develop and use more efficient process inks. Facsimile color printing from our tricolor separations requires a set of process inks in which each ink absorbs only one-third of the spectrum.

Most available yellow inks absorb principally blue and therefore come close to this requirement; but all magenta process inks also absorb some blue, typically from 30 percent to 70 percent as much as the yellow. Perfect magenta inks should only absorb green light; the added—but unwanted—blue absorptions shift their hue 30 percent to 70 percent towards red. Because a perfect yellow separation will print 30 percent to 70 percent yellow correctly in any color made with these reddish magentas, their blue absorption is doubled and all red colors become more orange whereas the blues and purples reproduce grayer.

While the fault lies entirely within the magenta ink because its absorption has gone beyond green to include some blue, the color correction is nevertheless applied to the yellow printer in order to reduce the doubled blue absorption wherever magenta and yellow would print together. Cyan inks also absorb some blue; consequently additional corrections must be made again to the yellow printer wherever cyan ink will appear in the reproduction.

Here is the root of the greatest misunderstandings in color correction. People who have not studied the subject cannot understand why we must apply the most correction to the yellow separation that prints with an almost perfect ink, with the result that we *then* need no correction on the cyan separation, in spite of the fact that the cyan separation is printed in a most inefficient ink. It is difficult for the theoretically un-informed to realize that cyan inks absorb light in all three-thirds of the spectrum and that corrections must therefore be applied in the other two separations. Nor do they understand that the red-light absorption of the cyan inks is not duplicated by good yellow or magenta inks and that, consequently, the red filter separation can fully control where cyan ink must print.

The most serious error of all available cyan inks is their considerable absorption of green light, which absorption is theoretically the sole function of magenta inks. This fault of cyan inks makes their hue bluer than it should be in a correct cyan, and this hue shifts even warmer when a magenta printer adds its own proper green absorption. Correction in the magenta printer consists in lessening the strength of magenta ink wherever cyan prints by the same amount that the cyan ink incorrectly absorbs green.

COLOR SEPARATION GUIDES

A valuable aid to judging color-separation negatives and color correction is a control strip such as GATF's Color Reproduction Guide. The suppliers of photographic materials make available color control patches of various design (Eastman-Kodak Color Control Patches were, for years, the standard such guide). The most distinctive feature of the GATF guide is that the lithographer produces his color reproduction guide with the inks he will use, the paper on which he will print, and incorporates also his own peculiar press variables. In a sense, GATF's Color Reproduction Guide is a miniaturized representation of GATF's Color Chart which, for some years now, has been in wide use. Since the GATF guide is produced in the plant, it will represent the variables in that plant's color separation process, something no ready-made standard color guide can do.

Solid Ink Patches. As in other color control guides, the solid ink patches of the GATF Color Reproduction Guide are used for the calculation of mask percentage, for the evaluation of ink trapping, and for the measurement of solid ink densities. In separation negatives or positives, the solid ink patches indicate the degree of color correction by the "Rule of Three." This rule requires that, in each properly corrected separation (except black), three of the six basic colors are as dense as black and three other colors as light as white.

Sometimes, it is convenient to have the three wanted colors side-by-side. With standard color guides, this is provided only in the yellow and magenta separations. In the new GATF Color Reproduction Guide, the addition of a second green patch between cyan and white keeps the three wanted colors together in the cyan printer also.

Tint Patches. Each solid patch of the GATF Color Reproduction Guide is followed by patches of ¾, ½ and ¼ tints of 150 lines per inch. These tints represent the dark, medium, and light portions of the halftone scale. They will show what amount of dot gain is to be expected through each stage of reproduction. Another use of the tint patches is to calculate proportionality failure. Proportionality failure makes the hue and grayness of lighter tints look worse (further from ideal) than the hue and grayness of solid ink. To correct for this phenomenon, mask curves must depart from a straight line. Negative masks must have a higher slope in the highlights than in middle tones or shadows. Positive masks require a flatter slope in their higher densities. The tint patches help to predict the correct mask curves. In color separations, they will indicate if proper mask curves have been used and show if the proportionality failure has been corrected.

Moiré Patterns. The rescreening of any tint or halftone may, under some conditions, produce an objectionable moiré pattern. In some cases, this also may happen to the tint patches of the GATF Color Reproduction Guide. To avoid this difficulty, the angle of each color of the reproduction guide is turned 30 degrees away from its customary position. The new angles are as follows:

Black:	$45° + 30° = 75°$
Magenta:	$75° + 30° = 105° (15°)$
Yellow:	$90° + 30° = 120° (30°)$
Cyan:	$105° + 30° = 135° (45°)$

When shot at regular screen angles, the tints of the reproduction guide will show only minimum pattern, visible through a magnifier as a slight irregularity in dot formation.

The precaution of adjusted screen angles may not prevent the appearance of moiré in some tints if the separations are not fully corrected and a tint appears where no tint of this color was present on the original color guide. We have a similar situation with tints of black. In the original, the black solid and tint patches print only black ink. In the standard color separation process, however, the black patches will reproduce in each separation. This makes is impossible to avoid moiré in each printer and it will be visible in some of them. The black printer is not important for color balance and the appearance of color moiré in black patches will do no harm because most of this pattern will be covered by the black printer with no pattern.

Most problems connected with moiré patterns can be eliminated when the copy and the Color Reproduction Guide are reduced.

Gray Balance. One of the basic requirements of the color reproduction process is to reproduce the gray scale with three process inks. Three-color overprints of tints of equal dot area will not produce gray but will look brown. To appear gray, the dot sizes of the gray scale in three-color printers should be properly unbalanced. The extent of the unbalance needed depends on the inks, paper, and press variables.

There are several ways to compute the gray balance requirements of color process reproduction. One method, for graphic solution, is to use the GATF Color Hexagon* to obtain color density measurements of a series of the following tints: (1) Yellow; (2) Magenta; (3) Yellow and magenta overprints; (4) Three-color overprints. GATF's Color Reproduction Guide includes all these tints and, consequently can be used with this method.

The new GATF color reproduction guide† contains all these patches. The guide also offers another simple way to find out the gray balance requirements.

The tints of each color in the original negatives or positives of the reproduction guide have equal dot area. The three-color overprints also originate from identical tints.

The original Reproduction Guide was printed with the thought that the final screened separation of the color copy and the guide would go through exactly the same reproduction stages. Consequently, to achieve facsimile reproduction, the final halftone negatives or positives of the color reproduction guide should be identical with the original negatives or positives. As a result, a simple rule can be applied. All three separations must be screened to equal dot size in the tints of three-color overprints.

* The method was described by Wulff, A, and Jorgensen, H. O. "An Analysis of the Controllability of the Separational Stages in Multi-Color Productions;" a report from the Graphic College of Denmark, Copenhagen, July 1964. While simpler than other systems which have been published, this method is still too involved for general use in the average plant.

† GATF's "Research Progress" No. 67, *The New GATF Color Reproduction Guide* (included in the back of this book), and *A Gray Balance Chart,* reported on in GATF's 1967 "Report of Progress," describe two other methods of computing gray balance.

If the brown three-color overprints will reproduce in the same manner as in the original color reproduction guide, the dot area of the gray scale tints will be unbalanced. This unbalance will be the gray balance requirements for a satisfactory reproduction of the gray scale.

In the evaluation of the final reproduction of all colors, we must try to reproduce the original negatives or positives of the GATF Color Reproduction Guide.

THE RULE OF THREE

The simple "rule of three" is derived from the way the six solid ink control areas were produced and how they, consequently, must be reproduced. Each of the process inks is printed solid in three of the six areas, and of course, not at all in the remaining three. A reproduced set of printing plates must repeat this condition. In our first color separation—the blue filter separation for the yellow printer—we must record where the yellow color block prints equally solid in the yellow, red and green areas as well as where no yellow is printed, namely in the magenta, cyan and blue areas. It is impossible to create this separation directly in one photographic step, no matter what color filter, spectral band of light or photographic emulsion is used. This is neither the fault of filters or photographic emulsions, nor that of yellow colorants (dyes or pigments); it is the fault of the two other inks.

Here, at the blue-filter separation, we are only concerned with the absorption of blue light by one ink and the reflection of blue by the other two inks. We can photograph yellow as black because yellow absorbs blue light, but we cannot record magenta and cyan inks as white because no available magenta and cyan inks completely reflect blue as they should. No conceivable blue filter can overcome this deficiency.

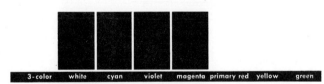

3-color | white | cyan | violet | magenta | primary red | yellow | green

Color Patches of Ideal Yellow-Printer Negative

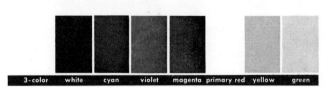

3-color | white | cyan | violet | magenta | primary red | yellow | green

Color Patches of Actual Yellow-Printer Negative
(Blue filter separation)

By examining the six solid ink control areas in a blue-filter separation negative, you can see the failure to fully reflect blue light by the fact that magenta and cyan photograph less dense than the white paper; this failure can also be noticed where magenta and cyan overprint yellow to make red and green. Under normal conditions, red and green will photograph that much stronger than yellow, as magenta and cyan photograph stronger than white. Perfect color correction for this condition would then require adding a controlled density to the separation negative in all areas where magenta and cyan inks will print. This correction density—whether applied by hand retouching or by photographic masking—must follow that "rule of three," thereby bringing up the densities recorded by the magenta, cyan and blue to equal the density from white, and therewith equalize the solid ink level in the yellow, red, and green.

Color Patches of Ideal Magenta-Printer Negative

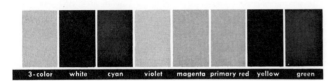

Color Patches of Actual Magenta-Printer Negative
(Green filter separation)

The second separation negative, made with a green filter, strongly records the three areas, magenta, red and blue-violet—in which magenta is printed solid—but fails to bring up all densities of the other three colors—yellow, cyan and green—to the density photographed by white paper. These photographed densities are, of course, a measure of green reflectance, and while most yellow-process inks record almost as dense as white, all cyan (or process-blue) inks absorb half or more of the green light ideal inks would reflect. Correct separations will also carry this same intrinsic error wherever cyan over-prints other

Color Patches of Ideal Cyan-Printer Negative

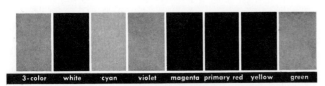

Color Patches of Actual Cyan-Printer Negative
(Red filter separation)

colors. This will be most noticeable in the blue-violet control area which will be that much clearer than magenta, as the cyan area is clearer than the white density in the negatives. We may judge the green-filter separation fully corrected when this condition is equalized in the magenta, red, and blue-violet—while the yellow, cyan and green densities are equalized to the white density.

The third separation negative, made with a red filter, may be judged as correct if three areas are equally strong, namely the cyan, green and blue-violet—and if the yellow, magenta and red areas are equally dense to white paper. Actually this condition can be practically reached with most sets of process inks, although some magentas are noticeably grayed and their lower red reflectance records a little less dense than white. A red-filter separation may then merely need this slight correction to be fully color corrected. But if the cyan, green and blue control areas are not as strong as the black area, a contrast increase or saturation correction must be applied. For more complete masking control, GATF now further recommends the addition of a tint area with each solid color so that the masking color corrections can be judged at at least two tone levels. This new GATF color reproduction guide is illustrated in the Research Progress #67 in the back of this book. It illustrates also the Rule of Three, with separate comparisons of each printer color.

HAND CORRECTION

Much of the color correction in lithography and other graphic arts processes has traditionally been done by hand-work of artists or etchers. Photo-engravers have long depended on local etching and burnishing of the copper printing plate to change color tone values with little or no work done on negatives. Early lithographic color printing in the "submarine process" also left much of the correction to the printing image. In the submarine process, direct halftone separation negatives were printed in bichromated albumin on lithographic stones, and left under water after inking and development. The name "submarine" was used because dot sizes were reduced by forced over-development consisting in locally rubbing with cotton while the albumin image was kept soft under water. Small runs were printed from these original stones while longer press runs were usually made from their images which were proofed and hand-transferred to larger stones or plates.

THREE-STEP, FOUR-STEP, AND TWO-STEP PROCESSES

One of the most used early hand-correction systems was the "Three-Step Process" in which most of the color correction was done on continuous-tone wet-plate positives made on ground glass. While tone values could easily be lightened by rubbing with pumice powder and erasers, or by shaving, scratching or rippling with a needle, positives were also often made lighter than normal density. In this case, correction consisted in building up the wanted image by penciling, stumping with graphite or opaquing. This was particularly good for reproductions needed in more than one size, such as calendars, and is still the best method when extensive changes in color or detail are needed. From the corrected positives, halftone negatives of any size were made for the albumin or surface type of press plates.

When deep-etch plates, requiring positives, became more universally used, a fourth step of contacting the halftone negatives to positives was sometimes added. More generally, the practice has been to shorten the process to only two steps, halftone positives being made directly from the separation negatives. This technique began the new era in lithographic color correction known as dot-etching, in which much of the color correction is accomplished similarly to photo-engraving by chemically reducing dot sizes where less color is needed. In lithography these dots are, of course, on photographic positives rather than in the metal and cannot be enlarged by burnishing. Local strengthening of dot images is obtained by starting with fuller positives, staging-out certain areas and etching-back the remainder to proper strength. This local strengthening cannot be accomplished on negatives as fully or as easily as on continuous-tone positives; it has therefore been general practice to locally reduce or open up the separation negatives with Farmer's Reducer before they are screened for positive retouching. When more than one size reproduction is needed, it is customary to minimize the dot-etching and lighten these tones by dye-staining the gelatine of the separation negatives.

COLOR CORRECTING BY MASKING

While hand artwork has been the backbone of color correction for lithography in the past, photographic methods, called masking, are becoming better understood and are now taking over an increasing amount of this work load. With masking methods matched to selected inks and controlled press conditions, regular work is now being accomplished without hand corrections. This is only possible when the several important color errors of process inks are balanced and specifically corrected for. In a rapidly increasing number of jobs, hand correction is done only when the customer wants a change from what was in the original copy.

In the past, many of the correction systems using masking still left considerable error and required handwork for completion. Some of this was due to poor selection of process ink hues, uncontrolled press conditions, or failure to consider the differences in ink trapping and dot gain characteristics of single-color, two-color, and four-color presses. Some error was due to failure to recognize the significance of paper surface efficiency* as a factor in process color reproduction. However, too often, handwork was needed because the intrinsic errors and their correction had not been understood. All too often the approach to color separation and masking was in imitation of hand-worked sets. Dozens of different approaches to color correction by photographic means have been patented; in spite of considerable ingenuity shown in their many variations, most of these processes have failed to consider all of the variable and inherent errors that we are now learning to consider important.

ADDING LIGHT FOR COLOR SEPARATING

The most basic errors of process inks lie therein that each of them fails to reflect fully the two-thirds of the spectrum that it should reflect. This failure is manifested in each separation

---

* A discussion of paper surface efficiency and how to measure it is in GATF's "Research Progress" No. 60.

negative, as copy colors—similar to two of the process inks—failing to separate out as dense as white paper, and to properly record, namely, only where the third ink will print. This problem was recognized long ago; an early proposed solution to it was to project more light onto the copy areas where more density was needed in the separation negative.

Both Levy and Robertson built special cameras to accomplish this effect by adding a small auxiliary camera-projector to standard gallery-type cameras. Levy mounted the small projector camera on tracks running at 45-degrees to the copy while the large separation camera directly faced the copy. Robertson had the projector directly face the copy, giving more useful light and eliminating angular distortion and focus problems; the large camera was then placed at right angles to copy and projector and picked up the image through a prism to give laterally-reversed negatives, the kind then desired for photoengraving.

These cameras made possible the applying of Edward Gamble's patent of 1912 (see: B. P. 6768). Gamble proposed making red- and green-filter negatives in the small camera, and projecting light from an arc through them individually while exposing the magenta and yellow separations. The degree of correction was established by balancing the strength of the direct copy illumination and the projected light. The modern Addmask camera (see: Frank Smith, "The Nicoll Addmask Auxiliary Unit," Process Engravers Monthly, May 1952, pp. 148–49 and Frank Smith, "A New Colour-Masking Technique," Penrose Annual Vol. 46, 1962, pp. 97–99) accomplishes the same ultimate goals more efficiently by use of a mirror system to project the added light image directly to the photographic plate instead of the copy.

FLUORESCENT DYE COPY

Alexander Murray (see: USP 2,108,503; A. Murray & John Yule, USP 2,278,114; and John Yule, USP 2,286,779-80) has developed a method to replace projection as the source of locally added light. The original artwork must be painted with a special pallet of watercolors some of which contain different fluorescent additives. These additives radiate blue or green light when stimulated by ultra-violet rays. The photographic density from these areas can then be made to match the density from white paper by controlling the ratio of ultra-violet to visible light. A special camera-light hood with ultra-violet filters and variable slit widths passes only this balanced light to the copy.

NEGATIVE MASKS

Another effective way of getting relatively more light to the exposing separation in the areas which otherwise would not be dense enough, is to put a mask negative in the camera back directly in front of the exposing separation. This mask is made with the same filter as though it were to be used to locally project added light to the copy. However, in this system the copy is evenly illuminated. Instead of actually adding light to the exposure, the mask here accomplishes the same purpose by holding back light in the white and the opposite color areas. For example, during a green-filter exposure, a red-filter negative mask holds back some light from white, yellow and red, and relatively more passes through the clear green and cyan areas.

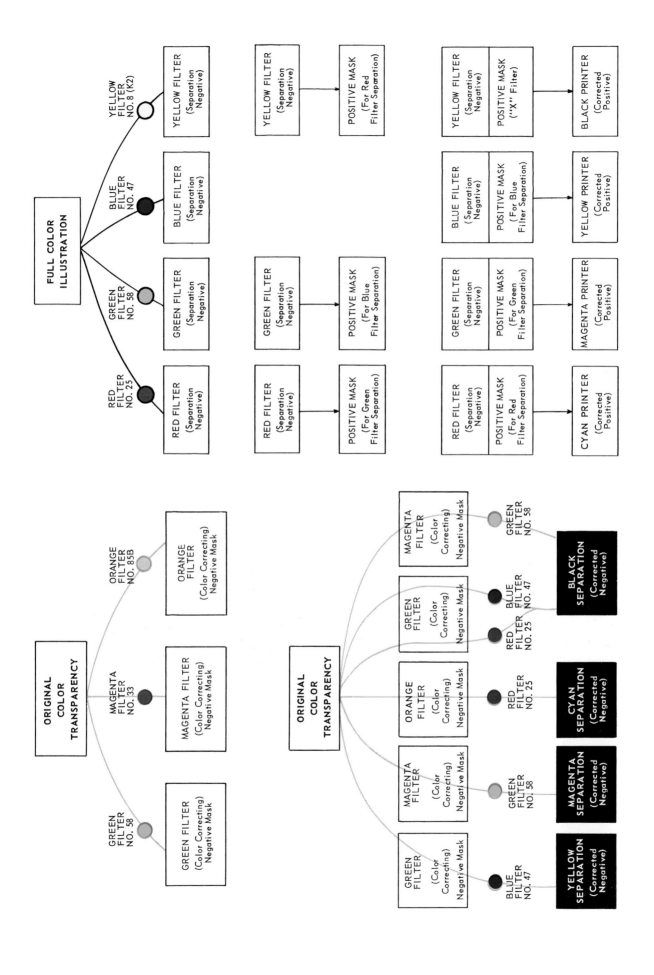

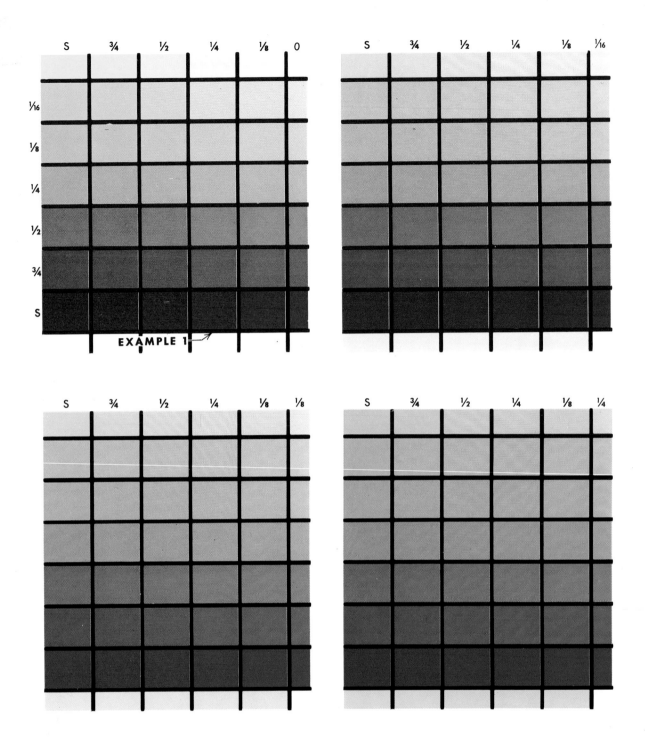

COLOR GATF CHART

The GATF Color Chart meets all of the important requirements for a good color chart and provides a means for standardizing color printing. It shows 1,760 different color combinations made with two, three, and four colors. These appear in 42 different color squares. The chart is designed primarily for printing on a single 22x29 inch sheet. However, all of the more important information can be run on a 17½"x22½" sheet. Lithographers can save much time and expense by purchasing sets of positives or negatives from GATF to print their own color charts using their own inks, papers, methods and equipment.

Seven color blocks are shown here. The basic block is composed of five vertical columns of yellow. The first column is solid yellow. The others are ¾, ½, ¼, and ⅛ tints. The six horizontal rows within each block are values of magenta printed over the yellow. The other blocks are overprinted with different tints of cyan.

These seven blocks show the full gamut of two and three color combinations. On the complete GATF Color Chart, these same seven blocks are duplicated in five more rows with tints of black overprints.

To specify a color, match it as closely as possible with a color patch on the chart, say the patch marked Example 1. By referring to the left of the row in which the patch appears, you see that one component is solid magenta; by referring to the top of the column in which the patch appears, you see that the other component is a ¼ tint of yellow.

Suppose the color matches Example 2. By referring to the left side of the basic block, you see that these fourth rows contain a ¼ tint of magenta. The top of the column in which the patch appears shows that it also contains solid yellow. Then by checking the upper right corner of the block, you see that the third component is the ¾ tint of cyan that overprints the entire block.

The GATF Color Chart also has solid color bars that help the pressman get and hold an even ink lay and a GATF Color Test Strip. This is a bar about ½" wide and 10½" long, composed of 21 different ½" blocks. These show solids and tints of the individual colors as well as two, three, and four color overlaps. Densitometric analysis of these colors provides valuable information on the color range producible with a set of process inks; that is, basic information for setting up photographic masking systems.

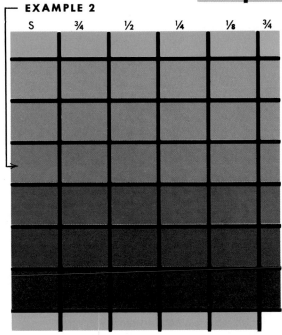

EXAMPLE 2

←— 1/16 BLACK—ROW B

A	B	C	D
PROJECTED MASKS	**CONTACT MASKS**	**INTEGRAL MASKS**	**CAMERA BACK MASKS**
MASKS USED WITH ORIGINALS			
Projected Negative Masks (image projected on copy)	Negative Masks (used for color transparencies) See Kodak Data Book Masking Trans- parencies for Photo- mechanical Repro- duction	Not used	Magenta Masks Silver Masks
MASKS USED WITH NEGATIVES			
Projected Positive Masks (image projected on negatives) Automasking (image of original used as mask)	Positive Masks 1. Color Correcting 2. Undercolor Removal Negative Masks 1. Highlight 2. Drop-out Two-Stage Masks 1. Pre-masks 2. Principal Masks	In color negative films	Not used
Masks of this type are used to project a modifying light pat- tern on the original or on the exposure plane when making separations or at a later stage, as when making positives.	One photographic image gets added density in certain areas from a second image mounted in contact. Example: a red-filter positive mounted in register with a green-filter separation negative.	Example: The orange color seen on Koda- color and Ektacolor negatives. This dye mask is produced automatically as an integral part of the negative and corrects for certain unwanted transmissions of the dyes.	A mask is made and used in the camera, just forward of the plateholder. The sep- aration negative is made through it. Its effect is to reduce the intensity of the image in those areas where it has density.

Masking for Reflection Copy

If these masks are made as normal silver images they are best developed to fine grain, at correct strength, and used in contact with the exposing separation. If spaced in use, normal silver grains scatter light and diffuse the image. Negative masks when spaced may give clearer separations if used during only part of the exposure. This requires that they be made considerably too strong. Special cameras were built to facilitate removing the mask during the separation exposure and to substitute a compensating glass of equal thickness in the optical path. Raschke's camera (see: Emil Raschke, USP 1,373,020), patented in 1921, had two swinging frames, while the Levy-Hahn camera (see: Francis Hahn, USP 1,576,118) used an additional sliding plate holder positioned just ahead of the halftone screen position.

CAMERA-BACK MASKING*

Camera-back masking is a method that is used mainly for reflection copy. The masks are made directly from the copy and before the separations. They are exposed on the camera back through suitable filters. After being processed, the masks are returned to their original position on the camera back over a piece of panchromatic film. The color separations are then exposed onto this film through the mask. The separation is thus color corrected at the same time that it is exposed.

COLOR TRANSPARENCIES

The most universal use of negative-type masks has been with positive color transparencies, and the manufacturers of such color materials have helpfully published detailed instructions for handling them. When the first dye-coupled three-layer films came into use, color-separation negative emulsions did not linearly record their long scale of tone values. The first most important benefit of masking came from the tone compression of these originals to a shorter density range which passed through lenses with less flare, and better matched the straight-line acceptance of separation negatives. These masks also selectively increase relative color saturation.

Color correction is controlled by choice of filters and individual mask strength for each color separation. Tone control is often introduced in transparency masking to improve highlight contrast and increase middletone color strength. This can be done in two different ways. When principal or tone compression masks are made as negatives with a shouldering tone-reproduction curve, separations exposed through them and color transparencies have greater high-light contrast than when made with masks of straight-line densities. Still greater highlight contrast with wider range of control is obtained when an additional masking step is used. A highlight pre-mask is first contacted from the transparency, and the principal mask exposed through the highlight protected transparency.

POSITIVE-IMAGE MASKS

The most widely varied use of masking for color correction has been with positive-image mask systems. Positive masks

* This technique is treated in detail in the Eastman-Kodak Q-Sheet No. 7A.

give color correction to separation negatives by adding their densities to local areas from which too much of a color would print. They are most often made from the regular set of separation negatives but may also be made from differently filtered negatives to vary the correction. Most often a positive contacted from the green-filter negative is used to correct the blue-filter negative; and a similar contact from the red-filter negative corrects the green-filter negative. Positive masks, of course, also lighten the strength of the printing color in black and gray areas, and the first masking patent (see: Dr. E. Albert, DRP 101,379) of Dr. Albert described this in 1897. His second patent (see Dr. E. Albert, DRP 116,538) extended the system to fuller color correction.

MASKING PUT ON SCIENTIFIC BASIS

Many other variations of masking were patented in following years but masking did not attract wide attention until 1935 when Kodak published "The Modern Masking Method of Correct Color Reproduction." This described Alexander Murray's infra-red improvement (see: Alexander Murray, USP 2,161,378) of the black separation and introduced the proper use of a densitometer to relate separation negatives and mask densities. Murray's work demonstrated that color correction can be divorced from visual judgment and personal opinion when guided by instrument control standards related to measurements of the color reflectance of the process inks and the variables in the processing steps.

REVIEW OF MASKING PRACTICE

It is desired that each color-separation negative present an exclusive record for each of the three process inks and their appearance in the print. In practice, however, uncorrected separations always also partially record some ink colors in areas where either only one or both of the other color inks should be present. Masks made directly from standard separations are usually adjusted to correct for the larger of these two errrors, and then leave a residual error to be corrected by hand, or an additional mask. The magnitude and relation of the two errors in each separation varies with the relation of the individual ink hues. It is most desirable to select ink hues having either very low secondary errors, or inks having such hues that their errors balance out together with standard mask conditions.

Some variations in masking techniques aim to cancel both errors from unbalanced ink hues through use of special masks made from differently filtered or doubly-filtered exposures. For example, when an orange-shade chrome yellow ink is used, the magenta printer must be lighter in all oranges—and this correction may be included by a partial blue-filter exposure added to the normal red-filter mask exposure. If the blues need relatively more correction in a yellow printer than the magentas, the mask exposure should shift yellower from green, either by help of a yellow filter or by added red-filter exposure. These variations should not be used unless the measured hue balances of inks used in the particular case show that they are required.

Some process-ink sets have opposite hue differences than the described ones and need still more complicated treatment. No extra photographic plates are needed in color correcting for this type of process inks. In negative masking their correcting means simply a different filter treatment, whereas positive masks may be made for this purpose by double exposure from two separations.

Common practice often makes use of additional thin film masks, sandwiched between the glass-separation negative and a glass-positive color-correction mask. These may each have a separate purpose; a "Highlighter" to improve light tone detail, or an "Opaquer" to cleanly drop out all white backgrounds. Extra film color correctors may also be included when the principal glass mask does not cancel all errors.

MASKING CAMERAS

Some early masking methods (see: Joseph Hatt, USP 1,349,956 and William Wilkinson, USP 2,124,679) combined all of these corrections into one intimate image with the separation. Separation negatives were first coated with a waterproof layer, and overcoated with bichromated glue, gelatine or collodion emulsion. Multiple contact exposures were then made from other reversed negatives or positives. The Long mask camera was designed to sequentially project up to four different images into one plate or film. The master images are pre-registered in separate frames and automatically move into exposure position by pushbutton control. Both these methods simplify the positive-making step by pre-assembly of all correcting units.

Another camera specially designed for masking color correction was patented in France by Nerot (see: Henri Nerot, FP 780,364; see also W. B. Hislop "Notes & Comments," Process Engravers Monthly, Aug. 1948, p. 255). The Nerot process contacted separation negatives to color-corrected positives without intervening mask layers. The camera was essentially a same-size fixed-focus lens system which projected mask images through the separation negative as the positive exposure light source.

Still another versatile masking camera is the Multichrome. This provides for making and using projected and spaced masks at precision register positions. Close image controls and illumination from both ends of the camera are provided. Color transparency masks and separations may be made and used without contact or register disturbance of the original. Routine color-corrected separation of transparencies may be accomplished by first positioning the original in the usual front copy-holder and focusing its image at the normal back plate-holder position. A highlight pre-mask is then made and returned to this position with the light source moved around behind it. This projects the mask image onto the transparency while spaced principal masks are exposed in a register position close behind it.

The degree of unsharpness of these masks may be varied by changes in the lens aperture controlling depth of focus. Studies by John Yule have shown that detail is more clearly reproduced when masks are suitably unsharp (see: John Yule, USP 2,455,849). The unique combination transparency and mask holder (see: W. Hislop, "The Latest Multichrome Addition," Process Engravers Monthly, June 1951, p. 173) allows changes of masks without disturbing the transparency so that a wide field of multiple masking is possible. The Multichrome camera (see: H. M. Cartwright, "Colour Masking by Projection," Penrose Annual, Vol. 46, 1952, pp. 93–96) most simply described, is a combination of two cameras facing each other and sharing a common lens to accomplish "distance" masking.

THE PROBLEM OF OVERCORRECTING

Color correction from simple negative or positive masks has not always been satisfactory. A common failure is over-correction of some color mixtures, such as removing too much yellow from browns or too much magenta from purples. The cause of this lies in the separation negatives rather than in the masks, but when it is present it may be controlled by use of two-stage mask systems. With positive masking, for example, to correct the yellow separation, a pre-mask film positive is first contacted from itself to protect red and brown areas. This is combined with the magenta separation negative while the corrected mask for the yellow printer is being exposed. This "two-stage" mask will still fully correct single ink-color errors of magenta while retaining full strength yellow in red and brown color mixtures.

When similar overcorrections occur with negative-mask systems, a thin positive-mask image of the printing color may be combined with the usual negative mask during the color-separation exposure. One application of this has been called "counter masking" by Frank Smith (see: "Colour-Masking in Graphic Arts Reproduction," Science and Applications of Photography, 1953, pp. 543–47) who has found it useful for color correction in three-color processes where full strength of each color is desired in black. A related variation of this avoids use of two masks at one time in the camera by using a blue-filter pre-mask negative, for example, during the exposure to make the usual green-filter mask which will be used during exposure of the yellow-printer separation.

The basic fault of separation negatives, which simple one-step mask systems overcorrect in two-color mixtures, is found in their failure to record color ink errors the same when overprinting as when printing alone. In other words, if with a blue filter, magenta ink photographs darker than the paper on which it prints, it must also photograph the same amount darker than any ink it overprints, in the overlap. Red must be as much clearer than yellow in a blue-filter separation, as magenta is clearer than the density from white paper. Some separation negatives fail to accomplish this from totally different causes. The most difficult error to compensate for lies in the overlapped process inks themselves.

Depending on increasingly high-hue error and surface-scattered light, some inks simply do not add their separate light absorptions fully when printed together. This can be measured with a reflection densitometer, and if the measured difference between yellow and red is not as great as between magenta and white, a broader band filter than the 47 used for measurement may compensate this photographically. If the measured differences are equal, such inks will photograph unequally under differing conditions such as narrower band filters, lens flare, or when they are underexposed in order to place color mixtures on the toe of the separations reproduction curve. Separation negatives, made under these incorrect conditions for masking, look better and are actually better for hand correction, because the strong colors in which all ink should equally print are in closer balance.

UNCOMMON LIGHT SOURCES

Most color separation is being accomplished with white-flame arcs or tungsten light and conventional filters, but other light sources, too, may have certain advantages; continuing research is therefore being devoted to this field. Any system that eliminates filters in the lens can avoid image shifts and astigmatism; such a system can also give slightly better shadow detail. One way of doing this has been the use of large sheets of colored theatrical gelatine over fluorescent tubes (see: "Color Separation by Filtered Light" Modern Lithography, September 1948, pp. 50 and 131). Another way of lighting copy with selected color has been with the Huebner Prismatic Light (see: William Huebner USP 2,614,042). The Huebner light is probably at its best for side-lighted texture effects, as its single-source traveling feature can give equal density from both sides of the copy. No single stationary light can do this as well.

Sylvania has created a radio-frequency lamp which shows great stability and excellent adaptability to condensing-lens illumination of color transparencies. Current designing by Sylvania is planned for increased power to compete with arc-light strength for larger areas. One of the most consistent and reproducible bright light sources for color separation is the strob-type discharge tube. The periodic charging of condensers acts as an efficient metering system, and several manufacturers have adapted it for graphic arts use.

CONTEMPORARY MATERIALS

Color separation with red, green and blue filters and three panchromatic plates is now almost universal practice but it has not always been so. Much early separation for the yellow printer was done with no filter and blue sensitive "colorblind" plates, while orthochromatic emulsions with yellow filters were used for the magenta printer. Reasons then given for this practice were that fully color-sensitized plates cost more, gave poorer halftone dots, and required longer exposure. The widest differences in plate use occurred in direct halftone separations where it was common to use a wet collodion plate for the yellow, an eosine-sensitized collodion emulsion for the magenta and a panchromatic dry plate for the cyan. The use of differently sensitized emulsions together in separation sets has been practically abandoned because of their different tone-reproduction curves which can make it difficult to match grays at all brightness levels. Exceptions to this have been with one-shot cameras and with enlarged separations where shortening of exposures has been of primary importance.

COLOR NEGATIVES

A promising step in the direction of automatic color correction has been made with the development of color negative films with built-in masking images. Ektacolor, (see: Frank Preucil "Ektacolor for Lithography" National Lithographer, Feb. & March 1950; Eastman Kodak, USP 2,322,027, USP 2,428,054 and USP 2,449,961) as one example, is a three-emulsion film which develops not only to a negative in colors complementary to the original, but also creates a yellow positive-mask image in the blue-sensitive layer, and an orange-corrective image in the green-sensitive layer. Positives color-separated from Ektacolor are color-corrected suitably for dye transfer prints.

For average graphic arts process inks, stronger correction is desirable. This is obtainable for the yellow by use of narrower band width in the blue filter. The orange mask image is not controllable by different green filters, and fuller correction must be obtained by making a contact mask for added strength during the magenta positive exposure. These color negative materials have shown their greatest help in composite forms, where transparency and reflected copy are used together and different enlargements or reductions must be composed into page layouts. By creating matched-size color negatives of all units, they may be assembled together and color-separated as one copy in perfect register and controllable density balance.

A more recent advance has been made in the use of color-sensitive multi-layered films designed specifically as a masking material. Each of the emulsion layers has a selective color sensitivity and contains a dye-forming coupler. A yellow filter layer prevents blue-light exposure in the lower layer or layers. Exposures through a single filter (primarily to absorb ultra-violet light) results in a single-film mask for producing corrected separations of each color when the separation films are exposed through the proper filters.

SCANNERS

Complete automation in the controlled production of color separation, color correction, and tone reproduction is the ultimate goal in full-color reproduction. We must remember that the limiting factors in facsimile reproduction of a full-color subject are: the need to resort to a halftone screen; the limitations of the printing inks available; and, the inherent inability of a lithographic press to print exactly as desired. However, the techniques for measuring these limiting factors are available, and this makes automatic color separation and correction possible. To accomplish this, color scanners utilizing electronics have come into increasing use within the past two decades. Some of these scanners do color separation and correction; others only color correction. Some scanners handle only transparencies as copy; others can handle reflection copy as well as transparencies. The most important consideration is the relation of the original copy to the demands of the buyer of the printed piece. Unless the buyer is willing to accept what can be produced with scanning, the advantages of this step toward automation cannot materialize. It must also be recognized that modern camera techniques of color separating and correcting can yield excellent results at costs which are competitive to scanning costs, when several copies are photographed together.

The color scanner can, in many cases, greatly improve the rate of production when sufficient work is available to run it full time. Of perhaps greater importance than rate of production is the consistancy which is possible when copy is properly controlled. It is possible to take care of a modest amount of local color correction of the scanner's product, but as soon as this becomes practice the amount of changes dictated is increased, resulting in a loss of the basic concept of scanning.

Recent Scanner Development. A number of major companies have devoted research and development time to reduce the problems of time and cost associated with full color reproductions. To date, four systems have been accepted by the industry in varying degrees. It should be of interest first, to have at least a glimpse of what has been attempted within the

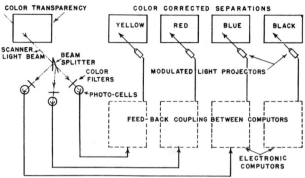

Schematic of a Scanner

last decade. Frank Preucil of GATF described the Acme color separation approach in 1954 (see: Frank Preucil "A New Color Scanner," National Lithographer, Sept. 1954, pp. 30–31). This scanner was designed primarily to produce continuous-tone positives for newspaper screening, using principles similar to those of the Springdale Scanner developed by Time, Inc. (see: Nathaniel Bishop, "The Time-Springdale Colour Scanner," Penrose Annual, Vol. 45, 1951, pp. 92–94). This scanner, now popularly referred to as the PDI Scanner, is the most widely used scanner at the present time. Interchemical Corporation developed a mechanical scanner which RCA adapted to an all-electronic system (see: A. E. Ohler, "The RCA-Interchemical Colour Corrector," Penrose Annual, 1955, Vol. 49, pp. 80–82). This equipment color corrected color-separation negatives or positives which were produced photographically. While referred to as a scanner but completely different in concept, the Hunter-Penrose scanner is essentially a feed-back copy-controlled light source for copyboard use (see: R. Kilminster, "The HPK Autoscan," Penrose Annual, Vol. 50, 1956, pp. 111–114).

The PDI Scanner. Printing Developments, Inc. (a wholly-owned subsidiary of Time, Inc.) offers the services of this equipment through several service centers on a "trade" service basis. The PDI Scanner accepts color transparency copy up to 8″ x 10″, producing a set of same-size continuous-tone color-corrected negatives or positives, in one operation. A number of transparencies can be grouped, such as four 4″ x 5″ transparencies, so long as all the transparencies in the group are in color balance and can be scanned satisfactorily with the same settings

Courtesy Printing Developments, Inc.

PDI Scanner

of the scanner. The continuous-tone films may be retouched if required, or the subsequently produced screened positives may be dot-etched. PDI offers full training to users of their service so that subsequent correction and screening operations will not nullify the basic advantages of using the scanner service. Recent development work has made it possible to extend the maximum size to 11″ x 14″, with auxiliary enlargement from 35 mm and 2¼″ x 2¼″ transparencies. Where only reflection copy is available, this is reproduced as color transparency copy for the scanner. This approach makes possible correction of original copy, to meet the customers' demands, before the scanning operation.

The Fairchild Scan-A-Color. The Scan-A-Color is, in general principle, similar to the PDI Scanner. However, it accepts reflection copy also, if the copy is sufficiently flexible to be mounted on the copy cylinder. The product produced is a same-size set of corrected continuous-tone negatives or positives.

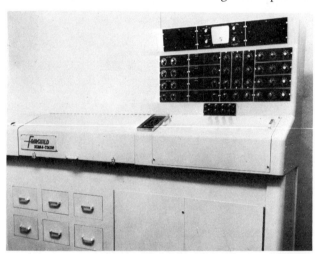

Fairchild Scan-A-Color Scanner

To forestall the problems associated with subsequent handling of scanned films, Fairchild trains the purchaser's men at the factory. Here the operators are taught to handle the equipment and process the films produced using live copy supplied by the purchaser of the Scan-A-Color equipment. When the trainees have demonstrated acceptable levels of proficiency, and the scanner has proven itself on the purchaser's commercial work, it is installed in the purchaser's plant. The Scan-A-Color handles copy up to 8″ x 10″, and may be leased or purchased.

The Crosfield Scanatron. This equipment is strictly for color correction. The Scanatron produces color-corrected, continuous-tone or screened positives from photographically produced color-separation negatives. The maximum size of the corrected films is 14″ x 17″. The separation used cannot be over 11″ x 17″ and must be shot and processed to very close tolerances. Crosfield meets this need by having its own technical people work closely with all the men in the purchaser's plant. The cameramen are taught how to consistently produce separations within the close tolerances required for efficient utilization of the Scanatron. The retouchers and etchers are shown how to handle the corrected films to minimize hand work and assure consistency of final screened negatives and positives. The

Scanatron has had good acceptance in the gravure field because the earlier models were perculiarly adapted to the needs of that process. Subsequently, development work has produced equipment which meets the needs of lithography and letterpress also.

Courtesy Merganthaler Division, Eltra Corp.

K. S. Paul Scanner

Crosfield Scanatron Scanner

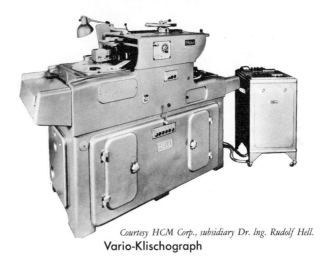

Courtesy HCM Corp., subsidiary Dr. Ing. Rudolf Hell.

Vario-Klischograph

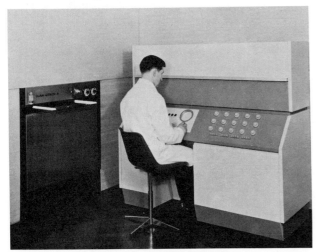

Crosfield Diascan Scanner

tives for lithographic use can be made by conventional photographic techniques. This equipment will enlarge 4 times and reduce 3 times to a maximum size 12.2″ x 17″. Dr. Hell is developing other scanners for specialized use such as the Helio-Klischograph for gravure, and the Hell Colorgraph to produce

Crosfield Diascan. Crosfield's latest scanner is both a color separation and color correction device. It works from color transparencies in size up to 14″ x 18″, with choice of 333, 500, or 1000 line scan. Positives or negatives may be produced.

K. S. Paul Scanner. Another European scanner for in-plant use is being promoted by the Mergenthaler Company (division of Eltra Corporation) in America. It also handles transparency areas up to 14″ x 18″ with a similar choice of three degrees of scanning line. It uses a divided spectrum rather than filters for color separation.

The Vario-Klischograph. This equipment, developed in Germany by Dr. Hell, is essentially an engraving machine devised to produce a set of engraved letterpress color plates. By use of a specially coated plastic, the Klischograph will produce a set of halftone separation positives from which contact nega-

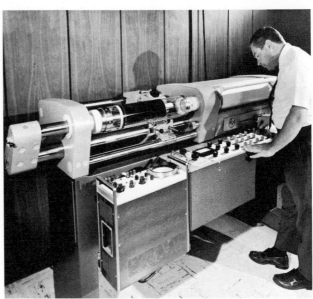

Courtesy Radio Corporation of America

RCA Model 70/8801 Color Scanner

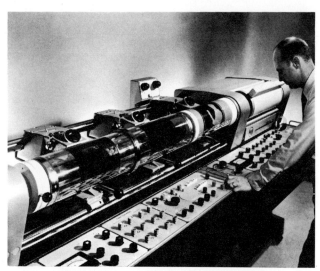

RCA Model 70/8821 CombiScanner

(Merges parts of two, or more, transparencies into one set of separations.)

continuous-tone separation negatives or positives from reflection or transparency copy, or from camera-separated continuous-tone negatives.

RCA Scanner. The modern trend for in-plant scanning is away from the large expensive four color machines to small faster compact units which produce one color at a time. These may scan an 8″ x 10″ area in 5 minutes.

RCA's version of Dr. Hell's colorgraph is similar to the K. S. Paul in scanning one color at a time. It also has complete control of tone reproduction with cathode ray tube display. It is completely transistorized and has a sensitometer exposure feature for stability evaluation. Besides a 14″ x 18″ model, a 20″ x 24″ model is available. Reflection copy may be scanned as well as transparencies.

Conventional Color Separation and Correction. What of the plant which cannot justify purchase or lease of a scanner, or make practical use of a trade service such as PDI offers? The fact is that Alexander Murray (USP 2,161,378), demonstrated that color correction can be scientifically done by conventional techniques. This eliminates the time lost through mistakes in visual judgment or personal opinion on rationalization. Color correction by photographic masking techniques is at least 30–35 years old, but the industry wouldn't take the trouble to adapt soundly developed scientific techniques to its handcraft. There has been an enormous amount of work done in this field of color reproduction which has resulted in better materials and vastly improved techniques. The entire field of so-called "pleasing color" is based on planning the reproduction steps on the results of instrumented analysis of the copy, and carrying out the steps under instrumented control. These techniques are adaptable to the finest commercial work just as readily. All that is required is the will to do it.

As color-print paper is improved, the color negative to color print sequence may replace much of the color transparency copy for reproduction because of the flexibility of retouching and combining artwork. We have already crossed the threshhold of a new era for color reproduction.

Section Two: Process Inks and Color Correcting

In this section you find a discussion of the relation between the qualities of process inks and color correcting. This discussion is divided into the following three main subjects: (1) The evaluation of process inks; (2) Measurements of ink trapping; and (3) The GATF Color Chart and its use for masking.

THE EVALUATION OF PROCESS INKS FOR COLOR CORRECTING

The range of colors that any set of process inks can produce, and the amount of color correction that they will require, can be judged from simple calculations. These calculations are based on reflection densitometer readings of the individual solid colors using filters over the densitometer aperture.

Four factors describe the most important working characteristics of a set of process inks. These are: (1) Strength; (2) Hue; (3) Grayness; and (4) Efficiency.

To make an evaluation, first make reflection density measurements of solid yellow, magenta, and cyan. Measure the density of each ink with a red (A25), green (B58), and blue (C5—47) filter over the densitometer aperture. Make readings of colors in the same general area of the sheet. Assemble the figures in a table like the example below.

		FILTERS	
INKS	Red	Green	Blue
Yellow	.00	.10	1.20
Magenta	.10	1.30	.70
Cyan	1.50	.60	.30

Printed Ink Strength. To compare the printed strength of different inks of the same hue, you merely compare the highest of their three filter density readings. In the case of the inks in the example above, the yellow has a density value or strength of 1.20, the magenta 1.30, and the cyan, 1.50.

The strength of an ink is important because it determines the range of colors and the depth of colors that you can produce with it. For example, the relative strengths of a yellow and a cyan overlap will determine whether the green that is produced will be a blue-green or a yellow-green.

It is just as important to control the individual strengths of inks as it is their hues. In single-color presswork, it is especially important to measure the strength of at least the first color down. Use a densitometer to make sure it is correct for your standard printing conditions. Evaluations of the strength of the colors that follow can be made visually by checking the colors produced by overlaps. For example, if yellow is down first and has the proper strength, you can check the strength of the magenta that follows by noting the shade of red produced by a solid overlap.

Color Hue and Hue Error. The hue of a color is determined by the colors of light that it absorbs and reflects. Perfect process inks would absorb one-third of the spectrum and reflect two-thirds. A perfect process magenta would absorb all green in the light and reflect all blue and red. A perfect process cyan would absorb all red and reflect all green and blue. Likewise, a perfect process yellow would absorb all blue and reflect all red and green.

The hue error of a color is determined by the extent to which the colors it reflects are not perfectly balanced. The ink hue number expresses this error as a percentage. A magenta with zero hue error reflects red and blue equally. If it had a 100 percent hue error toward red, it would reflect red and no blue. Such a color would, in fact, be red and not magenta at all. (Some plants are using "magentas" with hue errors as high as 90 percent.)

The hue error of a color can, therefore, be determined by measuring the amount of red, green and blue light that it reflects. As an example, consider the magenta shown in our table. This magenta had a density of .10 with the red filter, 1.30 with the green filter, and .70 with the blue filter. The red filter reading is the lowest of the three (L), the green filter reading is the highest of the three (H), and the blue filter reading is in-between or medium (M).

To calculate the hue error, use the following equation:

$$\text{Hue Error} = \frac{M - L}{H - L}.$$

Using this equation and the figures in our example, we have:

$$\text{Hue Error} \frac{.70 - .10}{1.30 - .10} = \frac{.60}{1.20} = 50\% \text{ error.}$$

Grayness. The purity of a process color is judged by its freedom from gray. Colors become gray when they reflect less light of their predominant color than the paper that the color is printed on. For example, a process magenta should reflect all red and blue. It becomes gray to the extent that it reflects less red than the white paper it is printed on. The grayness of an individual color will, of course, affect the grayness of color mixtures in which it is used.

The equation to calculate grayness is:

$$\text{Grayness} = \frac{L}{H}.$$

In this calculation, we again use the highest density reading (H) and the lowest (L). Using the figures in our table for the cyan ink we find:

$$\text{Cyan Grayness} = \frac{.30}{1.50} = 20\%$$

The lower the percentage grayness of a process color, the higher its purity.

Efficiency. In the discussion of hue, it was pointed out that a perfect process ink should absorb one-third of the spectrum and reflect two-thirds of it. How well it does this is a measure of its efficiency. A process ink's efficiency goes down in proportion to the amount of light that it should reflect but which it absorbs.

The efficiency of a process color can be rated from the percentage ratio of its incorrect light absorption to its correct light absorption. The equation is:

$$\text{Efficiency} = 1 - \frac{L + M}{2H}$$

If we again use the cyan ink in our table we have:

$$\text{Efficiency} = 1 - \frac{.30 + .60}{2 \times 1.50} = 1 - \frac{.90}{3.00} = 1 - .30 = 70\%.$$

The higher a process ink's efficiency number, the greater the range of pure colors it will produce with other process inks. Also, the higher an ink's efficiency, the less the color correction work that will be needed.

Efficiency values are perhaps the best single number to use in evaluating the color quality of a group of process inks. However, two different inks may have the same efficiency, but differ in their grayness and hue.

MEASUREMENT OF INK TRAPPING

Densitometer measurements of the single solid colors and overlapped solids in the GATF Color Strips can produce valuable data to check the trapping of your process inks. The procedure to measure trapping is described in this section.

Trapping of Magenta Ink. With a B-58 green filter over the densitometer aperture measure the density of: (1) The solid magenta patch; (2) The solid yellow patch; and (3) The overlap of solid magenta on solid yellow.

Subtract the yellow solid ink density from the red two-color overlap density. Compare number with the density of the magenta ink. For example: magenta density—1.22; yellow density—.07; subtraction number—1.15.

If undertrapping has occurred, the subtraction number will be less than the density number of the magenta's printed ink strength. You may assign an effective trapping percentage number to this magenta ink on yellow by dividing the subtraction number of red density (magenta on yellow) minus yellow density, by the magenta ink density. For example: subtraction number—1.15; yellow—.07; difference—1.08; 1.08 divided by 1.22; apparent trap—89%.

If the subtraction number of red minus yellow is equal to the magenta ink density the calculation will indicate 100% apparent trapping.

If the two colors together have printed with more gloss than the top ink, as printed separately, the calculated apparent trapping and its visual appearance may indicate 5 to 7% more ink than actually trapped. This is common on coated paper. If the calculated trapping is more than 107%, the overprint is physically overtrapping with more ink going to ink than to paper. This overtrapping surprisingly sometimes measures as much as 125 to 135%. This tendency is favored by low absorbent paper and also by highly absorbent matte yellow inks, particularly in the rotogravure process.

Trapping of Cyan Ink. With an A-25 red filter make density readings of: (1) The solid cyan patch; (2) The solid yellow patch; (3) The solid magenta patch; (4) The patch where solid cyan overlaps solid yellow; (5) The patch where solid cyan overlaps solid magenta; (6) The patch where solid magenta overlaps solid yellow; and (7) The patch where solid cyan overlaps the overlay of solid magenta on solid yellow.

To check the trapping of cyan on yellow, subtract the yellow density from the green (cyan on yellow) density and compare this number with cyan ink density. If it is smaller there is undertrapping. To assign a percentage trap number, divide the subtracted number (green density minus yellow density) by the cyan density.

Similarly judge the cyan trap on magenta by subtracting the magenta density from the blue (cyan on magenta) density and compare to the cyan density. The trapping of cyan on red (magenta on yellow) is typically the same as the trapping of cyan on magenta but may be verified by subtracting the red density (2 color) from the three colors, and comparing to the cyan density.

Photoengravers color bars and the new GATF offset magazine proofing bars include a black on cyan area. This permits evaluating the trap of black ink on cyan (also equivalent to black on three color).

Use a blue filter in the densitometer and measure the three areas involved; black, cyan, and black on cyan. Subtract the cyan density from the black on cyan, and compare to the black alone density.

It is typical for single-color presses to trap on dried ink films within 5 percent or 10 percent of the normal 100 percent on bare paper. Usually, the trapping is a little more than this 100 percent normal and ranges between 100 percent and 105 percent. If too much wax, compound, or an excess of some driers is used, trapping may drop as much as 20 percent to 30 percent.

Many two- and four-color presses are also trapping magenta and cyan on yellow within the range of 90 percent to 110 percent.

If measurements of your trapping conditions show that an ink is trapping below 90 percent, changes in the body or relative tack of the inks may improve it. Check also the way that the ink is handled or "doped" between the can and the press fountain. Also, running with an excess of fountain solution will increase the ink's emulsification with the water and reduce its trapping ability.

In wet printing on four-color presses where the order of the colors is yellow, cyan, magenta, it is common for magenta to trap on the cyan only 70 percent to 80 percent.

Rotation of Color. This description of the procedure to measure trapping applies to the pairs of printing of magenta on yellow, cyan on yellow, cyan on magenta, and black on cyan. If the top and bottom ink of these pairs is reversed the filter used in measurement must be changed. The basic rule is to use the filter which gives the highest density of the top color. With black ink on top, use the filter which gives the lowest density reading to the bottom ink.

THE ROLE OF THE GATF COLOR REPRODUCTION GUIDE IN MASKING

Color correction is (or should be) based on the inks being used—their hue, saturation, strength, and opacity. Other factors that affect the inks, like different papers or different trapping conditions, call for modifications of the basic requirements.

The goal in color separation photography is to produce three printers that are exclusive records of where yellow, magenta, and cyan should print. However, most process inks are not as pure as they should be. The result is that normal color separations always print some of their color in areas where it doesn't belong. In other words, some yellow may print in an area that should be only magenta or only magenta and cyan. Or, some magenta may print in an area that should be only yellow or only yellow and cyan.

Errors such as these can be analyzed by making density measurements of the colors on the GATF Color Guide. Such an analysis will permit you to set up the most efficient masking system for the conditions in your plant. Or, such information about the color errors that occur in your plant can help you select process inks that are more suitable for your work.

Measurements are made of the solid color patches on the GATF Color Reproductions Guide. It includes, in addition to the solid single-color, two-, three-, and four-color overlaps of solids, as well as overprints of one-quarter, one-half, and three-quarter tints.

The first step in a typical analysis is to make densitometer readings of the solid yellow, magenta, and cyan blocks in the strip. Measure each of these three colors with filters covering the aperture of the densitometer head. The filters that should be used are: Red (A25); Green (B58); and Blue (C5—47).

Let's suppose for a moment that we made these filtered densitometer readings of a set of perfect inks. If we then assembled the data in a chart it might look something like our table:

PRINTED INKS	FILTERS		
	RED (Cyan Printer)	GREEN (Magenta Printer)	BLUE (Yellow Printer)
Yellow Ink	.00	.00	1.60
Magenta Ink	.00	1.60	.00
Cyan Ink	1.60	.00	.00

These figures show that each of our theoretically perfect inks is strongly absorbing one-third of the spectrum and reflecting two-thirds of the spectrum. Reading horizontally across the chart we see that the yellow is absorbing no red light and no green light. It is strongly absorbing the blue light. Therefore, when blue is removed from white light the combination of the remaining red and green light produces yellow.

In the case of magenta ink, our theoretical figures show that it is strongly absorbing green light and is absorbing no red or blue light. So, when green is removed from white light, the remaining red and blue light combine to form magenta.

Likewise with the cyan ink. It is strongly absorbing red light and no green or blue. The reflected green and blue combine to form cyan.

Now let's read the chart vertically. The vertical columns show the relative densities that would occur in positives or printers from separation negatives. In the case of the red filter —cyan printer—no cyan will print in either the yellow or magenta image areas. Cyan will print only in the cyan areas.

With the green filter—magenta printer—magenta will print only in the magenta image areas. No magenta will print in the yellow and cyan image areas. Likewise with the blue filter—yellow printer—yellow will print only in yellow areas. No yellow will print in the magenta and cyan areas.

This is what we would have using theoretically pure inks. Such inks do not exist. As a result, the density measurements that we would be more likely to get using the inks that are available today would produce figures something like those in our chart.

PRINTED INKS	FILTERS		
	RED (Cyan Printer)	GREEN (Magenta Printer)	BLUE (Yellow Printer)
Yellow Ink	.00	.10	1.20
Magenta Ink	.10	1.20	.60
Cyan Ink	1.25	.40	.28

This more typical set of figures demonstrates errors in the light-absorption properties of inks. Any density in any area of the chart outside the diagonal lines represents additional light absorption of the inks that is incorrect and not desirable. It shows that inks can have two absorption errors. Again, reading across the chart, we see that the yellow is absorbing .10 of green light. This error is not too great. However, the absorption of some of the green light makes the yellow go very slightly toward orange.

The magenta ink in our example is absorbing .10 of red and .60 of blue which it should not do. The bigger error, the absorption of .60 of blue, adds yellow to the magenta which makes its hue shift toward red. The smaller error, the .10 absorption of red light, decreases the brightness of the magenta which makes it grayer.

The cyan ink in the chart is absorbing .40 of green light and .28 of blue light. The larger of these two errors, the absorption of .40 of the green light, adds magenta to the cyan which shifts

its hue toward blue. The smaller error, the absorption of .28 of blue, again decreases the brightness of the cyan making it grayer.

If these errors are greater than 10 percent of the ink's highest absorption, corrections either by masking or by handwork are necessary. The .10 magenta error in the yellow ink, for example, is less than 10 percent of the yellow's 1.20 blue absorption. There is little need for correction work in this case. Corrections are necessary, however, for both the other colors.

Reading the chart vertically, we see the relative densities that would occur in the positives or printers made from uncorrected separation negatives.

The figures for the yellow printer show that: (1) A density of 1.20 of yellow would print where yellow should be; (2) An additional .60 density of yellow would print where only magenta should be; and (3) An additional .28 density of yellow would print where only cyan should print.

In the green filter—magenta printer—column we see that: (1) A .10 density of magenta would print in areas that should be only yellow; (2) A density of 1.20 of magenta would print where magenta should be; and (3) A .40 density of magenta would print where only cyan should be.

The red filter—cyan printer—column shows: (1) There is no cyan printing where yellow should print; (2) A .10 density of cyan would print where only magenta should print; and (3) A density of 1.25 of cyan would print where only cyan should be.

The purpose of masking (or hand correction) is to correct for or cancel these densities which lie outside the diagonal lines in the chart. Masking systems usually correct a color separation for the larger of its two ink errors. At the same time, however, the mask may undercorrect or overcorrect the smaller error. This unbalanced condition most often occurs in the yellow separation because the average cyan and magenta inks do not reflect enough blue light. GATF's survey of color process work showed that with the inks now in common use, single masking would not be able to fully correct both errors in about 75 percent of the press runs represented. You can check your inks for their balance using the calculations for mask strength.

Section Three: GATF's Color Diagrams

In any study or analysis of color, the plotting of data on some sort of diagram is essential to visualize and evaluate any color. Through the years, many types of color-notation and color-diagram systems have been developed.

One of the best known of these is the CIE Chromaticity Diagram. This was developed by an International Commission of Illuminating Engineers. As shown in the figure, it takes the shape of a horseshoe within right angle coordinates. Color values are plotted on it in terms of "x" and "y." The diagram uses unreal red, green, and blue primaries that do not exist—that is, primaries that are purer and brighter than any in the spectrum. However, it does a good job of showing the properties of additive mixtures of different colors of light and of color differences as they appear to the eye.

The Munsell and Ostwald color systems are also well known. These are sets of standard colors to which you compare your colors. They are useful in industry to specifically identify colors wanted on merchandise, in art work, etc.

The Maxwell Triangle is related to the CIE diagram. Unlike the CIE diagram it is based on the use of real primaries. Plots are determined from densitometer readings made through red, green, and blue filters. This diagram is also good to show the properties of additive mixtures of colors of light.

One disadvantage of the CIE and Maxwell diagrams is that they require inconvenient calculations and plottings. Data for the CIE diagram, for example, has to be taken from spectrophotometric curves. Data for use on the Maxwell Triangle is based on percentage-reflectance densitometer readings. Some densitometers read this directly. However, it is much more common for the instruments to read in terms of density. The density readings must then be converted to percentage-reflectance values using tables such as those in GATF's Txb Optical Density.

There are also important disadvantages that are inherent in any color diagram. None of the diagrams show all of the possible characteristics of a color because diagrams are limited to two dimensions.

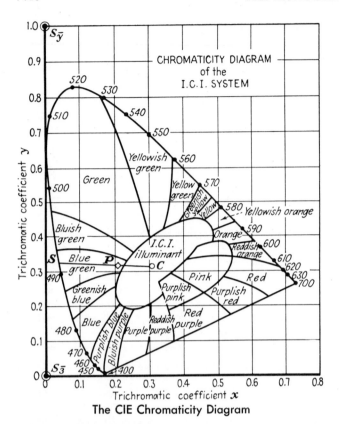

The CIE Chromaticity Diagram

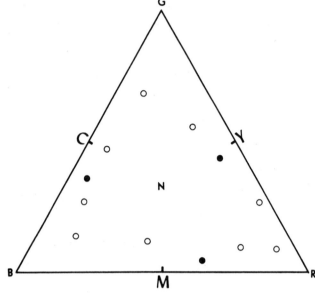

The Maxwell Additive Triangle

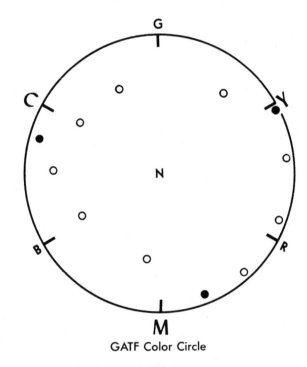

GATF Color Circle

Since the simplest description of any color requires three terms, conventional diagrams always omit at least one of the important qualities.

Still another disadvantage is that no one diagram is suitable for use with all types of color problems. When color is studied in different fields, new or different relationships of color properties become important. To best show these relationships, new diagrams are often required.

Until the introduction of the GATF Color Circle, this was the case in color studies for the graphic arts. None of the diagrams available before the Circle did a satisfactory job of picturing the special problems of color reproduction.

The main reason for this is that previous diagrams were mainly concerned with the effects of additive mixtures of different colors of light. The diagrams were therefore designed to show these effects and were based on the primary colors of light, red, green, and blue.

In graphic arts color reproduction, the conditions and needs are different. Here we are working primarily with subtractive color effects. In other words, and for example, yellow ink on paper looks yellow because it has subtracted or absorbed the blue from white light. The remaining red and green components of the white light are reflected from the paper and when combined, appear as yellow.

In studies of color reproduction, we want to be able to see and picture different qualities of the subtractive primary yellow, magenta, and cyan inks. A prime interest is to chart colors in terms of the way that they photograph and not necessarily as they appear to the eye. We want to be able to see what changes or corrections are required in photography to produce the best possible reproductions with different process inks, different half-tone screens, different papers, etc.

So far, GATF has developed three new diagrams for this work. They are directly concerned with the special problems of color printing. As such, they are not intended to act as new color systems or substitutes for previous diagrams.

THE GATF COLOR CIRCLE

The GATF Color Circle which is also called the GATF Ink Hue and Purity Chart was the first of GATF's new diagrams. It is described fully in GATF's Txb 509, "Color Separation Photography" and in GATF Research Progress No. 38. Its general appearance is shown in the figure; the intermediate plotting lines have been omitted.

The color circle is quite versatile. It will permit the plotting of a number of different pairs of factors.

In its most common use, the hue differences of inks are plotted around the circle and the grayness of the inks is plotted inward toward the center. The same diagram is also useful to plot hue and printed strength, or hue and another factor that is similar to saturation or chroma.

The two coordinates most commonly used to position a color on the color circle are called Hue Error and Grayness. They are described on pages 7:12 and 7:13. They are derived from red, green and blue filter densitometer readings by use of the Hue Error and Grayness equations also explained on page 7:12.

To position a color on the full circle, as shown in color before page 7:7, first take the Hue Error number and locate its position somewhere around the edge of the circle. The Hue Error number is a percentage number between zero and one hundred. There are, however, six pie shaped sectors around the circle which are scaled from zero to one hundred and you must determine in which one of these six areas the color should plot. This is done by comparing the red, green, and blue filter density readings. The color of the filter which gave the highest density readings is complementary to the sample color. For example, if the ink's highest density is given with a blue filter, the color is basically a yellow and you start counting Hue Error 2% lines from the zero yellow position, upper right on the circle diagram. You then do not know whether to count toward 100 green or 100 red, until you again compare the red, green and blue filter density numbers. A typical yellow process ink will have its red filter density reading the lowest of the three. You then count hue lines downward around the outer edge of the circle towards red.

The simple basic principles of plotting on the circle are that a color is somewhere opposite across the circle from the color of the filter giving the highest density reading and then from zero towards the color of the filter of lowest density reading. These instructions are explained in the GATF Research Progress #38.

The closer a plot is to the "ideal" yellow, magenta, or cyan shown on the outer rim of the circle, the greater is the purity of its hue, or, the less its "hue error" in process color printing. The farther a plot is away from the center, the less its grayness or contamination with the third primary.

The special features of the GATF Color Circle that are important in a study of process color reproduction are as follows: (1) the coordinate values of a color have a significant and understandable meaning in themselves—they specify such things as hue error or grayness rather than more or less of "x" and "y"; (2) changes in the location of a plot for a color are easily interpreted to show what change is needed in the color correction system; (3) equal graynesses are symmetrical; (4) subtractive color mixtures are shown and related more logically between the primary colors; and (5) subtractive complementary colors (not additive colors) are shown directly opposite one another across a neutral center.

A special form that was developed for use with the Circle provides for an orderly assembly of the data used to locate the plots and to record mask factors and information on hue shift, additivity, trapping, and other factors.

Despite the many advantages of the circle, there are two other desirable properties that are not shown well on it or on previous diagrams. These are: (1) the direct prediction of the

Special Data Form for Color Circle

color that can be produced by a two-color overprint; and, (2) the possible gamut of different colors from different sets of the three process inks. GATF has found an answer to this need with a simple modification of the Maxwell Triangle.

SUBTRACTIVE COLOR TRIANGLE

The comparison illustration shows how the same set of three process inks and their in-between colors, plot on two different diagrams. The triangles are oriented so that the key colors have the same relative positions. Note: These diagrams omit the intermediate lines of the actual triangles.

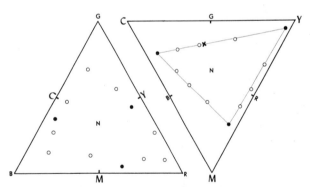

Comparison of the Maxwell Triangle and the GATF Subtractive Triangle

The triangle on the left is a conventional Maxwell Triangle. The additive primary colors of light (red, green, and blue) are positioned at the corners. Positions for yellow, magenta, and cyan are centered on the three sides. Neutral is in the center, and is indicated by the letter "N."

Typical plots of yellow, magenta, and cyan are shown on the diagrams as the solid dots. In this type of diagram, additive complementary colors are on the side opposite the plotted color. The exact spot falls at the end of a straight line drawn from the plotted point through the center neutral point.

A straight line drawn between any two of the plots of the three ink colors locates the possible in-between colors of additive light mixtures of the two colors. The open circles shown on the diagram are plots of printed in-between colors, that is, subtractive overprints of pairs of the primary inks. It is easily seen that you can't predict subtractive mixtures from the plots of the primary inks in this type of diagram.

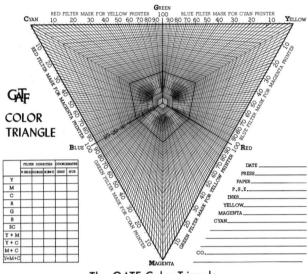

The GATF Color Triangle

GATF's new diagram is shown in simplified form as the triangle above. We call it the Subtractive Color Triangle. The ideal subtractive primaries—yellow, magenta, and cyan—are located in the corners. Ideal red, green, and blue that would be produced by ideal pairs of yellow, magenta, and cyan fall in the centers of the sides of the triangle.

Plotting Ink Colors. In using this or any of the other diagrams, the data is obtained from the GATF Color Test Strip or other patches of color that are printed on the sheets. Patches of solids of the individual inks and overlaps of pairs of the inks are required.

The first step is to make densitometer readings of the color to be plotted through each of three filters (Red No. 25, Green No. 58, and Blue No. 47).*

Next, calculate Hue Error and Grayness coordinate percentage numbers as explained on page 7:30. These are the same coordinates used for the color circle and, plotting on the subtractive triangle, follow the same rules as plotting on the color circle just described on the preceeding page and section.

The previous edition of this Lithographers Manual and also GATF's, Research Progress Bulletin #53 "New Color Diagrams" described a different way of plotting on a triangle. Equations for coordinates "C" and "M" were given. These may

---

*The Number 29, 47B, and 61 filters should not be used. Values obtained with them will not agree with GATF standards. Some densitometers are equipped at the factory with these filters. Before you use your densitometer, check the filters in it against a set of filters known to be correct.

be used on commercially available triangular coordinate graph paper, used by engineers and chemists. These charts did not directly show printing ink color properties well, so GATF redesigned the triangle to show hue and grayness directly as the color circle does.

How to Check Overprints. The example that follows, describes the procedure to show the trapping of cyan on yellow to produce green. The procedure for other pairs of the inks to produce red or blue is identical.

From the three filter densitometer readings, determine and plot the yellow and cyan hue and grayness coordinates on the triangle as shown in the Color Triangle. Draw a line connecting these two points. Possible ideal overprints of yellow and cyan should fall on this line.

To predict where on the line the expected green should fall, use the same densitometer readings already made. In the lower third of the chart are blocks for Y + M, Y + C, M + C, and Y + M + C. In this example, we are interested only in adding vertically the readings for the yellow and cyan ink solids.

So, the Y + C red filter prediction is .02 + 1.19 or 1.21. For the green filter, we add .08 and .37 to give .45. Likewise, for the blue filter, .97 + .13 = 1.10.

Now handle these figures the same as before to obtain hue and grayness coordinates. Omit the decimal points and add the three numbers (121 + 45 + 110). Divide the total first into the red value and then into the green value. Plot this point on the line connecting the yellow and cyan and indicate it as an "x." This shows where the predicted green should position on the diagram with ideal printing conditions.

The next step is to obtain the "actual" figures. This is done by making the three filter densitometer readings of the actual overprint yellow and cyan, that is, the green block in the test strip. Enter these readings (as well as readings for the other overprint colors) in the center blocks of the Color Triangle chart marked R, G, B, and 3 Colors.

Handle these figures exactly as before and plot where the actual overprint color falls on the diagram. Its position relative to the position of the ideal prediction (x) will give the following information. Assume here that yellow is first down:

(1) If the actual plot is the same as the ideal prediction, then the printing conditions are ideal. This doesn't happen very often.

(2) If the actual plot falls on the line, but is closer to yellow than the ideal x the cyan is undertrapping.

(3) If the actual plot falls on the line, but is closer to Cyan than the ideal x, the cyan is either overtrapping or the cyan ink is acting as though it is not fully transparent.

(4) If the actual plot falls outside the line (away from N), it indicates an increase or gain in the gloss of the over-printed inks.

(5) If the actual plot falls inside the line (toward the center), it indicates a loss of gloss due to possible excess drainage of ink vehicle or other causes.

It is possible to "predict" an overprint color only if transparent inks that are trapping properly are being used. However, the diagram is still useful to show the trapping of opaque inks. In this case, the original plotting would be made from the OK sheet. Later plottings during the run will show differences from the original. Opaque inks plot toward the top color similar to an overtrapping condition with transparent inks.

THE COLOR HEXAGON

Still another practically unfilled need has been a really simple way of charting color variations during a press run. To plot the printed strength of the separate primary inks (yellow, magenta, and cyan) only one number from a single densitometer reading is required. In process color reproduction, however, the accuracy or consistency of the overprint colors (red, green, and blue) are of even greater importance. This is because most of the colors in a reproduction are created by more than one ink. Changes in trapping or other press conditions may seriously shift the hues of the overprinted colors while the separate inks are still printing without change.

Although two different filter readings of overprint colors can detect shifts in their hue, we get the best information about changes from three filter readings. Getting these readings is now much more practical with modern densitometers that have push-button pre-zeroed filters. The problem then becomes one of how to chart hue and strength differences from these readings quickly.

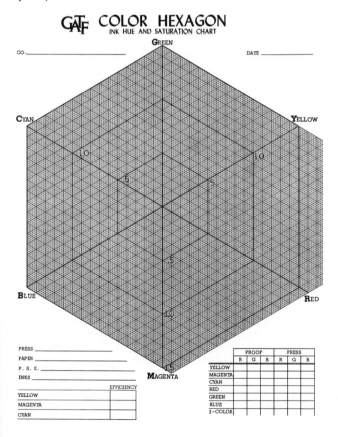

In reviewing the literature on color research, it was found that just such a system was already in existence. It had been used successfully in studies of Kodachrome film but had not been publicized to the Graphic Arts. It is a simple charting system in the form of a hexagon and is described in the book, "Principles of Color Photography," by Evans, Hanson, and Brewer*.

---

* Evans, R. M.; Hanson, W. T., Jr.; and Brewer, W. L., Principles of Color Photography, John Wiley & Sons, Inc., or Chapman & Hall Ltd., London (1953).

They called it a "Trilinear plot." We have adapted this chart to our requirements by modifying its range and working out the simplest alternative chartings.

The GATF Color Hexagon has separate lines which correspond to .02 increments of density. The single ideal primary inks—yellow, magenta, and cyan—plot along their radial lines from the center. The stronger the ink color, the farther away from the center it falls.

In using this diagram, no calculations, equations, or slide rules are needed. Color points are positioned directly on the hexagon according to the red, green, and blue filter density readings. To position a color, always start from the center of the diagram. First, use the red filter density and count toward cyan (away from red) the number of lines equal to this density. Now count downward the number of lines equal to the green filter density and then upward to the right toward yellow the number of lines equal to the blue filter density.

A slightly easier charting method is described in the book, "Principles of Color Photography," that was mentioned before. In this method, the lowest density reading is subtracted from each of the other two readings. In making the plot with the remaining two readings, again start from the center and count in the directions that are away from the remaining two filter colors. For example, suppose the three filter readings of the magenta are Red = .10; Green = 1.22; and Blue = .46. Red is lowest so subtract its value (.10) from green which leaves 1.12 and from blue, leaving .36. To make the plot, start in the center of the diagram and count down (away from green) to the 1.12 position and then upward to the right (away from blue) to the 0.36 position.

This diagram is particularly useful to check both trapping and the strength of the color being run while the run is in progress. To do this, make initial plots from the OK sheet. Make plots of the solid primary inks and the overprinted pairs of the primary inks that produce red, green, and blue. Then, as the run progresses, make additional plots onto the same diagram. Where these plots fall in relation to the original plots tells how close the printing is to the OK sheet.

If the plot for a primary color shifts outward, it indicates that the printed strength or density of the color has increased. A shift inward toward the center tells that the strength or density of the color is less than it was on the OK sheet. In either case, of course, the press ink feed or cylinder packing should be adjusted.

Suppose there has been no change in the densities of the primaries, but the plots for the overprint colors (red, green, and blue) have shifted toward one of the primaries. This tells that overtrapping or undertrapping is occurring.

A change in the printed strength of a primary color will naturally shift the hue of an overprint color produced with this primary. There may also be changes in trapping. This cannot be determined until the primary ink strength has been adjusted back to match the original plot from the OK sheet. The improved hexagon chart now has lines of .02 density difference to make charting more accurate. This is illustrated in the color section preceeding page No. 7:17.

SUMMARY

GATF's Subtractive Color Triangle, Hexagon Color Charts

and Color Circle are three diagrams which can be valuable aids in comparing and studying important graphic arts color reproduction problems. They have been designed specifically for visualizing subtractive color properties of printing inks and are not necessarily suggested as substitutes for diagrams used in other fields.

The GATF Color Circle is best suited to: (1) Visualize the hue and grayness of actual ink colors in relation to ideal colors; and, (2) Visualize the requirements of a color correction system for different inks, papers, etc.

The GATF Subtractive Triangle is best suited to show: (1) The gamut of pure color that is possible with a given set of inks; (2) Under or overtrapping; (3) Changes in gloss; and, (4) To directly predict ideal overprint colors.

The GATF Hexagon is the only diagram that requires no mathematics, formulas, or computations to plot color strength and hue differences. It is the easiest and quickest to use and is best suited for quality control or press control of the separate primaries and overprint hues.

None of these diagrams is necessarily in its final form. At the present time, there appears to be a need and a place for all three. The diagrams that are most important and useful can only be determined by their practical use in more plants. This will also help us to finalize their most useful format.

Section Four: Color Correcting by Photographic Masking

In this section you find a general and brief survey of color correcting by photographic masking. The subject matter is divided into the following six units: (1) What masking will do, (2) Masking Methods, (3) Types of masks, (4) Types of masking, (5) Masking Color Transparencies, (6) Recent masking developments.

Color separation negatives alone cannot give accurate color reproduction. Formerly, when the necessary added color correction steps were done entirely by hand retouching, color separation could be studied as an independent operation. Modern color reproduction processes now often use all photographic correction steps. So, it has become important to understand their relationship with separation negatives. This section is not intended to include complete working details of all correction methods, but sufficient description of most methods is given so that their purpose and control can be understood.

The term "masking," as we use it today, describes a photographic technique used primarily for color correction. It is neither new nor standard. As early as 1899, Dr. E. Albert was granted a German patent on a masking method to improve four-color reproduction. This method is only one of the many that have been proposed as a means of obtaining better color quality in reproductions at reasonable cost.

WHAT MASKING WILL DO

Briefly, a mask is a negative or positive image used with another negative or positive to modify the amount of light that passes through while exposing still another negative or positive. Masking methods can be used to correct colors and/or tones, to drop out backgrounds, etc. Photographic masking can do this without loss of detail. With the best inks and careful masking, plants are producing acceptable quality with a minimum of handwork. With balanced process inks and a moderate amount of care in the masking procedure, hand-correction time can be reduced by more than fifty percent in most cases. Specifically, masking may be used to accomplish the following:

Correct for the Deficiencies of the Process Inks. The failure of the magenta and cyan ink to reflect as much blue light as the white paper it is printed on is one of the reasons for color correcting the blue-filter separation. Masking adds density to the blue-filter separation negative (yellow printer) wherever

magenta and cyan are required in the picture and prevents excess yellow from printing in these areas.

The cyan ink does not reflect as much green light as the white paper it is printed on. We, therefore, have to add density in the green-filter separation negative (magenta printer) wherever cyan appears in the subject. This prevents magenta from printing in the areas that should be only cyan.

Color correction masking will also remedy some of the other minor ink deficiencies.

Correct for Deficiencies in Color Transparencies. A color transparency doesn't exactly reproduce the original scene. The yellows may be weaker, and the blues too strong. Other colors may also differ from the original scene. These differences may be due to the incorrect strength or hue of the three dyes in the transparency. Masking can be used to help bring the colors in the printed image closer to those of the original scene.

Reduce the Density Range of the Copy. Copy, such as dense oil paintings, transparencies, carbros, and dye transfer prints does have density ranges greater than those which can be printed by lithography. The effective density range of the copy can be compressed by using photographic masks.

Remove Undercolor in High Speed Wet Printing. In four-color wet printing it is sometimes difficult to trap three or four overlapping solids. Then, in the shadow areas, where yellow, magenta, and cyan would normally be printed, it helps to remove some of the color. Black is substituted for the shadow color removed. This undercolor removal, as it is called, can be done by masking.

Produce a Corrected Black Printer. Most of the separation methods will produce a black printer which will print some black in some of the pure colors. Masking the black printer can reduce the amount of black printing in these colors. A new method for doing this is described in Chapter 6.

Preserve Highlight Detail. In normal color separation and halftone procedures, the contrast of the highlights in the copy is generally reduced. When it is important to retain highlight detail, a highlight mask should be used. It maintains the highlight contrast of the copy.

Block Out White Highlights, White Backgrounds, Type Matter. An opaquer mask can be used to eliminate the need to opaque each of the separations. It blocks out parts of the copy, such as white backgrounds, highlights, type, etc., which would normally be opaqued on each separation.

MASKING METHODS

The most convenient way of classifying masking methods is according to the way that the masks are used, that is the mechanical arrangements of the various images. There are three principal ways of using masks. These are: (1) by projection, (2) in contact, and (3) in the camera back. A fourth class is the "integral" mask which is a part of the original art and not produced by the photographer.

Projected Masks. Projected masks were generally made in a special camera or camera attachment. They can be made from the original copy, or from the color separations. When made from the copy, filtered exposures are made on panchromatic plates. These masks are then projected to the copy or to the focal plane of the camera when the separations are made. When masks are made from the separations, they can be projected back onto the appropriate separations when the halftone or continuous-tone positives are made.

In the projection method, several special cameras have used masks projected in different ways. The Gamble process camera used an auxiliary small camera projector. This made 5″ x 7″ filtered negatives from the copy on an angle. Extra light was then locally projected to the copy through the mask negative during normal color separation with the large camera. The British Add-mask camera accomplishes this same effect by mirror projection to the exposing separation plate rather than to the copy. The British Multichrom camera uses light projection from either end and provides an excellent series of register positions to allow both projected masking and "distance" masking. The Nerot camera was more correctly a contact frame with same-size projection from positive masks to expose corrected positives.

Contact Masks. These can be made in a vacuum or pressure printing frame. They can be made from the copy (color transparencies) or from the separation negatives. When made from the transparency, filtered exposures are made on panchromatic emulsions. When masks are made from the separations color blind emulsions can be used.

Camera-Back Masks. These are made in the process camera from reflection or transparent copy. They are processed and replaced in the camera back. Additional masks or separations are made behind these masks. Both silver and dyed masks can be used.

Integral Masks. Integral mask layers are incorporated by the manufacturer in some color negative films. Integral color correction can also be obtained from reflection copy if it is prepared with special fluorescent water-color paints. When the copy is illuminated with ultraviolet light, the colors fluoresce and add extra density where needed in the color separation negatives.

Masks With Multi-Layered Color-Sensitive Film. These films, while similar to color-negative films, are designed specifically for color correction by photographic masking techniques. A single exposure of the film to the color copy through an ultraviolet filter, and color processing, results in dye masks for all three color separations in one piece of film. The color separation films are exposed to the copy, through the mask and normal color separation filters. How close to complete photographic color correction may be attained, by use of these materials, depends on how close to ideal are the inks and paper.

TYPES OF MASKS

There are many different types of photographic masks. They include highlight pre-masks, principal masks, dropout masks, shadow masks, and undercolor removal masks. Each type is used to produce a certain effect. Most of them can be made and used in projection, contact, and camera methods of masking.

Highlight Pre-Mask. The highlight pre-mask is a negative mask usually made from transparencies. It can be used to increase the highlight contrast of underexposed transparencies. It is a contrasty, short-density range mask. The density range may vary from .25 to .50 depending on the copy and the results desired. It records only the highlights. It is made on a high-contrast lith-type emulsion and developed in a diluted continuous-tone developer. This mask is used to protect the highlights when the principal or final mask is made. It is discarded after the final mask is made.

Highlight pre-masks can be made by projection, contact, or in the camera. When made in a contact printing frame, a contact negative is made from the transparency. The processed mask is then fastened to the transparency in register and the principal mask is contacted from the combination.

Highlight pre-masks can be made from either transparent or reflection copy in the process camera using a special plate bar or the halftone screen holder just ahead of the focal plane of the separation negative emulsion. The processed plate is then replaced in register in the camera back. The final mask can then be made behind the highlight pre-mask, but ahead of the position where the separation negative will be. The highlight pre-mask is discarded after the final mask is made.

Final or Principal Masks. When a mask is produced by the use of more than one step, such as the intermediate use of a highlight pre-mask, it is called a final or principal mask. The final mask for a transparency is a negative. It is used for tone and color correction. It may be made from the copy by any one of the three methods just described. It is generally an unsharp, full-tone scale, low-contrast negative. A continuous-tone panchromatic emulsion is used and processed in a continuous-tone developer.

When the final mask for a color transparency is made by contact methods, the combined transparency and highlight pre-mask are contacted to the panchromatic emulsion. This mask will compress the density range of the transparency so that the separation negatives can be developed to a higher contrast than would otherwise be possible. This will increase the saturation of colors in the final reproduction.

In the camera method, the final mask can be made from reflection or transparent copy. If a highlight pre-mask has been made, the final mask is made behind it, but ahead of the plane of the separation negative. The mask is then shot with the required filter. After exposure, it may be developed to produce either a fine grain silver image, or dye coupled to produce a magenta dye image. There is less light scattered from dyed images than from silver images. However, it is much easier to work with silver images and to obtain reproducible results. With either type, the mask is replaced in the camera back, and the separations are made behind it.

A second type of final mask is for separation negatives. These require a preliminary color-correcting pre-mask made from one of the other separation negatives.

Positive Masks. A positive overlay mask is a low-contrast, continuous-tone positive which is laid over a separation negative for the purpose of color correction. There are many variations in the way that they can be used. They are usually made by contact.

In the contact method, the masks are made from the color separation negatives. Colorblind or orthochromatic emulsions and continuous-tone developers are used. Positives made from one separation are placed over another separation in the set. For example, the blue-filter separation (yellow printer) is corrected by a positive contacted from the green-filter separation (magenta printer). The green-filter separation (magenta printer) is corrected by a positive contacted from the red-filter separation (cyan printer).

Highlight Mask. The highlight mask is a short-scale continuous-tone negative overlay mask. It is made to be used on separation negatives for the purpose of increasing the highlight contrast. It can be shot directly from the copy at the time that the separations are made, or a positive can be contacted from the separation negative containing the most highlight detail. This positive is then contacted back to a negative to make the final highlight mask.

Dropout Mask (Opaquer). This mask is a special form of highlight mask which is used to drop out white backgrounds that repeat in every separation. By making one mask which records only the white areas and then placing it over each separation when the positives are made, a considerable amount of opaquing can be eliminated.

One method of making a dropout mask is to make a strong contrasty, contact positive from the separation negative containing the most detail. All areas that are not dense enough on the positive are opaqued. This leaves only the white areas clear. A contact negative is then made on thin base film which is used as the dropout mask for all the separations.

A second method of preparing a dropout mask is to shoot a weak, contrasty, continuous-tone thin-base film negative at the time the separations are made. The purpose of this negative is to record only the white tones of the original copy. Any other tones held on the negative are eliminated with a standard reducer (such as Farmer's reducer). This negative is used as the dropout mask. If the camera has a reversing prism, the negative can be made so that it will be in emulsion-to-emulsion contact with the separation negatives. Even though the density of the

mask is not as opaque as in the previous method, it is dense enough to work.

Shadow Detail Mask. This mask is used on continuous-tone positives when it is important to keep or improve shadow detail. It is a contrasty, short-density range positive made with the same materials, and similar in appearance to the highlight mask. It is a record of the shadows only. The mask is made from the masked separation negative and placed over the positive. It adds density to the shadow end of the scale (dense portion of positive), increasing the shadow contrast.

Undercolor Removal Mask. This mask is used to reduce the amount of ink printing in the shadow areas of the picture. It is valuable in printing with multicolor presses. When you can't fully trap four wet solids in one area, the general practice is to reduce the amount of colored ink printing in these areas and substitute black. A weak contact positive is made from the black separation negative on thin base film. The mask is then fastened to the color separations when the halftones are made.

TYPES OF MASKING

These many types of masks may be used in different combinations to provide a great variety of systems.

Basically, only four systems are now commonly used. These are (1) single-stage positive masking, (2) two-stage masking for separation negatives, (3) camera-back masking using either multilayer dyed films or silver masks, and (4) transparency masking.

Positive Masking. The simplest system, which has also been in use the longest, is commonly called overlay masking. This is now technically classified as positive masking. These masks, added to uncorrected separations, give complete correction for properly balanced sets of process inks when printed on coated papers. Experience at the GATF Laboratory has shown that this system gives the most accurate reproduction of the widest range of colors when used with (1) the standard broadband filters, (2) sets of compatible process inks whose magenta and cyan ink errors balance with these filters, and (3) separation negatives with straight-line gray-scale tone reproduction.

Positive masking is a contact method. The following procedure is used to make the masks:

1. Make continuous-tone separations.
2. Make weak contact positive masks from the separations.
3. Bind the positive masks in register to the appropriate separation negative.
4. Shoot halftone positive through combination mask and separation.

MAKING THE CONTINUOUS-TONE SEPARATION NEGATIVES. The separation negatives are made with wide-band filters (Nos. 25, 58, and 47). This was described in Chapter 6.

MAKING THE WEAK CONTACT POSITIVE MASKS FROM THE SEPARATIONS. Continuous-tone colorblind or orthochromatic emulsions on glass, or dimensionally stable film base, are generally used. They are processed in continuous-tone developers. It is also possible to use high-contrast lithtype emulsions developed in a diluted continuous-tone developer to make continuous-tone masks.

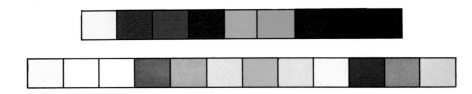

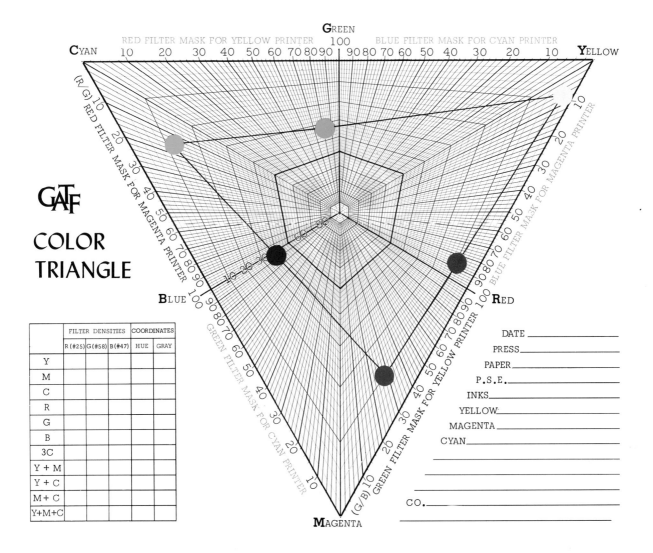

The GATF Subtractive Triangle is best suited to show (1) the gamut of pure color that is possible with a given set of inks, (2) under or overtrapping, (3) changes in gloss, and (4) to directly predict ideal overprint colors, (5) masking requirements for a given set of process inks.

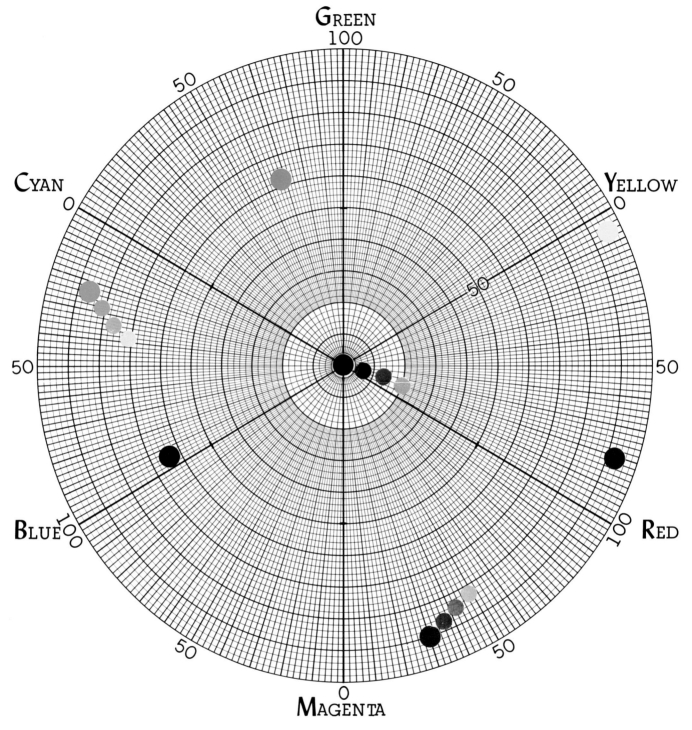

GATF COLOR CIRCLE
INK HUE AND PURITY CHART

GREEN
100

50   50

CYAN
0

50

YELLOW
0

50

50   50

BLUE
100

RED
100

50   50

0

MAGENTA

Note: Density measurements and plots are examples of the method of plotting ink on the GATF Color Diagram, and will only approximate the inks on these pages.

The GATF Color Circle offers an easy way to visualize the hue error and grayness of a number of process inks. Plots are shown for solid yellow, solids and tints of magenta and cyan, solid overlaps of the primaries, and overlaps of three color tints of equal dot sizes (center).

GATF COLOR HEXAGON
INK HUE AND SATURATION CHART

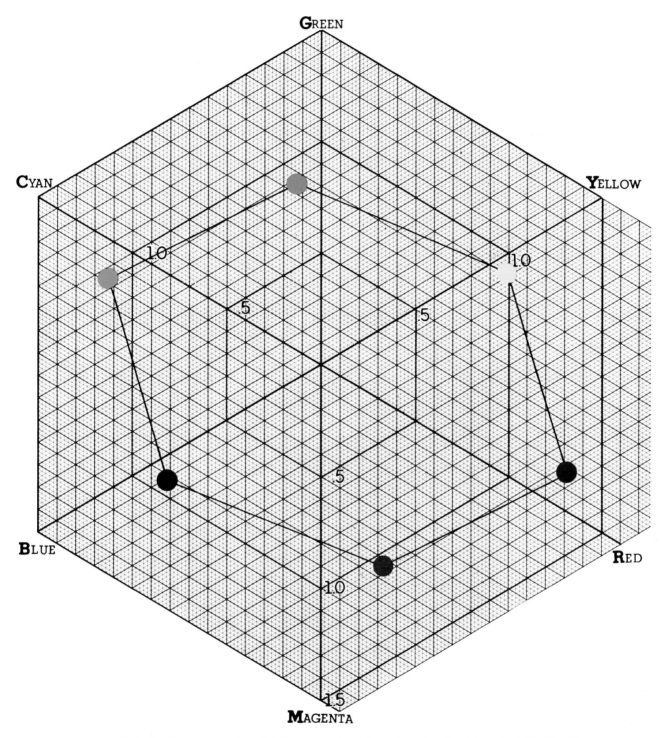

Note: Density measurements and plots are examples of the method of plotting ink on the GATF Color Diagram, and will only approximate the inks on these pages.

The GATF Hexagon is the only diagram that requires no mathematics, formulas, or computations to plot color strength and hue differences. It is the easiest and quickest to use and is best suited for quality control or press control of the separate primaries and overprint hues.

Reproduction of the same photograph with color correction by masking methods only. The clean colors more closely match those of the original.

Reproduction of a photograph made without color correction

The positive masks are contacted from the separations and combined with the appropriate separation negatives. The following combinations of masks and separations are ordinarily used: (The percentage values are explained later and are for an average range of process inks.)

1. Blue-filter separation negative (yellow printer) and a 30 to 50 percent positive mask from the green-filter separation negative.
2. Green-filter separation negative (magenta printer) and a 30 to 50 percent positive mask from the red-filter separation negative.
3. Red-filter separation negative (cyan printer) and a 20 to 30 percent positive mask from the black-separation negative.
4. Yellow-filter separation negative (black printer) and a positive mask from the cyan- or magenta-separation negative.

The masks for the blue- and green-filter separations are used primarily for obtaining color correction. The red-filter separation generally does not need much color correction. However, a positive mask from the black separation will increase the color saturation of the red-filter separation.

The black separation can also be improved by using one of the masks already made for color correcting the yellow or magenta printers. If the mask made from the green-filter separation negative is used, less black will print in reds, warm colors, and flesh tints. If the mask made from the red-filter separation negative is used, less black will print in greens, blues, and cold colors. Unfortunately, these masks add more black to the colors that they do not lighten.

You can make a better single mask which lightens black in all colors with a special "X" filter. The desired property of this filter is that it be able to record all colors, except yellow, as black. No single gelatin filter does this as well as desired. However, two common filters used together approach this goal. These are the Orange (No. 22) and the Cyan (No. 61). These filters, when overlapped, transmit only a narrow wavelength band of light near spectral yellow. Because of the decreased light transmission, the exposure factor is larger than for single filters. Camera negatives, therefore, have to be made with large lens apertures and bright lights. Shorter exposures and still more complete correction is expected with new interference filters that are now being developed for black correction.

DETERMINING THE PROPER STRENGTH AND PERCENTAGE OF COLOR CORRECTION MASKS. The strength of the correcting mask is determined by the printing inks that will be used to print the job. Once the mask strength has been determined for a given set of process inks, the same percentage mask is used for all types of copy.

Ordinarily, instructions for masking methods refer to different strength masks in terms of percentages such as 30, 40, or 50 percent masks. Such percentages have sometimes been misunderstood, and unsatisfactory results have been produced without knowing the cause. *Percentage figures represent the desired black-to-white density range of the mask divided by the black-to-white density range of the negative it will be used with.* In other words, the density range of a 40 percent mask will have to be different from one set of separations to the next, if the density range of the color separations that the masks are used with also varies.

In commercial production work, the photographer does not have to figure these mathematical percentages if he photographs process ink color separation guides with his copy. If the color

separation guide does not include good black and white patches, a gray scale should also be photographed with the copy. If this is done, the proper strength to make each mask can be determined directly from the separation negative in terms of density differences. The following examples will explain the procedure:

Example 1. *Determining the Mask Strength to Correct the Blue-Filter Yellow-Printer Separation Negative.* Measure the densities of the magenta-ink patch and the white patch as photographed on the separation negative. Subtract the magenta reading from the white reading to obtain the density difference. Make a positive mask from the green-filter separation. This mask will include the ink color separation guide that was photographed on the green-filter separation negative. Measure the densities of the magenta and white patches on the mask. Subtract the readings to obtain the density difference. The mask will fully correct the separation if the density difference of the mask is equal to the density difference of the separation. A quick visual check can be obtained by registering the mask over the separation. If the combined densities of the magenta and white patches are equal or appear equally dense, the mask strength is correct for this error.

Example 2. *Determining the Mask Strength to Correct the Green-Filter Magenta-Printer Separation Negative.* Measure the densities of the cyan-ink and white patches on the separation negative. Subtract the cyan reading from the white reading to determine the density difference. Make a positive mask from the red-filter separation negative. Determine the density difference of the cyan and white patches on the mask. The mask will fully correct the separation if the density differences are equal. As before, a visual check can be made by registering the mask over the separation to see if the combined densities of the cyan and white patches are equal.

While percentage calculations do not have to be figured each time the ink control patches are used, percentage strengths are important to know. They are especially useful when we wish to obtain these same degrees of correction for specific sets of process inks when the ink color guides are not photographed with the copy (such as transparencies).

The required percentage mask values may be calculated from previous sets which included color guides and a gray scale (if good black and white patches were not a part of the color guide), and which were satisfactorily masked. By "satisfactory" we mean that the masks raised the density of the magenta patch in the yellow-printer separation and the cyan patch in the magenta printer to exactly equal the density of the combined mask and separation white patch. The mask for the cyan-printer separation, made from the black separation, would be correct when the densities in black equal the density of the cyan-ink patch.

The percentage value of these satisfactory masks is calculated as described before. You measure the densities of the black and white patches on the mask and subtract one from the other to get the density range of the mask. Do the same thing for the separation that the mask will be used with. The density range of the mask divided by the density range of the separation is the mask's percentage value.

The alignment chart can be used to find mask percentages, or the required density range of the mask.

TO FIND MASK PERCENTAGES.
1. Measure the density range of the mask and the density

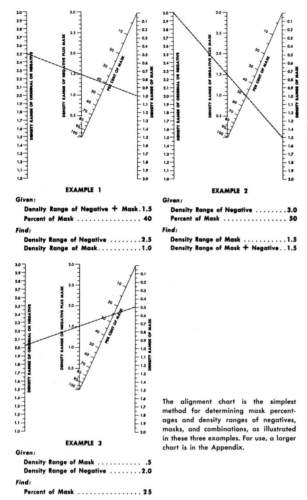

EXAMPLE 1

Given:
Density Range of Negative + Mask . 1.5
Percent of Mask 40

Find:
Density Range of Negative 2.5
Density Range of Mask 1.0

EXAMPLE 2

Given:
Density Range of Negative 3.0
Percent of Mask 50

Find:
Density Range of Mask 1.5
Density Range of Mask + Negative . . 1.5

EXAMPLE 3

Given:
Density Range of Mask 5
Density Range of Negative 2.0

Find:
Percent of Mask 25

The alignment chart is the simplest method for determining mask percentages and density ranges of negatives, masks, and combinations, as illustrated in these three examples. For use, a larger chart is in the Appendix.

Alignment Chart for Converting Mask Densities to Percentages

range of the negative or transparency with which the mask is to be used.

2. Place one end of a straight-edge on the appropriate figure in the left-hand column representing "Density Range of Original or Negative."

3. Place the other end of the straight-edge on the appropriate figure in the right-hand column representing "Density Range of Mask."

4. Read the actual percentage of the mask by the figure at the point where the straight-edge intercepts the diagonal "Percent of Mask" line.

For example, a separation negative has a density range of 1.5 and the mask density range of .60. If a straight-edge is placed at 1.5 at the left-hand scale and at .60 at the right-hand scale, it will intersect the "Percent of Mask" scale at 40 percent. The density range of the negative and mask can be read from the center scale.

To Find Required Density Range of Mask:

1. Measure the density range of the negative or transparency with which the mask is to be used.

2. Place one end of a straight-edge on the appropriate figure in the left-hand column representing "Density Range of Original or Negative."

3. Place the other end of the straight-edge on the "Percent of Mask" scale.

4. Read the required "Density Range of Mask" from the right-hand column.

For example, a separation negative has a density range of 1.5 and the mask is 40 percent. If a straight-edge is placed on 1.5 at the left-hand scale and on 40 percent on the diagonal "Percent of Mask" scale, it will intercept the "Density Range of Mask" scale at .60.

The single-stage masking described here will not give completely satisfactory correction with all process inks and printing conditions. This will be recognized by too little yellow printing in browns, and too little magenta in blues. Sets of process inks, whose magentas are redder than the magenta of the color separation guide or whose cyans are bluer or grayer, may need two-stage masking to prevent these overcorrections.

Two-Stage Masking. Two-stage masks are so called because they are made in two steps. First, a film positive called a premask is contacted from one of the separations. This is then registered with another separation through which the final or principal mask is exposed.

Two-stage masks for color correction of the yellow- and magenta-printer separations are made from the separation negatives which would be used to make corresponding single-stage positive masks. Their difference in correction comes from the use of a pre-mask. The pre-mask in each case (except for the cyan printer) is made from the separation which will be corrected by its final mask. The pre-mask can help control the amount of yellow that the final mask takes out of browns and reds and, similarly, the amount of magenta taken out of blues and purples. As most commonly made, two-stage masks leave the gray scale undisturbed with full solids of each color in black. A small amount of undercolor removal may be accomplished by giving longer exposure while making the final mask, or by using a lower contrast, non-canceling pre-mask. For a high degree of undercolor removal, an additional undercolor removal mask is preferable.

An outline of procedure is as follows:

1. Color separation negatives are made by exposure with the Nos. 25, 58, and 47B filters. Development is adjusted to give close to equal density range.

2. Positive pre-masks are made from the blue- and green-filter separations. These should have gray scale densities which will just cancel those of the separation they are applied to.

3. The pre-mask from the blue-filter separation is placed on the green-filter separation during the exposure for the final mask to correct the blue-filter separation.

The pre-mask from the green-filter separation is placed on the red-filter separation during exposure to make the final mask for correction of the green-filter separation.

These final mask exposures should be such as to give the right amount of correction in the wanted colors. Usually, this just creates a small density in blacks and whites. The length of development will control the contrast or amount of color correction in unwanted colors.

Suitable films for the pre-masks are continuous-tone commercial, or mask-type films capable of giving a straight-line tone reproduction at a gamma of 1.0. Most final masks may be made with the same type of film or plates, but in some cases higher contrast emulsions are used when stronger corrections are needed. More complete working details on two-stage and other masking, with specific recommendations of suitable emulsions, can be found in the film manufacturers' publications.

Camera-Back Masking. This masking system is a camera method of masking reflection or transparent copy. The masks are shot in the camera back, processed, and replaced in the camera. The separations are then shot through the appropriate masks.

These negative masks are made by exposing through the back of a film which does not have an anti-halation backing, and processing it. A mask and the separation-negative film are positioned in the camera, emulsion-to-emulsion. The exposure is made through the back of the mask. In this masking method, three such masks are made. For approximate corrections, these masks may be simply made with single-filter exposures; one with a Red (No. 25) filter, one with a Green (No. 58) filter, and one with a No. 80B or 85B filter.

To make the corrected separation negatives, films are exposed through the following mask and filter combinations:

1. For the green-filter separation negative, expose through the magenta-filter mask with the Green (No. 58) filter in the lens.
2. For the red-filter separation negative, expose through the No. 80B or 85B filter mask with the Red (No. 25) filter in the lens.
3. For the blue-filter separation negative, expose through the green-filter mask with the Blue (No. 47) filter in the lens.
4. Give the yellow-filter separation negative a double exposure. First, expose through the magenta-filter mask and then through the green-filter mask. Use the Yellow (No. 8 K2) filter in the lens.

Some sets of process inks will be better color corrected by masks made with two filters. If needed, blues can be more strongly corrected in the yellow separation by adding a short red-filter (25) exposure to the green-filter (58) exposure when

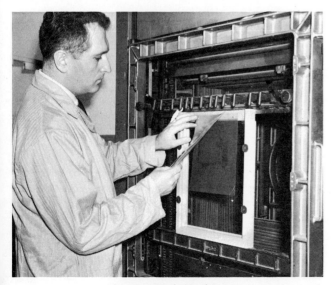

Camera-Back Masking

making this mask. Examine the color patches to judge the effect of the additional exposure. The aim is to eliminate yellow from both the magenta and cyan areas.

To more fully correct "orange" chrome yellow inks in the magenta printer, add some 47B blue filter exposure to the 25 red filter mask. In this case, you use the No. 25 and 47B filters. Again judge the effect of different exposure times with the two filters by examining the color patches on the magenta-color separation negative. The aim is to have both the green and cyan areas as dense as the white patch. (To balance this correction in process ink sets that are like the Kodak Color Separation Guide, Eastman suggests a trial of a ten percent No. 47B filter exposure added to a No. 25 filter exposure when making this mask.)

When making the masks it is important that they be exposed in the same image plane that they will be in when they are used. This is done by exposing the mask film while it is on top of another piece of film. This "spacer" film should be the same thickness as the separation-negative film. It should be fogged and developed so that it is completely black.

The mask film can be held in place over the spacer film by a large piece of thin film placed over both. An opening, about one-half inch shorter and narrower than the film being exposed, is cut out of the large piece of film. In other words, when the large "hold-down" film is in place, it will overlap the edge of the film being exposed about one-quarter inch all around.

After the mask has been exposed and processed, the fogged spacer is replaced by a piece of unexposed film for the separation negative. The mask is placed over it and both are again held in contact by the larger "hold-down" film.

To assure proper registration, the masks and separations must be prepunched and mounted on pins when they are exposed. The Eastman Kodak Register Punch and Pin System is one that can be used for this purpose. A metal strip with the two register pins mounted on it is fastened to the camera back for this work.* The punched masks and separations are placed over the pins for all exposures as shown in the figure, instead of using a register strip. The contact frame is mounted in the plate holder of the camera. The frame is kept in the same position throughout all the exposure operations.

Camera-back masking is an improvement over the *magenta masking method*. This method also employed the camera back, but used plates which were processed in magenta developers to produce a magenta-dyed mask. Exposure in this method is not through the back of the plate. A special plate bar for accurate repositioning of the mask and to permit placing it just ahead of the focal plane of the camera when exposing the separation negative plate, is required. Also, the separation-negative plate has to be focused through a cleared glass plate of the same thickness as the mask plate to assure accurate focusing.

MASKING COLOR TRANSPARENCIES

By a slight variation in the normal procedure, fuller color correction can be introduced into the separation negatives. The following procedure can be used when using the contact method:

* Such strips are available from a number of sources including the Condit Mfg. Co., 20 Oregon Road, Staten Island, N. Y.; Eastman Kodak graphic arts suppliers; or the Mechanical Color Registration Co., 418 East Maynard Ave., Columbus 2, Ohio.

Make Highlight Pre-Mask. To increase highlight detail from an underexposed transparency, a highlight pre-mask may be made.

The mounted transparency, along with the register marks and guides, is contacted to a high-contrast lith emulsion such as that used to make line or halftone negatives. The film is then developed in a diluted continuous-tone developer to produce a short-scale, contrasty negative. For data on the materials and procedure used to make the mask illustrated in figure see the table. Comparable materials are, of course, available.

	Film *	Wratten Filter No.	Exposure Time (in seconds) ‡	Development Time (in minutes at 68°F) **	Density Range of Mask
MASKS:					
Highlight (if necessary)	Pan Litho	.30 Neutral Density	3	2	.40
Principal	Pan Masking	85 B and .30 Neutral Density	3	2	30% to 40%
COLOR SEPARATION NEGATIVES:					
Cyan	Cronar Transparency Separation Negative	25	5	3½	
Magenta	"	58	10	3½	
Yellow	"	47B	60	3½	
Black	"	1.0 Neutral Density	10	4	

*Film used: Dupont
**Developer used: Dupont 16D diluted 1:2 with water.
‡Illumination: 7 footcandles at contact frame.

Masked Color Separation Data

A normal highlight pre-mask will have its maximum density in the range of .25 to .50. The density value needed in the mask will depend on the transparency and the effects desired in the

highlights. For a given transparency, the higher the density of the highlight pre-mask, the greater the highlight contrast in the separation negative. However, if the highlight contrast is too great, the result produced may not look natural.

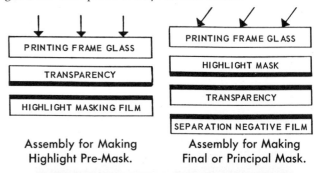

Assembly for Making Highlight Pre-Mask.   Assembly for Making Final or Principal Mask.

Principal Mask

Mounting Transparency for Masking.

1. The first step in making masks is to bind the step tablet and register marks to the color transparency.
2. Fasten transparency to the glass of the printing frame using cellulose or glue tape.
3. In making mask, the unexposed masking film is placed emulsion-side down in printing frame.

Highlight Pre-Mask

Make Final Mask. An unsharp final mask is made with panchromatic continuous-tone film. It is exposed with a filter placed on the printing lamp. Three masks are made, one with a Magenta (No. 25) filter, one with an 85B filter, and the other with a Green (No. 58) filter. The film is processed in a continuous-tone developer to produce a low-contrast, full-tone scale negative. The density range of the masks should be approximately 40 to 50 percent of the density range of the original transparency.

Make Separations. The highlight pre-mask is removed from the transparency, and the appropriate principal mask is bound to the transparency to make the separation negatives. The separations are made with filtered light using the Red (No. 25), Green (No. 58), and Blue (No. 47) filters over the printing lamps as described below. The panchromatic separations are developed in a continuous-tone developer.

Combination of Masks and Filters. The following combinations of masks and filters are used to make the separations:

1. To make the red-filter separation, expose through the No. 85B filter mask with the Red (No. 25) filter over the light source.
2. To make the green-filter separation, expose through the Red (No. 25) filter mask with the Green (No. 58) filter over the light source.
3. To make the blue-filter separation, expose through the Green (No. 58) filter mask with the Blue (No. 47) filter over the light source.

4. To make the black printer, a multiple exposure procedure can be used. Make the first exposure with the Green (No. 58) filter over the light source and the Red (No. 25) mask on the transparency. Make the second exposure with the Red (No. 25) filter over the light source and the Green (No. 58) mask on the transparency. After the second exposure replace the red filter with a Blue (No. 47) filter and make the third exposure through the same green-filter mask.

A simpler way of correcting the black separation negative is to make a special mask with the "X" filter as described previously. Mount this mask on the transparency and expose the black separation negative through the pair. If tungsten light is being used, the exposure can be made either with no filter or through an 80B filter if cleaner blues are needed.

If arc lamps are being used, a "no filter" exposure is equivalent to a tungsten exposure with the No. 80B filter. Arc light through a No. K2 filter is equivalent to tungsten light with no filter.

Section Five: Equipment for Masking

Nearly all masks for transparencies are done by contact printing. But even with color separation and masking of opaque full-color copy, most of the actual masks will also be done by contacting.

In this section we are not concerned with the customary equipment for contact printing in general. Rather, we are concerned with such auxiliary equipment as is specifically needed for masking, over and above the usual contact room equipment.

CONTACT PRINTING LAMPS FOR MASKING

Contact printing lamps, in general, should evenly illuminate the entire printing area, with as small a light source as is practical. These requirements are essential for making masks. In addition, contact printing lamps for masking should be operated through a precise timer and reliable transformer, and be equipped with a filter frame holder.

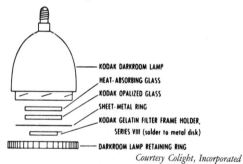

— KODAK DARKROOM LAMP
— HEAT-ABSORBING GLASS
— KODAK OPALIZED GLASS
— SHEET-METAL RING
— KODAK GELATIN FILTER FRAME HOLDER, SERIES VIII (solder to metal disk)
— DARKROOM LAMP RETAINING RING

Courtesy Colight, Incorporated

Darkroom Lamp Converted to Contact Printing Lamp

In plants where color separation and masking are only done once-in-awhile, a Kodak Adjustable Safelight Lamp can easily be modified to fit the requirements listed above.* An ordinary Kodak type dark-room lamp can also be converted to a contact printing lamp. Where at least a fair amount of full-color reproduction is being done, there are several ready-made exposure units available on the market. The more sophisticated units incorporate voltage selection, timer, and remote-control filter wheels.

Register Marks, Gray Scales, and Color Blocks. Each piece of copy should have a set of register marks. Place reg-

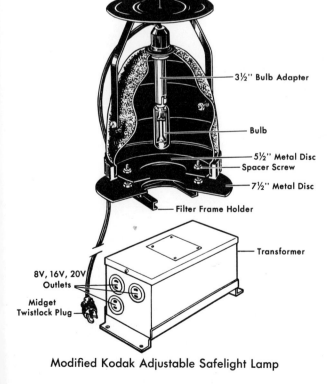

— 3½" Bulb Adapter

— Bulb

— 5½" Metal Disc
— Spacer Screw

— 7½" Metal Disc

— Filter Frame Holder

— Transformer

8V, 16V, 20V Outlets

Midget Twistlock Plug

Modified Kodak Adjustable Safelight Lamp

---

* Eastman Kodak's Q-80 Sheet describes this.

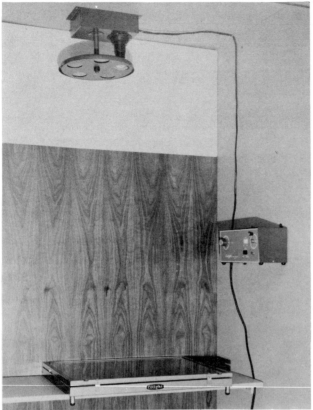

Courtesy Colight, Incorporated

Courtesy K & M Manufacturing Co.

**Small-Source Contact Exposure Units with Filter Turrets
and Electronic Timer Control**

ister marks on the exact vertical and horizontal centerlines of the copy, making sure they are square. A photographic gray scale and color control blocks should be mounted next to the copy, but outside the crop marks. Transparencies should be mounted with transparent gray scales, register marks and, if possible, a transparency of the color block made with the same type of material as the transparency.

Attaching Color Guides. On reflection copy attach gray scales, color blocks, and register marks with masking or drafting tape. This tape can be removed more easily than transparent tape and without damaging the copy. Pressure-sensitive transparent tape can be used with transparencies. The gray scale should be mounted so that it receives the same illumination as the copy.

Color separation guides should include a photographic gray scale and process ink color blocks. Ideally, these ink patches should be sample printings of the same inks and ink strengths that will be used on the press. Color blocks that have been purchased should be used *only* to identify the various separation negatives. Only color blocks that match the inks that will be used to print the job can give an accurate indication of the color separation of the copy.

REGISTER DEVICES

When shooting black-and-white copy, requirements for the photographic equipment used for holding the negative or positive in position are not too critical. The only strict requirement is that it hold the sensitive emulsion flat in the focal plane.

When working with color, however, greater precision of image placement is necessary. When separations are made to be used in photo-composing machines, the centermarks of the copy should be within one-eighth of an inch of the center of the plate on all separations. Some masking techniques require that a mask be shot, processed, and replaced in the identical position within the camera, so that a negative can be shot through the mask. In this case, it is imperative that the mask registers with the image of the original art being shot.

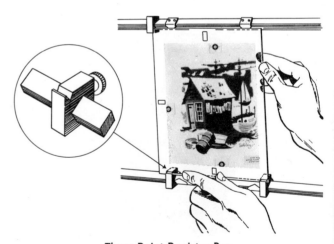

Three-Point Register Bar

Three-Point Register System. Three-point register systems have been developed which will position a series of glass plates in exactly the same place in the camera back every time. The bar used in these systems is designed so that the glass plate rests on two elevated knife edges and butts up against a third. The plate makes contact with the holder at only three points.

Punch Register Systems. A number of registering devices have been designed for working with films. They range from a very simple punch and contact frame combination for small

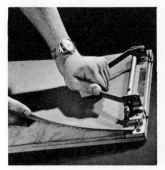 

Kodak Punch and Contact Frame

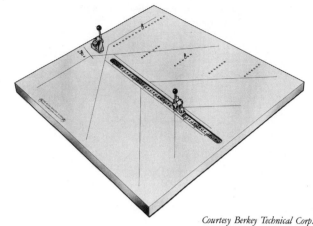

Courtesy Berkey Technical Corp.

Berkey-Aldis Camera Punch

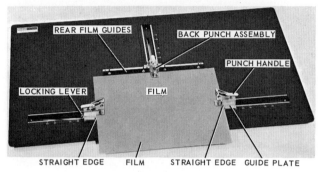

REAR FILM GUIDES — BACK PUNCH ASSEMBLY — PUNCH HANDLE — LOCKING LEVER — FILM — STRAIGHT EDGE — FILM — STRAIGHT EDGE — GUIDE PLATE

Kodak Register Punch

work, to elaborately designed and manufactured precision punch units which can handle up to 30″ x 30″ films, and even larger. These systems make it possible to pre-punch sets of films so that separations and masks can be made in perfect register with each other. Some of the more elaborate units can be correlated with pin set-ups which are permanently installed in the camera back, vacuum frame, or photo-composing machine.

Section Six: The GATF System for Calculating Mask Strength

In this section you find a presentation of the GATF system for calculating mask strength. The subject is divided into a discussion of single masking and two-stage masking.

SINGLE MASKING

Our presentation of calculating mask strength in single masking covers the following three points: (1) The yellow printer, (2) The magenta printer and (3) The cyan printer.

Yellow Printer. The redder the magneta (process red) ink being used, the greater the mask strength needed to correct the yellow printer (blue filter negative). The percentage strength of the mask for the yellow printer is usually determined by dividing the following densitometer readings of the magenta ink patch:

$$\frac{\text{Reflection density of magenta patch through blue filter}}{\text{Reflection density of magenta patch through green filter}}$$

= percentage strength of mask for yellow printer

If, for example, you get a reading of .60 for the magenta patch through the blue filter and a reading of 1.20 of the same patch through the green filter, then the percentage strength of the mask for the yellow printer should be:

$$\frac{.60}{1.20} \text{ or } 50\%$$

This mask should be made from the green filter magenta separation, and developed to 50 percent of the density range of the blue filter yellow separation negative.

Since the cyan ink also introduces an error in the yellow separation a calculation should be made to measure its extent.

Use the same formula as before. This time, however, substitute the density values that you determined for the cyan patch using the blue and green filters. If these values are those in the chart shown, the calculation is:

$$\frac{.28}{.40} = 70\%$$

The first calculation called for a 50 percent mask for the yellow printer. If the second calculation had also produced a value of 50 percent, then a single mask for the yellow printer would give perfect correction for both errors.

In this case, however, the second calculation produced a value of 70 percent. This tells you that a single mask cannot perfectly correct both errors. The residual cyan error will be 20 percent undercorrected if you match the magenta error which requires a 50 percent mask. Or the magenta will be 20 percent overcorrected if the mask is made to correct the cyan error which needs a 70 percent mask. Usual practice would leave one color undercorrected rather than overcorrected, and, in this case, an extra mask could be added from the cyan printer negative.

The term "balanced inks" has been applied to sets of process inks in which the magenta and cyan have close to a matching ratio of blue and green absorption, and thus color correct most efficiently with a single mask.

Magenta Printer. The percentage strength of the mask for the magenta printer (green filter negative) is computed by dividing the following densitometer readings of the cyan (process blue) color patch:

Reflection density of cyan patch through green filter
———————————————————————————————————
Reflection density of cyan patch through red filter

= Percentage strength of mask for magenta printer

For example, if the reflection density reading of the cyan patch through the green filter is .40 and 1.25 when measured through the red filter, the percentage strength of the mask for the magenta printer should be:

$$\frac{.40}{1.25} \text{ or } 32\%$$

This mask should be made from the red filter cyan separation negative, and developed to 32 percent of the density range of the green filter magenta separation negative.

Cyan Printer. The basic determination of a mask for the cyan printer is not similarly made directly from the set of color filters density numbers as the masks for the yellow and magenta printers were. All color correction masks, of course, are always expected to clean out the printing color in the unwanted color areas, such as yellow out of blue and magenta out of cyan and green. They also do other important things such as increasing the saturation of the printing color relative to black in the picture and may also adjust the gray scale tone values relative to the other color printers. In the uncorrected cyan printer the unwanted color areas of red and magenta need only a small degree of lightening but the cyan areas still need almost as much strengthening relative to black as the magenta printer does.

When using a Trimask Type of single film mask for camera back or transparency masking the degree of gray scale correction of the cyan separation is very much the same as its reduction of the magenta separations gray scale. The required imbalance of the cyan gray scale to the yellow and magenta gray scale for printed ink gray balance is then adjusted in the development of the three color separation negatives which can then be screened alike. With separate negative, silver, camera-back, or transparency masks, the same principle can be followed. Make the mask for the cyan printer the same percent density range as the mask for the magenta printer. This mask for the cyan is commonly made with an 85B filter to give approximately the low degree of color correction required in red. With typical positive masking of color separation negatives with equal density ranges, the mask for the cyan printer may be approximately 85% of the mask for the magenta to permit giving printed gray balance from equal positive screening.

TWO-STAGE MASKING

Our discussion so far has dealt only with single masking. Under certain conditions of printing, single masks may overcorrect and remove too much color. In such cases, twice as many masking steps or additional handwork will be needed to correct the separations. Just what the situation is for a given combination of paper and set of process inks can be determined by density measurements of the GATF Color Test Strip on the Color Chart. Keep in mind that the situation will be different for each combination of different papers or sets of process inks.

Yellow Printer. Measure the density of the solid area of yellow and the density of the solid area of magenta. Make these measurements with the blue filter over the densitometer aperture. Add these two density values. Then measure the density of the area where the solids of yellow and magenta overlap (the red block). If the sum of the densities of yellow and magenta when measured separately is higher than the density of the red overlap patch, then you'll know that a single mask will probably overcorrect the yellow printer. A single mask will take some yellow out of the reds and browns.

In such a case, you'll need a second mask or additional handwork on the yellow printer. This second mask is called a pre-mask. It can be a 50 percent to 100 percent positive made from the yellow separation negative. A positive made from this combination is the final mask for the yellow printer.

Magenta Printer. To determine whether a single mask will overcorrect the magenta printer follow the same procedure just described for the yellow printer. In this case, however, use the green filter over the densitometer aperture. Measure the density of the solid blocks of cyan and magenta separately and add them together. Then measure the density of the block where the cyan and magenta solids overlap. (With ideal inks, the color produced by overlapped cyan and magenta will be blue. With commonly used inks, the color is usually a purple.)

If the density of the individual cyan and magenta blocks when added together is higher than the density of the overlap block, then a single mask would probably overcorrect the magenta separation. It is likely to take too much magenta out of the purples and blues and shift their hues toward green or cyan.

The pre-mask required in such a case is a 50 percent to 100 percent positive of the magenta separation negative. Make this positive and attach it to the cyan separation negative. The combination positive and the cyan separation negative are then used to expose the final mask for the magenta separation negative.

TONE REPRODUCTION CURVES OF MASKS

The formulas and procedure given to obtain the percentage strength of masks can also be used to prepare tone reproduction curves for the masks for the yellow and magenta separations. Briefly, the way that this can be done is as follows:

Mask for the Yellow Separation Negative. Make two sets of densitometer readings of the solid, three-quarter, one-half, and one-quarter magenta tints in the GATF Color Test Strip. Use the green filter over the densitometer head for the first set and the blue filter for the second set. Now make a graph on paper ruled with 20 lines to the inch and used sideways (see our illustration). Let each ruling represent .01 density unit. Set up these values on both the X (horizontal) axis and the Y (vertical) axis.

The X axis is used for density readings made with the green filter. The Y axis is for the blue filter density readings. One point for the curve is established by using the green and blue values of the solid patches, another by using the green and blue values of the ¾ tints, the third by using the values of the ½ tints, and the fourth by using the ¼ tint values.

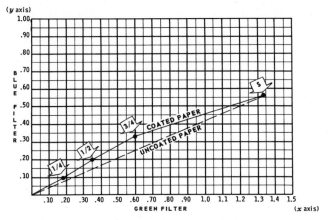

Proportionality diagram showing positive mask curves for reproductions on coated and uncoated papers. The ¼, ½, ¾ and "S" points represent reflection densities of ¼, ½, and ¾ tints; and magenta when measured through blue and green filters.

This proportionality curve now represents the green and blue filter tone values for magenta as they are printed in your plant and with the paper and ink used for this particular color chart. Your aim now is to prepare a mask for the yellow separation with tone values that match this curve.

Put a gray scale on the original copy so that it photographs in all of the separations and in the masks made from the separations. To check the tone reproduction curve of the mask for the yellow printer, plot the curve on the same graph that you prepared of the printed tint values. Use readings of the gray scale on the mask for the vertical Y axis and density readings of the gray scale on the original copy for the horizontal X axis.

Mask for the Magenta Separation Negative. Curves for the cyan tone values and the mask are prepared the same as for the mask for the yellow. In this case, however, you would measure the densities of the cyan patches on the GATF Color Test Strip using first the red filter over the densitometer aperture, and again using the green filter. Plot the red filter readings on the horizontal X axis and the green filter readings on the vertical Y axis.

Curve Patterns. In general, mask curves for 133- to 150-line screens are almost a straight line on offset paper. On coated paper, the mask strength is about 20 percent to 25 percent stronger in the middletones than in the solids. On metal, the middletone curvature is 30 percent to 40 percent stronger than the solids.

The curve for a good positive mask will have the same shape as the curve for the printed tone values. If you are using negative camera back or transparency masking, the curve should be proportionally opposite to the curve for the printed tone values.

The production of a positive mask that matches the curve for the printed tone values usually requires shouldering, that is, the use of overexposure and film that normally would produce high contrast, but which is developed with a weak developer.

The production of a negative mask is just the opposite. The usual need here is to create more of a toe in the curve by underexposing and using materials and methods that produce lower contrast in shadow tones than in the highlights.

For precise work, use a densitometer. Take density measurements of the colors or tints that you are concerned with from the master set of negatives or positives that were used to print your color charts. Compare these densities with readings taken from the job's halftones and adjust the halftones accordingly. *Do not* adjust the job's halftones to match density readings made from printed color charts. Printed densities have been affected by all of the variables involved in your plant's platemaking and presswork conditions.

Section Seven: Undercolor-Removal Masking for High-Speed Wet Printing

The masking methods described previously are designed, in general, for three-color printing or for four-color printing in which only a skeleton black printer is required. In these methods, no account has been taken of the darkening of the picture by the black printer because it will not cause trouble unless it is too heavy. In high-speed wet printing, where the piling-up of the three colors in the same area has to be avoided, special measures must be taken. Wherever ink would be deposited by all three color plates, the same effect can be obtained by carrying the image on the black plate plus a smaller amount of color on one or two of the color plates. A much heavier black printer is then substituted for combinations of the three colored inks, and it is necessary to compensate for this by reducing the amount of the three colored inks which print in neutral areas. The masking method described here, and known as "undercolor removal," takes the colors out of the grays. Our presentation of the subject is divided into the following six units: (1) Outline of an undercolor removal masking method, (2) Making the color-separation negative, (3) Making the undercolor-removal mask, (4) Making the continuous-tone positives, (5) Making the halftone negatives, and (6) General considerations for undercolor-removal masks. Each of these is presented in the following.

OUTLINE OF THE KODAK UCR MASKING METHOD

This method is applicable to any kind of original and is quite simple in principle. The three color-corrected separation negatives, along with the separation negative utilized for the black printer, are made in accordance with any of the procedures described in this chapter. A positive, undercolor-removal (UCR) mask is then made from the corrected black-printer separation negative. This UCR mask is, in turn, registered with the other three color-corrected separation negatives when the positives are being made.

The UCR Mask in its Relation to the Color-Separation Negatives. The UCR mask adds an equal amount of density to each of the three color-separation negatives wherever black is to be printed. However, to produce a neutral with conventional process inks, different amounts of density are required in the three printers. This is achieved either by adjusting the balance when making the color-corrected separation negatives so that the magenta and yellow printers have less contrast than the cyan, or by adjusting the contrast of the individual halftones made from a set of matched separation negatives.

Black-Printer Negative and UCR Mask. The chief secret of success with this method lies in making a good black-printer negative and in flattening the highlights of the UCR mask and the highlights of the black-printer positive. The tone gradation should be similar in the mask and in the positive, since the chief object of the black printer is to replace the amount of black that was taken out of the other three printers by the UCR mask.

MAKING THE COLOR-SEPARATION NEGATIVES

Any of the methods described in this chapter can be used for making the color-separation negatives. If the balance of the separation negatives is to be adjusted at this stage, the gray-scale density ranges of the negative printers including any color-correcting masks should be about 1.25 for the yellow, 1.25 for the magenta, and 1.4 for the cyan. In the case of the Two-Stage Masking Method, all should have density ranges in the gray scale of about 1.4. Exact values depend on subsequent steps of the process, particularly the balance of the printing inks.

The Black-Printer Negative. A well-corrected black-printer negative is essential, and it should be further corrected by hand, if necessary, to remove excessive black which may still be present in pure-colored areas. It has been found, however, that black printers which are corrected entirely by hand are unsatisfactory for undercolor masking.

Correcting the Black-Printer Negative. In correcting and retouching the black-printer negative, the chief object is to add density to the areas of pure color in the negative. The theoretically ideal black-printer negative for making a UCR mask would have a density in every area equal to the color-separation negative which is the darkest. If the negatives differ from each other in highlight density, allowance should be made for this effect. With such a perfectly corrected black-printer negative, it would be possible to carry all the gray component of the picture in the black printer. One advantage of this undercolor-removal masking system is, however, that minor errors in the black-printer negative are compensated for in the reciprocal action of the UCR mask and the black-printer positive.

MAKING THE UNDERCOLOR-REMOVAL MASK

A positive UCR mask is made by contact printing through the black-printer negative. If a color-correcting mask has been made for the black-printer separation negative, it should be used

while exposing the UCR mask. The UCR mask can be exposed on a Kodak 33 Plate if a diffusion sheet is used as a spacer to produce the desired unsharpness in the mask. The plate is tray developed for about five minutes at 68°F. In masking methods where color correcting masks have been made on plates rather than on film, the UCR mask must be made on film. This will allow the register of two plates, emulsions facing each other, with the film mask between them. B. S. Masking developed for about 3¼ minutes in a tray of soft developer (1:12) at 68°F. can be used for the UCR mask in this case.

It is important that the proper amount of flattening of the highlights in the UCR mask be obtained. In this way, excessive undercolor removal is prevented in colors which are not perfectly rendered in the black printer. This flattening of highlights can be accomplished either by under-exposing the UCR mask or by using a fogging exposure in making the mask similar to that described in connection with obtaining bow-shape separation negatives—as presented in the "Color Separation Photography" chapter in our Manual. The latter method gives more definite control of curve shape. The amount of fogging exposure required can be estimated by determining how much fogging exposure will give a density of 0.3, and then taking three-quarters of this value. The exposure through the black-printer negative and the development should then be adjusted

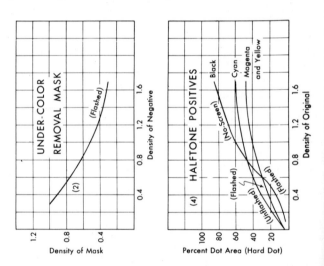

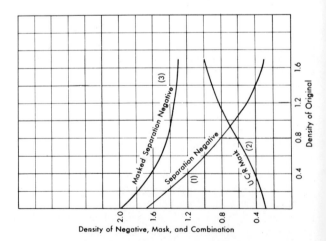

UNDERCOLOR-REMOVAL MASKING REPRODUCTION CURVES

so that the UCR mask has a highlight density of 0.3 and a density range that depends upon the amount of undercolor removal desired.

MAKING THE CONTINUOUS-TONE POSITIVES

Using the color-corrected separation negative (yellow, magenta, or cyan printers) that contains the strongest color, register the UCR mask, and set it up in the transparency-holder of the process camera to make the positive. If this particular separation should contain any solid colors, the positive should be developed to a density range of 1.3 to 1.4 between white and the solid colored areas. If no solid colors are required in the picture area, the appropriate color patches in the color control patches (or, preferably, patches of the actual inks to be used) should then have this range. The highlight density of the positives should be no less than 0.4. Precaution should be taken to minimize lens flare in making the positives, as this might cause too much loss of highlight detail.

The UCR mask is next registered, in turn, with the other two color-corrected separation negatives, and the positives from them are made in the same manner. These positives should be developed for the same length of time as the first positive. (If the separation negatives do not all have the same highlight density, the exposure times for the positives can be calculated with the Kodak Graphic Arts Exposure Computer.)

The density range in the picture areas of the different positives may vary considerably and, if the subject does not require any solid colors in one or more of the printers, may be quite low. Do not attempt to equalize the density ranges of the three positives in the picture areas, as this may throw the whole picture off balance.

The black-printer positive is made without using the UCR mask. The highlights of this positive, much like those of the UCR mask, should be flattened by the use of underexposure or fogging. The fogging exposure is determined in the same manner as described above for the UCR mask. However, the development time, and hence the contrast, of the black-printer positive should be higher. A density range of about 1.3 to 1.4 can be obtained with tray development in Kodak Developer D-11 for about six minutes at 68°F.

The black-printer made in this way should have about the same amount of highlight detail as the UCR mask, or slightly more. Halftone, instead of continuous-tone, positives could, of course, be made at this stage.

MAKING THE HALFTONE NEGATIVES

The positives obtained by this method are very unusual in appearance, and some experience will be required in adjusting the balance of the halftone negatives. When working with a masking method, in which the relative contrasts of the separation negatives have been adjusted, the same screen-exposure conditions can be used with all the printers. It is suggested that the printer requiring the most solid color should be made first, and then the other two made in the same manner. For a masking method, such as the Two-Stage Masking Method, where matched separation negatives are used, the screening conditions of each printer must be adjusted to obtain a neutral gray scale. The cyan printer should have greater highlight contrast than the magenta or yellow printers. The exact balance depends upon the printing inks and the printing process.

GENERAL CONSIDERATIONS FOR UNDERCOLOR-REMOVAL MASKS

This method of undercolor-removal masking has sufficient flexibility so that it can be adjusted easily to suit the requirements of the operator. The gradation in the first few steps of the gray scale will be carried by the three color printers, the rest of the scale being supplied by the black printer. The middletones and shadows of the three color printers will be completely flattened or even slightly reversed by the UCR mask.

When reproducing copy of lower density range, such as watercolor drawings and similar artwork, and when printing on uncoated paper, the contrast of the separation negatives should be increased to avoid further compression of the scale. The color control patches should not be used in this case, but should be replaced by color patches printed with the inks to be used on uncoated paper. The density range of the color-corrected separations should be such that, when screened in the normal manner, the color patches are produced as solids. In original copy where color saturation of the shadows is especially important, less bowing of the separation-negative curve may be more desirable.

It is strongly recommended that, in the first few attempts to employ this method, curves of the negatives, positives, and masks be plotted, and a color proof be made from the plates, since their appearance is so unusual. Such a set of reproduction curves is shown. In photoengraving, the flat etched plates should be proofed. It is safe to carry the flat etch considerably further than with uncorrected color separations. The further the flat etch can be taken, the more benefit will be gained from the process.

CHAPTER EIGHT

The Litho Art Department

Section One: Equipment of the Litho Art Department

The litho artist or color etcher works with tone values on negatives or positives and interprets them in terms of color values in the printed job. Although there are instruments available to aid in this work, many of the corrections will require a visual evaluation of the color copy. He must also estimate allowances for the printing process variables. This dependence on his eyesight makes it important that working conditions and equipment be such that they will aid the color etcher's work. Our presentation of the subject is divided into the following three groups: (1) General considerations for the litho art department; (2) Furniture and fixtures; (3) Instruments and tools. Each of these is briefly discussed in the following. A more extensive treatment of the subject can be found in GATF Skilled Craft Text #510/11, *Tone and Color Correcting for Offset Lithography,* by Bernard R. Halpern.

GENERAL CONSIDERATIONS FOR THE LITHO ART DEPARTMENT

Some of the requirements for favorable working conditions are: (1) Color environment, (2) Good illumination, (3) Water supply, and (4) Proper working habits. Each of these points is now briefly discussed.

Color Environment. Walls, ceiling, large equipment, shades and other prominent objects should be neutral gray, white or black in color so that they do not add their reflected color values to that of the color original.

Illumination. General room lighting can be white or cool white fluorescent. It should, if possible, match the lighting used to illuminate the color copy. It has been customary in the past to locate the color-correction department with its windows facing north so as to reduce the variables caused by changes in sunlight. It is preferable to block-out all daylight and to use artificial lighting throughout the color-correction department in order to maintain constant light and color values.

Water Supply. Water supply for dot-etching sinks should be delivered through a temperature control valve set to 70° F. The water should also be filtered if sediment or rust is noticeable on the dried negatives or color printers.

Proper Working Habits. Cleanliness, the orderly arrangement of equipment and tools, provisions for temperature and humidity control, and clean filtered air are conducive to good workmanship and improved efficiency.

FURNITURE AND FIXTURES

The furniture should be simple and functional, preferably a neutral gray in color. It should be resistant to staining, warping, or rusting from the water, opaques, dyes, and the etching chemicals used. In the following you find a few notes on: (1) Artist's stand and stool, (2) Easels, (3) Light tables, and (4) Dot-etching sinks or stands.

Artist's Stand and Stool. Continuous, close concentration for color correction requires a stand and stool that

Courtesty Mueller Color Plate Co.

Artist's Stand, Stool and Easel.

will be comfortable and convenient. The working surface of the stand must be uniformly illuminated. A white reflector in the stand or an opal diffusing glass is best as neither causes glare, hot spots, or concentrated light bands to appear through the glass. The light source behind the glass surface may be variable in intensity or fixed at about 50 to 60 foot-candles. The lighting should be white or deluxe cool white fluorescent to agree with that used for illuminating the copy. A black roller curtain fastened to the top of the stand should be provided to confine the illuminated area to the height of the negative or positive so as to reduce glare and eyestrain.

Easel. The easel for holding artwork is best attached to the artist's stand so that it can hold the copy securely without interfering leg supports. It should be equipped with a pair of adjustable fluorescent fixtures to illuminate the copy uniformly. Deluxe cool white fluorescent lamps should be used for normal color judgment unless the customer's viewing conditions require special lighting. Provisions should also be made to house the transparency viewer when working from color transparencies.

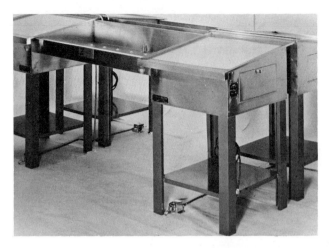

Courtesy Zarkin Machine Co.

Dot-Etching Stand with Sink and Footvalve Controls.

INSTRUMENTS AND TOOLS

Satisfactory equipment and tools contribute to the color etcher's efficiency and good workmanship. Here we discuss the following nine kinds of equipment: (1) Equipment for inspection; (2) Color viewers; (3) Magnifiers; (4) Densitometers; (5) Gray scales; (6) Color combination charts; (7) Airbrushes; (8) Needles and knives; and (9) Trays and brushes.

Equipment for Inspection. As the color of the copy under inspection during color correction is directly altered by the type of illumination used, all lighting should be the

Light Table.

Light Table. A light table, similar to a stripping table, is used for squaring-up negatives, and to rule, opaque, border or add register, trim, and other reference marks. Its internal illumination should be uniformly diffused without hot spots or undue glare. Squared, machined edges and a stainless steel T-square are useful additions.

Dot-Etching Sink or Stand. As the dot-etching sink or stand is used for extended periods of time, its height and the location of the water controls must be convenient. Its housing construction should be of stainless steel to withstand the chemicals and the water. The internal lighting beneath its glass surface must be uniformly diffused to avoid glare and eyestrain. The sprinkler pipe and flushing hose are best controlled through foot-operated valves.

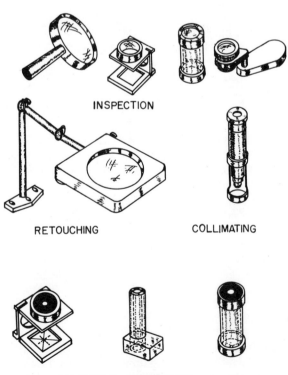

Magnifiers.

same throughout the art department. The only exception is where special lighting must be used in a transparency viewer to provide a specific color temperature. Close, intricate work requires a level of illumination on the working surface of between 50 and 100 foot-candles. This is least tiring to the eyes.

Color Viewers. Color comparison is best judged and matched at the higher values of color temperatures, such as 7,500° Kelvin. However, color itself can be better interpreted as it will be seen by the consumer, when viewed at a lower color temperature, such as 4,500° Kelvin. Accordingly, this lower value is more commonly used in the color-etching department. The deluxe cool white fluorescent lamps are usually rated at about 4,500° Kelvin.

Magnifiers. Magnifiers are a useful extension of the eyesight in both continuous-tone and dot-etching corrections. Those used for dot-etching should be of at least 10-power to 15-power. The pocket microscope with magnifications from 20-power to 50-power, or higher, is excellent for judging dot size. High-powered magnifiers are essential for observing and evaluating dot size during the progress of the etching operation.

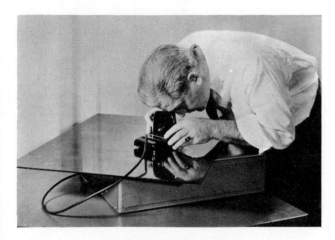

Using the Densitometer.

Densitometers. A transmission densitometer measures the proportion of light that will pass through selected areas of the separation negative or positive. It scales this transmission in terms of density units. The density scale runs from 0.00 to 3.00, or higher. A density of 0.00 represents a completely transparent area. A density of 3.00 is practically opaque.

Density values are calibrated to a logarithmic scale to keep the numbers low and in comparable proportions. The density numbers are the logarithm of the ratio of the percentage of the incident light that is transmitted through the negative. An area with a density rating of .30 will transmit twice as much light as .60 area, or five times as much as an area with a density of 1.00. Similarly, an area with a density of 2.00 will let through only one-tenth of the light that an area with a density of 1.00 will transmit.

Gray Scales. Where densitometers are not available, the commercial calibrated gray-scale filmstrip can be used as a simple comparison densitometer for approximate val-

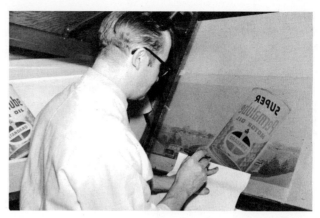

Using an Airbrush.

ues. When using the gray-scale filmstrip, observations must be made over a light table having a uniformly diffused illumination. The neutral-gray spotting cards must also be used for comparing the density value in the subject with the gray scale.

Color Combination Charts. Several fairly complete color combination charts or "Color Atlases" are commercially available. They represent a range of color combinations of three selected process-ink colors and black, usually in ten-percent dot size steps. Similar color combination charts in a limited range are obtainable from some of the ink houses.

Every lithographic plant actively engaged in color work should have its own color chart. The most effective and the most economical way in which a color chart can be made is by following the GATF method. The Foundation provides the necessary negatives or positives as well as complete instructions for making of your own color chart. For further information consult the GATF publication, Bulletin #320, *The GATF Color Chart.*

Airbrush. The airbrush has limited application for adding density to continuous-tone negatives or positives. It provides the means for increasing density uniformly within the bounds of frisket-paper masks, or applying it gradually as a vignetted density change. Its principal applications are for adding density to required areas of con-

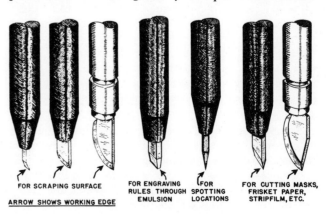

FOR SCRAPING SURFACE FOR ENGRAVING RULES THROUGH EMULSION FOR SPOTTING LOCATIONS FOR CUTTING MASKS, FRISKET PAPER, STRIPFILM, ETC.

ARROW SHOWS WORKING EDGE

Needles and Scrapers.

tinuous-tone positives or negatives, for increasing contrast of curved surfaces where a gradual density change is required, or for adding or changing color values as applied to a transparent overlay over the copy.

Needles and Knives. Scraping and engraving tools are sometimes used for local partial removal of negative or positive densities. They can also remove the emulsion completely as when scribing line detail in negatives, or for cleaning up the highlight points in the positives. Knives

and needles used for scraping and engraving must be carefully stoned to provide clean, sharp edges. Round needles make poor engraving tools as they tend to furrow and tear the emulsion.

Trays. Enameled or plastic trays are preferred over stainless steel or Monel Metal trays for dot-etching purposes because of possible chemical reactions with the metal. Translucent or transparent plastic trays are particularly desirable for staging or flat-etching halftone printers.

Section Two: Materials Used in the Litho Art Department

Our discussion of the materials used in the litho art department is divided into two units. Materials used for manual color correcting and opaquing form the first group. Materials for dot-etching are described in the second.

MATERIALS FOR MANUAL COLOR CORRECTING AND OPAQUING

Hand color-corrections consist of physically adding or removing density from the photographic image. They require considerable skill and good tools to conform to the photographic detail and to produce the required color proportions in each element of the subject. Our discussion of the materials used in hand color correcting and the related opaquing includes the following ten items: (1) Stumps and graphite powder; (2) Pencils; (3) Dyes and neutral groups; (4) Red dyes; (5) Opaques; (6) Artist's brushes; (7) Farmer's reducer; (8) Abrasives; (9) Bleaching agents; and (10) Litho crayons and tint sheets.

Stumps and Graphite Powder. The stump consists of a roll of soft paper shaped like a pencil. It is provided with a blunt point. When rubbed into fine graphite powder, it picks up some of the graphite. This grapite is then applied to the negative surface. It is worked in gradually. Additional graphite is added a bit at a time to blend it into the subject detail.

Pencils. The pencils used may range in hardness from 4B to 6H depending on the amount of density to be added and whether fine lines or corrective re-working of areas are necessary. The pencils are sharpened with a long gradually tapered point to retain their working tips as long as possible. Small, circular-arc strokes usually are used and are blended together to avoid a visible pattern. Hard pencil lines can be used for delineating outlines, textures, designs, or highlight detail.

Stumps, graphite and pencils serve to increase the density on continuous-tone separations or positives. The dry plates that are usually used for making separations are provided with a fine matte surface on the emulsion. This surface will accept the retouching pencil or graphite. Where other negatives or positives are used, it is necessary to flow or wipe a thin coating of a commercial retouching fluid over its surface to provide a "tooth" to hold the graphite.

Dyes and Neutral Grays. Dyes and neutral grays are commonly used on continuous-tone separations and positives to add density wherever required. They can be applied more smoothly than pencil or stump and graphite. They are generally used for area corrections.

Red Dyes. Red dyes are still used as they provide a more readily visible record of the areas in which the corrections have been applied. The experienced color etcher can interpret the red application in terms of total negative density. This can be confirmed by looking at the negative through a green filter, and the total density in any area directly related to a corresponding step on the gray scale. Red will photograph the same as gray or black when the halftone positives or negatives are made.

Opaques. Opaques are used to border the printing subject and block-out the surrounding marginal non-printing areas of a negative. They are applied with brush and ruling pen. Opaques are also used to fill in solid color detail on positives and to provide clean highlights on both continuous-tone and halftone negatives. Colloidal graphite opaques are usually preferred since they can be applied as a thin, smooth coating, free from pinholes, granularity and lumps.

Artist's Brushes. Red sable and camel's hair brushes are used for applying dyes and opaques. Good quality, medium-sized brushes such as No. 4 or No. 6 are generally suitable. They can be used for applying fine detail, as well as covering larger areas, since they carry a good reserve of opaque or dye.

Farmer's Reducer. Farmer's reducer in reducing photographic density will also decrease the contrast range of detail, within the areas on which it is applied. It should, therefore, be used sparingly on continuous-tone negatives or positives.

Abrasives. Abrasive erasers and abrasive pastes are sometimes used for local reduction of density values. They are useful particularly where quick corrections are to be made, or where chemical reducers cannot be applied conveniently, as in working on the inclined surface of the artist's stand.

Bleaching Agents. Where complete removal of all photographic detail is required in large areas, common bleaching solutions of hypochlorite ("Chlorox" or equivalent) work fast and clean. Detail surrounding the area to be cleared should first be painted out with a protective staging lacquer or asphaltum.

Litho Crayons and Tint Sheets. Texture effects can sometimes be applied when adding density to continuous-tone negatives or positives in fake-color work. The litho crayon, Ben Day tints, or commercially available screen texture patterns can be applied to the surface. When patterns are applied, they must be proportional for the color combination required. They must also be positioned so that the angle of the texture will not produce a moiré pattern when making the halftone.

MATERIALS FOR DOT-ETCHING

Dot-etching is the careful application of an etching solution to the exact areas and for the exact time that is needed to reduce the local dot size to that required so that it will produce the wanted color value. The materials used to control this operation are discussed under the following three headings: (1) Staging lacquers and resists; (2) Combining staging materials. of different solubility; and (3) Etching solutions. Each of these is now individually discussed.

Staging Lacquers and Resists. Asphalt varnish is usually mixed with a small proportion of printing ink or varnish, to prevent embrittlement and improve its working properties. This is further thinned down with turpentine to a consistency suitable for application with a camel's hair brush. The asphalt resist is used widely for staging-out areas so as to control density reduction on continuous-tone images or dot size by dot-etching. Lacquers are also available for staging. Staging lacquers are usually transparent red in color. Their transparency makes errors in staging readily visible. Many of the lacquers can be stripped off the emulsion surface after use, without requiring a solvent.

Combining Staging Materials of Different Solubility. Several staging resists can be used together advantageously to reduce correction time. The areas requiring the least etching can first be bordered with a lacquer resist. The areas requiring slightly more etching are then bordered with an asphalt resist. After the first etching the asphalt is washed off with a solvent that will not dissolve the lacquer. The second etching is then made.

Etching Solutions. Farmer's reducer is most commonly used. It is safe, can be easily controlled, and exhausts itself after use so that etching is definitely stopped. Some plants use a cyanide-iodine etch for fast work. This etch has some disadvantages and the trend has been away from its use.

Other reducing solutions are sometimes used for their particular properties. Their formulation and action are described in folders or booklets issued by the graphic arts film manufacturers. However, it is best to become thoroughly familiar with the working of Farmer's solution and adhere to it so that a uniform and efficient control over color correction is maintained.

Section Three: Opaquing

Almost every lithographic job needs opaquing of some kind or another. For this reason the subject is treated here rather extensively. Our presentation of opaquing is divided into the following seven main points: (1) Spotting and patching; (2) Eliminating unwanted areas and lines and adding wanted ones; (3) Opaquing for silhouettes and highlights; (4) Adding register and trim marks; (5) The use of stains, pencils and stumps; (6) Opaquing of positives; and (7) Opaquing troubles.

SPOTTING AND PATCHING

Spotting and patching is treated under four headings: (1) Spotting of type negatives; (2) Spotting of line negatives; (3) Repairing breaks and holes in halftone negatives; and (4) Patching breaks in halftone negatives.

Spotting of Type Negatives. A common form of opaquing is the spotting of type negatives. When these negatives come from the camera, they usually have fine, white pinholes scattered throughout the type. These pinholes would reproduce as spots, if they were not spotted-out. If the pinholes are numerous and no corresponding specks appear on the original copy, then check with your cameraman to see if there is dust on the copyboard glass, or if the darkroom area is dusty. Either condition can cause excessive pinholes. For display type use a #2 or a

Defective Lettering and Pinholes.

#3 brush and follow the type line-for-line. Remove scratches and cuts as around letters A and F and above J in our illustration. As you follow along, look for letters that are misformed or broken, as in letter D. Use your brush first to clean up the excess white areas around the letters; then finish by scraping with the round or oval needle. When working on fine type, the use of a crowquill pen under an enlarging glass will enable you to do the job more accurately.

Spotting of Other Line Negatives. Line negatives may be handled in the same manner as type negatives. First spot-out all the pinholes in areas that will not be later covered by goldenrod or other masking. Then check for broken or fogged-over lines. These should be cut open with a fine, flat needle that is sharpened for engraving lines. Fit the size of the needle to the work at hand. When the line is badly broken in a section, it is sometimes advisable to paint over that area with red stain or a thin coating of red opaque, just light enough so that the lines show through faintly and then cut in the faulty section. Curved or irregular lines may be cut by hand, but a curve will help a lot. Straight lines can best be cut with the help of the ruler or straight-edge. A ruling pen will also be found handy in straightening ragged edges.

Repairing Breaks or Holes in Halftone Negatives. Repairing a break or hole in a halftone or screen negative is one of the most difficult things to do. The mechanical formation of dots is such that the slightest irregularity of

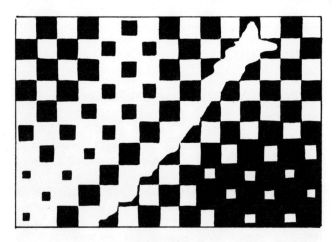

Damaged Halftone.

spacing in a repair is immediately visible. A break in the screen tint can be patched in a number of ways. If the black dot is very small, it can best be repaired with a fine, stipple or crowquill drawing pen and thinned black opaque. Work under a magnifier. Be careful to put the dots in perfect alignment with the other dots. It will take a great deal of practice and steadiness of hand to accomplish this. See *"Retouching and Adding Detail"* in Section Five of this chapter.

Patching Breaks in Halftone Negatives. If the dots are large and it is not a rubber-coated negative, you can patch the break by drawing fine parallel lines of the same width as the dots, following the dot line in any one

direction. These parallel lines can then be cut through with an engraving needle under a magnifier so as to form square dots. Do not try to cut in both directions on a dry plate; because of such cutting, the emulsion will separate from the glass.

ELIMINATING UNWANTED AREAS AND LINES AND ADDING WANTED ONES

Eliminating unwanted and adding wanted areas and lines is discussed under the following four headings: (1) Opaquing for key-outline jobs; (2) Eliminating unwanted tint areas; (3) Opaquing on color separations; and (4) Adding solid areas or lines on screened negatives.

Opaquing for Key-Outline Jobs. A set of negatives to provide individual color separations are made from original color artwork or from key drawings with color overlays indicating where the different colors are to be placed. It is the job of the opaquer to separate the colors on the negatives by opaquing the areas or lines not wanted on each negative. This work is then completed on the contact positive that is made from the negative by filling in with opaque those solids not already created in the negative stage. Sharpness and accuracy are vital. Where color overlap between adjacent color areas is not provided for, this can be added on the positive. Where colors run into heavy, black lines or black solids, the amount of overlap can be more than where color meets color, or color meets a thin, black line. Judgment and experience are the best guides for the amount of color overlap to be used.

Eliminating Unwanted Tint Areas. Where original key drawings are provided, tones of the solid colors are made by flat, halftone tints placed on the negative or perhaps on the positive. If put on the negative, the excess may be opaqued off sharply to the outlines. If put on the positive, the excess may be scraped off, trimmed off, or the tint may be staged-out with asphaltum or lacquer and the unwanted part etched away. Where different strengths of tones are desired, a stronger tint can be placed down and by successive stagings and etchings the different tones can be obtained.

Opaquing on Color Separations. When you have become very proficient at opaquing, the retouchers will probably call upon you to do some of the opaquing necessary on their color-separation negatives. Black water opaque is most often used. Be careful and accurate. Do not touch the work area with your hands as fingermarks will show up on the positive. Use an arm board or ball-stick, or a piece of clean paper for resting your arm while working. Usually lettering, panels, or background sections must be opaqued out. Be accurate when following contours.

Adding Solid Areas or Lines on Screened Negatives. If there are solid blacks in the copy, they can be reproduced by scraping away the dots on the negative. Even fine lines can be cut in with the aid of a fine, flat needle. Only as much need be done as is required by the customer for whom the job is being done. Some will not expect every tone or line, but others will. When positives are to

Separate Pieces of Copy Grouped.

Opaque Masks.

be made, all lines and solids can be put in with india ink or opaque much easier than they can be scraped in. Red or black water opaque may be used, as may stain, tinfoil, and masking paper, according to conditions.

OPAQUING FOR SILHOUETTES AND HIGHLIGHTS

Opaquing for silhouettes and highlights requires exceptionally high skill. Here we discuss the following three points: (1) Opaquing for highlights; (2) Opaquing the background of silhouetted negatives; and (3) Making opaquing masks for multiple use.

Opaquing for Highlights. Most pictures, particularly pictures of mechanical subjects, have numerous highlights. Since the normal halftone reproduction gives a dot all over the negative, it is necessary in reproducing such pictures to opaque out all highlights. It takes considerable skill to do the job cleanly and sharply. Any roughness or carelessness will detract from the quality of the finished reproduction. The larger white areas of the original copy (the dark parts on the negative) can best be stopped-out with a brush. Use your opaque just heavy enough to completely cover the dot. Any excess amount of opaque that dries as a ridge or lump will hold the negative out-of-contact in making the positive, whether on glass or plate. For irregularly shaped highlights, use a fine, pointed brush; for straight lines, guide your pen or ruling pen along a straight edge.

Opaquing the Background of Silhouetted Negatives. Some drawings are silhouetted against a white background. In this case the background must be opaqued out in the negative. Use a #3 or #4 brush and opaque up sharply to the picture, taking care to retain the character of the original. Where there are soft, blend-out tints in the original, opaque them a little way from the margin where they fade out, so that the fine dot can be blended off. This blend-off can be accomplished in a number of ways. You might use lithograph crayon, or spatter applications by airbrush. With a little practice with the crayon, you will be able to produce quite satisfactory results.

Making Opaquing Masks for Multiple Use. Some color jobs are made up of elements which are silhouetted against a white or a one-color background. Other jobs have numerous white highlights. It is unnecessary to repeat the same opaquing on each negative. One mask may be prepared and used on each of the color negatives in turn, thus saving the time required to opaque each of the color negatives. The mask is clamped, or taped, in register with the continuous-tone negative and does not interfere with any previous retouching.

Because of the fact that the opaquing is done only once, each of the plates is identical and the finished positive is much sharper than if each had been worked on individually. This mask plate is made on a continuous-tone positive obtained by contact. Use the negative that shows the best outline for making this contact positive. Opaque out all the parts that are to be white with a turpentine or lacquer base opaque. Then etch out all the tones not wanted. Be sure not to disturb the opaque during this etching operation.

ADDING REGISTER AND TRIM MARKS

Register and trim marks are discussed under the following four headings: (1) Register marks; (2) Corner marks and bleed marks; (3) Marks for double and for multiple exposures; and (4) Indicating the top of the sheet.

Register Marks. The marks for any job that is to go in the photocomposing machine should be in the exact center on all four sides of the sketch and should be at right angles to each other. They should be made as fine as possible, since the engraved lines in the register device of the

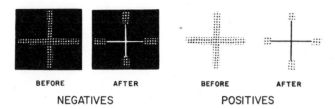

BEFORE   AFTER   BEFORE   AFTER
NEGATIVES   POSITIVES

Re-worked Register Marks.

photocomposing machine to which they are positioned are very fine. Registering to either side of such a mark may cause a discrepancy of as much as .005 of an inch. These marks are called centermarks. They are used to position the print on the plate. They are also used by the prover and the pressman when registering the printed sheets. Therefore, the necessity for fine accurate marks cannot be over-emphasized. If a lineup table is available, be sure to rule in the marks with the aid of this machine.

Corner Marks and Bleed Marks. Marks indicating the extreme size of the job are called corner marks. If there is to be a bleed (an extra amount of area to allow for folding and trimming variation), there will be a second mark called a trim or bleed mark beyond the corner mark. This outside line is a guide for opaquing away the waste area on the outside of the job. The corner marks along with the centermarks help in laying out the job on the photocomposing machine, and guide the pressman, the folder, and the cutter in their operations.

Marks for Double and for Multiple Exposures. When double or multiple exposures are made, there are identical extra long marks placed on each blueprint glass to make it easier for the registry of the separate exposures. If diecutting is to be done later, as on display work, outside guide lines may be put on. To help in folding, special marks may be put on also.

Indicating the Top of the Sheet. It is advisable to ring three of the four centermarks or to opaque out the fourth mark so that the same top is always taken. As the four marks are seldom square with each other, this will assume that the same three marks will be used on each color to provide a good color fit.

THE USE OF STAINS, PENCILS AND STUMPS

If you are going to use stain, do all the staining before starting to opaque. If you use either stain or airbrush, be sure the surface of the negative is free of grease or finger-

prints as they will make the finished job spotty. Here we discuss first the application of stains, and then the use of soft pencils and stumps.

The Application of Stains. To use stain take a small wad of damp cotton and moisten the surface to be worked. Any surplus water left on the negative will cause the stain to run. Use the stain greatly reduced to avoid steps in the blend-off. Hold the brush in one hand, the damp cotton wad in the other. Apply the stain and immediately wipe it off. Apply the stain again, just a little back from the edge of the first application, and wipe again. Each application increases the density of the stain and, if you repeat this process carefully time after time, you will get a smooth, even blend from a tone that is barely perceptible to the full strength of the stain. Do not be discouraged if your first attempts are rough and irregular. It will take a great deal of practice to do the job smoothly, but it can be done. Blending can also be done with an airbrush, but that is a job for a litho artist.

The Use of Soft Pencils and Stumps. If the negative has a matte or ground glass surface, a soft pencil can be used. A paper or chamois stump and graphite, or lampblack, will do a very smooth job. Some use the stump dry, while others prefer an oil stump. Be sure to do your opaquing before using the lampblack or graphite, as they will repel the opaque.

Courtesy Colorcraft Litho Plate Co.

Applying Graphite with Stump.

OPAQUING OF POSITIVES

A positive is the exact reverse of the negative. The areas which were transparent in the negative are solid black in the positive. Most of the things that you have learned in handling negatives can be used equally well on the positive.

All areas which should print as solid color must be opaqued if they are not already solid in the positive. This includes panels, outline lettering, or halftone lettering which should be solid and solid shadows in the design. Whenever possible, use black water opaque on positives as it is thinner, lies flatter and smoother, and will not pick off on the print. When blending a strong halftone into a solid, the same methods can be employed as were explained in handling blend-offs on the negative. See "Blending" in Section Five of this chapter.

OPAQUING TROUBLES

No matter at what trade you work, they all have their troubles, and the lithographic trade is no exception. Here are some of the difficulties you will encounter and also the remedies. As you gain experience, other little tricks of the trade will suggest themselves to you. We discuss the following five kinds of opaquing troubles because they are the most common ones: (1) Greasy negatives; (2) Powdering of greasy negatives; (3) Dirt spots; (4) Loose ends; and (5) Re-coating troublesome negatives.

Greasy Negatives. First we will discuss greasy negatives. Occasionally you will run across a negative which seems to have a greasy film over the surface which repels or fights the opaque. You will make a stroke with the brush and the opaque immediately creeps back, leaving you a rough or saw-toothed edge. When you use the ruling pen, the fluid is reluctant in leaving the pen, and when it does, the line is not sharp and clean, but broken or ragged.

Powdering Greasy Negatives. The cause of this greasiness is either in the making of the negative, excessive handling, or a condition of the coating. When you run across one, first try cleaning the negative with cotton or tissue and a grease solvent. Commercial negative cleaner solutions are available for this purpose. If still slightly greasy, try powdering the negative with powdered talc

(french chalk). Dust off the excess powder and try opaquing again. If that doesn't work, add a few drops of a wetting agent to the opaque dish and stir it in. Or use acetate or turpentine opaques that will adhere better to greasy surfaces.

Dirt Spots. Sometimes in going over a negative you will find dirt and lint specks adhering to the emulsion. In most cases they can be removed with a little piece of cotton on the handle of your brush, and water. If that doesn't remove it, test a little gasoline or alcohol on the outside edge of the negative and, if they do not affect the negative, try removing the spot. Be very careful not to use a solvent on a plate which will dissolve the coating or the emulsion of the negative.

Loose Ends. On all stripped jobs it is good practice to examine the negative carefully for loose ends and corners before starting to opaque. If you find any, take the plate back to the stripper and he will cement these down. If the corner or edge is such that it can be removed without losing work area, it can be trimmed off with a sharp razor blade or cutting needle. Be very careful not to cut into the work.

Re-Coating Troublesome Negatives. When you have a stripfilm negative assembly that repeatedly gives you trouble, it can sometimes be given a top coat of rubber and collodion. Better let the man who does the coating do this. He will know whether it can be done without ruining the negative. When opaquing a stripped negative, use your opaque as dry as possible as this will help to prevent the opaque from creeping under the film. When using the ruling pen, use as little pressure on the pen as possible as you might cut the film.

Section Four: Procedure for Manual Color Correction

Manual hand methods of color correction are used on continuous-tone negatives and positives. They consist of adding or subtracting density to the photographic separations in proportion to the ink-color density required in printing. Even where most of the shop procedure is based on dot-etching, some preliminary work on the continuous-tone separations can reduce the amount of etching required. This is especially true where color changes are specified in local areas that cannot be done by photographic masking techniques.

Work on continuous-tone separations is also needed where retouching is done to remove blemishes in skin tones, wrinkles, photographic defects, or unwanted spots on objects. Where a color job is to be reproduced in several sizes, the total correction time can be reduced materially by partial corrections on the continuous-tone separations. Details for planning the amount of hand correction to be done, and the procedure, follow. They are discussed under the following seven headings: (1) Evaluating a set of color separations for manual color correcting; (2) Inspecting for manual color correcting; (3) Establishing job standards; (4) The black printer; (5) Subtracting densities from separations;

(6) Adding density to separations; and (7) Density corrections on continuous-tone positives. Each of these subjects is briefly discussed in the following. (Readers interested in more detailed information are advised to consult the GATF Skilled Craft Text #510/11, *Tone and Color Correcting for Offset Lithography*, by Bernard R. Halpern; chapter IX in particular.)

EVALUATING A SET OF SEPARATIONS FOR MANUAL COLOR CORRECTING

The main source for job evaluation is the job jacket; it should contain the following minimum information: (1) Kind of plates to be made; (2) Number of colors to be printed; (3) Size of final job; (4) Kind of paper to be used; (5) Type of color correction and degree of photographic masking to be used; (6) References to previous printings of the same job; (7) Special instructions; and (8) Time schedule. Most of these points do not need further discussion for the purpose of our presentation. Several points to be checked are:

Number of Colors to be Printed. Determine whether standard three-color-and-black printings are to be used, or if additional printings are required. If special colors are to be used in place of the standard process colors, they must definitely be established and agreed upon before color correction can be undertaken.

Type and Degree of Photographic Masking. Determine whether masking corrections have been used or are to be used on all separations. Also if highlight and other additional corrective masking will be provided. Usually all such corrective masking is agreed upon in advance and accompanies the separations. However, the color etcher may be required to specify the exact type of masking that will be needed for a particular job.

Special Instructions. Determine how much color-correction work is required. This should be stated as total number of man-hours or cost allowed in the estimate. This may also be coded by the job quality symbol. Are there any general and local color changes specified? Is the entire copy to be reproduced? Will it be cropped down to a selected portion? What particular color areas must be held? Few color jobs are accurately reproduced in entirety or the cost would be prohibitive. Accordingly, important color areas must be established. Is special lighting to be used for viewing the transparency or copy?

INSPECTING FOR MANUAL COLOR CORRECTING

The separation negatives must be inspected for the following four points: (1) Defects; (2) Registration; (3) Density range; and (4) Color change areas. Each of these points is briefly discussed.

Inspecting for Defects. Study each separation carefully. Compare them with the copy to make certain that there are no serious physical defects such as scratches or tears. Look for photographic defects such as blocked-out areas due to light reflection; out-of-focus areas due to copy movement, negative movement, or an off-square camera; slurred detail due to out-of-register masking; or development defects such as clear spots due to air bells; or cloudy, discolored, or stained areas. If these defects cannot be corrected the separation should be replaced.

Inspecting for Registration. Separations that are exposed on film, or made in part on different days, or temporarily interrupted by other camera work before the set was completed, may not agree with each other in size or proportions. A quick visual check for register between film separations can be made on a light table. If the separations are on glass, the thickness of the glass may make such a comparison difficult. A collimating magnifier can be used to align the register marks and the detail through the thickness of the glass.

When any serious questions arise concerning the possible misregister between a set of separations, such as may be due to the copy shrinking or stretching during the exposures, a photographic check gage should be made. This consists of a photographic contact print that is made from one of the separations. It can be exposed on film or on a dry plate depending on the degree of accuracy that is required between the separations. The contact print gage is used to check each of the separations in succession by registering it with them on a light table.

Inspecting for Density Range. Check the gray scale and color patches on each separation, or masked separation, with the densitometer. Make certain that the range of densities of the gray scales are in agreement between the set. Check the color patches, where masking has been added, to see how effective the photographic color corrections are in neutralizing the unwanted color. The amount of under-correction as well as over-correction can be measured from the total densities of the masked color patch areas.

Courtesy Ketterlinus Lithographic Mfg. Co.

Color Separation Negative with Color Controls.

Inspecting Color Change Areas. In areas where color changes have been specified, make certain that the amount of density correction will not be so great that extensive etching or added dye will flatten or obliterate the subject detail. Except in flat color areas, a great density change on a separation will usually require complete reworking of the subject detail and texture by hand-retouching.

The alternatives are (1) obtaining a new separation made through a different filter; (2) masking locally during photography or by use of a special contact mask; (3) combining areas of the subject by double-exposure methods of stripping. These should be weighed against the hours of retouching work that would be necessary otherwise.

ESTABLISHING JOB STANDARDS

Under this heading we discuss the following four points: (1) The standard color chart; (2) Compensating for non-standardized inks; (3) Wet printing and dry printing; and (4) Charting density and dot values. Each of these points is now briefly discussed.

The Standard Color Chart. If possible, obtain a color combination chart prepared in your own plant with the standard process-color inks to be used, and on the grade of paper stock specified. Such a chart can be made by following the instructions of the Graphic Arts Technical Foundation and with material supplied by it. (See the GATF Bulletin #320, *GATF Color Chart Book.*)

If such a chart is not available, any color combination chart will be helpful for interpreting approximate color values. If no commercial color chart or atlas is available, some guidance can be obtained from a previously printed color job whose colors and tone values are similar in range.

Compensating for Non-Standardized Inks. If the color process-inks are standard and have been used to prepare the color combination chart, no ink compensations are necessary. If the inks are not standard, then printed samples of the solid ink colors with percentage tint blocks of each ink must be used to guide in the allowances to be made for their use. These can be taken from the ink supplier's specimen book, if the inks have not been used before.

Wet Printing and Dry Printing. If allowances must be made for wet printing and only a dry color combination chart is available, the gain to be allowed may range up to 25 percent of the printing value in all areas. Approximate allowances for color gain can be made proportional through the range of color values.

	PER CENT										
Desired Color Value	5	10	20	30	40	50	60	70	80	90	100
Dot Size Required	4	8	16	24	32	40	48	56	64	72	80

Color Gain in Wet Printing.

Color gain in wet printing is greatest with the first color printed, and least with the last, usually the black. This is due to the dot size spread caused by the wet ink on the sheet transferring to the blanket of the following press color units.

Charting Density and Dot Values Required for the Job. Draw a rough sketch of the color job; obtain a light photoprint from the black or blue separation; or use a transparent overlay sheet attached to the copy to chart the color corrections to be made. Start with a principal color area on the copy. Use standard or specified illumination. Select a pure color spot that is not textured or variated with shadows and highlights.

Directly compare this spot with the color combination chart. Use the neutral-gray spotting cards for viewing to avoid the influence of adjacent colors. When a close match has been found, note the percentages of ink composing the color block.

Add or subtract to these ink percentages any allowances necessary for the difference between inks that will be used on the job and those used to prepare the chart. Make similar adjustments for the paper stock, overprint varnish, or other factors such as wet printing. Write the final half-tone printing dot size values of each ink color for this area on the sketch. This can be simplified by using code numbers in sequence, such as 641P to show that the color desired will consist of 60 percent yellow, 40 percent red (magenta), 10 percent blue (cyan) and a pinpoint dot in black.

Repeat the same procedure for all other principal color areas until a fairly good charting of the desired dot size values for the job has been prepared.

. THE BLACK PRINTER

Our short discussion of the black printer is restricted to the following points: (1) Black in three-color printing; (2) Black used for type; (3) The effect of overprinted black on colors; and (4) Black in dry printing and in wet printing.

Black in Three-Color Printing. Dense blacks cannot be obtained by overprinting the three process colors. Fine outline detail that is not printed in black would require the overprinting of the three colors in exact register. A black printer is therefore used for extending the shadow density range and for providing the fine detail outlines to simplify the register problem in printing.

Black Used for Type. As most color jobs are printed together with type composition, the black printer is usually available for use in the color reproduction. While three-color printings may provide satisfactory reproduction, the added black printing will improve the appearance and tone range of the job with no need for an additional press run for this purpose.

The Effect of Overprinted Black on Colors. When black is overprinted on a color it changes the value or brilliance of the color. It does not change the color hue aside from the slight undertone, usually blue, that may be incorporated into the black ink. If a particular area has a mixture of all three colors, the black printer can be used to substitute in part for these colors. In so doing, each of the three color densities should be reduced in proportion to the gray balance value of the process color inks used and to the extent that the black will substitute for the colors.

Black in Dry Printing and in Wet Printing. For runs on single-color presses the use of the color inks in the highlight and lighter tone areas and the practical elimination of the black, other than for outline detail, results in cleaner and more brilliant reproductions. In multicolor wet printings, however, the greater gain in the dot size of each color will gray the highlights.

For wet printing it is best to remove from the highlights the common gray value in all three colors, and leave only the excess of the predominating color or two colors. The black printer is then used to provide all of the common gray value of the three color printers, plus the usual detail and modeling outlines or texture.

SUBTRACTING DENSITY FROM SEPARATIONS

Our discussion of the subject is divided into the following three points: (1) General exposition of subtracting density; (2) Procedure for subtracting densities by chemical etching; and (3) Subtracting density by scraping. Each of them is taken up in the following.

General Exposition of Subtracting Density. A decrease of negative density on continuous-tone separations can be done chemically by use of Farmer's reducer, assisted by some local fine detail work with a scraper. Density corrections are usually limited to those separations where such corrections have not been made by photographic masking. Such work on separations, sometimes called "back-etching," is also done where important color changes are to be made, or where several different sizes of reproductions are required.

With the indirect method of color correction, it is usually better to limit the density changes made on the separation negatives to the major corrections. Further density corrections are more easily made later on the continuous-tone positives that are made from the separations.

Where masking corrections have been used, the added density corrections (such as for local color changes) must apply to the total densities of the separation and its mask. Density can then be added or subtracted from either the separation or mask, or from both, depending on which is easiest to do.

Procedure for Subtracting Density. Here we list the many steps taken in the subtracting of density. The reader can find their detailed discussion in the already mentioned GATF Skilled Craft Text #510/11, *Tone and Color Correcting for Offset Lithography,* by Bernard R. Halpern, P.115-118. First, the overall density range of the separations is checked. Then the density scale relationship to dot size value is established. Finally the required density for the first control area that will produce the desired color value is determined. Then determine the required density in all the other control areas that have been charted.

Next, decide whether local or general density reduction is needed. If the entire subject has excess density, flat-etching can be applied until the area with the least density difference is brought into line. If some density areas are already low or correct in value, these will be staged-out so that the excessive density areas can be reduced to the desired values. The treatment with Farmer's reducer is applied in several stages until all areas are reduced in density to agree with the charted density values. This is repeated for the other separations. Washing and drying are the final steps in the process.

Subtracting Density by Scraping. Following density reduction with Farmer's reducer, study the separation carefully, comparing it with the copy, to see if important fine detail in the highlights and elsewhere has been subdued by the etching. If the highlight detail contrast is partly obscured, or if the shadow outlines are veiled, proceed to clean them out with a scraper. Do not try to remove too much at each stroke. When sufficient density is removed to provide the highlight contrast or shadow detail outlining

required, proceed with the next area. After all areas have been cleaned out, dust off scrapings with a wide camel's hair brush.

ADDING DENSITY TO SEPARATIONS

Our discussion of adding density to separations is divided into the following three points: (1) General exposition of adding density; (2) Procedure for adding density; and (3) Adding detail density. Each of these points is now discussed.

General Exposition of Adding Density. When all density reduction operations have been completed, study the first separation again. Compare it with the chart. Use the densitometer again to check areas that require an increase in density. Mark these areas on the chart, preferably with a red pencil, noting the density values that are needed.

Density can be added by use of neutral gray or red dyes, pencil, graphite and stump, or opaque. If areas are to be made denser, dyes should be applied by artist's brush or airbrush. If outline detail or highlight points are to be intensified, a pencil or a fine artist's brush with dye or opaque is used.

Procedure for Adding Density. After preparing the dye solution and adjusting it to the proper concentration the required density is slowly built up by repeated application of light washes of the dye, blotting with damp cotton and by checking the increase in density. Apply the dye to blend gradually with the work detail. The gray scale on the negative can serve as an approximate guide in checking the density obtained.

After the first area in work is built up to the required density, the other areas are treated in the same manner. If the dye application increases the density beyond that needed, some of the density can be removed by wiping the surface lightly with a tuft of cotton that is dampened with the solvent. This may be water or alcohol, depending on the solvent required for the dye in use.

Adding Detail Density. Density additions to detail such as may be needed to add texture contrast or highlight points, or to retouch negative defects, cannot easily be measured. Their areas are too small to read with a densitometer. The color etcher must judge such additions by visual comparison with the gray scale. Brilliant highlight points may be completely opaque, but all other added density for texture contrast will be in various densities of gray. Prepare the diluted grays. Then place opaque, spotting brushes, crowquill pen in holder, wiping tissue and other materials needed on the table or stand where they will be convenient. A magnifier on an extension arm stand or a spectacle magnifier is helpful for applying grays or opaque to fine detail in the approximate density values needed.

DENSITY CORRECTIONS IN POSITIVES

Our discussion of density corrections in positives is divided into the following three points: (1) General exposition of density corrections in positives; (2) Procedures for density corrections in positives; and (3) Finishing and checking the work. Each of these points is now discussed.

General Exposition of Density Corrections in Positives. The indirect method of color correction, where continuous-tone positives are made from the separation negatives and the final halftone negative printers are made from these positives, usually requires much of the density corrections to be applied to the positives.

The correction of positives is easier to master as density increases are *directly* related to the increase of the printing color needed. The subtraction and addition of density to continuous-tone positives require the same techniques as are used in making such corrections on continuous-tone separation negatives, except that the density values will be reversed.

Procedures for Density Correction in Positives. The first step is to prepare a chart of halftone printing values required for each important color area in which color is to be held. Then this chart is marked with the related positive density values required to produce the correspond-

ing dot size. For removal of density as well as for addition of density the same techniques are used on positives as were previously described for negatives in this section.

Finishing and Checking the Work. After all required changes in density values have been made to the point where the remaining color corrections needed can be more easily completed by dot-etching, check the work done. Re-calculate and re-check several important color areas as well as color change areas. Then prepare a chart or note for the process cameraman to inform him what dot sizes are required on the halftone printers. Show these in two or more important color areas or for specific density steps on the gray scale. Try to extend this across a maximum range of important densities.

The dot size requested must allow for any final dot-etching planned for the halftone negatives. Where the halftone negatives are later to be contact printed to provide positives, the negatives will be laterally reversed.

Section Five: Dot-Etching

Dot-etching for color correction consists of reducing the dot sizes of the halftone printers to provide the printing values desired. Dot-etching is generally done on halftone positives. This accords with the deep-etch platemaking process where halftone positives are required. For surface or other plates where halftone negatives must be used, they are usually prepared by contact from reversed halftone positives after corrections have been made by dot-etching. Positives agree in dot size to printing value and so are easier to correct.

Our subject is discussed under the following eleven headings: (1) Suitability for dot-etching; (2) Charting a color value; (3) Dot size and integrated density; (4) Flat-etching; (5) Staging and etching; (6) Local reduction; (7) Blending; (8) Intensification; (9) Retouching and adding detail; (10) Checking the progress of correcting; and (11) Negative color printers. Each of these points is here discussed in full detail.

SUITABILITY FOR DOT-ETCHING

To permit any etching whatsoever, the entire halftone dot must have a density greater than .80 over its entire effective dot size, if it is not to print through in platemaking. This corresponds to holding a solid 6 on the GATF Sensitivity Guide in platemaking. This dot density can only be measured with a micro-densitometer. Such an instrument is not normally available to the color etcher.

Comparing Dot Density. An approximate indication of the dot density can be obtained by direct comparison of the dots with a continuous-tone gray scale on film, as seen under a good microscope. The more a dot is to be reduced in size, the greater its central density must be. The normal camera halftone dot increases in density towards its center. Dot-etching dissolves the silver off the top as well as the sides of the dot in reducing its size.

Different Types of Halftone Screens Produce Different Dots. A halftone dot made through a glass screen may be prepared with one or more exposures. Usually a "flash" exposure is added to produce a hard central core. A glass screen dot has a relatively steep density gradient from the core to the dot margin. A halftone dot made with a contact screen is usually softer. The density

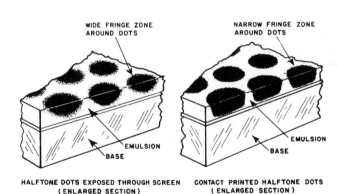

Halftone Dots. Camera and Contact.

gradient between its center and margin is much less. Consequently halftone dots prepared with the ruled glass screen are usually capable of greater size reduction by dot-etching.

Dot Size Reduction. Reductions as great as 40 percent to 50 percent of dot size would be necessary for some color printers such as in the yellow, if masking corrections or back-etching have not been applied to the separations. Extensive dot-etching could also be needed for some specified color changes from the copy if compensations have been omitted in the masked separations. However, in most work where masking has been used, the dot size reduction will seldom reach 40 percent. A good contact screen halftone is then also satisfactory for dot-etching.

Making Duplicate Positives by Contact Printing. If the corrected dots, after dot-etching has been completed, have an insufficient density so that doubtful printing values will result, it is best to duplicate the positives by contact printing. Halftone positives, that are duplicated by contact printing, have a very dense dot structure with a very narrow fringe border. They are preferred in platemaking as their dot size or color values are less altered by exposure or other variations in platemaking.

Halftone positives made by contact printing have too dense a dot structure to be suitable for further important corrections by dot-etching. This dense structure will seldom permit more than a 10 percent to 15 percent further reduction without destroying the central density of the dot itself.

CHARTING A COLOR VALUE

In the preceding section we discussed the subject of charting density and dot values in general; here you find specific step-by-step information on procedure.

Preparatory Steps for Charting Color Values. Obtain an outline chart or use an overlay sheet on the copy on which to chart the required color combination values. Select the first principal area on the color copy. Use spotting cards and the specified illumination for color matching. Locate the color block on the chart that closely matches this

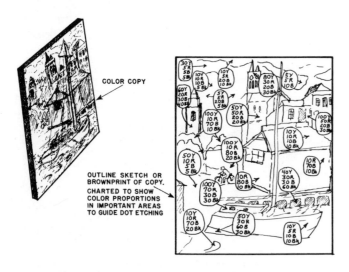

Charting Color Proportions for Dot-Etching.

area. Note on a scratch pad the percentages of color required to print this color. Allow for differences if an exact match is not obtained. If one or more of the inks were non-standard, note also the color composition of each. If an allowance is to be made for wet printing, refer to the chart for proportional dot-size reduction to be allowed for each color.

Color Sequence. Color density gain is greatest for the first printed color and least for the last. If black is to be used to replace a portion of the gray component produced by the three colors in this area, note the percentage of black to be used.

Special Considerations. Finally, note any special allowances to be made for overprint varnish, tinted stock, color overprints, or plastic laminates.

Calculating Color Percentages. Then calculate the percentages of each color required in this area. This will require starting with the three-process color dot-size values of the color block on the chart that matches the copy area. Subtract from each color (where non-standard inks are used) the proportion of this color contained in the other color inks to be printed in this area. Then subtract the proportion of color to be carried by the black. If wet printing is to be used, the net dot size is further reduced to allow for gain on the press.

Noting Color Values in Code Form. Write this final set of color values in the circle for the first principal area: Y stands for yellow, M for magenta, C for cyan, BK for black. A coded notation of the required color values may read, for example: Y-80, M-30, C-20, BK-10; it may also be expressed in figures alone in the following form; 8321.

Repeat this for all the other important color areas on the copy until the entire job has been charted.

DOT SIZE AND INTEGRATED DENSITY

Dot-size measurements can be made either by direct comparison with a halftone gray scale or by use of a densitometer A halftone gray scale for dot-size measurements can be prepared on the process camera by exposing a calibrated ten-step gray scale onto film so that the steps range in dot size from a pinpoint dot to a pinpoint opening with a 50 percent dot in the center step.

Dot-Size Measurement by Comparison. For accuracy the halftone scale should be prepared by contact printing from the camera scale so it will have opaque dot formation. The steps are then numbered as to their dot size. Dot-size measurement can be made with this scale by direct comparison under a high-powered magnifier.

The Extinction Method of Dot Measuring. The extinction method can also be used to select the step that just blanks out the space between a set of dots. The scale must be rotated to the same screen angle as the halftone for taking dot-size readings.

Densitometric Measurements of Integrated Dot Density. Densitometer measurements of integrated dot density are more accurate for contact halftones than for camera halftones. Camera halftones may transmit less or more light due to the wider fringe areas on the halftone dots and the lower dot density. This is particularly noticeable in the highlight areas on positives. However, this condition will be fairly uniform in any particular plant. A dot-size-to-density-value chart can be prepared for use with the densitometer that is based on integrated light transmission through a halftone area.

FLAT-ETCHING

If the halftone positives have a slight general fog, particularly in the shadow areas, or if the highlight dots are generally too large and the shadow dots are almost closed up, an overall etch in Farmer's reducer will be helpful. Farmer's reducer should be mixed just before use. It is self-exhausting and its activity declines rapidly after mixing.

Technique of Flat-Etching. First paint out half the length of the halftone gray scale with staging asphaltum or lacquer to provide a record of the amount of etching done. Dry thoroughly. Then immerse the positive in a tray of water containing a few drops of a wetting agent (at about 70°F) for about one or two minutes. This softens the emulsion and aids in uniform penetration of the etch.

Pour out the water, and pour in sufficient Farmer's reducer to completely cover the positive. Rock the tray in alternate directions or swab lightly with a tuft of cotton. Every 15 or 20 seconds remove the positive, flush with water and examine under a magnifier.

When the etching has proceeded far enough, immerse the positive in a tray of running water for about three to five minutes. Remove it and dry. Overall etching may be used to reduce the printing density of the black printer if exposed too full on the camera.

As the smaller or highlight dots reduce more quickly, there will be a slight increase of overall contrast as the flat-etching proceeds.

STAGING AND ETCHING

Dot-size reduction by staging is carried out in trays with the etching confined to specific areas. The procedure is as follows:

Preparations for Staging. Place the first halftone positive of the set on the light table. The positive must be thoroughly dry. Put the asphaltum varnish or staging lacquer solvents, brushes, lintless rags or wiping tissue, rule, arm board, and other materials required in a convenient position.

Planning Staging to be Done. Refer to the prepared dot size chart. Check the dot size for the first color positive in all the principal areas marked on chart. Use the film halftone scale or densitometer for the dot-size measurements. Opposite each charted dot-size value for the first color, write the percentage of dot-size reduction necessary.

Starting Staging Work. Apply the staging asphaltum or lacquer with the brush. Apply it first to the border areas around the subject. Also cover register, corner and trim marks. Leave half the length of the halftone gray scale uncovered.

Applying First Stage. Next paint out all areas where an "O" has been marked on the chart. These are areas where the dot size is correct and no etching is required. If the edges of these areas follow the borders of the subject, the staging asphaltum or lacquer can follow their outlines. (If the edges must be graduated, as in following the folds of drapes, break the sharp edge of the staging by use of a litho crayon or grease pencil so that its texture will gradually reduce the etching action towards the staged area.) Fan the asphaltum or lacquer dry.

Prepare for Etching. Place trays for Farmer's solution, hypo solution, and running water in the etching sink or on the etching stand. A translucent tray for Farmer's reducer solution is desirable. Have stock solutions ready for use. Note the minimum dot-size reduction required for the positive as noted on the chart.

Condition Positive for Etching. Place the halftone positive in water containing a few drops of wetting agent. Allow it to soak for a minute. Then transfer the positive to the etching tray.

Mixing Etch, First Etching. Mix Stock A of Farmer's reducer into the required quantity of water, and then add Stock B. Stir rapidly. Then pour the solution over the positive in the etching tray. Rock the tray gently and alternately in different directions to etch uniformly. If the first dot-size reduction is five percent, watch the highlight dots and the five percent step of the halftone gray scale. These will show the etching action first. When the five percent dot is noticeably reduced in size, transfer the positive quickly to the water tray and wash it thoroughly with water. Then examine the five percent dot as well as the lightest tone areas on the positive to see if the dots are sufficiently reduced.

Checking Extent of First Etching. Examine the other areas requiring the same minimum dot-size reduction (such as five percent). Depending on their area and nature, decide whether these will be reduced to size by a further staging and partial etching, or whether this etching can be completed more easily by local brush application.

Second Staging. If the examination shows that further etching is required for the darker tone areas of the first staging, you repeat the steps outlined previously under "Applying First Stage." First dry the positive thoroughly. Then stage-out the areas that have been sufficiently etched.

NOTE: The positive must be thoroughly dry each time the staging is applied. The grease pencil or litho-crayoned edges in areas that are to be staged again should first be wiped off with a suitable solvent.

Second Etching. Etch again by repeating the steps outlined previously under "Mixing Etch, First Etching." Stop the etching every 15 or 20 seconds by dipping the positive into a tray of water for 10 to 15 seconds. Then examine the dots in the lightest of the darker areas. Check to see if they have been reduced to the desired size. If etching is insufficient, repeat the etching operation for another 15 to 20 seconds. Continue until the dots in these areas have etched down to the required size. Then wash the positive well in water and dry.

Checking Extent of Second Etching. Examine the dots under a magnifier again. Note what additional etching may be required in the shadow areas. Also check other highlight areas that originally required more reduction to see whether the second etching has brought their dot sizes close to the desired values. Check the dot size with the halftone dot size strip or the densitometer.

Third Staging. Again paint in all areas that have been etched sufficiently. Also those that can be finished up more easily by local etching with the brush after the staging operations are completed. Blend-off hard edges where necessary.

Sub-Staging. Refer to the chart again. If the next stage is 5 percent or less, it can be worked as in first etching. If the next stage calls for a ten percent or greater dot reduction, it is best to work it in three or more sub-stagings. In each sub-stage, work in the bordering edges slightly to graduate the edges to the staged areas, so that noticeable density changes along the etched margins will be avoided.

Etching and Staging to Final Values. Repeat the etching, staging, and inspection until the entire positive has been fully etched to provide dot sizes indicated by the chart.

Removing Staging. Strip or wash off staging lacquer or asphaltum varnish with a solvent. When using a solvent, wipe off the surface of the positive at least four or more times, after the staging has been removed. Use clean solvent and tissues each time to be certain that all lacquer or asphaltum has been wiped away. Remaining traces of the staging resist will interfere with subsequent local etching or corrections.

Checking for Satisfactory Etching. If the staging and etching operations have completed all necessary dot-etching, and corrections and local etching are not required, wash the positive thoroughly and dry. Check the highlight dots under a high-powered magnifier to see if they are still sufficiently opaque for platemaking. If they are not, then request a duplicate contact positive to be made from the etched positive. Check to see that the duplicate positive retains the same dot-size values that were obtained by the etching corrections.

LOCAL REDUCTION

For finishing corrections after staging, or where further local dot-etching is required, Farmer's reducer can be applied with an artist's etching brush. Small quantities of the solution can be mixed every 15 or 20 minutes as the work progresses. For extensive small etching corrections, some color etchers prefer to keep Stock Solutions A and B in separate containers as the mixed solution rapidly loses its strength.

When used separately, the hypo solution is first applied to the area to be etched with a brush. The excess is blotted off. Another brush is then dipped lightly in the ferricyanide solution (Stock A diluted down in eight parts of water). The excess solution is wiped off the brush, and the brush then applied to the area to be etched. Work the etch from the central uniform color area outward, gradually enlarging the etched area so that no etched outlines will show. Every 15 or 20 seconds, stop the etching action with a swab of cotton wetted with water.

Whether Farmer's reducer is mixed or used in separate parts, the action is approximately the same. Examine the dots under a magnifier between each etching cycle, or use the densitometer for measurement. Continue the etching cycle until the desired dot size has been obtained. When all the local reductions have been completed, wash the positive in running water for at least five minutes. Then dry.

BLENDING

Large displays, pictorial subjects, or posters are sometimes split up into two or more joining sections, when limited by the size of the camera, the halftone screen, or by the size of the negative-holders used on the photocomposing machine. These sections are later recombined during stripping or platemaking. In reconstructing the subject, the joining edges must blend together so that the finished reproduction will not show the joining line. The satisfactory recombination requires careful consideration of the following points.

Size Agreement. Exact register must be held between sections. Additional center and fine register marks are usually placed on the copy before the separations are made. If the subject is to be recombined by stripping, these marks are located along the margins adjacent to the dividing line. If the photocomposing machine is to be used, the marks must be located along the centerlines of the split portions, so that they will be centered on the individual negatives or positives in photography. When intended for stripfilm, the marks may also be within the subject, along the joining line. When so used, they are kept small and located in inconspicuous variegated color areas. They are later retouched out by the stripper or platemaker after they have served their purpose for registration of the adjoining portions.

Register marks must be clearly visible to the stripper or platemaker. When exposing halftones on the camera, the marks are broken up by the screen pattern and are spread out in area. Whenever possible, the cameraman should double-expose the marks in position on the camera, so that they will appear as line instead of halftone marks. Otherwise it may be necessary to re-work the halftone marks to permit accurate registration. When re-working register and centermarks, it is advisable to allow portions of the original screened marks to remain, so that the accuracy of the rules or scribed marks can be checked.

Matching of Detail. Subject detail must fit together along the joining edges. An out-of-square camera will distort the image on the negatives or positives. Separate exposures of the sections of the copy will not provide matching detail along the joining edges. This condition can be checked by placing the positives over each other, or by double-printing the negatives down on brownprint paper. The photographer can sometimes compensate for such distortion when exposing the halftones, by reversing the original heads-up or heads-down placement of the copy on the copyboard or on the transparency-holder. He should then have his camera squared-up for later jobs.

Uniform Density Values. Slight variations in tone or color values will show up prominently when flat tint color areas extend across both portions. Flat color areas, or similar critical color value detail on adjacent sections, will require very close tolerances in holding the exact printing dot size across the joint. The use of the densitometer, and direct comparison of the dot sizes under a high-powered magnifier, are advisable. Halftone positives can be placed emulsion-to-emulsion for dot size study under the microscope, so that the adjoining dots will both be in focus.

Invisible Joint. The joining line of each section of the color printers should follow detail borders if at all possible. The joining line should also be displaced irregularly between the individual halftones in the color set, so that they will be diffused between the different colors and will not coincide in printing.

Blending Procedure. Before the halftone printers are made, make certain that the adjoining sections of the continuous-tone separations are identical in density and contrast range so that the dot size along the adjoining edges and the color values throughout the subject will be in balance with each other. When the halftones printers are received, study them carefully under a magnifier or with the densitometer to make certain that the balanced relationship has been retained.

When preparing the dot size chart of important color areas, include additional control areas for any color combination that extends across both sections. Then make a note of the actual dot size on these areas on each of the adjoining halftone printers for the first color in work. This will show whether one section is consistently fuller than the other, so that flat-etching can be applied, or whether the dot-size difference varies along the joint and necessitates local corrections.

If flat-etching is indicated, check the other important color control areas on the slightly fuller printing section to determine whether flat-etching is also required in these areas. If the dot-size values in the other important color areas are correct, then the blending must be confined to the areas along the joint. The boundaries of subject detail are the preferred limit of such blending. Otherwise a gradual blending of tone values will be necessary. This blending should extend over a sufficient width so as not to be readily noticeable. In such blending, it will be necessary to repeat the operations in the other color printers, so that the color proportions will remain consistent between them. Normal dot-etching techniques are used. As the tolerances for dot size are very close, it is better to dilute the etch further so as to slow its action, and thereby prevent over-etching.

INTENSIFICATION

Intensification of halftone positives has limited usefulness. Dot size can be increased a few percent by intensifying the fringe area. Once the dots are intensified they are not as suitable for later dot-etching. Where dots are weak, and may print through in platemaking, intensification may help if the lack of density is only slight, and the dots are sharply defined. Otherwise it is better to duplicate the positive by contact-printing methods, particularly where the subject size is small; where color values are not too critical; and where the halftones are on film. With large glass positives, and where a small amount of local intensification is desired to increase color printing value, chemical intensification can be used. The positive must be thoroughly washed, before intensification, if stains are to be avoided.

For intensification, commercial dot size intensifiers are available through suppliers. Immerse the halftone positive in a tray of intensifier or apply the solution locally with an inorganic plastic-fiber etching brush. Do not use hair brushes or cotton swabs. Circulate the solution over the area until sufficient intensification has been obtained. Then flush the positive with water and place it in a tray of 25 percent hypo solution for two or three minutes. Rock the tray to circulate the solution. Intensification should not be carried on in direct sunlight. The intensifier solution will stain the hands. Film tongs or rubber gloves should be used for handling the positives.

Intensification by Local Staining. Some increase of the apparent dot size is sometimes obtained by local staining with light washes of dye. This means is not desirable. Dyes tend to concentrate around the dot so as to hold back the light during exposure in platemaking. In this way the reduced exposure light intensity will print a larger dot due to the extended effective zone of the fringe area. Some dye will also remain between the dots, to under-exposure these areas during platemaking.

Airbrush Spatter Techniques. Dot value Intensification can be obtained by spatter technique with an airbrush. The nozzle and distance are adjusted so that fine droplets are produced instead of a spray. This is tested first on a clear film. When satisfactory opaque droplets are produced, that have a diameter approximating the pinpoint highlight dots on the positive, the color etcher can apply them to the areas needing intensification. He can control the airbrush to apply the random droplets in direct ratio to the increase in printing value required as well as to smoothly blend-off subject contours. The densitometer can be used to check total printing value. The use of spatter technique is limited to last-minute corrections of halftone printers. The resulting dots are printable in platemaking and on the press, but as they are irregular, and sometimes very small, there is more difficulty in holding their values through the press run.

Local Photographic Intensification. Local photographic area intensification can sometimes be provided by the cameraman through dodging methods, particulary when large areas are involved. Such dodging is best made on continuous-tone conversions from negative to positive. Once the halftones are made, the dodging method can still be used, but to a much lesser degree. When making duplicate positives through an intermediate contact negative, the use of dodging methods, during the exposure of the intermediate, can hold back some of the light in the required areas, so that the fringe areas of the dots will add their value to the dot sizes. The intermediate halftone negative is then printed down by contact to produce the contact positive needed for platemaking.

RETOUCHING AND ADDING DETAIL

Finishing operations on halftone positives may require adding line detail as well as halftone dots. This may be needed to emphasize subject outlines, or to correct photographic defects. The artist's brush, ruling pen, crowquill pen, needles, opaque, and a high-powered magnifier are usually required.

Adding Line Detail. Line detail, such as ship's rigging, machinery component outlines, type matter, or the product being merchandised, can be retouched on the appropriate color printer with pen or brush where such outlines or areas can print as solids. Opaque is usually used, slightly thinned down, so that it will flow freely from the pen or brush, and yet leave an opaque deposit on the emulsion. Where less than solid printing values are required, or where some dots are missing because of photographic defects, the crowquill pen, with slightly thinned down opaque, can also be used. Work under a high-powered magnifier. First test the pen on a clear piece of film, and when the correct size dots are produced, apply the pen immediately to the area in work. Match the dot spacing and pattern, so that the retouching blends inconspicuously into the subject.

Adding Halftone Detail. Halftone detail can be added with greater accuracy with a needle than with the crowquill pen, but errors in such work are more difficult to correct as the emulsion is engraved. Skill should be acquired on waste positives before working the needle on a job. In the highlight and under 25 percent areas, a sharp pointed round needle (or one with the point slightly stoned-off flat to increase dot size) is used to prick through the emulsion.

Work under a high-powered magnifier. Follow the dot pattern for spacing and size in agreement with the printing values desired. Then rub in black litho crayon, and wipe the surface clean with the finger or preferably with a clean tissue or cotton to remove the excess of crayon. For values larger than a 25 percent tint, apply a thin coating of black (colloidal graphite) opaque to the area. In the areas where disconnected dots having less than 50 percent value are required, use a needle sharpened for ruling lines in negatives. Rule through the opaque in agreement with the screen angle, so as to produce dots that have the same area (even if not the same shape) as the adjoining dots they are to match.

For printing values of 50 percent or greater, the ruling needle, or the square needle, sharpened diagonally to provide a triangular point is used. For these values, a flake of opaque with some of the underlying emulsion is removed for each dot to be formed. Follow dot line and spacing along a straight edge. Dig the cutting edge slightly into the emulsion where the dot is to begin, and lift out where the dot is to end.

Random Stippling. Random stippling with pen and opaque, or scraping with a needle is sometimes used for fast work. Much depends on the skill of the color etcher to provide a uniform-appearing tint to the unaided eye. The color etcher should retouch and correct dot-by-dot under a high-powered magnifier where good workmanship is required. Carefully worked dot corrections are necessary to prevent such retouching from showing up on the press after the run gets under way.

CHECKING THE PROGRESS OF CORRECTING

Proof plates should be made and progressive proofs pulled as each corrected halftone color printer is completed.

Don't wait for the set. In this way, color errors that develop may sometimes be compensated for in the later color printers. Where possible, the defective halftone should be corrected before the balance of the progressive proofs are printed, and a new proof made. In this way, the complete re-proofing of the job can be avoided. Any color errors noted should be checked immediately to learn whether any of the control equipment, charts, inks or variations in proofing are at fault. In this way their recurrence can be prevented.

Photographic color proofing methods are sometimes used to check the progress of dot-etching corrections. Since their color values do not agree with printing ink values, their color combinations must be interpreted so as to avoid errors in color judgment. These newer color proofing methods are available in a wide range of materials, techniques and processes. Each has its advantage in some type of color procedure. Learning to handle them properly can lead to much saving of labor as well as improved quality. One important key to their use is proper evaluation. This is easily mastered with some attention and experience.

Finishing a Set of Color Printers. Bordering, opaquing, emphasizing register marks, introducing trim or fold marks, stripping in type matter, and adding job number and other identification markings are necessary to complete the set of color printers. In many plants this work is assigned to the stripping department. Because of job load division, or for other reasons, part or all of these finishing operations may be assigned to the color etcher. Details are given in the GATF Skilled Craft Text #512, Color Stripping.

Additional Corrections Before Platemaking. Before releasing the set of color printers for platemaking, certain additional corrections may be necessary. These may be indicated by the progressive proofs themselves, or the customer's markings on the color proofs. Where such corrections are minor, they can usually be made without re-proofing. The color etcher must then doubly check such corrections to be sure they will provide the right color printing values or other details. Otherwise costly press-plate makeovers, lost press-time, and wasted paper stock may result.

Re-Checking the Color Printers in the Absence of Proofing. Where proofing facilities are not available in the plant, the color etcher should re-check each color printer. Repeat the process of selecting the important color areas on the color copy, re-evaluating them for dot size by comparison with the color chart, and re-calculate any necessary dot-size allowances. The color etcher should then check the computed dot sizes with the corresponding dot-size values on the color printers.

Here, too, the gray balance proportions, that were removed from each color printer and added to the black printer, should also be checked to make certain that all compensations in each printer have been completed. The additional time that is spent in re-calculating and checking the color values, before releasing the set of printers, is small when compared with the possible added costs and lost time that result when some serious error is discovered after the job has gone to press.

NEGATIVE COLOR PRINTERS

Negative halftone color printers are required for surface plates; some types of bimetallic plates; or where the positive color printer is to be prepared by contact from the halftone negative. In low-cost color reproduction, the separation negatives are screened directly during photography, so that they can be used for platemaking of surface plates. The color correction procedure for halftone positives that is covered in this chapter also applies to corrections on halftone negatives. Where an intermediate continuous-tone positive is made from the color-separation negatives, most of the corrections will be made in the density values of the positives. The same techniques are used as were applied to continuous-tone negatives except that the density values will be reversed.

The Quality of Dot-Etched Negatives. The halftone negatives that are made from the corrected continuous-tone positives are finished by using dot-etching methods as described in this chapter. The dot-size values will be inverted as will the allowances made for color value gain on the press. The shadow areas will usually carry an opaque ten percent or slightly larger dot that will not fill up in printing. The highlight pinpoint dots must be completely transparent when viewed with a high-powered magnifier against a diffused white light source. Any fog or extended dot fringe area can result in these dots going blind in platemaking or on the press. Brilliant highlight points can be opaqued-out by artist's brush or pen, so that only pinpoint dots of the principal reflected color will print in these locations.

Color Combination Charts for Negatives. The color combination charts that are used for charting and dot-etching negative halftone printers should be prepared by using the platemaking method and inks that are scheduled for the job. GATF masters for preparing color combination charts are available as either positives or negatives. Where both surface plate and deep-etch plate methods are in use for color process jobs, separate charts should be prepared. Printing dot sizes will be inverted from those obtained on the halftone negative.

Color Correcting on Direct Negatives. Where direct halftone negative separations are supplied for low-cost color reproductions, work by the color etcher may not be required, or it may be limited to approximately correcting one or two principal color areas. Fast working techniques, using the artist's brush and Farmer's reducer to open up areas for increased dot size, or the use of dye, crayon, or splatter tints to add density and reduce printing dot size, may be applied. The dot structure in direct halftone separations is frequently soft with a wider fringe zone than on other process halftone jobs. This results from the use of faster negative emulsions that are required for making the separations. The dots will etch faster and they cannot be reduced as much in size. They are far more critical to exposure time and other conditions in platemaking. The GATF Sensitivity Guide must be used with such negatives to control the required color printing values.

Checking Contact-Printed Negatives. When the negative halftone printers are made as photographic contacts from color-corrected halftone positives, the color etcher must check the dot-size values in all principal color areas. Variations during contact printing exposure and development can change the printing dot-size values just as it does in platemaking. This is particularly important in the highlight areas.

Section Six: Manual Color Separation Techniques

In this section we discuss some of the commonly used manual color-separation techniques. Our presentation is divided into the following four points: (1) Key-line jobs; (2) Pre-separated film-pack transparencies; (3) Fake-color separations from black-and-white photographs; and (4) Duo-tones. Each of these subjects is briefly presented in the following. A more extensive treatment of these subjects can be found in the GATF Skilled Craft Text #510/11, *Tone and Color Correcting for Offset Lithography,* by Bernard R. Halpern.

KEY-LINE JOBS

Non-process color reproductions, such as are used for the preparation of maps and fake-color work, represent a simple separation and combination of color printings. The colors are usually printed as solids or as uniform area tint values. Color combinations are obtained the same as in process-color work, by proportioning the dot-size values for each color of printing ink. Our discussion of key-line jobs is divided into the following four main points: (1) Color-separation drawings; (2) Charting the key-line separations; (3) Making the individual separations; and (4) Making the final separation negatives and their treatment.

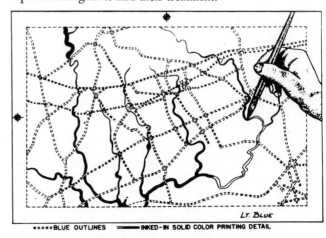

LT. BLUE

= = = = BLUE OUTLINES   ——— INKED-IN SOLID COLOR PRINTING DETAIL

Inking-in Blue Board for Light Blue Plate.

Color-Separation Drawings. The copy furnished for most map work and for simple color jobs such as for labels, posters and displays, usually consists of a black-and-white key outline drawing. The required colors are either marked on an overlay sheet, or shown on an accompanying sketch. When the color etcher is required to prepare the separation drawings, he must obtain a set of identical blueline prints. These blueline prints are made by first preparing a line negative from the key outline drawing.

Each of the blueline prints is then marked for one of the printing ink colors. The first of these color drawings is then inked in wherever the color is to print. Solid color areas are inked in solid with india ink or covered with red acetate overlays. If the color tints all have a common value, such as a 25 percent blue, a separate drawing will be inked in solid or covered with red overlays wherever these tints are to appear. A variety of different tint values may be necessary in a printing color, such as in fake-color work, so as to build up different color combinations in various areas on the job. These tint values are added to the same drawing on which the solid color areas were filled in with india ink.

The percentage values of the tint sheets correspond to dot-size values. The tint values can be printed down with ink into masked areas using Ben Day screens. More commonly, the tint sheets are procured through supply houses as a thin cellophane or plastic sheet with uniform rated tint values printed on them, such as 10 percent, 25 percent, and 50 percent. These sheets are backed with a pressure-sensitive adhesive so that they can be attached directly to the drawing. The fineness of the texture is chosen so that the printed tint values in the final size of the color reproduction will be similar to the halftone screen rulings that would be used.

Charting the Key-Line Separations. Chart the colors to be obtained for the job in terms of percentages of ink-color values. Study the colors on the sketch, swatches, color notation system, previously printed job, or whatever material is furnished to identify the required colors. If the inks to be used for printing the job are the standard process-inks used in preparing the color chart, the dot-size values on the chart will be used. If the inks differ in hue or value, a printed color sample of the ink should first be compared with the color chart to determine its color composition. The color values of the ink will then be divided between the printing values of the process-inks as obtained from the chart.

Making the Individual Separations. The making of the individual separations includes a variety of steps such as the inking in of borders and reference marks, as well as of solid areas; the selecting of the tint values; the preparing of the tint sheets; the setting of the screen angle; the applying and adhering of the tint sheets; and the trimming of the sheets to the required outline.

Making the Final Separation Negatives and Their Treatment. When the color-separation drawings are completed, the process photographer will prepare a line negative from each drawing. The color etcher will retouch these negatives where tint sheet cut-marks or other defects

may print. These negatives can be slightly modified in dot-size values by dot-etching techniques if necessary. Camera exposures from line copy usually provide a slight vignetted density edge around the printing detail. Such vignetted detail permits some size reduction by dot-etching.

Dot-etching on the line negatives may also be desired for a gradual increase of tint values. Any such work on one color printer must be duplicated on the other color printers to keep the color hue in balance. If a wider latitude for dot-etching is desired, as for modeling curved surfaces, the photographer can usually provide a more suitable variable density dot.

PRE-SEPARATED FILM-PACK TRANSPARENCIES

Pre-separated color transparencies are sometimes furnished for reproduction. They consist of a set of three or more colored films on a clear base that are fitted to each other through register marks or perforated holes. The printing design on each film is prepared in a single color. This colored design may be obtained through photographic dye-coupling methods, or be applied as hand-drawn artwork. Color changes can be made by the removal of color or the addition of similar dyes or transparent inks.

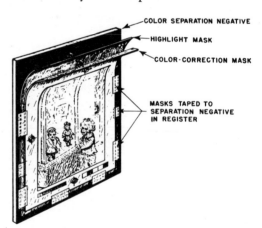

COLOR SEPARATION NEGATIVE
HIGHLIGHT MASK
COLOR-CORRECTION MASK

MASKS TAPED TO
SEPARATION NEGATIVE
IN REGISTER

Masked Separation Assembly.

Pre-separated color transparencies, prepared with colors to match the printing inks for the job, will require little masking or color etching. If the colors on the overlay films do not match the ink colors to be used, the photographer can prepare compensating masks when making the separations. If masks are not prepared, the color etcher should regard the color pack as full-color copy. He will then chart the color proportions for the inks in each important color area. Color correction will consist of normal density compensations by back-etching or additions on the separations, and by dot-etching on the halftone printers.

FAKE-COLOR SEPARATIONS FROM BLACK-AND-WHITE PHOTOGRAPHS

A black-and-white photographic print may be furnished as "color" copy, accompanied with a sketch or instructions as to the colors desired. Most of the color values must be obtained by extensive density changes on continuous-tone "separation" negatives or positives. Back-etching is usually preferred instead of adding density, especially where considerable detail is involved. The negatives, therefore, will usually be shot higher to allow for density reduction. Such reduction of density must be controlled through density measurements so that the final halftone printers made from them will provide the correct color proportions needed to fake the colors that are required. Most of the outline detail will be carried in the black printer.

Our very condensed discussion of the procedure is restricted to the following seven main points: (1) Selecting color values; (2) Charting color values; (3) Relating color values to densities; (4) Reducing density; (5) Etching highlight areas; (6) Adding density; and (7) Finishing. Each of these steps is now individually described, if ever so briefly.

Selecting Color Values. Refer to the accompanying dummy color sketch or instructions for color values desired. If the sketch or instructions are vague, obtain some other color copy that has similar subject matter so that color values can be approximated from it. Study the photoprint for clues as to color tones.

Charting Color Values. Use the ink color combination chart, preferably prepared with the standard process-inks and the paper stock used in the plant. Based on the color sketch, or other considerations, select a color square on the chart that will provide the required color combination. Then mark the color proportions in the selected areas using the color code in *"Charting a Color Value,"* Section Five of this chapter.

Relating Color Values to Densities. Refer to our "Continuous-tone density and dot-size" table which charts the continuous-tone density values required to produce corresponding dot-size printing values. Select a density range than can be held on the set of negatives after the density corrections have been made. Then mark the chart of the job with the density values that are necessary to obtain the dot sizes that were circled.

Reducing Density. By either staging or local application of Farmer's reducer, reduce the density of the first area charted. Work gradually with diluted solutions so that the density reduction can be safely watched without its acting too fast. Continue until all required density reductions have been obtained.

Etching Highlight Areas. Finally study the local detail, particularly in the highlight areas (densest areas on the negative). See if contrast can be added to local detail by fine etching with the brush and Farmer's reducer.

Adding Density. Next study the areas where density must be added. This may be required in local areas where

etching has been excessive; where an increase of subject brightness requires a reduction of color; and for highlighting texture detail. Density can be added with neutral grays, with pencil, or with stump and graphite, depending on which is best suited to the work required.

DENSITY					DOT SIZE	
					POSITIVE %	NEGATIVE %
2.55	2.20	1.55	.	.	5	95
2.45	2.07	1.45	.	.	10	90
2.30	1.88	1.30	.	.	20	80
2.15	1.68	1.15	.	.	30	70
2.02	1.50	1.02	.	.	40	60
1.91	1.36	.91	.	.	50	50
1.80	1.22	.80	.	.	60	40
1.66	1.03	.66	.	.	70	30
1.48	.64	.48	.	.	80	20
1.25	.50	.25	.	.	90	10
1.10	.30	.10	.	.	95	5

Continuous-tone-Density-to-Dot-Size.

Finishing. Finish the negative by opaquing the borders. Mark the job name and printing color along one edge.

DUO-TONES

Duo-tones are two-color printing jobs. They consist of a principal darker color, and a lighter color that may be of the same or a different hue. The two colors increase the density range of the printed job; provide better detail modeling, particularly in the highlights; and add an undertone of color to the job. The principal color is usually screened at 45-degrees. The lighter color of the duo-tone is normally prepared with its screen angle displaced by 30-degrees from the principal color, either to 15-degrees or to 75-degrees.

Where possible, separation negatives are first made for duo-tones. The principal negative will be exposed and processed for normal contrast, but somewhat higher (denser) to allow for some back-etching. It will retain only outline values in the highlights. The lighter printing color separation will be exposed with the highlights more open to provide good contrast of detail, particularly in the lighter or highlight areas. The color etcher's work will be limited to adding detail contrast and further dividing printing values between the two separations to accord with their nature on the copy.

CHAPTER NINE . .

The Stripping and Photocomposing Departments—

Section One: Review of Modern Stripping Techniques

Stripping formerly referred to the removal of sections of the photographic emulsion from wet-plate or dry-plate negatives. These emulsion sections were then transferred, assembled, and adhered in position on a glass plate. The stripping of emulsions off of photographic plates was discontinued when manufactured stripping films became available.

In stripping films the photographic emulsion is applied to a thin membrane. This membrane is temporarily adhered to a heavier film or paper support. The membrane remains attached to its base for the exposure and processing of the negative. The membrane with its photographic image is removed from the base when it is stripped to a new support. Stripfilm is currently used for the more intricate jobs. This is usually limited to older established plants where personnel skilled in its handling are available.

Stripping is now commonly used to describe the methods for splicing cut films together. This serves the same purpose as a stripfilm assembly. Stripping operations include the preparation of the layout for stripping; the cutting and attachment of the films; the addition of printing controls; and the necessary corrective or supplementary

work on the films that may be needed to complete the printing detail. In popular stripping procedure, the cut films are usually attached to a supporting sheet of goldenrod paper or plastic film.

Tabs of pressure-sensitive cellophane tape are applied to hold the films in position. Such stripping with cut film sections is easier and less costly than when stripfilm is used. Cut film assemblies are also suitable for a large proportion of all lithographic stripping requirements.

In this section we first review the main kinds of stripped-up assemblies, and then discuss the subject of negatives and positives as it relates to stripping.

THE MAIN KINDS OF FLATS

The stripped-up assembly of film sections is called a flat. There are many types of flats in use. Here we present the following six kinds of commonly used flats: (1) Goldenrod flats, (2) Film flats, (3) Blueline flats, (1) Partial or sectional flats, (5) Complementary flats, and (6) Miscellaneous film assemblies.

Goldenrod Flats. These are an assembly of film negatives on a sheet of goldenrod or orange-colored paper. The goldenrod paper serves three purposes. It is used as (1) a drawing base to indicate the subject locations on the printing layout; (2) a support to hold the individual films in correct location; and (3) a mask to prevent the exposure light from reaching the non-printing areas of the press plate during platemaking.

Film Flats. Films can be joined to each other to produce a flat, without using a goldenrod or plastic supporting sheet. This can be done when the available film sections will cover the entire printing area of the press plate. Film flats may consist of assemblies of negatives or of positives. The individual films are positioned and attached to each other with strips of tape directly over a prepared layout. Holes can be punched in each film in register location in advance to permit rapid and accurate assemblies of film flats to pegboard layouts.

Stripped-up goldenrod flat.

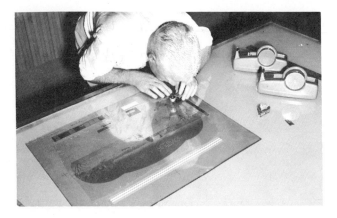

Blueline flat.

Blueline Flats. For the highest degree of stripping accuracy, with stripfilm, the film sections are attached in position to blueline images. These images are photographically printed down on a set of sensitized plate glass or plastic sheets. The prints are made from a master or key flat. This key flat consists of an assembly of films or register marks that include all the location detail needed to fit the films on each flat.

The blue image serves as a visible guide for accurately locating each film. Its blue color is transparent to the actinic exposure light used in platemaking. For this reason, the blue image does not show up on the press plate. Acetate, vinyl, and polyester plastic sheeting are also used for preparing blueline flats. The vinyl or polyester sheeting has better accuracy where plant humidity variations are experienced. Plate glass is used where the highest degree of location accuracy and register is required from a flat.

Partial or Sectional Flats. A flat may be prepared to cover only a part of the press plate. This is common

practice when printing subjects are to be duplicated by step-and-repeat methods on the press plate. Such flats are provided with marks or mechanical attachments. These positioning guides enable the platemaker to accurately step the flat across the press plate on the photocomposing machine or in the vacuum frame.

Partial flats may be stripped-up as related sets of small groupings of films. The printing detail from the several partial flats are then combined together on the photocomposing machine when making the press plate.

Complementary Flats. It is frequently desirable to divide the printing detail for a press sheet between two or more flats. This is commonly done when the printing detail consists of many small illustrations with close-fitting text.

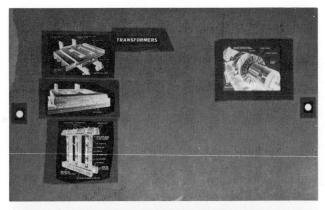

Set of complementary goldenrod flats.

In such work the films would be troublesome to splice together and could cause platemaking difficulties. The division of detail is also necessary where printing is to surprint or print over other printed matter.

The complementary flats are exposed successively in register with each other so as to combine their detail on the same sensitized press plate. Location register between the flats is obtained by adding register marks, by use of butterfly cutouts, or with the aid of plastic hole tabs attached to each flat.

If hole tabs are used, mating sheet-plastic dowels must be temporarily secured to the press plate so as to register the two flats to the same location.

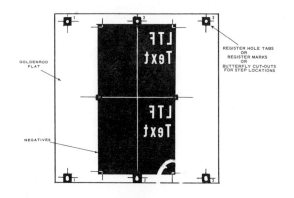

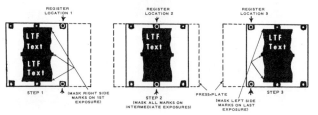

Partial flat.

Miscellaneous Film Assemblies. Stripping practices are used for combining films together when assembling transparencies as camera copy. Acetate pulls from type composition can be combined with each other or with films. This is done to eliminate camera work when no size changes are required in the text. They may be used directly as positives or be contacted if negatives are needed. Galley lengths of photocomposition on film are usually cut apart into column or paragraph sections. They are then combined with other films of running heads, borders, or display matter to obtain page make-up. Spreads, chokes, and outline characters of display type or line-color printing areas are also produced with film assemblies. Many of these practices require the use of photographic contact-printing facilities to produce the final films that will be used for stripping-up the flat.

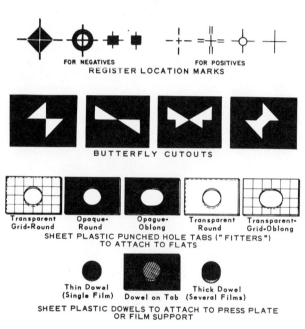

FOR NEGATIVES
REGISTER LOCATION MARKS
FOR POSITIVES

BUTTERFLY CUTOUTS

Transparent Grid-Round — Opaque-Round — Opaque-Oblong — Transparent Round — Transparent-Grid-Oblong
SHEET PLASTIC PUNCHED HOLE TABS ("FITTERS") TO ATTACH TO FLATS

Thin Dowel (Single Film) — Dowel on Tab — Thick Dowel (Several Films)
SHEET PLASTIC DOWELS TO ATTACH TO PRESS PLATE OR FILM SUPPORT

Registering aids used on flats.

NEGATIVE AND POSITIVE STRIPPING FLATS

Negatives are required for preparing flats that are to be used for making surface or albumin press plates. Positives are used when the press plate is to be made by deep-etch or reverse methods.

Surface Plates. In making a surface plate, the image is exposed through the transparent portions of the negatives. This image becomes the ink-receptive printing design. Accordingly all the printing detail in the negatives must be completely transparent. The remaining areas of the flat must then completely block out the exposure light. The blocking out is obtained from the opaque portions of the negatives. The area surrounding the work detail on each negative is then masked by cutting away portions of the goldenrod paper. The remaining paper then serves as a mask. Further detailed masking is obtained by using pressure-sensitive red or black cellophane tape, with the aid of masking foils, or by opaquing.

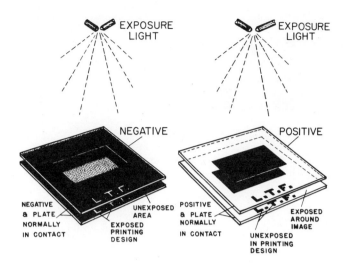

EXPOSURE LIGHT   EXPOSURE LIGHT

NEGATIVE   POSITIVE

NEGATIVE & PLATE NORMALLY IN CONTACT — UNEXPOSED AREA — EXPOSED PRINTING DESIGN

POSITIVE & PLATE NORMALLY IN CONTACT — EXPOSED AROUND IMAGE — UNEXPOSED IN PRINTING DESIGN

Schematic comparison of surface and deep-etch platemaking.

Deep-Etch Plates. When making deep-etch or other reverse plates with the use of positives, the areas that surround the printing detail are exposed in platemaking. Development dissolves away the unexposed image detail and so uncovers the metal surface of the intended printing areas. The remaining exposed and insoluble coating then serves as a temporary stencil resist for etching. The uncovered metal printing areas are next treated to make them ink-receptive.

Positive Flats Are Very Critical. Positive flats that are used for making deep-etch plates must consist of opaque printing design areas on a completely transparent support. Any foreign material, stains, deep scratches, or cut edges on a positive flat that cause shadows during platemaking exposure, can introduce printing defects. Some such edge shadows are unavoidable and must be staged-out by the platemaker to prevent their printing. The edge effects can also be eliminated by double exposing the press plate with a mask flat. A second exposure made with the mask flat will "burn-in" the defective markings between film sections and unwanted detail. Positive films are stripped by attaching them together or to a transparent plastic or glass base with

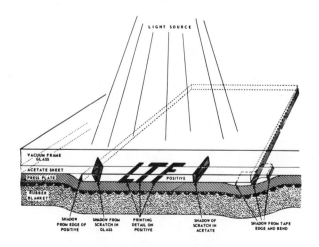

LIGHT SOURCE

VACUUM FRAME GLASS
ACETATE SHEET
PRESS PLATE
RUBBER BLANKET

SHADOW FROM EDGE OF POSITIVE — SHADOW FROM SCRATCH IN GLASS — PRINTING DETAIL ON POSITIVE — SHADOW OF SCRATCH IN ACETATE — SHADOW FROM TAPE EDGE AND BEND

Difficulties with positive flats.

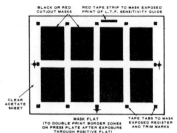
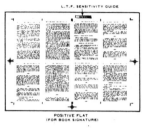

Mask flat.

tabs of transparent pressure-sensitive tape. If stripfilm is to be applied to blueline flats, a stripfilm cement is used to adhere the stripfilm membrane to the glass or plastic sheet.

Combining Positives and Negatives. Positives may be combined with negative film sections. This is done to produce reverses, such as when white display characters are required on a solid, tinted, or halftone background. Negatives and choked positives are also combined to prepare outline display characters.

Section Two: Layout and Equipment

As the stripping department is a production department, it should be arranged to facilitate production. This is more easily done in the planning stages of a new plant, or at periods when major plant expansion moves and reorganization are in progress. In some of the older plants, many of the preliminary processing departments such as camera, color correction, stripping and platemaking have been considered as secondary to the press department. They were, therefore, crowded into undesirable and limited space with poor production facilities. Even under such conditions it is possible to gradually modify and improve the efficiency of the stripping department.

The Small Stripping Department. The small stripping department is frequently required to do a variety of work that may extend into copy preparation, contact printing, proofing, and other fields. As the department increases in size, the stripping operations become more specialized. Additional operators and departments are introduced to perform the different operations.

The Large Stripping Department. In the larger plants each operation for inspection and spotting out films, preparing the layout, stripping the flat, proofreading, and checking are assigned to different individuals. The stripper is then responsible only for assembling and securing the films to the flat, and for masking between the films. Opaquing is limited to that required after the films are assembled, such as the removal of register marks or other detail that was required for stripping, but which are not to print on the press plate. The layout is prepared by a layout man, and preliminary opaquing and retouching are done on the individual films by artists before releasing them for stripping.

In this section you find a presentation of the layout and the equipment for a black-and-white as well as for a color-stripping department.

THE LAYOUT OF A STRIPPING DEPARTMENT

The layout for the stripping department depends on a variety of factors. The exact location selected, the separation between supporting columns, the plumbing facilities, windows, and the relation to adjacent departments will all influence the preferred floor plan arrangement.

In the following you find a discussion on several points essential for the efficient functioning of a stripping department. These points are: (1) Flooring, (2) Walls and ceiling, (3) Windows, (4) Lighting, (5) Ventilation, and (6) Plumbing.

Flooring. Preferably covered with linoleum, rubber, wood, or other resilient material. Concrete floors are tiring to the stripper who usually is on his feet all day. Concrete is also injurious to instruments or films that may be dropped accidentally and is a source of grit and dust.

Walls and Ceiling. These should be sealed and painted in any light color to aid in providing a clean, cheerful area.

Windows. Preferably sealed-off, if a filtered air supply is provided. Venetian blinds or other light screening shields should be used to block direct sunlight from entering.

Lighting. A uniformly distributed, relatively shadowless lighting preferably cool white in color, is essential to efficient operation. The illumination level of the room should be in balance with the internal lighting in the layout, stripping, and retouching tables. A satisfactory balance would provide about 25 to 35 foot-candles from room illumination on the table tops when the internal lighting of the tables ranges between 100 and 150 foot-candles. Doubling this by use of higher intensity lighting in the tables, ranging between 200 and 300 foot-candles, will also permit an increased room illumination level of about 40 to 60 foot-candles. This is less tiring to the eyes. If the tables have too low an intensity, such as under 75 foot-candles, it is preferable to increase their internal lighting by the addition of strips of fluorescent lamps rather than to reduce the general room illumination.

Ventilation. The best working conditions combine air filtration with humidity and temperature control. They also extend these conditions to the camera, stripping, and platemaking departments, so that all phases of copy, film, and flat handling are kept under size control. Complete control should be included in the plans for any new plant. In existing plants, the high installation costs for adding ducts, insulation, vapor seals, and for clearing existing structural members and production facilities, may dictate a gradual improvement of atmospheric conditions over a long range program, in keeping with financial considerations.

Plumbing. The black-and-white stripper has very little need for water supply in flat preparation, and a small sink can supply these requirements. If the water supply contains rust or other undissolved solids, a small filter is advantageous. If brownprints are to be made in the stripping department, then a large trough with water supply and drain are essential. In such instances the water supply should include a temperature-control water valve that is either manually or thermostatically controlled. Normal drainage facilities are usually adequate in accordance with local plumbing codes, as the limited range of chemicals used are non-corrosive and are also greatly diluted in water. Where photographic contact prints must also be made, the water supply and drain must be adequate to meet these additional requirements.

EQUIPMENT FOR STRIPPING

The equipment selected for stripping must be in keeping with the quality levels required for the class of lithographic printing normally produced. The cost of equipment in the stripping department is relatively low in relation to the labor costs, as compared to other departments. The additional investment for high-quality equipment is also relatively low, especially when this is compared to the cost of lost time that results from the breakdown, inaccuracies, and inefficiency of cheaper equipment.

In the following you find first a description of the equipment for black-and-white stripping, and then a description of the additional equipment needed for color stripping.

EQUIPMENT FOR BLACK-AND-WHITE STRIPPING

The main items of equipment for black-and-white stripping are stripping tables, layout and line-up tables, worktables, shelves, cabinets and racks. All of these are now individually discussed.

Stripping Tables. The primary function of the stripping table is to provide an illuminated working surface on which films can be positioned and stripped-up to make a flat. The working surface is a sheet of plate glass, usually grained on the underside to diffuse the internal lighting. The internal lighting usually consists of several fluorescent lamps, located to provide a fairly uniform distribution of light under the area of the glass top. Internal reflectors and diffusers may be used to help improve the uniform quality of the light.

Many stripping tables are equipped with straight-edges on two or all four sides. If these edges are machined or ground true, and adjusted to square, they permit the stripping table to serve also as a layout table, particularly where small forms are concerned. Straight-edges should be checked for accuracy, as some commercial equipment uses strips of cold rolled or formed steel for this purpose. The irregular edges of such inaccurate straight-edges can cause much trouble in positioning and alignment.

Layout and Line-Up Tables. A precision layout and line-up table is almost indispensable for the efficient and accurate preparation of layouts, and for checking the accuracy of the completed flat. Commercial line-up tables range from modified stripping tables equipped with straight-edges or steel scales, to rigidly constructed units that in-

corporate micrometer-adjustable straight-edges and that have carriages to hold scribing, ruling, and locating attachments. In selecting a line-up table, the highest level of accuracy normally encountered in stripping should be the determining factor. In specialized plants, where ruled-form or similar ruled jobs are produced, the ruling and scribing attachments available with some machines will permit this unit to serve also as a production unit. When selecting equipment having lower levels of accuracy, the straight-edges and positioning scales should be checked with a precision scale, straight-edge, and square to determine if they will be acceptable for the class of work to be done.

Worktables. A worktable should be located close to every stripping table. The worktable serves as a safe location for temporarily placing completed flats, dummy layouts, complementary flats, and other reference material. Shelves underneath the table serve to carry a working stock of goldenrod, vinyl, and other flat materials, as well as tint sheets and masking supplies. Metal, plywood, pressed-board or linoleum-topped tables are available in most large industrial centers. In remote areas, where shipping costs are important factors, such tables are usually constructed locally.

Shelves, Cabinets, and Racks. All necessary stripping supplies and tools should be accessible and placed in individually-marked compartments or hangers in which the tool outlines are painted.

Storage cabinets for completed flats can consist of horizontal shallow drawers or shelves. The flats themselves should be held in fiberboard folders. Each folder should hold from ten to twenty-five flats. The folders should be indexed with numbers that correspond to filing locations. A routine inventory system should be established to eliminate "dead" flats from cluttering up the storage facilities.

EQUIPMENT FOR MAKING PROOFS AND FOR COLOR STRIPPING

The equipment needed for black-and-white stripping is augmented by many other items when brownline or other proofs are to be made and when color stripping is to be done. To make proofs from flats, the normal platemaking units consisting of troughs, whirlers, vacuum-printing frames, and printing lamps are required. These may be duplicated in the stripping department when the normal platemaking units are already used to capacity. Color stripping on glass may necessitate carriers for glass flats, troughs for glass salvage, and storage racks for glass flats. If contacts or duplicates are to be made, a contact-printing frame with controlled exposure light and darkroom facilities are needed. Production setups may require pegboard assembly equipment. Each of these subjects is described briefly in the following.

Trough. Glass flats require thorough cleaning prior to sensitizing with the blueline coating. This is best accomplished in a trough provided with an inclined platform, drain, and flushing facilities. The platform should consist of slats, or be covered with a white vinyl or rubber-ribbed matting, to prevent suction adherence in lifting the glass. The same or a similar trough is required for making brown-lines or other proofs. If used solely for making proofs, the trough should be equipped with a tilting tray instead of slats.

Whirler. The whirler is required for sensitizing glass or vinyl blueline flats. When glass is used the whirler should be selected with a large cover opening to simplify insertion and removal of the plate glass, as well as to permit cleaning and processing of the flats in the whirler when necessary. The whirler bed must be level. When used for glass flats, the rotating bed should be provided with intermittent supports, or with a ribbed rubber or vinyl blanket, to prevent suction adherence and to permit finger space for lifting the glass. Stop pins or guards are essential for glass flats, and hold-down clips must be used on the corners of vinyl sheeting.

Vacuum-Printing Frame. The glass-side-up vacuum frame is the type preferred for proofing and duplicating from flats. It is used for the ease in handling flats and avoids scratching the glass. The glass-side-down frame is advantageous where a set of blueline flats are to be made from a key or intermediate. The key flat can be left in position on the glass in the frame for the exposure of the entire set of bluelines.

If the vacuum frame is to be used exclusively for blueline flat preparation the glass-side-down frame is the preferred unit in the color stripping department.

Printing Lamps. An arc lamp similar to that used in platemaking will be needed for exposing the blueline flats in the vacuum printing frame as well as for making proofs from flats.

Carriers for Glass Flats. Caster-mounted carriers, slightly larger than the largest glass flat and provided with wood or rubber strip for finger clearance, are desirable for movement of glass flats between departments. If constructed locally they should be provided with two fixed wheels and two caster wheels. The wheels should be rubber- or fiber-tired and at least three inches in diameter. Where subjected to rough flooring, or movement on elevators, a canvas safety strap with end clasp should be incorporated to secure the plate glass.

Trough for Glass Salvage. Where a separate department is provided for removing stripfilm and work from "dead" flats, a soaking trough is needed. This trough can be similar to that used for press plates, or improved by equipping it with a mechanically tilting or elevating tray or platform. The platform can be ribbed or dimpled or provided with glass support strips. The movable platform permits the glass flat to be successively immersed for soaking and raised out of the bath for cleaning and flushing. A standpipe drain, equipped with a large diameter screened overflow to catch stripfilm waste, is required for the trough.

Storage Racks. Large glass flats should be stored in racks with individual slots. The slot runners and base are preferably constructed of hardwood. The baseboard should extend at least six inches outside the rack to support the tail end of the glass on removal. There must be no exposed screws, nails or other possible glass-to-metal contact that may cause chipping or cracking of the glass. A small rubber-topped dolly about $\frac{1}{4}$ inch higher than the baseboard, with two fixed non-swiveling wheels and two caster wheels, will aid in storage and removal of large glass flats. The surrounding flooring should be wood, linoleum, or rubber-covered to minimize accidental glass damage.

Contact Printing Frame. The vacuum printing frame used in platemaking or for making intermediates or blueline flats can also be used for occasional photographic contact printing when necessary. However, a darkroom contact printer provides a more versatile and efficient unit and produces a better quality film. As a considerable percentage of contact printing involves exposing the image through the thickness of the film base, or simultaneouly through several films, a point source of light, such as the GATF Contact Printing Lamp, described in *GATF Research Progress No. 20,* is essential for retaining dot size and image detail. An alternate diffused light source can also be used for line work where emulsion-to-emulsion contact is obtained. The diffused source will undercut dust and other defects on the glass and so reduce the amount of opaquing needed on the contacts. All contact exposure lights should be equipped with an electrical interval timer to control the exposure. The remaining equipment needed in the contact darkroom will be the same as is used with the process camera.

Pegboard Assembly Equipment. Pegboard assemblies are usually a plant specialty. They are used for standard production work such as signatures or forms. The pegboards are constructed to meet the job specifications. The positioning pins, or pegs for locating the films may be installed in the tabletop itself where a standard layout is in continuous use. However, they are more frequently mounted in hardboard, aluminum sheets, or in sheets of heavy rigid plastic $\frac{1}{8}$ inch to $\frac{1}{4}$ inch thick. The plastic is preferred for use over a layout table as it permits inspection of the films by transmitted light. The pegs are usually $\frac{3}{16}$-inch diameter pins that are shouldered and threaded for screw installation. The register punch fixture that is used in conjunction with the pegboard perforates two or more holes along one margin of the film. These holes fit on the pin sets on the pegboard. One of the punched holes is usually round, and the other is slotted so as to allow for dimensional changes in the films.

Section Three: Tools for Stripping

Good tools contribute to efficiency and good workmanship. Tools are required to drawn upon, measure, scribe and cut films or flats. A good cutting tool that is correctly sharpened will, for example, turn out better work in less time, and with less effort than a dull or improperly sharp-ened one. Descriptions of the various tools used by the stripper follow:

Rules and Scales. These are primarily intended for measurement and not for drawing straight lines. At least one good precision steel scale should be in every stripping department. Steel or stainless steel scales with fine etched or engraved divisions are preferable. The heavily etched, printed, or plastic rules cannot be relied upon for accurate settings. Numbered "easy reading" fractional graduations in 32nds, 64ths, or 100ths of an inch aid in reducing measurement errors. The pocket rule is a useful asset for rapid checking of dimensions but should not be used for laying out a flat. The glass scale with graduations on its underside is a valuable addition in specialty plants where accurate measurements must be taken without injuring the copy.

Straight-Edges. Straight-edges are used for scribing or drawing straight lines. The better quality straight-edges are made of steel or stainless steel. They have beveled edges that are machined or ground true. Some straight-edges are graduated to serve as a scale also.

T-Squares. T-squares can be used for squaring-up small sections of film, such as bodies of text or display type matter, or for ruling borders or blocking out the margins of illustrations. Few T-squares are true or square enough for preparing accurate layouts. Long T-squares in particular can produce serious errors. A good T-square should have its straight-edge secured to its head by machining or doweling. The straight-edge of the T-square and the contact face of its head should be machined or ground true. In use the T-square should be held with its head firmly against the straight-edges of the layout table when it is positioned.

Triangles. A variety of triangles are available to the stripper. These range in construction from transparent plastic cutouts to stainless steel triangles with accurately squared edges. The plastic triangles are useful for squaring-up small sections of negatives or for penciling location lines wherever high accuracy is not required. They should never be used to guide razor blades, steel needles, or scribers. The best triangles have ground edges that are true and square. One or more of the edges may be beveled. The 30-60 degree triangles are most popular in the stripping department. A 45 degree triangle should also be available.

Protractors. The small 3-inch or 4-inch semi-circular protractors are of little value to the stripper. They are difficult to use, and lines extended from them are frequently in error. Where angled lines are occasionally drawn and are different than those obtainable with standard triangles and their combinations, the adjustable protractor triangle that can be set to the required angle is preferred. Where the highest accuracy of angle position is required, the calculated coordinates that are based on trigonometric tables should be used.

Irregular Curves. Two or three plastic irregular curves belong in every stripping department. They permit more accurate opaquing of curved lines or irregular shapes than is possible by freehand means. They are available in a wide variety of shapes for special applications.

Dividers. Dividers are useful for locating small sections of films so that their printing detail is parallel to each other before taping them down to the flat. They are also used to transfer small measurements accurately from the scale to the flat or film. The most convenient dividers have thumb-screw adjustment to permit setting their points accurately to the scale.

Beam Compass and GATF Register Rule. Wherever longer dimensions than those possible with a divider must be transferred accurately from the scale to the flat, the beam compass or the GATF Register Rule can be used. Although a precision layout and line-up table will supply most of the needs for locating lines accurately on the layout, the GATF Register Rule and the beam compass are still valuable instruments. They are portable and can be used to compare measurements between flats, press sheets, and press plates.

They also serve to check the source of difficulty when a deviation has occurred between measurements on the flat and on the printed sheet. They are desirable for angled measurements, and for drawing accurate angles or squares. Detailed instructions covering the use and adjustments on the GATF Register Rule can be obtained from the Graphic Arts Technical Foundation Inc.

Ruling Pens. The ruling pen is used principally to draw border lines for cropping down illustrations with opaque, for retouching solid printing detail on films, or for drawing rules on positives. The stripper's ruling pens should be reserved for this purpose and must not be used for tusching in lines on press plates.

When ruling pens become dull so that they show a noticeable flat spot, they must be carefully sharpened on a fine oil stone. When correctly sharpened, they will neither cut the film when ruling a line, nor show a flat shiny surface around their inking points. The better-quality ruling pens have inlaid tool steel or carbide tips.

Compass. The draftsman's compass can be used instead of the dividers for transferring small measurements, dividing lines or angles, or marking parallel locations on the flat. With its inking pen attachment, the compass also serves to outline or border circular illustrations. For larger circles, the beam compass is used.

Pencils and Ballpoint Pens. Hard lead drawing pencils are used for penciling lines in layout preparation. These usually range from 4H to 8H in hardness. They are sharpened to a chisel point for increasing their useful life between re-sharpenings. The ballpoint pen is becoming increasingly popular for drawing layout lines. It produces uniformly thin lines at a fixed distance from the guiding straight-edge. These lines provide more contrast and so are easier to register to than penciled lines in assembling films on the flat.

Needles and Scribers. Lithographic needles are available in different diameters and cross-sectional shapes. These are sharpened by the stripper by grinding and then stoning them to the desired shape. The round needles are usually sharpened to a gradually tapered point. They are used to mark locations on a film or flat along a thin scale, and to transfer locations from one flat or film to another that is placed in register beneath it.

By stoning the point of a tapered needle so that it is flat, it can also serve as a scribing tool on film. As a scriber, it is generally not as satisfactory or as uniform in scribing width as are tools intended for scribing purposes. Needles with square or flat rectangular cross-sections are usually ground-down and honed to a sharp edge to serve as scrapers for removing photographic defects in the film emulsion.

For scribing lines in films, commercial scribing tools are available. They are sharpened to specified widths and are usually better than hand-sharpened tools. They are often less costly, if the time spent in sharpening the tools is considered. Scribing cutters are also available as attachments to some of the precision layout and line-up tables.

Screen Tint Ruling Measurement Scale. While the black-and-white stripper is not ordinarily concerned with the ruling used in halftone screens, some means for measuring screen rulings are helpful in selecting tint sections. Commercial scales are available for this purpose. They consist of a series of screen patches of different rulings or a scaled set of radiating lines. The correct ruling is determined by the patch that shows the largest moire pattern to the point that it disappears, as the scale is rotated slowly over the halftone film. The radial line indicator curves the moire pattern to the number of the screen ruling.

Screen Angle Indicator. A screen angle indicator is useful in black-and-white as well as color work where flat tint sections are to be used, and where overlapping tint or halftone areas might otherwise produce a moiré pattern. It also can be used to check or determine the color separation of a halftone printer. Some screen angle indicators are available commercially.

If not readily obtainable, an improved screen angle indicator can be made from a piece of a uniform screen tint of the same ruling as used for halftones or tints. A section should be selected with the value of a 20% or 25% tint (75% or 80% printing value if negatives are normally used). With the aid of a magnifier and a straight-edge, a line is drawn across this tint, in line with a row of dots. This line will be the 45° angle line and will be used for black or for single-color printing. Based on this line, the tint section will be trimmed as a polygon with angles differing by 30°, 45°, and 60° from the 45° line. The edges are then marked with the screen angles.

For use, rotate this indicator over the halftone or tint section until the largest moiré pattern forms and almost disappears. The screen angle of the film can be read off directly at the top of the indicator.

Dot-Size Measuring Scale. A scale for measuring dot sizes of screen tints is helpful to the stripper for laying down tint areas specified on the copy. Such scales are not available commercially at the present time, and are accordingly improvised in many plants. The cameraman can prepare an approximate scale that is satisfactory for most measurements.

He does so by exposing a halftone from a calibrated ten-step gray scale. He controls his exposure for straight line reproduction and development so that he obtains a square 50 percent dot for the middle step and a fine pin-point dot or opening at the end steps of the scale. This is then contacted onto another piece of film to provide a hard dot structure with the same dot-size range. The stripper can then approximately number these steps as 5%, 10%, 20%, 30%, 40%, 50%, 60%, 70%, 80%, 90%, and 95%. If a densitometer is available, the steps can be measured for integrated dot value and then accurately numbered. This scale is used in contact with the tint sheet and the value of the tint is determined by direct comparison under a high-power magnifier.

Razor Blades and Knives. Most strippers prefer to use single-edged, metal-backed razor blades for their cutting operations. These blades are convenient, relatively inexpensive, and are discarded when both ends are dull. The thin, double-edged safety razor blades should never be used, even if in holders. They are dangerous and brittle, and may break off or twist when making a cut. The artist's knife or frisket knife, with replaceable blades, is convenient for certain operations, such as cutting intricate outlines in masking materials, or marking locations from a scale on a film or flat.

Magnifiers. The stripper requires several types of magnifiers to aid him in his work. A low-power stand magnifier with an adjustable arm is useful for spotting pinholes and defects in printing areas, such as between rows of type composition. A higher powered magnifier from 9X to 15X, extending from a supporting base, is helpful for fine-detail work with a scraper or pen. This is useful for repairing halftone dots or fine type matter. A pocket-type or shop microscope, with a magnification of forty or fifty diameters, is invaluable for examining halftone dots. Such a microscope can show if the dots have adequate density. It can also be used to determine the dot size or printing value of screen tints.

Brushes. It is advisable for each stripper to have his own set of brushes so that he can care for them properly and keep them in good shape and ready for use. A suggested set of brushes includes:

2 — No. 0 Red Sable Water Color Brushes; 2 — No. 2 Red Sable Water Color Brushes; 2 — No. 4 Red Sable Water Color Brushes; 2 — No. 6 Red Sable Water Color Brushes; 1 — One-half inch flat red sable lettering brush; 1 — Two and one-half or three inch wide camel's hair dusting brush.

Brushes for rubber cement, non-water soluble lacquers, and opaques for vinyl application, plus a stiff one-inch wide bristle brush for cleaning the layout and line-up table racks, should also be available in every stripping department.

Section Four: Materials and Supplies for Stripping

The materials used by the stripper can be divided, according to their application, into the following four main groups: (1) Base materials for flats, (2) Photographic materials, (3) Masking materials, and (4) Miscellaneous supplies. Each of these four groups is now discussed and described.

BASE MATERIALS FOR FLATS

The four most commonly used base materials for flats are: (1) Goldenrod paper, (2) Tracing paper, (3) Plastic sheets, and (4) Plate glass. The choice depends on the type of flat prepared, the degree of accuracy desired, its quality level and its costs. Some data on each of these materials follow.

Goldenrod Paper. Goldenrod paper is the most popular stripping material for negative flats. It serves the several functions of providing a drawing surface for preparing the layout, as a satisfactory support for holding the film assembly together, and as a mask for the non-printing areas of the press plate. Its color prevents the passage of nearly all actinic light during platemaking exposures. Its weight, usually seventy or eighty pound stock (25" x 38" basis), provides durability and flatness.

The difficulties with its use are largely due to its thickness and its size variations with changes of moisture content. Its thickness can cause out-of-contact areas between the film and the press plate when fine printing detail is close to the goldenrod paper. The safe clearance limit for goldenrod paper masking will depend on the thickness of the press plate used, the degree of vacuum in the vacuum frame, and the nature of the exposing light.

Double thicknesses of goldenrod paper, or the reinforcing of goldenrod paper with tape close to fine line detail or halftones must be avoided. The added thickness aggravates the out-of-contact condition. The result of using goldenrod paper to crop halftones to size is usually a thickening of dots from negatives (a loss of dots with positives), along the paper margins.

Goldenrod paper, red masking paper, red pressure-sensitive tape, and strippable red-coated plastic sheets are normally safe for masking the flat for one or several exposures. However, they may let enough light through to scum the plate when four or more exposures are made on a step-and-repreat or surprinted jobs. Such multiple exposures overlap their masked areas and accumulate their effect.

Goldenrod paper will change its size with changes in temperature and humidity as can be seen from our table: "Dimensional Characteristics of Base Materials for Flats." Goldenrod paper is satisfactory for stripping use in hu-

midity-controlled plants, or for making small flats. It is not suitable for precision stripping, particularly where humidity control is lacking.

Tracing Paper. Tracing paper is used as a substitute for plastic sheets when preparing low-cost positive flats. It is also used as a flat base material for paper negative assemblies, or for film negative assemblies when the goldenrod flat, after cutting, would normally be too flimsy for handling.

The layout on tracing paper is prepared with light-blue pencil or light-blue ink lines. The blue lines serve for positioning the films or paper negatives but will not hold back the exposure (actinic) light in platemaking. A good quality tracing paper is relatively free from mottling or dense spots. It may be plasticized or otherwise treated to increase its transparency and size-holding properties.

The use of tracing paper usually requires an increased exposure time in platemaking. This may range from 25 percent to 50 percent over that needed without its use. When tracing paper is used for paper negative or film negative flats, the masking needed between negatives is completed by adding strips of red pressure-sensitive tape or red masking paper.

Plastic Sheets. Plastic sheets are used principally for the preparation of positive film flats. They are sometimes used for negative assemblies when size and register must be closely held. This is more likely to occur in plants experiencing considerable humidity variations. Plastic sheets are available in several types of acetate film, vinyl film, and polyester base. They are also stocked in several thicknesses.

Acetate is the least costly and is used where humidity variations are not a problem. The .0075" thickness is usually satisfactory. Low-shrink acetate sheeting (acetate butyrate) is more stable dimensionally. Vinyl sheeting is widely used where high dimensional stability and accuracy is required from a film flat. The .010" thick sheeting is popular as it lies flat and provides a substantial working base. The .007" thick polyester sheet is also used for high accuracy and durability. Plastic sheets coated with a red strippable lacquer are time savers for intricate or exacting masking operations in flat preparation.

Glass. Plate glass is rarely used for black-and-white stripping in the lithographic industry. When used it is to combine stripfilm sections of highly accurate and close-fitting work. Such stripping is usually done to blueline images printed down on the glass. Details covering this use are to be found in the GATF Skilled Craft Text No. 512, "Color Stripping."

PHOTOGRAPHIC MATERIALS

The most important photographic materials used in the stripping department are: (1) Photographic films, (2) Stripfilms, (3) Paper negatives, (4) Brownprint paper, (5) Diazoprint paper, and (6) Tint sheets. Each of these is now briefly discussed.

Photographic Films. The black-and-white stripper normally works with film negatives or positives. These are usually exposed in the camera so that their emulsion side

Dimensional Characteristics of Base Materials for Flats		
Material	Approximate Expansion	
	(1)	(2)
Goldenrod Paper	.006" (3)	.0015"
Goldenrod Paper	.020" (4)	
Acetate Film	.007"	.0035"
Vinyl Sheet	.001"	.0038"
Polyester Film	.001"	.0015"
Plate Glass	.000"	.0005"
(1) In 10" for a 10 percent increase in RH.		
(2) In 10" for a 10°F increase in temperature.		
(3) With grain (4) Across grain.		

will be in contact with the press plate. The image will, therefore, be reverse-reading on the emulsion side. When mounting films on goldenrod or plastic sheets in flat preparation, the emulsion side will be upward. The back of the film will be in contact with the goldenrod or other flat material.

Films are commonly available in two thicknesses. The "regular base" material is about .005" to .0075" thick. It lies flat and is also thick enough so that it is not easily cut through when cutting out the goldenrod exposure windows in the assembled flat. Thin base films are about .0035" to .004" thick. They are gaining in popularity and are also used when it is necessary to assemble two films over each other or to expose through its base thickness with its emulsion side out-of-contact with the plate. Polyester based films are preferred whenever accuracy in dimensions or location is essential for the job.

Stripfilm. Stripfilm has similar photographic properties to the other films. They are supplied as laminates that consist of a thin removable emulsion membrane that is temporarily attached to a sheet plastic support. The thin emulsion membrane can be removed or "stripped off" and adhered to clear areas on other negatives or positives. This is sometimes done when adding halftone illustrations to close-fitting line detail.

Stripfilm can be attached to film, sheet plastic, or blueline glass. Its adhesion is aided with a liquid stripfilm cement. When the stripfilm section is placed in position on the film or flat, it is wiped down in registered location by using small squares of lintless blotting paper. Working details for the use of stripfilm are covered in the GATF Skilled Craft Text No. 512 "Color Stripping". The black-and-white stripper in a small or medium-size plant will rarely use stripfilm.

Paper Negatives. Paper negatives are used for low-cost flat production. Such work will consist largely of line detail, though halftones may be included if their resulting printing values are not too critical. These jobs are largely of the store bill, direct mail, railway tariff, and throw-away handbill varieties.

Brownprint Paper (also called Silverprint or Van Dyke paper). Brownprint paper is commonly used to prepare positive proof prints from negatives or negative flats. Brownprints are used for proofreading and for checking the lay and arrangement of the flat before platemaking. In this way the customer can approve or request changes in the job without the added costs of preparing proof plates and printing a short run on a lithographic proof press or on a production offset press.

Diazoprint Paper (also called Whiteprint, B. & W., Ammonia Process and by various trade names). Diazoprint papers are direct-positive light-sensitive papers. They are used for producing positive proofs from film positives. They are exposed in the vacuum frame, under conditions similar to that used for brownprints. Development of the exposed image is obtained either by moistening the surface with a special developer, or by subjecting the exposed sheet to warm ammonia fumes, depending upon which commercial product is used.

Tint Sheets. Tint sheets carry uniform dot-size values over their entire area. They are used by the stripper to introduce tinted backgrounds as different shades of black or color in printing. Tint sheet are prepared photographically on thin base film. Commercial tint sheets in graded tint values are available. The cameraman also prepares such tint sheets by making contact prints on film from uniform halftone tint masters.

MASKING MATERIALS

The masking materials used by the litho stripper can be divided into these kinds: (1) Red masking paper, (2) Masking foils, and (3) Pressure-sensitive masking tapes.

Red Masking Paper. Masking is usually applied over the face of the films. It should be as thin as possible to prevent out-of-contact conditions and embossing of the plate in platemaking. This is particularly important when a small flat is prepared for use on the photocomposing machine.

Red masking papers have the advantages that goldenrod paper has in low cost and in permitting penciling the outlines of the section to be cut out. It also has sufficient translucency to show if work detail has been accidentally masked-out. Several types of red masking paper are in use by strippers. These include the lightest weights available of deep-red or maroon glazed label paper (about 13 lb. to 16 lb.), and similar lightweights of machine-finished red sulphite stock.

Masking Foils. Thin metal and plastic sheets are used for close masking to work detail to reduce the amount of opaquing otherwise required. Tin or aluminum foil is used for accurate masking or cropping of halftone areas, particularly on small flats intended for the photocomposing machine.

Metal foils are not normally used on goldenrod flats as they are easily damaged in the normal handling of these flats. Metal foils are about one-thousandth of an inch in thickness. When removed from the roll they are relatively free of pinholes. However, pinholes develop if the foil is wrinkled or mishandled. Thin red acetate films are also suitable for masking.

A red coated clear plastic sheeting is commercially available that is suitable for the rapid preparation of complementary and mask flats. The red coating can be outlined with a knife in the intended exposure areas. The coating is then lifted and peeled away.

Pressure-Sensitive Masking Tapes. Pressure-sensitive cellophane or polyester tapes in red, brown, or black coloring offer a fast and effective means for securing film sections together and masking the film joint at the same time. The red and brown tapes are translucent and so permit seeing the sections that are masked while the tape is applied to crop printing detail areas to size.

These colored tapes are also useful for blocking-out words or other detail where two identical negatives are to be masked-out as complementaries, so as to separate the color areas between them. This is frequently done to print paragraph headings, or display lines or trade names in a different color than that used for the text. Red and brown pressure-sensitive plastic tapes can also be used for cropping or vignetting illustrations so as to closely outline printing detail. In many instances this method is faster and more easily applied to negatives than is opaquing.

MISCELLANEOUS STRIPPING SUPPLIES

The black-and-white stripper uses a variety of expendable materials in his work, such as inks, adhesives, opaques and register marks or holes. The color stripper will also require blueline solutions and stripfilm adhesives. Some of these supplies are briefly discussed in the following.

Transparent Tapes. Transparent, colorless pressure-sensitive tapes are used to attach positives to plastic flats, and negatives to goldenrod flats. The cellophane-type tapes are satisfactory for most goldenrod flat preparations. The polyester tapes are somewhat more difficult to use, as some of them may be electrostatically charged when they are removed from the roll. However, they are more transparent, more durable, and are preferred when the tape must extend across image areas, and where flats must be stored for extended periods of time.

Cements. Rubber cement is used for attaching masking materials, principally on positive flats, where it is undesirable to permit the tape to extend beyond the masked areas. Rubber cement should always be applied sparingly. It should be allowed to set for fifteen or twenty seconds before applying the mask.

India Ink. India ink is a dense black ink. It can be applied with brush, ruling pens, or special fountain pens. It serves to provide improved visibility of layout lines, particularly when such layouts are to be used repeatedly.

Plastic Drawing Inks. Special "acetate" inks are available that will take to films, acetate, vinyl, and other plastic sheets. Black, blue, and red are the preferred colors. Black is used for permanent markings that are required to hold back light. A light-blue ink is used wherever non-printing marks are needed for positioning films on plastic flats. Red is used to block-out areas on positive flats, particularly on complementary flats or in color jobs.

Marking Inks. These are intended for and commonly used with felt-tipped marking pens. They are desirable for prominently marking flats with such information as job number, job name, printing color, and direction of movement for a step-and-repeat job.

Opaques. Both red and black opaques are used by strippers. They serve to block-out defects or unwanted printing detail on negatives and are used to retouch printing detail defects in positives. The black colloidal-graphite opaque is preferred for fine work. It covers well, and is extremely thin.

Red opaque is somewhat easier to apply over large areas and is less likely to stain the emulsion when errors in opaquing are corrected. The black opaque is better for scribing purposes. In such work the negatives are spotted-out before scribing. Red opaque must be applied carefully and uniformly. If it is permitted to dry in lumps close to halftone areas or to fine line detail, the lumps can cause an out-of-contact condition similar to that produced by heavy masking papers.

Register Mark Tabs. For the average run of commercial stripping, register marks can be applied to the flat as small tabs of film. These marks can be made photographically in quantity by first preparing master groups of positives or negatives of such marks. These groups are then cut into strips and scored so each can be broken off as needed. A desirable type of mark consists of cross lines with segmented portions of a surrounding heavy circle.

Register Hole Tabs and Dowels. Plastic register hole tabs and dowels are commercially available. They provide a fast means for positioning complementary flats on a press plate or on brownprint paper so that they can be successively exposed in register with each other. They are also used for simple step-and-repeat jobs.

Color Blocks. Color blocks are small rectangles applied as an opaque area on each positive flat, or as a transparent opening on each negative flat. They are located in the trim area of the sheet. Each is positioned so that it will print adjacent to the color blocks for the other colors. These blocks show the colors already printed and guide the pressman in determining whether he is carrying a full body of ink.

Halftone Step Scale. Also located in the marginal trim area, the gray scale is an added guide to the pressman. It provides a visual check of the ink control and density for each color. Any tendency towards filling in shadow detail or blinding the highlights can readily be detected with such a scale. These scale strips may appear on the separation films where they have served as controls for the photographer and dot-etcher.

The GATF Sensitivity Guide. The GATF Sensitivity Guide consists of a continuous-tone gray scale with numbered step densities. It should be temporarily applied to every flat as an aid to the platemaker for determining whether his exposure and development are correct. This guide helps in establishing standard controls for uniform color reproduction. It also informs the platemaker if any of his operations are deviating from their best conditions. (See GATF Research Bulletin No. 215, "The Sensitivity Guide").

Blueline Solutions. The blueline solution is applied as a light-sensitive coating to glass or plastic sheeting. Exposure through the key or intermediate flat and development produces a blue image that can be registered to in stripping, yet will transmit actinic light. The color stripper positions his films to this blue image. The blue image can be converted to brown or black by a local or general application of a stain or developer. The brown or black image will reproduce in platemaking. A flat so prepared can serve as intermediate in printing down blueline flats.

Stripfilm Adhesives. Stripfilm, when applied wet, will adhere well to clean glass, acetate, or film base if it is "flopped" so that its emulsion side is in contact. When stripfilm is transferred to the flat without "flopping," an adhesive must be used.

Cleaning Solutions. Before cleaning a film with a solution, first dust off any surface particles. Use a wide camel's hair brush. This removes abrasive particles that could scratch the emulsion if they were wiped with a rag or tissue. For cleaning films, toxic solutions such as carbon tetrachloride and benzol have been replaced with safer proprietary solvents. These are available through most suppliers. A good cleaning solution should evaporate completely without leaving a greasy film or other residue.

Scratch Fillers. Scratches or accidental lines cut into the exposure areas of negatives or positives can cast shadows during platemaking exposure or contact printing. These shadows will show up in the reproduction. Minor hair scratches on films can usually be ignored, as the exposure light will burn through them. Major scratches or accidental razor blade cuts in work areas will require correction. If they are on the back of the film, they can be wiped over with commercially available film-scratch fillers.

Section Five: Auxiliary Stripping Operations

In simple jobs the negatives or positives delivered to the stripper are ready for stripping-up a flat without any additional work. In many cases they will require intermediate steps to prepare them for stripping. Here we discuss six types of such auxiliary stripping operations: (1) Inserting negative sections, (2) Adding rules and borders, (3) Adding tints, (4) Fake color work, (5) Double printing and surprinting, and (6) Making corrections and changes. Instructions concerning each of these operations follow.

INSERTING NEGATIVE SECTIONS

Negative sections can be inserted into a larger negative by various methods. Here we present the following three in detail: (1) Use of stripfilm, (2) Attaching the negative to the surface of the larger film as an overlay-insert, and (3) Cutting an opening and splicing-in the insert, or window-inserts. Double-printing methods can also be used to obtain the same results. These techniques are presented later in this section.

Inserting Negatives by Use of Stripfilm. To use stripfilm, or to attach a film to the surface of a larger negative, the area it is to occupy must be clean and transparent. This can be anticipated in copy preparation by attaching red or black cutouts that are cut to size and mounted in position on the paste-up copy. These blocked-out areas will remain clear on the developed negative.

If the areas are not completely transparent they can be cleared by local removal of the silver image. An emulsion remover such as commercial sodium hypochlorite solution ("Chlorox" or equivalent), a concentrated Farmer's reducer, or a cyanide etch, as may be used by the camera or color correction departments, is carefully applied to the area. The chemicals are then removed by washing the film in water and drying. Stripfilm requires highly skilled handling techniques. Its application is described later in this chapter, Section Seven, and in GATF Skilled Craft Text #512, *Color Stripping*.

Overlay-Inserts. Overlay-insert sections are prepared on thin base film. This reduces the out-of-contact image spread of adjacent printing detail. The overlay-insert should always carry the halftone or the finer printing detail. This permits the detail to be in contact with the press plate in platemaking. The insert films should be cut to a size slightly larger than its printing area. The extended border

permits taping the film down without running the tape over the image area.

If the overlay-insert is a halftone and is to be cropped down to size, this should be done first. Masking is applied

Opaquing to crop illustration to size.

to the back of the film. This is usually done by first ruling in opaque border lines to the crop marks. Additional opaque is then applied by brush up to these border lines.

Cropping can also be done with strips of red or brown pressure-sensitive cellophane tape. While this method is faster than opaquing, it must be used cautiously as some marginal dot spread could result from its added thickness.

If the overlay-insert has register or other crop marks for use in positioning it on the larger negative, these marks are allowed to remain until after the insert is taped down in

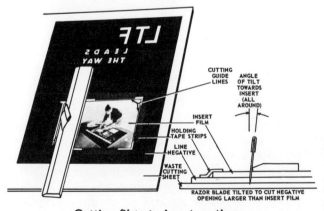

Cutting films to insert section.

position. If no location guides are provided on the copy or dummy, the stripper must square-up the insert to important detail. In cropping unmarked inserts to size, the detail must be selected to provide good composition that is centered and balanced on the subject matter. When attaching the overlay-insert, it may be necessary to first cut the tape into narrow strips so that these strips of tape will not overlap printing detail.

Window-Inserts. If both the insert and the adjacent film areas have close-fitting and fine printing detail, it is best to insert the film into an opening cut into the larger negative. This aids in obtaining good contact in plate-making. To produce a good fit in a minimum of time, both films are cut together.

First square-up the insert with the large film and attach it in position. Use strips of pressure-sensitive tape. Then place the attached films, emulsion-side down, on a waste cutting film. Position a steel straight-edge or triangle to the first edge to be cut. Use a sharp razor blade or frisket knife. Make several light cuts until both films are cut clean through, up to and slightly past the intended corners.

It is best to tilt the knife slightly in, away from the insert. In this way the opening in the lower film will be

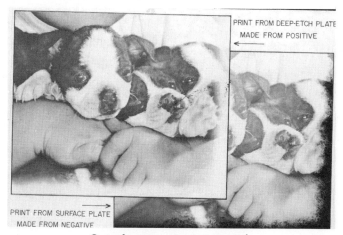

PRINT FROM DEEP-ETCH PLATE MADE FROM POSITIVE

PRINT FROM SURFACE PLATE MADE FROM NEGATIVE

Out-of-contact image spread.

slightly larger than the film to be spliced in. Otherwise it may be necessary to double-trim two sides of the insert to prevent an interfering overlap of the insert edges. Then use strips of red or brown pressure-sensitive cellophane tape to secure the insert in place. This will also mask-out the cut edges.

When taping the insert in location it may be necessary to first slit the tape into narrow strips so that the tape will not overlap the printing detail. If the printing detail comes very close to the joint line in places, a wider red or brown cellophane tape can be applied that covers some of the detail. Then, using a sharp razor blade, cut lightly through the tape. Cut to a straight or irregular line that clears the printing detail. Lift away the interfering tape. Avoid overlapping tape in the corners where possible as the added thickness can produce an out-of-contact condition in plate-making.

ADDING RULES AND BORDERS

The transparent areas on negatives will transmit light to produce the printing image. Wherever the blackened emulsion is removed from a film, light can pass through to expose the press plate. To produce rules, grids, or borders on a negative, strips of emulsion are shaved away with a scribing tool to form transparent lines.

Good scribing tools are ground to the correct widths for

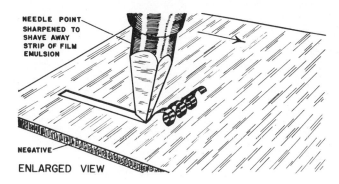

NEEDLE POINT SHARPENED TO SHAVE AWAY STRIP OF FILM EMULSION

NEGATIVE

ENLARGED VIEW

Scribing lines in negative.

specified line thicknesses. When drawn across the emulsion side of a negative they will shave away a strip of the emulsion and produce a sharply defined rule. A needle point or a blunt tool will furrow the emulsion and produce a ragged line. The emulsion for ruling must be clean and dry. It should not be excessively hardened in fixing or excessively dried by forced heating. The scribing tool should always be tested along the waste margins of a film for its ability to shave away a clean ruled line, before it is used in the work areas. Some emulsions are better scribed when slightly damp.

To Add Rules on a Negative. First square-up the negative to the layout table. Select a table area that is clean and free from scratches. Then tape the film down securely and flat with strips of pressure-sensitive tape. Mark the location of the lines to be scribed along the margins of the negative, outside of the trim area of the job.

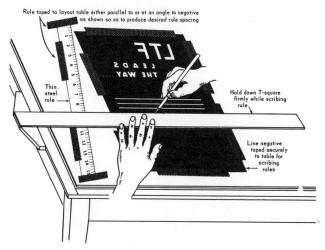

Rule taped to layout table either parallel to or at an angle to negative as shown so as to produce desired rule spacing

Thin steel rule

Hold down T-square firmly while scribing rule

Line negative taped securely to table for scribing rules

Scribing or ruling at uniform intervals.

Ruling Uniformly Spaced Rules. If the rules are to be uniformly spaced, a thin steel rule can be taped down alongside the form. The T-square or triangle is then positioned to the scale graduations for each line to be ruled. If the uniform spacing is not a full fractional value of an inch, such as when 21 rules are to be spaced uniformly in $5\frac{1}{4}$ inches, the steel rule can be tilted at an angle and taped down.

The angle is selected so that the space is divided into the desired number of full graduations.

Duplicating a Previously Printed Form. If a previously printed form is to be duplicated, the form can be squared up and taped down alongside of the negative. The T-square is then positioned to the printed rules. Before scribing the rules, pencil in an outline on the negative to show the limits for the lengths of the rules. Then spot out any large pinholes or other defects in the area to be ruled. Set the T-square to the location for the first rule. Hold the scribing tool perpendicular to the edge and slightly inclined in the direction of ruling.

Start slightly beyond the penciled limit and scribe with a steady uniform stroke across the negative to slightly past the other limit line. If the stroke was too light so that all of the line is not cleanly removed, repeat the stroke without disturbing the T-square or the angle of the scriber. Continue with all the remaining lines to be scribed.

Scribing Horizontal and Vertical Rules. If both horizontal and vertical rules are to be scribed, first make certain that the two edges of the layout table are square with each other so that the rules will be at right angles. Otherwise it is best to release the negative, rotate it 90 degrees, square it with the T-square and steel triangle, and tape it down again, before scribing the other set of rules.

Opaquing the Ruled Negative. After all the rules are scribed in, release the film and flop it over, emulsion-side down. Square it to the layout table and tape it down. Use a ruling pen and opaque to draw the marginal borders that will mask-out the ends of the successive ruled lines. Red or brown pressure-sensitive cellophane tape can also be used for this purpose if it is carefully applied and guided straight along the edge of the T-square or triangle.

To Border an Illustration. The same procedure is used as in scribing rules on a negative. First lightly pencil in the border on the negative. This will locate the lines and prevent scribing short or long lines. Apply a thin covering of a colloidal-graphite opaque with a brush to any pinholes or unwanted transparent areas in the location of the intended border lines. When the opaque has dried, carefully scribe in lines of the required thickness. Follow the procedure previously detailed for adding rules. Opaque out the excess lengths of the border rules at the corners. This is best done on the back side of the film. If opaque is applied to limit the length of a scribed rule on the scribed side of the film, the opaque may creep in along the line.

Bordering Halftone-Inserts. When bordering halftone-inserts, the scribed border may be applied either to the large negative or to the insert. This will depend on its required location and in providing adequate clearance for the tape that is used to secure the insert. If the fit is so close that it will not permit scribing the border on the negative or insert, it may be possible to double print the border in location. This can be done by use of a flap section on the flat or by preparing a complementary flat.

Adding Rules to Positives. Rules can be added to positive films by drawing them in with opaque and a ruling pen. First lay out the rules on a sheet of paper. Then position the positive over the layout and tape it down. Always test the ruling pen for its ruling properties immediately be-

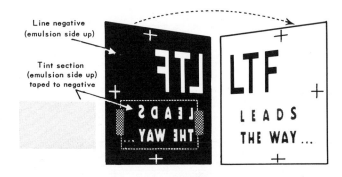

Line negative
(emulsion side up)

Tint section
(emulsion side up)
taped to negative

Applying tint sections to negative.

fore drawing on the positive. The positive should be clean and free from greasy fingerprints. If difficulty is experienced with ruling on positives, it is advisable to use "acetate inks" for such ruling. If only a few short lines are to be added to a positive such as register or trim marks, the scriber can be used to engrave these marks. The scribed lines are filled in by rubbing them with a black crayon or litho crayon. The excess crayon is then wiped away with a soft clean tissue.

ADDING TINTS

Tints are added to negatives or positives to produce uniform tone values of the printed color. Several different tint or tone values may be used for a single color. A color combination of tint values in two or more colors can also be applied to any area.

This is done in fake color preparations. The use of tint values makes possible the printing of a job in fewer press-runs. Otherwise each shade of gray or color would require a separate press-run to be printed with a specified ink.

Selecting the Required Tint Value. The percentage steps in an ink specimen book or the color blocks in a color combination chart will guide the stripper in selecting the required tint value whenever the values are not specified on the dummy or copy. This requires that he match the color swatch or spotted colors on the dummy with the chart to determine the dot size needed in each color. Tint sheets can be prepared photographically by the cameraman or are available commercially. They come in standard screen rulings and are rated in nominal values such as 10, 20, 25, 30, 40, 50 percent etc. If the values of the tint sheets are not marked, the dot-size measuring scale previously described should be used.

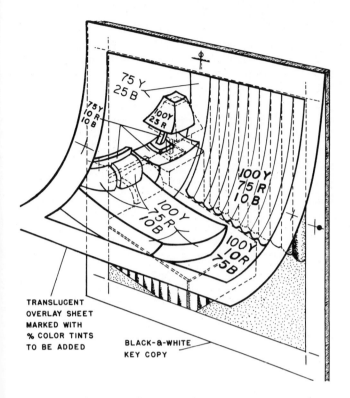

Copy marked for fake color tints.

Dot-Size Gain. When working with negatives, the dot size on the tint sheet will be the reciprocal of its printing value. That is, if a 60 percent tint is to be printed, the dot size on the tint sheet will be a 40 percent dot and cover 40 percent of the area. Whenever the specified tint value is greater than 50 percent, it is desirable to know the dot-size gain that is experienced on the press on which that job is to be printed. For example, it may be necessary to use a 65 or 70 percent tint if an 80 percent printing tint is specified.

Locating the Screen Angle on Tint Sheet. It is also important to locate the screen angle of the tint sheet section to be used. When the printing is to be done in black or with a single color, the screen angle of the tint section

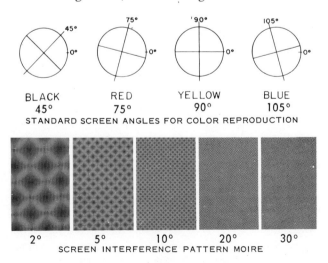

STANDARD SCREEN ANGLES FOR COLOR REPRODUCTION

| BLACK | RED | YELLOW | BLUE |
| 45° | 75° | 90° | 105° |

SCREEN INTERFERENCE PATTERN MOIRE

| 2° | 5° | 10° | 20° | 30° |

Color screen angles and moiré.

should be selected for use at 45 degrees. If several tint values of different colors are to overprint each other, the angle selected for each color should be the same as that used in a color process job. Popular angles are: black-45°; red-75°; yellow-90°; blue-105° (15°). These angles are selected to avoid a moiré pattern from forming in the overprinting color tint areas. The same applies in single-color work when a tinted background bleeds into a halftone illustration.

Reducing an Area to a Specified Tint Value. If an area on a flat or on a negative is to be reduced to a specified tint value, it is usually photographed clear. This is anticipated in copy preparation by attaching a red or black cutout to the copy.

Any defects in this area on the negative such as fog, specks, or streaks must first be cleared by using the sodium hypochlorite solution or the concentrated Farmer's reducer, as previously described.

The bordering areas are then opaqued-out where necessary so as to limit or crop the tint areas to size. A section of the tint film that has the required printing value is inspected and selected for uniform dot value and freedom from de-

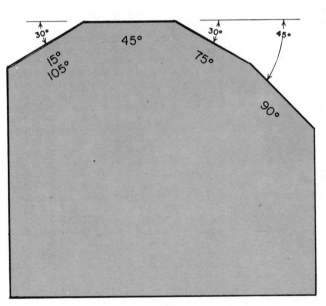

Screen-angle determination gage.

fects. Its angle is determined. It is then placed emulsion-side up and at the correct angle over the negative area it is to occupy. A light line is penciled or scribed on the tint sheet about $\frac{3}{16}$ or $\frac{1}{4}$ inch outside the tint area limits. This excess margin will be trimmed closer along those edges where the tint may overlap adjacent printing detail.

The tint sheet is then cut to size. It is finally secured in place on the negative, emulsion-side up. Use tabs of cellophane pressure-sensitive tape. Cut the tape into narrow strips, if necessary, so that it will not extend into the tint area. It is not advisable to cut away openings in a larger film to provide clear areas for receiving tint sheets. If this is done the unbacked margins around the tint area may result in a thickened printed border due to an out-of-contact condition in platemaking.

Preparing Tint Sheets for Positives. In cutting tint sheets for use on positives, the tint sheet is selected to have the same dot size that is to be printed. Its angle is selected, and its edges cut cleanly to the exact size of the tint area it is to print. In attaching it to a positive, it is advisable to use a thin application of a clear rubber or film cement to hold it in place. Clear tape that is attached to the surface of tint sections can result in printing defects.

FAKE-COLOR WORK

Tint sheets can be used to produce fake-color jobs for some classes of work by the methods described in the previous section. Wherever the color areas are of uniform tone value, color can be added and limited in its coverage so that it will follow detail outlines. The tint sheets applied to negatives can be opaqued locally to produce clear areas or highlights in printing. The dots can also be removed locally by brush application of sodium hypochlorite or concentrated Farmer's reducer (as previously detailed) to form solid-color printing sections in the tint areas.

With some experience in dot-etching techniques, the dot-size values can also be modified locally. The dot sizes can then be made to conform with the subject modeling and with required changes in color values. For such work, color process procedures are followed. The printing dot size for each color on each section of a color combination area must first be determined. This is done by spot color matching with a color combination chart. The color combination chart should be prepared in advance with the inks that are to be used for printing the job.

DOUBLE PRINTING AND SURPRINTING

Double printing and surprinting are photographic procedures that are used to combine the detail from two or more films into a single film. This is done to simplify stripping practices. By combining printing detail into a

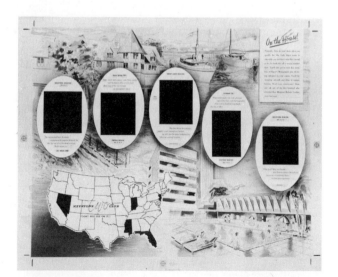

Copy with blank cutouts for illustration strip-in.

single film it is possible to eliminate the close-fitting of film sections and the need for complementary flats. This is used for combining close-fitting line and halftone detail. The photographic combination also improves the quality of the printed reproduction. The single film eliminates out-of-contact difficulties, and provides a more opaque dot structure than can be obtained from the original camera halftone negative or positive.

Equipment for Double Printing and Surprinting. Double printing and surprinting require darkroom processing facilities; a vacuum-contact printer; and a point-source exposure light. The darkroom methods for exposure and development of the film are described elsewhere in this manual, as they are usually done by the cameraman or by a specialized contact man. The stripper is required to prepare the negatives or positives so that they can be double printed or surprinted accurately in relation to each other. He does this by using one of the following methods:

Flap Methods. This requires a supporting base, such as a sheet of $\frac{1}{8}''$ thick plastic, pressed-board, or a section of metal press plate that is free from kinks. The base size must fit within the contact frame. The two negatives to be double printed (or surprinted) are first registered to each other. They are then trimmed if necessary so that each negative has one side that projects beyond the margin of the other film.

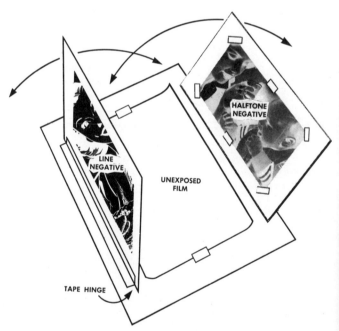

Flap method of double printing.

A white sheet of paper, the size of the film that will be exposed, is placed on the base. The two films are then carefully registered to each other in position on the paper. Each film is then taped to the baseboard along its extended side. In this way each negative will be hinged to the supporting base. If the negatives are small, the hinged sides can be opposite each other. If the negatives are large and nearly fill the contact frame they are usually hinged along the same side with separate strips of tape. In use, darkroom safelight conditions are employed.

The sensitized film to be exposed is placed emulsion-side up on the base in place of the white sheet of paper. It is taped down securely. The first flap negative is lowered over the film. The vacuum frame is closed, the air exhausted, and the first exposure made. Vacuum contact is then released. The second flat is lowered against the sensitized film in place of the first, and the second exposure is made.

If the negatives were large and hinged along the same side, the sensitized film is secured only along the opposite side to that used for the negative sections so that it also is hinged to the base. The sensitized film is first interleaved between the top and lower film and the first exposure is made. For the second exposure, the top film is removed and the sensitized film is hinged below the second film.

Punched Hole Methods. Registration for double printing or surprinting two films may use standard peg-

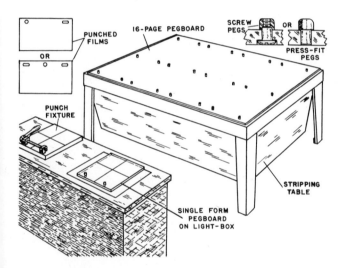

Pegboard assembly with punching fixture.

boards and a punch fixture for punching the films. Punched holes and plastic dowels can also be used. The two films to be double printed or surprinted are first registered to each other over a light table. They are then taped securely to each other to hold register.

The two films are next punched together along a waste margin, to obtain two register holes. (Three holes can be used for large films. When three holes are used, a combination of one round and two slotted holes, or three slotted holes are desirable. When three slotted holes are punched the intermediate slot is at right angles to the others.) To use the punched films, a pegboard with spring-loaded or removable pegs is required.

The peg locations must match the hole locations on the films. These holes permit the successive exposure of each negative in registered location on the sensitized film. The sensitized film can be taped in exposure position to the pegboard. Holes can also be punched in the sensitized film (under safelight conditions) so that it can be mounted on the same pegs. If plastic dowels are used, they are located

and attached to the baseboard through the punched holes of one of the negatives. This is then used as a pegboard.

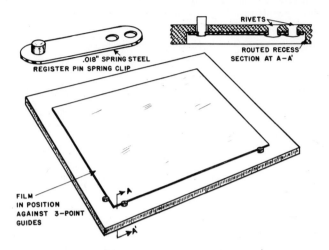

Three-point register for double printing.

Edge-Register Methods. Edge register or "three-point register" is sometimes used for positioning each negative in register when exposing them to the sensitized film. This is done by first registering the two negatives together over a light table and taping them to each other. Two of the adjoining edges of the negative assembly such as the top and left hand side are then trimmed off together. The other edges are notched or the opposite corner clipped off so that the correct edges will be used for locating the negative in the contact frame. Positioning each negative for contact printing is done by pressing it against the three pins. The negative is then temporarily taped down in register location to secure it for the exposure.

There are other methods for double printing or surprinting. Some utilize specialized equipment, such as the double-negative printer. Under suitable conditions, the photocomposing machine can also be used for this purpose.

Double Printing with Positives. When double printing with positive films, it is necessary to mask-out each positive in the areas that the other positive will contribute its printing detail. Otherwise the double exposure will blank out printing detail. When surprinting with positives, both positives are first registered and taped to each other. They are then exposed simultaneously to the sensitized film.

MAKING CORRECTIONS AND CHANGES

When combining new film sections with older films, it is essential that the printing detail in each be similar if the new section is to be inconspicuous in printing. This is especially important where text matter is involved. Changes in exposure times or in development conditions in preparing the film can result in noticeable changes in the body weight between the older and the new text matter. The stripper should not try to compensate for such differences. He should request new negatives that are made to match the old printing detail whenever this is possible.

Compensating for Differences in Type Body Weight. If the cause of the difference in body weight is directly due to the reproduction proofs used for copy, and new proofs cannot be readily obtained, the cameraman can determine how much compensation he can provide in sharpening or thickening up the text by photographic methods so that it will be less conspicuous in printing.

Replacing Lines of Type or Paragraphs. When introducing a new line, paragraph, or illustration to replace an old one, it is best to attach the new film in register over

the older film. Then carefully cut through both films as was described for making an insert. If the new text matter differs in composition and arrangement from the old, the old film area can still be used to locate and line-up the new printing detail, before it is cut away.

Some corrections, such as changing the typeface of scattered display material throughout a text, are more easily made by stripping-up a complementary flat or flap section with the new film sections in location. The words to be deleted on the first negative are then opaqued out.

Section Six: Goldenrod Flats for Black-and-White Stripping

Our discussion of goldenrod flats for black-and white stripping is divided into these major parts: (1) Securing the essential information and the materials for the job, (2) Preparation for stripping, and (3) The assembly of the films in stripping-up the goldenrod flat.

ESSENTIAL INFORMATION AND MATERIAL FOR STRIPPING

Under this heading we discuss six points: (1) The layout of the job, (2) Dimensions of each form, (3) Press requirements, (4) Quality control standards, (5) A complete set of negatives, (6) The necessary equipment, material and supplies for stripping.

A Layout of the Intended Printing Arrangement. This may consist of a visual, mock-up, or dummy, or it may be specified on the job jacket as consisting of a definite number of pages or forms on the press sheet.

Dimensions of Each Form. The trim size, bleed allowances, and double trims needed must be known. Signature lays are prepared for correct imposition of both sides of the press sheet. They must allow for folding, wraparound, binding, and other finishing requirements. This subject is discussed in Section Eight, *Imposition,* of this chapter.

Press Requirements. Flats must be prepared for the particular model and size of offset press to be used. Each press has its own requirements for gripper distance, non-printing gripper margin, and printing conditions. These requirements may indicate a change in layout to accord with ink distribution limitations, to compensate for shrinkage or stretch of the paper stock, or to circumvent specific press difficulties. Some pressmen use a system of pins or scribed marks for positioning the press plate when clamping it to the cylinder so that they can reduce press adjustments. These reference points must then be used when preparing the flat for a specific press.

Quality Control Standards. The job jacket should indicate the quality level and accuracy specified for the job. If too much time is applied to a competitively priced job it can easily result in a financial loss. Too little time and inferior handling in flat preparation can result in a disappointed customer and a loss of further business. Good

stripping practices require the best degree of workmanship and the use of expedient shortcuts that will produce a satisfactory job within the limits of a specified quality level.

A Complete Set of Negatives. Each negative should first be checked for correct size, its provisions for register, and for errors and defects. Corrections are best made on the individual negatives before they are stripped-up on the flat.

The Necessary Equipment, Materials and Supplies for Stripping. The equipment must provide the degree of accuracy in alignment and register position that is required of the printed job. T-squares or layout tables that are out-of-square, or straight-edges that are not true will result in inferior workmanship. Good tools and equipment will provide a much better job for the same amount of work. A good craftsman first checks that all the needed supplies are on hand. He locates each item in an established convenient position where it can be reached with a minimum of effort.

PREPARATION FOR STRIPPING

The stripping layout is usually decided in advance by the agency, office, or the job planning department. A dummy of the job or the required dimensional data is furnished. These include all normal printing allowances. The stripper can sometimes use the dummy directly to strip up part or all of a flat. He does so by assembling the negatives over the dummy, placing the negatives emulsion-side down. If the dummy has not been accurately drawn, as is frequently the case, the stripper must prepare an accurate layout to which he can position the negatives.

The exact procedure for preparing a stripping layout will vary with the available equipment. It must also be guided by the accuracy required in the imposition of the forms. The general procedure follows:

Preparing the Goldenrod Base. Place a sheet of goldenrod paper on the layout table. Square-up its leading edge (the gripper edge) to the straight-edge, front stops, or with the aid of a T-square. Then tape the sheet down with tabs of pressure-sensitive tape. Make certain that no waves exist or appear when the sheet is taped down. The goldenrod paper should be purchased or cut to a size equal to or slightly larger than the press plate. For certain plate sizes, the paper may be an inch or two less than the around-cylinder dimension of the plate. This may permit economical use of standard goldenrod sheet sizes. The platemaker will later cover this area along the back edge of the press plate with a strip of goldenrod paper after he positions the goldenrod flat on the press plate. NOTE: Where higher accuracy in location is required, orange colored plastic sheets are used in place of the goldenrod paper.

Drawing the Basic Reference Lines. Draw the basic reference lines.

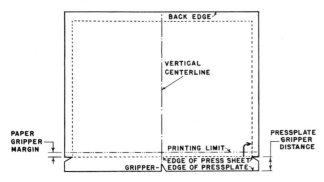

Reference marks used on flats.

This consists of the gripper-edge line and the vertical-center line. The gripper-edge line is the location of the front or gripper edge of the press sheet in relation to the press plate. It varies in distance for each size or model of press. Also draw a second line parallel to the gripper-edge line to represent the non-printing gripper margin of the press sheet. This will also be determined by the press to be used. This gripper margin distance ranges from $\frac{3}{16}$ to $\frac{3}{8}$ inches.

Selecting the Gripper Edge. If no printing detail comes within the gripper-margin distance, the gripper edge of the sheet can be used as part of the printed job. This is necessary when the full sheet size must be used. If the sheet is larger than needed for the forms, it is best to allow for trimming away the gripper edge. This will help prevent press markings such as gripper finger-marks and ink or dampener roller slur from showing up on the trimmed forms along the gripper edge of the press sheet.

The Vertical-Center Line. The vertical-center line must be exactly at right angles to the gripper line. This is very important for work-and-turn or other backed jobs. An off-vertical line will double its error in backing when the other side of the sheet is printed. The gripper-edge line and the vertical-center line are the basic lines from which all the other lines on the layout will be measured. This will avoid accumulated errors that may result if the measurements are taken from subject to subject in preparing the layout.

Center Line on Work-and-Tumble Jobs. For work-and-tumble jobs, draw another horizontal line to locate the horizontal-center line of the press sheet. This center line will be used as the basic reference line in place of the gripper-edge line. Its use will reduce the amount of

press adjustments that are otherwise necessary for printing the back of the sheet.

Indicating the Margins of the Press Sheet. It is also advisable to add lines on the layout that show the margins of the press sheet. The press sheet outlines will show if the trimmed forms and all printing detail are correctly placed on the sheet. The sheet-margin lines also serve to guide in locating the centermarks, trim and fold marks, color blocks or bars, halftone scales and other controls, so that they will print in the waste trim margins of the press sheet.

Locating the Layout Position of the First Subject. Lay out the location of the first subject. This is usually the central form, or it may be another form that is located along the gripper margin. If the negative has centermarks, the positioning lines will be drawn to locate the first form to the centermarks.

If centermarks are not provided and trim marks are used, the positioning lines will be drawn to locate the negative by its trim marks.

If no marks are provided, or irregularly located register marks are used, the form outlines should be drawn to the form size that is indicated on the job jacket or dummy. Where positioning marks are omitted, each film must be stripped-up by squaring to work detail, and by measurements taken from the mechanical, dummy, or copy.

When trim marks on the negative are to be used for positioning, always measure the separation between them, and check these measurements with the specified trim distance on the job jacket. These marks are frequently incorrectly spaced on the negative. This may be due to errors in copy preparation or to size changes resulting from relative humidity variations.

Layout Techniques for Different Levels of Accuracy. With the average stripping job where high accuracy in register or position is not essential, the layout lines should be drawn to the correct dimensions as specified

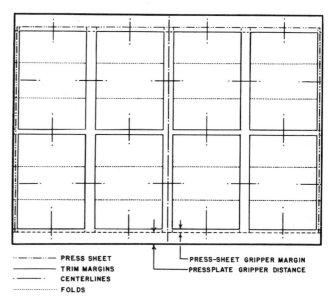

--- ---   PRESS SHEET
--- --- TRIM MARGINS
--- --- CENTERLINES
.... FOLDS

PRESS-SHEET GRIPPER MARGIN
PRESSPLATE GRIPPER DISTANCE

Layout locations for negatives.

rather than to measurements taken from the films. When stripping-up the films, the difference between the drawn and actual film dimensions can be approximately split up between the marks. For accurate register jobs, additional marks should be added at the corners of each subject location on the layout to agree with the negative measurements. The negatives can then be exactly aligned to these marks. The highest degree of accuracy in layout preparation is obtained by working to subject center lines.

Handling Asymmetrical Forms. If the first form is not centrally located along the gripper edge, make certain that its location lines are drawn in a laterally-reversed position, so that it will print correctly on the press plate.

Locating Adjoining Forms on the Layout. Lay out the location lines for the adjoining forms to either center or trim marks as provided on the negatives. Include all the specified allowances for double trims, folds, wraparound, or other cutter and bindery requirements. Calculate all distances from the basic reference lines. Measure and mark down the position of each layout line from these reference lines.

Continue to draw in the lines until all of the locations for each negative have been laid out.

Adding of Additional Location Marks. Locate and add the marks that are needed to strip in the center or trim marks that are to be printed on the press sheet. Also mark the location of the color blocks, color bars, halftone scale, GATF Sensitivity Guide, and other reference controls that are to be printed down on the press plate.

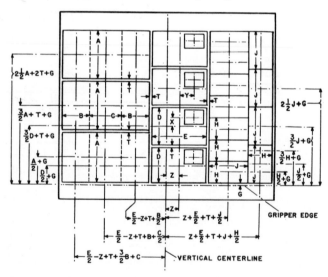

Layout calculations.

Checking the Completed Layout. Check all principal dimensions. It is best to check with another steel scale or tape than was used to draw the layout. This will disclose errors such as those that may result when the one-inch mark of a scale, rather than its zero end, is used for marking the layout.

ASSEMBLING GOLDENROD FLATS

The procedure by which goldenrod flats are assembled is

described in our Manual in all detail, as you can see from the listing in the following paragraph.

Stripping-Up the Goldenrod Flat. When the stripping layout has been completely drawn, prepare to strip-up the negatives. Place the tape dispensers, razor blades, brushes, and opaque in established, convenient locations. Put the negatives in their approximate locations on the layout with their emulsion-side up. If additional register marks, register hole tabs, masking foils, tint sheets, or other materials are required, make certain that they are on hand. Then proceed to strip up the goldenrod flat by taking the following steps: (1) Trim the negatives to size, (2) Strip-in the first negative, (3) Strip-in the second and the following negatives, (4) Add controls, (5) Add notches to the flat, (6) Check the taping of negatives, (7) Cut windows in goldenrod base, (8) Check for loose masking, (9) Check all printing areas, (10) Mark the flat, (11) Make brownprint proofs, and (12) Transmit the completed flat to the platemaker. Each of these steps is now individually discussed.

Trimming the Negatives to Size. Note the overlapping areas of adjacent negatives as temporarily placed in location on the flat. Mark each negative where it should be trimmed off so that it will not overlap the adjoining negative when they are stripped-up. Select a trim location that is midway between the work detail on each negative, or that is at least $\frac{3}{8}$-inch away from any fine printing detail or halftones on either negative when this is possible.

Then trim the negative if register or other reference marks are not removed in so doing. If needed marks are in the area to be trimmed, do not cut the film. This edge can be trimmed off later after the negative is attached in location on the flat.

In simple jobs where only trim marks are used and where printing detail does not come close to the trim margins of the form, it may be expedient to trim each negative down to the trim size. This is done by first taping down a waste clear plastic cutting sheet and then squaring the negative over it on the layout table and taping it down. Using the T-square, a steel square, and a sharp razor blade or frisket knife, cut through the film in line with the trim marks. Do not trim off the margins that will extend along the outside edges of the flat.

Stripping-In the First Negative. Start with any negative. Locate it accurately so that its center or trim marks align with the positioning lines drawn on the layout. Then attach it in position with tabs of cellophane pressure-sensitive tape. Locate one tab near the center of each edge. Make certain that the negative is flat against the layout and that no waves or twists are evident.

Stripping-In the Second and the Following Negatives. Register the next negative alongside the first one. If the negatives do not overlap, tape it down as before. If the second negative overlaps the first, as may occur when register marks are retained, position the second negative in register with its layout lines. Then tape it down on the three non-interfering sides.

Applying a negative to a flat.

Next insert a heavy strip of waste film under the intended cutting line below both negatives. Using a straight-edge or steel triangle, hold it down firmly with its edge along the intended cut. Then cut through the negatives with a sharp razor blade. It is usually better that the apprentice use several light strokes instead of one heavy stroke to cut through both films. This will avoid twisting a film or cutting too deeply into the underlying waste film.

Do not release the straight-edge until the cut is completed. Test this by lifting the cut edge. Then remove the cut off strips and the waste strip underneath. Apply tabs of pressure-sensitive tape to secure the newly trimmed edges.

Repeat this operation for the remaining negatives, until all are attached in position to the goldenrod flat.

Adding Controls. If prepared press-sheet register marks on film tabs are used, strip these in place. If the non-printing margin of the negative interferes with locating these tabs, cut away a slightly larger section of the negative. The register mark can then be positioned to the layout without overlapping the negative. Attach the mark in position with several tabs of pressure-sensitive tape. Most other marks for trim and fold locations can be scribed into the outside margins of the negatives that are stripped-up on the flat.

Carefully scribe each in location as a short mark ($\frac{1}{8}$- or $\frac{3}{16}$-inch long). Line up each scribed mark to the trim or fold lines that were drawn on the layout. Scribe each mark so that it will print on the trim margins of the press sheet. If the negatives do not extend into the area where the marks are required, attach small sections of negatives in location, emulsion-side up. The marks can then be scribed in each section as previously detailed.

In recent years, presses have been equipped with pins over which the plates are placed. This facilitates obtaining correct

lay on the sheet. There is supplied, for such "pin register" systems, punches which will perforate the leading edge of the plate corresponding to the pins set in the plate cylinder clamps. Plastic strips attached to the flat are also punched in the same device; or the flat itself is punched. Flat and plate are registered by visually lining up the holes or by the use of dowel pins.

Adding Notches to the Flat. Notch out the half "V" cutouts at the ends of the gripper-edge line and the vertical-center line of the flat. These will be used by the platemaker when he positions the flat to lines that he will scribe or pencil on the press plate. The notches should extend to about $\frac{1}{4}$-inch to $\frac{1}{2}$-inch inside the edges of the press plate. For more accurate positioning where stop pins are used to locate the press plate on the plate cylinder of the press, the notch locations should also agree with these pins. In notching the flat, add two notches that are positioned to exactly match the locations of the pins on the press. This is especially desirable when using re-grained plates, whose edges have previously been distorted on the press.

Checking the Taping of Negatives. Check to see that all negatives are securely attached. Then release the flat from the stripping or layout table. Flop it over, negative-side down.

Cutting Windows in Goldenrod Base. Using a sharp razor blade or frisket knife, carefully cut out the exposure openings behind each printing area.

First test the cutting pressure on a waste piece of goldenrod paper placed over a waste film. A single cutting stroke should cut clean through the paper but only lightly mark the film.

When cutting the exposure openings try to clear all fine printing detail and halftones by at least $\frac{3}{8}$ inch. This reduces or eliminates the thickening of printing detail due to out-of-contact undercutting of the exposure light in plate-making. If narrow paper strips remain between negatives, cut them away. Replace them with strips of red or brown

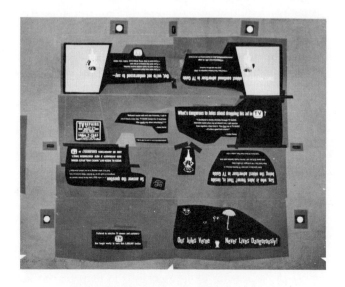

Exposure cutouts on goldenrod flat.

pressure-sensitive cellophane tape so that they cover the exposed gap between the negatives.

Also, cut the goldenrod paper away behind register, trim, halftone gray scale, and other marks or controls that are to print on the press sheet. Finally cut an opening in the flat for attaching the GATF Sensitivity Guide so that it will be exposed on the press plate outside the press sheet area.

Checking for Loose Masking. Note any loosely attached edges around the cutout openings. Fasten them down with tabs of pressure-sensitive tape so that the flat assembly will be securely held together.

Checking All Printing Areas. Check the detail of the entire flat against the dummy and copy. Make certain that no work detail is covered by the goldenrod paper, opaque, or by bits of tape that may accidentally have adhered to the film surface. If pinholes or light exposure gaps remain, spot them out with opaque or cover them with tabs of red or brown pressure-sensitive cellophane tape. If large

areas require spotting-out and do not contain printing detail, time can be saved by covering them with thin red masking paper or foil.

Marking the Flat. When the flat is satisfactory, mark the job name, number, and other required detail on the margins of the flat. Then enter the job time records. Make notes of any difficulties or defects that required additional time, or that will detract from the quality of the job.

Making of Brownprint Proofs. If the job jacket requires brownprint proofs, make them, or have them made by the platemaker. This will depend upon the location of the vacuum frame and other equipment that is required for this purpose.

Transmitting the Completed Flat to the Platemaker. If the flat is large or must be transported some distance, use a heavy manila or fiberboard folder to protect it in transit.

Section Seven: Color Stripping

Our presentation of color stripping is divided into the following six subjects: (1) Introduction to color stripping, (2) Color flats on goldenrod paper, (3) Flats on plastic or plate glass, (4) Blueline flats, (5) Blueline stripping with stripfilm, and (6) Final inspection of color flats. Our discussion is restricted to the essentials of the subject, a much more detailed treatment can be found in GATF Skilled Craft Text No. 512, *Color Stripping for Offset Lithography,* written by the author of this study.

INTRODUCTION TO COLOR STRIPPING

In multicolor reproductions, it is usually necessary to prepare a set of flats. A separate flat is made for each color to be printed. For some simple color jobs where color overlap is not required, a single flat can be used for all colors. This requires changes in masking to separate the colors when making each press plate. Where a set of flats must be prepared, it is important that all of the printing detail in each color flat be in register with the detail on the other color flats. This is necessary not only at the time the flats are made, but also at the time each flat is used to print down the press plate.

Where a high degree of register accuracy is required, it is essential that humidity control be provided in the stripping and platemaking departments. If such control is not possible, the materials used for stripping must be selected so that they will be dimensionally stable with the humidity variations that are experienced.

A set of color flats can be made to register with each other by either of the following methods:

(a) Stripping-up the first flat to a drawn layout. Then using the first flat as a key; the other flats are stripped directly to agree with the locations of the films on the first flat.

(b) Using identical blueline images on a set of plastic or plate glass sheets; the films for each color are then attached to a separate blueline flat.

These methods require that the blueline key, or the first flat stripped-up, must carry all of the necessary positioning marks or detail that will be needed for the other flats. The key flat may therefore carry a combination of detail that are to print in several colors. This may require duplicate negatives or positives of this detail for use on the key. If the key flat is also to be used in platemaking as one of the color flats, this additional color register detail or films must be removed or masked out after the set of bluelines has been completed, and before the key flat is sent to the platemaker.

COLOR FLATS ON GOLDENROD PAPER

The stripping of the first of a set of color flats on goldenrod paper is similar to the procedure used for preparing a goldenrod flat for single-color printing. The layout is first drawn (laterally reversed). The negatives for the first color, usually the black printer, are stripped-up in position. The exposure openings are then cut through the back. The sheet centermarks can also serve as the color register marks. Sheet corner marks, that may also be trim marks, are helpful to trace the cause of fanning out, or other misregister difficulties that may show up on the press sheet.

Using First Flat as Key. After the first color flat is completely prepared, it is again squared-up with the layout or stripping table, emulsion-side up, and taped down securely. A sheet of goldenrod paper for the second color flat is then placed over it. The sheet is squared to the first flat, and then taped down. Make certain that no waves or other distortions exist in either flat.

Handling Close Fitting Color Jobs. If a close color fit is necessary, first cut small openings through the top goldenrod flat in spot register locations where the subject register marks or fitting detail are located. Slip a waste plastic cutting sheet between the flats in the area each cut-out is to be made, so as not to damage the negatives on the lower flat. If close register is not essential, the upper negatives can be located to the lower through the thickness of the goldenrod paper.

Collimating for Close Register Jobs. When positioning and attaching the negatives to the second color flat, be careful to sight straight down over each register mark or matching detail. Otherwise the combined thickness of the film and the goldenrod paper may permit a parallax displacement. A small sighting tube or collimating magnifier is desirable to direct the line of sight straight down.

Registering a film by superimposition.

This helps to avoid misregister errors. The sheet color register marks are also attached to the second flat. Identify each flat by its printing color, such as "Yellow," "Blue," or "Cyan." Then cut away the exposure openings for each as previously described.

The remaining color flats will be prepared similarly. Use the first flat as a key on which to assemble the negatives for each of the other colors by superimposition. Identify each flat by name and job number.

FLATS ON PLASTIC OR PLATE GLASS

If goldenrod flats cannot provide the required accuracy, or if positive flats are to be stripped-up, it will be necessary to use sheet plastic or plate glass as the base material. The layout can be drawn directly on the plastic or glass base by using a light-blue transparent "acetate" ink. This ink will guide in placement of the films but will not interfere with exposure in platemaking.

More commonly, the layout is first drawn on a sheet of white paper or tracing paper. The plastic sheet is then se-

cured in position over this layout. The films are attached to the plastic sheet with tabs of pressure-sensitive tape. If the films are positives, a transparent tape is used. The spaces between positive films are left uncovered. If the films are negatives, the gaps between the films are blocked-out with strips of red masking paper or tape. Alternately orange colored vinyl plastic sheets are available and can be used the same way as goldenrod paper.

Standard stripping practices are used to prepare the layout, and to position and attach the films. As the thickness of the plastic sheet can cause a parallax displacement, it is essential to sight straight down in positioning each film. A sighting tube or collimated magnifier will aid in such registration as was previously described.

BLUELINE FLATS

For high accuracy stripping, particularly if plate glass is to be used as the flat material, color register is best obtained by printing down the same blueline guide image on each of the set of plastic or glass plates to be used for the color set. To make a set of blueline flats, several steps are necessary. These are described in the following:

Preparing the Key Flat. Prepare a key flat that carries all the register marks and detail that is needed to position all of the films on every color flat. Either negatives or positives may be used on the key flat. Negatives are preferred. If the key is to be used solely as a key, its layout must be correct-reading.

The bluelines printed down from a correct-reading key flat will then be laterally reversed, as is required for stripping.

Blueline Keys for Plate Glass and for Plastic. A correct-reading key or intermediate should always be used for making bluelines on plate glass. If the key is prepared on a sheet plastic base, it can serve as one of the color flats and also as a master to print down bluelines on the other flats. When this is done the key is laid out and stripped-up in the laterally reversed arrangement.

Printing Down the Bluelines. In printing down the bluelines the key flat is placed on the sensitized blueline sheet or plate with the film side towards or away from the sensitized blueline surface depending on the reading order required in the flats. By using a single-arc lamp for printing down, the bluelines for the remainder of the set made from a key flat with its film side out-of-contact with the bluelines will also be sharply defined and will also be laterally reversed as is required for stripping.

Sensitizing the Plastic or Plate Glass. Sensitize each of the plastic sheets or plate glass with a blueline solution. While this solution can be mixed to formula, it is better and more economical (time considered) to purchase prepared solutions for this purpose. Each sheet surface must be thoroughly cleaned to de-grease it and to remove foreign material. This can be done by washing with a fine scouring powder, or with any good water-soluble glass cleaner, followed by flushing with water. The blueline sensitizer is applied to the plastic or glass sheet in a whirler at about 35 to 40 rpm and dried.

Exposing the Sensitized Plastic or Plate Glass. Each sheet is then exposed. The exposure time is about the same as that used in platemaking. Development is done under running water, assisted by light circulation of a cotton wad. The image can be intensified by flowing a one percent solution of hydrochloric acid over the developed image. Then flush the blueline with water and dry it. Exact procedure may vary slightly with the proprietary solutions used. Detailed instructions are usually available from the supplier.

BLUELINE STRIPPING WITH STRIPFILM

If stripfilm is to be used to strip-up a set of blueline flats, the cameraman will supply the film in either dry or wet condition. For immediate stripping, they are usually supplied wet just as the films are removed from the wash water after development and fixing. More commonly, the cameraman will dry the stripfilm and turn over the complete set of dried films to the stripper.

Materials and Tools for Working with Stripfilm. Before working with stripfilm, all the necessary materials must be obtained and placed conveniently for use. This includes: (1) *Acetic acid solution.* You need a photographic tray containing a three percent solution of acetic acid. The tray should be slightly larger in size than the largest stripfilm section to be used. (2) *Blotter squares.* These should be cut to about two by two inches in size from lintless photographic blotting paper. The squares are used as squeegees to wipe down the stripfilm in position and to remove the excess water or cement. (3) *Stripfilm cement.* A cement is necessary if the stripfilm is to be attached emulsion-side up, or if the film is to be applied to a vinyl or polyester base. (4) *Miscellaneous tools.* Razor blades, artist brushes, litho needles, dividers, straight-edge, and other tools should all be ready before you begin to work.

The Wet and the Dry Technique of Handling Stripfilm. Stripfilm will usually adhere well to clean glass or acetate flats or to the emulsions of other films when it is transferred and flopped emulsion-side down. For wet application the stripfilm may first be soaked in the acetic

acid solution for about fifteen seconds to soften the gelatin emulsion.

In dry stripping, the stripfilm membrane is carefully released from its base by the stripper. Depending on the technique used, either the released dry stripfilm or the soaked stripfilm on its base is then placed in approximate position over the blueline image on a small puddle of stripfilm cement.

In the wet stripping technique a razor blade or a frisket knife is used to separate the stripfilm from its base along one edge. The base is then carefully peeled away, leaving the stripfilm membrane section on the flat. (Some stripping films require a warm water solution to aid in their separation.) The blotter squares are then used to carefully shift the stripfilm membrane by light wiping action so that it registers with the blue image. Light wiping strokes are further applied from the center of the film outward, so as to squeegee out the excess water or cement and to secure the stripfilm in registered position to the blueline base.

Joining Stripfilm Sections. It is usually advisable to leave an excess margin around each film section if it does not interfere with the adjoining film sections. If printing detail between adjoining sections is to be closely fitted, both sections should be applied in position to overlap each other. The two stripfilm membranes are then trimmed together. This is done while they are still damp, immediately after they are squeegeed down. Use a sharp razor blade and a straight-edge or steel triangle, if necessary, to obtain a clean cut. Then remove the waste film strips. Squeegee the released margins down once more. A little additional cement can be applied sparingly along the margins with a brush, if the stripfilm edges are too dry to adhere properly.

Using Stripfilm Emulsion-Side Up. When applying stripfilm emulsion-side up, it is necessary to use stripfilm cement to securely adhere the film to the flat. The procedure is similar as when flopping the film. In wet stripping the membrane is made to slide off its base into location. If stripfilm is to be applied to a vinyl or polyester base to obtain increased accuracy of location, the plastic base should be purchased already coated with a gelatin substratum. This will aid in obtaining good adhesion of the stripfilm. Otherwise special stripfilm cements must be used. Stripfilm applied directly to uncoated vinyl and without special cements will usually come loose after drying.

Opaquing Stripfilm Flats. When applying opaque to stripfilm flats, use single brush strokes. Thick opaque applications or repeated strokes in an area that is already moistened with opaque can release the stripfilm edges. For this reason, non-water soluble opaques that are made with an alcohol, turpentine, or petroleum solvent are preferable for use on stripfilm flats.

FINAL INSPECTION OF COLOR FLATS

After any flat or set of color flats is completed, they must be thoroughly checked against the job jacket, dummy, copy, and other instructions for completeness and accuracy. Ex-

Applying a stripfilm section.

cept in simple or low-cost jobs, it is usually advisable to make brownprint proofs from the flats. These proofs should simulate the press sheet. They may consist of a single print for a simple one-side printed job. A partial flat should be

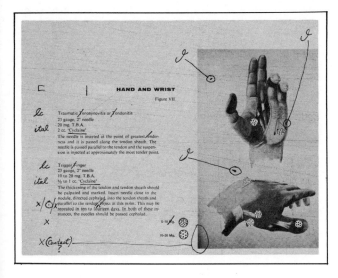

Brownprint proof.

repeated when printing down the brownprint just as will be done for its step-and-repeat use in platemaking. Alternately blueprint paper can be similarly used for negative flats.

If the job is a work-and-turn or work-and-tumble job, two brownprints can be made for pasting together. It is better to use a brownprint paper that is sensitized on both sides. The prints are made on the opposite sides of the brownprint paper and are keyed to each other through butterfly cutouts or through punched holes.

In a multicolor job, each of the color flats is successively exposed to the same sheet of brownprint paper in register with each other. Butterfly cutouts, register marks, or plastic hole tabs and dowels can be used to obtain this register between successive exposures. The exposure times used are different for each flat. The black printer is given the full exposure time. Those for the other colors are reduced by about 50 percent or more each time. In this way there will be a noticeable difference in the shades of brown that are developed from each color flat that was exposed.

These brownprints serve the same purpose as galley and press proofs in printing. They are used for editing and for checking folding and other finishing operations. Needed corrections are then added to the flats before the press plates are made.

Section Eight: Imposition

Imposition is the arrangement and positioning of pages, checks, labels, bags, box covers or other units of a job on a sheet or section of a web of paper to meet the requirements of the job. These requirements vary with each job depending upon specifications. Without some systematic approach to certain fundamentals, the matter remains confusing regardless of the amount of experience we may have had.

Our study of impositions is divided into the following seven points: (1) Basic information, (2) Arrangement of pages, (3) Positioning of pages, (4) Kinds of binding, (5) Kinds of impositions, (6) Units other than pages, and (7) Summary. Each of these seven points is individually discussed in the following.

BASIC INFORMATION

One of the first things that must be determined is the stock size. If this has been determined, we arrange the units on this size to the best possible advantage to meet the requirements. If the stock size has not been determined, then someone must figure the minimum stock required for each unit and how many such units can be run together on a sheet or section of web, allowing for essential trims and gripper edge, and considering the length of run, the limitations of press, cutting, folding and other finishing equipment.

Basic Information for Jobs to be Folded. Let us first consider the imposition of pages of a job which must be folded so that the pages appear in numerical order with proper margins after the job is bound and trimmed. The information we must have is as follows: (1) Type page size, (2) Trimmed job size, (3) Trims — top, outside and foot, (4) Untrimmed page size, (5) Kind of binding: Saddle stitch, side stitch, sewed, pasted or glued, and (6) Margins — position of type page on trimmed stock for one page.

A Typical Example. Let us fill in the above items of information for a typical job:

1. Type page size: 4″ x 6½″
2. Trimmed size: 6″ x 9″
3. Trims: Head ¼″, outside ¼″, foot ¼″
4. Untrimmed page size: 6¼″ x 9½″
5. Saddle stitch (no stock allowance for binding)
6. Margins: Bind ¾″, top 1″, outside 1¼″, foot 1½″.

With 6¼″ x 9½″ of stock required for each page, it is a simple matter to figure the amount of stock required for any number of pages. We could print 16 pages on one side of a 25″ x 38″ sheet — 32 pages on both sides. Maximum sheet size is determined by press and folder capacities. Let us assume that our press size confined us to 16-page plates and that our folder confined us to a 32-page signature. A signature is the folded sheet as it comes from the folder. This would require 25″ x 38″ stock.

In some plants all the foregoing information is shown on an exact size page layout.

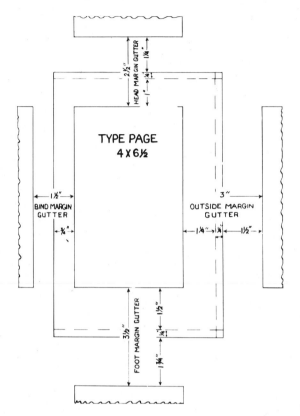

Page layout containing all information regarding the individual page and its position in relation to surrounding pages.

ARRANGEMENT OF PAGES

Before we can position the 16 pages in a form, we must determine where and how to place each page so that the head will come at the top of the book and so that the page numbers will appear in consecutive sequence. To do this, we must have a folded dummy, folded in the same way that the printed sheet will be folded and with the folder guide edges marked. This should be made or approved by the person in charge of the folding operation.

Making a Folder Dummy. The binding edge and the top of this dummy will be evident. With scissors, cut a notch in the top to show page heads and trim along dotted lines so corners can be folded back for numbering.

Arrangement of Signatures. Before numbering the dummy, we must determine whether the signatures are placed on top of one another as for a side stitch or sewed book or whether one signature is inserted inside another as is required for a saddle stitch job. For this job, we are considering a saddle stitch, one signature inside the other, and the first signature would contain the first 16 and last 16 pages of the job. If the job was 64 pages this dummy would be numbered 1 to 16 on the first half and 49 to 64 on the last half.

Outside Plates and Inside Plates. This 32-page signature is to be printed with two 16-page plates, each containing the pages shown on one side of the dummy. The plate containing the low page of the signature is called the "outside" plate because this low page is always on the outside of the folded signature. The plate containing the next to the low page is called the "inside" plate because this page is always on the inside of the folded signature.

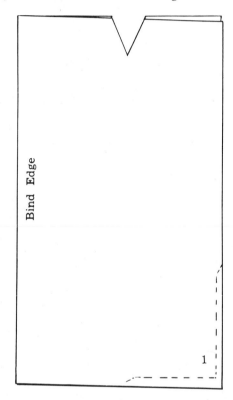

Folder dummy with notch cut in top to show heads. Dummy is trimmed along dotted lines so corners can be folded back for numbering.

Folder Dummy. The folder dummy shows us the following: (1) Press gripper edge and side guide. These correspond with folder guides on dummy. (2) Which way to place page heads. (3) Which pages go into each 16-page plate. (4) How to arrange the pages for consecutive pagination of the finished job.

POSITIONING OF PAGES

Each page is positioned at the head and binding edge. As we examine a 16-page print, plate or one side of a folder dummy, we observe two head-margin gutters (space between heads of type pages) and two bind-margin gutters. We need only locate the centers of these gutters.

For the job under consideration each page requires $6\frac{1}{4}''$ x $9\frac{1}{2}''$ of stock or a 25" x 38" sheet for a 16-page plate. The centers of the head-margin gutters will be $9\frac{1}{2}''$ from the center of the 38" dimension. The center of each bind-margin gutter will be $6\frac{1}{4}''$ from the center of the 25" dimension.

The Lay-Sheet. To position the pages for an offset plate, we first prepare a lay-sheet. A sheet of 70- or 80-lb. coated yellow or orange masking paper slightly larger than the press plate is used for this. One edge is marked to identify the gripper edge.

Paper Line, Gripper Edge, and Clamp Margin. Next mark the "paper line" across the gripper edge of the lay-sheet. This shows the position of the gripper edge of the printed sheet in relation to the gripper edge of the press plate. This information should be available for each press. If not, obtain it from the pressroom or from the manufacturer. This is different on each press but let us assume that it is 2″ back from the edge of the press plate. We measure and mark the lay-sheet two inches back from the gripper edge to show the position of stock in relation to the press plate. This is called the clamp margin. Later when we position the lay-sheet to the press plate in the printing frame, we simply make the front edge of the press plate flush with the front edge of the lay-sheet.

Bind Margins. To find the center of the bind-margin gutters, we measure 12½″ back from the paper line and mark the center of the 25″ sheet dimension. The centers of the bind-margin gutters will be 6¼″ in both directions from this center of the 25″ sheet dimension.

Head Margin. To find the center of the head-margin gutters, we mark the center of the lay-sheet crosswise, at the gripper edge. The centers of the head-margin gutters will be 9½″ in both directions from the center of the sheet crosswise.

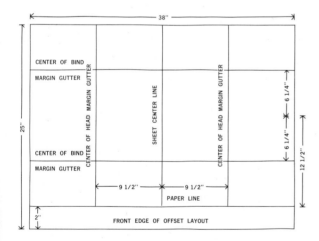

Lay-sheet showing paper line; center of head-margin gutters, 9½″ from center — crosswise; and center of bind-margin gutters, 6¼″ from center of 25″ dimension.

Page and Marks. Next select the pages for the plate you plan to make as shown on one side of the folder dummy. These pages should have marks showing the centers of the head-margin gutters and the bind-margin gutters.

Indicating Page Marks. They can be printed with hairline rules when pulling reproduction proofs. Usually two or four pages are proofed together. They can be drawn on positives or scribed through the opaque area on negatives. The bind-edge marks are on the left of odd numbered pages 1, 3, 5, etc. and on the right of even numbered pages, 2, 4, 6, etc.

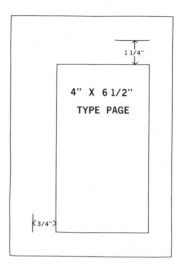

Marks on each page showing centers of bind-and-head-margin gutters.

Positioning of Pages. The pages are placed for proper arrangement and each page is positioned by registering the marks on the negatives or positives with the bind- and head-margin gutter centerlines on the lay-sheet.

For an 8-page plate the feet of pages will be to the gripper edge. We locate the center of the head-margin gutter by measuring back from the paper line a distance corresponding with the total length of stock required for each page, 9½″. For 32 pages we have two head-margin gutters parallel with the gripper edge. The center of this second head-margin gutter would be the amount of paper required for three page lengths or 28½″ from the paper line. The centers of the bind margins on a 32-page plate would be 6¼″ and 18¾″ (3-page widths) in both directions from the center mark.

The side of the lay-sheet to which the negatives are attached must be against the coated side of the press plate. It is customary to secure the page negatives on top of the

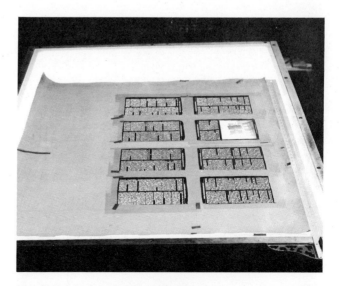

Finished lay-sheet with masking paper cut out over type pages.

lay-sheet, emulsion-side up, to correspond with a face-down folder dummy, and then turn the lay-sheet over before exposing the plate.

After the negatives for a plate are all arranged and positioned in the above manner the lay-sheet is turned over and the lay-sheet masking paper is cut away over each type page.

It is sometimes possible to attach the negatives to the bottom side of the lay-sheet. When this is done, the lay-sheet is not turned over and the page numbers must correspond with the face-up folder dummy.

Lay-Sheets for Surface Plates and for Deep-Etch Plates. The foregoing applies specifically to the positioning of negatives on a lay-sheet for surface plates. When positives are used for deep-etch plates, a transparent key sheet is sometimes used in place of a lay-sheet but the fundamentals of imposition (arranging and positioning the pages) require the same detailed information and involve identical figuring.

Regardless of page size or number of pages, the fundamentals are the same. We need a page layout or equivalent information shown in any way. We need a folder dummy, made or approved by the person in charge of folding and showing the best way to fold a sheet containing the specified number of pages. We prepare a lay-sheet showing the paper line and the centers of the head-margin gutters and the bind-margin gutters. We place the pages to correspond with the face-up or face-down folder dummy depending on whether the negatives are attached to the top side or bottom side of the lay-sheet. We position each page at the head and bind edge.

Imposition, Stripping and Paste-Up. There is a tendency to confuse imposition with stripping and paste-up. Generally stripping and paste-up are involved in making up a page or unit; imposition is the arrangement and positioning of the made-up units.

However, there are other factors we need to consider, specifically: (1) Different kinds of binding, and (2) Different kinds of imposition.

KINDS OF BINDING

The various kinds of binding are of interest to the man who prepares the page layout depending on whether or not they influence the visible margin at the bind edge.

The saddle stitch, sewed job or glued job permits the bound job to show the entire bind margin. These require no consideration with one exception — the saddle stitch "push-out."

Saddle Stitch Push-Out. When a number of signatures are inserted, one inside the other for a saddle stitch,

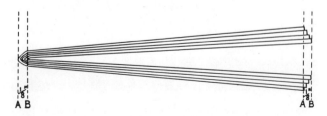

Illustrating the push-out on a saddle-stitched booklet.

each folded signature is pushed out slightly, about $\frac{1}{32}$" for each 16-page signature of .003" stock with a resulting loss of the outside margin. Allowance is made for this by reducing the bind-margin gutter and adding this amount to the outside-margin gutter every three or four signatures on a many-signature job.

Extra Bind Margins on Side-Stitched Binding. On a side-stitch, pasted binding or fastener that does not permit the job to open up to the fold, allowance must be made in the page layout for the amount of bind margin that is lost (for example, on a side stitch where the stitches are placed in the stock about $\frac{1}{4}$" from the binding edge). We must allow for this $\frac{1}{4}$" plus extra bind margin lost.

Preparing a Binding Dummy. The best way to determine how much is lost is to make up a blank dummy and stitch it, then observe just how much of the bind margin is lost. Such jobs require more stock, less margins or narrower type pages than if saddle stitched, sewed, glued or spiral bound. Many side-stitched jobs must allow $\frac{3}{8}$" extra for lost bind-edge margin.

KINDS OF IMPOSITIONS

Different kinds of impositions are employed depending upon press and folder sizes, length of run, nature of job and other factors. Those most commonly employed are as follows: (1) Sheetwise, (2) Work-and-turn, and (3) Work-and-tumble.

Sheetwise Impositions. When a different plate is used for each side of the sheet with the same gripper edge, the imposition is termed sheetwise.

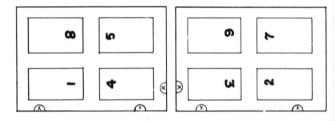

Two 4-page sheetwise plates for an 8-page booklet.

Work-and-Turn Impositions. When one plate is used for both sides of the sheet with the same gripper edge, the imposition is termed work-and-turn.

Work-and-Tumble Impositions. When a sheet is turned for back-up so that the gripper edge on the first side becomes the tail edge for backing up, this is termed work-and-tumble. It can be printed with one plate for both sides or a separate plate for each side depending on the nature of the job.

Any job with pages on both sides of the sheet can be printed with two sheetwise plates. Most such jobs can be printed with one work-and-turn plate. We illustrate this with an 8-page booklet. The folder dummy is 8 pages. The job could be printed with two 4-page sheetwise plates or one 8-page work-and-turn plate.

Back-Up on Different Impositions. It will be observed that with the two sheetwise plates, pages 2, 3, 6 and

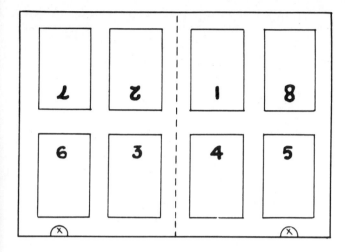

One 8-page work-and-turn plate for an 8-page booklet.

7 on one plate back-up pages 1, 4, 5 and 8 on the other plate. Now on the 8-page work-and-turn plate, observe how pages 2, 3, 6 and 7 on half of the plate back-up pages 1, 4, 5 and 8 on the other half of the plate when the sheet is turned over.

The work-and-turn plate produces two printed copies and after backing up, the sheet is cut in half.

Folder Dummy and Imposition. One 8-page folder dummy is used for either the sheetwise or the work-and-turn impositions. For sheetwise impositions one side of the folder dummy shows the pages that go into one sheetwise plate. The press guide edges should be the same as the folder guide edges. For the 8-page work-and-turn imposition the short dimension folder guide edge becomes the press gripper edge and the long dimension folder guide edge becomes the cut edge in the center of the press sheet. Each side of the folder dummy becomes half of the work-and-turn plate.

3		9	1
10		7	12
9		8	11
4		5	2

A work-and-tumble sheet printed with one plate. This is a 12-page booklet on 17" x 28" stock. The back edge of the first side becomes the gripper edge for the back-up so that page 1 will back-up page 2. After printing, the sheet is cut on the heavy line, producing two identical 12-page sections. Two sheetwise forms would have to run on a strip of paper 8½" x 28" and would double the impressions.

Work-and-tumble sheets are printed only when conventional impositions are not practical. Work-and-tumble sheets should be trimmed to produce uniform size around the cylinder.

Selecting the Right Kind of Imposition. The choice between sheetwise and work-and-turn impositions involves number of pages, sheet sizes, length of run, press and folder capacities and any other factors which determine the number of press impressions and the number of sheets to be folded. With few exceptions, the aim is to produce the job on the equipment available at the lowest cost and this is basically a matter of mathematics.

Reduced Spoilage. In some cases the matter of keeping spoilage at a minimum is a factor in choosing work-and-turn impositions. With sheetwise impositions more allowance must be made for spoilage to avoid re-runs when the back-up spoilage is excessive. With a work-and-turn imposition any shortage on back-up can be immediately made up with the plate on the press which prints both sides of the sheet. This permits reduced allowance for spoilage.

UNITS OTHER THAN PAGES

The arrangement and positioning of units other than pages require a unit layout or equivalent information. We must have the following: (1) Trimmed or diecut shape and size of unit, (2) Stock required for unit — allowance for bleeds and diecutting, and (3) Position of printed matter on unit stock.

On work where there is white space on all sides of printed matter, we need only know the unit stock size and the position of the print on this size, as a 3" x 5" print centered on 4" x 6" label.

Where bleed edges come together no extra stock need be allowed. A continuous print produces two bleed edges when two units are cut apart. Where a bleed comes next to an unprinted edge some extra stock must be allowed for cutting off the printing beyond the bleed. Sometimes the unit is composed of two or more individual units as in checkbooks, stamps, and cigar bands.

Unit Size and Stock Size. An individual check and stub may require $3\frac{1}{16}$" x $10\frac{15}{16}$" of stock. When this check is to be printed and bound in books, three to a page, the trimmed size would be $9\frac{3}{16}$" x $10\frac{15}{16}$". If $\frac{1}{16}$" trim was allowed for head, outside and foot of each book, the stock required for each untrimmed page of three checks would be $9\frac{5}{16}$" x 11". In this case a 3-check unit size would be practical. We could get 6 such 3-check units out of a 22" x 28" sheet as follows:

$$\begin{array}{l} 9\frac{15}{16}" \text{ x } 11" \text{ unit size} \\ \underline{3 \quad\quad \text{ x } 2 = 6 \text{ out}} \\ 27\frac{15}{16}" \text{ x } 22" \text{ press sheet (28" x 22")} \end{array}$$

With small units like stamps or cigar bands a number of individual units are positioned on a negative. This group of images is a practical unit size and involves less figuring. Stamps $\frac{3}{4}$" x $\frac{7}{8}$" may be grouped 100-up on a negative, ten rows in each direction, requiring $7\frac{1}{2}$" x $8\frac{3}{4}$" of stock. It is a simple matter to figure how many $7\frac{1}{2}$" x $8\frac{3}{4}$" units come out

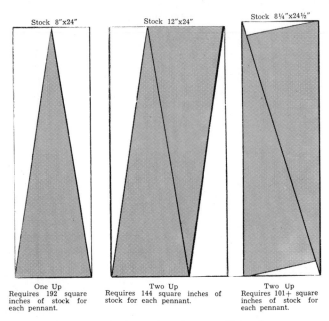

Stock 8"x24"   Stock 12"x24"   Stock 8¼"x24½"

One Up
Requires 192 square
inches of stock for
each pennant.

Two Up
Requires 144 square inches of
stock for each pennant.

Two Up
Requires 101+ square
inches of stock for
each pennant.

Laying-out triangular shapes efficiently.

of any sheet or what stock size would be required for any number of units this size.

Keystone-Shaped or Triangular Designs. With many keystone-shaped or triangular designs to be diecut, a unit of two or more represents a great saving of stock. The value of different layouts for 8" x 24" pennants is evident from the illustration of imposition for pennants.

Diecut Folding Boxes. Diecut boxes present an interesting challenge in arranging and positioning several units on a sheet for greatest economy. The first step is to reduce a box to a flat diecut section or sections. The next step is to see how multiple boxes or sections can be arranged on minimum stock, making sure that bleeds and cutting and creasing can be handled with this arrangement.

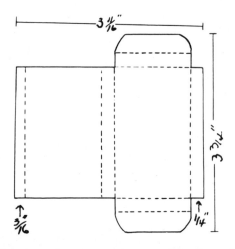

A one-piece box opened to a flat sheet 3¾" x 3 11/16". Solid lines are die-cut edges. Dotted lines are creased for folds. The 3/16" strip, on left, folds under and is pasted to the ¼" strip at right.

Nesting for Economy of Stock. It will be observed that the shape of each diecut box or section presents all kinds of possibilities for arrangement that results in economy of stock. This requires accurate sheet layout which should always be approved by the die-maker.

Bags must be reduced to flat sheet by opening them up at the glued edges. Then we can see exactly what operations were necessary to produce them and make the unit layout accordingly.

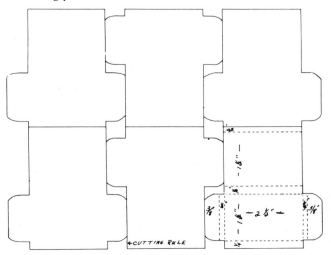

Six boxes arranged for greatest stock economy. This box could be arranged in a similar manner for 8, 9, 10 or 12 up. After figuring such an arrangement, check any bleed edges. Also check with die-maker.

Layouts for Straight Cutting. Wherever a sheet must be cut in a straight line as with a conventional cutter or chopper be sure a straight line cut can be made. This limits us on certain arrangements that would otherwise be possible.

Margins on Gripper Edge Sheet-Fed Jobs. All sheet-fed presses require blank margin at the gripper edge. This normally is somewhere from 5/16" to ½" depending on press size. We can only print so close to the front edge of the blanket and this front edge of the blanket must clear the grippers which hold this sheet. Where the print on the unit layout allows less than this, extra stock must be allowed. Many check jobs do not have enough margin at head, outside or foot. However, at the bind edge, there is adequate margin. On check jobs, we must run the bind edge to the gripper or allow extra stock for gripper bite.

Press-sheet guide edges should correspond with the two edges to which these sheets must be jogged for cutting, binding or other operations. On checks the head and bind edges are used for cutting and binding. The units should be arranged and press guide edges used so this is possible.

Impositions for Roll-Fed Jobs. Imposition for roll-fed presses is basically the same as for sheet-fed presses. We must have a page or unit layout or equivalent information. We must have a section of a web equivalent to one full cylinder revolution. This must be marked showing the specific pages or units that must appear on one or both sides of this web section and how they are arranged. Where multiple rolls are used a web section for each roll must be marked. The web sections used for imposition are obtained from or approved by the person in charge of the press.

SUMMARY

Imposition as used herein implies the arrangement and positioning of pages or other units on a sheet or web section: (1) We need a page or unit dummy containing all the information pertaining to the individual page or unit; (2) We need a folder dummy or a web section showing what pages go on each side of the stock and where and how these pages are arranged; (3) The page or unit dummy is prepared from the job specifications; and (4) The folder dummy is determined by the stock used, the size of the job, the press and folder limitations.

Like anything else, we learn from practice. Study one step, practice it, then go to the next step. This will make each step clear and give you the fundamentals of all imposition.

Section Nine: Photocomposing

Photocomposing in the original sense of the word is a lithographic technique for combining many images according to a predetermined plan into a single unit. In the more recent time, photocomposing has become a vague term because the same word is also promiscuously used to indicate the setting of type by means of photography. In this study the word photocomposing is exclusively used in its original sense of combining many images other than letter forms into a single unit.

The Products of Photocomposing. The products of photocomposing can be divided into two kinds: (1) press plates, and (2) multiples of images on a photographic material such as film or plates. Each of these two kinds of products is arrived at in a different way and is used for different purposes.

Kinds of Photocomposed Press Plates. Press plates with many exposures on them fall into two main categories. A press plate where many images of the same subject appear is called a step-and-repeat or "duplicate" plate. The press plate that has many images, all different, is called a "combination" plate.

Some plates are a combination of both, such as those found in label shops. A plate may have four labels for one customer, six for another, and two for another. Thus when this plate is put on the press for a twenty-five thousand run, one customer will get 100,000 labels, another 150,000 and another 50,000.

Photocomposed images on Photographic Materials. The photocomposing machines are also used for making multiple images on photographic film or plate. In such cases the product of the photocomposing machine is known as a negative or positive assembly, or as multiple negatives or multiple positives. Negative or positive assemblies are often intermediates to be further used in the photocomposing of press plates. But they can also be used directly for stripping or platemaking.

How Images Were Assembled in the Past of Lithography. The need for combining several images was recognized very early in the history of lithography, and a means of making duplicates was soon found. This was very important to lithography because in those days the lithographic process was devoted almost entirely to pictorial subjects. The method for making multiple images was termed "hand-transfer" and resembled the decalcomania method of transferring images.

The original was drawn by hand on a flat grained limestone. The image was inked-up and several impressions made on transfer paper. The several images were then transferred to a larger stone which became thereby the press form made up of multiples of the original. In multicolor work, register was accomplished by fitting to register marks by eye.

During the transition from handwork to the present photomechanical method, certain shortcomings became apparent in the hand-transfer method of making multiples. The greatest shortcoming was the difficulty of exact register. Another was that there were certain losses of tone between the negative and the final images on the plate. As long as originals were made by crayon, fine details of drawing did not reproduce in all colors. But now the camera picks up such details in every color. Exact register, to pinpoint accuracy, must be obtained between the black and the color plates. Tone loss became important because lithographers wanted to print in fewer colors.

Shortly after the turn of the century, these facts were recognized by William C. Huebner, a lithographer who was gifted with a tremendous inventive and mechanical talent. He envisioned a means of making every duplicate a perfect reproduction of the original and of positioning these reproductions on the plate with precise mechanical accuracy. This aim would require a machine that would expose a negative directly upon the press plate many times and in exact predetermined positions: expose-and-shift; step-and-repeat. By 1915 such a machine was put into operation. The photocomposing machine was born.

At the present time photocomposing is one of the important lithographic techniques. Our study follows the GATF Skilled Craft Text No. 515, Photocomposing, originally written by the author of this section. The reader finds the following subjects discussed: (1) the Rutherford Precision Photocomposing Machine, (2) the Lanston-Monotype Huebner Vertical Photocomposing Machine, (3) the layout of a photocomposing department and the maintenance of its equipment, (4) job layouts for photocomposing, (5) operating procedure, (6) register, (7) making multiple negatives, (8) contact, (9) nesting forms, (10) troubles in photocomposing, and (11) other modern machines. Each of these eleven points is individually presented in the following.

THE RUTHERFORD MACHINES

Two models of the Rutherford Photo-Composing Machine are manufactured. One is the standard semi-automatic model and the other is the fully automatic Ruth-O-Matic. Both models can be furnished either in the RM series in four different sizes, or in the PL series in three different sizes.

The Rutherford PL is a semi-automatic model. This is an upright machine made in three sizes. The PLB takes plates up to 48" x 60", and negatives or positives up to 28" x 32" standard and 32" x 32" special. The PLC takes plates up to 50" x 69", and transparencies up to 28" x 32" standard and 32" x 32" special. The PLD takes plates up to 58" x 78", and transparencies up to 30" x 40" standard and 40" x 40" special.

Plate Movement and Register Carrier Movement. On this machine the negative carrier moves only up-and-down, for vertical positioning. The plate moves sideways for horizontal position. Movement is accomplished by large precision screws, and the amount of movement is controlled by the number and fractions of turns of these screws. The screws are manufactured either for power operation, or for hand. The number of turns is counted by devices that indicate a movement of .001".

Courtesy Rutherford Machinery Co.

Rutherford Photocomposing Machine

Two-Movement Measuring Devices. The Rutherford Precision Composing Machine has two measuring devices. Each consists of a Veeder counter that counts inches and tenths. The dial registers hundredths and thousandths of an inch; the hand wheel is used for the final few thousandths of movement.

Centralized Control Board. The machine has a centralized control board with valves for the vacuum and for the air cylinder that moves the plate bed back. There is a gage for indicating the amount of vacuum and also a timing device. At top center of our illustration three push-buttons can be seen. The top button raises the negative carrier, the

bottom one lowers it, and the middle one stops it. Right below these buttons are three more. The left button moves the plate to the left, the right button moves it to the right, and the center one stops it. Other buttons are for vacuum pump and other auxiliary equipment.

Registering on a Rutherford Precision Photo-composing Machine. Register is accomplished between colors and to the register device by fine register marks that must be put on the original copy before photographing. These marks are carried through each step and are used in the final positioning of the negative in the machine chase. After that, they are covered up and ignored because a series of registering dowel pins and bushings take care of the rest of the registering steps.

Our description covers merely a few of the more important features of this machine. For more detail see its presentation in the "Resources Section" of this chapter.

THE RUTH-O-MATIC PHOTO-COMPOSING MACHINE

The Ruth-O-Matic machine is fully automatic. It is just like the standard semi-automatic model, except that the setting of the layout positions is also automatic.

The Ruth-O-Matic is an automatic photo-composing machine that is operated from a pre-punched tape or by simple dial controls. It is capable of vertical and horizontal positioning accurate to .001 inch throughout the entire range of the machine. All spacings are measured from the zero reference and not as a distance from the last position. In other words, the machine will programme any number of regular or irregular steps in any manner desired and with an accuracy within .001 inch.

The macine operates much faster than a conventional photo-composing machine as both the vertical and horizontal settings are made simultaneously and the complete exposure cycle is automatically handled by mechanical and electrical controls with no need for attention from the operator.

Perfect register of all plates in a color set or similar layout is assured, regardless of the operator or the shift, since all the plates are produced from the same tape.

The entire step-and-repeat pattern is contained on a 4-inch wide roll of plasic tape. The tape is prepared with a manual punch and punchboard containing 140 hole positions. Each hole is numerically identified and represents a vertical or horizontal coordinate point for positioning the negatives on the plate. Numerical settings, corresponding to the positions of the image drawn on the layout sheet, are transferred to the tape by a punching operation. Additional instructions can be noted on the tape, regarding the chase to be used, number of exposures, top to bottom or to either side, positioning, etc. After punching, the tape can be inspected visually for accuracy. Corrections, if necessary, can be made by patching unwanted holes with pressure sensitive tape and repunching with either a common paper punch or the manual tool. The spool of tape snaps into place in the tape reader and is driven through the reader by a motor.

All operations which the machine can perform automatically are punched on the tape. The tape can also be punched to start a buzzer which signals the operator to perform a manual function, such as inserting a negative or positive or changing its position. While the buzzer is sounding, if so desired, the macine can be programmed to lower the chase automatically to a convenient loading height and held at that position until the operator does his job. Then the chase automatically returns to the proper position for the next shot. The tape is not affected by oil or dirt. The same tape can be used over again to duplicate the original layout with perfect uniformity and accuracy.

The Ruth-O-Matic reader is the control center of the automatic positioning system. The reader contains 140 spring loaded pins which sense the information being fed through it on the tape. The reader automatically controls all vertical and horizontal movements according to the data placed on the tape.

When the sequence of exposure is completed, the reader automatically rewinds the tape, the vacuum holding the press plate is released, and the machine is ready for a new job. If the number of exposures is small, the tape does not have to be used. Coordinates can be taken from the layout sheet and fed directly into the reader by manually dialing the proper settings on the reader control panel. From this point, the machine will position and expose automatically. The Ruth-O-Matic also can be operated manually if this is desired for any reason.

THE LANSTON M-H MACHINES

These are upright, pedestal machines in which the negative carrier moves both vertically and horizontally. The plate does not move. The plate is put into position from the front. The Lanston M-H machine is a fast, entirely hand-operated machine that takes up little room.

Courtesy Lanston Monotype Co.

The Lanston Vertical Photocomposing Machine.

Our illustration shows the machine with a plate in place and the lamp moved out of the way on its overhead rail.

The negative holder is shown, supported by the cross rail and carriage saddle. The chase, with negative, is shown clamped in the carriage. The vacuum pump and motor can be seen behind the machine and the gage at the top. The foot-treadle near the floor applies the vacuum. The vacuum hose to the saddle is not connected in this picture. No timing device is shown.

The Movement of the Negative Carriage. Vertical rails and slides upon which the cross rail is supported may be seen at each side of the backboard. Gear racks on the vertical rails and gears on the cross rail are used for the vertical movement of the negative carriage. The gears are actuated by a hand crank on the right side of a horizontal shaft. The carriage is moved sideways by a gear running on a rack. The rack is fastened to the cross rail.

There are one inch spacers called notch bars on all three rails. Notch segments or keys on each end of the cross rail engage vertical notch bars exactly to the inch position desired. The notch bar assembly runs in a groove and has a one-inch controlled movement. The movement is controlled by a screw at the top of each assembly. These screws are operated by the crank at the upper right corner. One turn of the screw and the micrometer-type cylindrical dial moves the notch bar $\frac{1}{10}$th of an inch. The dial is divided into one hundred scale divisions, therefore, each division represents $\frac{1}{1000}$th of an inch.

The sideways movement of the negative carriage is obtained in the same manner. The saddle is moved by a hand crank, a gear and a rack to the desired notch. The notch bar assembly is then moved by a screw, and readings are made on the $\frac{1}{10}$th scale and the thousandths dial.

The Negative Holder. On this machine the negative holder is made up of a two piece metal frame. One piece is movable within the other and moves with the glass. There is an air-seal frame that also serves as a rest for the glass negative. This may be adjusted for various thicknesses of glass. The movable part of the frame contains the glass clamps and has a rubber air seal that contacts the plate. This inner frame is the one that can be adjusted so that it carries the glass into register.

Registering on the Lanston M-H Photocomposing Machine. Placing the negative in the frame and leveling it is the first step toward register. The glass is then clamped in securely. The frame is placed in the register device using the dowel pins for positioning. A lever is used to move the frame towards the ground glass. The emulsion side of the negative is thereby put in contact with the ground glass. The ground glass has a fine etched, vertical center-line and a series of horizontal lines, one for each size frame. The inner frame and negative is now registered to the lines by using the thumbscrews, and is then locked into position. The images or at least the marks on the negative are now in register relationship with the dowel pins of the negative holder. As these pins fit into identically located bushings in the machine saddle, the register of the negative to the notch bar key is complete.

Making Multiple Negatives on the Lanston M-H Photocomposing Machine. Multiple negatives may be made right on the Lanston M-H machine. If regular film is used, it is necessary that the machine be placed in a darkroom. If some type of slow emulsion film such as Kodak Autopositive is used, orange illumination, as normally found in most photocomposing rooms, is suitable.

When a step-up positive or negative is to be made on glass, an aluminum mask is used so that the glass may be recessed into it, affording a flush surface. The glass fits snugly into the opening of the aluminum plate and is taped around the edges. If the step-up is to be made on film, it is fastened to a plate with sticky-back and put into the machine in the usual manner. The original is set up in the chase in the usual manner. A small bulb or contact lamp with a split-second timer should be used for the exposure. The step-up may then be made exactly like a plate.

Our description of the Lanston M-H machine is not more detailed than the preceding description of the Rutherford product.

THE ATF-GERSON MACHINE

The ATF-Gerson Multiplater is a medium-duty piece of equipment designed for a wide variety of the work most commonly done in moderately sized plants.

The equipment is 6'10-1/2" high, 6'3-1/2" wide, and 34-1/2" deep. It can mount a plate up to 48" x 52" and can expose a maximum of 40" x 50" of this area. The maximum size of the flat or negative that can be placed in the chase is 22" x 28" of which an area of 19" x 25" can be exposed at one time. A smaller chase is also available — 15" x 22" with an exposure area of 12" x 19". Each chase has its own matching arc-lamp hood.

The arc lamp used with this equipment has motor-driven carbons and is separate from the machine itself. It is mounted on wheels and is moved into position for each exposure. The lamp hood fits into the chase so that light curtains or masking screens are not needed. Exposure times are controlled by an automatic reset timer.

The chase can be moved both vertically and horizontally in increments of 1/16th inch. Each increment position is accurate to .001 inch. Built-in controls eliminate any possibility of accidentally scratching the plate. The chases use an acetate cover instead of glass. The manufacturer claims that this makes for better vacuum, less refraction, and easy access for changing flats without removing the chase.

Plates are accurately positioned in the back-board by a horizontal and vertical hole/pin arrangement. The stripping department is provided with a layout grid that mounts register pins. Negatives are stripped onto special, dimensionally stable plastic sheets. These are pre-cut to fit the chase and pre-punched to fit (1) the pins on the layout grid, and (2) matching pins on the chase. This simple pin-hole system matches the layout grid to the chase. If the negative is accurately registered on the grid, it will be registered with equal accuracy when the flat is mounted in the machine chase.

Shooting layouts of machine positions are calculated from a zero reference point on the machine. The conventional center-to-center machine layout calculation method is not used.

The arc lamp used with this equipment has a reversible reflector that is white on one side and black on the other. The black reflector, which tends to make the arc more of a point light source, provides the best quality of exposing light. It is suggested for use with grainless plates such as the presensitized and wipe-ons. The more diffuse light that results when the whiter reflector is used, provides a faster exposure that is sometimes desired when exposing grained plates.

The Multiplater is also suitable for making multiple negatives or positives on film. For film exposure, a special "pinpoint" lamp is available.

Because of its simplicity, the manufacturer claims that a competent platemaker can be trained to use the equipment in less than a hour.

Larger sizes of the equipment and equipment for special applications can be built on order. An example is the Model FP Multiplater which was developed for forms printing. The horizontal movement increments of this model have been modified so that they are more suitable for production on standard rotary forms printing presses. In addition, a special micrometer-equipped horizontal chase carriage can be furnished for applications that require vernier compensations between steps.

CONSOLIDATED STAR STEP-AND-REPEAT PHOTOCOMPOSER

This machine is fully automatic and suited for multiple negative work up to the capacity of the machine which is 26" x 32" and, with a pin indexing system, step and repeat work up to 32" x 50".

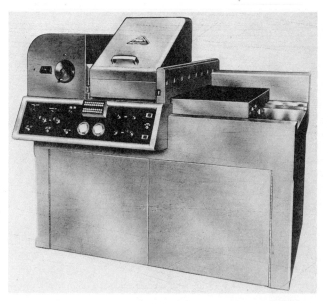

Consolidated "Star" Step and Repeat Photocomposer

The macine requires two settings for the movements of the vertical and horizontal steps. Programming of the machine is accomplished by setting dials which give the exact number of steps required in each row and the total amount of steps for the entire job. An illuminated, visual counter indi-

...es, at all times, which step is being exposed so that on combination jobs, the operator can stop the machine, and handle set-ins etc. Pushing the start button starts the machine and it operates independently and automatically without any assistance of the operator. When the steps for the entire job are completed, a bell will ring.

The lighting system is of the indirect type using a pin-point light source which is reflected off the surface mirror at 45 degrees to the negative holder, giving a uniform, sharp exposure. A precision-built register frame registers the negatives to fine scribed lines. The movements are operated and affected by hydraulic cylinders and valves which move the register frames. Original settings are set on dials graduated in thousandths of an inch and can be set to accuracies of a split thousandth of an inch.

Another feature built into the new machine is the interchangeable plug-in type system so that two spare relays can be used to service all twelve relays in the machine. The photograph displays a read-out device which tells the operator at any time, the number of steps the machine has made and the exact location. The machine has a larger 8" x 10-1/2" negative chase size, with a 27" x 33" table size, which can be increased to 33" x 50" when equipped with an extension table.

THE LAYOUT OF A PHOTOCOMPOSING DEPARTMENT AND THE MAINTENANCE OF ITS EQUIPMENT

The layout of the department can do much to save work, steps, time and mistakes. It is of course possible to make plates in a room just containing a whirler, a printing frame, one sink and one table. But the efficiency of such a room is very low. No flow chart of any value can be devised for such a layout, and when the platemaker needs a helper, it is impossible to use him to full advantage.

Essentials of a Good Photocomposing Department Layout. Besides equipment and work space, a good layout will provide ample storage space and a specific place for all utensils needed, such as rags, wipers, graduates, spare equipment and chemicals. These things must be kept

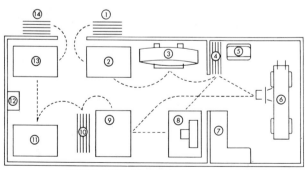

DOTTED LINES INDICATE FLOW OF WORK

1 Freshly grained plate rack	6 Lanston photo-composer	11 Developing and clearing sink
2 Sink for washing and c'etching	7 Work bench and cabinets	12 Chemical and supply cabinet
3 Vertical plate whirler	8 Vac. frame—overhead lamp	13 Etching and gumming table
4 Plate conditioning rack	9 Developing inking table	14 Finished plate rack
5 Neg. register device	10 Vertical soaking tank	

Layout for a photocomposing department.

conveniently at hand, and yet not be in the way during working.

A Schematic Floor Plan. Our diagram shows a compact plateroom with a vertical whirler, an overhead lamp on the printing frame, and a Lanston Photocomposing Machine. Where space is at a premium, this layout is very practical, even for two men. The flow of work, shown in dotted lines on our diagram, is excellent. One worker can follow the other worker from station to station and yet never cross his path.

Air-Conditioning. Note that only the photocomposing room is air-conditioned, and also note that there is a plate-conditioning rack in this room. When a plate is taken right from the heated whirler it may have a relative humidity of 30 percent; some ammonia will also still be present in the coating. If a plate is placed in the photocomposing machine in such a condition and if exposures start immediately, either the first shots will be underexposed or later shots will be overexposed.

Therefore, we provide a rack where plates can come up to room humidity and where they can be left until the ammonia has completely evaporated. The room is air-conditioned to slow up dark reaction while the plate is being shot. In such a set-up, plates can be almost fully controlled as to quality. It is understood by itself that the plates to be exposed in the printing frame also partake of the advantage of air-conditioning.

Where the entire lithographic plant is not air-conditioned, the photocomposing department should have a small air-conditioning unit in the room where the photocomposing machine stands. The wet end of platemaking does not require air-conditioning. In fact the sinks, whirler, and heaters put a heavy load on an air-conditioning machine, and the little good that might be derived by air-conditioning would be very expensive.

Cleanliness and Lubrication. Cleanliness, lubrication and frequent testing and adjustment are very essential to good performance on precision equipment such as a photocomposing machine. The negative frames must not be handled roughly and stored carelessly, or they will become burred, scratched and their fine adjustments and fit will be impaired. The adjusting screws must not be allowed to become rusty, bent or noticeably worn; air seals must neither be damaged nor allowed to become oily, dirty, or hard and cracked.

Keeping Check on Wear and Looseness. All dowel pins and bushings, particularly, must be kept in like-new condition. Screws, gears, racks and other fine mechanical parts of the machine must always be meticulously clean and well-oiled. Any looseness or play must be taken up as soon as discovered. There are many means provided in these machines for compensation of wear; they should be used.

Instruction Manuals. The book of instructions for the care, maintenance and lubrication of the machine should be kept handy and used frequently. A well-kept and well-adjusted machine saves the operator a lot of annoying troubles and saves the plant a lot of lost time.

The operator should feel a responsibility for his machine

and department. Cleanliness and order are important to accuracy, quality of work and safety of operation. Carelessness with equipment and the work in general can only lead to sloppy results.

Good Housekeeping. A man can be judged by the house he keeps. Men who work in cluttered surroundings often have the same mental condition. That there is no time to clean up is just a poor excuse. Does lack of time account for disorder? Isn't it rather the other way around? Isn't the lack of order responsible for the lack of time? Good housekeeping in the photocomposing room, as everywhere else, will pay off in better work and less fatigue.

JOB LAYOUTS FOR PHOTOCOMPOSING

The photocomposing machine operator must have a layout of moves before beginning to shoot the plate. He generally makes this layout himself from the layup that appears on his shop order. Some photocomposing layouts are quite simple while others can be very complicated. But a few basic rules apply to all layouts.

Basic Rules for Photocomposing Layouts. The first rule is that all figures on the layout refer to the centers

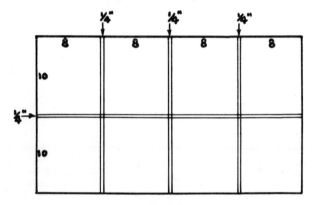

A typical job layout.

of the images. Not necessarily the centers of the pictorial work but rather to the centers of the trimmed or folded piece or page. Another rule is that all vertical movements start with zero and at the gripper edge of the plate, while all horizontal movements start with the center of the machine.

A Typical Example. For a simple layup of eight pieces $8'' \times 10''$ with $\frac{1}{4}''$ trim between, the layout is made as follows:

Let us assume that we are using a 70-inch machine and that the horizontal movement is 64 inches. Then, our center reading for all layouts will always be 32 inches. We work both ways from this center line in calculating our readings. An 8×10 inch piece then will be centered on the machine center at 4 inches plus half the trim—in our case one eighth of an inch. The unit to the left of center will be shot at 32 minus $4\frac{1}{8}$ or $27\frac{7}{8}$ or 27.875.

Layout Figures Must Be Carried to the Third Decimal. All machine layouts must be indicated in decimals carried out to three places, because machine indicators

read to thousandths. The succeeding horizontal moves are each one full trim size plus one full trim-off size away from this first position.

Locating the Vertical Centers. To locate the vertical centers, we must now allow for the gripper-edge margin of the paper. Presses cannot print right out to the gripper edge of the sheet. There must be some white paper left for the grippers. As our example is a trim-to-bleed job, we

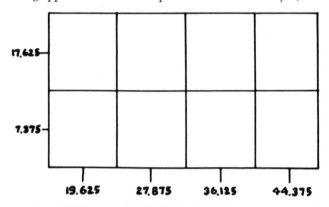

A final layout for photocomposing.

must allow for both a gripper margin and $\frac{1}{8}$ inch trim. Suppose our gripper-margin allowance on the press is $\frac{1}{4}$ inch. Then we must have a plate "set-back" to take care of the margin of the plate required for plate clamps. Assume this margin to be 2 inches. Our total set-back, etc., comes to $2\frac{3}{8}$ inch. We add this figure to half the trim size (10 inches) of our piece and come up with $7\frac{3}{8}$ inch for the reading of the first-row centers. The center of the second row will be $10\frac{1}{4}$ inch away. The final layout for shooting looks like our diagram.

Combination Forms. On combination forms, and where two or more jobs or sizes are put on the same negative, the layout becomes quite complicated. The method of making the layout remains the same but there are more opportunities for making mistakes. Combination sheets, turnover jobs and work-and-flop back-ups are discussed in detail in the aforementioned GATF Skilled Craft Text No. 515, *Photocomposing*, chapter four, pages 37 to 42.

Cutting Difficulties Must be Considered. There is more to making a layout than just getting the images on

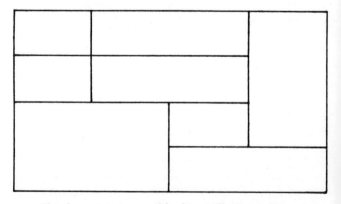

This layout is impossible for guillotine cutting.

the sheet. A layout man must pay attention to any possible difficulties in cutting. It is quite possible to make a layout that cannot be cut in a guillotine cutter.

The "Far Corner" of the Sheet. A good layout man will also pay attention to where, on the sheet, he places very fine register work. The most difficult part of the sheet to control in the press is the "far corner." This is the corner that is farthest away from the front and side guides. When possible, work that is not too critical will be placed in this corner. Small detail and fine register pieces are put close to the guides, when there is a choice. Heavy work will be placed to avoid ghost images.

Developing a Layout. A complicated layout is something to be studied and worked out. It should not be made by the photocomposing machine operator who has a full day's work laid out for him. When the operator is working on layouts, his machine is idle. The hourly rate of a photocomposing department may be three times as much as that of someone in the production department. If there is not enough work to keep the machine busy, and if there is idle time for the operator, he will probably make his own layouts. But when his department is busy, someone else should make them.

Whoever makes a photocomposing layout should have all the information available. Any information lacking on the shop order may lead to expensive mistakes. The person concerned should have a drawing board or a layout machine and a quiet place to work.

OPERATING PROCEDURE

The operator first reads the shop order. It will give him the required information so that he will know what size plates to use and how many, where to put cylinder marks, size of paper, size of units and layup of the job.

Preparing Negatives and Press Plate. On simple film jobs the operator may mount the negatives to a suitable glass. If it is a combination job, it will have been stripped to glass in the stripping department and will be ready to go into the chase. Busy operators and platemakers should not do their own stripping.

If the operator coats his own plates, he will select a fresh plate of proper size, counter-etch it, wash it and coat it. He will check his plate bed for dirt or tape residue. Dirt under the plate can cause trouble.

Operating the Rutherford Machine. He will choose the proper size chase and place it in the register device, insert the negative, square it to register and lock it up. He then inserts the three positioning pins in the plate bed and positions the plate to them. He tapes the edges of the plate down firmly. The plate bed may now be swung up into position and locked

Going to the front of the machine he attaches the chase, the vacuum sealing frame, and the hose, and then moves the carrier to position for shot number 1. In making his moves he will run the plate by power to the right side; then run it back to take out backlash. He will use power most

of the way and then give it the last slight movement by hand. Next, he runs his carriage to the bottom and brings it back by power, again making the last adjustment by hand.

He now checks his carbons and swings the lamp into position, starts his vacuum pump, pulls in the back for contact, and checks vacuum gage. When all is in order, he sets the timer and presses the switch for the first exposure.

Operating the Lanston M-H Photocomposing Machine. The operator places the proper size negative-holder on a table, face-side-up, while the plate is whirling dry. The negative is placed in the inner frame and leveled with a piece of plate glass. The clamps are then set-up tight and the whole frame put on the dowel guides of the register device. The frame is moved into contact with the register glass. The inner frame, with the negative, is now adjusted to register with the fine lines on the glass.

The plate is punched, put into the machine with screws and taped down. The negative chase is removed from the register device pins and set into the saddle carriage of the machine on corresponding pins. The hose is attached to the saddle. Then by use of hand cranks the whole assembly is moved to the first shooting position which on this machine is the upper left corner.

Preparing the negative holder.

To position the chase, first the saddle is moved to the correct notch on the cross bar and locked in. Then the micrometer screw is turned to the correct thousandth. To position vertically, the cross bar is run up by crank to the proper notch and the screw turned to the right thousandth.

After the operator starts the pump, checks carbons, tests vacuum etc., he positions his lamp, installs the hood and starts shooting. After the plate is fully exposed, it is removed from the machine and put through the usual procedure of finishing exposed plates.

REGISTER

On plates made for color work, each color must be exactly superimposed upon the other in perfect register. Some sort of guide to register must be used and this consists of cross marks or register marks. They have been used since the beginning of hand-transfer and for photocomposing are placed on the copy by the cameraman. In this way we are assured that every color image will have a guide that is in perfect relationship with the image on every negative. But we cannot position a negative directly to a plate by the use of register marks alone, because there are no marks on a freshly coated plate to which to register.

Registering Both Negative and Press Plate With the Photocomposing Machine. In order to make a negative register with the plate it is necessary to register each with the machine. That is, the plate must register with the plate bed and the plate bed must register with the machine frame. Also, the negative must register with its chase and the chase must be made to register with the machine frame. Things that correspond to the same thing will correspond to each other.

Register Marks and Dowel Holes. So we start out by putting register marks on the copy before the first negative is made. We now must establish a perfect relationship between these marks and the dowel holes in the chase. This is done in the registering devices as previously described.

There is a set of dowel pins on the carriage of the machine that exactly duplicates and corresponds to the set on the registering device. These pins are made to register with the machine frame through large screws in one case and notch bars on the other. We therefore get our register between register marks on the copy to the machine frame and to the plate.

Sequence of Positioning. When a negative-holder is positioned in the register device and its negative is positioned to the scribed lines, all succeeding negatives can be positioned to the same exact position. And when successive negative-holders are placed in the machine and moved to the same numbers, each color negative will occupy exactly the same spot as every other color negative, no matter how many color plates are made.

Causes of Inaccuracies. There are only a few ways in which inaccuracy can occur on any machine that is kept in good condition. One cause may be that the register marks are not exactly on each color. Another cause may be that the operator is careless in lining them up. Still another cause may be carelessness in making movements to the wrong number on the counter, or a mistake in the layout.

Register marks themselves cause the most common error. This is so because many workmen who have something to do with register marks develop careless habits. But register marks are the heart of register; if they are not perfect, no machine can compensate for the ensuing errors.

Alignment and Placement of Register Marks. Starting with the copy, the marks must be thin and of a type that will not distort and are easy to see, even in half-tone negatives. The marks must be aligned and placed squarely with the work or with the cutting lines. Register marks must not be cocked; they should really be put on in a line-up machine. The register marks must also be placed both ways in the exact center of the unit trim size.

Although the operator uses only three, there should be four marks put on the copy. The operator will use the two marks that are farthest apart and select as the third the more convenient of the remaining two marks. The scratching-in of these marks by the retoucher should be done under strong magnification. The retoucher should use a sharp needle and he should split the mark exactly in half.

The photocomposing machine operator must use care in lining-up the negative register marks with the marks on the register device. He should use a magnifier of the columnar type.

Registering Head-to-Head Forms. Anyone who has ever had anything to do with photocomposed plates of the head-to-head type knows of the trouble they can cause. One row of images can be made to fit perfectly while the opposing row may be over $\frac{1}{16}$th" out between the red and the blue or black. This lack of fit seldom is the fault of the machine or the registering device but nearly always that of the register marks. The register marks are either too thick or they do not show up sharp in a halftone, or they are not cut in accurately.

Small Mistakes Add Up to Big Ones. Marks that are sloppy, or cocked, or a poor type of mark to start with, may be cut-in by the retoucher a little low or high on a straight plate without causing serious consequences. It just means that the images will all be off in one direction; the pressman simply makes a shift that fixes everything. But suppose that, on a head-to-head job, the retoucher scratches his marks one line low on the blue negative and one line high on the red. A line is only about .010 inches wide. Then the blue rows will be .010 inches too close to the center line which makes them .020 inches too close together. But the red images will be .020 inches too far apart. If the pressman fits the blue and red on one row, the other row will misregister by .040 inches. If the photocomposing machine operator is also careless, the total error can easily amount to 1/16 inch.

Plate-To-Press Register. The series of images on a press plate do not have to register closely with the edges of the plate. Re-grained plates seldom have straight edges. A small discrepancy is easily compensated for by the pressman in adjusting his clamps. However, much press time is lost during makeready in trying to put the plates into register with the plate cylinder.

The photocomposing machine operator can be of great

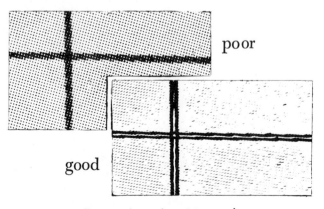

Poor and good register marks.

help to the pressroom in cutting down press makeready time. This may be done in one of two ways. One is called the pin method and the other the cylinder-mark method.

Registering With the Pin Method. The pin method consists of having corresponding pairs of pins on the presses and on the photocomposing machine. If the operator is always careful to see that his plate registers with his pins, and if the pressman sets the plate to his pins, positioning is almost perfect on the first try.

Registering With the Cylinder-Mark Method. The cylinder-mark method consists of carrying register marks to the press cylinder. Here the machine operator shoots marks to the edges of the plates that are a specified distance back from the gripper edge. The pressman then lines-up these marks with two cylinder marks that have previously been put on the cylinder. This method eliminates much shifting of plates during makeready, and the saving of expensive time on four-color presses makes such practice worthwhile.

MAKING MULTIPLE NEGATIVES

When the subject to be photocomposed is so small that shooting it one at a time would take too many hours on the machine, the negatives are grouped. The hand-transferrer used to do this too by transferring the original to an intermediate plate ten or twenty times. He then had only to pull a reasonable number of groups for the press stone.

Making Multiple Negative Assemblies by Stripping. The grouping of multiple negatives may be done in several ways. A simple way to do it in single-color work, is to make several negatives in the camera of the same copy and to strip them up on the photocomposing machine glass. Or, from one negative, several paper-prints can be made, and these grouped on the copyboard for one large negative.

Making Multiple Negatives in the Camera. Some cameras have step-and-repeat backs. With this arrangement, an exposure can be made in one corner of the film, and then by moving the negative a measured distance each time, succeeding exposures can be made for a group of negatives. The arrangement is the same as that used on the photocomposing machines.

Making Multiple Negative Assemblies in the Photocomposing Machine. Both the Rutherford and the Lanston machines have special auxiliary equipment for making multiple negatives and positives in the same manner as plates are made. In making a step-up positive from a single negative, the negative is registered in a special frame on the register device and placed in the carriage. Next, a large unexposed film is fastened to a press plate with sticky-back; this plate, with the film on it, is in turn mounted to the back of the machine. From there on, the step-up is made exactly like a press plate except that a small lamp is now used in conjunction with a fine-setting timer.

Making Step-Up on Glass. If a step-up is wanted on glass, the Rutherford machine has a segment of the back than can be removed to accommodate the glass. The Lanston machine has an aluminum plate with a segment cutout that serves the same purpose. Where only a few step-up negatives are made, and where they are to be used for color work, they are generally made in the regular photocomposing machine as just described.

Special Photocomposing Machines for Negative Assembly. Where a great amount of this work has to be done, special machines are used. These are complete photocomposing machines in miniature. They are placed in a darkroom and are used only for multiple negative and positives. These can be made either on glass or film. Several companies make such machines, as you can see from the descriptions contained in the "Resources Section" of this chapter.

CONTACT

Perfect contact is necessary for obtaining good sharp prints between negative and plate. The pressure must be firm, but gentle and evenly distributed or the glass will crack. Contact on some of the older machines was obtained with mechanical pressure, and it was never entirely satisfactory. On present machines a vacuum is used to exhaust the air between negative and plate. This allows atmospheric pressure, acting on the outside surfaces only, to force the inner surfaces together with an even pressure of as much as twelve pounds to the square inch. This insures good contact unless there is foreign matter between the inner surfaces.

Watch Out for Air Leaks. To obtain and maintain vacuum between negative and plate, all possible air leaks must be sealed off.

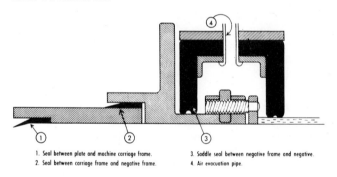

1. Seal between plate and machine carriage frame.   3. Saddle seal between negative frame and negative.
2. Seal between carriage frame and negative frame.   4. Air evacuation pipe.

Four areas that must be sealed on a photocomposing machine.

There must also be channels to allow trapped air to bleed off. These channels or grooves, which can be seen in several of our illustrations, prevent accumulations of air from holding the plate and negative apart.

Rubber Gaskets and Their Placement. Air leaks are sealed off with rubber gaskets. They must be placed on the negative frame at a point where air would normally enter between plate and frame. They must also be placed where air would leak between the negative glass and the frame. Very little mechanical pressure is used to obtain contact between the rubber seals and the glass or metal. The actual sealing edges of the rubber gaskets are quite thin, so that atmospheric pressure acts to make the sealing contact.

The Vacuum Gage. Because these gasket edges actually do the work of sealing they have to be thin and pliable. If they are allowed to be damaged or become hard and stiff they will not work. The vacuum gage is the best indicator of whether or not the gaskets are doing their work. If perfect contact is not obtained a condition called undercutting will occur. This means that the light will penetrate inward from the edges of the dots, thus exposing a greater area of plate than was intended. It will cause thickening of tones on surface plates and sharpening on plates using positives.

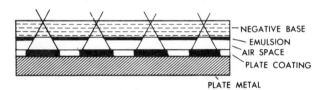

Undercutting.

NESTING FORMS

One of the most difficult jobs to do in a photocomposing machine is the multicolor job where the images are placed head-to-head. This is sometimes done on cutout pieces in order to nest them together and get more pieces on the sheet. As a rule, the first time it is tried there will be a wide discrepancy in fit between the upright pieces and the upside-down ones. Generally the machine is blamed and a serviceman is called in to tighten it up.

Causes for Misregister on Nested Forms. What is the answer to misregister on nested forms? It can be cured with better register marks and more care in scratching and aligning, but most of all, everyone concerned must know how it occurs. The reader who is interested in this subject can find a detailed discussion of it in the already mentioned GATF Skilled Craft Text No. 515, *Photocomposing*.

Forms With Units Turned at Various Angles. Probably the most difficult of nested forms are the ones that are turned at various angles. Two pieces are seldom at the same angle. These forms occur with envelopes and some bottle labels. Because these forms are so intricate it requires special machines to make the layout, to photocompose them, and to check the plate later for possible errors.

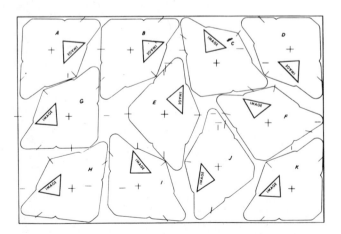

Nested layout.

Special Equipment for Nesting. Of course, to shoot a plate with such a layout requires a photocomposing machine with a rotating negative-holder like the Huebner Rotary Head machine or the Rutherford circular negative-holder. After the plate is shot it can be put in the layout machine for checking. If the register marks on the plate correspond to the machine readings of the layout, the plate is okay. This machine can also be used to check the accuracy of hand-transferred plates.

Due to the cost of special equipment, most lithographers make these intricate layouts by the stripping or hand-transfer methods rather than photocomposing.

Photocomposed Press Plates for Stretched Sheets. It often happens that paper stretches in the press around the cylinder. Usually the pressman can compensate for this by shifting the packing from its position under the plate to a position under the blanket. This makes the press "print longer" and therewith possible to maintain register. But making the press print longer than normal is equivalent to the inviting of slurs. If the paper stretches a little too much, for example on a job that has large areas of three-quarter flat tints and where the paper has a high finish, the third or fourth color may slur badly.

Elongated Press Plates. It is up to the photocomposing machine operater to make an elongated plate so that the pressman can run with normal packing on his latter colors. If there are four or more rows of images on a step-and-repeat plate, the problem is quite simple. It is only necessary for the pressman to go back to a normal packing under the plate in the press and then to print a few sheets. These will indicate the amount of stretch that is in the sheet. The stretch on the longest sheet pulled with normal packing must be measured. Thereafter, look at the layout and add a portion of the stretch to each vertical move. If the stretch is .060 inch, for example, and there are four rows, add .020 inch to each distance between rows.

How the Amount of Stretch Must be Established. Do not try to find paper stretch by comparing a sheet with a plate. All plates print longer than their image size. This would just confuse the issue and result in more lost time. Measure the actual stretch on the printed sheet after going back to normal packing. Measure it with a fine transparent scale showing divisions of .010 inch. The photographer can make such a scale on film from a one-tenth ruler. Every operator should have such a scale. Or, use a pair of sharp dividers to measure the error on the sheet and then lay the points of the dividers on a fine scale.

Using a Register Rule. In shops that check all of their first printed sheets with a Register Rule and record the readings, set-out plates are easy to make. By this method, not only can paper stretch be found but "fan" across the back as well. When the image "fans across the back," the corner images can be set out to fit in the same general manner.

TROUBLES IN PHOTOCOMPOSING

In this our final unit on photocomposing, we discuss the following five kinds of photocomposing troubles: (1) plate embossing, (2) poor contact, (3) insufficient vacuum, (4) poor register, and (5) uneven exposure.

Plate Embossing. A plate is said to be embossed when, after exposure, ridges appear in the surface of the plate. This is caused by atmospheric pressure behind the plate pushing it into an unsupported area around the frame or glass. Using too small a piece of glass can cause a wide gap around the glass, and embossing will result. Use only full-size glass.

It is dangerous to use too high a vacuum on thin plates. Even though the gaps around the frame are small, a high vacuum on a thin plate will cause embossing. Thin plates, if there are no kinks in them, need only a light vacuum for good contact.

Poor Contact. Poor contact is possible even with a high vacuum. A plate embossed on a previous job will give trouble unless the graining has removed the ridges. Plates should be inspected before and after coating with a low-level reflected light. Plates carelessly handled get kinks that are difficult to remove. With such plates contact good enough for fine halftone work is not possible.

Dirt on the bed or on a plate may cause pimples and prevent contact. Dirt in the plate coating or on the face of the negative will do the same thing. Poor stripping practices or the use of improper front masking can ruin a job.

Whenever contact is questionable, a pen-type flashlight held at an angle with the glass will throw shadows of the dots than can be seen with a magnifier.

It is also important that the glass be flat in the negative-holder. It has been explained how the glass is leveled in the different frames. This should be done carefully and re-checked after the clamps are tightened. Dirt must not be allowed to accumulate at the base of dowel pins, as this keeps the whole frame out of level with the plate. Contact must not be forced by raising vacuum excessively. If everything is in good condition, fifteen to twenty inches of mercury is sufficient.

Insufficient Vacuum. If the gage registers a low vacuum, this means pump trouble, motor trouble or an air leak. An air leak may be in the relief valve that is stuck open due to dirt. Or, the leak may be in the hose or the hose connections. Such leaks can usually be heard and easily located.

The leaks most often occur around the gaskets on the chase. This may be the case when the seal extends beyond the edge of the plate. If plate edges have been damaged by rough handling or are not taped down carefully, a leak will occur.

A leak may be between glass and frame or between chase and plate if the gaskets are not kept in a soft and pliable condition. Rubber surfaces become hard due to oxidation and do not seal properly in such a condition. Or, the seals may be damaged by careless storing of the frames. In storage, nothing should touch the thin edges of the seals as this will put permanent waves in them. Hard or distorted seals should be replaced.

Poor Register. Reading the dials incorrectly causes much of the poor register. Another cause of poor register is failure to keep out backlash errors due to not always approaching the final mark from the same direction on every plate. Dials should be kept clean and well-lighted.

Misregister is also caused by worn or dirty dowel pins and bushings. These should be periodically tested for any play; when worn, they must be immediately replaced as they are the heart of register.

As a rule there are two adjusting nuts on every lead screw arranged so that they take up excessive backlash. These should be tightened and oiled occasionally. The lead screws also have some type of thrust bearing and take-up that need periodic attention.

It is also possible for dowel pins to become loose on a chase or on the register device. Sometimes the lined glass on the device becomes out-of-square with its pins. A check should be made of everything that affects register when poor register occurs. Then test the machine by making a cross-mark check. Use a negative that has a perfect cross mark on it in addition to very accurate register marks. Lock it up, put it into the machine and step it up on a plate or Vandyke Paper. Calculate the steps so that the lines of each cross printed just touch those of adjacent crosses. Step-and-repeat both up and down. An error, if it exists, will be clearly shown.

Uneven Exposure. If possible, all arc lamps should be on separate power lines of ample capacity, running back to the source of electrical power in the building. Lamps must be kept free of arc dust and rust. The carbon clamps must be free of pits and burned spots, and in good working order.

Uneven exposures may be caused by fluctuations in light intensities or color. If arc lamps are on the same circuit with other equipment of high electrical consumption, fluctuations in line voltage will occur. After a few months use, any lamp can lose some of its compensating ability. A compensating, integrating light control is a big help provided it is maintained in good working order.

Dark reaction is a frequent cause of uneven exposure on warm, humid days. The plate starts to harden or to tan as soon as it dries, and this continues until it is developed. As dark reaction progresses the plate becomes more sensitive. If a plate stays three or four hours in the photocomposing machine the first exposure will be different from the last. This error in uniformity can be eliminated by air-conditioning. Many of our pre-sensitized plates do not have the tendency to dark reaction.

CHAPTER TEN

The Platemaking Department

Section One: Introduction

The offset lithographic plate is the hub around which the lithographic process revolves. Platemaking is the step at which the lithographic process clearly demonstrates the principle that grease and water generally do not mix. A lithographic plate must consist of two areas: the printing areas which accept grease and repel water; and the nonprinting areas which accept water and repel grease. The wider the difference between the ink-receptivity of the image and the water-receptivity of the non-image areas the better the plate and the easier it will run on the press. Many plates prior to 1948 were difficult to run because of the small differences between the ink-receptive areas and the water-receptive areas.

Some of the most significant developments in lithography since World War II have been made in the area of platemaking. Practically all of these developments have helped to increase the difference between the ink- and water-receptivity of the image and non-image areas; they have improved platemaking to such an extent that plates are no longer the serious source of trouble they used to be. Science has given the lithographic craftsman materials, techniques and knowledge which makes possible the present state of the art, *where there is little excuse for bad plates to go to press.*

There are a number of ways of putting an ink-receptive image on a lithographic plate. Plates are generally classified according to the method used.

Original Plates. Original plates are plates on which the artist has drawn an image with a greasy crayon or a special ink called *tusche.* The artist may also apply a mechanical dot pattern or *benday* with a greasy ink. This technique provides a method for creating various tone values. Most original plates were on stone. Some artists still use stone as their medium, and stone lithography is taught in many art schools. The modern "direct image" plates are, strictly speaking, original plates. However, they are so different from lithographic stones that discussion of the direct image plates is combined with other contemporary plates in Section Nine.

Hand Transfer Plates. When two or more identical images were to be printed from the same plate, the artist did not draw the same image two or more times. Instead, he drew a single design from which the required number of ink impressions were duplicated on hand transfer paper. Hand transfer paper is coated on one side with a gummy or gelatinous layer. The duplicate transfers were then laid face down in the proper positions on a new plate, and their ink images were pressed against the plate. The transfer paper was then soaked with water and peeled, leaving the inked images on the plate. This was the procedure used for the first metal printing plates.

CONTEMPORARY LITHOGRAPHIC PLATES

Original and hand transfer plates are seldom used today. They have been almost entirely replaced by photomechanical plates made from negatives and positives. Direct image plates, discussed in Section Nine, are also in current use, but not to the extent of photomechanical plates.

The Photomechanical Principle. A photolithographic plate is a metal, paper, or plastic plate that is cleaned, treated, and coated with a thin film of light sensitive material. This material is naturally soluble in some solvent such as water, but becomes insoluble after it is dried and exposed to light. A negative or positive of the image is placed in close contact with the coated plate, usually under vacuum, and then exposed to a controlled light source. The light that goes through the transparent parts of the positive or negative hardens the plate coating and makes it insoluble. Where the coating is shaded by the opaque parts of the negative or positive, the coating remains soluble. After the light exposure, the plate is developed to make the image areas ink-receptive; then it is treated to make the non-image areas water-receptive. (For positive-working presensitized and wipe-on plates, discussed more fully in Section VI, the solubility is reversed by selective solvents. On these plates the exposed area is rendered soluble, while the unexposed area becomes insoluble.)

THE MAIN TYPES OF CONTEMPORARY PLATES

For the purpose of this manual, lithographic plates are divided into four groups: (1) Surface plates—albumin, presensitized, wipe-on, and photopolymer; (2) Deep-etch plates; (3) Bimetal plates; and (4) Direct Image, Projection, and Electrostatic plates. Each of these is briefly described in this introduction and more fully discussed in following sections.

Surface Plates—Albumin, Presensitized, Wipe-On, Photopolymer. On surface plates made from negatives, the light sensitive coating becomes the printing surface. In the *albumin* type plate, the light sensitive coating may consist of albumin, casein, or soybean protein, sensitized with ammonium bichromate.

Cross section of a surface plate.

Presensitized plates provide the ultimate in simplicity in platemaking. They are called presensitized because they are sensitized when purchased. They will generally keep their sensitivity for six months to one year. Presensitized plates consist of a thin film of a light sensitive material, usually a *diazo* compound, which is coated on a specially treated aluminum or paper base plate. Both negative and positive types are available.

Wipe-on plates are chemically similar to presensitized plates, but they are coated in the plateroom by hand, or in a simple roller coater. A specially treated aluminum is coated with the diazo coating, exposed through a negative, and developed. Positive wipe-on plates are also available.

Photopolymer plates consist of cinnamic acid esters and a sensitizer which combines during exposure to produce a tough, long wearing image area. Photopolymer plates are made with negatives. The exposed coatings require special organic solvents for processing. There are presensitized and wipe-on photopolymer plates. Photopolymer plates, developable in water-soluble solutions, have also been developed.

A full discussion of these and other surface plates is contained in Section Six of this chapter.

Deep-etch plates are based on a light-sensitive coating which

Cross section of a deep-etch plate.

serves as a stencil to produce the printing image. They are made from positives. After the image is produced, the stencil is removed. Most deep-etch plates are coated in the lithographic plant. The coating for in-plant produced deep-etch plates is a mixture of gum arabic, or polyvinyl alcohol (PVA), and ammonium bichromate. A full discussion of deep-etch plates is contained in Section Seven of this chapter.

Bimetal plates are excellent for exceptionally long runs and for printing with abrasive inks, papers or boards. Bimetal plates have the widest difference obtainable between the ink- and water-receptivity of image and non-image areas. All of the plates described previously—surface plates and deep-etch plates—have been single-metal plates. Bimetal plates consist of two different metals, one for the image areas and the other metal for the non-image areas. *The metals of bimetal plates are chosen so that the image metal is ink-receptive under the same conditions which render the non-image metal water-receptive.* All bimetal plates in present use, except one, have copper as the image metal. The one exception uses brass (alloy of copper + zinc) as the image metal. The usual non-image metals are aluminum, chromium, or stainless steel. When copper and chromium are used together, they are usually electroplated as layers on a third metal such as aluminum, mild steel, stainless steel, or zinc. Such plates are often called trimetal or polymetal plates even though the third or base plate metal takes no part in the formation of the printing of the image.

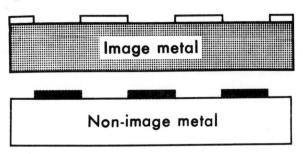

Cross sections of the basic types of bimetal plates.

There are two basic types of bimetal plates: Type I which has the image metal above the non-image metal; and Type II which has the image metal below the non-image metal. Examples of the first type consist of copper on stainless steel, or copper on aluminum. These plates are usually processed with negatives but some are also available as presensitized plates for processing with positives. Examples of the second type consist of chromium on copper or brass, chromium and copper on a zinc, mild steel, aluminum, or stainless steel base. These plates are always made from positives. A full discussion of bimetal plates is contained in Section Eight of this chapter.

Direct image, projection, and electrostatic plates are generally used for offset duplicating or on small offset presses.

DIRECT IMAGE PLATES are made of a specially coated paper which permits direct use of the plate in the typewriter for applying the greasy printing image. Direct image plates are used extensively in systems printing and in encoding checks for MICR (magnetic ink character recognition) sorting.

PROJECTION PLATES are the simple means for making printing plates directly from other copy. They can be made directly in a camera or projector, and special processor in approximately one minute. Projection plates eliminate the intermediate step of making a photographic negative, and the image can also be an enlargement or reduction of the original copy.

ELECTROSTATIC PLATES are made with the Xerographic and Electrofax processes.

Direct image, projection, and electrostatic plates are discussed in detail in Section Nine of this chapter.

Section Two: Equipment for Platemaking

The platemaking room should be large enough to provide ample space for all equipment. It should be well ventilated to remove fumes from evaporation of lacquers, alcohol, and other solvents, and should be air conditioned.

Hot and Cold Water Supply. The plate room should be so situated that ample supplies of hot and cold running water are readily available. Water temperature as high as 120°F is occasionally needed. Many plate troubles, and even failures with some processes, have been traced to the lack of a sufficient supply of hot water.

Illumination. Room lighting is also important. Plate coatings are sensitive to ultra-violet and blue light. When coated plates are being handled they should not be exposed to any stray blue or ultra-violet light. Direct daylight or sunlight should be blocked out, or by fastening yellow or orange plastic sheets over the windows. Yellow insect bulbs or yellow fluorescent tubes make suitable safe lights for the plate room without sacrificing good viewing conditions. The plate room should also be wired so that the yellow lights are always lit when the room is in use; regular white lights should either have individual switches or be wired to a separate switch.

PLATEMAKING SINKS

Sinks for platemaking are generally made of stainless steel or plastic covered wood or steel. If stainless steel sinks are used, the steel should be a good grade of 18-8 stainless steel with a high gloss finish. A polished surface resists corrosion much better than a rough surface. Wood, plywood, or steel sinks which are covered with fiberglass or polyvinyl chloride materials are also satisfactory.

The sink should be approximately one foot larger in each dimension than the largest plate used. A flat platform should cover the entire area inside the sink. This platform should be placed about three inches below the rim of the sink, and should be sloped away from the working side of the sink.

Mixing Valves. The water supply to the sink should come through a thermostatically controlled mixing valve. A movable pipe about two feet above the sink, to which is attached a cheesecloth sock, is preferable to a perforated pipe along the front edge of the sink, as iron and other minerals collect in the perforations and may cause corrosion streaks on the plates.

WHIRLERS

Plate whirlers are gradually going into disuse as a result of the increasing use of presensitized, wipe-on, and pre-coated plates. But whirlers are still needed for conventional deep-etch and bimetal plates.

The plate whirler is designed to coat lithographic plates. The whirler is actually an oversized turntable. The plate is fastened or mounted on the turntable, the sensitized coating is poured on and centrifugally distributed over the plate while it is turning. The whirler should be equipped with a positive variable-speed drive and accurate controls for setting and measuring whirler speed. The coating is dried by heat and/or forced air as the plate revolves.

There are two types of whirlers in general use—horizontal and vertical. The horizontal whirler distributes the coating solely by centrifugal force. The vertical whirler, which has the turntable placed at an angle of 15° to the perpendicular, distributes the coating by a combination of centrifugal force and gravity. There is little difference in the quality of the coatings produced by these two types of whirlers; neither produces a perfectly even coating over the entire plate. Coatings are generally slightly thicker in the centers and on the edges of the plates. The vertical whirler has the advantage of taking up less space. The horizontal whirler is better suited for coating fragile materials such as plastics and glass.

Whirlers should be equipped with thermostats to control inside temperatures. They should also be equipped with thermostats for controlling the temperature of the water used to flush the plate immediately prior to coating. If a thermostatically-controlled water valve is used in the plate sink, the same control can be easily connected to the whirler by running a special line to it.

Roll Coaters. Simple two-roll coaters, with the coating pan under the lower roller, are used for coating wipe-on plates. The machine consists of two soft synthetic rubber rollers mounted one over the other. The lower roller rotates partly submerged in a trough containing the coating solution. The plate is passed between the rollers face down. Adjustments on the upper roller help govern the thickness of the coating applications. The coating is dried under a fan. These coaters are very effective, productive, and economical with regard to consumption of solution, if a large number of plates are coated. It is wasteful, of course, for coating single plates intermittently.

Coating a plate with a roll coater.

VACUUM PRINTING FRAMES

The vacuum printing frame holds the negative and plate in intimate contact during exposure. The frame consists of two wooden or metal frames, one of which holds a corrugated or channeled rubber blanket with a rubber-bead gasket around its edges; the other frame contains a sheet of flawless plate glass. In smaller vacuum frames the two frames are usually hinged together on one side. The rubber blanket is connected to a vacuum pump by a flexible rubber tube. Special frames with glass on both sides are also used.

Operating the Vacuum Frame. When the printing frame is open, the blanket is horizontal and the glass is raised up out of the way. The sensitized plate is laid on the blanket with the coated side up. The positive or negative, or a stripped up flat is laid on the plate in exact position, emulsion side down. The glass frame is lowered and the two frames are locked together. The vacuum pump is then turned. The pump sucks the air from between the blanket and glass, thus forcing the sensitized plate and the negative or positive together. A reading of from 20″ to 28″ of vacuum is considered satisfactory. When this has been done, the printing frame is rotated so that the glass faces a controlled light source which, when turned on, gives the necessary exposure. On a flip-top frame the glass is inverted through 180° since the exposing light is underneath.

Making Good Contact. Good contact between the negative or positive and the plate is absolutely essential, otherwise undercutting or spreading of the light during exposure will occur. This is a serious problem with aluminum plates, especially the thin presensitized plates. To insure good contact, the frame must be checked periodically for air leaks. The reading on the vacuum gauge does not necessarily correspond to the actual vacuum in the frame, and a high reading on the gauge could still not indicate an air leak between the gasket and the glass. The gaskets must be kept smooth and clean and replaced immediately if they dry out, crack, or chip.

Another way to insure good contact between the flat and the plate is to cover the flat and plate with a thin sheet of clear flexible plastic, such as polyethylene. The plastic should be large enough to cover the gasket areas of the frame. When the frame is closed, the glass is above the plastic. The air is exhausted between the plastic, flat, and plate. Because the plastic is flexible it conforms to the irregularities in the thickness of the flat. This results in much better contact between the flat and the plate than is possible with glass alone.

Testing Contact. An easy way to test the contact between the plate and the negative or positive in a vacuum frame, or on a photo-composing machine, is to illuminate the area, which is

Checking contact between flat and plate.

to be checked with a pen flashlight. The light is held at a 45° angle to the glass and the area examined with a magnifying glass. If there is enough vacuum for good contact, there will only be one image. If a sharp shadow appears along the side of each dot or line, the contact is poor and the exposure should not be started until the shadow disappears.

Photo-Composing. The photo-composing machine, sometimes called the step-and-repeat machine, is used for exposing lithographic plates. The machine produces a series of exposures in register on the same plate or successive plates. The same precautions as described for conventional vacuum frames holds true for the photo-composing machine. The types of machines and the techniques for using them are described in the chapter on "Stripping and Photo-Composing."

LIGHT SOURCES

A number of light systems are available for exposing lithographic plates. The following factors govern the choice of a good light source:

SPECTRAL DISTRIBUTION. Most light-sensitive coatings are only sensitive to blue and ultra-violet light. Sources which are rich only in ultraviolet light are not ideal because the frame glass and some photographic film bases absorb much of this spectral energy. The light source used for exposure should have appreciable energy in the near-ultraviolet and blue part of the spectrum. Special *water-white glass* should be used on printing frames as this glass transmits more ultraviolet light than ordinary plate glass.

LIGHT INTENSITY. The stronger the light the shorter the exposure time.

POINT SOURCE VERSUS DIFFUSE SOURCE. A point source of light produces sharp shadows and reduces risks of undercutting. Diffuse light, or light from a broad source, can give trouble with undercutting when there is insufficient vacuum or poor stripping.

EVENNESS OF ILLUMINATION OVER THE EXPOSURE SURFACE. Light intensity from a point source will vary in illumination from the center to the edges of the image. This can be corrected somewhat by reflector design. A common rule is to place the light at a distance from the plate equivalent to the diagonal of the plate. Greater distances will produce more even illumination but lengthen exposures since light intensity varies inversely as the square of the distance.

CLEANLINESS. Dirt is a platemaker's worst enemy. A light source should be used that creates a minimum amount of dirt. Where open-flame carbon arc lamps must be used, they should be so vented as to exhaust as much of the carbon ash as is practical.

Arc Lamps. A lamp with a single arc is preferred for exposing the plate. Multiple arc lamps or banks of fluorescent lights usually undercut the negative or positive, especially when there is a lot of tape on the flat or layout. Multiple arc lamps and banks of fluorescent lights tend to spread the image areas, plug the shadows in halftones located near masking paper and tape on surface plates, and sharpen deep-etch plates. There are two general types of arc lamps.

Solenoid Arcs. In the older type of arc lamp two carbon rods are used as electrodes for creating a spark gap. The gap, or length of the arc, is controlled by an electromagnet or solenoid. As the carbon ends burn, the gap becomes longer. At a given distance in the gap, the solenoid acts to shorten the gap, where it then holds the carbons in the new position until the gap again reaches its maximum length. This intermittent adjustment of the carbons causes a periodic variation or flicker in the light intensity. These lamps are practically obsolete.

Motor Driven Arcs. Motor driven carbon arcs were introduced in 1947 to overcome the variation in light intensity of the solenoid arc. An electric motor gradually moves the carbons as they burn down. The length of the gap remains practically constant. The light output from motor-driven carbon arcs is, therefore, more constant in intensity and color quality than the light from solenoid models.

Maintenance of Arc Lamps. Arc lamps may be a source of considerable trouble if they are not properly maintained. The manufacturer's instructions should be followed carefully. An occasional check of the arc length and the steadiness of the light should be made. Check for excessive friction in the mechanism and readjust the length occasionally. Only the carbons that are recommended by the manufacturer should be used. The reflectors must be cleaned often.

Pulsed Xenon. Pulsed Xenon lamps, which are already replacing carbon arc lamps in process photography, are gaining acceptance in platemaking. The 4000 watt and 8000 watt helical pulsed Xenon tubes have been mounted in suitable reflectors and are now being used extensively on photo-composing machines and on vacuum frames.

Other Lights. Photoflood lamps and quartz iodine lights provide enough light to expose presensitized and other smaller offset plates. There are also available special ultraviolet tubes which are mounted so that they travel across from the face of the vacuum frame. The stripping operation, and vacuum, become more critical with these broad-source lights as undercutting of the image may occur.

Important advantages of these newer light sources are that they are much cleaner than carbon-arc lights, and do not change in light intensity or color temperature as much as carbon-arc lights do.

Integrating Light Meters. Integrating light meters for controlling platemaking exposures were used as early as 1940, but did not come into general use until after World War II.

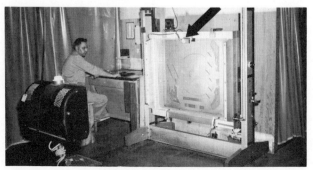
Integrating light meter photo-cell on vacuum frame.

Integrating light meters adjust the exposure in terms of light units reaching the plate, integrating the light intensity with time much as a water meter measures water volume in cubic feet regardless of its rate of flow. All lights are influenced by line voltage variations. When arc lights are used, or when exposure times are critical, it is desirable to have a light integrating meter for controlling the exposure times.

Light Lines and Power Lines. In some areas, power companies have separate service lines for light and for power. The voltage in the light line is usually more stable than the power line. If the plant happens to be in one of these areas, it should operate the arc lights from the light line. The intensity of the light will not vary nearly as much as it will when the arc lights are supplied from the power line.

DEEP-ETCH DEVELOPING TROUGHS AND PADS

The deep-etch developing trough has a level grid or island in the center of which is laid the exposed deep-etch plate for the developing and deep-etching operations. The trough should be about twelve inches larger in each dimension than the largest plate. Since the tray is used for both developing and deep-etching, it should be lined with an acid proof material. The drain and trap should also be acid proof.

The Exhausts. The trough should be in a well-ventilated area and should preferably have its own exhaust system. A down draft or surface type of exhaust is safer and more efficient than an overhead type, since the vapors of plate-making chemicals are all heavier than air.

The Grid. The grid or island which sits inside the trough should be one-inch smaller at each edge than the plate. This allows the platemaker to squeegee off the spent developer or deep-etching solution without the danger of dragging the chemicals back onto the plate. If plates of different sizes are made, it is a good plan to have the grid the same size as the largest plate. For smaller plates, individual pieces of three-fourths inch marine plywood for each plate size should be placed on the grid to raise and support the plate on a suitable-sized smaller platform.

Provision should be made for a water tap either in the trough under the grid or close by so that the trough can be washed after each use. Drenching the waste developer and deep-etching solutions will dilute them and therefore reduce the danger of corrosion to the water drain line. Care should be taken that the water does not splash or leak on the plate during processing.

Deep-Etch Pads. The deep-etch pad is a plush covered wooden or plastic block. The platemaker should have separate special pads for development and for deep-etching. After each plate is finished, the pads should be rinsed thoroughly with alcohol, squeegeed as dry as possible, and placed in a rack to dry. At the end of the day, the pad should be thoroughly washed with water, squeegeed as dry as possible, and left to dry overnight. The pads should not stand with developer or deep-etching solution in them, as these solutions absorb moisture from the air. The excess water in the pad could damage the next plate by speeding up the reaction rate of the chemicals in the solutions.

Automatic Plate Processors. Several automatic plate processors have been designed. Most plate processors are designed for use with a particular plate. There are automatic processors for bi- and tri-metal plates. Several are versatile and can be used for different kinds of plates. There are, also, processors for presensitized and wipe-on plates.

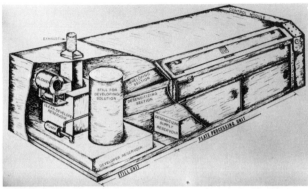

Courtesy Ball Brothers.

Cut-away sketch of an automatic plate processor.

As the trend toward presensitized and pre-coated plates increases, the interest in automatic processors will also increase.

Processors will not only speed up production, important in such areas as web offset newspapers which work on edition deadlines, but processors will increase general printing production, improve consistency, and reduce down-time, as well as reduce makeovers of plates already on the press. These factors can result in real savings that can pay for the equipment in a short time. Automatic processors should be as effective in platemaking as they are in photography.

Air Conditioning. Air conditioning is almost a necessity in plate rooms where bichromated coatings are used since these coatings are affected by both temperature and relative humidity. The system should have provisions for controlling both temperature and relative humidity. Good conditions are $75° \pm 3°F$ and $45\% \pm 5\%$ RH in the United States and Canada. In Europe, coatings are designed for use at relative humidities as high as 85%.

Air conditioning is not as necessary where presensitized and wipe-on plates are being made exclusively, except that if film negatives and positives are used they can change size before and during exposure. Film size is extremely important for color separation in the camera, stripping, and plate-making operations. All three departments should therefore be at the same conditions for optimum register or fit of images on the plates.

Section Three: Platemaking Materials

The materials for platemaking consist of the metals used for lithographic plates, the mixtures of substances used for coating them, and the chemicals used for processing the plates.

Unlike letterpress, flexography, or gravure in which the difference between image and non-image area is accomplished mechanically, lithography maintains this difference chemically by the principle that grease (ink) and water, generally do not mix. So that the platemaker can understand what is happening in this process, an examination of the properties of the materials and solutions used may be helpful.

LITHOGRAPHIC PLATE METALS

Today, lithographic plates are all thin metal sheets except some direct-image and similar special-use plates. Aluminum is used in most plants, but some plants use zinc as well. Bimetal and trimetal plates are also used. Plates are the full size of the press cylinder, and must be thin and flexible enough to wrap snugly around the cylinder. The thickness of regular zinc and aluminum "lithoplate" used for surface and deep-etch plates varies with the press size, from .009" to 0.12" for 17" x 22" presses up to .025" for 55" x 78" presses.

Metal litho plates are made in rolling mills and are reduced to their final thickness by cold rolling. Cold rolling makes them harder. They are then carefully inspected to be sure that: (1) They meet the required gauge tolerance; (2) They are flat; and (3) At least one side is free from scale, dents, or scratches.

Uniform Thickness and Flatness. Uniform thickness and flatness of plates are extremely important. Plates in the size range up to 25½" x 36" should not vary more than .001" in thickness. For example, a .012" plate must not be less than

.115" nor more than .125" in any area. This is called "gauge tolerance" and is usually expressed as ±.0005". For larger plates the gauge tolerance is ±.001".

Flatness is important to insure good register. If there are any buckles or waves in the metal plate it will not lie flat on the photo-composing machine, the vacuum frame, or the press cylinder. Any movement of the buckle or wave will result in misregister on multicolor work, or misfitting where die cutting is involved. Vacuum backs on photo-composing machines are a must when making plates for multicolor close register work, especially when using aluminum.

SOME COMPARISONS OF POSITIVE AND NEGATIVE-WORKING PLATES

A review of some of the features, advantages and disadvantages of negative- and positive-working plates may be of some value at this point.

Costs. Plates made from negatives are almost always cheaper from the standpoint of labor and material. However, on complicated multicolor stripping jobs that demand the making of positives, the contacting back to negatives can more than consume the savings. In these cases, positive working plates should be considered.

Tone Control. Where critical tone values are concerned, such as on four-color process, the press plates should usually be made sharper than the proofing plates by 1 or 2 steps on the GATF Sensitivity Guide. This can be done, when using positive working plates, by increasing exposure and using a separating film.

Dirt Spots. Positives that have been used over a period of time will become marred and dirt infested, requiring excessive staging and dirt-picking, particularly on multi-image deep-etch plates. Negatives can be kept clean by opaquing out dirt and pinholes so it would not be necessary to clean up negative-working plates.

Photo-Composing. On certain combination press layouts masking must be done while the material is locked in the machine. Positive-working plates permit the operator to see the last exposed image. Also, white lettering in multicolor areas can be shot out in exact register by superimposing.

Press Life. With the exception of bimetal negative plates and some photopolymer plates, the deep-etch or positive-working plates are completely acceptable for long run jobs.

Press Performance. Deep-etch or positive-working plates have the capacity to carry excess ink and still print reasonably sharp. Halftones and fine work will thicken faster on negative-working plates.

Plates for Web Presses. Positive working deep-etch plates, and bimetal positive and negative plates will give better performance than most other plates. However, because of high operating cost of a web press, negative-working presensitized and wipe-on plates are often used since these plates can be made faster and thereby reduce down-time. One-piece negatives of the full press form are used so that the plates can be made quickly in a vacuum frame.

COATING MATERIALS

Ammonium Bichromate. Ammonium bichromate is the main ingredient of plate coatings made with albumin, casein, soybean proteins, gum arabic. It is the sensitizer of the coating and it is responsible for producing the image through the action of light. Ammonium bichromate is the result of reacting chromic acid with ammonia. The chemical is poisonous if taken internally, and can cause dermatitis—skin irritation—to personnel with specific sensitivity to bichromates. The "Photo Grade" is considered satisfactory for lithographic use.

Albumin, Casein, and Soybean Protein. These proteins are used on certain types of surface plates, most of which are now practically obsolete.
Albumin is a protein derived from the whites of eggs. It is sold as spray-dried powder and as dried scales in a variety of grades. The best form for lithographic use is "edible" egg albumin scales. The powders do not work as well.
Casein is a milk protein. Because it has a much higher molecular weight than albumin, casein is not as readily soluble in water and must be dissolved in an ammonia solution. Satisfactory grades of casein for lithographic use must also be fat free.
Soybean protein, like casein, has a large molecule and must also be dissolved in an ammonia solution. Since it is considerably cheaper than albumin or casein, one of its major uses is as a substitute for casein in paper coatings.

Gum Arabic. Gum arabic is the main organic ingredient of deep-etch coatings. It is also the main ingredient of plate etches and gums. Gum arabic is a natural gum that comes from acacia trees in the Anglo-Egyptian Sudan area of North Africa. Clean gum arabic is an edible product used extensively in the manufacture of candies. It comes either in lumps or as a powder. The type preferred by lithographers is called "Select Gum Arabic Sorts." There are two crops of gum arabic annually, and some of the early crops show a characteristic known as stringiness. Solutions of stringy gum are unsatisfactory for preparing coatings but can be used in etches and as plate gumming solutions.

Glue. Glue has also been used for deep-etch coating and, sometimes, as a mixture with albumin for surface plates, but these uses are almost obsolete. Fish glue is most commonly used. The glue is a specially prepared fish glue known in the trade as liquid photoengraver's glue. The main advantage of glue coatings for deep-etch was that they were water-developable; but this made it difficult to control tone values.

PVA. Polyvinyl alcohol (PVA) is used extensively in Europe for making deep-etch coating. PVA is very similar to photoengraver's glue in that it can be developed with water and does not require special developers or alcohol. However, as with glue, tones made on a PVA coating cannot be controlled by development. Processes using PVA have not been very popular in the United States, and although it is used to some extent in photoengraving and in the production of printed electrical circuits, it has not found acceptance in lithography. Some work is being done in Europe to make PVA plates solvent-developed in the same way as gum arabic coated plates so that tones can be controlled to some extent during the development step.

Diazo. Diazo sensitizers are used for presensitized and wipe-on plate coatings. Most of the diazos in use are condensation products of formaldehyde and diazo diphenyl amine stabilized with a compound like zinc chloride. Some diazo oxides are also used. Diazos differ from colloids such as albumin, casein, and gum arabic in that they are themselves light sensitive. Exposure to light converts them directly to insoluble resins that have good ink receptivity and reasonable wear characteristics for printing.

Photopolymer Coatings. One type of photopolymer coating for surface plates is a cinnamic acid ester of an epoxy resin sensitized with a suitable organic compound. This coating is insoluble in water but soluble in organic solvents, and can be used for presensitized or wipe-on plates. On exposure to light, the exposed parts of the coating become insoluble in the organic solvents which dissolve the unexposed portions. The resultant images are very tough, and the plates generally withstand long runs. Since photopolymer coated plates are not affected by temperature and relative humidity, the plates can be pre-coated and stored for long periods of time prior to use. The process, however, suffers from high cost of materials and the necessity of using organic solvents in processing. Photopolymer plates are used extensively for making printed circuits for electronic components. Photopolymer coatings of the water-developable type have also been introduced.

PROCESSING CHEMICALS

A number of chemicals are used in making a lithographic plate and in running the plate on the press. "Chemically Pure (C. P.)" grades of chemicals are always acceptable for use, but they are too expensive for large quantities when a cheaper grade will do equally as well. A published formula will usually state the quality level required of the ingredients. The most commonly used, and most important litho platemaking chemicals are listed below under their chemical types, such as acids, alkalies (bases), and salts. For specific information about the availability of the chemicals refer to the many standard references published annually by the major chemical houses. Some of these are: The Merck Index of Chemicals and Drugs (Rahway, N. J.: Merck & Co., 1960); Fisher Chemical Index-67-C (Pittsburgh, Pa.: Fisher Scientific, 1967). Eastman Organic Chemicals (Rochester, N. Y.: Eastman, Kodak Company, 1966). Aldrich Chemical Catalog (Milwaukee, Wisc: Aldrich Chemical Company, 1966).

Acids. A number of acids are used in lithographic platemaking. All of these acids are corosive in their purchased form, and MUST be handled with extreme safety precautions.

Acetic Acid, Hydrochloric Acid, and Hydrofluoric Acid are acids used as counter-etches to clean litho plate metal. Hydrochloric acid is used as an ingredient of etches for zinc, aluminum, and chromium-copper, bi- and tri-metal plates.

Nitric Acid is used to some extent in the treatment of bi-metal plates on the press.

Phosphoric Acid is one of the most important ingredients of most plate etches and fountain etches. It is used as a counter-etch for aluminum. Phosphoric acid is used extensively as a press treatment for bimetal plates.

Sulfuric Acid is an ingredient of surface treatments and is also used for cleaning aluminum, bimetal, and anodized aluminum plates.

Carbolic Acid (Phenols) are used as preservatives for gum.

Lactic Acid is used in deep-etch developers as a solvent for unexposed gum arabic.

Oxalic Acid is used as a treatment to eliminate ink-dot scum on aluminum plates on the press.

Tannic Acid is used in the fountain solution to help the gum desensitize the plate. It is also used as an ingredient of plate etches.

Alkalies (Bases). Two common alkalies used in lithography are:

Ammonium Hydroxide (Ammonia) preserves the coating solutions by keeping the pH high. It is also used to assist the development of surface plates.

Sodium Hydroxide (Caustic Soda) is used to clean zinc plates prior to graining, and as a counter-etch for aluminum plates.

Salts. Many salts are used in the various treatments on lithographic plates, both during platemaking and on the press.

Alums. Ammonium alum is an ingredient in surface treatments. When mixed with hydrofluoric acid it is used as a special counter-etch before adding work to aluminum plates.

Chrome Alum is used in desensitizing plate etches to help harden the gum arabic so that it will not dissolve readily from the plate, and yet allow the gum to hold the water. It is also used in fountain solutions.

Bichromates. *Ammonium bichromate* is used as a coating sensitizer (see Coating Materials), as an ingredient of plate and fountain etches, and as a corrosion inhibitor in surface treatments for zinc and aluminum plates.

Sodium Bichromate is also a corrosion inhibitor and may be used in graining and in surface treatments.

Chlorides. *Calcium chloride, magnesium chloride,* and *zinc chloride,* are used in deep-etch developers and deep-etching solutions.

Ferric Chloride is used in deep-etching solutions. By itself, it is used as an etch for copper on stainless steel bimetal plates.

Aluminum Chloride is an ingredient of chromium etching solutions.

Cuprous Chloride is an ingredient of chemical copperizing solutions for aluminum and steel.

Nitrates. *Ammonium nitrate* and *zinc nitrate* are ingredients of press fountain etches.

Magnesium nitrate is an ingredient of plate etches made with cellulose gum (carboxymethyl cellulose) and is also used in press fountain etches.

Ferric nitrate is used as an etch for copper on copper-aluminum bimetal plates.

Phosphates. *Ammonium dihydrogen phosphate,* or *ammonium phosphate (monobasic)* is used in many press fountain etches.

Trisodium phosphate (TSP) is used as a cleaner for plates during graining. It is also used as a counter-etch or pre-treatment for aluminum.

Cellulose Gum, the sodium salt of carboymethyl cellulose (CMC), is a synthetic gum which is used as a substitute for gum arabic in press fountain solutions.

Gum Arabic is used in plate etches, as a gumming solution, and in press fountain etches. It has already been described under "Coating Materials."

SOLVENTS

A number of solvents are used in lithography. They are divided into three classes: (1) Solvents for chemicals; (2) Lacquer solvents; (3) Ink and grease solvents.

Solvents for Chemicals. Alcohols are used as solvents for chemicals where water might have some effect on the process.

Anhydrous ethyl alcohol is used in the deep-etch process to dissolve and remove the salts left from the developing and deep-etching solution. It is also used as a main ingredient in chemical copperizing solutions.

Anhydrous isopropyl alcohol may be used for the same purposes as anhydrous ethyl alcohol. Isopropyl alcohol (not anhydrous) is also an ingredient of fountain solutions for the Dahlgren, Miehlematic, Dampen-Orr and other new dampening systems. Concentrations up to 25% of alcohol are recommended for these systems.

Ethylene glycol is a dihydric alcohol which absorbs water and holds it like glycerin. For this reason it is used in the copperizing solution for steel, where some water is needed to get good deposition of copper. Ethylene glycol is also used in some press washup solutions to dissolve and remove gum from the rollers.

Cellosolve is a combination of alcohol and ether. Its chemical name is ethylene glycol monethyl ether. It does not evaporate as readily as alcohol and is a substitute for alcohol in the deepetch process. With the use of non-blinding vinyl lacquers, it has been found that the use of Cellosolve must be followed with anhydrous alcohol prior to applying the lacquer, or the lacquer will not adhere properly to the image areas.

Secondary Butyl Alcohol is used as a solvent for hydroquinone in the manufacture of Litho-Kleen. Litho-Kleen is a preparation for preventing glazing and tackiness of rubber blankets.

Lacquer Solvents. The solvents for vinyl lacquers are ketones. Ketones are organic liquids with varying rates of evaporation. Acetone evaporates extremely rapidly. Methyl ethyl ketone (MEK) dries less rapidly, as does hexamone; isophorone is the slowest drying ketone used in lacquers. Because ketones are expensive, lacquer thinners often contain other less expensive chemicals such as toluene, butylacetate, and others. These liquids are not solvents for the lacquer, but they are compatible with the lacquer and with the other solvents. These liquids are used to control the evaporation rate and working properties of the lacquer. Since they are considerably cheaper than the pure ketones, their use helps reduce the price of the lacquers.

Ink and Grease Solvents. The most common solvents for ink and grease are the petroleum solvents. These, too, have different evaporation rates and are classed by flash point, or the temperature at which the vapors will ignite in the air. Their use is regulated by fire departments and insurance companies.

White gasoline has a flash point below 0°F, and is considered an extremely dangerous fire hazard. Benzine (VM & P Naphtha has a flash point of about 45°F. It is safer than white gasoline but is still considered hazardous. *Stoddard solvent* has a flash point of over 100°F and is considered safe for use if kept in safety cans.

Chlorinated solvents like carbon tetrachloride, monochlorethylene, and trichlorethylene, are good solvents for grease and ink. They are non-flammable but are very toxic. *Carbon tetrachloride is a deadly poison and should never be used under any circumstances.* The other chlorinated solvents are less toxic, but they should be used with extreme caution and only where the area is very well ventilated.

Turpentine is a natural solvent obtained from the resinous wood of southern pine and is used for washing out plates in platemaking and on the press. It is available either as gum spirits of turpentine or steam distilled wood turpentine, both of which are satisfactory for lithographic use. Although it is an excellent solvent, turpentine is a skin irritant to many people, and its use should be avoided.

Lithotine is a solvent developed by GATF as a substitute for turpentine. It consists of a mixture of pine oil, caster oil, ester gum, and petroleum solvent. Lithotine works exactly like turpentine but is not an irritant to the skin.

Air Pollution. Many solvents are considered causes of air pollution and many regulations have been put into law to restrict their use. Plants with many presses using large quantities of solvents will be required to install expensive exhaust and/or catalytic oxidation systems.

OTHER MATERIALS USED IN PLATEMAKING

A number of other materials are used in platemaking. Most of these materials are proprietary or ready-made. They are described in general classes without reference to different brand names.

Abrasive Sticks are used to remove unwanted areas from plates. There are two types: snakeslips and scotch stones. Air erasers are also available. This is an airbrush type of gun which uses compressed air and pumice. The air eraser does an excellent job of removing unwanted work in platemaking and on the press, and still leaves a grained surface to carry water. The trouble with most abrasive sticks is that they polish the metal and affect the ability of the treated area to carry water, thereby they may cause a scum or tint in the polished area.

Asphaltum is used to protect the plate image after the developing ink or press ink is washed off. Plates are usually stored "under asphaltum" since ink would tend to dry or harden while the plate is in storage. Asphaltum (gilsonite) is a natural mineral resin available in a variety of forms. Acceptable lithographic asphaltum should be completely soluble in Lithotine.

Asphaltum-Gum is an emulsion of asphaltum and gum arabic solution used in place of the gum solution. When used properly, the solution applies a film of protective gum to the non-printing areas while the asphaltum imparts good grease receptivity to the image areas. The emulsion helps to eliminate the failure of plates to roll up properly on the press due to gum laying on the image, or developing ink rubbed down too thin. The asphaltum-gum emulsion can be used on all types of plates.

Developing Inks are used in platemaking to apply a greasy surface to the image areas. They are essentially stiff, non-drying greasy black inks thinned with solvents so that they can be rubbed to a smooth, even film on the plate. Developing inks are commonly available in different consistencies. Surface plate inks are rather thin; deep-etch inks are thicker. Special heavy-bodied inks are also supplied in tubes for use on bimetal and fine grained plates.

Lacquers are used to strengthen the image and to make it resistant to solvents, acids, and gum. Lacquers were formerly made of shellac, nitrocellulose, Bakelite and other synthetic resins. Practically all such lacquers have been replaced by new ones made from vinyl resins. These form the basis of the modern non-binding lacquers.

Lacquer Emulsion is used extensively on presensitized and wipe-on plates, and consists of an emulsion of a lacquer resin and a desensitizing gum. Plates on which lacquer emulsion is used are sometimes difficult to roll up on the press.

Staging Lacquer or stopping-out lacquer is used on deep-etch plates to block out unexposed areas in order to prevent them from developing. As staging lacquers are composed mainly of shellac, which is alcohol soluble, the staging lacquer is removed in the alcohol wash.

Tusche is used for adding work to plates. There are two basic types: One is formed by rubbing litho crayon in water. The soap in the crayon emulsifies the wax and grease and produces an emulsion with the approximate consistency of heavy coffee cream. Tusche can be applied to a cleaned plate with a brush to produce solids, or with a pen to draw lines. Before it can produce a printing image, however, the tusche must be dried thoroughly on the plate and reacted upon by the plate etch; otherwise it will be soluble in water. The acid in the etch converts the soap to a water-insoluble fatty acid which is ink-receptive.

The other type of tusche is used when images are added to aluminum presensitized plates. This tusche is applied to a dry plate by rubbing the solution on the area and then tapping in press ink. The plate is then etched.

Image Remover is a thickened solvent used for the removal of unwanted image. The formula varies with the type of plate—positive working, negative working, zinc, or other metal. The remover is applied to the area with a brush or swab, and after allowing the solution to react for approximately a minute, the plate area is flushed with water or the area is wiped dry.

Section Four: Chemistry of Platemaking

Chemistry is the foundation of platemaking. Chemical reactions are involved in: (1) the production of the image by light; and (2) wettability of the image area by ink and the non-image areas by water.

LIGHT SENSITIVITY
OF BICHROMATED COATINGS

The following discussion is limited to the light sensitivity of bichromated coatings because they are still in use and little is known about factors that affect the light sensitivity of organic type coatings such as diazos and photopolymers, and the electrostatic processes.

When Alois Senefelder invented lithography his patent and subsequent book made known that lithography was a chemical process based on the phenomenum that water and oil are generally insoluble in each other. Probably the most important advance since Senefelder has been the development of photolithography—the use of photographic negatives or positives and light sensitive chemicals to produce printing images on lithographic printing surfaces.

Two things are common to the conventional photo-lithographic processes of the albumin, deep-etch, and bimetal types of plates; they are a bichromate and a colloid. A colloid is a material with a large organic molecule that forms a uniform, continuous film. The colloids of value in photolithography are water soluble. When mixed with a bichromate, coated on a stone or plate, and exposed to light through a negative or positive, the molecules which are exposed to light become insoluble. When the unexposed parts of the coating are washed away during the development steps, an image remains. Albumin and casein were the first colloids used extensively for making "surface" plates prior to the introduction of presensitized and wipe-on plates. Gum arabic is the colloid, used for making "deep-etch" plates and the various types of bimetal plates. In Europe, bichromated PVA is also used for deep-etch and bimetal plates.

From the beginning of the twentieth century, many chemists have studied the reactions by which bichromated colloids become insoluble under the influence of light. But these reactions are so complex that, even now, we still cannot write chemical equations for the complex chemical reactions which occur during exposure. In the first place, the colloids in themselves—albumin, casein, gum arabic and others—are such complex materials that we cannot even give them chemical formulas. In fact, many are not simple compounds but mixtures of compounds. Secondly, when bichromate is added to one of these colloids, and the mixture is exposed to light, only a small fraction of the bichromate becomes changed. Chemical analysis has shown that the changed parts have been reduced and part of the bichromate's oxygen is absorbed by the colloid, which then becomes oxidized. In some way, the reduction product of the bichromate (Cr_2O_3) or $(Cr_2(OH)_6)$ attaches itself to the colloid. The known result is that the new combination is insoluble in water or at least much less soluble than the original mixture. It is this reaction to light that makes bichromated colloids so important to platemaking. The results of GATF's studies on this subject are published in its Bulletin No. 218, "The Sensitivity of Bichromated Coatings," by G. W. Jorgensen and M. H. Bruno. A recent revision to this publication is found in Appendix III, of textbook 502/4, "Offset Lithographic Platemaking."

While scientists do not know all the chemistry of the light hardening process, it has been possible to study the process and learn enough to control it. Before this basic work was done, lithographers did not know what was causing variations, so they could not possibly avoid them. Most of this trouble was caused by unexpected changes in light sensitivity of the dried plate coatings which in turn caused the coatings on successive plates to be hardened to different degrees by the same light exposure.

SIX PLATEMAKING VARIABLES

The variables that must be controlled in order to produce coatings of the same light sensitivity consistently are:
1. Bichromate—colloid ratio in the coating solution.
2. pH (alkalinity) of the coating.
3. Coating thickness.
4. Age of the dried coating.
5. Temperature.
6. Relative humidity.

Intentional or accidental changes in the first three variables may be made by the platemaker. The fourth variable often depends on the nature of the job—in other words, the length of time it takes to complete the light exposure and start the development. The last two variables are continually changing in most shops, but they can be kept somewhat under control by air conditioning. The following discussion tells how these variables affect the light sensitivity of coatings and what the lithographer can do to control them.

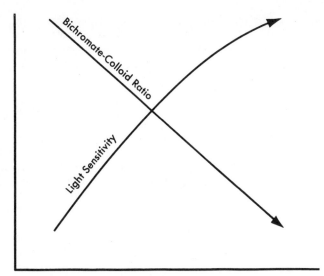

Light sensitivity increases as bichromate : colloid ratio decreases.

Bichromate: Colloid Ratio. The light sensitivity of the coating increases as the ratio of ammonium bichromate to the colloid is increased, at least to a limiting point after which the bichromate precipitates. In other words, if the amount of bichromate increases without increasing the albumin, casein, gum arabic, or PVA, the coating will be increasingly light sensitive up to the limiting point. If the bichromate is decreased, the coating will be less light sensitive. In either case, the regular light exposure will produce a different degree of hardening than with correctly made coatings.

Most albumin coating solutions have a bichromate-colloid ratio of 1:3 (one part by weight of dry ammonium bichromate to three parts by weight of dry albumin). Casein coatings have bichromate-casein ratios ranging between 1:3 and 1:10.

Deep-etch coatings have bichromate-gum ratios ranging between 1:3 and 1:5. The GATF published formula for a deep-etch coating is based on a ratio of 1:4.18. If the shop changes from one brand of coating to another, the bichromate: colloid ratios may be different and the exposure times may have to be changed.

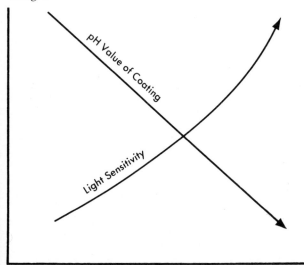

Light sensitivity increases as coating pH decreases.

pH (Alkalinity) of the Coating. All coatings contain ammonium hydroxide in addition to ammonium bichromate and the colloid. The bichromate-colloid mixture, by itself, is acidic and unstable. It becomes useless after a few hours. However, if the coating is made alkaline with ammonium hydroxide, the mixture will be more stable, and keep awhile.

The amount of ammonia has an effect on the light sensitivity of the dried plate coating. Most of the ammonia evaporates within a half-hour after the coating has dried. The amount that remains in the coating at any given time depends on the pH of the coating solution. The more ammonia there is in a coating, the less light sensitive the coating will be. This is the reason why it is important to maintain the pH value of the coating solution at all times.

Coating Thickness. Thick coatings require longer exposures than thin coatings, because light hardens the coating from the top down. The thicker the coating, the longer it takes for the light to penetrate to the metal surface. Hardening to the metal surface is necessary for both firm adhesion and proper development of the coating. The effect of changing the coating thickness is therefore the same as that of changing its light sensitivity.

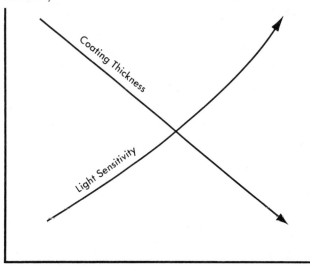

Light sensitivity increases as coating thickness is decreased.

Keeping the coating thickness constant from plate to plate is also very important, and these factors must be taken into consideration:

1. Plate grain.
2. Solids content of the coating solution.
3. Viscosity of the coating solution.
4. Temperature.
5. Amount of moisture on the plate when the coating solution is applied.
6. Volume of coating solution used on each size of plate.
7. Relative humidity.
8. Whirler speed.

The plate grain must be consistent from plate to plate. A coating on a coarse grained plate and a fine grained plate will not be equally thick, with the same coating solution and keeping all other factors that affect coating thickness the same. If the coating has the proper thickness for the fine grained plate, it will be too thin for the coarse grained plate. The high peaks of the

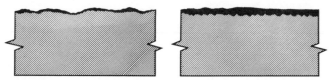

With equal amounts of coating, peaks of coarse grain (left) are not well-covered.

coarse grain will be covered so thinly that in surface plates the ink covers the peaks and on deep-etch plates the light-hardened coating may be penetrated by the developer and deep-etching solutions. This would produce a scummy plate. Conversely, if the coating is thick enough for the coarse-grained plate, it will be too thick for the fine-grained plate. Thick coatings increase the danger of undercutting.

The solids content of the coating solution is the amount of dry solids (ammonium bichromate plus colloid) in a gallon of the solution. As long as the coating solution formula is kept constant, the solids content will be the same. Any one brand of commercial coating solution should always have the same solids content. The best way to check solids content is to test coating solutions with a Baumé hydrometer.

The viscosity (resistance to flow) of the coating solution may vary with different lots of colloid. If the plant makes its own coating solution, it is difficult to control the viscosity unless the plant uses a viscometer, maintains constant room temperature, and selects or blends its own colloid. Commercial coating solutions, which are made under laboratory control, should have fairly constant viscosities.

Temperature changes will cause changes in viscosity of the coating solution. The higher the temperature, the thinner (more fluid) the coating solution. In order to obtain dried coatings of consistently uniform thickness from plate to plate, the temperature of both the plate and the coating solution should be as nearly constant as possible. This is why the plate should be flushed with a large amount of water at room temperature just before coating. The effect of temperature on viscosity is another reason for keeping the coating solution at room temperature.

The amount of moisture on the plate affects the final coating thickness. This moisture dilutes or thins the solution. The more moisture, the thinner the final coating. The plate must, of course, carry some moisture. A dry plate is not instantly wet by the coating solution, and therefore it may be difficult to coat evenly. To be sure there is always the same amount of moisture on the plate, whirl the plate for a definite period of time between shutting off the water and pouring on the coating solution.

The volume of coating solution also affects the coating thickness. More than the right amount of solution gives a thicker coating since the coating will be only slightly diluted by the moisture on the plate. Likewise, less than the right amount of solution produces a thinner coating.

Relative Humidity. The higher the relative humidity, the slower the coating will dry. Consequently, all other factors being equal, more of the solution will be whirled off the plate on humid days than on dry days. High humidity, therefore, produces thin coatings and low humidity results in thick coatings. If the plant is not air conditioned, the whirler should be slowed down on humid days and speeded up on dry days. Thin coatings on deep-etch plates dry harder and resist penetration by the developer better than thicker coatings.

The whirler speed controls the thickness of the coating, if all the above factors are held constant. The whirler makes the coating solution flow from the plate center to the edges where the excess coating is thrown off the plate. Centrifugal force causes this outward flow, and the force increases with increases in the rotational speed of the whirler platform. Hence, the faster the whirler speed, the thinner the final coating. If changing the whirler speed does not produce thin enough coatings, the coating itself should be thinned.

The most important factor in coating plates is to perform the sequence of steps the same way everytime; to have a fixed procedure. If the coating is too thick or too thin, a correction can be made on the next plate. Usually, the simplest way to change the coating thickness is to change the whirler speed.

One clue to early recognition of too thick or too thin a coating is glossiness of the dried coating on the plate. On grained plates, the thicker the coating, the glossier and shiner it will appear. The experienced platemaker soon learns the relative degree of glossiness to look for.

Variations in coating thickness will, of course, show up after the plate has been exposed and developed, especially on deep-etch plates. By watching the development carefully, the plate-

At the same whirler speed, coating thickness increases as relative humidity decreases.

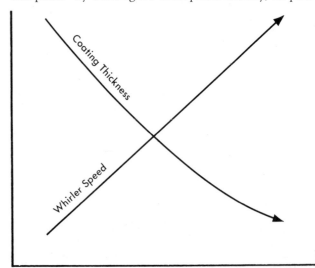

The higher the whirler speed, the thinner the coating.

maker can detect when he has a plate with a coating that is not normal. If the coating is not normal the platemaker makes an adjustment, perhaps a change in whirler speed, when coating the next plate.

Age of the Dried Coating. A freshly dried coating does not have its maximum light sensitivity, partly because the coating loses its ammonia rather slowly. Until the ammonia is completely gone, the coating is constantly becoming more light sensitive. From the time the dried plate is removed from the whirler, it takes about one-half hour for the coating to lose enough of its ammonia for its light sensitivity to become reasonably constant.

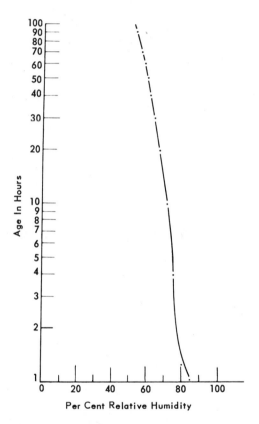

Time required for deep-etch coatings on plates to reach same degree of hardness or insolubility due to dark reaction at different relative humidities at 78°F. Same is true for surface coatings, but age is generally less.

Except when the relative humidity is above 70%, a good rule to follow is to allow half an hour from the time the plate is taken from the whirler before starting the exposure. This half-hour interval insures: that the plate has lost the residual ammonia; that the plate will have cooled to room temperature; and the coating will have come into balance with the relative humidity of the room atmosphere. All of these factors are necessary for uniform light sensitivity at the time the plate is to be exposed.

How long the coated plate can be kept, before the entire coating becomes too insoluble to be developed, depends on the temperature and relative humidity. As soon as the plate coating has dried, it begins to harden, even without the action of light. This spontaneous hardening is called "dark reaction." Dark

reaction is much slower than the hardening produced by light; but if dark reaction continues, the entire coating may become insoluble. If such a plate is exposed in the vacuum frame, the unexposed area will not develop; hence a poor plate. Whether the plate ages before or after the exposures makes little difference; the dark reaction is faster at the higher temperatures and relative humidities.

Temperature. The light sensitivity of the dried coating is greater, the higher the temperature, and as we have mentioned above, the dark reaction is also faster with increasing temperature. The dry plate coating, therefore, should be protected as much as possible from temperatures higher than room temperature. *The greatest damage from high temperature comes from leaving the plates in a heated whirler after the coating has dried.* It is a good idea to set an alarm clock just after the plate has been coated, the whirler closed, and the heat turned on. By checking a few plates to see how long it takes them to dry, the platemaker can establish standardized drying times. The plate should be removed immediately at the end of the predetermined time limit.

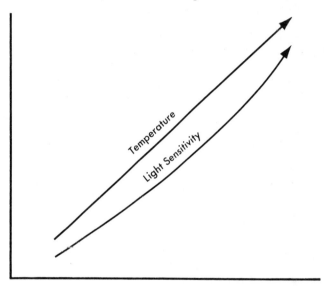

Light sensitivity of dried coating increases as temperature increases.

Relative Humidity. The light sensitivity of the dried coating increases with increased relative humidity. In non-air-conditioned shops where the relative humidity is continually changing, the light sensitivity of coatings will vary from plate to plate. Coatings of uniform light sensitivity can be made only if the platemaking room is air conditioned.

If the plant does not have air conditioning, the platemaker can adjust the light exposure or coating thickness to compensate for changes in relative humidity. The first requirement for making the necessary adjustments is to have an accurate hydrometer and to know how to use it. Check the relative humidity before coating the plate. If the relative humidity has increased since coating the plate, shorten the exposure. If it has decreased, lengthen the exposure accordingly. If the change in relative humidity is 20% or more, changing the exposure is not enough. In this case, the coating thickness must also be changed.

If the relative humidity is high in a non-air-conditioned plate room, it is advisable to protect the plate with a coating of wax or

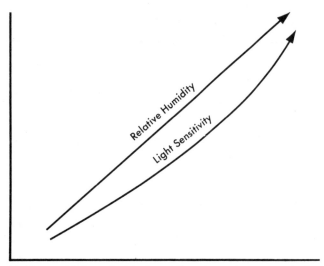

Light sensitivity of dried coating increases as relative humidity goes up.

asphaltum as soon as the plate is taken from the whirler. A coating of thin lacquer may also be used. Coatings of lacquers keep the gum in deep-etch coatings from getting tacky and prevent the softening of the gum by atmospheric moisture. These protective coatings also stabilize the light sensitivity and assist development, especially if the plate is dried carefully before starting the processing steps.

Unimportant Factors. Some factors which have little or no affect on the light sensitivity of the coating are given below.

1. The plate metal. Whether the plate is zinc, aluminum, or stainless steel makes no noticeable difference on the plate coatings, provided the grain and other factors are the same.

2. Surface treatments. Cronaking zinc plates or Brunaking aluminum plates has no noticeable affect on the light sensitivity of coatings, although these treatments do retard dark reaction to some extent.

3. Color of the coating solution. Some commercial deep-etch coating solutions contain a dye, usually blue, that gives the solution a green tinge (yellow bichromated colloid + blue dye). Careful checks show that this color has little or no effect on the light sensitivity of the coating.

Diazo and Photopolymer Coatings. Diazo and photopolymer coatings are not affected at all by most of the major platemaking variables. Diazo coatings do not seem to be affected by relative humidity, although they are temperature sensitive above 125°F. Higher temperatures than this can cause the coatings on presensitized plates to become insoluble, usually resulting in scummy plates. Diazo deteriorates rapidly when exposed to heat. For best results the dry diazo material should be kept in a refrigerator as well as the coating solution. The coating solution should be mixed daily. Photopolymer coatings do not seem to be affected by either relative humidity or temperature. Some plates of the cinnamic ester type were exposed two years after they were coated and were still acceptable for printing.

COMPOSITE EFFECT OF ALL FACTORS

The hardening of bichromated colloids is a chemical reaction.

The rate of hardening is a function of the product of all the factors mentioned. The most important variables are: bichromate-colloid ratio; pH; temperature; and relative humidity. *Since the product of these factors controls the reaction, the total result is small if the affect of any single factor is small.* This partially explains why coated plates can be kept in a plant for a long time during the winter when the relative humidity is low even though the temperature of the plant is comparatively high. It explains, also, why coated plates will keep in a refrigerator where the temperature is low but the relative humidity is comparatively high. If some way can be found of keeping the pH of coatings high until the time of exposure, we will have a way of presensitizing plates with bichromated coatings. Several commercial coatings are available which make this claim.

CONTROL OF THE PLATEMAKING VARIABLES

The GATF Sensitivity Guide. Most of the factors affecting plate coatings cause trouble only when they get badly out of hand. Usually this appears when the temperature and relative humidity suddenly become high or vary considerably from day to day. During most of the year the effect of most of these variables is hardly noticed.

The biggest source of trouble in the past was the lack of some way of measuring the total effect of all the variables. Most plates looked good in the platemaking department. Their appearance, however, was deceiving. It was never really known whether the plate was acceptable, or whether it would print satisfactorily until the plate was on the press and running; too late for corrective action.

GATF's research changed this situation when it developed the Sensitivity Guide for platemaking. The Sensitivity Guide is a simple photographic measuring device which integrates the effect of all the variables affecting the plate coating, its exposure, and the development. As soon as the plate is developed, the Guide tells the platemaker if the image areas are properly exposed and developed and if the non-printing areas are apt to cause trouble.

The GATF Sensitivity Guide is a narrow strip of special continuous tone transparent gray scale about one-half inch wide and five inches long (12½ x 125 mm). There are 21 different density steps in the Guide. These steps are numbered from 1 to 21 with the low numbers at the clear end of the scale. The gray scale is so selected that the density difference between steps is about 0.15, and 0.30 between every other step. This means that the light transmission of every other step is cut in half or

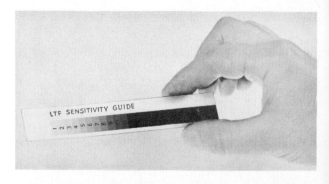

The GATF Sensitivity Guide; a 21-step gray scale.

doubled depending on whether the numbers increase or decrease. Step 7 on the scale has about one-half the light transmission of step 5, step 4 lets through about twice as much light as step 6.

HOW THE GUIDE IS USED. To use the Sensitivity Guide, it is stripped into the flat, or on the photo-composing machine glass. Any prominent place on the plate is satisfactory; some plants use several guides on different parts of the plate.

On surface plates—when the plate is exposed, inked, and developed—a number of the steps of the Guide will also show. Ordinarily, step numbers 1 to 5, or 1 to 6 are solid black. If step 5 is the highest numbered solid black step, steps 6, 7, 8 (and perhaps more) will show as a gray tone. These gray tones get weaker and weaker as the numbers go higher.

THE CRITICAL STEP. The highest numbered solid black step is called the critical step. This is the one to watch. With the same exposure time, the critical step will change when the sensitivity of the coating changes, or when changes in the amount of dark reaction have occurred. The more sensitive the coating, the higher the number of the critical step that will appear. A difference of two steps means that the coating was twice as sensitive as it should have been, or that the exposure should have been cut in half. In addition the number of gray steps that show on the plate should be checked. Too many gray steps are a warning that a plate may be sensitive to scum or sharpening on the press.

THE GATF GUIDE ON DEEP-ETCH PLATES. On deep-etch plates the Guide is even more important than on surface plates because it can be used as a control in compensating for slight errors of exposures or changes in sensitivity. When the Guide is used properly, deep-etch platemaking with the bichromated gum process becomes an exposure-development process like ordinary photography with silver halides. Changes in sensitivity, or errors in exposure, can be compensated for by changes in development. This is true also for bichromated PVA processes which use solvent developers.

The Guide on deep-etch plates is reversed in appearance to a Guide on a surface plate. The high numbered steps are solid and the low numbered steps are clear, with possibly one or two gray steps in between the gray area and the solid black areas. Development is usually carried to approximately one step from the critical step. Deep-etching removes the one step. The ideal critical step is determined by experience but here, again, it has been found that a critical step of 5 or 6 is satisfactory under most operating conditions.

WHAT THE GUIDE TELLS. The GATF Sensitivity Guide is the most important tool the platemaker has. He has a device by which he can exercise control over the platemaking process. It will tell him when a change in coating sensitivity has occurred and how much of a change has taken place. It will not tell him what has caused the change. For this he must depend on his experience.

CONTROL OF TONE VALUES IN PLATEMAKING

The GATF Star Target. The GATF Star Target is a small (⅜″—9 mm diameter) circular pattern of solid and clear pie-shaped wedges. When correctly reproduced on the plate, the center of the target will be open, just as it is on the original film. If the center of the target appears filled in on the plate, dot spread is indicated; if the center of the target appears broken or enlarged, dot sharpening has occurred. The actual amount of spreading or sharpening is magnified 23 times. This requires the use of a magnifying glass or microscope with a calibrated reticle, if specific calculations are to be made. More information on the GATF Star Target will be found in GATF's Research Progress 52.

GATF Star Targets: left, positive; right, negative.

The GATF Dot Gain Scale. The GATF Dot Gain Scale is a small (¼ x 2″—6 x 50 mm) strip, available in either negative or positive. The Scale consists of numbers from 0 to 9 in a fine screen pattern against a coarse screen pattern. The dot values in the numbers vary in increments of 3% to 5%. In the original negative or positive the number "2" appears to have exactly the same density as the background, at normal viewing distance, and therefore is "hidden." When the Dot Gain Scale

Printed images of Dot Gain Scale: top, sharp; center, shows dot gain without slur; bottom, dot gain caused by slur.

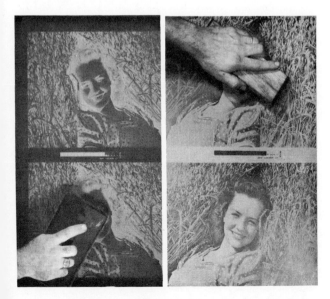

Appearance of the Sensitivity Guide: left, on a developed deep-etch plate; right, on a finished surface plate.

is reproduced on a plate, one number blends with the background tint; higher numbers are lighter, lower numbers are darker. The number that disappears is a measure of dot-size change. If the hidden figure advances a single number from one plate to the next, the dots have spread about 3%–5%. For more information on the GATF Dot Gain Scale see GATF's Research Progress 69.

WETTABILITY OF IMAGE AND NON-IMAGE AREAS

The principle on which lithography is based—that grease and water don't mix—is not completely true. Grease and water do mix under certain conditions. We also have evidence which indicates that a plate will not print if ink and water do not mix to a slight degree on the press. The process, therefore, seems to work within limits. These limits cannot be too narrow, or the process would never work as successfully as it does. If the limits within which the water and grease mixes get too wide, then we run into trouble.

While it has been found that some mixture of water and ink is necessary in printing on the press, in platemaking, nevertheless, any such tendency must be prevented. If the image areas could be wet *only* by ink and not by water, and the non-image areas *only* by water and not by ink, the ideal lithographic plate would be the result, and such a plate would run with the least amount of trouble. When the image areas are wet by water and not by ink, trouble results with "blinding." There is trouble with "scum" when the non-image areas are wet by ink and not by water. The wettability of the image and non-image areas, by ink and water respectively, is related to the physical chemistry of the surfaces.

INK-RECEPTIVITY OF IMAGE AREAS

Different kinds of image areas are used in lithography depending on the type of plate. Each type of plate has a different kind of image, and each kind of image may have different characteristics with respect to ink-receptivity.

Albumin Surface Plates. The image areas on albumin surface plates consist of hardened protein covered with ink or lacquer. Dried protein, in contact with ammonium bichromate, when chemically reduced by exposure to light, becomes insoluble in water and ink-receptive at the same time. This ink-receptivity is enhanced further by application of developing ink. The hardened protein will eventually absorb water on the press if water and acid are used extensively. As the image absorbs water, it swells and loses its affinity for ink, resulting in a blind image. This tendency is eliminated, or at least retarded, by the use of a lacquer prior to the application of developing ink.

Presensitized Plates. The image areas on most presensitized plates in commercial use consist of diazo compounds that are either polymerized or reacted upon in some other way by light. In general, these materials have excellent ink-receptivity and resistance to wetting by water or gum. They have, however, poor resistance to abrasion, especially with the thin coatings which can be produced on these relatively smooth plates. Images wear more rapidly on these relatively smooth plates unless pressures are watched carefully and abrasive conditions are kept to a minimum.

Wipe-on Plates. The images on wipe-on plates are similar to those on diazo presensitized plates. The images, however, are more resistant to abrasion because wipe-on plates are grained. This condition is also true of those presensitized plates which are grained.

Photopolymer Plates. The image areas on photopolymer plates of the cinnamic ester type consist of an organic resin insolubilized by light. The material is completely insoluble in water and has excellent resistance to wetting by water and gum. The resin also has good resistance to abrasion so that long runs are one of the characteristics of these plates. The image areas on the water-soluble type of photopolymer plates also have good ink-receptivity and resistance to wear, if the images are treated before the plates are put on the press.

Deep-Etch Plates. The image areas on deep-etch plates consist of a chemically etched metal to which a lacquer and an ink are applied. The ink-receptive properties of the image seem to be related to the surface characteristics of the chemically etched area, and to the chemical nature of the lacquer.

If the coating has not been completely removed from the image area by the developing and deep-etching operations, the lacquer does not adhere well, and the image blinds in printing. The same thing will happen if moisture is allowed to condense on the image areas during the alcohol wash, or after the water wash on PVA plates. Leaching of bichromates from the stencil can also cause similar trouble. These image areas will corrode or oxidize, and corrosion prevents good adhesion of the lacquer.

Another cause of poor adhesion of the image on aluminum deep-etch plates, especially copperized images, is the presence of loose iron. Iron is deposited in the image wells as a result of the chemical reaction between the ferric chloride in the deep-etch solution and the plate metal itself. Some of the iron is tightly bonded to the aluminum, but some is rather loose and spongy. Copper will deposit on this iron, but because the iron is loosely bonded to the surface it dislodges when the plate is running on the press. The result is "spotty blinding." Some chemical suppliers try to eliminate the iron by recommending a redevelopment step after deep-etching, but this does not completely remove the iron deposit. GATF has found that the iron deposit can be completely removed with a solution of nitric acid and cellosolve (Nicohol—see GATF's Research Progress 43). Another remedy for the problem is to use a deep-etch solution that does not contain ferric chloride. Still another method is to eliminate the deep-etching step. When this is done, development must be extended approximately one-half step further on the GATF Sensitivity Guide. Recently modified iron etches have been developed which, when properly used, do not leave loose iron on the image area.

Lacquers are used primarily to make the image resistant to acids and solvents. The first lacquers were of the nitrocellulose type. Although these were resistant to acids and solvents, they were readily wet by water and gum. Many deep-etch plates went blind because of gum sticking to such lacquers. The introduction of vinyl lacquers eliminated this problem because vinyl lacquers have much less tendency to be wet either by water or gum. Formulation of the lacquer, however, is important. If the dye, pigment, plasticizer, or solvent mixture is incompatible with the other chemicals in the lacquer, even a vinyl lacquer may show poor resistance to blinding. Dyes, pigment, or plasticizers, which float to the surface of the lacquer on drying, can readily be wet by water or gum. The solvent mixture should be so balanced that all solvents evaporate together, leaving a hard tough film of lacquer on the image. If one of the solvents dries more slowly than the others, it either allows too much of the lacquer to be rubbed off, or the slow drying solvent gets trapped in the lacquer film so that the lacquer film remains soft and has little resistance to abrasion.

Bimetal and Copperized Deep-Etch Plates. The image areas of all but one of these plates consists of copper covered with a lacquer. Copper has two main advantages as a printing surface: (1) It is very ink-receptive and water- or gum-repellent in the presence of nitrates and phosphates; (2) It has greater resistance to abrasion than have the lacquers. Lacquers are used on copper images mainly to protect the copper during platemaking, and to start the plates printing faster on the press.

One of the main reasons bimetal plates have been so successful is that copper *is ink-receptive under the same conditions that render the non-image metal water-receptive.* In the presence of nitrates and phosphates, the copper is ink-receptive, while aluminum, chromium, and stainless steel are water-receptive. This means that if the image areas start taking water, or if they become blind, and if the non-image areas start taking ink, or if they scum on the press, a single treatment with a fairly strong (10%–25%) solution of phosphoric acid is usually sufficient to bring both areas back to their original printing condition. Copper can be readily blinded by exposure to sulfur compounds, chromic acid, or excessive bichromates. Copper will also corrode quickly if exposed to the air. The corroded copper becomes dull and dark when the oxide forms, and then interferes with the ink-receptivity. The copper image areas, therefore, should be protected as much as possible. If by accident corrosion does occur, the oxide can easily be removed with a treatment of weak nitric acid and a solution of phosphoric acid, or a good commercial preparation. A small amount of bichromate in the fountain does not seem to hurt the copper and even seems to help bimetal plates on the press. However, an excessive amount of the bichromate can cause blinding.

By far, the greatest advantage of copper is its resistance to abrasion. Lacquers are somewhat brittle, and when printing under abrasive conditions (too much pressure, abrasive inks, papers, or sprays), images will blind when the lacquers are worn off. Copper, on the other hand, is rather ductile and is not as easily worn off the plate by abrasive printing conditions. There are instances on record, where, with just the use of chemical copperizing on aluminum deep-etch plates, *all other conditions being equal,* the life of the plates on the press were increased as much as tenfold.

Other Types of Plates. The image areas of direct image plates consist of carbon black in wax transferred from a special paper typewriter ribbon. These images are easily abraded so that the plates do not have a very long life.

The image areas on projection plates consist of tanned gelatin which is not especially resistant to blinding or wear, and these plates are also short lived.

The image areas on plates made by the electrostatic processes of Xerography and Electrofax consist of baked organic resins. These resins can be selected so as to have good ink-receptivity and resistance to blinding and abrasion.

WATER-RECEPTIVITY OF THE NON-PRINTING AREAS

The water-receptivity of the non-image areas is affected by the metal used in the plate and how that metal has been treated. As in the case of image areas, water-receptivity is dependent on the type of plate. The items that most affect the water-receptivity of non-image areas are: (1) The metals themselves; (2) The surface treatments given the metal; (3) The desensitizing process; (4) The fountain solutions with which the plate is run; (5) The gumming.

Differences in Water Wettability of Metals. Metals that form hard, tenacious oxides, such as aluminum, chromium, and stainless steel are easily wet by water and retain their wettability for a long time. Anodized aluminum is especially superior in this respect. Metals such as zinc or iron, which form loose corrosion products similar to rust, are not wet as readily by water. The wettability of these metals changes as they go through different stages of corrosion.

In lithography, the ability of a metal to be wet with water is further enhanced or reinforced by the application of a solution of a gum, for example a gum arabic etch. How well the gum or etch sticks to the metal depends on the composition of the etch and the condition of the metal surface. Metals such as aluminum (especially anodized aluminum), chromium, and stainless steel hardly need the gum to be water-receptive. Zinc could not be used at all as a lithographic metal without the use of gum. Many troubles are encountered with zinc because the adherence of the gum and its ability to wet with water (desensitized) is affected by the presence of other materials and by corrosion. If the zinc is clean, gum sticks to it very well and the zinc becomes very water-receptive (well desensitized). If the zinc is corroded, or if a foreign material like unremoved or residual albumin is attached (adsorbed) to its surface, the gum will not stick; then the zinc is not water-receptive, or it is said to be poorly desensitized. Residual coating will also affect the desensitization of surface plates on aluminum.

Surface Treatments. Surface treatments have been developed to: (1) Eliminate difficulties caused by residual coatings and corrosion; (2) Improve the wettability of metals. A surface treatment is a combination of chemicals which react with the metal leaving a stable, tenacious coating. A surface-treated metal does not corrode, does not react with coatings like diazos, and is not affected by the solutions used in the lithographic process; coatings and gum stick very well to the treated metal.

The first of the surface treatments used was for zinc. The Cronak process, as it was called, was originally developed by the New Jersey Zinc Company and modified for lithographic use, in the mid-1940's, first at the Army Map Service in 1944, and then at GATF in 1946.

Surface treatments have been developed for aluminum, but largely for a different reason. Aluminum does not corrode or rust like zinc; it does form a hard, tenacious oxide. When the oxide film is continuous and unbroken, it is an excellent water-receptive surface. If this film of oxide is damaged in any way, minute corrosion pits form at the points of damage. The aluminum is soon covered with a peppery type of ink-receptive corrosion pit that we call "ink-dot scum." It has been found that this type of corrosion can be inhibited or stopped by the use of the Brunak treatment. (See GATF Txb 502/4, "Offset Lithographic Platemaking.")

It is believed that the Brunak treatment of aluminum distributes a mixture of chromic oxide and chromium trioxide on the aluminum oxide, and that these compounds inhibit the electrolytic corrosion of the aluminum when the aluminum oxide surface is damaged. If ink-dot scum forms on the press, the scum can usually be removed by a 5% phosphoric or oxalic acid solution.

Aluminum must be surface treated before it can be coated with the type of diazos used for negative presensitized or wipe-on plates. The diazos, which become ink-receptive when exposed to light, react with metal. Several types of surface treatments are used; the most popular seems to be a silicate treatment. A number of other treatments have been developed and used for this purpose. Anodizing is one; potassium zirconium fluoride is another; a third makes use of an organic phosphoric compound. These are just a few of the metal treatments used. (See Section Five.)

Anodizing the aluminum plate is an especially popular surface treatment in Europe. Anodizing is a means of electrolytically producing a film of aluminum oxide of controlled thickness on the surface. This film is highly water-receptive and resistant to chemical and abrasive attack on the press. It is used primarily for deep-etch plates, but is also used for presensitized and wipe-on plates.

Composition of Etches. The purpose of an etch is to deposit a water-receptive material on the non-image areas of the plate. A good etch should leave a film of water-receptive material which lasts for a long time on the press, and wets with a minimum of water.

An etch usually consists of a gum, an acid, and one or more salts. The main ingredient of the etch is the gum, usually gum arabic. Only one other material has been found that works as well as gum arabic, and this is cellulose gum (carboxymethylcellulose) (CMC). It works well as an etch on zinc, but not on aluminum. However, it is used effectively in press fountains on plates of both metals.

Much searching has been done to find a substitute for gum arabic. In the first place, the industry is entirely dependent on a foreign source of supply; in the second place, since gum is a "natural" material, it varies widely in composition and purity. But gum arabic is a very unusual material; it has a low viscosity for a gum; has good adherence to metal; forms a highly water-receptive film. Gum arabic is the major ingredient of etches, gumming solutions, and deep-etch coatings. It is believed the reason gum arabic sticks so well to metal is that it contains free organic acid groups in the molecule. These groups are commonly referred to as carboxyl groups. A firm bond is made between the gum and the metal, through these carboxyl groups. The gum swells in the presence of water, but the carboxyl bond keeps the gum from dissolving away from the metal.

The acid commonly used in plate etches is phosphoric acid. The purpose of the acid is to convert more of the groups in the gum molecule to carboxyl groups in order to improve the adhesion. There is a limit to the amount of acid that can be used because too much acid attacks the metal. In this case, instead of forming a film on the metal the etch removes metal. Much

more acid can be used in plate etches for aluminum, without danger of the plate metal being attacked, than can be used for zinc. Anodized aluminum is an exception to this because the acid can attack the anodized oxide layer. A good plate etch for aluminum is the so-called 1:32 etch, which consists of 1 oz. of 85% phosphoric acid to 32 oz. of 14° Be' gum arabic.

Caution: *This etch should not be used on anodized aluminum plates as the acid will destroy the oxide surface.*

With all plate etches, except on anodized, presensitized, and wipe-on plates, it has been found that the etches must be dried on the plate to produce a good water-receptive layer. When materials composed of very large molecules like gum arabic, cellulose gum, albumin, or casein are dried, they undergo a physical change which makes it difficult to dissolve them on re-wetting. Thus, non-printing areas on which etches have been dried will wet well with water, but the gum layer adsorbed to the metal will not be removed by the water. This explains, too, why freshly made albumin or casein plates might blind if put on the press immediately, and might run for 100,000 impressions if allowed to stand overnight. Light-hardened albumin and casein absorb some water in processing. If the plate is put on the press immediately, the image areas continue to absorb moisture and swell until they lose their affinity for ink and are easily destroyed by abrasion. The images go "blind" or "walk off." If the moisture is removed from the image by standing or heating, the images are toughened and refuse to absorb water unless extreme conditions of excessive water and acid are encountered in printing.

Fountain Etches. Fountain etches are similar in composition to plate etches, but much less is known about their action on the plate than is known about plate etches. It is known that if plates are properly desensitized in platemaking, they can be run on the press with just plain water in the fountain. Water has been used in spray and other types of dampening systems; but with the conventional system, using molleton, cloth or parchment paper covers, the dampeners grease rapidly when only plain water is used in the fountain. Greasing of the dampeners causes poor wetting as well as spreading of the ink into non-image areas, especially in halftones and reverse lettering. The use of solutions containing 1 ounce of 14° Baumé gum arabic, or one-half ounce of a 6% solution of cellulose gum in one gallon of water, as a fountain solution greatly reduces this tendency of dampeners to grease. Greasing of the dampeners in a conventional dampening system, however, always occurs to some extent. The addition of a small amount of acid such as phosphoric acid, at a pH value of 4.0 to 5.0, and salts such as nitrates, phosphates, and bichromates to the fountain solution seems to overcome greasing and promote better wetting. A typical formula for a fountain etch may be found in GATF Txb 502/4, "Offset Lithographic Platemaking."

With alcohol fountain solutions the amount of gum should be reduced to one-half this value, since gum is not as soluble in alcohol and can cause glazing of rollers and blankets.

There are a great number and variety of fountain etch formulas. They are not divided by classes or types for different kinds of plates, as are plate etches. As long as the fountain etch formula contains a nitrate salt, it can be used on zinc or aluminum surface and deep-etch plates, presensitized and bimetal plates. For some unknown reason, fountain etches do not work well on aluminum plates unless they contain a nitrate salt. While bichromates are undesirable in fountain etches because of their tendency to cause dermititis, they are of help in preventing the stripping of steel rollers on the press. With the introduction of hard rubber, nylon, and copper rollers, as well as copperizing treatments for steel rollers, this stripping tendency has decreased considerably. Many plates now are running successfully with etches of zinc nitrate, phosphoric acid, and either gum arabic or cellulose gum. This eliminates the necessity for bichromates in press etches with a resultant decrease in the incidence of dermititis. A typical formula for this type of fountain etch may be found in GATF Txb 502/4, "Offset Lithographic Platemaking."

Gumming. Gum is normally applied to the non-printing areas of lithographic plates to protect them against accidental damage from finger-prints, air, dirt, and grease. There is evidence to indicate that gumming also adds to the desensitization of the plate. A plate which is etched and gummed is always better desensitized and always prints cleaner with less water on the press than a plate which is just etched and not gummed. Gumming on the press helps to reinforce the water-receptivity of non-printing areas. Care should be taken, however, not to gum plates too frequently on the press. Too frequent gumming can cause sharpening and eventual blinding of images. Gum arabic works best as a gum when thinned to a Baumé of 7°–10°. This will help prevent gum streaks. Cellulose gum has been used; but if it is not used properly it can cause gum streaks, blind images, and/or difficulties in washing off asphaltum after plates have been stored. Larch gum, mesquite gum, and arabogalactan have been used successfully for gumming plates on the press. These gums do not adhere as tightly as gum arabic and are therefore less likely to produce gum streaks. Also, they do not serve as desensitizers.

Section Five: Graining or Surface Preparation of Metal

Before a metal can be used as a base for a lithographic plate its surface must be properly prepared. This can be done by roughening the surface mechanically, or treating it chemically or electrolytically. If this is not done, the plate will not coat or perform properly in the lithographic process. The roughening process, whether it is done mechanically, or chemically, is called graining. The only exceptions are anodizing and the chemical treatments used for presensitized plates.

Graining. There are a number of mechanical methods for roughening a metal surface. They are "rotary tub" graining, "sandblasting," "dry brush" graining, "wet brush" graining and a combination of rotary tub and wet brush graining called "ball-brush" graining, and a combination of rotary-tub and wet-brush graining.

Rotary tub graining is sometimes called ball graining, because it is done in a graining machine which consists of a tub with a rotary motion. Small steel marbles, which are usually reject ball bearings, are rotated over the surface of the plates. Water is added and then an abrasive material. The actual roughening is done by the abrasive. The character of the grain is determined by: (1) The hardness of the surface of the metal; (2) The amount of water used; (3) The weight and uniformity of the marble load; (4) the nature, amount, and size of the abrasive; (5) the speed of the grainer. The problems with this type of grain are inconsistency from plate to plate, scratchiness, dirt, and imbedded abrasive.

Sandblasting is used for roughening plates both for wipe-on and other platemaking processes. The plates are mounted on a rotary drum and a dry abrasive is impinged on the surface at an angle to the plate at right angles to the direction of rotation of the plate. Nozzle wear can cause variations in grains with this method, and imbedded abrasive can also be a problem.

Dry Brush Graining is used for treating some plates prior to presensitizing. This can be done with brass or steel wire brushes. The main advantage is that dry-brush graining can be done in line with the treating and coating of presensitized plates.

Wet Brush Graining takes a special machine in which the plates are fed onto a conveyor belt under nylon brushes and the graining is done with a mixture of pumice and water. Even with new aluminum plates, several passes through the machine are needed to get an evenly grained surface without indications of rolling-mill streaks. The grain is very fine and is satisfactory for presensitized and wipe-on plates. This type of grain is usually too fine for good moisture control on larger presses.

Ball-Brush Graining is a combination of rotary tub and wet brush graining. In this type of graining good depth is obtained in the tub graining operation and a fine, even texture is produced by the wet brush technique. These plates have the texture for good quality printing and the depth for good moisture control on large presses.

Chemical and Electrochemical Graining. Several methods of roughening plates chemically and electrochemically are in commercial use. They are used primarily for treating plates prior to coating in the manufacture of presensitized plates. The most widely used method is the electrochemical treatment of aluminum in a solution of hydrofluoric acid. This produces a fine grain which is used as a base for wipe-on and presensitized plates. It is also used as a preliminary treatment to anodizing.

Anodized Aluminum is a process by which a uniformly controlled thickness of oxide is produced electrolytically or chemically on aluminum. When produced, the oxide surface is very sensitive and must be sealed. Usually hot water is the sealant. The sealed surface is very inert to most chemicals, hard, and abrasive-resistant, as well as being highly water-receptive. Anodizing is very popular in Europe but has not gained much acceptance in the United States or Canada for deep-etch plates. This could be due to the fact that copperized aluminum plates were already well established when the anodizing treatment became available.

Chemical Treatments. In addition to roughening the surface, chemical treatments are also needed for some processes, especially negative diazo presensitized plates. The diazo compounds used for sensitizing these plates, and which are ink-receptive when exposed, will in themselves react with metals. The diazo compounds can only be used if the metals are specially treated to prevent or inhibit this reaction.

Over the thirty years since Kalle's original work, many treatments have been proposed or developed. Among them are: Brunak; silicate (U.S. Patent 2,714,066-1955); acrylic acid monomer (U.S. Patent 3,064,562); metal phosphate glass and a fluoride (U.S. Patent 3,148,984); fluorides sealed with chromic acid (U.S. Patent 3,160,506); hydrophyllic adhesive containing a mineral pigment, coated on a thermoplastic carboxylated polymer (U.S. Patent 3,161,517); hydrolized organic titanates (U.S. Patent 3,161,521); acrylic compound treated with vinyl tri-substituted silane (U.S. Patent 3,163,534); insolubilized titanium tetrachloride (U.S. Patent 3,196,785); Böhmite (U.S. Patent 3,210,184); organic phosphonic acid (U.S. Patent 3,220,832); sealed phosphomolybdates (U.S. Patent 3,247,791);

tetraisopropyl titanates (U.S. Patent 3,211,376); Alpha-alumina hydrate under an adsorbed metal dichromate (U.S. Patent 3,266,900); phytic acid (U.S. Patent 3,307,951-1967).*

When positive presensitized diazo plates are made, these special surface treatments are not necessary, although cleaning and usually some type of fine graining precedes the application of these positive-working diazos.

More information is available in GATF publications #401, "Chemistry of Lithography; #502/4 "Offset Lithographic Platemaking;" and #218 "Standardization of Graining Procedures."

---

* Excerpted from "Some Studies on Wipe-On Lithographic Plate Coatings"; a paper delivered at the 1967 TAGA Convention by Dr. Albert R. Materazzi.

Section Six: Surface Plates—Albumin, Presensitized Wipe-on, Photopolymer

Surface plates are defined as those plates on which the exposed coating becomes the printing image. Plates of this type include albumin, casein, presensitized, wipe-on, and photopolymer. With the exception of positive presensitized and wipe-on plates, all are made from negatives.

ALBUMIN AND CASEIN PLATES

Historically, albumin surface plates were the first photo-mechanical plates used in lithography. They are still the most difficult to make from the standpoint of quality and consistently satisfactory performance. Because there are few operations and the cost of the materials is low, a few plants still make albumin plates. Actually, albumin and casein plates are almost obsolete and are rapidly being replaced by presensitized or wipe-on plates.

The coating solutions for these plates are bichromated proteins like albumin, casein, and soybean protein. Zinc or aluminum can be used as the base metal, although there is a slight difference in the process depending on the metal used. The plate must first be grained. It is then counter-etched (cleaned) in a weak acid solution. After cleaning, the plate is rinsed, placed in a whirler, and coated. When dried, the plate is exposed to a negative, in a vacuum frame. After exposure, developing ink, or lacquer and developing ink are applied to the plate and dried down carefully. When dry, the plate is developed with water, or a weak ammonia solution if the coating contains casein or soybean protein. For best results the plate should be post treated with a solution like Post Nital for zinc, or Brunak for aluminum. The plate is then etched and gummed. For details on making these plates see GATF Publication No. 502/4, "Offset Lithographic Platemaking."

PRESENSITIZED PLATES

Presensitized plates are so-called because they come already coated, and are ready for exposure and processing when purchased. Presensitized plates are used for the making of one press

plate if they are coated on one side, or for two press plates if they are coated on two sides. These plates are not regrained and coated again, but they can be stored after use for later reprinting of the same image.

Presensitized plastic coated plates were originated in Germany by Kalle and Company just prior to World War II. The base of the plate was plastic-coated paper. These early plates, and those which are now used, are coated with a diazo sensitizer. Such sensitizers are not affected as much by temperature and relative humidity as bichromated coatings, as long as temperatures do not exceed 120°F.

Presensitized plates on aluminum are available with a variety of treatments of the aluminum. The earliest presensitized metal plates were made on aluminum with an electrolytically produced grain. Recently, plates with this type of surface have been marketed in the larger sizes. Presensitized plates with chemically produced and mechanically produced smooth grains are also available. For longer runs, presensitized plates on which the surface of the aluminum has been mechanically hardened, are also available.

Presensitized plates are sometimes designated by the manufacturers as being *additive* or *subtractive*. These terms are descrip-

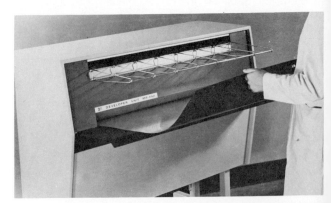

Courtesy 3M Company.

Processor for presensitized plates.

tive of differences in the processing procedures. A presensitized plate is an "additive" type when the platemaker adds image—reinforcing materials to the image areas during processing. The coating on non-image areas is either removed or rendered water-receptive during processing. With some additive presensitized plates, image reinforcing is optional; if the run is short this step in processing may be skipped. A presensitized plate is a "subtractive" type plate if it comes to the platemaker with the image-reinforcing material already on it (applied at the time of manufacture). During processing, the platemaker removes the unexposed coating from the background. The image-reinforcing material on the unexposed coating comes away at the same time.

Negative-Type Presensitized Plates. The steps in making the "additive type" of presensitized plates from negatives are as follows:

Exposure is made through a negative. Diazo coatings have higher speed than bichromated coatings. Less exposure is required to produce step 5 or 6 on the Sensitivity Guide.

Developing is accomplished with a special acidified gum solution which either removes the unexposed diazo coating or renders it water-receptive.

Application of Lacquer is required to assure good image life. A special lacquer emulsion, to improve image life, is applied to the plate so that the image areas are covered by lacquer.

Gum is applied to the plate and dried down. This is a special gum solution.

All manufacturers market single solutions for processing presensitized plates. These solutions combine the developer and lacquer emulsion.

The general procedure for making a "subtractive" plate is as follows:

Exposure is made through a negative. Exposure time, on these plates, is about the same as for deep-etch plates—1½ times the exposure normally required for the presensitized plates described above—to step 5 or 6 on the Sensitivity Guide. On subtractive plates, exposure is somewhat more critical, and plate life on the press may be affected. The manufacturers exposure recommendations must be followed to obtain the best possible results.

Developing is accomplished with special developer which removes the lacquer applied when the plate was originally coated by the manufacturer. This also renders the unexposed diazo water-receptive. The plate is thoroughly rinsed with water to remove residual chemicals from both the background and image areas.

Gum is applied to the plate and rubbed down smooth and completely dry. A special gum solution is used.

Positive-Type Presensitized Plates. As with negative-type plates, there are additive and subtractive types of positive-working presensitized plates. On positive-type plates, the unexposed areas which form the image are ink-receptive. However, the exposed areas, which are the non-image areas, must either be removed or converted to water-receptive surfaces during development. The processing includes one more step than in the negative process as the image must be "fixed" to render it insensitive to light.

The steps in processing the "additive type" of positive presensitized plates are as follows:

Exposure is the same as negative plates except that positives are used.

Developing is accomplished with a special developing solution that is wiped over the plate until all the exposed sensitizer is removed; the plate is then washed with water.

Fixing is done with a special solution that is applied to stop the action of the developer.

Application of Lacquer, to intensify the image, is made by applying a lacquer emulsion to the plate.

Gumming is done with a weak gum arabic solution.

More complete information on the various presensitized plates is available from the manufacturers of the individual plates.

With the subtractive type of positive-working presensitized plate, the lacquering step is eliminated. This type of plate is generally considered to be capable of longer life than the additive type of presensitized plate.

WIPE-ON PLATES

Wipe-on plates are similar to presensitized plates in that specially treated metal is needed and diazo coatings are used. They differ in that coatings are applied by hand or with a special roller coater, and either aluminum or zinc can be used. Also, the plates used for wipe-on coatings all have comparatively fine grains. The graining can be done in graining machines, by dry sandblasting, and by brush graining. The grained plates offer more latitude in printing than the grainless presensitized plates, without sacrificing appreciable printing quality.

Negative-Type Aluminum Wipe-On Plates. A number of wipe-on processes are available for use with negatives. They are all similar.

Coating is first prepared by mixing the diazo powder with the liquid base solution immediately before use. The coating is applied to a dry aluminum plate. All aluminum plates sold for wipe-on procedures are pre-treated and sold ready-to-use. The pre-treatment produces an inert barrier between the metal and the diazo coating. Diazo coatings require such a barrier. Using a cellulose sponge, cheesecloth, or cotton swab, the coating is spread with long strokes in both directions to make sure that the entire surface is covered with coating. Some wipe-on processes require wiping down until dry; others are dried, after spreading, by use of a fan. The manufacturers instructions must be followed for optimum results with their particular process.

Exposure is through a negative. Exposure time is about the same as for presensitized plates. Exposure to steps 5 or 6 on a GATF Sensitivity Guide is considered satisfactory.

Developing is done by one of two methods. One uses a desensitizer as in presensitized plates. This is followed by an emulsion lacquer. The plate is finished with another application of the desensitizer which is dried down.

Another method uses a lacquer emulsion which removes the unexposed coating from the non-printing areas and desensitizes the background while the lacquer deposits on the exposed image areas. This operation is followed by the application of a gum etch or an asphaltum-gum emulsion.

Negative-Type Zinc Wipe-On Plates. Negative-type zinc wipe-on plates were developed by GATF in cooperation with zinc plate manufacturers and the International Lead Zinc Research Organization (ILZRO). Only one chemical supplier is now manufacturing the chemicals for zinc wipe-on plates. The plate is made exactly as an aluminum wipe-on plate except that specially treated, fine grained zinc is used rather than aluminum, and an "Ink-Developer" is used in place of the lacquer emulsion.

Positive-Type Aluminum Wipe-On Plates. A great deal of work has been done to develop a positive-working wipe-on plate. The processing ease and low cost of the wipe-on plate, coupled to the need for using positives, has stimulated this interest. One of the specific needs is a proofing plate which reproduces a dot structure similar to that of a copperized deep-etch aluminum plate. To date a few of the efforts have met with success.

One approach has been to formulate a diazo coating whose processing would be the reverse of a negative-working wipe-on plate. In such a plate the unexposed coating (image area) is retained and made grease receptive during development, while the exposed coating (background) is removed or converted to a water-receptive layer. Another approach has been to use a material other than diazo for the light-sensitive coating.

A more recent approach to the problem of producing a positive-working wipe-on plate is based on supplying a finely grained plate coated with a grease-receptive resin cured on the plate by high heat. Processing this type of plate is as follows:

Coating is not of the diazo-type. It is supplied ready for application by either the wipe-on or roller-coating technique.

Exposure is through a positive. Step 6 on the GATF Sensitivity Guide is obtained in about half the time normally required for a deep-etch coating.

Development is accomplished with a special emulsion developer. During development, the lacquer phase of the emulsion removes the unexposed coating and covers the baked-on resin with the ink-receptive lacquer. The hydrophyllic phase of the emulsion converts the exposed coating to a water-receptive surface. The excess developer is rinsed off with water. *There is no stencil-removing step.*

Desensitization is completed by scrubbing the plate with a solution of phosphoric acid and water. After thorough scrubbing the plate is rinsed with water.

Gumming is done in the normal manner with regular gum solution.

Screenless Lithography. Presensitized and wipe-on plates became possible largely as a result of three developments. They were: 1) The discovery of light-sensitive coatings other than bichromated colloids such as gum, albumin, casein; 2) Improved desensitizing materials and techniques as well as plate-surface treatments; 3) The ability to successfully run a lithographic plate with little or no grain.

During some of this development work it was discovered that under certain conditions the combination of very fine grain and new-type coatings produced a plate capable of holding up to ten steps on a 21-step wedge as compared to 3 steps with a conventional, surface or deep-etch, plate. This phenomenon gave rise to the thinking that screenless lithography could be done if photographic methods could be adapted to plate-making procedures. Some very fine color lithography has been done using "continuous-tone" plates exposed to suitably produced continuous-tone positives. As of this date, however, the process has not proven itself commercially feasible except for special applications.

PHOTOPOLYMER PLATES

For many years, organic coatings such as Syrian asphalt, or asphalt sensitized with iodoform, have been known and used in lithography and as resists for etching metals. These coatings were not very successful in commercial lithography because they were slow and required organic solvents for development. This in turn, made the process inconvenient and expensive.

In the past twenty years, considerable work has been done on synthetic photopolymers which are light sensitive in themselves, or can be sensitized to enhance their own light sensitivity.

The photopolymers most used presently in lithography are light-sensitive cinnamic acid esters, usually of epoxy resins modified with hydrocarbons, amines, nitro compounds, ketones, quinones, and various other organic compounds. These are organic-soluble compounds which require special solvents for development. In this sense, they are inconvenient and expensive like the old Syrian asphalt processes. But, the new photopolymers do have many advantages. The photopolymers are exposed to light through a negative, and during exposure the cinnamate units in the polymer chain are cross-linked to form a rigid, insoluble structure with excellent acid and abrasion resistance, while showing good ink-receptivity. Photopolymer plates of this type have produced runs in excess of a million impressions. In addition to wear resistance, they have excellent shelf life and they are hardly affected by changes in temperature and relative humidity. Their acid-resistance has made them very popular in the production of printed circuits, now almost exclusively used for making electronic components for radio, TV's, computers, etc. The availability of photopolymer plates gives the lithographer another possible method for making a long-run plate that can be made from negatives. As of this writing, processing is very critical. Whether these photopolymer plates will encourage a trend to the use of more negative-working plates for long-run printing, remains to be seen. Presensitized photopolymer plates of this type are also offered to the industry. These plates combine the long-run advantages of the photopolymers with a potential processing ease comparable to the popular diazo-type presensitized plates.

Lithographic photopolymer plates of the cinnamic ester type can be coated in many ways: roller coater; the wipe-on method; whirler; spraying. The procedures for making these plates are slightly different than for other plates.

Counter etching is done with the same technique and solutions used on deep-etch plates except that aluminum must have a special pre-treatment before coating.

Coating with a roller coater may require that the sensitized photopolymer be thinned, prior to use, with a special thinner. For wipe-on coating, the techniques are the same as diazo coating since a fine grain is required for the photopolymer plate.

Exposure is made through negatives and the exposure time is about the same as for presensitized and wipe-on plates.

Development is done with chlorinated solvents such as trichlorethylene, and is best done in a vapor degreaser. It is absolutely essential that the work areas be properly ventilated as trichlorethylene is very toxic.

Sensitizing and Inking requires a special etch which contains glycerine, and is used in place of the gum. This is necessary because there is no ink to protect the photopolymer image areas. The special etch keeps the image from blinding, yet prevents the non-image area from greasing while the image areas of the plate are being rubbed up with ink.

Etch and Gumming is done after inking. The plate is etched and gummed like any other plate. Any regular etch can be used.

Photopolymer Presensitized Plates. There are two types of photopolymer presensitized plates: a cinnamic ester type, and a water-soluble type. The cinnamic ester type is similar to the plate just described and is developed in organic solutions. One manufacturer of these plates uses an automatic processor, which is essentially a vapor degreaser, for development. Another uses a lacquer emulsion. The steps in making these plates are simple. The plate is exposed, developed, etched, and gummed. The plate has good ink receptivity, wear resistance, and long life on the press.

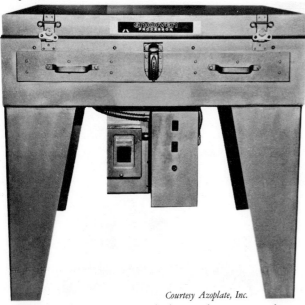

Processor for presensitized photopolymer-type plate.

The water-developable type of presensitized photopolymer plate is developed in a water-base solution. After exposure, the plate can be developed in one minute, after which it is gummed. A post exposure, of four to five minutes, to a strong light source, or a heat-treatment is required to insure long life on the press. The image is very ink receptive and has good chemical and wear resistance. The non-image areas have good water receptivity. Runs up to 250,000 have been reported for these plates.

REMOVING AND ADDING WORK

Removing Work from Surface Plates. Small areas up to two square inches can be erased with a Snake Slip, Scotch Stone, or an air eraser. This is done as follows:

1. The ink or asphaltum is washed off the unwanted work area with naphtha or gasoline.
2. The gum arabic is then washed off the immediately surrounding area with water.
3. While the area is wet, the unwanted work is polished out. The area is cleaned with a water sponge and blotted dry.

4. *On zinc plates,* the area is regrained with a flat-sided glass marble and 240- or 300-mesh aluminum oxide abrasive or fine graining sand, moistened with hydrochloric acid counter-etch. A mushroom-shaped glass bottle stopper is even handier than a marble. The abrasive is washed off and the area blotted dry.
   On aluminum and stainless steel surface plates, hydrochloric acid counter-etch, acetic acid counter-etch, or weak nitric acid (one ounce concentrated nitric acid in a quart of water) is used when regraining the cleared area. For stainless steel plates either hydrochloric acid counter-etch or weak nitric acid may be used.
5. The cleaned area is desensitized with the appropriate plate etch. On zinc, the etch is applied twice, and dried down both times. On aluminum, only one application is made.
6. The entire plate is washed and re-gummed.

If the image area to be deleted is large, the following method is more practical and effective:

1. The ink or asphaltum is washed off the unwanted area.
2. The lacquer is removed with a lacquer solvent. The area is gone over several times with the solvent to be sure it is clean, then the area is blotted and dried.
3. The gum arabic is washed off the surrounding areas with water and blotted dry.
4. *On zinc plates,* lye solution (two ounces of lye to a pint of water) is applied. This is done by use of a stick with a wad of cotton rag tied firmly to one end. The lye solution is allowed to act on the image for a few minutes and then blotted off.
   On aluminum and stainless steel surface plates, concentrated sulfuric acid is applied. To do this a stick with a wad of wool flannel tied firmly to one end is used. The acid is permitted to act on the image and then blotted off.
5. *On zinc plates,* the area is rubbed with wet cotton to remove as much of the image material as is possible.
   On aluminum and stainless steel surface plates, the area is scrubbed several times with wet cotton. A little pumice powder can be used to remove all traces of the image.
6. *On zinc plates,* lye solution is applied a second time and the image is scrubbed with a rag wad until all traces of the image are gone. A little powdered pumice helps.
   On aluminum and stainless steel surface plates, the cleaned area is counter-etched with acetic acid counter-etch and blotted dry.
7. *On zinc plates,* the lye solution is blotted and the area scrubbed several times with wet cotton.
   On aluminum and stainless steel surface plates, a piece of flannel dipped in aluminum plate etch is used to go over the area thoroughly with pumice or fine graining abrasive. This is done with a circular motion. The abrasive is then washed off, and the area blotted dry.
8. *On zinc plates,* the cleaned area is then counter-etched. Several applications are made, each one being blotted. The lye will neutralize the first applications of counter-etch.
9. The cleaned area is etched with the appropriate etch. On zinc, two applications are made, each being rubbed down dry. On aluminum, only one application is made.
10. The entire plate is washed and re-gummed.

Work Additions on Surface Plates. The method used in adding work depends on the plate metal and the type of image to be added. Of the metals zinc, aluminum, and stainless steel, zinc is naturally the most ink receptive. Therefore direct additions of work with tusche or greasy ink are easiest to make on zinc plates, and are more durable on zinc than on the other metals. On the other hand, additions of solids with lacquer hold equally well on all three metals provided the metal surface has been properly prepared. Since photographic additions (shooting in of halftones or line work) require a localized surface platemaking procedure, there is essentially no difference in the results obtained with the three metals, when additions are "shot in."

ADDING TUSCHE WORK. The procedure in adding tusche work is as follows:

1. The gum is washed off an area considerably larger than that to be occupied by the new work. This is done with a clean water sponge or wad of cotton, and the area is blotted dry with newsprint or blotting paper.
2. *On zinc surface plates,* the washed area is treated with a strong counter-etch (three ounces of concentrated hydrochloric acid to a gallon of water). This is applied with a wad of cotton for about one minute, then blotted dry. The treatment is repeated once again.
   On aluminum and stainless steel surface plates, the following counter-etch is used:

	Metric Units	U.S. Units
Ammonium Alum, NH$_4$Al(SO$_4$)$_2 \cdot$12HO	7.5 g.	1 avoir. oz. (28 g.)
Hydrofluoric Acid (HF), 48%	7.8 cc.	1 liq. oz. (29 cc.)
Water to make	1000 cc.	1 gallon

The area is treated three times, blotting off after each application.
3. The desired additions are made with tusche in the counter-etched area. The tusche must be allowed to dry thoroughly.
4. The added work is powdered with a 50-50 talc-rosin mixture.
5. The entire area, from which the gum was originally removed, is etched with the appropriate plate etch; two applications on zinc, one on aluminum.
6. The entire plate is washed thoroughly, and re-gummed in the usual way. The plate image is then washed out with Lithotine and put under asphaltum.

ADDING SOLIDS WITH LACQUER. To produce a solid with lacquer, the gum is first removed from an area somewhat larger than the solid to be added. The area is then counter-etched with a counter-etch appropriate to the metal being worked on. The procedure is the same as steps 1 and 2 in adding tusche work (above). After this has been done the desired solid is outlined with gum arabic solution, using a pen or brush; the surrounding area is then painted out with the gum arabic. The entire area that was counter-etched, outside the outline, should be covered with the gum. After the gum has dried thoroughly, a non-binding deep-etched lacquer is applied. The lacquer is rubbed down and dried, then developing ink is applied and powdered. The entire area is washed with water to remove the developing ink and gum from the areas around the added solid. Finally the area is re-etched with the appropriate etch, the etch being dried down, and the entire plate washed with water and gummed.

ADDING HALFTONES OR TYPE MATTER. Images containing halftones or type matter have to be added (usually as the result of an error) by the regular photographic platemaking procedure. Following is the procedure:

1. The ink is washed off the unwanted work with naphtha or gasoline.
2. The lacquer is removed with a lacquer solvent. The lacquer supplier can recommend the best solvent to use. The area to be removed is gone over several times with solvent to be sure it is clean, then the area is blotted and fanned dry.
3. The gum is washed off the area and its margins with water, and the area blotted dry.
4. *On zinc plates,* lye solution (two ounces of lye to a pint of water) is applied. To do this a stick with a wad of cotton rag tied firmly to one end is used. The lye solution is allowed to act on the old image for a few minutes, then blotted off. The area is scrubbed several times with wet cotton to remove as much of the lye as possible.
   On aluminum or stainless steel plates, a concentrated sulfuric acid is used and applied with flannel instead of a cotton rag.
5. Using powdered pumice or a fine graining abrasive, the deleted image area is rubbed with a piece of flannel or felt dipped in the plate etch appropriate to the metal being worked on. This is done with a circular motion.
6. The plate is placed in a whirler, the gum washed off, and the entire plate coated in the usual way.
7. The negative of the new work is placed in correct position, with the remainder of the plate being covered with masking paper or foil. The exposure is made.
8. *On zinc plates,* lacquer and developing ink are applied and the plate developed and finished just as is done in making the original plate. The lacquer and developing ink are applied only in the new image area.
   On aluminum and stainless steel plates, the plates should be Post-Brunaked after development.
9. The entire plate is etched and gummed up. The appropriate etch for the metal being worked on is used.

Removing and Adding Work from Presensitized and Wipe-on Plates. Deletions and corrections on presensitized and wipe-on plates are relatively easy to make. Unwanted work can be removed with an eraser, Scotch hone, or snake slip, dipped in plate etch or fountain solution. Suppliers also furnish image removing solutions under such names as stop-out solution or image eradicator, with instructions for their use.

Repairs to image areas are made by scratching with a needle, stylus or sharp pencil, followed by an application of tusche, special ink, or even press ink.

If the repairs or additions needed are extensive, it is less expensive and less time-consuming to make a new plate.

Section Seven: Deep-Etch Plates

Deep-etch plates are defined as single-metal plates made from positives in which the exposed coating serves as a stencil to protect the non-printing areas while the image areas are produced on the metal base. Until recently, there were no presensitized deep-etch plates. Several have been developed and are in various stages of field trials and use. To make these plates, the manufacturers' chemicals should be used and his directions followed carefully.

There are two processes for making conventional deep-etch plates: one using bichromated polyvinyl alcohol (PVA) as the coating; and the other using bichromated gum. The gum process is most widely used in the United States (see Coating Materials). Therefore, this section deals primarily with the gum process. Instructions on the processing and use of PVA coated plates are available directly from the manufacturer.

THE GUM-BICHROMATE PROCESS

The steps in deep-etch platemaking using bichromated-gum coating are counter-etching, coating, exposure, stopping out, development, deep-etching, alcohol wash, copperizing (optional), lacquering, inking, clearing, etching, and gumming. Each of these steps is discussed in some detail in the following.

Counter Etching is cleaning the grained plate surface without damaging the grain. The counter-etch is usually a weak acid solution, preferably one ounce of hydrochloric acid in a gallon of water for zinc, and four ounces of phosphoric acid in a gallon of water for aluminum.

Coating. A number of commercial deep-etch coatings are available. A typical formula for a deep-etch coating follows:

DEEP-ETCH COATING SOLUTION

Gum Arabic Solution, 14° Baumé	3 quarts	(1000 cc.)
Ammonium Bichromate, 20% stock solution	1 quart	(340 cc.)
Ammonium Hydroxide, 28%	4¾ liq. oz.	(50 cc.)

Exposure. To expose deep-etch plates, the plant must have an arc or other intense light source and a vacuum printing frame or a photo-composing machine. The positives must be clean, dense, with sharply defined lines and without fog. If possible, two or more GATF Sensitivity Guides should be included in the layout.

Stopping-out Before Development. To protect unexposed borders and unwanted work areas during development and deep-etching, one of the commercial stop-out shellacs or lacquers available from suppliers should be used. The unexposed borders and unwanted areas should be exposed out or painted with the stopping-out shellac or lacquer using a soft camel's hair brush.

Development. The developer removes the unhardened bichromated gum from the image areas in preparation for deep-etching. Numerous commercial developers are available. A simple deep-etch developer formula follows:

REGULAR DEEP-ETCH DEVELOPER

Calcium Chloride Solution 40°–50° Baumé	1 gallon	(1000 cc.)
Lactic Acid, 85%	6¾ liq. oz.	(53 cc.)

The action of the regular developer changes with temperature. Therefore, the Baumé should be adjusted for the room temperature. Most commercial developers are stabilized so they are not affected as much by temperature. If commercial coating is used, the developer designed for the particular coating should be used. The sink or deep-etch developing trough should be clean, have a level grid or island, and a clean, dry developing pad should be used.

To develop a plate, it is placed in the deep-etch developing sink and a liberal quantity of the developer poured over it. This developer is worked evenly over the entire surface with the developing pad, using moderate pressure. In two to three minutes the image areas should clear. The development should be stopped when Step 8, or possibly Step 7 has appeared on the image of the GATF Sensitivity Guide. The developer is squeegeed off the plate and a fresh supply poured on. This fresh developer is worked over the plate until Step 6 is cleared.

The GATF Sensitivity Guide step numbers mentioned above are examples only. Sensitivity Guides vary somewhat in light transmission. The platemaker can vary his development one step in either direction from the figures given, depending on what exposure he finds best for his positives.

In developing plates on which it was impractical to include the Sensitivity Guide, the following method may be used:

The developer is poured on and worked over the plate with the developing pad. In two or three minutes the image areas should begin to clear. A note of this time is made. The developer is squeegeed off the plate and a fresh supply poured on. This is worked over the plate for exactly the same length of time as the first application. This second application of developer is squeegeed off and one more application is made for the same length of time. When this third developer is squeegeed off, the plate is ready to be deep-etched. Normally, *complete* development should take from five to eight minutes.

Deep Etching. The purpose of deep-etching is to etch the image areas slightly below the non-image areas. If the plant uses a commercial deep-etch coating solution, the deep-etching solution designed for that coating should also be used. The formula for a typical deep-etching solution for aluminum is:

ALUMINUM DEEP-ETCHING SOLUTION

Calcium Chloride 40°–41° Baumé	1 gallon	(1000 cc.)
Zinc Chloride, Technical	51 av. oz.	(380 gm.)
Iron Perchloride Solution 50°–51° Baumé	36¼ liq. oz.	(285 cc.)
Hydrochloric Acid 37%–38.5%	1¾ liq. oz.	(14 cc.)
Cupric Chloride	3½ oz.	(27 gm.)

This type of solution can cause problems with spotty blinding due to loosely bonded iron deposits. To help avoid these problems the plate can be redeveloped (with the deep-etch developer) after deep-etching for approximately one minute. Nicohol can also be used. Some chemical manufacturers have formulated deep-etching solutions without ferric chloride to avoid the iron deposit problem. These solutions, as well as the new modified iron etches, are quite satisfactory.

Alcohol Wash. Anhydrous (water-free) denatured alcohol is used to remove the deep-etching solution and to prepare the image areas to accept copper, lacquer, and ink. Other materials like Cellosolve can be used, but anhydrous alcohol should always be used as a final wash. Some anhydrous alcohol is poured on the plate while it is still in the developing sink. With a wad of deep-etch paper wipes, the plate is rubbed evenly and thoroughly over the entire surface. As much of the dark deposit as possible should be removed from the image areas. This wash will remove any stop-out shellac or lacquer. The alcohol is wiped off and the plate is washed with the alcohol an additional three times, using fresh alcohol and clean paper wipes each time. After the fourth wash, the work areas are rubbed thoroughly with clean paper wipes to remove as much of the alcohol as possible. Then the plate is fanned dry.

Paper wipes are better than a squeegee which slides over the surface and leaves some alcohol in the image areas, particularly in halftones. Paper wipes absorb the alcohol and leave the image areas dryer and cleaner. The alcohol should be poured on the plate without spattering, since this may cause spots in halftones. A good way to prevent spattering the coating is to lay one or more paper wipes on the plate and pour the alcohol on the wipes. The same wipes are used to rub the alcohol over the plate.

Copperizing. Copperizing is an optional step which deposits a thin layer of copper on the deep-etched image areas. A typical formula for a copperizing solution follows:

COPPERIZING SOLUTION FOR ALUMINUM

Isopropyl Alcohol, 99%	1 quart	(1000 cc.)
Cuprous Chloride	1 av. oz.	(31 gm.)
Hydrochloric Acid, 37%–38.5%	1 liq. oz.	(32 cc.)

To copperize a plate, some copperizing solution is poured on it and spread over the entire surface with a plush-covered pad. The solution is worked over the plate for three to ten minutes, or until a reddish copper deposit is formed on the image areas. The time depends on the solution used and the conditions of temperature and relative humidity. Some fine-grain coppers can take as long as ten minutes to deposit. The plate is given one or two washes with anhydrous alcohol to remove the copperizing solution and then wiped dry. Cleanliness is very important here. Let the plate warm to room temperature before applying the non-blinding lacquer.

Applying Non-blinding Lacquer. Non-blinding lacquer is used to coat the deep-etch areas with a strongly ink-receptive material. This material forms a base for the printing image; one that is not affected by the usual cleaning solvents, and will not become water-receptive.

The non-blinding deep-etch lacquer is applied to the image areas of the plate by spreading the lacquer over the plate with a paper wipe, then rubbed down smooth with a soft, lintless rag. As much lacquer is left on the plate as is possible, but not enough to interfere with removing the gum stencil.

In drying the lacquer, the manufacturer's instructions must be followed. The improved non-blinding lacquers generally work best if they are dried thoroughly before applying the developing ink.

Applying Developing Ink. Developing ink coats the lacquered image areas with a film of greasy ink which prevents the lacquered image areas from being covered with gum during the etching and gumming operations. For fine-grained plates a heavy deep-etch developing ink is needed. There should also be on hand a 50:50 mixture of French chalk (powdered talc) and powdered rosin.

Some developing ink is poured on the plate and spread over the image areas with a soft rag or paper wipe. Then, with a clean soft rag, the ink is rubbed down to a smooth, even film and fanned dry. Finally, the ink is powdered with the French chalk-rosin mixture.

Clearing the Plate. Clearing the plate is the operation of removing the light-hardened gum stencil from the non-image areas. Warm water at 90°–100°F. and a bristle brush are used.

After the stencil has been removed with warm water, turn on the cold water and rub the image with a clean deep-etch pad. The cold water sets the ink and rubbing sharpens the image by removing the feathery edges of ink caused by scrubbing in the clearing operation.

Etching. Etching forms a water-receptive film on the non-printing areas. A good etch for aluminum is the "1:32" etch which consists of 1 ounce of phosphoric acid to 32 ounces of 14° Baumé gum arabic.

Plate etching (and gumming) should be done on a separate table, reserved for these operations. If the plate has been tusched, or any corrections have been made, the plate will be dry. The etch can be applied directly to the dry plate. If the plate is wet, all excess water is removed with a clean squeegee or sponge before etching. Any excess water remaining on the plate surface will dilute the etch and make it less effective.

If a good developing ink was used and applied properly, the image will be ink-receptive and refuse to be wet by etch. If the image does wet with etch, the plate will be difficult to roll up on the press. To avoid this difficulty, the plate can be rubbed with developing ink while it is under etch. The same rag which was used for applying the developing ink is rubbed over the image areas of the plate while the etch is on the plate. After the image is thoroughly rubbed up, the ink and the etch are rinsed off with water and another application of etch is made and dried down. If asphaltum-gum emulsion is used for gumming, the rubbing-up is not necessary as the asphaltum makes the image ink-receptive.

Gumming the Plate. Gumming the plate applies an additional coating of gum. This additional coating protects the non-image areas of the plate while it is being handled and when it is washed out and put under asphaltum. A gum arabic solution at 8°–10° Baumé, or asphaltum-gum emulsion, can be used. Plates should be gummed on a table reserved especially for the etching and gumming operations.

The etch should be washed off with water, before gumming, with a "wash off" sponge reserved exclusively for washing etch or gum from the plates. The plate is sponged two or three times with fresh applications of water each time. The plate should be only slightly damp, after each sponging, especially the last one.

More complete information about deep-etch plates is available in GATF textbook 502/4, "Offset Lithographic Plate-making."

DEEP-ETCH PLATES ON ANODIZED ALUMINUM

Deep-etch plates on anodized aluminum are widely used in Europe. The steps in making deep-etch plates on anodized aluminum are similar to those followed on untreated aluminum. Special chemicals are used and no copperizing of the image is done. Manufacturers' instructions for use of the plates and chemicals should be followed carefully. In this process perhaps more than any other, the chemicals are closely related to the metal treatment used.

Preparing the Plate. Anodized aluminum plates are not counter-etched prior to coating. They only need be scrubbed well using a soft bristle brush and tap water.

Coating the Plate. The plate is coated using the same techniques as with a conventional deep-etch plate. However, the coating is poured while whirling about 45 rpm, but then the whirler is speeded up to about 100 rpm and dried with moderate heat.

Exposing the Plate. Exposure time is generally less than for copperized aluminum deep-etch plates. Correct exposure time is easily established by test shots through a GATF Sensitivity Guide.

Stopping Out. A special stop-out solution is recommended, using the same techniques as for conventional deep-etch plates.

Developing. Developing of anodized aluminum deep-etch plates is somewhat faster than with conventional plates; four to five minutes using three applications. Clearing of the unexposed areas will usually be reached at about two minutes. Again, the GATF Sensitivity Guide can be very useful in establishing standard development times. Where long intervals between coating and development are unavoidable, as with a long step-and-repeat job, a "fast" developer is available. The developer, however, is more sensitive to high humidity than the standard developer. Where development is excessively long, it is a clear indication that: coating is too thin; over-exposure has occurred; or dark-reaction has been encouraged. Incomplete development will show up as excessive image sharpness, loss of highlight dots, partial blinding.

Deep-Etching. When development is complete the excess developer is squeegeed off and a special deep-etching solution is poured and spread quickly and uniformly over the plate. A cotton wool swab or a brush should be used. From three to six minutes should be allowed, with several renewals of the deep-etching solution. The time required is dependent on type of work and length of run. When etching is complete, spent etch is squeegeed from the plate.

Alcohol Wash. This is carried out, on an anodized plate, just as on a conventional deep-etch plate. The purpose is the same, procedure is the same, possible troubles from high humidity are the same. After the alcohol wash, stopping out may be required again. A special stop-out solution for use at this particular stage is recommended. The plate must be thoroughly dry before proceeding to the next step—lacquering.

Lacquering. This step is carried out exactly as with conventional deep-etch plates. Several lacquers are available; they differ primarily in their rate of drying.

Inking-in. This step is also identical to its counterpart in conventional deep-etch platemaking. Powdering the dried-down ink film with French chalk is also recommended.

Removing the Stencil and Desensitization. This is a combined operation when making deep-etch plates on anodized aluminum. The plate is soaked in warm water until the stencil begins to lift. Then the plate is scrubbed lightly with a fine bristle brush until all the stencil has been removed. Under no circumstances should any acid be used since this would destroy the anodized surface treatment. This also holds true for the 1:32 phosphoric acid-gum etch even though it is the best etch for aluminum. The plate is now rinsed with clear cold water and gummed up. No further desensitizing is normally necessary.

Gumming. As with conventional deep-etch plates, final gumming serves to protect the non-image areas while the plate is handled through mounting in the press. Gumming is also required if the plate is to be washed out by the platemaker.

DEEP-ETCH PLATES WITH PVA

One direction in which much effort has been expended to simplify the deep-etch platemaking process has been to find a coating which does not require special solvents. During the 1930's the glue-reversal process, using photoengraver's glue as the coating colloid, was developed. This has been successful, but only in highly standarized applications in certain specialty fields. For general commercial lithography the process suffers from the fact that it does not offer the platemaker any latitude in development to sharpen the image on the plate or make it fuller.

Polyvinyl alcohol is easier to use than photoengraver's glue for making the coating solution. PVA lends itself to better manufacturing controls than photoengraver's glue which frequently yields a coating with considerable amounts of undissolved particles. PVA is developable in water, and the entire platemaking process is simpler than in the gum process. However, as with glue, there is no development latitude. There is no need for an alcohol wash, and copperizing is optional. As with anodized aluminum, all chemicals and solutions used are specially formulated for the process.

The latest work with PVA is leading in the direction of development with materials other than water. The result sought is to give the platemaker some controllable latitude to compensate for unintentional changes in sensitivity or exposure, as well as to make up for minor deficiencies in the position. It should be kept in mind that in general practice the platemaker needs latitude to adjust his procedures to meet specific press requirements. Quite often halftone color separation positives are completed before a decision has been made as to the press on which the job will run; or the type of plate or paper to be used. Sometimes the sequence of colors hasn't been determined. These decisions will affect the degree of sharpness or fullness which the platemaker will strive for during development.

A final outcome of all this development work, with PVA, could be the establishment of two PVA processes; one for a highly standardized operation using water as the developer, and another for use where platemaking flexibility is desirable.

REMOVING AND ADDING WORK

Removing Work. Small areas of unwanted work, up to one or two inches square, can be erased with a Snake Slip, Scotch Stone, or an abrasive air gun. The following are the steps:

1. The ink or asphaltum is washed off the unwanted work area with naphtha or gasoline.
2. The gum arabic is washed off the immediately surrounding area with water.
3. While the area is wet, the unwanted work is polished out. The area is thoroughly cleaned with water using a sponge and blotted dry.
4. *On zinc plates,* the area is regrained using a flat-sided glass marble and 240- or 300-mesh aluminum oxide abrasive, or fine graining sand, moistened with hydrochloric acid counter-etch.
   On aluminum plates, an acetic acid counter-etch or weak nitric acid is used.
5. The area is desensitized with an etch appropriate to the metal being worked on. *On zinc,* the etch is applied twice, rubbing down each application. *On aluminum,* only one application is made.
6. The entire plate is washed and re-gummed.

If the image area to be deleted is large, the following method is more practical and effective.

1. The unwanted work area is cleared of ink or asphaltum by using naphtha or gasoline.
2. The lacquer is removed with a lacquer solvent. The unwanted area is gone over several times with the solvent to be sure it is clean. The area is then blotted and fanned dry.
3. *On zinc plates,* the cleaned area is double-etched each application being dried down.
   On aluminum and stainless steel, the cleaned area which is to be etched is first gone over thoroughly with pumice or fine graining abrasive using a piece of flannel or felt dipped in aluminum plate etch. The scrubbing should be done with a circular motion. Then the area is washed clean of abrasive and a single application of etch is dried down thoroughly.

4. The entire plate is washed and re-gummed in the usual manner.

Work Additions on Deep-Etch Plates. Solids can be added on deep-etch plates by hand, using tusche or deep-etch lacquer. To add type matter or halftones, however, it is necessary to repeat the deep-etch platemaking process locally, since these additions can best be made photographically. Broken lettering or lines, and spots in solids can be repaired by scratching through the gum layer with a needle and applying developing ink or press ink directly to the uncovered metal. The method, therefore, in adding work depends on the type of image to be added. Of the three metals, zinc, aluminum and stainless steel, zinc is naturally the most ink receptive. Therefore, direct additions of work with tusche or greasy ink are easiest to make on zinc plates and are more durable on zinc than on the other metals. On the other hand, additions of solids with deep-etch lacquer hold equally well on all three metals provided the metal surface has been properly prepared. Since photographic additions (shooting in of halftones or line work) require a deep-etching procedure and the application of deep-etch lacquer, there is essentially no difference in the results obtained with the three metals when additions are "shot in."

ADDING TUSCHE WORK. This is accomplished as follows:

1. The gum is washed off an area considerably larger than that to be occupied by the new work. This is done with a clean water sponge or wad of cotton, and the area blotted dry with newsprint or blotting paper.
2. *On zinc plates,* the washed area is treated with a strong counter-etch (three ounces of concentrated hydrochloric acid to a gallon of water). This is applied with a wad of cotton for about one minute and then blotted dry. The area is counter-etched again for one minute and blotted dry. The counter-etch should not be washed off with water.
   On aluminum and stainless steel plates, the special counter-etch should be used. (See formula on page 10:24).

The counter-etch is applied three times, and blotted off after each application.

3. The desired additions are made with tusche in the counter-etched area. The tusche is allowed to dry thoroughly.
4. The added work is powdered with a 50-50 talc-rosin mixture.
5. *On zinc deep-etch plates,* the entire area from which gum was originally removed is double-etched with a zinc plate etch, each application being dried down.
   On aluminum and stainless steel deep-etch plates, an aluminum plate etch is used, but only one dried-down application is made.
6. The entire plate is washed thoroughly and re-gummed in the usual way.

The plate image can now be washed out with Lithotine and put under asphaltum.

ADDING SOLIDS WITH DEEP-ETCH LACQUER. To produce a solid with deep-etch lacquer, the gum is first removed from an area somewhat larger than the solid to be added, and then counter-etched. This is done in the same way as when adding tusche work; the appropriate counter-etch is used depending on the metal being worked with. Next the solid is outlined with gum arabic solution using a pen or brush, and all the surrounding area is painted out, also with gum arabic. After the gum has dried thoroughly the non-binding deep-etch lacquer is applied. The lacquer is rubbed down and dried. This is followed by an application of developing ink. The developing ink and gum from the areas around the newly-added solid are washed off with water. Finally the area is re-etched with an etch appropriate to the metal being used, and with the technique appropriate to that metal. Then the entire area is washed with water and gummed up.

ADDING HALFTONES OR TYPE MATTER. Images containing halftones or type matter have to be added by the regular photographic platemaking procedure. The steps to do this are as follows:

1. The ink is washed off the unwanted work area with naphtha or gasoline.
2. The lacquer is removed with a lacquer solvent. The area is gone over several times with the solvent to be sure it is clean, and then the area is blotted and fanned dry.
3. The gum is washed off the area and its margins with water.

4. With a piece of flannel or felt dipped in the appropriate etch, the deleted image area is rubbed, using a circular motion, with pumice or fine graining abrasive.
5. The plate is placed in the whirler, all the gum washed off, and the plate coated with deep-etch coating solution in the usual way.
6. The positive is placed in the correct position, the remainder of the plate covered with masking paper or foil, and the exposures made. This can be done in either the vacuum printing frame or the photo-composing machine, depending on the job itself.
7. The new image area is developed, deep-etched, and finished locally, just as in making the plate originally. The appropriate chemicals are used depending on the plate metal.
8. The plate is put under running water and the new gum stencil scrubbed off.
9. The plate is etched and gummed up in the usual way, using the chemicals and techniques appropriate to the metal being worked on.

Section Eight: Bimetal Plates

As was stated in Section One, bimetal plates are composed of two metals, one of which forms the image areas and the other the non-image areas. The metal forming the image areas is selected for its ability to take ink. The metal forming the non-image areas is selected for the ease with which it is wet by water and its ability to be desensitized to ink under the same conditions which render the image metal ink-receptive. To simplify the discussion, these two metals will be referred to as the image metal, and the non-image metal, respectively.

Theoretically there are four possible types of bimetal printing plates. These are best classified by the methods used to manufacture and process the plates.

TYPE I. An image metal is electroplated on a plate of a non-image metal; an acid-resistant positive image is formed on the layer of image metal; the image metal is etched away from all areas except the image areas; the acid resist is removed from the image areas.

TYPE II. A non-image metal is electroplated on a plate of an image metal, or on a plate which carries a surface layer of an image metal. A stencil or negative image is formed by means of acid-resistant coating on the layer of non-image metal. The non-image metal is etched away to lay bare the image metal in the positive image areas. Then the protective stencil is removed from the non-image areas.

TYPE III. An acid-resistant positive image is formed on a plate of an image metal; a non-image metal is electroplated on the remaining areas; and finally the acid resist is removed from the image areas.

TYPE IV. A stencil or negative image is formed by means of an acid resistant coating on a plate of a non-image metal; an image metal is electroplated on the bare image areas; and finally the protective stencil is removed.

While all four types have been tried, only Type I and Type II have been generally successful. Types III and Types IV gave trouble because of difficulties in finding photo-resists that could

withstand the electroplating operation, and because of the inability to obtain uniform electro-deposits of metal.

Trimetal and Polymetal Plates. So-called trimetal and polymetal plates are made with more than two metals. The most common consists of three metals; (1) A base plate of zinc, mild steel, stainless steel, or aluminum; (2) An electroplated layer of copper (image metal) on the base metal; (3) An electroplated layer of chromium (non-image metal) on top of the copper layer. However, only the electroplated layers of copper and chromium are affected by the platemaking process, and take part in the printing process. For all practical purposes therefore, trimetal and polymetal plates are the same as Type II bimetal plates. The advantages of using zinc, steel, stainless steel, or aluminum instead of copper or brass as the base plates are that these metals reduce the weight and cost of the plates, and the plates are easier to handle both in platemaking and on the press. For use on web offset presses, some of these plates are backed with mylar to keep them on the plate cylinder if they should break at the clamp edges.

Several plates have been made using more than three metals. One has two platings of copper, one from an acid solution and the second from an alkaline solution; each is claimed to have different degrees of adhesion and ink receptivity. Another plate has coatings of silver and antimony, in addition to copper and chromium, on a base metal.

MAKING BIMETAL PLATES

Type I Bimetal Plates. Bimetal plates of Type I are available with the copper protected with a gum, or as presensitized plates on stainless steel or aluminum. These bimetal plates are similar to surface plates because they are made from negatives, and because their copper image areas are very slightly raised above the non-image areas. However, the process and ma-

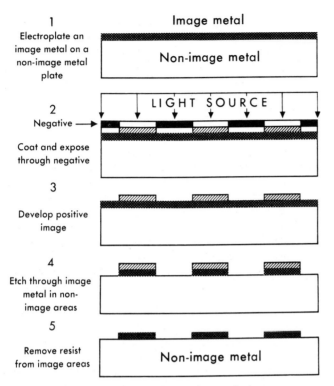

1

Electroplate an image metal on a non-image metal plate

Image metal

Non-image metal

2

Negative →

Coat and expose through negative

LIGHT SOURCE

3

Develop positive image

4

Etch through image metal in non-image areas

5

Remove resist from image areas

Non-image metal

Steps in making a Type I bimetal plate.

terials used in making them are much the same as for deep-etch plates. The following steps briefly describe the processing of Type I bimetal plates.

Counter-etch. The copper coating of the plate is cleaned by counter-etching with a diluted acid, usually sulfuric or nitric acid.

Coating. The cleaned plate is coated in the usual way with regular deep-etch coating solution and dried. The same techniques and precautions are used as with deep-etch plates. Since most of these plates are relatively smooth, coating solutions with lower density (Be') should be used. Otherwise the dried coatings may be too thick.

Exposure. The coated plate is exposed through a negative with a GATF Sensitivity Guide attached. Generally, higher guide numbers are used than on deep-etch or surface plates. This means longer exposures.

Development. The plate is developed with deep-etch developer to remove the unhardened coating from the non-image areas. The Sensitivity Guide, and the manufacturer's instructions, should be followed carefully.

Copper Etch. The copper is removed from the non-image areas by means of a special etch that has only a small effect on the stainless steel or aluminum underneath. The etch on stainless steel plates is essentially ferric chloride solution; for aluminum base plates, it is mostly ferric nitrate.

Clearing. The hardened coating, which protects the image areas, is removed by scrubbing the coating with a soft bristle brush and the nitric or sulfuric acid counter-etch.

Sensitizing the Copper. The copper image areas are sensitized to ink with sulfuric or nitric counter-etch, or with one of the several proprietary products on the market especially designed for this purpose. In addition, these products will serve the dual purpose of removing the stencil and rendering the copper ink-receptive.

Rubbing Up. The image areas are then rubbed up with ink.
Etch and Gum. The plates are etched and gummed as in other platemaking processes.

Techniques have been developed for making Type I bimetal plates from positives, but this is a rather complex operation. More information about this and other procedures are available directly from the suppliers or manufacturers.

Courtesy Printing Developments, Inc.

Processor for bimetal plates. Shown is the developing section; a similar section, hooked up in tandem, takes care of finishing.

Presensitized Bimetal Plates already have a light-sensitive coating applied to the plates by the manufacturer. Usually, the presensitized coating is such that the plate is exposed through a positive transparency. The basic steps in presensitized bimetal platemaking are given below.

Exposure. The plate is exposed either through a positive or negative transparency, depending on the specific light-sensitive coating. A GATF Sensitivity Guide should be used.

Development. The plate is developed with a special developer which removes, or at least makes water-receptive, the unhardened coating in the non-image area. With some plates, it may be necessary to apply a resist to the image area.

Stage. The light-sensitive coating is removed from any unwanted areas; film edges, dirt, etc.

Copper Etch. The copper is removed from the non-image areas by swabbing a special etch over the plate. The etch does not attack the stainless steel or aluminum backup metal.

Clearing. Clearing is normally not necessary as the resist in this case is ink-receptive. However, the resist may be removed by a solvent. If the resist is not removed, the copper need not be sensitized, or the image rubbed up. However, if alcohol is used in the fountain solution on the press, the resist should be removed.

Gumming. The plates are gummed as in other plate-making processes.

Detailed instructions and information is available from the manufacturers.

Type II Bimetal Plates. Type II bimetal plates are closely related to deep-etch plates because; they are made from positives; their copper image areas are very slightly recessed below the non-image areas; the process and materials used in making them are similar.

Bimetal plates, which have a solid copper base, are electroplated on one side with chromium to a thickness of .00005 to .00007 inch. These plates are available in the smaller sizes on special order only, from one manufacturer. Another manufacturer produces plates with chromium plated on a solid brass sheet. These plates are used mainly on web offset presses.

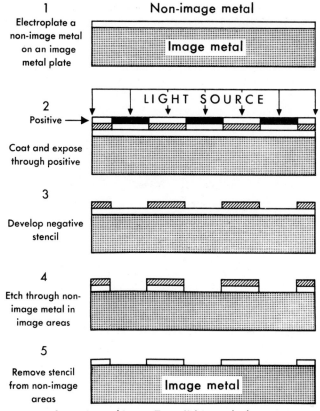

1
Electroplate a non-image metal on an image metal plate

Non-image metal

Image metal

2
Positive →

LIGHT SOURCE

Coat and expose through positive

3
Develop negative stencil

4
Etch through non-image metal in image areas

5
Remove stencil from non-image areas

Image metal

Steps in making a Type II bimetal plate.

Trimetal plates usually have a zinc, steel, stainless steel, or aluminum base. These plates are electroplated on one side, first with copper, and then with chromium. These layers are extremely thin: the copper thickness ranges from approximately .0001 to .0003 inch; the chromium from approximately .00005 to .00007 inch. As mentioned above, some plates are also available with an additional sheet of mylar laminated to the base aluminum sheet.

Suppliers can furnish trimetal plates either grained or ungrained. The ungrained plates are made by electroplating ungrained base plates. To make grained trimetal plates, the base plates are first grained in the usual way and then electroplated with copper and chromium.

The chromium layer on trimetal plates is not like the bright chrome plating on an automobile bumper; instead it has a dull matte appearance, even on ungrained plates. This is necessary for the plate to carry water properly during the printing operation.

Again, as we have mentioned above, the process of making a trimetal plate of this type is essentially the same as that for making a deep-etch plate on a single metal. There are, however, a few important differences, pointed out in the following brief instructions.

Plate Treatment Prior to Coating. Trimetal plates come with a protective coating of gum arabic on the chromium layer. This gum layer should be removed, before applying the coating, by scrubbing the plate with a brush under running water. Under certain conditions, however, the chromium surface may need to be counter-etched or chemically cleaned after the gum is removed. The supplier should be consulted regarding this and the chemicals required.

Coating and Drying the Plate. The regular bichromated gum deep-etch coating solution is used on trimetal plates to produce the light-sensitive coating. For grained plates the full strength coating is used, the same as for grained zinc or aluminum plates. For ungrained plates the coating should be diluted with water to make it thinner. Otherwise the thickness of the dried coating on the plate will be too great.

Good, sharp positives are required but, for the best results, halftone positives should be made a little "higher" than for deep-etch plates. By "higher" is meant that all tones should be lighter or sharper. The reason for this is that in etching through the chromium layer, after the image has been developed, there is a slight sidewise etching that enlarges the dots. So, to produce the same tone values on a trimetal plate as on a deep-etch plate, the halftone dots on the positive must be slightly smaller. If the same positives are used as for deep-etch platemaking, the halftones will print heavier or darker. The GATF Sensitivity Guide should be used since it is important to control the exposure. The GATF Star Target and GATF Dot Gain Scale are also helpful in controlling dot size.

Stopping-out Before Development. Unexposed borders and other unwanted areas that can be seen easily, after the plate has been exposed, can either be stopped-out with shellac or lacquer, or exposed out. Minor imperfections such as dust spots and tape marks that are not easily seen at this point should be stopped-out after development.

Developing the Plate. The developing solution and method of development are in every way the same for trimetal plates as for aluminum deep-etch plates. Use of the GATF Sensitivity Guide is essential in securing proper development.

Etching Through the Chromium Layer. Etching through the chromium layer, to bare the copper in the image areas, corresponds to the deep-etching operation. To do this, a special chromium etch is required. A suitable etch and the instructions for its use can be obtained from the plate supplier.

Clearing the Copper Image Areas. Removing the chromium etch from the copper image areas is done by washing the plate three or four times with anhydrous alcohol in exactly the same way as cleaning the image areas on a deep-etch plate.

Sensitizing the Copper Image Areas to Ink. After the copper image areas have been washed with alcohol, they are immediately coated with a thin film of straight asphaltum or asphaltum containing a fatty acid like oleic acid. From this point, the treatment may vary, and it is best to follow the recommendations of the plate supplier.

Removing the Gum Stencil. The gum stencil is removed by soaking the plate in warm water and then scrubbing with a bristle brush in the same way as for deep-etch plates.

Desensitizing the Non-Image Areas. Since the non-image areas on bimetal plates are chromium, which is very easily desensitized, there is no need to remove the residual stencil or to give these areas any sort of post-treatment. Therefore, immediately after scrubbing off the gum stencil apply a desensitizing plate etch, and gum up the plate.

REMOVING AND ADDING WORK

Work can be removed from or added to finished bimetal plates. It is advisable to consult the platemaker about this as he will have the most up-to-date methods for the particular type of plate and process.

Small spots that show up on the finished plate can be removed by polishing with a snake slip or pencil eraser. Even though this abrasion bares the copper, the copper can be desensitized with a plate etch and should stay clean for some time. However, a more permanent repair can be made by electroplating chromium on the bared copper spots. This can be done by applying chromic acid solution and using a pencil- or spatula-type electrode. The plate supplier can advise on this type of equipment.

Broken lettering or lines, and spots in solids, can be repaired by scratching through the chromium layer with a needle, and applying ink.

If it should be necessary to remove one image area and replace it with another, this can also be done. The procedure is as follows:

1. Wash all ink off the area to be corrected with gasoline or naphtha.

2. The surrounding area is painted or staged out with stop-out shellac or lacquer so that it will be protected.
3. Chromium etch is applied to remove all the chromium in the bare area.
4. The area is washed thoroughly with alcohol to remove the chromium etch. The alcohol will also remove the shellac or lacquer from the surrounding area.
5. The bared copper is scrubbed with fine pumice and water using a felt pad. This slightly roughens the copper. The pumice is washed off and the area dried.
6. Using a roller-type electrode and chromic acid solution, the bared copper area is replated with chromium. The plate supplier can advise where this equipment may be obtained.
7. The area is washed with water to remove the chromic acid.
8. Deep-etch coating is applied, the new work is shot in, the area is developed, etched and finished locally in the same way the plate was originally made.

Section Nine: Direct Image, Direct Photographic and Electrostatic Plates

Direction image, camera or projection, and electrostatic plates are presently being used for duplicating or reprography on smaller presses. The quality and wear resistance requirements for such lithographic work are not as demanding as plates for larger presses. It should not be assumed from this, however, that these plates do not represent a large sales market, and are not capable of excellent quality or longer runs. Direct image plates are used extensively in bank check printing, especially for encoding in magnetic ink character recognition (MICR) printing. The specifications for this type of printing are quite restrictive. The photographic plates (camera and projection), which are relatively new, are of value to a sales market that may be larger than all other duplicating printing plates combined. Electrostatic printing offers many possibilities for future development.

DIRECT IMAGE PLATES

The direct image process is similar to the old "original plates" (see Introduction) in that the greasy image is applied manually or mechanically to the printing plate. The plates are called "masters" and can be made of specially coated paper or plastic, or of specially grained aluminum foil laminated to a paper base. The image can be drawn, lettered, painted, ruled, traced, typed or written on the master by using pencil, crayon, ink, carbon paper, fabric or carbon paper ribbon, rubber stamp, numbering machine, brush or air-brush. The image can also be printed directly on the plate by offset or letterpress. Only oil base materials can be used for producing images from which we can print. If guide lines and instructions are required on the master, they are applied with water color inks so that they will not print.

Most direct image plates are made directly on the typewriter and are used on offset duplicating presses. An increasing number of plates are being made by transferring the image from existing letterpress plates or standing forms. These direct image plates are used for reprinting books, price lists, and rate books where only minor changes are needed. Such plates have also been considered for printing publications and newspapers in an effort to combine the use of existing typesetting and stereotyping facilities with the speed and other advantages of offset reproduction.

Direct image plates are ideal for systems work since they eliminate the need for pre-printed forms. All of the information that would normally be on the form can be pre-printed on the master, and the last minute data can be typed or drawn in. When the master is printed, all of the information prints at the same time. This is the way most MICR printing is done.

Direct image plates for offset duplicating use are made in different quality and price ranges, depending on the number of copies expected from the plate. In general, quality of the plates is determined by the number of sheets required to print before a readable image can be obtained. With the best plates, a readable image is obtained with the first or second sheet printed.

Making Direct Image Plates is very simple. The steps are essentially the same for all manufacturers' plates.
1. The image is transferred to the plate by any of the methods mentioned above. Care in handling the plate is extremely important. The plate surface must be protected from grease spots such as finger prints, or grease and oil from the machine, as these spots will print.
2. Paper and plastic base plates are mounted on the press, the plate surface wiped with a special etch, the press started running, the ink and dampening rollers dropped on the plate and the printing started. The etch and fountain solution used must be those specifically designed for the plate.

Detailed information on individual plates and processes is available from the manufacturers.

DIRECT PHOTOGRAPHIC PLATES

Photographic plates can be produced in either projection or camera types of equipment.

Projection Plates. Projection plates are lithographic plates made in a projector similar to an enlarger, or in a camera. The original image is projected onto the photosensitized plate *through a lens system.* This is the feature which distinguishes so-called "projection" or "camera" plates from conventional lithographic plates which are made by *contact* exposures. The use of the term "projection," in this section, does not cover *poster plates* which have been made by projection for many years. Poster plates use bichromated albumin or casein coatings, and require very long exposures to 125-150 ampere arc lamps through condenser-projection lens systems.

The new projection plates have photographic-type emulsions whose speeds are high enough to make possible reasonable exposures in cameras equipped with light sources of average energy. They can be considered as direct-image plates in that the original reflection copy is photographed directly on to the plate. These plates are used on small lithographic presses. Two systems have been developed for this process; one utilizes a paper-based plate, the other a plastic-based plate.

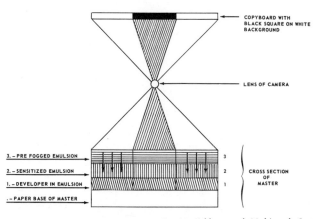

Courtesy Addressograph-Multigraph Corp.

Relationship of copy, lens, and master in a typical direct photographic platemaking unit.

The paper-based camera plate is coated with three layers: (1) A photographic developer suspended in a gelatin emulsion; (2) A silver-sensitized coating similar to that used on photographic print paper; (3) A silver-sensitized pre-exposed, or fogged, coating. This last layer becomes the printing surface of the finished plate, after the processing steps have been completed.

On exposure to a positive, in a camera, the light reflected from the white portions of the copy penetrates the fogged layer and exposes the silver salts in the second emulsion layer. The areas corresponding to the black portions of the copy do not reflect any light and do not expose. When the plate is placed in an activator solution after exposure, the activator penetrates all coatings and starts migration of the developer in the bottom layer into the other layers. In the areas that were exposed the developer is exhausted in the second layer. In the areas that were not exposed the developer penetrates to the prefogged top layer and develops it. Putting the plate in the stop bath, stops

the action of the developer. The top layer then contains areas of developed silver which are ink-receptive and correspond to the image areas or black portions of the copy; and undeveloped emulsion which is water-receptive corresponds to the non-image or white areas of the copy.

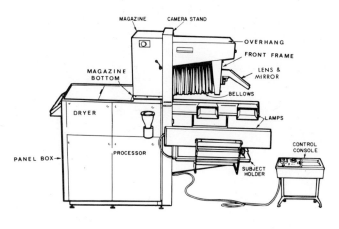

Courtesy Itek Corp.

Complete diagram of a direct photographic platemaking unit.

Because there is only a small difference between the ink- and water-receptivity of the image and non-image areas on this plate, it is rather critical with respect to exposure, processing and printing on the press. A special ink and fountain solution are desirable as well as a clean press with proper roller and cylinder pressure settings. Some inks give more latitude in exposure and printing than others. With a little experience excellent results can be obtained with these systems as long as the contrast range of the copy is not too great. It is difficult to mix line, halftone, and solids on one plate as each requires different levels of exposure or different inks for optimum printing results. For best results manufacturers' instruction should be followed carefully.

A modification of this material is used for reproducing enlargements from microfilm. The material is designed to work from negatives. As with the positive-working plate, these plates are exposed and processed in specially designed projection and processing equipment. The plate is ready for press as soon as it comes out of the processing machine.

The plastic-based camera plate features a plastic base and a non-printing area from which all the emulsion-imaging layer has been removed. Pre-screened halftone copy—up to 110 line—can be reproduced. This makes possible the use of a much broader range of copy than is presently possible on the paper-based camera plate.

While the plate must be started up by wiping with a special "starter" solution, conventional dampening solutions and standard inks may be run on the press.

ELECTROSTATIC PLATEMAKING PROCESSES

To date two electrostatic processes for making printing plates have been developed—Xerography and Electrofax. The Xerographic process was invented by the patent attorney Chester

Photograph of a direct photographic platemaking unit.

electricity. The areas affected by light lose their charge, leaving a photographically positive image on the charged surface which attracts a special oppositely charged powdered resin.

Xerography. In the Xerographic process, the photo-responsive surface is selenium, which is a photoconductor. A positive charge is produced on the selenium surface by a corona discharge source. The charged plate is exposed to the light image in a camera. The charge leaks off in the areas of exposure, leaving a charged positive image on the selenium. The plate is developed by cascading a negatively charged resin powder over it. The resin powder image can be transferred to a paper or metal lithographic plate and fused to the plate with heat or a solvent vapor. The image may also be transferred to a transparent or translucent material and fixed. This material can then be used as a positive for exposing positive-working presensitized plates.

Complete information on this and other applications of the Xerox process are available directly from the manufacturer.

Electrofax. In the Electrofax process, the photo-responsive surface consists of zinc oxide photo-conductor in a resin binder which is coated on paper or a lithographic metal. A corona ion source produces a negative charge on the zinc oxide. Like selenium, the zinc oxide loses its charge on exposure to light. The image is dusted with a positive charge resin powder. The powdered image is then fused on the paper or metal, by heat. No transfer is required.

To make a lithographic plate with an electrofax sheet, the zinc oxide and binder must be removed in the non-printing areas and the plate etched and gummed, or, the zinc oxide and binder must be made water-receptive.

F. Carlson and developed by Batelle Memorial Institute. It is marketed by the Xerox Corporation. Electrofax is an electrostatic process developed by the Radio Corporation of America.

In both processes an image is produced by the action of light on a photo-responsive surface which has been charged by static

Section Ten: Platemaking Troubles

Intensive research in platemaking has resulted in knowledge which gives the platemaker excellent control of his craft and its product. Improved materials and supplies also help assure consistently good plates. The variety of platemaking methods now available makes it easy to choose the best possible plate for a particular need. But despite all this, troubles in platemaking do occur. The following is a brief discussion of the more commonly experienced troubles, their probable causes, and suggested remedies. Page references are to GATF Txb 502/4 "Offset Lithographic Platemaking."

ALBUMIN AND CASEIN SURFACE PLATES

Plates of this type are being replaced by presensitized wipe-on plates. However, this type of surface plate does have important applications which warrant a discussion of the troubles associated with it.

Plate Coating Is Not Uniform. A coating which is not completely smooth and uniform across the entire plate may be due to three factors: 1) A plate which doesn't accept a smooth coating; 2) Blisters in the dried coating; 3) Solid particles in the coating.

Plate Is Hard To Develop. Some causes of this trouble are: dark reaction; too thin a coating, resulting in over-exposure; plateroom lights not completely safe; masking paper not opaque enough or of too light a color; negatives with insufficient density; developing water too cold.

Plate Has Scum. A plate may be scummy due to the causes which make the plate hard to develop. In addition, this condition may be due to: residual coating; improper desensitization; new, natural sponge; asphaltum not properly applied; too thin a coating; pitting oxidation; masking tape not suitable for lithographic use.

Plate Develops Too Sharp. This trouble is usually due to under-exposure. Increasing exposure time is the obvious remedy. Proper use of the GATF Sensitivity Guide should make possible proper balance between coating thickness and exposure time to assure a correct image on the finished plate.

Plate Develops Too Fast. This trouble is usually due to too thick a coating. Reversing the remedies suggested previously, for increasing coating thickness, should eliminate this problem.

Weak Image. A weak image may result from a coating which doesn't adhere well. This can be due to incomplete counter-etching. Pre-etching unnecessarily, that is when RH of the plateroom is low, may also contribute to this problem. A weak image may also be the result of too thin an application of developing ink.

Broken Halftone Dots. Some of the troubles already discussed also may result in broken halftone dots. They are: too thin an application of developing ink; too thick a coating; coating not uniform and even. In addition to these, broken halftone dots—as distinguished from too sharp an image—may be due to: plate grain too coarse; excessive "halo" or fringe in camera negatives; dirt or specks on the vacuum frame glass.

Excessive Dirt Spots. Dirt spots in the non-image area are usually due to pin-holes in the negatives. The negatives should be checked before they are forwarded to the plateroom.

Tacky Coating. The dried coating on the plate may become tacky when RH is high (above 70%). Air-conditioning in the plateroom, or at least a dehumidifier, is the best long-term remedy, but often it is necessary to work in less than ideal conditions. One way to minimize this problem is to expose the plate while it is still warm from the whirler. Dense, sharp negatives are very important in such conditions. Use of the Sensitivity Guide to assure proper exposure is advisable. If the plate is to be shot on a photocomposing machine, especially when a large number of shots are required, an application of wax, lacquer or thin asphaltum will help prevent the coating from becoming tacky.

GATF Sensitivity Guide on a finished plate; steps 1 through 6 are solid, steps 7, 8, and 9 are gray.

Thickening of Work; Plugging of Shadows and Fine Reverses. These are problems generally caused by: too thick a coating; poor contact; a diffused light source; smearing of developing ink; improper desensitization. Coating thickness and remedies are discussed on page 121.

Plate is Hard To Wash Out. This may be caused by: too thin a film of developing ink; developing ink drying too hard;

gum over the image. The problem of too thin a film of developing ink is discussed on page 122.

PRESENSITIZED PLATES

Presensitized plates are one of the types which have gone far to make albumin, casein, and similar surface plates largely obsolete. Presensitized plates lend themselves to greater consistency because the supplier treats the metal and coats the plate under mass manufacturing procedures which lend themselves to excellent quality control. In addition, the manufacturer supplies processing chemicals which he developed to work easily and well with his particular plate. Following are brief discussions of some of the more commonly-experienced troubles with presensitized plates.

Scummy Background On Negative-Working Plates. There are three likely causes of this trouble: plate was exposed too long to daylight or room light; rubbing up of the developed plate with lacquer was continued until it got too dry; lacquer sponge not clear of old lacquer.

Lacquer Comes Off During Rub-Up. This is caused by excess lacquer in the rub-up sponge.

Halftones Are Plugged or Bridged. Working the lacquer too long or until it is dry will cause this. When this problem is faced, it may be overcome by squeegeeing excess water off the plate, then applying a liberal quantity of fresh lacquer to dissolve the previously applied lacquer. The plate should be washed out with water using a thoroughly rinsed-out sponge. The excess water should be squeegeed off and the usual lacquer rub-up started and properly done.

Mottled and Spotted Halftones and Screen Tints. A likely cause is poor contact during exposure. It is essential, because presensitized plates are so smooth, that the vacuum frame be in good working order. When the photocomposer is used, it must also provide proper vacuum especially when large chases are being used. Poor contact will aggravate problems when over-exposing. Exposure should be held down to the time necessary to produce an even screen. Placing a sheet of grained or frosted plastic between the flat and cover glass may improve contact. The frosted side of the sheet should be toward the negative.

WIPE-ON PLATES

Wipe-on plates have become very popular in recent years, partially because of their simplicity. As is the case with presensitized plates, the supplier furnishes a treated plate along with chemicals compatable with a specific process. This lends itself to the possibility of completely standardized procedures. Some troubles do occur now and then. Following is a discussion of the more commonly encountered problems.

Streaked and Chalky-Colored Coating. This is the result of too thick an application not being wiped and rubbed down properly. Excess coating should be wiped off the plate and the coating rubbed down until it is uniform and clear. The indi-

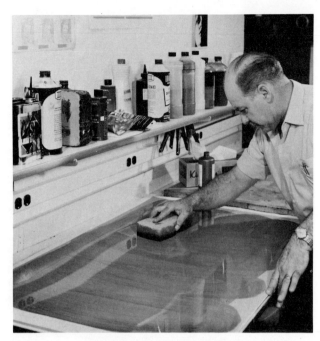

Applying a wipe-on coating.

vidual manufacturer's instructions should be closely followed with respect to coating the plate, especially the wiping and drying of the coating.

Fibers or Lint In The Dried Coating. The lint or fibers come from the paper wipes or cloth. Care should be taken not to use a paper wipe which shreds, or a linty cloth. Proper wiping technique will tend to remove lint.

Weak Image. Excess water in the rub-up sponge, an oxidized plate, or a plate that has not been pre-treated are the causes of a weak image or one which refuses to accept lacquer or ink during the developing procedure.

Plates which have not been pre-treated will not work with the diazo coatings used for most wipe-on processes. The pre-treatment is best done by the plate supplier, and should be compatible with the coating and developing chemicals. Pre-treated plates have an indefinite shelf-life provided they are not stored in a damp atmosphere which can deteriorate the pre-treated surface.

When applying the lacquer-developer emulsion, care should be taken that the rub-up sponge does not contain too much water. If it does, a dilution of the lacquer-developer occurs which upsets the chemical balance of the emulsion.

Scummy Background. A scummy background, after processing has been completed, may be caused by: too long exposure to room light of the dried coating; insufficient lacquer-developer used during development; or, too coarse a grain for wipe-on coatings which are normally quite thin.

DEEP-ETCH PLATES

The copperized aluminum deep-etch plate is the work horse of the lithographic industry. Most color and medium to long run jobs (50,000–500,000) are produced from these plates. The research and development of the late 40's and early 50's resulted in controls, techniques and materials which, in turn, made possible consistently good deep-etch plates. This, in turn, contributed significantly to the growth of web-offset. The deep-etch process is still, however, a complicated one as compared to presensitized and wipe-on methods.

Following are brief discussions of the more commonly encountered troubles when making deep-etch plates. Many of the problems parallel experiences with negative-working surface plates. These are referred to. All that has to be kept in mind is that the deep-etch plate is positive-working.

Plate Coating is Not Uniform. The causes of this are discussed on page 125, and are applicable to deep-etch coatings. In addition to those, a deep-etch coating which is not uniform may be due to making the coating with a "ropy" gum or gum which contains suspended gelatinous material. Where a plant makes its own coatings, care must be taken in selection of the gum arabic sorts. The gum solution should be thoroughly strained before it is used in making the final coating solution, and the finished coating strained again when poured into the coating pot.

Plate Requires Prolonged Development. Dark reaction and excessive exposure to room lights are two causes of this, and are discussed on page 125. In addition, too high a developer Baumé will result in prolonged development. The Baumé of the developer should be adjusted to give complete development in 5 to 8 minutes with two or three applications of developer.

Plate Develops Too Fast. This is due to too low a developer Baumé for the existing conditions of temperature and RH. A developer with a higher Baumé should be used.

Broken Halftone Dots. Grain, dark reaction, and dot fringe in camera films, as causes of broken dots, are discussed on page 126. In addition to these causes, broken dots may result from incomplete development, or lack of good contact during exposure. Contact, as a source of trouble is discussed on page 126. There, it was pointed out, poor contact will cause thickening of the image. With deep-etch plates (positive-working), poor contact may result in a broken image.

Some judgment, and use of the GATF Sensitivity Guide, should prevent trouble with broken dots due to incomplete development. If coating and exposure have been properly standardized (see Section Seven), then the developer Baumé should be adjusted to produce clear work areas in two to three minutes after the first application of developer.

Excessive Dirt Spots. Problems due to bubbles in the coating, and dirt or dust from the whirler itself as well as the room, are discussed on pages 126 and 127. In addition, specks of dirt on the clear areas of the positive will result in dirt spots on the finished plates. Positives should be clean when they come from the camera or stripping departments.

Tacky Coating. This problem, its causes and remedies, is discussed on page 127.

"Spider-Web" Scum. This is caused by excessive drying of the coating which results in shrinkage cracks. This is not likely to happen in an air-conditioned plateroom. Thinning the coating should help. Another remedy is to add up to two ounces of glycerin to a gallon of coating solution. When handling the coated plate avoid, as much as possible, bending it.

Fine, Over-all Scum. This may be due to too thin a coating failing to sufficiently protect the grain peaks from the developing and deep-etching solutions. Another possible cause is excessively high humidity resulting in a coating not completely dry. Too thin a coating is best remedied by a thicker coating, a longer exposure, or both.

Scum Areas Where Masking Tape Contacted The Coating. Masking tape as a source of trouble is discussed on page 127.

Plates Cannot Be Washed Out. This difficulty is usually due to dried gum over the image, or developing ink drying so hard it cannot be dissolved by the regular solvent. Both of these are discussed on page 128.

Oxidation Scum On Aluminum Plates. This problem is discussed on page 128. In addition to the causes and remedies mentioned there, oxidation scum can be caused by the preservatives used in the gum arabic solution. The preservative used must be mercury-free.

Embedded abrasive may also contribute to oxidation scum. After counter-etching, the plate grain should be examined for embedded abrasive. If any is detected, the plate should be discarded.

BIMETAL AND TRIMETAL PLATES

Most of the troubles encountered with these plates are similar to those encountered in surface and deep-etch platemaking.

In tracking down the trouble, it is necessary to consider whether the plate is negative-working or positive-working. The parallel discussions, in this section, under surface and deep-etch headings, cover most of the commonly encountered troubles in bimetal and trimetal plates. However, when working with these plates, it must be borne in mind that two different metals are always involved: the image-bearing metal (copper), and the water-carrying metal (chromium, stainless steel, etc).

Refusal of the copper to take ink is one of the more common troubles. On a negative-working plate, this is usually due to incomplete removal of the light-hardened gum coating from the image areas. This can be overcome by application of an image remover which the plate supplier can furnish. Sometimes a repeated acid sensitization of the copper image may do the trick.

On a positive-working plate, this same trouble with the copper image area is caused by failure to remove all the chromium etch from these areas. A thorough washing of the plate with anhydrous alcohol, followed by an application of asphaltum or lacquer, should eliminate this problem. In those platemaking procedures which call for removing the stencil by scrubbing under water, but omitting the alcohol wash, an application of a sensitizing solution followed by a rub-up with ink should bring the image up satisfactorily. The rub-up should be carried out while the plate is wet by the sensitizing solution.

Section Eleven: Handling Plates on the Press

This section should rightfully belong in Chapter Twelve: Lithographic Presswork, as it applies to operations which the pressman performs. It is included in this chapter on platemaking: (1) To complete the information on plates, their behavior on the press, and the problems associated with their use; (2) To acquaint the platemaker with conditions plates encounter on the press; (3) In the hope that it will encourage pressmen who refer to and read this chapter to learn more about the plates they run.

To get the best results from any printing plate, the plant must maintain the best possible press conditions. Bearer pressure and packing of the plate and blanket should follow the press manufacturer's instructions. All ink rollers should be free from glaze. Form rollers should be set lightly, with slightly more pressure against the ink drums than against the plate; the rollers should be set firmly against the plate, but should not bounce at the gripper edge. Dampener covers when used, should be clean and resilient. The blanket should be free from glaze and embossed areas. The back-cylinder pressure should be just enough to produce a good print—no more than that.

Unless the press conditions are right, no plate will produce the quality and length of run of which it is capable.

CHECKING THE PRESS

Printing from fine-grained or ungrained plates requires particular care and precision when adjusting pressures and setting rollers. Since the plates are relatively smooth there is less traction between plate and form rollers, as well as between plate and blanket. Therefore, there is more tendency to skidding. Form rollers and dampeners must, therefore, be more nearly perfect and must be set with a minimum of pressure against the plate.

Checking Form Roller Setting. The best way to check form roller settings is as follows:

1. Gum up the plate and dry it.
2. With a normal amount of ink on the form rollers, and the press standing still, drop the form rollers onto the plate and immediately raise them.
3. Jog the plate around and inspect the bands of ink that the rollers have left on the plate. The ink bands should all be the same width and should be uniform from one end of the cylinder to the other. For grained plates they can be one fourth to three-eights inch wide, depending on the size of the press.

For ungrained plates, one-eighth to three-sixteenths inch is sufficient. If the form rollers cannot be set this lightly to get uniform ink bands, the chances are the rollers need to be reground or replaced.

Dampening Rollers. The dampening rollers should also be set as lightly as possible, as smooth plates take less roller pressure than grained plates, in order to obtain uniform dampening.

The Blanket. A hard blanket gives the best reproduction from fine and ungrained plates. The squeeze between plate and blanket should be kept to a minimum. Ordinarily packing for .003 inch to .004 inch squeeze for grained plates is sufficient, but the closer to .002 inch squeeze as is possible is best for smooth plates.

STARTING PLATE ON THE PRESS

Plate Image. When the pressman receives the plate, the non-image areas will be under gum, and the image areas will be either under developing ink or asphaltum. Plates under developing ink are generally preferred because they are easier to check. Covering the plates with developing ink is acceptable as long as the developing ink does not dry hard, or is not covered with gum. The plate can then be washed out easily and completely with Lithotine. Broken lines, lettering, and spots in solids can be repaired by the pressman by simply scratching through the gum with a needle and dabbing ink on the uncovered metal. Depending on whether the plate is for black ink or color, different treatments are recommended for starting the press run.

TREATING BLACK PLATES ON THE PRESS

The gum should be washed from the plate with the water sponge, inked up, and the lay (position or register on the sheet) obtained. When the sheet position is satisfactory and the image is printing satisfactorily, the run is started. On the other hand, if the image is not printing properly, the plate should be wet-washed before proceeding to print. To wet-wash the plate, first the plate is washed with the water sponge. While the plate is still wet, the ink is washed off with Lithotine. Then the plate is wiped twice with a clean water sponge to remove the solvent. The press is started, and the form rollers dropped. Washing the plate with water removes any gum that may have been covering work areas and causing blindness, broken dots, or streaks. The ink can then be washed off easily, and the image should roll up and print properly.

TREATING COLOR PLATES ON THE PRESS

Depending on various conditions, one of the following two methods should be used in starting color plates. As the governing conditions lie mainly in the press washup preceding the job, these two methods are distinguished as A and B.

Method A would be used under the following conditions: (1) If there will be no change from the previous color run on the press; (2) If the change will be to a color that will not be altered or dirtied if the press washup hasn't been very thorough, as in going from a light to a dark color; (3) If an improved press washup method is used and the press rollers are thoroughly clean.

The procedure is as follows: (1) After checking the work, the developing ink is washed out with Lithotine and asphaltum applied, the asphaltum being rubbed down smooth and thin; (2) The plate is put on the press; (3) The press is inked up; (4) The gum is washed off the plate; (5) The form rollers dropped, and lay okay obtained; (6) The plate is wet-washed, and a color okay obtained.

The final wet wash before printing is worth the extra effort. It makes clean, sharp printing possible from the start. Without it, tone values may change somewhat after the run has been started.

If a delicate color such as light yellow or a tint is run, the asphaltum on the plate image may dirty the print. In this case asphaltum should not be applied after the developing ink is washed out. Instead, press ink of the color that is to be run is applied and rubbed down with a clean rag.

Method B should be used if there is a change of color that will alter or dirty the job if the press washup has not been thorough, for example, from a dark to a light color.

The procedure for the method B is as follows: (1) After the work is checked, the developing ink is washed out with Lithotine, asphaltum applied and rubbed down smooth and thin; (2) The plate is put on the press; (3) The press is inked up with as little ink as possible; (4) The gum is washed off the plate; (5) The form rollers dropped and an okay on the lay obtained; (6) The press is washed up and fresh clean ink applied; (7) The plate is wet-washed and color okay obtained.

CONTROLLING INK AND WATER

An important part of the pressman's art is his ability to balance the ink and water. Poor plates make this very difficult, but with well-desensitized plates that resist blinding, it is relatively easy. Here are a few general rules that should be followed:

1. Enough ink is run to print good solids without noticeably squashing the halftone dots. Printed halftone dots should be sharp and clean, and close to the same size and shape as those on the plate. The amount of ink needed will vary with the ink requirements of the paper. High-finish coated papers require the least ink, rough uncoated papers the most. The shadows should not be filled in or the dots slurred.

2. Crowding the ink to get color should be avoided. It is better to mix the ink stronger and run an amount that will print the halftones right without squashing and filling in. The use of GATF's Star Target, Quality Control Strip, and Dot-Gain Scale enables detection of these troubles.

3. Running the ink too spare should be avoided. If the color is too strong, a reducer like alumina hydrate may be added to the ink. If quick-set or heat-set ink is being run, the ink supplier should be consulted for the proper reducer to use. There must be enough ink on the plate image to protect it from any blinding action of the fountain solution.

4. Excessive additions of compounds and driers to the ink should be avoided. These may cause the ink to waterlog which, in turn, may cause blinding of the plate, improper ink transfer, piling, or stripping of the rollers.

5. A minimum of dampening water should always be run. Well desensitized plates require very little moisture to keep them clean. Poorly desensitized plates need excessive moisture which makes it necessary to crowd the ink, thereby causing a series or chain reaction of troubles. Excessive water slows ink drying, causes register troubles and curling of paper.

6. Well-desensitized plates need very little acid in the fountain water (pH 5.0 to 6.0) to keep them clean with most inks. For very soft or greasy inks, the pH may have to be considerably lower. Fountain waters more acid than pH 4.0 will slow the drying of conventional inks. With well-desensitized plates, acid and gum in the fountain water are needed mainly to keep dampening rollers clean.

The grain on the usual lithographic plate acts as a reservoir for water. It carries more water than is actually needed in printing and, because of this excess water, more ink must be run than is actually needed to print the density of color that is wanted. But when printing with a very fine-grained or smooth plate there is no such reservoir, and the water feed must be cut back. The following suggestions should be of help in adjusting the water feed and getting the proper ink-water balance on fine-grained and smooth plates, especially presensitized and wipe-on plates.

When a fine-grained or smooth plate is started, an excess of water will show up in two ways: (1) Rivulets or drops of water will be seen along the back edge of the plate and blanket; (2) Beads of water will be seen riding between the ink rollers. In this case, the water feed should be cut back until this evidence of excessive moisture disappears.

When the water has been cut back, it may appear that too much ink is being fed. If halftone dots appear to be squashed, or if shadows are starting to fill in, the ink feed should be cut back a notch or two. Compensating for too much ink by feeding more water will lead to trouble or result in poor print quality.

As the run is continued with less ink, beads of water may again show up on the rollers. This is because there is less ink to take up the water. In this case, the water feed should be cut back still more. When the water beads disappear, the halftones should be checked again. It may be that the ink can be cut back still further.

By following this system it is possible to reach the proper balance between ink and water for the particular plate. Of course, if cut-backs are carried too far, the plate will catch up. But the idea is to run with as little water as possible. A pressman may be surprised as to how little water and ink fine-grained and smooth plates require; and how much their printing quality is improved by proper water and ink adjustments. Colors will print brighter, and conventional inks will dry faster.

This system of water and ink adjustment is helpful, not only with smooth plates, but with all types of grained plates as well. With well-desensitized plates of any type, it will help to get the maximum in printing quality.

GUMMING-UP AND ETCHING PLATES ON THE PRESS

It is not as easy to gum up or etch a plate properly on the press as it is in the plateroom. Many plates are damaged or ruined because the pressman will not take the time and precautions to do a careful job. While properly made plates will stand more abuse and careless treatment, certain precautions are necessary if the best results are to be obtained in day-to-day production. The following suggestions are made for avoiding trouble and saving time when plates are etched or gummed-up on the press.

When Plates Should Be Gummed Up. Plates made with modern techniques and materials do not need to be gummed up for stops up to 15 to 20 minutes while getting started on the press. For longer stops and shutdowns during the run, they should be gummed-up and left under the press ink. For stops longer than one hour, plates should be washed out and put under asphaltum; otherwise, the press ink is likely to dry. By avoiding gumming-up for short stops at the start of the run there is a saving of time and much less chance of plate damage.

Gumming-Up a Plate. To gum up plates on the press, the first thing done is to protect the printing image with enough ink to resist gumming or etching. To do this, the dampeners are first lifted, and then after about three cylinder revolutions, the form rollers are lifted and the plate allowed to dry. This will leave a good charge of ink on the work areas. In order to dry the plate as rapidly as possible (to avoid oxidation), the press should be running while the plate is drying. Fanning the plate while the press is rolling will hasten the drying.

Since press ink is relatively soft and smears easily under the gum sponge, the next thing that is done is to powder the image. This is accomplished with a mixture of half-and-half French chalk and powdered rosin. (French chalk alone can be used, but it tends to make the image hard to wash out.)

For gumming-up the powdered plate, gum arabic solution at 6°–8° Baumé is used, and the plate fanned dry. The rub down should be made thin enough so that none of the image areas are left covered. The gum should be thin because gum that dries over the image will make it hard or even impossible to wash out. If necessary, the work areas should be gone over with a slightly damp cloth just before the gum dries to remove any overlying gum film.

Press ink contains drier and will often dry if left on the plate longer than about two hours. So, if the press is to be shut down much more than an hour, it is advisable to wash-out the plate and put it under asphaltum. Otherwise, the work may not take ink unless the area is washed with a special solvent mixture.

Putting a Plate Under Asphaltum. To put a plate under asphaltum, the plate is first gummed up, making sure that the gum is thoroughly dry. Then all the ink is washed out of the image areas with Lithotine. Asphaltum solution is applied with a soft rag and rubbed down to a smooth light tan color. If the image has vinyl lacquer on it, it can be left without asphaltum.

If the gum is not dry before the asphaltum is applied, the asphaltum will penetrate the gum and scum the plate. If the asphaltum is put on too heavy, or is streaked, the water sponge may not remove the asphaltum when the job is ready for printing. When this happens, the only thing that can be done is to wet-wash the plate.

If a plate has finished a run and it is to be stored for a re-run, it is best to have the final gumming-up and application of asphaltum done by the platemaker.

Etching a Plate on the Press. Correctly made plates seldom need etching on the press. However, if a plate shows a tendency to scum, the pressman should try etching it a few times before increasing the strength (lowering the pH) of the fountain solution.

To etch a plate on the press, the image is first rolled up with ink, and powdered in the same way as for gumming-up. For best results, the same etch which the platemaker uses should be used. The etch is applied just like plain gum solution, rubbed down thin, so it does not cover any work areas, and dried. The etch is washed off thoroughly with water before proceeding to print. If this washing is not thorough, the phosphoric acid left on the plate may cause the steel ink rollers to strip. If the plate is to stand longer than one hour, the etch film should be washed off and the plate gummed with gum arabic; then the ink is washed out and asphaltum applied.

If the scum comes back, it is usually because the ink is too soft, or the dampeners are too greasy or improperly adjusted. In any case, the fountain solution should not have a pH lower than 3.8. It is better to clean the dampeners, check the rollers, and stiffen the ink, if at all possible.

More information on the handling of plates on the press is available in GATF publication Txb 502/4 *Offset Lithographic Platemaking,* Txb 501 *Press Troubles,* Txb 505/6 *Offset Press Operating,* Txb 513 *Advanced Pressmanship.*

CHAPTER ELEVEN

The Proofing Department_____

Section One: The Purposes and Methods of Proofing

The risk of error is high in all manufacturing processes, but it is nowhere higher than in printing, and particularly in lithography. Almost every job is custom-made, almost every job is produced under enormous time pressure, almost every job is a composite of many pieces that must be properly related by the lithographer. Add to these conditions the fact that imperfections are more detrimental to the printed product than to many other ones, and you realize the hazards of this business. The main purpose of proofing is that of catching errors and mistakes before they become fatal.

PROOFING HAS MANY PURPOSES

But proofing has many other purposes and reasons, in addition. Most jobs are turned over to the lithographer in many pieces out of which he must make a harmonious whole. Very often the customer, a busy advertising agency, for example, wants to see how the job will look before it goes to press.

Customers may demand proofs for many other reasons, too. Very often they want to send advance copies of forthcoming sales literature to salesmen, distributors or dealers. Or, they may need proofs for the purpose of guiding other people who supply material belonging to a specific campaign in their work.

PHOTOMECHANICAL PROOFING AND PROOFING WITH INK

How are lithographic jobs proofed? The posing of this question may sound silly to letterpress printers or photo-engravers to whom proofing means clearly the taking of a few prints in a proof press. Things are very different in lithography. Here jobs are proofed in many techniques of which the proofing in proof presses is only one, and—to say it right away—by no means the most important proofing technique at all.

It can be stated—with all due reservations—that proofing with ink is much less common and much less generally used in lithography than photomechanical proofing. The use of photomechanics for proofing is an achievement of lithography and peculiar to it. The use of photomechanics for lithographic proofing is closely connected to the methods and procedures of lithographic platemaking and must be discussed in relation to platemaking itself.

In letterpress printing the final printing form consists either of original material, or of duplicate plates or of a mixture of both. The printing form for a flatbed cylinder press may combine type set in any hot metal machine technique, original photo-engravings, electrotypes or stereotypes. All these elements are physically assembled during imposing and fastened into proper position by lock-up.

In lithographic platemaking the assembly precedes the making of the physical printing plate. Stripping has the function of assembling the material — negatives or positives — and of putting it in its correct place. As the material consists of photographic images, it is suitable for photomechanical proofing. Photomechanical proofing aims at paper-prints on which the transparent image of the photographic material is recorded in an opaque form. Like every other generalization — and definitions are nothing but a special kind of generalizations — this one too tends to cause trouble. How is the image recorded? As a negative or a positive? How accurately is it recorded? These and several other questions will be discussed in the following sections of our study. But, no matter how critical we may be toward our definition of photographic proofing, no matter how many holes we may be able to tear into this fabric of words, one fact should emerge clearly: A photomechanical proof is a paper-print and not a transparency.

Even this very restricted assertion needs qualification. As you will see further down in the discussion of photomechanical proofing for full-color printing, some very useful photomechanical proofing methods produce transparent images on clear plastic sheets where each of the process colors is recorded in color. But, our definition holds nevertheless because these images are placed on white paper and viewed on it as if they were directly made on the paper.

SUMMARY OF PROOFING PURPOSES AND TECHNIQUES

If we want to summarize the preceding paragraphs we may state that lithographic proofing serves a variety of purposes and utilizes a variety of techniques. The two main purposes of proofing are: (1) proofing for production control or proofing for internal use in the lithographer's own plant; and (2) proofing for submission to the customer or for other external use. The two main techniques of proofing are: (1) proofing with ink; and (2) photomechanical proofing. We might add two additional distinctions that cross the lines of purposes and techniques. These are: (1) proofing for register; and (2) proofing for color. All following discussions of proofing are made with these six points in mind.

CRITERIA

If we ask ourselves what proofing indicates we can generalize again by saying that proofing conveys information on two groups of criteria which are essential for the evaluation of a lithographic job. These criteria are: (1) quality; and (2) accuracy. Both of them need to be discussed.

Few words cause more heated arguments in the printing business than the word quality. Every printer and lithographer, and most certainly every printing salesman, speaks of his firm as a "quality" house! Everybody sells "quality," everybody considers his own jobs quality jobs and those of his competitors something different, to say it mildly. Quality is a term that expresses our personal judgment; it is not an objective term but a highly subjective one, if used in this manner.

Like many other "value" words, quality, too, has become almost meaningless in this world of exaggerated advertising. In most cases a quality printer is merely a printer who knows his business but by no means a printer of outstanding performance. Those who still hold that it is no merit to know one's business, but something understood by itself, will object to being thrown into this undistinguished quality barrel.

In this study the word quality is used in a different and very special sense that must be explained to the reader. We understand by quality the degree to which a lithographer has achieved the result desired by the customer and promised by the lithographer to his customer. Thereby we want to emphasize that many lithographic jobs are problems of intuition and interpretation rather than tasks of exact and faithful reproduction. There are, of course, many cases where facsimile reproduction is demanded. But the majority of commercial lithographing, for advertising in particular, is neither prepared for facsimile reproduction nor so intended.

QUALITY IS A SUBJECTIVE TERM

Commercial lithographing is highly competitive business. Advertising is a Moloch with never-ending appetite. Every advertising job is a problem of getting the results of which the customer dreams with the least possible expenditure. Advertising has the taste of a millionaire and the means of a miser. The individual lithographer proves his mettle by ingenuity with which he bridges this constant gap.

Quality is, therefore, in our eyes a relation more than anything else. It is the expression of the extent to which the lithographer has been able to achieve what he set out to do. Used in this sense, the word quality is highly subjective; only the parties concerned in a specific transaction are capable of making such quality judgments.

Seen in this manner the experience and wisdom of lithographer and customer alike are the main criteria for quality. Intuition, psychology, knowledge of the customer's business are not less important for the quality lithographer in our sense than his standing as a technician in lithography itself. If such a lithographer meets an equally equipped buyer, the highest quality becomes possible.

ACCURACY CAN BE CLEARLY DEFINED

Accuracy, the other kind of information conveyed by proofing is the supplement and in a sense even the contrary of quality. There is nothing vague about accuracy; it can be clearly defined. In the following discussion of proofing you will meet many aspects of lithographing that can be accurately described and discussed in the terms of their own accuracy.

Finally, a word on the division of this study into single-color and multicolor proofing on the one hand and full-color proofing on the other. Full-color is used in this study as a more precise synonym for what is often called process work. Full-color printing is so very different from other kinds of lithographic printing that it must be treated by itself.

Single-color and multicolor proofing comprise in this study the vast bulk of line and halftone printing in one or several colors. Single-color and multicolor proofing are of the greatest importance to the average lithographic plant. A thorough understanding of this subject is also a prerequisite for the understanding of full-color proofing.

Section Two: Single-Color and Multicolor Proofing

At the outset of this discussion we want to emphasize that there are no generally accepted rules or techniques for proofing in the lithographic industry. Every shop, every organization has its own problems, its own equipment and its own techniques. Every organization develops in its own particular way. The kind of work done by it is responsible for the method developed in it. Price, delivery requirements, nature and purpose of jobs, equipment and personnel are all important factors that vary from company to company.

The lithographic industry is not a staid, saturated guild but a living and vigorously growing organism. For this reason it is still far from uniformity. The following discussion of proofing is not a statement of generally valid and ubiquitously applicable practices but rather a loose description of methods and techniques that are more or less consistently used by lithographers in many cases. The purpose of this study is stimulation of the reader. The practical lithographer will be the best judge as to how other people's experiences can be applied to his own benefit.

Our presentation covers the following four main groups: (1) Accuracy as it is related to proofing; (2) Photomechanical proofing techniques; (3) Proofing with ink; and (4) Special proofing techniques. Each of these groups is now individually discussed.

ACCURACY

The four main aspects of accuracy in single- and multicolor proofing are: (1) Accuracy of the assembled material; (2) Accuracy of position; (3) Accuracy of imposition; and (4) Accuracy of register. All four aspects of accuracy are closely connected. Serious errors in accuracy are inexcusable and must be caught before they cause real damage.

Accuracy of the Assembled Material. Lithographic jobs are often turned over to the printer in fragmentary form. Some pieces can be photographed as they are, others must be scaled. It is often necessary to make intermediate composites out of various art and copy elements for the final assembly of a job. The accuracy of the assembled material must be checked in several respects. One pertains to its completeness, including the elimination of not-belonging matter. Another aspect of accuracy is that of the size of each individual element. Photomechanical proofing permits control of this kind of accuracy, but it must not be overlooked that not all photomechanical proofs are of exact dimension. Where this point counts, blueprints, for example, must not be used indiscriminately.

Accuracy of Position. Accuracy of position seems implied in the preceding aspect of accuracy. But this is often not so, particularly in multicolor jobs. There it happens very often that various copy or art elements in one color cannot be checked for correct position without reference to other colors. Where accuracy of relative position counts, multiple exposure proofs are required, if photomechanical proofing is used. Accuracy of position will again attract our attention at the discussion of proofing with ink, and also under the heading of special proofing techniques.

Accuracy of Imposition. The accuracy of imposition is much too often neglected. Many lithographers are much more concerned with the quality of their print than with its proper imposition. But the imposition must not be neglected; it is a most essential consideration in all jobs that are printed on both sides and must be folded before they attain their final form.

Impositions are particularly exacting in book work. The position of the page on the sheet, its back-up, the inside and outside margins, head and foot trims, and last but not least, shingling, are all items with which a lithographer should be thoroughly familiar. Proofing is the last opportunity for making sure that the job is imposed according to the bindery imposition which should always be the basis of the lithographer's plate layout.

Accuracy of Register. Register is another essential of all lithographic printing that can be checked in proofing. To quote Mr. Charles Latham (GATF Skilled Craft Text #505/6, "Lithographic Offset Press Operating," p. 67) "The term register is loosely used to denote the position of the image on the sheet or the position of one color with respect to another. *Technically there should be a distinction between register and fit, or external and internal register.* If every sheet goes through the press and is printed in the same position relative to the gripper edge and the guide side, the press is printing 'in register.' If the plate has been made incorrectly, or if the paper distorts and some of the images are out of place in relation to others on a sheet that are printed in register, then the term should be 'misfit' or *internal misregister.*"

Photomechanical proofing is an excellent check for internal register, at least inasmuch as the plate is concerned. Paper shrinkage, of course, cannot be controlled in this manner. External register cannot be checked by photomechanical proofing but only on the press. The checking of external register is normally not a task of proofing but constitutes one of the responsibilities of the pressman and is considered part of makeready on the press previous to running.

PHOTOMECHANICAL PROOFING TECHNIQUES

Photomechanical proofing techniques are in general executed by contact printing. We can distinguish three main kinds of materials used for photomechanical proofing of single- and multicolor work. (The photomechanical proofing techniques for full-color work are discussed in section three of this chapter where you find several other processes described.) The three most commonly used materials for photomechanical proofing are: (1) Blueprint papers; (2) Brownprint papers; and (3) Diazo papers. Each of them is discussed in the following.

Blueprint Papers. Blueprint papers are commercially available products. They are widely used by architects and engineers for photomechanical copying of plans and technical drawings. Blueprints are based on the light-sensitivity of organic iron compounds, in particular of potassium ferricyanide to change into ferric ferrocyanide, a compound commonly known as prussian blue. Blueprint paper is exposed together with negatives, in most cases a stripped flat, in a vacuum-printing frame to arc light. The transparent image areas of the negatives permit light passage and therewith the formation of prussian blue. The result is a photomechanical positive proof showing the image areas in dark blue on a more or less white or light blue background. The exposed blueprint paper is developed in water and air-dried.

Blueprints are not dimensionally stable, nor do they retain their original color during aging. They are, nevertheless, very widely used because they are very inexpensive and very easy to make. Blueprints afford sufficient information on three aspects of accuracy, that of the assembled material and its position as well as of the imposition. As to the fourth type of accuracy with which proofing is concerned, namely, the accuracy of internal register or fit, blueprints may or may not be sufficiently indicative. By and large, blueprints are considered satisfactory in most simple jobs, particularly in single-color book work.

Brownprint Papers. Brownprint papers are known under a variety of other names such as Van Dyke, Solar, silver print, print-out or P.O.P. and developing-out papers. Brownprint papers are silver salt papers. But their image is formed very differently from that in bromide papers — our most common kind of photographic printing papers. In bromide papers the visible image is obtained by development of the latent image. In brownprint papers there is no latent image; here the image is formed entirely by exposure to light. The longer a brownprint paper is exposed, the darker becomes the exposed image. This fact is of greatest importance for photomechanical proofing, as you can readily see.

Brownprint paper is used for making positive photomechanical proofs from negative flats. The paper is exposed together with the stripped flat in a vacuum-printing frame to arc lights. The exposure time is approximately the same as for albumin or surface plates. The exposed brownprint is developed in water, fixed with hypo, and dried after rinsing. It should be remembered that brownprints change dimensions, just like blueprints.

Brownprints afford information on all aspects of accuracy, not only that of the assembled material, its position and imposition, but also that of internal register or fit in multicolor jobs. This feature we owe to the peculiar way in which the brownprint image is created that permits us to identify various flats on the same brownprint in different tonal values.

The following discussion of brownprints and their use is quoted from the GATF Skilled Craft Text #507, "Offset Stripping (Black and White)," by Bernard R. Halpern (Chapter X).

"For simple color jobs, the brownprint proof can show the fit and relationship between the several printing colors. In such work, the flat for the darkest printing color, or black, is exposed first. The full normal exposure time is used. The next lighter color flat, such as a blue or red printer, is registered in position and exposed for about half the time. If a third color is to be printed, its flat is also exposed in register with the others for a still shorter period of time. Such a series of exposures may be 2½ minutes for the black, 1 minute for the blue, and 30 seconds for the yellow. Upon development, the different exposure times produce different shades of brown on the paper. Color overlap areas produce darker lines. Halftone or tint areas may be confusing due to their tones being lighter than the solid printing color. Such areas should be noted in pencil with the color they are to print.

"For proofs of publications, work-and-turn jobs, and similar work, the brownprint is folded and cut up to simu-

late the format of the printed job. Jobs printed on both sides of the sheet can be prepared by pasting sheets of brownprint paper together to represent the front and back printings. This pasting can be done with rubber cement. Or the two-sided brownprint paper can be used. When exposing each side of the double-coated brownprint paper, butterfly cutouts along the brownprint sheet centerlines or punched holes are used so that the exposures on the two sides will register with each other. In development, both sides are developed simultaneously."

Diazo Papers. Diazo papers are also known as ozalids (even though this name belongs to the Ozalid Company), white-prints, ammonia-prints and gas-prints. Similar to blueprints, diazo papers, too, produce, under the influence of light, images of colored pigments. The exposed diazo print must be treated either with a liquid or a gaseous chemical for development of the colored image. In many cases, diazo prints are developed with ammonia fumes, hence the colloquial designations of gas-prints or ammonia-prints.

Diazo prints are distinguished by two features: (1) They produce positive images from photographic positives and are therefore used for the photomechanical proofing of positive flats, and (2) they do not change their size during development. The procedure of exposing is the same for diazo papers as for the other two described kinds: They are contact-printed in a vacuum frame with strong lights. Diazo prints afford information on all other aspects of accuracy than internal register or fit. For this purpose brownprints remain unsurpassed. But diazo materials play another very important role in photomechanical color proofing. In the following section on full-color proofing you will meet them again.

PROOFING WITH INK

Proofing with ink can be divided in many ways, according to the kind of equipment, the kind of plate and last but not least the point at which proofing takes place in the production of a job. Let us first take a look at the equipment. Proofing can be done on special proof presses or on

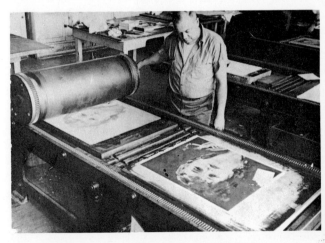

Proofing on a Hand-operated Proof Press.

regular production presses. The plate used in proofing can be either an intermediate plate or it can be the final press plate. Proofing can be done at different stages of production, either as a step preliminary to putting the job on the press or as part of the presswork.

If we look at these six points we see that some of them can be combined with others in several ways. A press plate can be proofed either on a proof press or on a regular production press; proofing with a press plate can be an independent preliminary step or it can be done as part of presswork. For practical reasons we divide the subject in the following three groups: (1) Proofing on proof presses, (2) Preliminary proofing on production presses, and (3) Proofing as part of presswork. Each of these subjects is now discussed in detail.

Proofing on Proof Presses. Proofing on proof presses is not too important in the average lithographic plant for single and multicolor work. Proof presses are much more important in full-color printing. For this reason, they are not discussed in this section of our study but rather in the following section on full-color proofing. It should not be assumed that single- and multicolor production does not use proofing on proof presses at all; this is not so. In many specialized cases such as label work, for example, it is customary to proof the intermediate plates on proof presses before the final press plate is made.

Another and quite different use of the proof press in single and multicolor work should not be forgotten. Presentations and other very short runs are sometimes produced on proof presses rather than on production equipment. In these cases the proof press functions not as a proof press but as a production machine. (You can see how difficult it is to generalize in our so very highly diversified industry. Now the proof press has at last changed its function completely!)

Preliminary Proofing on Production Presses. Proofing on production presses is much more often done in single- and multicolor printing than proofing on proof presses. In some cases the plate to be used for proofing is not the final press plate but an intermediate or unit plate. Such plates are proofed before the final press plate containing several times the material of the unit plate is made. Proofing of intermediate unit plates is a safety measure primarily. It is much easier to correct the small unit plate than to remake the final and much larger press plate.

Proofing of the final press plate preliminary to the running of single- or multicolor jobs can have many reasons. The customer may request proofs because he wants to see finished prints before the run is started. Or, the customer may need samples for advance distribution. But preliminary proofing is also often done because the lithographer himself desires information that cannot be provided in any other way. We are referring here to all cases where a job is either very critical, or where some of its component elements are unknown to the plant where the job is produced.

In many cases proofing is the only way in which the necessary information on paper, ink, overprinting, and so on can be obtained. It is always dangerous to rely on verbal information alone when new materials must be used. Even

if we give everybody connected with the asking and answering of such questions the benefit of the doubt, there are still too many points that cannot be taken care of by verbal means. How new materials will behave under very specific job conditions can in most cases only be found out by trying. Preliminary proofing is often the best and least expensive way of experimenting with new materials and techniques.

Proofing on production presses requires accurate setting of the press and does not become conclusive before approximately 500 waste sheets are run. At this time, hickeys and gear- and roller-streaks will show up. After the job is perfectly adjusted, final proof sheets are taken for customer submission.

Proofing as Part of Presswork. Whether a job should be proofed or not depends entirely on the case and on the terms of sale. Most lithographers do not include press proofs in their contract price but charge extra for such services. In some cases, particularly where the lithographer and his customer know each other well and are used to cooperating smoothly with each other, a customer representative is invited to the plant at the beginning of an important run, particularly in case of a difficult color. Such a procedure saves the customer the expense of proofing, but it is obviously only workable with highly experienced people on both sides.

A Fully Powered Lithographic Proof Press.

The press is inked, and the color is adjusted in cooperation between plant personnel and customer's representatives who are very often artists. But care must be taken not to waste too much time in this procedure. Many firms make extra charges for idle time of their presses; such charges have often rather surprising effects — colors that needed a lot of adjustments become passable if it costs a lot to work on them. Many a job is improved by a more strict procedure; very often long fooling around with colors does make the result worse rather than better.

SPECIAL PROOFING TECHNIQUES

Under this heading we want to discuss two techniques that have proved their usefulness in many cases. One is proofing by means of the strike-sheet, the other is proofing for pre-separated artwork.

Proofing by Means of the Strike-Sheet. Proofing by means of the strike-sheet can almost be classified as part of starting certain jobs on the press rather than proofing. The purpose of this kind of proofing is control of internal register or fit in multicolor jobs. The strike-sheet is a print of the key color, mostly but by no means necessarily, the black.

Proofing by means of the strike-sheet is done on production presses with actual press plates. The first step consists in printing a good and sufficient number of sheets from the key-color plate. These are the strike-sheets. After the strike-sheets are printed, the key plate is taken off the press and the job is started. Every color is first printed on strike-sheets where it is possible to check its relation to the rest of the job and to make sure that all colors fit as they should. The strike-sheet technique is particularly valuable in such artwork where color is used discontinuously and where it is impossible to tell from an individual color print whether it is in register or not.

Proofing for Pre-Separated Artwork. In this technique, proofing is used in the making of pre-separated artwork. The artist makes a drawing of the key color; a plate is made from this drawing and prints are taken in a "non-photo blue." The artist uses these prints for making finished artwork. As the key color does not photograph, each of the separation sheets can be used for the camera without further preparation.

This technique concludes our discussion of single- and multicolor proofing. Our next subject is proofing for full-color reproduction.

Section Three: Full-Color Proofing

Proofing for the process color work, or as we prefer to say, full-color reproduction shares many problems and techniques with single- and multicolor proofing but has in addition many aspects peculiar to itself. It might be stated that proofing for full-color reproduction is that operation where all phases of full-color printing meet; color separating, color correcting, platemaking, presswork, ink and paper, and last but not least, the viewing of the full-color proof in comparison with the original. All play their role in this seemingly simple and innocent step of proofing.

The reader who wants to follow the discussion of the subject must be at least superficially conversant with the main steps and problems of full-color printing. Readers lacking this background will not be able to absorb the meaning and implications of many points discussed in the following.*

Full-color printing is here discussed under the following six main headings: (1) Photomechanical proofing; (2) Standardization and controls for full-color printing; (3) The scope of color proofing with ink; (4) Proofing on proof presses; (5) Proofing on production presses; and (6) Proof plate and press plate. Each of these six topics is individually treated in the course of this study.

PHOTOMECHANICAL PROOFING

Photomechanical proofing for full-color printing utilizes of course many techniques of single-color and multicolor proofing. These are described in the preceding section of our study. Here, we do not need to repeat this information but will rather concentrate on photomechanical proofing techniques in color. The color-separated and color-corrected material from which the plates are made is, as the informed reader knows, not in color but in the form of photographic images having different tonal values or densities of the black silver deposit. It is very difficult to interpret these black-tone images, or halftone images, as colors — and it is

even more difficult to "visualize" them as full-color reproductions. Experienced litho artists have acquired a measure of this ability, but it is nevertheless even for the most experienced, not possible to be sure and precise in their interpretations. The densitometer is in many cases the most reliable guide, but instrument readings are confined to very small areas.

It is easy to see why workers in the field have persistently tried to find ways for providing images in color that correspond to the resulting prints which will finally be made from corrected separations, after these have been converted into press plates and the latter have been printed. But, there is many a slip betwixt cup and lip, and full-color printing drinks from many different cups! For this reason, many systems that looked "ideal" to their proponents have come and gone in the years. At the time of this writing, several systems are on the market. Here we will discuss two types of such systems: (1) colored-diazo transparencies; and (2) pigmented light-sensitive materials. It must be emphasized that all such systems have their value in the hand of the well-informed worker who knows their nature and limitations. But none of these systems produce true replicas of the future press print. They provide guides for the litho artist or color etcher but nothing else.

Colored-Diazo Transparencies. Diazo materials are, as you remember, direct positive materials meaning that they produce positive images from photographic positives. For this reason, diazo transparencies are not suitable with negatives but are mainly used with continuous-tone positives before they are screened or with halftone positives to be used for deep-etch plates.

Colored-diazo films are available in a variety of colors; the diazo films closest in color to the inks selected for a specific job are used for the proofing of this job. You notice that we speak of diazo films closest in color to the selected ink colors. Keep this in mind: Diazo films are close but almost never a match of our inks. The importance of this fact must not be forgotten.

The detail of operation is not presented in this part of our study but can be found in the following resource

* For a discussion of process color work, see chapters six, seven and eight of this Manual.

section. Here we merely give a brief summary. The diazo film is first flashed in a vacuum-printing frame for a pre-determined time. Then it is exposed together with its own color-separation positive, e.g., the yellow diazo film is exposed with the yellow positive printer, the magenta with the magenta printer, and so forth. Development takes place either in a diazo machine or in another suitable manner by impingement of ammonia fumes on the exposed diazo films.

Diazo color proofing is not a replica of the future print, nor can it be — of course — a replica of the original. Diazo proofs are guides and must be evaluated with their limitations in mind. One of them is the difference in color, another is the fact that three or four diazo films are put over each other for viewing. The color of the transparent material has a graying effect as you can easily see by comparing densitometric readings of the paper on which the job will be printed and of the paper plus the three or four diazo foils, read in a totally clear area.

Pigmented Light-Sensitive Materials. Pigmented light-sensitive materials are used for photomechanical color proofing of negatives. Such materials are available in a variety of colors and different tradenames. Photomechanical color proofing with pigmented light-sensitive materials avoids the superimposing of several plastic sheets because here each colored material lies directly on the base plastic and on the preceding color layer.

Pigmented light-sensitive materials are sold as liquids suitable for whirling. Color proofing takes place on a sheet of white opaque plastic. This white opaque plastic — mainly a vinyl — stands for the paper to be used in printing. The different pigmented solutions stand for the printing inks; the negative stands for the press plate and whirling; exposing and developing stand for making the impression in the press.

First the solution colors are compared with the ink colors to be used on a specific job; then the closest pigmented light-sensitive solutions are selected. Now a sheet of clear white plastic is put in the whirler and coated with that color solution corresponding to the first ink color of the future run, yellow, for example. After coating, the plastic sheet is exposed with the yellow printer to arc light in a vacuum-printing frame. Then the exposed sheet is developed with ammoniated water. The image appears in yellow, and is an assimilation of the yellow to be printed on the press.

After the development of the first color coating, the plastic sheet is again put in the whirler and again coated, this time, of course, with the next color solution, the magenta, for example. Exposure and development follow with the result that both colors are now deposited over each other in direct contact on the plastic sheet. The procedure is repeated as often as is necessary; in three-color printing, the cyan is the last; in four-color printing, it is followed by the black.

The finished result is a photomechanical color proof that serves many useful purposes if its limitations are understood and if it is interpreted with them in mind. For detailed instructions of execution see the resource section of this chapter.

STANDARDIZATION AND CONTROLS FOR FULL-COLOR PRINTING

Full-color printing or process work is the most intricate and the most sensitive kind of printing. This holds true for all branches of the industry, letterpress and gravure not less than lithography. In full-color printing we reproduce an enormous gamut of colors by the use of very few inks — three, four, five or six — as the case may demand. It is not possible to produce faithful reproductions of full-color jobs unless every detail is very strictly controlled. If a single element is left uncontrolled, the harm resulting must obviously be much greater in full-color printing than in any other kind of printing where we do not try to obtain such a wide range of effects with such a narrow selection of means.

This study is not concerned with the fundamental problems of full-color printing. Here it is assumed that the reader is familiar with the subject. For the sake of continuity and completeness, several points bearing on the subject matter of this study of full-color proofing are briefly discussed. They are six: (1) The role of paper and inks; (2) The GATF Sensitivity Guide; (3) The GATF Color Chart; (4) The GATF Color Test Strips; (5) The use of the densitometer; and (6) The comparative viewing of original proofs and press sheets.

The Role of Paper and Ink. In the context of our subject we are not concerned with the general problems of ink and paper as related to full-color printing. Here we are only concerned with the correspondence of proofing and production. Many and diversified reasons may move the management of a lithographic plant to select a given set of process-color inks as standard for this particular plant. In the proofing department we are not concerned with these reasons, but we are vitally concerned with staying within these selected standard inks. It cannot be said too often that a set of standard inks is an absolute necessity if full-color work is to be produced and proofed with economy, accuracy, and reliability time and time again.

While the foregoing is true, in general, it is based on the comparatively young concept of using "balanced" process colors in printing because this simplifies the problem of color correction. However, this concept may be comprised when unusual demands in a specific job either preclude use of the "standard" set of balanced inks or require use of specially formulated inks to meet either end use demands of the particular piece of printing, or the nature of an unusual surface on which the printing is done. In such cases, both the inks and paper to be used for the job should also be used for proofing. Whenever possible and practical, color proofs should be pulled using the combination of special inks and papers. This can serve to guide the preparatory department during color-separation, masking and/or hand color-correction. During such proofing it is possible that the ink maker may better see where he can come closer to a balanced set of process colors without sacrificing the special demands which required unusal ink formulations in the first place.

If the process inks change from job to job, each full-color job, and each proofing with it, becomes a new venture into the unknown. Such ventures may appeal to people who are bored by the humdrum existence of our times. But lithographers do not fall into this category, for them — and particularly for those engaged in full-color work — life is one challenge after another. They aim at speed, accuracy and reliability, and therewith at low cost, more than at a romantic experience.

Nor should we forget the role of paper over the so very important part played by the inks. Every job must be proofed on the paper on which it will finally be printed. It is impossible to enumerate and describe all the points where paper tells in a printed job. But things become very simple the moment you see the same job proofed on different papers. Plates, inks, press, the work itself can all be the same — but you see a world of difference if you look at proofs pulled on different papers. If proofing is to be representative for final production, the paper must be the same here and there.

The GATF Sensitivity Guide. The GATF Sensitivity Guide should be incorporated into all proof plates in such a manner that it will appear in all colors on the finished proof. The presence of the Sensitivity Guide in all colors enables you to judge whether all plates were produced in a standardized manner. Standardization by means of the Sensitivity Guide is a must for reliable plate production. The GATF Sensitivity Guide is the most valuable tool in every effort of compensating for variations between proof plates and press plates. Additional information on this subject can be found in the "Platemaking Department" chapter of this manual and in the GATF Bulletin #215, "The Sensitivity Guide."

The GATF Color Chart. With the publication of the GATF Color Chart the industry has a very simple and most effective tool for standardizing proofing of full color work. The proofing department should use the sets of positives and negatives supplied by GATF and make proof plates from them. The proof plates made should include every kind of plate made in a particular plant. These various proof plates should be proofed with the standard set of inks as they are selected for a specific plant on all kinds of paper used for full color printing in this plant.

The proofs should be combined into proof-books by kind of plate and kind of paper; they can be bound in looseleaf binders for protection. These books of progressive proofs should become the standard source of reference for all future jobs. Such proof-books are standard setting for everybody concerned, for the proofer, but not less for photographers, color etchers, platemakers, and pressmen, all of whom can use them for visual or densitometric comparisons. For further information on this subject see GATF Bulletin #320, "The GATF Color Chart Book."

The GATF Color Strip. The GATF Color Strip, as described in the already mentioned Bulletin #320, contains 21 blocks. Listed from left to right they are:

1, Solid yellow.
2, Solid yellow and solid magenta producing red.
3, Solid magenta
4, Solid magenta and solid cyan producing blue or purple.
5, Solid cyan.
6, Solid cyan and solid yellow producing green.
7, Solid cyan, magenta and yellow producing black or brown.
8, Solid cyan, magenta, yellow and black producing maximum black.
9, Black
10, 11 and 12, three-quarter, one-half and one-quarter tints of yellow.
13, 14 and 15, three-quarter, half and quarter tints of magenta.
16, 17 and 18, three-quarter, half and quarter tints of cyan.
19, 20 and 21, three-quarter, half and quarter tints of equal dot sizes of yellow, magenta, and cyan.

The inclusion of the GATF test strip on every proof makes it possible to check ink-film thickness and ink distribution across the sheet either by eye or with the aid of a reflection densitometer. Variations in ink balance on the press are immediately visible by studying the last three blocks, #19, #20 and #21 on the Color Strip. These three blocks are, as already listed, the three-quarter, one-half, and one-quarter equal dot-size blocks of yellow, magenta and cyan. The GATF Color Strip should, of course, also be put in the press plate and appear on the press sheet. By assembling duplicate films a row of test strips can be made to print across the back of the sheet.

The Use of the Densitometer. The densitometer plays a very important role in evaluating proofs and press sheets. For this purpose a reflection densitometer is needed. It is used for checking the thickness of the ink film during proofing by reading the solid squares of the yellow, magenta and cyan color strip with the blue C5 or C47 filter, the green B58 filter and the red A25 filter, respectively. It is, of course, understood that every ink must be read with the complementary filter.

By keeping records of these densitometric readings it becomes possible to set densitometric or numerical standards for each color ink. Proofing has then the task of taking the readings of the color blocks, adjusting the ink until the proper reading is obtained and making sure that the readings are uniform throughout the sheet.

There should be no tampering with the ink balance by running different amounts of ink in different areas of the sheet. If the positives or the plate is faulty it should be changed, but the amount of ink being run on the sheet should be the same throughout the total sheet area for every color. Many plants use a long color bar for each color across the back of the proof sheet; the GATF Color Strip is preferable because it occupies less space and because it affords additional information. (See GATF Bulletin #320 for further detail.)

The Comparative Viewing of Originals, Proofs and Press Sheets. The lithographer and his customer should have an understanding on the light in which the reproduction of a full-color job, in particular a job made from color transparencies, is to be viewed. Here we are not very much concerned with the best kind of light and the most advisable color temperature of a light source; here we want to emphasize the necessity for using the same light source by customer and lithographer for the viewing of all elements having a role in full-color printing.

Eastman Kodak's #1 viewer is inexpensive, not heavy and easy to carry around. The Macbeth (Philadelphia, Pa.) Chromocritic Viewer contains two light sources that can be mixed and measured and the pair of readings can be given to the lithographer by his client for each color transparency. This enables the lithographer to view the job in the same light in his own plant.

Most plants use various kinds of daylight fluorescent lighting for the viewing of artwork and proofs. It is better to depend on artificial light for this purpose because daylight varies too much. Care should be taken to make certain that the same kind of lighting is used throughout all departments where color work is produced in a lithographic plant.

The Macbeth Corporation of Newburg, New York, sells a packaged lighting system usable for viewing transparencies as well as proofs or press sheets. This seems — to date — to be the best approach to the problem because it makes it possible to view transparencies, artwork, proofs and press sheets under similar lighting conditions.

THE SCOPE OF COLOR PROOFING WITH INK

Color proofing with ink is a complex subject with many ramifications. It is full of ifs and buts because it has so very many variables. Our first step in the study of color proofing with ink consists in isolating four groups of variables for an introductory discussion. These four kinds of variables are: (1) The plate used in proofing; (2) The press used for proofing; (3) The purpose of proofing; and (4) The evaluation of the proof. Each of these four kinds of variables is now discussed in some detail.

The Plate Used in Proofing. We distinguish between two kinds of plates for proofing: (1) The unit or intermediate plate; and (2) the final press plate. The unit plate or intermediate plate is a plate made for the purpose of proofing exclusively. In full color proofing we mean, of course, a set of plates when we speak of a plate. Unit plates proof the result of color separation and color correction. In many cases the final press plate is not made by the same organization that took care of color separation and color correction. This situation prevails very often when a trade shop is involved. The trade shop supplies a set of color-corrected halftone negatives or positives to the lithographer who will print the job. The final press plate is very often not supplied by the trade shop but made in the lithographic plant. This is particularly so when jobs are printed "many-up."

In the case of such jobs we may have several proofings for the same job. The first proof may be a unit or intermediate proof. This proof may or may not be made in the lithographer's own plant. Assuming the best case, namely that the first proof needs no corrections and that it is enthusiastically approved by the customer, the final press plate is made from the same negatives or positives which were used for the making of the intermediate plate.

The final press plate can have a variety of proofing experiences. We must number the cases because they become too unwieldy by themselves. We distinguish four possibilities: (1) The final press plate is not proofed at all; (2) The final press plate is used for preliminary proofing, independent of presswork; (3) The final plate is proofed as part of presswork; and (4) The final plate is proofed two times, preliminary to presswork as well as in the course of presswork. These four possibilities do not include makeover and other contingencies.

The last ten years has witnessed an enormous change in lithographic plate-making materials and techniques. While this has been a boon to the industry, it has tended to complicate proofing. This is especially so where proofs are not merely a guide to how the final job should look but an absolute standard to be followed. The problem of matching wet-printing to dry proofing has always been recognized. But the problem of matching press prints made with one type of plate on the press, to proof prints made with another type of plate has not been carefully thought out except in rare instances. This problem has been aggravated by the practice of using low-cost platemaking materials and techniques in proofing jobs which are to be run from deep-etch or other long-life plates on the press.

A bit of thought, planning, and some cost can reduce this problem to a minimum, and often eliminate it completely. Despite the wide variety of plates available, most plants do standardize on from one to three plates depending on the range of work done in the plant. For an investment in a proof plate and several press plates made up of a series of halftone scales, or the GATF Color Chart, the differences between a proof print and press print can be calculated. This in turn serves to guide the proofer in how to distort his plates and proofing techniques to match what the press plate and press combination will produce under production conditions.

The Press Used for Proofing. Proofing can be done on five kinds of presses. Three of these are proof presses and two are production presses. The three kinds of proof presses are discussed in the unit on proof presses; the two kinds of production presses are: (1) production presses used for proofing but not for the final running of a job; and (2) production presses used for the final running of a job.

The variety of proofing techniques becomes clear — or should we rather say bewildering — when we combine the possibilities discussed under the preceding heading with those of presses used in proofing. Then we arrive at the five following major groups: (1) Unit plates proofed on proof presses; (2) Unit plates proofed on production presses; (3) Press plates proofed on proof presses; (4) Press plates proofed preliminarily on production presses; and (5) Press plates proofed as part of presswork. Each of these groups will be discussed in the course of this study.

The Purpose of Proofing. Proofing of full-color jobs has the same purposes as proofing of single and multicolor jobs, namely, proofing for internal and for external use as well as proofing for accuracy. But full-color proofing has one additional purpose which is so important that many people believe it to be the only purpose of full-color proofing — this purpose is, of course, color fidelity. Color fidelity is the most important single feature of a finished full-color job. But it is by no means the only feature of importance. In ganged-up jobs accuracy of register is just as important if not more so than fidelity of color. Accuracy of register is a paramount requirement in all jobs for packaging, particularly if the press sheet must be diecut in the course of production. This kind of accuracy must, of course, be incorporated into the final press plate.

The Evaluation of the Proof. Whatever other purpose a proof may have, in some manner it must also serve as a guide for final production — if this is not its main purpose. It is most important to understand that various kinds of proofs must be evaluated in various ways. Lithographic production is a very intricate and sensitive process. Variables in plate, ink, press and atmospheric conditions, all express themselves in the finished product. Whether lithography is more sensitive than other high-speed color printing processes or not is a moot question that has no bearing on the subject of our discussion. Here we want to point out that great care and circumspection is needed for highest quality results. Lithography has demonstrated its capabilities time and time again and has therewith attested to the high qualities of its craftsmen, their sense of judgment, and their concern for very small detail. A proof will serve its purpose better, the better informed the people are who must read and understand it. You will read more on this subject as our discussion progresses.

In recent years, there has been considerable increase in knowledge concerning full-color reproduction. Coupled with this there have evolved improved inks, especially in the area of process colors. These two factors among others, have made it possible to vary color sequences when running. Sequences are varied not only to meet the color demands of a specific job, but to accomodate differences due to running dry or wet, or a combination of these. In some cases, color sequences may be determined by the type of press being used. This is especially true with some of the newer two-color presses which pose different trapping problems than older, conventional press designs.

PROOFING ON PROOF PRESSES

Three kinds of presses are available for proofing of lithographic plates: (1) Hand proof presses; (2) Power proof presses; and (3) Automatic proof presses. Each of them is briefly described in the following:

The Hand Proof Press. The hand proof press is a simple machine made up of two metal beds positioned side by side. Two gear racks are so situated that a rubber-covered cylinder can be guided by hand back and forth across both, carrying ink from the plate attached to one bed to a sheet of paper located on the other.

The plate is lightly dampened with a sponge and while still wet with water, ink is applied with a hand roller. When the plate is fully charged with ink, the excess water is fanned dry and the cylinder is rolled over the plate bed. Here the ink impression is picked up on the rubber blanket

cylinder as it rolls over the sheet of paper on the impression bed and leaves the ink image there.

The dampening and inking operation has to be repeated for each sheet to be printed. When hand proofing a four-color job, fifty sheets is the usual number used. This number should be sufficient to yield two proof-books and half a dozen proofs for the customer.

The Power Proof Press. The power proof press is operated in the same way as the hand proof press, but the movement of the blanket cylinder back and forth from plate to paper is motor driven. Dampening and inking is still done by hand.

There are two advantages in the use of a power proof press: (1) The rate of speed the blanket cylinder moves from plate to paper has some bearing on print quality and ink-film thickness. The power press enables the proofer to maintain a uniform printing speed and consequently higher quality and more uniform proofs. (2) The increased efficiency of the power press makes longer proofing runs possible.

The Automatic Proof Press. The automatic proof press prints from two flatbeds just as do the two already described presses, but now the inking and dampening systems are automatic just as they are on production presses. The automatic proof press has a set of dampening rollers and a water fountain, a set of ink rollers and an ink fountain. Uniformity of proof sheets is assured and production speed is increased enough to make short edition runs possible. Sheets are hand-fed, however. The speed of an automatic proof press is consequently much slower than that of a production press.

The usual proofing procedure in use in most plants is to proof color work on proofing equipment smaller than the final press size. When full-size press plates are made after proofs have been okayed, the register and color accuracy of these press plates can only be checked by going to press.

An automatic proof press large enough to accommodate full-size press plates can be used to check their register and color accuracy without taking up valuable production press time.

PROOFING ON PRODUCTION PRESSES

Proofing on production presses can be divided into two groups: (1) Proofing of unit plates; and (2) proofing of the final press plate.

Proofing on Unit Plates. A single-color press, generally a smaller one than the final production press, is set aside for proofing. This press is used in the same way as any of the previously described flatbed proof presses. Here, too, units or section of a job are proofed for color and register. These units or sections are later stripped and assembled for photocomposing onto the final press plates.

Proofing of the Final Press Plates. In this kind of proofing, a set of finished press plates is proofed preliminary to the press run. Preliminary proofing will be done for particularly fussy jobs or for particularly long runs. Proofing of final press plates can be handled in several ways.

On single-color presses there is no other choice but to proof all four plates in succession; generally the order is (1) yellow, (2) magenta, (3) cyan, and (4) black. On two-color presses, however, it is very often possible to use a technique similar to the "strike-sheet" described under the heading of "Special Proofing Techniques" in the preceding section of this study. On two-color presses the plates to be run as the third and fourth (the third and fourth *down* plates to use the pressman's language) are put first on the press. After printing sufficient sheets for register and uniform color, the press is worked up and the plates exchanged for the first and second plates of the job. Thereby it is possible to check all four colors before the beginning of the run. If everything is okay the saving is considerable because the first and second plates are already on the press, ready to run.

PROOF PLATE AND PRESS PLATE

The result of printing a plate on a hand proof press and on a production press is not the same. The press plate tends to print heavier than the proof plate, particularly when the proof plate was printed on a hand proof press. This fact must not be ignored in the planning of the press plate. If it is neglected, you are headed for trouble: Either the whole set of plates must be re-made or every plate must be run with less ink than normal. The result of running with insufficient ink is, of course, a flat and unattractive job.

The technique whereby you compensate for this consists in making press plate and proof plate intentionally different. The proof plate is made full and the press plate is made sharp. An example explains what we mean by full and sharp. In the case of deep-etch, the proof plate is made to have a reading of 5 to 6 on the GATF Sensitivity Guide. The press plate will be made to have a reading of 8 or 9 on the same guide.

If a color is too heavy or too full on proofing, the positives should either be re-etched or made over in order to obtain a lighter image. It is not advisable to re-make the plate from the same positives and to reduce the image by overexposure.

Another point worth remembering is the difference between camera positives and contact positives. On contact positives there is very little halation present around each dot. Small variations in plate exposure have, therefore, little effect on the dot size of the plate. This is not the case when camera positives are used because camera positives have a softer dot formation; press plates made from camera positives are very noticeably different if made with different exposure times. It is therefore a good principle to use contact positives for platemaking and to stay away from camera positives. The problem of matching proof sheets and press sheets is thereby greatly simplified.

Lithographic Presswork

Section One: Introduction to Presswork

In all the graphic arts, with only a few exceptions, the equipment which produces the salable sheets is the focal point of a particular process. This is true even though the printed or lithographed sheets are very often processed in some finishing steps, and even though the finishing may be an expensive procedure during which the appearance of the lithographed sheet may be completely changed in order to attain its final product form. All preparatory steps, while they are designed to utilize as much as possible the inherent advantages of the lithographic process, are determined nevertheless largely by the capacity of the pressroom equipment. It is true that the choice of press may depend on the demands of the finishing processes. However, once this choice has been made, all further activity is aimed at deriving maximum output from the lithographic press at the least possible cost.

This chapter is devoted to an analysis of the lithographic offset press. The stress will be on the general capabilities and characteristics of the lithographic offset press, and how it functions as a part of this closely integrated process.

This presentation considers the many types of presses and their particular features, but stops short of one particular subject: No attempt is made to indicate the superiority or inferiority of various press makes. Discussions of this kind are here omitted; they are left to the buyer and seller of printing equipment.

This chapter describes the press in terms of the principles and operation of feeding methods, registering systems, insertion devices, inking, and dampening mechanisms, rollers, blankets, deliveries and printing units. But we are no less concerned with the many control methods used throughout the printing operation. Our description will not be made in the sense of an instructional manual for prospective operators, but rather for the purpose of imparting general information on what to expect from a press, how to achieve those expectations, and which factors to consider when planning the purchase of a lithographic offset press.

Omission of the small "duplicator" type of offset press is not due to an oversight. It is admitted that such presses are capable of doing an excellent job in their own field, and are even used for fine work in some special cases. The fact remains, however that they are essentially office equipment replacing the stencil duplicators, rather than production machines for a commercial printing plant. There is no denying that they are limited in ink-covering power, impression rigidity, and pinpoint register when compared to the production type of equipment.

It will be obvious that the writer deliberately avoids the use of the term "offset" when discussing our printing process. The reason is that "offset" as such merely describes one *method* by which lithography can be produced. The "offset method" can be, and is indeed, used in other printing processes as well — in both relief and intaglio printing, for example. Therefore the distinguishing characteristic is not offset, but lithographic or lithographic-offset. As the offset principle is the most common one in lithography this chapter discusses primarily, presses which produce lithography by the offset method.

It is customary to discuss presswork under the three separate headings of makeready, operation and maintenance. From a management point of view this is essential, in order to accurately allocate costs and estimate selling price. In a discussion such as this, however, it is impossible to draw a sharp line of demarcation between these three classes of work. Is the checking and setting of cylinder pressures, for example, better discussed under maintenance or makeready? Or, take the case of a job which is already running but not printing as it should, and where it is discovered that the pressure between plate cylinder and blanket cylinder is not quite right. Is the checking and adjusting part of makeready or of operation? For the sake of readability as well as efficient production, all aspects of getting good quality and high production out of a lithographic offset press must be considered in every single step of presswork: during checking, adjusting and setting of the press no less than while getting the press ready to run; during the running no less than at the final delivery of the job out of the pressroom.

Before going any further, it should be understood that the material in this section covers specific points concerning generally accepted principles of pressmanship. However, the details of operating a particular press cannot be included here. Such information can be found in the manufacturers' instruction manuals.

It should also be kept in mind that the writer's point of view demands unceasing efforts of everybody concerned to come as close to perfection as is mechanically and humanly possible. This may sound at first glance like a blue-sky illusion on the possibilities of practical operation. However, the writer firmly believes — and has so proven through many years of practical printing experience — that *it does not take any longer to do the job right than it does to do the job in a slipshod manner.* In the long run, it always costs less; and costs are, in today's competitive world, of paramount importance for the prospering and growth of every lithographic business.

Section Two: Describing a Lithographic Press

In general, lithographic offset presses are described by using as criteria their size, number of colors, sheet or roll feed, and whether or not they are perfecting.

Size. When the size of a press is stated, reference is being made to either the maximum size sheet that can pass through the press, or the largest optimum size. Largest optimum size is seldom more than one-half inch smaller than the absolute maximum size, and almost always in the longer dimension. This dimension is the one parallel to the axis of the press, sometimes described as the "across-the-cylinder" direction. Take, for example, the ATF "Chief 22" which handles a maximum size sheet of 17½" x 22½". Its optimum size is 17" x 22". The range of standard sizes in lithographic offset presses, other than duplicators, runs from a 14½" x 20½" capacity to 54" x 77". Special presses have been built in larger sizes, but they are not available as standard models.

Web-fed press sizes are generally stated in much the same way as sheet-fed presses. However, while sheet-fed press sizes are given as the maximum size sheet which can be fed through the press, all these presses can handle sheets which are smaller in both directions. For example, a 17½" x 22½" press can handle a sheet as small as 8½" in the around-the-cylinder direction and 11" in the across-the-cylinder dimension. A web-fed press is quite different; the around-the-cylinder direction, referred to as the "cut-off," is fixed. The across-the-cylinder direction is usually given as the maximum width roll which can be handled. For example, 22 5/16" x 38" press will deliver a sheet (or signature) exactly 22 5/16" in the around-the-cylinder direction with the 38" dimension flexible up to a maximum of 38". While in most cases the shorter dimension stated is the cut-off length, this is not always the case.

Number of Colors. When discussing a press in terms of "number of colors," reference is being made to the number of printing units, if it is a sheet-fed press. It is understood, of course, that each printing unit will be run with a different color and that the number of colors describes how many separate colors can be printed on the sheet with one pass through the press. It is obvious, of course, that a "split" ink fountain on one or more of the units results in more "colors" being layed down during one pass through the press. The considerations in such cases must then include ability of the particular press to handle the job requirements and the imposition.

The design of multi-color presses has followed two basic approaches. As the lithographic process grew, multi-color presses developed primarily by assembling single-color units in tandem with transfer devices between units. This was originally available only in larger press sizes, and the larger sized multi-color presses are still designed this way. Smaller size multi-color presses, which have come into extremely wide use during the past decade, are built as integrally-built two-color units. Two such units are set up in tandem with a transfer device between them to become a four-color press. Three such units become a six-color press.

The range of colors on most presses used for the general run of lithographic work is from single color to six colors. In the metal decorating field there are presses which "roller-coat" a lacquer or base tint on the metal blank before it is passed into the first printing unit. There are, however, presses in existance which are described as eight-color presses. Before discussing this further, let us first consider the last two items previously listed as possible criteria when describing lithographic presses.

Feeding. One criterion for describing a press is whether the press handles sheets or rolls of paper. This criterion designates whether the press moves cut sheets through the feeder, or is fed by threading a web of paper from a roll through the press. Hence "web press" or "roll-fed" are the common terms for a press which prints on paper fed

Courtesy of The Miehle Co.

A Six-Color Sheet-Fed Press

directly from a roll. Sheet-fed presses which utilize a roll sheeter in place of or to supplement a sheet feeder, are best described as "roll-fed through a sheeter." This terminology leaves much to be desired, but as this feeding technique becomes more widely used, a less confusing description may develop.

Perfecting. The last criterion to be considered is that of perfecting. A perfecting press is one which prints on both sides of the paper in one pass through the press. Perfecting presses may be sheet- or roll-fed, single-color or multicolor. Most web-fed presses are perfecting multicolor presses of the blanket-to-blanket design. However, if equipped with the necessary white-roll stands, these presses can be used as single-color perfecting. For example, a four-unit blanket-to-blanket press can run four colors on

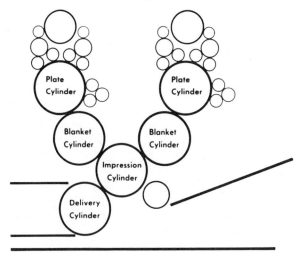

Schematic of a Perfecting Press.

both sides of a single web (split-fountain running is not being considered here), or this same press can run one color on both sides of four separate webs if the press is equipped with four white-roll stands. Between these two

Courtesy American Type Founders

A "Two-over-Two" Web Press. In this case instead of running two colors on both sides of a single web, two webs are being printed with one color on both sides. Note the folder set-up for a typical publication installation.

extremes a variety of combinations is possible on the same press.

Most sheet-fed perfecting presses are basically one-color presses. Interesting combinations, however, are becoming available. In one instance, it is possible to use the same press as a two-color (on one side of the sheet), or as a one-color perfecting press. In another case, single-color and perfecting units are tied together in such a way as to produce both perfecting and color during one pass of the sheet through the press.

Terminology. The terms used up to this point to describe a press are both generally known and yet somewhat arbitrarily employed by this writer. There are a number of reasons considered valid by him for this. In the first place more and more presses are being designed and built to do a special job or a special type of printing. In the second place, presses may be described with respect to special auxiliary features in addition to the four criteria used in the preceding paragraphs. And, in the third place, there are many variations and combinations possible within the basic criteria. For example, mention was made previously of a six-color press. This can be a sheet-fed press which prints six colors in one pass of the sheet through the press, but it can also be a six-color roll-fed perfecting press, which prints four colors on one side of the web and two on the reverse side during one pass of the paper through the press. Or we can have a five-unit drum-type press running from a half-width roll with a "double-ender" principle, printing five colors on one side and five on the reverse side using split fountains of all five units. And so, ad infinitum.

Common and Technical Designations. The matter of describing a press in greater detail by reference to special auxiliary features can also become complicated because of the myriad of combinations possible. Some of the simple, more frequent descriptions state whether a sheet-fed press feeds from a pile or feeds continuously (from a ramp), or whether the press delivers sheets in a single or double pile. But whether a perfecting press prints blanket-to-blanket; or whether a multicolor press uses a common impression cylinder, goes beyond the commonly known and carries us into the realm of technical and engineering detail. These points, too, will be covered later in our chapter.

Auxiliary Features On Web Presses. There is one particular time when it is important to describe a press with reference to its special auxiliary features. This is the case when web-fed web presses are being discussed. There it is important to know immediately — in addition to size, colors and perfecting — the manner of delivery and what special attachments exist between the last lithographic unit and the actual delivery. Special attachments may include such items as perforators, slitters, numbering heads, punches, etc. Delivery may cover such systems as re-wind, sheeter, fold, fan-fold; or the subject may even lead us into a completely different operation, such as a continuous cutter-creaser attachment. These attachmens will help produce such items as multiple forms, interleaved sets, spot-carboned leaves, cellophane windowed pieces, insertions, cartons, etc.

Auxiliary Features On Sheet-Fed Presses. Such features are limited, up to this time. Units are added to lithographic offset presses which will perform such auxiliary operations as bronzing, perforating, slitting, imprinting, numbering, die-cutting, etc.

Section Three: Feeders

The lithographic offset press, in common with printing presses in the gravure and relief processes, can be either sheet-fed or roll-fed. Roll feeding, as generally thought of, is in Section Ten of this chapter as part of the web-offset press discussion. In this section we are therefore, exclusively concerned with sheet feeding. Our presentation in this section is divided into two main parts. First there are presented the different types of feeders; then the setting of feeders is discussed.

TYPES OF FEEDERS

Sheet feeding is accomplished in one of two ways, either as successive-sheet feeding or stream feeding. Either of these two methods can be combined with one of three means in which the paper can be placed in the press. These are known as continuous feeding, pile feeding, and roll feeding. Our presentation is therefore further divided into the following five different subjects: (1) Successive-sheet feeding; (2) Stream feeding; (3) Continuous feeding; (4) Pile feeding; and (5) Roll feeding. Each of these is now presented individually.

Successive-Sheet Feeding. In this type of feeding the top sheet is separated from the paper supply (almost always a pile) and advanced to the feed board, table, tapes or ramp (depending on feeder design). The following

A Successive-Sheet Feeder — One sheet on the ramp.

sheet is not separated from the pile or main supply until the tail end of the preceding sheet has cleared the advancing mechanism. There is therefore a distinct space and time interval between sheets. In successive-sheet feeders the original advancing of the sheet almost always takes place at the gripper edge of the paper. The significant point to observe in this type of feeder is that *the sheet must travel forward*

at approximately the same speed as the press operates, since one full sheet is advanced at a time to the registering and/or insertion device.

The speed of the moving sheet is, consequently, very rapid, and special attention must be paid — especially on lightweight, large-size sheets — to holding the sheet down during forwarding, and to keeping it moving at press speed without any drag or cocking. Successive-sheet feeders generally employ some kind of a "slow-down" or pre-register device just ahead of the registering or insertion point. Slow-downs or similar devices, therefore, are used to prevent the sheet from buckling or bouncing as a result of the momentum built up during the rapid speed of the forwarding operation.

A Stream Feeder — Note the overlap of sheets on the ramp; from front stops to forwarding wheels, generally four sheets.

Stream Feeding. In this system a continuous flow of sheets is separated from the supply (either a pile or a continuous flow from a ramp-and-drum device) and advanced to the forwarding mechanism. In stream feeding, however, the separation *and* original advancing of the sheet takes place at the back end of the paper. There are some exceptions to this general design. As soon as one sheet is advanced onto the forwarding devices the following sheet is separated and also advanced. Thus a number of sheets are moving forward all the time. The sheets therefore overlap each other by some part of their length, and the speed of forwarding is proportionately reduced in comparison with the forwarding speed on successive-sheet feeders.

Because of this over-lapping, as one sheet is drawn into the nip by the impression cylinder grippers, the following sheet has only several inches of travel to reach the registering device. This slow travel of the sheet to the registering position on stream feeders simplifies some of the sheet control problems prevalent on a successive-sheet feeding mechanism. Another important advantage of stream feeders is that preceding sheets themselves tend to control the following ones as a result of their large overlap.

The guide edges of each sheet are, to some extent under control of the preceding sheet almost to the very point of register. This coupled with the slow rate of travel almost completely eliminates the problem of bounce or buckle at the register point. The stream feeder is, at the time of this writing, used on almost all late model presses with the exception of the smaller ones.

In some cases the feeder is so designed that it can be converted very easily from successive-sheet feeding to stream feeding and vice versa depending on the needs of a particular job. This is a feature of some advantage when running heavy board stock.

Mention should be made of one precautionary, but debatable point with respect to stream feeders, whether pile or continuous. There appears to be a tendency for static to develop, especially when such a feeder is operating in a very dry pressroom. Such a pressroom, for example, is one located in a building which is heated in the winter but not humidified. Where it is ascertained that static is developing in the feeder, neutralizing bars should be installed.

Continuous Feeding. Continuous feeding as such is not new. Practically all modern folding machines are equipped with continuous feeders. These feeders, however, haven't proven practical for lithographic presses. They are not sufficiently flexible for the wide range of sheet calipers run on lithographic presses. On large-size presses, extra paper handlers are required to keep the press running continuously. In recent years, the need for continuous feeding has been met by making it possible to load a pile feeder while the press is running and bringing the fresh load into feeding position before the proceeding load has run out.

Courtesy of Harris-Seybold Co.

Rods in Place, New Skid Coming Up in a Feeder
Continuous

The fresh load is placed into elevating position when the preceeding load still has some time to run. By means of supplementary elevator bars, the weight of the small load is temporarily supported on rods inserted under or near the bottom of this load. The pile elevator bars are lowered to the fresh load and this is elevated up to the bottom of the preceeding load. The rods are withdrawn; there is now a single pile in the feeder. If care is used in this series of operations, all comparatively simple, there is no interruption to the running of the press.

While the advantage of increased productivity is self-evident, there are important advantages to continuous feeding that are overlooked by those contemplating the purchase of a modern lithographic press. The advantages referred to are lower spoilage and consistent quality. It is well-recognized that the more steadily a lithographic press runs, the easier it is to maintain consistent color. In critical work, it is not necessary to pull the off-color sheets which are produced as a new pile is started in a press not equipped for continuous feeding.

Rear View of a Typical Pile Feeder.

Pile Feeders. This type of feeder is simply described as its name is very indicative of its nature. Here, the paper to be run is piled on a platform in the press feeder. This pile must, of course, be straight and neat and it must be positioned in correspondence with the settings of the register and insertion devices and for placement of the sheet. All these points are covered more extensively in the discussion on the setting of feeders.

The pile feeder raises the paper automatically to a constant level during printing. As of this writing, the pile feeder is the most versatile and flexible method for handling sheets. The main disadvantage of the pile feeder lies in the fact that the press must be stopped for its loading. In very long runs this drawback is a very important one. In short run work where the total quantity of the paper to be lithographed does not exceed the capacity of the pile feeder this limitation does, of course, not count at all. Attempts to reduce this drawback to an irreducible minimum resulted in means for loading a succeeding pile in the press before one pile is exhausted. It is then possible to start the new pile with the loss of only seconds rather than minutes.

Sheet Feeding from Rolls. Of even more recent date is the development of sheet feeding directly from a roll. As everyone knows, paper is manufactured in rolls at the mill, and is converted into sheets thereafter. Then, if mill trimming is specified, the sheets are trimmed on one, two, three, or four sides as specified. One of the important advantages of roll-fed presses — web presses — is the fact that paper bought in rolls is significantly less costly than sheeted paper. Some plants buy paper in rolls and sheet the rolls in the plant. However, sheet-fed presses are the backbone of the lithographic industry and their flexibility is a factor which will, in all likelihood, keep them in this status.

The interest is, therefore, in how to cut costs on sheet-fed equipment. One way to do this is to replace our present feeders with sheeters. In this case, a roll of paper is placed into running position in a sheeter. There the web of paper is converted into individual sheets, and the cut sheets are fed directly into the press. In addition to the savings in paper costs, there accrues also the advantage of continuous operation. As we know, this advantage so far can only be realized where continuous feeding is used.

A disadvantage of sheeting directly on the press is that the paper will be passed through the press with the grain the short way. This is not good practice if the sheets will be put through a press more than once. Sheeters are being made available which are set at the side of the press. This makes possible cutting the sheets at a right angle to the press and therefore the cut sheets are actually being fed into the printing unit "grain long." It should also be borne in mind that the difference in cost between roll and sheet stock is about 12 percent. The higher cost of sheeted paper is due to the cost of inspecting and sorting as well as sheeting and trimming. Inspecting and sorting of paper may be important for certain classes of jobs. In these cases sheet-fed printing is, of course, indicated.

No further mention can be made here of sheet feeding on lithographic offset presses from rolls. This method is, at the time of this writing, still in the development stage. It can be said however, based on experience to date, that the method does show considerable promise and that it could very well become widely used, especially in the long-run field when web-press production is not feasible.

SETTING THE FEEDER

After the exposition of various types of feeders we turn to a discussion on the setting of feeders. Here we begin with the loading of a feeder and end at the point where the sheet is forwarded down to the guides and/or registering pre-registering devices. These are not included in our present discussion but treated in "Section Four: Guides, Grippers and Insertion Devices" following immediately after this section.

In this part of our presentation we are concentrating on the following three topics: (1) Loading the feeder; (2) Pile-height governor and sheet detector; and (3) Separating and forwarding.

Loading the Feeder. On smaller presses the paper is loaded into the feeder directly. On larger pile feeders a

platform or skid is piled with the paper, away from the press, and when required this skid is wheeled into the feeder. Also on these larger presses, the skids of paper, as received from the mill, may be wheeled directly into the feeder. In any of the above mentioned cases the side-guide edge of the sheet is placed in such a position as to reach the front guides or insertion devices within the area in which the side guide operates. For example, on a press

Loading a Pile Feeder.

equipped with a rotary (roller type) guide, the edge of the sheet must be between the lower roller or finger and upper roller so that the upper roller — when it comes down — can pinch the sheet and pull it against the face of the side guide.

There is either a pair of matching scales across the feed board near the side guide, and across the front of the feeder, on the feeder platform or simply a scribed centre-line. A side pile-guide is set at the point corresponding to the operating area of the side guide and the paper piled against it. Where the paper is being piled away from the

Sheet Separator — Note Combing Wheel.

press one of two methods may be used to pile the stock properly on the skid or platform. In one case, a vertical line is drawn on the wall or a specially set-up back jogging board. The skid is placed in such a way that its center matches the center of the sheet when measured from the vertical guide line. The other method is to build a piling jig similar to those used for (large volume) padding work.

In any case it is imperative that the pile be perfectly straight and even. At the gripper edge of the pile there must be no overhanging of mutilated edges. And the stock must be carefully and thoroughly winded, especially if the paper has gone through the press before and is now to receive a succeeding color and/or be backed up. The skid or platform is now positioned in the feeder and the chains and supporting bars fastened into operating position.

Sheet Separator Using Air Jets

At this point the pile is raised, in the manner prescribed by the manufacturer, to a point a little below the normal operating height. If the feeder is equipped with a side pile-guide on both sides of the pile, set the one away from the guide side against the pile. Now, set whatever devices, if any, are supplied for holding the back edge of the pile in place. Then position the separator and sheet advancing devices to the operating position recommended by the manufacturer. On smaller presses, where separating and advancing devices are one unit, there may be little or no setting required unless changing from a minimum size sheet to a maximum size. On other presses the separating device and back-edge pile controls may be one unit. At this point notice the contour of the pile, especially on presses with capacity for large sheets. The importance of this will be discussed later in this section.

Pile-Height Governor and Two-Sheet Detector. Start the press running at idling speed until the pile reaches its normal operating height. On all feeders this is automatic but requires proper setting of the pile-height governor in accordance with the manufacturers' instructions. Now, set the two-sheet detector device, sometimes called the "choke." This is done easiest by inching the press to the tripping position as indicated in the manufacturers' instruction book. Tear off a strip of the stock to be run, about two inches wide, and fold it over with an overlap of a few inches.

Next, insert the single end into the detecting device and adjust its clearance so that the single thickness slides through easily. Then, push the strip further until the double thickness of your stock is in the device. Finally, re-adjust the two-sheet detector until a single thickness *just* goes through, but a double thickness of paper jams or trips the device. The position of the two-sheet detector on stream feeders is usually such that in normal operation there are several sheets under the choke at the same time. In this case you set the device exactly as described but with the normal number of sheets in the choke under the test strip.

Separating and Forwarding. When automatic feeders were described earlier in this section it was stated that the feeder functions by accomplishing two things: (1) It separates the top sheet from the pile; and (2) It forwards the separated sheet to the guides and/or insertion device. In order to have the separator devices function properly, the pile must be at he proper height in the feeder, and the contour of the top of the pile reasonably flat. This is especially important on presses with the capacity to hande large sheets.

At this point the difference in feeders of various designs is most noticeable. The manufacturers' instructions must of course be followed in all cases. It is well, however, to keep in mind several principles which apply, generally speaking, to all feeders.

In the first case, separation and forwarding may be accomplished entirely by air. Air blast nozzles fluff the rear corners of several sheets on the top of the pile. Suckers drop down and pick the top sheet up. Another set of air nozzles comes under this top sheet and floats it on a cushion of air. Then the same suckers, or a set of separate forwarding suckers, guide the sheet into the forwarding devices at the top of the feed ramp.

On differently designed feeders — especially the larger ones — separation is started, generally, mechanically, at the rear corners of the sheet usually by a combing device of some kind. Then telescopic suckers come down and pick up the corners of the top sheet while it is being combed. At this point, blower tubes — shaped like a foot — descend

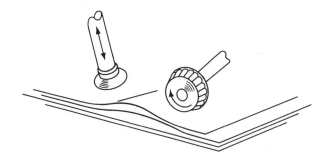

Schematic Showing Action of Combing Wheel.

and enter under the top sheet, resting firmly on the pile. Then, a blast of air from the blower feet separates the entire top sheet. This blast of air floats the sheet up to a second set of suckers while the first pair still have the sheet under control. The second set of suckers are the ones which generally advance the sheet to the forwarding mechanism.

While principles remain the same, there are considerable variations in the structure and operating details of the feeders supplied by the various manufacturers. Even within the line of presses of one manufacturer, there are wide differences—especially as between the larger and smaller presses. The brief descriptions above, of two basic types, apply generally to the larger presses. Most of the modern smaller presses use "centre" separation devices.

It is obvious that control of the amount of air and of the direction of the blower tubes or feet is critical. The sheet must be positively floated without riffling, waving or flapping. The sheet being forwarded must be completely separated from the pile so as not to drag the next sheet, or stumble on its leading edge, especially in feeders where no blower foot device is provided. The sheet must be under such positive and complete control that it reaches the forwarding devices at the right time and perfectly straight. If both of these conditions are not met, in the first instance proper timing of the sheet is lost, and in the second place a sheet coming down the ramp in a cocked position will either jam at the side-guide mechanism or reach the guides or insertion devices in such a way that it will jam and/or trip the press.

After the sheet is separated and advanced to the forwarding device, the press is inched and all parts of the device are checked for proper operation. The operator should especially note whether the sheet is coming down straight, whether it is balanced on the tapes, and whether it is being held down without dragging. The sheet is inched until its leading edge is in the side-guide mechanism. The operator notes whether it clears the side-guide face-plate but not by so much as to miss being guided. On all presses, except the smallest ones, there is provision for moving the pile slightly in either direction to make up for any error in judgment at the original setting of the side pile-guide. On the smaller presses the pile of stock can be pushed to the proper position without seriously upsetting the condition of the pile.

The sheet is advanced by continual inching, and the operator makes sure that it arrives into the guides or insertion device before the side guide starts its cycle of operation. The feeder has then accomplished its mission.

Section Four: Guides, Grippers and Insertion Devices

In the preceding section on feeders we were concerned with the separation of each sheet of paper from the pile, and with its forwarding to the registering position. Once this has been accomplished, the feeder has fulfilled its function. At this point, a completely different set of devices takes over control of the sheet. Among these devices we find great differences between equipment of various manufacturers as well as between some models of the same manufacture. Our presentation divides the subject into several groups. Our interest turns first to the most important problem of register and fit. Thereafter we review the main types of insertion devices, guides and grippers in general. A discussion of the setting of all these devices concludes our section on guides, grippers and insertion devices.

REGISTER AND FIT

Before going further it is necessary to clearly understand the true meaning and significance of register.

Register. As we use register in lithography we mean the positioning of the sheet with respect to the image on the blanket. Fit has a different meaning which is explained further down. During the registering operation, the press aligns the sheet in such a manner that when the impression-cylinder grippers take hold and draw the sheet through the printing nip, the front edge of the paper will be a set distance from the image. This distance is determined when the plate is clamped into proper position and the front guides set. In addition to the front edge of the paper, one side edge is also a fixed distance from the image edge. This distance is also determined when the plate is put on the press and the side guide set in its proper position. The purpose of all these operations is a most important one: Each and every sheet must be aligned *exactly* alike. With the sheets under proper control, and the registering devices properly set and operating, register will be accomplished.

Fit. Proper register does not guarantee "fit" but misregister makes the problem of fit a strictly academic subject. One can talk about fit but cannot do anything about it in such a case. The term fit is used to describe the *juxtaposition of all image elements in the printing area without regard to the sheet margin* (determined and maintained as a result of registering the plate and sheet). This is best clarified by using an example with figures.

Let us assume a job on the press whose front- and side-guide margins are exactly one inch. In running the job we check sheets, and each one has *exactly* these margins without *any* variation. The job is therefore registering. However, on checking further we note that the image on the plate measures 40 inches across the back edge, whereas measuring the image on the sheet shows a distance of 39.98 inches. We do not have fit. While this slight variation may not be significant on the average black-and-white job, it could be important if the job were a close tolerance business-machine form. This variation would certainly be noticeable on a four-color process job.

This section of our chapter is primarily devoted to the problem of register and how it is achieved on the modern lithographic offset press. Fit will be mentioned here once in a while, but the discussion of the overall problem is not in this section. Further discussion of fit can be found in the sections on "Cylinders," and "Running the Press" in this chapter, as well as in the "Ink and Paper" chapter in this Manual.

REGISTER AND INSERTION METHODS

In general, we can classify register and insertion methods in three groups: (1) The simple three-point guide system; (2) Feed-roll Insertion; and (3) Swing- or Transfer Gripper Insertion. It should be pointed out that the simple three-point guide system is not an insertion device. However, the system does fix the sheet in printing position just as is done for any insertion device. However, on presses equipped with insertion devices the positioning of the sheet before the insertion device starts its cycle of operation is generally referred to as "pre-registering." Therefore we will discuss the three-point register system from two points of view: (1) A simple three-point register system, where the impression-cylinder grippers *take* the sheet directly from the guides; and (2) Where the three-point register system pre-registers the sheet in proper position for an insertion device.

Three-Point Register System. In this method the sheet is forwarded to front guides (two to four, usually), and while it is held against the front guides a side guiding mechanism pushes or pulls the sheet into proper side alignment. In the simple three-point register system, the sheet is held in this position until the impression cylinder grippers take hold. At this time the front guides or stops are lifted out of the sheet's path of travel. As soon as the entire sheet clears the feed board the guides drop back into position to align the following sheet.

In the simple three-point register system, the guides are mounted on a shaft which is above the feed board. The guides can be moved sideways along this shaft in order to properly balance the particular size of the sheet being run. The guide itself is essentially a flat face plate. In the registering (lowered) position of this guide its bottom edge straddles a metal tongue protruding under the feed board, or a register plate. Very often the guide has built-in devices for preventing buckling of the sheets against the plate. Buckling happens either if the sheet comes down too fast or if the sheet is very lightweight. The guide may also have built-in slow-downs (they may be a separate mechanism), which not only prevent the sheet from buckling, but also prevent the bouncing of heavyweight or stiff sheets. Sheet detectors (not two-sheet detectors or chokes) may also be built into the guide; they trip the press if a sheet is not where it should be when the impression-cylinder grippers come into their taking position. The guide is designed for up and down adjustment along the tongue or register plate. This serves the purpose of obtaining desired position when only a small shift is required. Even though this adjustment is built into the guide, it should be used with great care. Any change in the guide affects the amount of gripper bite. Too much gripper bite may cause trouble when the sheet is transferred to the delivery-chain grippers. Too little gripper bite is not less dangerous; sheets may be pulled out of the grippers when going through the nip or when separating from the blanket after the impression has been transferred to them. If the sheet is too far out-of-square it may buckle against the side guide or be pulled away from the far stop by the action of a pull-guide.

Where the three-point register system is supplemented by an insertion device the general principle and construction are similar. However, in this case the front guides are generally constructed so as to drop *down* out of the forward path of the sheet *after* the grippers on the insertion device take hold of the sheet. Another point that should be noted in this case is the likelihood of less freedom for sideways movement of the guides. In the simple three-point register system, the position of the impression cylinder grippers is the principal limiting factor to such movement. With an insertion device, additional clearances must be taken into consideration which may seriously limit, if not completely prevent, such freedom of movement.

Feed-Roll System. In this system, the impression cylinder grippers do not take the sheet from the feed board. The device actually inserts the sheet into the grippers of the impression cylinder or an intermediate device. After the sheet is forwarded down the feed board, it is pre-registered against a number of stops (front guides) spaced across the entire width of the feed board. While the sheet is held against these stops, it is side-guided.

While the sheet is at rest, it is firmly gripped in its pre-registered position by being pinched between "upper" and

Courtesy Harris-Intertype Corp.

A Feed-Roll Insertion Device.

"lower" "feed rolls" or "cams." The front guides then drop down or lift up (whichever the case may be). As soon as they are clear one set of the feed rolls (upper or lower depending on individual press design) starts rotating and positively drives the sheet against gage pins (or stops) which are located on either an intermediate cylinder (sometimes called a feed or transfer cylinder) or the impression cylinder, depending on the model or make of press involved. These stops may be nothing more than slight lips protruding above the gripper pad. When the sheet is inserted into the grippers, it is held against these cylinder stops until the grippers have closed firmly on the sheet. At this instant, the low points of the upper feed-rolls have come around, and the sheet is completely under the control of the grippers. Where an intermediate feed or transfer cylinder is used between the feed board and the impression cylinder, complete control of the sheet is maintained by having the grippers of the intermediate device positively grip the sheet while the impression-cylinder grippers close on it. For a short distance of travel both sets of grippers are actually holding the sheet. This point is worthy of special note, because on all presses, where a sheet is being transferred from one set of grippers to another, transfer is never accomplished "on-the-fly." At some point during the transfer both sets of grippers are actually holding the sheet.

Swing-Feed or Transfer-Gripper System. The design of a swing- or transfer-gripper system is completely different from that of the feed-roll insertion devices. In this system, the sheet is forwarded down to the feedboard and brought to rest against front stops. Then is is side-guided. Here the similarity ends. After being properly guided, the sheet is picked up by a set of grippers usually mounted over the feed board and the front guides move out of the forward path of the sheet. This pick-up mechanism is called a swing-feed, transfer cylinder or transfer-gripper assembly. After the sheet has been picked up, the mechanism forwards the sheet and inserts it into the impression-cylinder grippers. In this system, too, positive control over the sheet is maintained during the transfer of the sheet from the insertion device to the impression cylinder.

Courtesy Miehle Printing Press & Mfg. Co.

A Swing-Feed or Transfer-Gripper Device.

SIDE GUIDES

Guides are divided into front and side guides. Front guides are classified as multiple-stop, or two-point drop

guides or stops. As we know, front guides may form part of insertion devices and are discussed under that heading. Side guides operate completely independently of the front guides or guiding device, and are the subject matter of the following presentation.

Neither the design of the side guide or the cycle of its operation are affected by the type of front guiding, insertion device, or gripper action on the press. Side guides can be described according to their motion or by the manner in which they operate. As far as their motion is concerned, side guides can be either push-guides or pull-guides. This is true disregarding the side edge (left or right) of the sheet to be guided. Some presses are so equipped that when one side guide is pulling, the guide on the opposite side may be set to push at the same time.

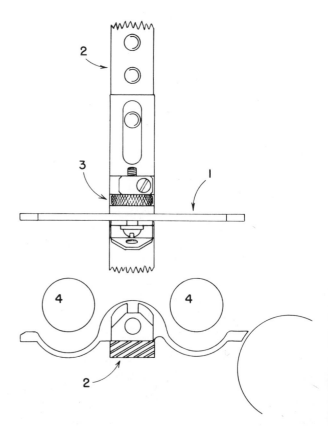

Cross-Section Schematic of a Push-Type Side Guide. (1) Push Plate; (2) Side Guide Bar; (3) Adjusting Nut; (4) Corrugating Bars.

Push-Guides. All push-guides are essentially the same. The sheet is forwarded into the front guides or insertion device. Then the side guide acts by pushing the sheet into its predetermined position. Whether the side guiding is done at the near side, or at the far side of the press, does not alter the actual guiding operation.

Push-guides are generally found on smaller size presses and those running heavy, rigid material such as metal and cardboard. They do not function very well where large size, light-weight paper must be handled. Along with the push-guide type of mechanism on paper presses we usually find some type of corrugating or stiffening device. This device serves to put a slight buckle in the sheet to stiffen it against the action of the push-guide.

Pull-Guides. Pull-guides are of three general types: (1) The finger type; (2) The rotary type; and (3) A combination of these. In all types the side-guide plate is fixed in the desired position, and the sheet pulled up against it after the sheet has been positioned at the front guides or stops.

Finger-Type Pull-Guide. The finger type of guide advances over the sheet, closes on it by pinching the sheet against a lower plate and pulls the sheet to the side-guide plate. The tension on this finger is adjustable. The finger must be so adjusted that it slips over the surface of the sheet without buckling it once the sheet is stopped by the side-guide plate. This adjustment of the finger pull-guide is possible for any weight stock. Even though the mechanism is rather simple the adjustment is, nevertheless, quite critical.

Rotary or Roller Guides. The rotary or roller guide is prevalent on most presses. Built into this mechanism is a lower roller which constantly rotates when the press is running. The sheet is forwarded to the front stops in such a position that the side edge rides over this lower guiding roller. After front register has been accomplished, a second spring-loaded roller, mounted above the lower one, drops

Courtesy Miehle Printing Press & Mfg. Co.

A Rotary or Roller Side Guide Assembly. On the left the locking device and the vernier adjustment; on the right the rollers.

down and pinches the sheet against the rotating lower roll. Friction causes the sheet to be pulled against the side-guide plate. As with the finger-type of side guide, the tension is adjustable in order to accommodate a wide range of paper calipers.

Roller-Finger Guide. In this type of side guide a finger slides under the front-guided sheet. When it has

reached the end of its forward movement, a spring-loaded upper roller pinches the sheet against the lower finger. Then the finger starts to move back and pulls the sheet with it until the side edge of the sheet is stopped by the face plate of the side guide.

GRIPPERS

Grippers are classified either as tumbler grippers or as grippers. Presses using a three-point register system without an insertion device require tumbler grippers. Presses which embody either a feed-roll or swing-feed (rotary-gripper) insertion device employ a "low-lift" gripper. Each of these two types is discussed in the following, as well as the general construction of grippers themselves.

Tumbler-Grippers. A tumbler-gripper rotates through a rather large arc when it opens and actually drops back into the impression-cylinder gap below the surface of the impression clyinder. It must do this in order to clear the gripper edge of the sheet as the impression cylinder comes around to its sheet-taking position. At this point the gripper rotates into the closed position, pinching the sheet against gripper pads, and pulling the sheet into the impression nip. The term tumbler is derived from the mechanism which imparts the opening and closing motions to the gripper shaft on which the impression-cylinder grippers are mounted.

"Low-Lift Grippers. (Low-lift is not a term used in the trade. It has been adopted here only for convenience.) Presses with insertion devices almost always have a gripper motion in which the grippers open just enough to allow the sheet to be inserted.

Instead of a mechanism which imparts a complete "tumbling action," low-lift grippers are mounted on a shaft which is rotated slightly through a cam and cam-roller device set at the end of the gripper shaft.

Construction of Grippers. Grippers may be of one-piece or two-piece construction. A one piece gripper has its "finger" part constructed as an integral part of, and an extension of the base or gripper clamp. In some cases the base is a solid piece of metal drilled to fit snugly on the gripper shaft. A set-screw is installed into the base in such a way that when the set-screw is tightened it clamps the gripper firmly on the shaft. In other cases the base may be split forming an open collar around the shaft. The set-screw, instead of being turned down directly on the gripper shaft, or gripper-shaft shoe, is threaded through both ends of the collar. When the set-screw is tightened it closes the collar around the shaft thereby clamping the gripper firmly to the gripper shaft. In this case the finger itself may be an extension of one side of the collar, or the collar is formed on the opposite side of the gripper shaft from the gripper finger.

In two-piece construction, the finger and the collar are actually two separate pieces. They are so assembled that while the finger opens and closes as an integral part of the assembly, provision is made for spring loading the gripper finger itself. This tends to simplify attaining a more nearly perfect, uniform gripper-bite pressure on the sheet. This

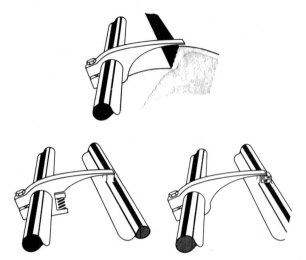

Three Common Types of Gripper Construction. Top — a one-piece gripper; Left — a two-piece spring-loaded gripper; Right — a one-piece gripper with a spring-loaded gripper pad.

same aim is accomplished in the case of some one-piece grippers by spring loading the gripper pad set in the top of the gripper post.

An important detail in construction and functioning of grippers is the character of the gripping face of the gripper finger on the top of the gripper pad. It is obvious that there is considerable pull on the sheet as it passes through the impression nip. Not only must the grippers guide the sheet through the nip but they must also hold the sheet against the pull of the nip. Quite often, the pressure of the gripper against the pad may not be enough. Too much bite pressure may mar the sheet and cause difficulty in later passes of the sheet through the press.

Several techniques have been used to accomplish this. Some newer presses have grit-faced grippers to prevent slippage of the sheet during the critical printing cycle. Others will face the gripper pad to accomplish this. On older presses, the grippers or gripper pads may be faced with light-weight emery cloth if proper bite pressure can not be developed through the spring-loaded grippers or gripper pads.

Grit-Faced Gripper

The significance and importance of gripper bite and gripper-bite pressure are discussed under the heading of "Setting the Grippers," further down in this section.

SETTING AND OPERATING THE SIMPLE THREE-POINT REGISTER SYSTEM

The three-point register system is here extensively discussed. First we will follow the travel of the sheet from the moment when it arrives at the guides to the point when it is carried into the impression nip. Then we will discuss the setting of front-guiding devices, and finally turn our attention to the adjusting of the gripper bite.

The Functioning of the Simple Three-Point Register System. We begin our analysis with the front- and side-guided sheet. As the impression cylinder comes around to its sheet-receiving position, the grippers start to rotate backwards (toward the leading edge of the cylinder) to the closing position. They reach the point of actually closing on the sheet. But while they are doing this the cylinder is rolling in its forward motion toward the impression nip. The sheet is held motionless in its guided position. As the grippers actually close on the sheets, the front guides lift clear of the sheet's path of travel to the impression nip.

Sheet Control in the Simple Three-Point Register System. Two things have happened which are important and critical. For a very brief instant the sheet is not under positive control. This is due to the fact that the guide must clear the sheet before it starts its forward motion. Since the gripper action and the cylinder travel are continuous, there is no way for the gripper to firmly close on the sheet before the guides are lifted. In actual practice, proper timing and setting prevents loss of register during this brief instant. In addition, on presses equipped with a corrugating device, timing of this device is such that it tends to control the sheet during this critical period.

However, something else happened at the same time. The sheet was lying at rest in the guides when the grippers took hold of it. Immediately, the sheet was then jerked into full press speed. On small presses, this may not be too important. But on large presses, overcoming the inertia of a large motionless sheet is a serious problem. It is for this reason that practically all modern larger presses have true insertion devices as standard equipment. Some medium size presses can be purchased with either the simple three-point register system or an insertion device. Most small presses are equipped with simple three-point register systems as are a few of the larger ones.

Setting Front Guides on Three-Point Register System. On smaller presses there are two guides, or stops; larger presses may have three or four. (The simple three-point register system is not found on any modern press over 35 inches, for the previously discussed reasons.) The front guides are set across the press to align and balance the sheet while it is side-guided and at the same time held against the front guides. The guides can be moved across the press on their mounting shaft. They must be carefully set to come down properly on the register plate or tongue. Make sure when you shift them that they are always placed *between* a pair of grippers and not over a gripper. And they must be so positioned, in the case of an insertion device, that the stops will clear the motion of the swing or transfer assembly.

They should be so set that they do not bounce on the register plate or guide tongue when they descend, but meet it gently. Where the guides are mounted with a keyway on the shaft, correct setting for easy seating is almost automatic. After the guides are set, a sheet should be placed against them and slid back and forth as a test that the contact of the sheet and the front face plates is smooth.

When setting the guide tongues or register plate it is important to note that they do not cause a bulge in the sheet when the impression-cylinder grippers take it. These tongues should be so set as to support the gripper edge of the sheet perfectly flat. Also check to see that the tongues are not depressed when the guides come to rest on them. If the tongues give, they will rise when the guides do and cause misregister or a bulge in the paper. Such a bulge can easily lead to a wrinkle when the sheet goes through the printing nip.

Anti-Buckle Devices. Guides of this type always have some kind of adjustable metal plate that holds the sheet down in order to prevent buckling against the guide. The space should be set to permit free movement of the sheet by the side guide without permitting buckling.

Timing the Front Guides. Now the press is inched forward until the guides just begin to lift. Here, perfect timing is essential. The timing should be such that the face plate of the guide *just* clears the sheet as the impression-cylinder grippers finally close. If the front guides are set too late, the edge of the sheet is nicked or torn; if they rise too early, there is loss of register.

Adjusting the Gripper-Bite. These guides are also adjustable up or down, that is, to increase or decrease gripper-bite or head margin. This adjustment, however, should be used only as a last resort. *The guides should be set to give exactly the gripper-bite recommended by the press manufacturer.* If the gripper-bite adjustment must be used, the face plate should be returned to its recommended position as soon as the job is finished. Actually, the primary purpose of this adjustment is to make certain that the sheet is taken by the impression-cylinder grippers with a uniform bite across its entire front-guide edge. Improper gripper-bite can cause trouble at three points: where the grippers first take the sheet; at the impression nip; or at the point where the sheet is transferred from one set of grippers to another, for example from impression-cylinder grippers to delivery-chain grippers.

SETTING AND OPERATING THE FEED-ROLL INSERTION SYSTEM

The feed-roll system is a true insertion device because here the sheet is *inserted* into the impression-cylinder grippers (directly or indirectly), whereas it is *taken* by them in the simple three-point register system. Let us again follow the travel of the sheet for our operational analysis of this device.

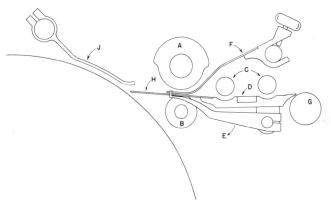

Schematic of an Insertion Device. A — Feed Roll Cam. B — Lower Feed Wheel. C — Corrugating Bars (if push guide). D — Side Guide Bar. E — Guide Stop Fingers. F — Upper Guide Fingers. G — Conveyor Rollers. H — Feed Plate. J — Sheet Holddown Fingers.

The Functioning of the Feed-Roll System. When the sheet comes down the ramp it is pre-registered against a series of stops spaced across the press and mounted on a common shaft. The sheet is held against these stops and side-guided. At the proper time the upper and lower feed-rolls pinch the sheet, holding it firmly. The stops now drop out (or raise) out of the forward path of the sheet. The feed-roll cams rotate and drive the sheet forward, exactly when the impression-cylinder, feed-cylinder, or transfer-cylinder grippers reach the sheet-receiving position.

Sheet Control in the Feed-Roll System. The cams themselves are so designed that they start the sheet slowly and then accelerate it to a speed *slightly faster* than the surface speed of the cylinder. *As a result, the edge of the sheet*

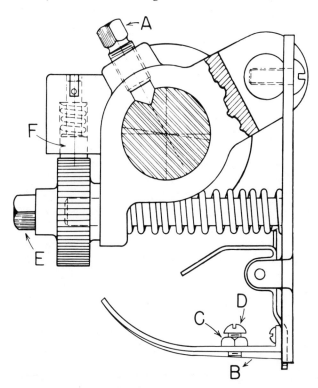

A Typical Front Guide of a Simple Three-Point Register System. A — Setscrew for locking guide assembly on shaft; B — Anti-buckle plate; C and D — Anti-buckle adjustment; E and F — Face plate adjustment.

is driven positively into the grippers and against another set of stops built into the impression, feed, or transfer cylinder, either along a separate bar or as part of each individual gripper pad. The sheet actually buckles slightly, just as the gripper closes.

This action is called overfeed, and the amount of this overfeed is adjustable in order to accommodate papers of varying thickness or stiffness. This method of forwarding and inserting assures consistent register, because it is possible with such an insertion device to have the cylinder grippers close positively on the sheet before the insertion device releases it. It is important that surface of both upper and lower rollers be absolutely clean. They should ride directly over each other. The free-turning feed-rolls should be constantly checked to make sure that they are turning freely.

SETTING AND OPERATING THE SWING-FEED INSERTION SYSTEM

The swing or transfer insertion system is the second true insertion system. In this system, just like in the above described feed-roll system, the sheet is *inserted* into the cylinder grippers, not *taken* by them. Again, we follow the travel of the sheet for our operational description of this insertion device.

The Functioning of the Swing- or Transfer-Gripper System. This system is so designed that the sheet is forwarded against a set of front guides similar to those in the simple three-point register system. The sheet is pre-registered and is side-guided, then a set of grippers — usually mounted on a shaft over the feed ramp — take hold of the sheet. When the grippers close, the guides move out of the forward path of the sheet. The transfer mechanism starts slowly to rotate — and accelerates until it reaches the same speed as the impression cylinder. At this time, the impression-cylinder grippers are in their sheet-receiving position and the sheet is inserted into them. Also, at this point, the transfer mechanism is momentarily locked into the impression-cylinder motion so that both sets of grippers travel together while the impression-cylinder grip-

pers close on the sheet. At the actual point of transfer, both sets of grippers are holding the sheet, guaranteeing positive control.

Timing and Gripper-Bite on Swing- or Transfer-Gripper Insertion Devices. It is important that timing on this device be checked periodically. The bite of all grippers should also be checked. This is best done by inserting strips of tissue paper, or .001 feeler gage, into each gripper and by closing them for testing. A strip should first be inserted between the cam and stop pin of the gripper shaft. The thickness of this strip is specified by the press manufacturer. By feeling the pull on each strip of tissue or feeler it is possible to make certain that the tension is equal on all grippers. The tissue strip or feeler should barely pull out if everything is set right. (The manufacturers' instructions should of course always be followed in re-setting and timing of insertion devices.)

CHECKING SHEET CONTROL AT THE POINT OF GUIDING

When the sheet is against the stops, all sheet-control devices used for controlling the sheet at this point should be checked. For example, on successive-sheet feeders are the tail brushes riding on the *end* of the sheet? Are the drive-up wheels, or balls riding free at the very edge of the sheet? This is important in order to make certain that the sheet is held in its forward position and still sufficiently free to be smoothly side-guided.

IMPRESSION-CYLINDER STOPS AND IMPRESSION-CYLINDER GRIPPERS

These devices are the last subject of our presentation in this section. First, impression-cylinder stops are discussed and then comes the setting and adjusting of impression-cylinder grippers.

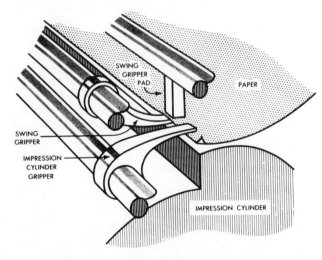

Schematic of Swing-Gripper Device.

Courtesy Harris-Intertype Corp.

Cylinder Stops for a Feed-Roll Insertion Device. Note the stop adjacent to each gripper.

Impression-Cylinder Stops. Presses using a feed-roll insertion device have stops built into the impression or feed cylinder, or into each impression-cylinder gripper pad. The shaft or bar on which these stops are mounted is capable of being bowed. Bowing then makes it possible to accommodate, to some extent, paper that has a bow cut into it. The bowing adjustment can also help to some extent when wavy-edged or tight-edged paper must be run. (For a discussion of various paper conditions as they influence presswork, see the "Ink and Paper" chapter of this Manual.) A wavy-edged sheet tends to compress at the back end, as it goes through the nip. Checking the image with the GATF Register Rule across the back corner marks shows this distortion. Bowing the stops — so that a slightly greater gripper bite is possible towards the ends of the sheet — tends to minimize the problem of fit. Always start a new job by making certain that the stops are set straight and parallel to the leading edge of the cylinder.

Some of the newer presses using swing- or transfer-gripper systems also offer the possibility of easily cocking the gripper edge of the sheet when this is unavoidable. It's important, of course, that this be done carefully to make certain that neither too little nor too much gripper bite is developed across the sheet. To handle the possible need for bowing the gripper-edge of the sheet, the shaft on which the front stops are set can be bowed slightly.

Impression-Cylinder Grippers. The setting of impression-cylinder grippers demands particular care because they are very easily damaged and go out of adjustment very easily. The manner of setting is carefully outlined by the manufacturers in their instruction manuals. Here, merely a few general points are stressed. When a gripper closes on the sheet it must do so firmly. Inch the press as the gripper closes on the sheet. Now, inch it very slowly and watch the grippers closely. See if they appear to "duck" — either down or up. Any such motion must be eliminated because it is a clear signal that the grippers are set wrong. Also notice if the entire closing cycle is absolutely smooth and devoid of any jerky motion. Check each gripper for even pressure and consult the manufacturer's press manual

for instructions before you begin correcting for this condition.

On tumbler-gripper mechanisms, with one-piece grippers, it should be borne in mind that even one gripper set too tight will cause the other grippers to have a looser bite. All grippers should, consequently, be checked carefully.

While the bite on impression-cylinder grippers gives trouble if it is set too tight, no less serious consequences result from too weak a gripper setting. It should be realized that there is a considerable pull of the sheet by the blanket — especially on coated stock — and even more so when coated stock is printed with a heavy lay of ink. If, as the sheet leaves the nip there is the slightest tendency for the sheet to pull out of the grippers, there will also be trouble at the point of transfer to the delivery grippers. Delivery grippers are discussed in Section Seven of this chapter which treats of deliveries. It is important to realize that impression cylinder grippers are set quite differently than the grippers of a swing-feed or similar insertion device. The reason is that there is comparatively little tendency for a sheet to pull out of swing, rotary, or transfer grippers unless there is something radically wrong. The same holds true for grippers on a transfer or feed cylinder. However, there is tremendous drag on the sheet as it passes through the impression nip. The impression-cylinder grippers must hold the sheet without any slip and yet do this without in any way marring the gripper edge of the sheet. A very heavy bite is not the answer. Rather, what is required is a firm bite — absolutely even — completely across the sheet. And this must be accomplished in a smooth operation, free of any binding or springing of the gripper mechanism or any of its parts. This explains why the manufacturer's instructions must be followed explicitly. Gripper motions of different design require different handling as do grippers of different construction. Gripper pads, where used, also affect the manner of setting the grippers.

Our presentation of guides, grippers and insertion devices ends here. In the following section we will familiarize ourselves with the three cylinders of the printing unit where the sheet is placed by means of feeder and insertion devices.

Section Five: The Printing Unit, I: Cylinders

The printing unit is the heart of the lithographic press. (It is sometimes — particularly on multicolor sheet-fed presses — referred to as "the frame.") Our discussion of the printing unit is divided into two sections. In this section we present the three cylinders, in the following — Section Six — The Inking and Dampening Systems.

THE THREE CYLINDERS AND THEIR FUNCTIONS

Everything about the actual printing cycle in the process centers around the three cylinders in the printing unit. They are: the plate cylinder, the blanket cylinder, and the impression cylinder. A fourth assembly, called the delivery

or skeleton cylinder, is not a true cylinder, nor does it function as part of the actual printing cycle. It merely serves to guide the printed sheet away from the impression cylinder, helping the sheet to change its direction of travel without being marred, marked, buckled or whipped. Set against the plate cylinder is a dampening system and an inking system. These are so placed as to permit the plate to be dampened before it is inked.

Arrangement of the Cylinders. In general, the three cylinders of the printing unit of a one-color press, or a multi-color press of unit construction are positioned with the plate cylinder uppermost, the blanket cylinder under the plate cylinder, and the impression cylinder behind the blanket cylinder. One important exception to this general scheme is found in metal-decorating presses. There the cylinders are mounted in a vertical row to increase the pressure between blanket and impression cylinders. Another reason for this design can be found in the necessities of handling metal blanks, which cannot be wrapped around an impression cylinder. Lithographic presses for the printing of paper, however, benefit by the flexibility of paper. Placing the impression cylinder behind the blanket cylinder makes possible a lower overall

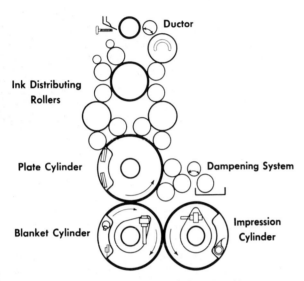

Schematic of a Typical Printing Unit.

height and a simpler design for feeding and inserting of the sheet. All three cylinders are similar in the materials from which they are made and as to the manner in which they are made and as to the manner in which they are mounted in the press. The differences are due to the function of each cylinder, as well as whether or not a cylinder must be rigidly mounted in the press.

The Printing Cycle. During running, the plate cylinder revolves in a counter-clockwise direction — counter-clockwise, that is, if you are facing the operating side of the press with the feeder to your right. The direction of rotation causes the form rollers of the dampening system to contact the plate *before* the form rollers of the inking system deliver a charge of fresh ink to the image. During actual operation of the press, the sheet is drawn around the impression cylinder, brought into contact with the blanket cylinder, and then transferred to the delivery chain which carries the sheet around the skeleton or intermediate cylinder to the delivery. Some presses employ intermediate or transfer cylinders between the impression cylinder and the skeleton or delivery cylinder. Plate cylinder, blanket cylinder and impression cylinder will now be individually discussed. The discussion will be confined to the one-color press because the wide variety of designs found in multi-color presses would make a clear-cut discussion impossible to achieve. A brief discussion of cylinder arrangements on multi-color presses will be found at the end of this section.

THE PLATE CYLINDER

As the name implies, the plate cylinder is designed to carry the lithographic plate. For this purpose the cylinder on sheet-fed presses is considerably larger in circumference than the plate itself. The cylinder is not a continuous, complete surface but one that has a gap in its surface where plate-clamping devices are installed. These are used to mount the plate on the cylinder.

Position and Mounting of the Plate Cylinder. The plate cylinder is, as already noted, the uppermost cylinder. In addition to the already stated reasons, this arrangement is necessary because of the inking system design, and last but not least, for convenience of operation. Since much work is done with the plate when it is on the press, placing it toward the top of the press makes the work more convenient. The inking system, too, is more easily designed for a position over the plate cylinder. The mounting of the plate cylinder is rigid in a fixed position in the press frames and cannot be adjusted for either pressure or alignment. However, it can be rotated independently of its gear.

Plate-Cylinder Bearers. The true shape and size of the cylinder is noticeable when looking at the bearers. (In actual practice there is no way to look at the entire bearer on an assembled press. However, enough can be seen so that *watching* the bearer while slowly turning the press will accomplish the same purpose.) All American presses and some presses of European manufacture are built so that the plate and blanket cylinders run on their bearers; that is the bearers are in firm contact when the impression is on. Bearers, as we know them, are rings of hardened steel that are pressed on the cylinder spindle, shaft or body — as the case may be — and are an integral part of the complete

The Plate Cylinder. Note the bearers at each end, the groove between bearer and cylinder body, and the plate locked in plate clamp.

cylinder. The plate cylinder gear is bolted to the cylinder through slots rather than holes. This is done to facilitate forward or backward movement of the cylinder, and therefore the image, without opening or shifting the plate

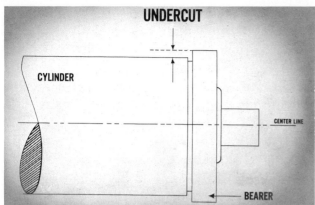

Schematic Showing Cylinder Bearer, Groove, Body and Undercut.

Courtesy Harris-Intertype Corp.

A Typical Blanket Cylinder Mounting. Note adjustments on the eccentrics.

clamps. This plate-cylinder movement is a limited one; therefore it is necessary that the stripper and the platemaker allow for proper plate-clamp margins when making the plate. With a little care, by all concerned, very little time need be spent in getting a plate into its correct position with respect to the gripper edge of the sheet. This is greatly facilitated on modern presses by the use of pin-register systems.

The Undercut of the Plate Cylinder. The surface of the bearer is the pitch line of the cylinder. All plate cylinders have their body cut down below the level of the bearers. The difference between bearer and cylinder radius is known as the *undercut.* The undercut serves to accommodate the plate and whatever packing may be required in order to bring the plate surface up to the correct printing height.

The Plate Clamps. The plate clamps are so set that one clamps the leading edge of the plate while the other holds the tail end of the plate firmly. Both clamps are designed for a slight sideways or cocking movement of the plate when it is necessary that a plate be shifted to attain its proper register or its fit. There is also some leeway for forward and backward movement. But care by the stripper and platemaker can and should hold such shifting operations to a minimum. To say it again: Total down-time during makeready can be considerably cut by a little standardized care on the part of everybody. As previously mentioned, intelligent use of available pin-register systems accomplishes the desired standardization.

THE BLANKET CYLINDER

Immediately below the plate cylinder is the blanket cylinder. In general appearance it is pretty much the same as the plate cylinder, consisting of a heavy metal shell with a gap across its length and with bearers fixed to each end. The gap accommodates bars for attaching the blanket, the bar at the tail end usually being so designed as to make possible winding of the tail end of the blanket for tightening purposes. On some presses the blanket is tightened at both ends.

The Mounting of the Blanket Cylinder. The blanket cylinder is mounted in the press in a manner quite different from that of the plate cylinder. Blanket cylinders are, generally, mounted by means of eccentric bushings in the press frames. On such installations, if the bushing is turned, the blanket cylinder can be moved toward the plate cylinder or away from it. The possibility of this motion facilitates adjustment of bearer pressure between plate and blanket cylinders. This is important because in time, no matter how carefully maintained, bearings and bushings will wear. Such an adjustment is also necessary in order to achieve and maintain proper parallel alignment of the plate and blanket cylinders.

Disengaging the Blanket Cylinder. Because of the relationship between the three cylinders, the blanket cylinder is so mounted that it can be pulled into contact or out of contact with the plate cylinder while the press is operated.

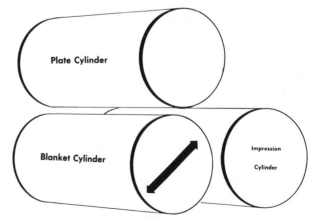

Schematic Showing Relationship of Three Cylinders When Press Is Tripped.

This is necessary for makeready and, of course, essential during running. When a sheet is missed, or when the pressman desires to idle the press, the blanket cylinder is moved away from both the plate and impression cylinders, automatically.

Blanket-Cylinder Bearers. Like the plate cylinder, the bearers on the blanket cylinder are rigidly attached to the cylinder body, but the blanket-cylinder gear is permanently bolted because a forward or backward adjustment is here undesirable. The reason for this is the need for exact timing between the blanket cylinder and the impression cylinder.

Blanket-Cylinder Undercut. The blanket cylinder is undercut in exactly the same way as the plate cylinder. However, the depth of the undercut is much greater since blankets average from .055 inch to .070 inch depending on size, ply, etc; lithographic plates range from .008-inch in the small sizes to only about .022-inch in the larger sizes. The undercut is always sufficient to allow for some packing in addition to the blanket itself. Like the plate-cylinder bearers, the bearers of the blanket cylinder represent the true circumference or diameter of the cylinder. Some presses of European design require two blankets on the blanket cylinder. The undercut is such as to accommodate them.

THE IMPRESSION CYLINDER

The impression cylinder is different from the plate and blanket cylinders. Like them it has a gap. It accommodates a gripper shaft, sometimes a gripper pad shaft and/or a stop shaft for control of gripper bite on the sheet. However, the relationship of the impression-cylinder body with that of its "bearers" is quite different. In the first place there is no provision made for packing the impression cylinder. In the second place provision must be made for changing the distance between the blanket and impression cylinders in order to achieve transfer squeeze on the particular paper being run. For example, if we run our press with a transfer squeeze of .003 and the paper being run calipers .003 then we set the distance between blanket and impression cylinders to give us no clearance or squeeze be-

Courtesy Harris-Intertype Corp.

The Impression Cylinder. Note apparent lack of undercut.

tween the surface of the blanket and the body of the impression cylinder when the impression is on and no sheet in the impression nip. When sheets are run, the caliper of the sheet will build up the required transfer squeeze. If the stock being run is .005-caliper, the clearance between blanket and impression cylinder surfaces with impression on and no sheet in the nip would be .002. (The figures used above are only for illustrative purposes; actual squeeze pressure will vary depending on type of job and especially on type of paper being run.)

Pressure Adjustment on Impression Cylinder. This method generally confined to smaller presses.

The Ends of the Impression Cylinder. The impression cylinder does not have bearers in the same sense that we have them on the plate and blanket cylinders. We may have ground and polished steel rings on the ends of the impression cylinder, pressed-on and bolted to the impression-cylinder body, or as an integral part of the body itself. But these steel rings do not ride the bearers of the blanket cylinder. These impression-cylinder ends are nevertheless generally known as bearers in the lithographic industry. We too will use the term in the course of this study, but the reader should keep in mind that the so-called impression-cylinder bearers are not bearers in the true sense of the word.

The impression-cylinder bearers are used for the alignment of the impression cylinder, though merely as reference points. The alignment is made by setting the space between blanket-cylinder bearers and impression-cylinder bearers so that they are exactly equal at both ends. It is again worth noting at this point that some foreign-built presses now available in this country have bearers on their plate and blanket cylinders which do not ride. They are used as reference points when cylinder pressures are being adjusted and set, just as we do with the impression cylinder on American-built presses.

Pressure Adjustment of the Impression Cylinder. On most smaller and some older presses the impression cylinder is adjustable, for obtaining squeeze pressure against the blanket cylinder. This is done from the operat-

Courtesy Harris-Intertype Corp.

Pressure Adjustments on Blanket Cylinder. The adjustment to left of cylinder mounting is for alignment between blanket and impression cylinder.

ing side of the press. With the impression on — blanket cylinder in contact with the plate cylinder — the impression cylinder carries the sheet into contact with the blanket cylinder and through the printing nip. On presses where the impression cylinder is in a fixed position, the blanket cylinder is mounted in a second set of eccentric bushings which allow for adjusting of the *blanket-to-paper* pressure without changing the *blanket-to-plate* pressure.

This matter of blanket-to-impression-cylinder adjustment is extremely critical, not because it is difficult to accomplish but because neglecting it leads to many troubles. The pressman must always keep the necessity for blanket-to-impression-cylinder adjustment in mind. For example, every change in the blanket-cylinder diameter caused by shifting the packing between plate and blanket cylinder must be accompanied by a change in the impression-cylinder squeeze or pressure adjustment. This subject is discussed in detail further down in our section.

THE BLANKET

It must be emphasized again that the blanket cylinder, and with it the blanket, is the heart of the lithographic offset process. That this is so is not always realized by many people, be they experienced or inexperienced in the lithographic process. But it is an undisputable fact that the transfer of very fine images onto a wide variety of paper finishes, including cloth and other materials, is best accomplished by the "offset" method. A lithographic plate is capable of retaining and transferring very fine images, up to 400-line halftones. The combination of the lithographic process with the offset method gives us indeed a superb printing technique.

The modern offset blanket gives us very little trouble other than that caused by improper selection and handling. Our presentation of the blanket is, corresponding with the great role played by the blanket, quite extensive. You find

the following eleven points individually discussed in the course of this section: (1) Selecting the blanket; (2) Checking-in the new blanket;; (3) Preparing the blanket for mounting; (4) Mounting the blanket;; (5) Adjusting blanket tension; (6) Breaking-in the new blanket; (7) Leveling the new blanket; (8) Treating a battered blanket; (9) Restoring the blanket; (10) Compatability of blanket, inks and solvents; and (11) The spare blanket.

Selecting the Blanket. Different types of blankets are available. For example some work better with coated papers than others. Specially formulated blankets must be used with some inks, heat-set inks for example. Therefore we have two responsibilities governing the blanket itself: (1) We must select the blanket best suited to the paper and ink being run; and (2) We must handle it properly. It should not be inferred that this is time-consuming or costly. One doesn't change the blanket for every change of paper. In actual practice a plant, which only once in a while runs a coated paper job, will do well to have a special blanket available for that purpose. As we previously stated, some of the newer ink formulations require special blankets. Which blanket is best for these should be determined by discussing the problem with the suppliers.

Checking-In the New Blanket. When a new blanket is received it should be checked immediately for proper size, with the warp line or directional arrows (on the back of the blanket) in the around-the-cylinder dimension. Then it should be checked for squareness of the across-the-cylinder edges with the warp lines. Next, it should be checked for any obvious defect on either side, and finally, for correct caliper. The best blanket thickness for a particular press is the thickness recommended by the press manufacturer. Checking caliper is best done with GATF's Blanket Thickness Gauge. In the first place, the Gauge is so designed as to indicate the caliper that the blanket will have after stretching around the cylinder. In the second place, measurements can be taken over the entire surface of the blanket. Thereby it is possible to arrive at an average figure for calculating the proper amount of packing. Recently, the manufacturers of bench-type paper micrometers are offering them with specially designed anvils and pressure rods to accomplish this "miking" of the blanket. These micrometers, however, do not allow rolling the blanket behind the anvil. This is necessary if measurements all over the blanket are desired.

Preparing the Blanket for Mounting. Most presses require that blankets be mounted in blanket bars

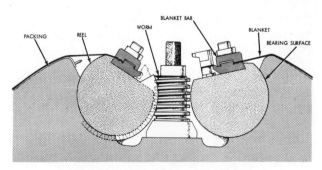

Blanket Reel Tightener and Support

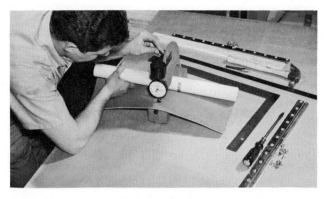

Checking Calipher of Blanket with GATF Blanket Thickness Gage.

Tracing Hole Locations with Blanket Bar.

Punching Holes in Blanket.

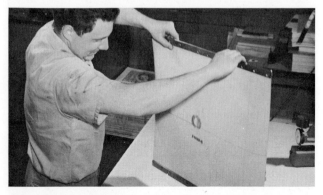

Permitting the Blanket to Seat Itself Properly.

for use on the press. Some presses are so designed that the blanket, once it is cut properly for size and squareness, is mounted directly into blanket clamps built into the blanket reels. The discussion on handling blankets which are punched and fastened to mounting bars is lengthy and detailed because many printing and running troubles are traceable to improper mounting.

On some small presses the blankets come specially pre-punched to match the specific blanket mounting device. On most other presses the blankets are mounted in their bars by the press crews. A new blanket should be prepared for mounting in its bars with great care. A little special attention at this point adds greatly to the life of the blanket as well as to reducing possible performance trouble. If the points mentioned in the preceding paragraphs have demonstrated that the new blanket is acceptable, preparing begins by laying the blanket face down on a clean flat surface. This applies to presses which mount their blankets to blanket bars by use of bolts.

Lay a blanket bar down flush with one end of the blanket, and check with a large carpenter's square to be certain that the blanket is square to the warp lines. Then lay a straight-edge against the back of the bar, remove the bar, and draw a sharp pencil line across the blanket against the straight-edge. Lay the straight-edge aside. From the center of this line, measure one-eighth of an inch back — away from the edge of the blanket — and mark this point. One-eighth of an inch is the distance on blankets up to about 38-inches wide; on blankets 76-inches wide the distance should be one-quarter of an inch; on 56-inch blankets, three-sixteenths of an inch will be correct.

Place the blanket bar along the line and trace the two end holes with a sharp pencil. Hold one end exactly over the traced hole and swing the bar until the center meets the point which was measured back from the original straight-edge line. Now trace all holes working from the center to the edge that was held firm over the end-hole. Then you swing the bar back to the original line, and check that both end-holes line-up with the originally traced two end-circles. Using the opposite end-hole as the anchor point, you swing the center of the bar up to the center point back of the original straight-edge line. Now you trace the holes on the other half of the blanket. The whole operation is repeated for the opposite end of the blanket. Finally the holes are punched exactly as traced.

Mounting the Blanket. Mounting begins by loosely screwing the blanket into its bars. Hold the blanket up by one set of bars and shake to seat the blanket smoothly. Lay one end of the blanket on the table with the other end hanging down. This position applies some tension to the blanket. Tighten the screws in this pair of bars; work from the center out, and tighten each screw successively, a little at a time until all are tight. When you have finished one end, reverse the blanket and tighten the other end.

The new blanket should now have its back — the fabric side — washed thoroughly with water, soaked well, and hung for a few days to dry out. This will bring back to their original size all fibers of the fabric, should they have been compressed in shipment or during the mounting operation. If blanket mounting in bars is not required, the back of the new blanket should be washed thoroughly etc., as mentioned above, before it is installed in the press.

Soaking the Fabric Back of the Blanket.

Adjusting Blanket Tension. The described method of mounting assures a smooth, even pull on the blanket when the blanket-cylinder reels are tightened. For putting the blanket on the press, follow the manufacturer's instructions for applying the proper tension.

Neither a show of brute strength nor a scientific knowledge of leverage guarantees the proper working of the blanket when it is tightened on the press.

Tightening the Blanket on the Press.

Breaking-In the New Blanket. A new blanket requires one further treatment. After it is installed in the press, the surface should be scrubbed with pumice, blanket solvent and water. Wet the rubber with water, sprinkle pumice on it and scrub the pumice with a clean soft rag that has been wet with a blanket solvent. Scrub until you attain a smooth, even "satin" finish. Do this with a side-to-side stroke, rather than a circular action. Wash off the pumice with water, then wash again with blanket solvent and dry the blanket. Now it is ready to print. When doing

Pumicing the Surface of the Blanket.

this kind of work on the blanket, care should be used to avoid soaking the ends of the blanket. Such soaking will cause the edges of the fabric to swell.

Leveling the New Blanket. A new blanket requires one further test to make sure that it is in printing condition. Remove an amount of packing equal to about one-half of the squeeze-pressure. (Squeeze-pressure is discussed further down.) Roll up the plate solid, print it on the blanket, and check the ink transfer. The slightest thickness deviations will now show up as light areas on the printed blanket. To make certain whether the blanket is at fault, remove it from the press and install it back in the reverse position. Now you print on it again. If the cylinders are okay the weak areas will still be in the same areas of the blanket.

According to the result of this test, either the cylinders, or the blanket, or both need patching. Patching must be done with great care and precision. If cylinders need to be patched, use shellac. This makes the patching reasonably permanent and avoids repeating this operation when blankets are changed. When patching the blanket, remove the rear bar from the press and trace the low spots with a pencil pressed against the back. Watching the face of the

Checking the Blanket for Levelness. Note that this should be done with .002 less squeeze pressure than is normally used for running.

blanket as you trace will guide you for correct marking. Build up a low spot gradually with thin tissue preferably .0005 inch thick. Do not *cut* the tissue to fit the mark but tear it. The feather edge of the tear prevents the edge of the patches from showing when solids are printed. Use the same caliper of tissue and tearing technique, if you are patching the cylinder.

This same procedure also applies to an old blanket which has been treated and given a rest off the press.

Treating a Battered Blanket. Battered blankets can usually be restored to a like-new condition. Wash the blanket with a blanket wash and with water to remove all ink, solvents, and gum; and dust it with a half-and-half mixture of talc and sulphur. Remove the blanket from the press and soak it in water for several days. If soaking the blanket in a container is not practical, hang it and keep swabbing it with water from a sponge. When a batter occurs on the press, the rubber is seldom damaged unless something like a piece of wood or a nail goes through the press from the feeder. If this happens, not only is the rubber cut but the fibers of the backing-cloth are also damaged. But this is the exception. In the usual paper batter, the cloth fibers are merely compressed, and soaking the blanket in water will almost always bring them back. After the blanket has hung sufficiently long, give the rubber a good pumice treatment, then dust with talc and sulphur mixture; and finally, store the blanket in a cool dry place, with the rubber rolled in, for a rest and future use.

Restoring the Blanket. A blanket should not be used until it is completely shot. Blankets should be removed in time from the press and treated as outlined in the preceding paragraph for a battered blanket. Treating them this way periodically gives them a good rest and preserves the fabric as well as the rubber. In addition, the solvents, ink vehicles, etc., are dispersed throughout the material, and the surface can become again like new. Running blankets too long causes permanent embossing. Embossing is caused by concentrations of absorbed materials — ink, vehicle and solvent — in the image areas. Besides becoming embossed, blankets that are run too long can become so badly glazed and oxidized that no amount of pumicing and rest can restore them.

There are a few other steps which the pressman can take to assure long life and excellent behavior by a blanket while on the press. When a rested, used blanket is put back on the press, reverse its position. Do not always use the same edge as the leading edge. Another precaution which is helpful is to release tension on a blanket if the press stands more than a few hours. Do not loosen the blanket reel completely, just slack off a few teeth, and "flag" the starter button to remind you or the next pressman how many ratchet teeth were slacked off.

Compatibility of Blanket, Inks and Solvents. A word of caution on materials for the treating of blankets as well as their selection is in order. Pay attention to the recommendations of your suppliers and follow their instructions. Then, and only then, can you hold them responsible for results. *The blanket manufacturers, ink makers and suppliers of solvents will fill your needs satisfactorily, if you only learn to define your needs accurately.* The suppliers cannot produce miracles, although on occasion it may appear as if they could. Do not expect more than they promise to do unless you want to be in trouble!

The Spare Blanket. In every pressroom there should always be at least one blanket for each press size — in perfect condition and fastened in its bars — ready for immediate use. If a blanket gets battered on the press it should *not* be patched up, but replaced. A spare blanket, if previously mounted in the blanket bars, can be installed just as quickly as the blanket which has been battered can be patched up. The battered blanket can usually be restored to a like-new condition — if it is not further mutilated by running it with patches. Properly handled, blankets will last a really long time and make possible trouble-free, good quality printing, as well as very high production. Having a spare blanket, completely mounted in its bars, reduces the tendency to run any one blanket too long.

PRINTING PRESSURE

The pressure required to transfer printing ink from the press plate to the blanket depends on two things: (1) Bearer pressure; and (2) Height to which blanket and plate are packed. On presses which do not run on bearers, the clearance between cylinders — when impression is on — is the determining factor; assuming, of course, that the total thickness of the press plate with its packing and the total thickness of the blanket with its packing are in accordance with the manufacturer's instructions. Emphasis on manufacturers' instructions for presses without bearers should not be misunderstood to mean that presses with bearers — and all presses made in America do have bearers — can be operated without regard for the instructions of their manufacturers. All presses, with or without bearers, must be operated by closely following the instructions of their makers.

We are not concerned with particular presses and their features. The press-manuals available from the manufacturers amply fulfill this task. Our interest is with the principles of printing pressure and their various aspects. These are divided into the following ten points for our study: (1) Impression squeeze; (2) Cylinder undercut; (3) The packing gage; (4) Packing and squeeze pressure; (5) Plate-image size and printed-image size; (6) The GATF Register Rule; (7) Preparing for bearer-contact check; (8) The thumbprint test; (9) Too much pressure?; (10) Checking impression-cylinder pressure. Each of these ten points is individually discussed in the following.

Impression Squeeze. Let us now discuss this matter of transfer pressure. It is known that we need more than just ink if we want to transfer ink from the press plate to the blanket, and from the blanket to the paper. We also must squeeze quite a bit to get the proper ink transfer. It is generally accepted, as a result of practical and long experience as well as research, that the plate-to-blanket squeeze required will range from .002 inch when running presensitized plates to about .004 inch for conventional plates such as aluminum deep-etched plates. A general rule for this setting is that the smoother the plate the less pressure required, while the coarser the grain (of a grained plate) the greater the pressure required. If a deep-etch plate is etched too deeply, even greater pressure may be required for the blanket to pull-out the full ink charge. Plates used on poster work often require considerably more than .004 inch squeeze pressure since much of this work is done from coarse-grained plates. The important points to bear in mind are: (1) The less pressure that is used the longer the plate life will be; (2) The plate-to-blanket squeeze pressure must be sufficient to pull out from the plate a clean, full charge of ink. It is important, also, to consider the type of blanket being used.

Plate and blanket packing alone do not guarantee adequate pressure. If a press has worn cylinder journals, whose play has not taken up properly, good ink transfer will be unattainable. The problem is to hold the cylinders together when the pressure is applied, because the squeeze-pressure is trying to force the cylinders apart. Assuming the cylinders are holding true as a result of proper setting at the cylinder journals, and that the amount of plate and blanket packing are correct, according to the manufacturers specifications, all is well. But if overpacking is resorted to in order to counteract loose or improperly set cylinder bearings (not the bearers), then not only may quality of ink transfer suffer, but the cylinder circumferences are affected. If the packing of both cylinders is not reasonably close to manufacturers' specifications, the cylinder circumferences will be out of balance. Granted, there is some leeway; but any approach to either extreme of the existing leeway may cause loss of fit as well as poor image transfer and premature plate wear.

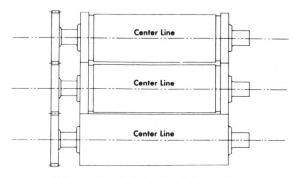

Schematic of Cylinder Relationship.

Cylinder Undercut. The plate and blanket cylinders are so designed that the body of the cylinders is below the level of the bearers for presses with bearers as well as for those without bearers. The difference in height between the surface of the bearer and the surface of the cylinder body is called the undercut. Each manufacturer's instruction manual lists the exact undercuts. But on old presses, it may be necessary to check the undercut. This is best done with a packing gage.

The Packing Gage. A packing gage is essentially a height gage. The body of the gage is held against the cylin-

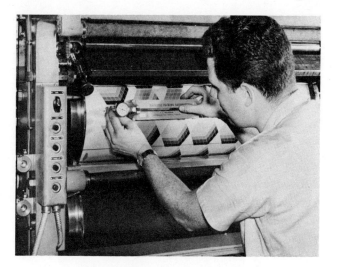

Using a Packing Gage to Check Plate Packing.

der body, and the gage itself is zeroed-in. Then the instrument is moved so that its body rests against the cylinder body while the gage itself is over the bearer. The reading shows the height difference between bearer and cylinder body. The packing gage is not only used for checking cylinder undercut; it is even more useful for checking the exact height to which either the blanket or plate cylinder have been packed. This measurement is most critical.

Packing and Squeeze Pressure. The amount of undercut on the plate cylinder is always more than the thickness of the lithographic plate itself. The same condition holds true on the blanket cylinder. This is done deliberately to allow for shifting of packing from one cylinder to the other in order to affect a change of printed-image size in the around-the-cylinder dimension. Transferring packing from under the blanket to under the plate produces a shorter image on the printed sheet, and *vice versa*. But the total thickness of the plate with its packing, and of the blanket with its packing must always be the same in order to produce the desired squeeze pressure.

Let us demonstrate this rule with an example. The undercut of the plate cylinder is .025-inch, the plate thickness is .020-inch. In order to bring the plate to *bearer height* .005-inch of packing material must be put under the plate. The undercut of the blanket cylinder is .070-inch and the blanket thickness is .065-inch. In order to bring the blanket to *bearer height* .005-inch packing material must be put under the blanket. But the total thickness of plate and blanket, plus their respective packings is not sufficient to produce image transfer. Therefore, an additional .002-inch to .004-inch (depending on press size and kind of blanket) must be added to the packing material. Where this additional material is put depends on the specific press design. This additional material *must* always be added where the manufacturer specifies — at least to start the job. If, after starting, change of image size is required to attain *fit,* then the appropriate packing shift is made. On a large sheet, the image can be elongated or shortened one-eighth of an inch to three-sixteenths of an inch before bad effects are visible.

Plate-Image Size and Printed-Image Size. In connection with change in image size it is important to understand that the printed lithographic image tends to be longer than the image on the plate when the plate is lying flat, that is, before it is curved around the plate cylinder. This is due to the stretch of plate, as well as the image too, when the plate in bent around the cylinder. Some stretch may also take place as a result of excessive pulling on the plate clamps when they are tightened. In addition, the nature of the lithographic press tends to stretch the sheet during printing, due to the ironing action in the nip as well as possible moisture pickup by the sheet. It may appear as if all these items would prevent good, controllable printing. This is far from true. But they must be understood and can then be very well controlled. In the "Ink and Paper" chapter you will find a discussion of paper and its control on the press. Here we are concerned with control of printed-image size.

The only way to be certain that a job starts with the correct printed-image size is to check the image size at the very beginning. Checking the image size is especially important with color jobs. If the first color is not printed to correct size, each succeeding color becomes more difficult to fit. Size checks should be made even on black-and-white close-tolerance jobs, or black-and-white jobs that are backed-up. The most practical way for checking size is based on the use of the GATF Register Rule.

The GATF Register Rule. This is a specially designed ruler with an adjustable vernier scale at one end. The plate image is measured both in the around-the-cylinder direction as well as across the back end before the plate is put on the press. These measurements are best made against the trim or corner marks. The measurements are noted, and when the first "try" sheets come off the press, the same measurements are made against the printed image. Any difference in image size, in the around-the-cylinder direction, calls

for a shift in packing to attain proper image size. If there is a difference in the across-the-cylinder direction, we are faced with an entirely new set of problems that will be discussed later in this section as well as in the "Ink and Paper" chapter.

Preparing for Bearer-Contact Check. With the proper packing on the cylinders, it is now essential to ascertain whether the bearers are riding in proper contact. A new press, installed by the manufacturer, is not likely to require any attention to this point. But the test for proper bearer-contact is a simple one; it should, therefore, be made periodically, especially on older presses. First you make certain that plate and blanket are packed exactly to the correct *printing* height. Roll up the plate solid, after making sure that it is properly gummed, and permit the blanket to contact the plate for one revolution. Examine the blanket for any areas where ink transfer seems to be weak. These areas should be underlayed with tissue until a uniform print is produced on the blanket as was described in the section on "Leveling the Blanket." Wash the blanket and the plate with an ink solvent, and apply apshaltum to the plate, rubbing it down smooth and dry.

The Thumbprint Test. Now put a good thumbprint of ink on each of the blanket-cylinder bearers, a few inches back of the lead edge of the gap. Make sure the thumbprints are equal as to amount of ink and sharpness. If the bearers are perfectly clean and dry it will be easy to get a nice,

Thumbprints on One Set of Bearers and Position of Sheet Before Test.

sharp thumbprint on the bearers. Put another set of thumbprints on the same bearers but about six inches further back. Take a sheet of .004-inch stock, wide enough to go clear across the blanket. Place its lead edge halfway between the pairs of thumbprints.

With the trip off (impression on), inch the press forward until both pairs of thumbprints pass through the nip. Inch the press *off* the impression until the original thumbprints come in view. Examine the plate cylinder bearers to

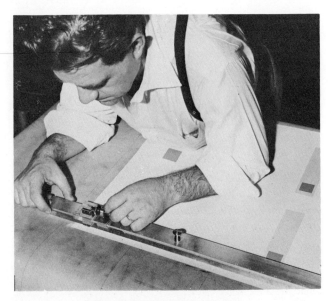

Using the GATF Register Rule.

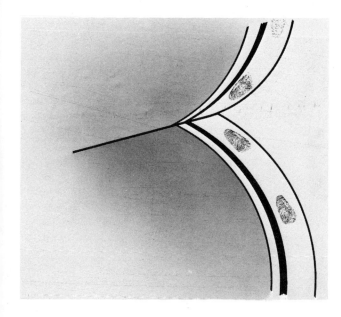

Thumbprints After Test.

see whether a clear set of prints has been transferred from the sets which were put on the blanket cylinder bearers. What you have done, is tried to transfer one set of thumbprints with normal squeeze pressure and another set of thumbprints with .004-inch excess squeeze pressure. If both sets are not fully transferred, it means that the bearers are not riding in firm contact and that they should be set by following the manufacturer's instructions for this particular press.

Too Much Pressure? We have concentrated on not enough pressure but it is often asked, how about too much pressure? Too much pressure it not likely to develop; presses wear, bearings become loose, and the result is to lose pressure, rather than to gain it. But, if by some chance the cylinder adjustments have been brought up too far, resulting in excess squeeze at the bearers, there will be a noticeable slowing down of the press when it goes on impression.

Checking Impression-Cylinder Pressure. Earlier in this section, when we first described the impression cylinder, the reasons for lack of "riding" bearers were discussed. It is timely, at this point, to go into greater detail on the subject of impression-cylinder pressure. Many people in the industry use the term "back-cylinder pressure." In the previous section there was a detailed discussion of pressure adjustment and maintenance between plate and blanket cylinders. Here we are concerned only with the relationship of blanket and impression cylinders, so let us assume that plate and blanket cylinders are properly set.

On many of our smaller presses, but not all, a simple means of moving the impression cylinder towards or away from the blanket cylinder is provided. With the impression on, and in the nip a sheet of the job being run, an experienced pressman can "feel" when he has the proper pressure. On some presses calibrated scales mounted on the press will

show the amount of movement being made. However, before this is done we must be certain that the impression cylinder is perfectly parallel to the blanket cylinder. Feeler gages inserted between blanket- and impression-cylinder bearers, with the impression on, will verify this. To make this paralleling adjustment you must follow the manufacturer's instructions, since the details of construction are quite different on presses of different make and even on presses of the same make but of different size or model.

On the larger presses, and some of the smaller ones, the impression cylinder is rigidly mounted in the frame and all adjustments between blanket and impression cylinders are made at the blanket cylinder. The design of the presses has taken this into consideration and these adjustments can be made without upsetting the relationship between plate and blanket cylinders.

The most important thing to remember about back-cylinder pressure is that it is critical. The fact that it is an easily made adjustment is no reason to change this pressure in the hopes of overcoming poor printed-image quality due to some other cause. The good pressman develops skill in running with minimum squeeze and constantly checks his printed image with a glass. If he spots a fault that might be due to faulty pressures, he checks pressure settings *before* he changes them. If they are correct he looks elsewhere for the trouble. It is important to beware of excess pressure at the impression cylinder because excess pressure will *not* hide print defects resulting from other faults. But excess pressure causes other trouble, mainly resulting in poor image transfer. Steps taken elsewhere to counteract the effects of excess pressure will only compound the troubles.

PUTTING THE PLATE ON THE PRESS

It is assumed that the reader understands the nature of the lithographic plate, if not from experience then from reading "The Platemaking Department" chapter of this manual. Every lithographic journeyman pressman should have this knowledge, although it is not expected that he actually knows how to make a plate himself. In watching the making of a plate, we recognize that it is of a planographic nature because the image and the non-image areas are on the same plane. Observing platemaking makes it obvious that either the printing or the non-printing image area of the plate is protected at each step in preparation for the next operation on the opposite area. The same alternating protection takes place on the press too, during printing. The dampening system protects the non-printing area before the plate passes under the inking form-rollers. Since the ink film on the image is split during transfer to the blanket, the ink remaining on the image protects it against the dampening solution. Neither of these protective treatments could be effective for any length of time if the plate was not made well to begin with. However, there is little excuse for a poor plate with today's techniques and materials.

Our presentation of handling the plate on the press is divided into five parts: (1) Handling the plate to the press; (2) Calipering the plate; (3) The micrometer; (4) Determining the packing height; (5) Inserting the plate in the plate clamps. Each of these points is discussed in the following.

Handling the Plate to the Press. The basic rule for handling plates on the press is to maintain the qualities of printing and non-printing areas. But before we go into the details of accomplishing this, let us consider the base material of the plate itself — the metal. Regardless of the metal used, with the possible exception of steel, a lithographic plate is rather unlike the boiler-plate used to build a battleship. The plate metal is quite thin (pre-sensitized plates are as thin as .005-inch) and therefore easily injured. In handling the plate *to* the press care must be observed not to get any kinks in it. And, of course, the face of the plate should not be scratched nor should any moisture be permitted to get at it — not even perspiration.

Calipering the Plate. When the plate leaves the plateroom it will be under gum and usually under asphaltum. The gum protects the non-printing area and the asphaltum, which is applied after the plate has been gummed, has replaced the developing ink. The pressman should first check that the clamping edges of the plate show no signs of breaking, if the plate metal has been used before. The next operation is to caliper the plate. If a GATF Blanket Thick-

Miking the Plate.

ness Gage has been installed in the pressroom, use it for greatest accuracy. (A description of the GATF Blanket Gage can be found in the Resources Section of this chapter.) Where the GATF Blanket Thickness Gage is not available, the micrometer will do a good job, if properly handled.

The Micrometer. The successful operation of an offset press is almost impossible without the proper use of the micrometer. Packing of plate and blanket must be accurate within a tolerance of approximately .001-inch. The micrometer is a simple precision tool and its use, with a little practice, is easily mastered.

The basis of the micrometer is a screw which turns through a fixed nut to vary the opening between the two measuring faces. The graduations on the barrel and thimble indicate precisely the amount of the opening between the measuring faces. Graduations on the barrel conform to the pitch of the measuring screw, one line for every revolution. The graduations on the beveled edge of the thimble accurately subdivide each revolution of the screw so that readings may be taken in units of .001 of an inch.

Each line on the barrel represents .025 of an inch. Each line on the thimble represents .001 of an inch, as already stated. Each visible line is counted and added to the figure on the thimble. The result is a reading in thousandths of an inch. If, for example, you see 9 lines on the barrel, then you have .225 inch (9 x 25). If you then see 16 on the thimble, the result is .225 plus 16 which equals .241 inch. Beginners are advised to practice on paper or any material, under one inch in thickness. A proper understanding of the micrometer is essential for the skilled offset pressman. When "miking" a plate, be sure it is on the table and lying flat or hanging straight in the front clamps. Any flexing of the plate while miking will give a reading greater than the actual caliper of the plate.

Determining the Packing Height. If you subtract the thickness of the plate from the plate-cylinder undercut, the difference is the required packing to bring the plate to bearer height. The manufacturers' instructions dictate whether or not the plate is to be packed above bearer height. If so, add the required thickness of packing. Before actually mounting the plate, make certain that the back of the plate is clean of any foreign material such as paper, grease, ink blots, and so on. Check the plate cylinder and make certain it is clean; be sure that the plate clamps are centered and that the lead clamp is up against the face of the gap. Starting every plate at the same point makes it easier to obtain lay, especially if the platemaker has a standard distance for each press. This distance can be agreed on, for example, as the paper line on the flat. Lines can be inscribed in the groove between bearer and cylinder body to which the pressman always aligns the plate marks. Most

Packing the Plate.

of this is of course unnecessary on presses equipped with pin-register systems, provided the preparatory work is standardized to such a system, and the plates punched and accurately lined up with the punched flat.

Inserting the Plate in the Plate Clamps. The plate should be inserted in the lead plate clamps and locked. Then the packing sheets should be placed behind it in such a way that the front edge of the sheet or sheets extends beyond the edge of the cylinder body. This will lock-in the sheets and prevent their shifting or wrinkling. Sideways, the sheets should be a trifle narrower than the plate. With the impression on, inch the press until the tail clamps are in a convenient position. The squeeze of the blanket cylinder helps wrap the plate snugly around the cylinder. Then you insert the back edge of the plate into the clamps

and draw the plate up tight. In this step the pressman should use his judgment. It is not necessary to exert such a strong pull that the threads of the tightening screws are stripped or the plate torn. Inch the press off impression and then tighten and lock the lead clamp screws. Check to see that the plate is still properly aligned, and then lock the screws on the tail clamp.

On small size presses the angle between the plate clamps and the cylinder body is rather acute. In such cases it is helpful if the clamping edges of the plate are bent before mounting it on the cylinder. This is best done by making a plate-bending jig similar to that illustrated. The dimensions are those for an ATF Chief 22. The measurements for any other press are easily obtained by measuring a plate that has been removed from the press.

Section Six: The Printing Unit, II: Inking and Dampening Systems

In this section we present the second half of the printing unit, the inking and dampening systems. Each of the two is first described and then operationally discussed.

THE INKING SYSTEM

The lithographic process makes more demands on its inking system than any of the other printing processes. Some people have said that the size of roller train and the number of rollers are due only to traditional beliefs. The fact is, however, that all attempts to simplify the system have so far failed. This is still true, even though the working and running properties of today's inks are vastly improved over those which existed when the lithographic offset press entered the printing field.

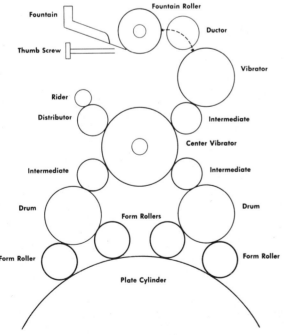

Schematic of Typical Inking System.

Ordinarily, one might think of an inking mechanism as a device whose function is to deposit ink on the printing image. This is true in all printing processes. But on a lithographic press the inking mechanism must perform other functions too, and with far greater efficiency than is demanded of their inking units by the intaglio or relief process. The lithographic image carrier is planographic; its image area is on the same plane as its non-image area. The form rollers of the ink train, therefore, contact both image and non-image areas at the same time. This condition imposes in itself a severe demand on the image-inking operation.

The Five Main Functions of the Inking System. The inking system on a lithographic offset press must perform the following functions: (1) It must "work" the ink by conditioning it from what is essentially a plastic state to that of a semi-liquid; (2) It must distribute a small, comparatively thick band of ink on the ductor roller to an even, thin film around all the form rollers; (3) It must deposit a uniformly even, thin film of ink on the image; (4) It must pick up fountain solution from the lithographic plate, emulsify some of this into the ink, and evaporate the rest into the atmosphere; (5) It should pick up from the lithographic plate any particles of foreign matter and hold them until the entire mechanism is cleaned.

The Controversial Role of Water. Much of the above is open to argument. Some say that emulsification takes place when the press is not being operated properly. Others say that the lithographic process itself would not function if a controlled amount of emulsification did not take place. Actually, we have a condition similar to that of the drunkard, who — on seeing a giraffe for the first time — said: "I don't believe it." It is stated here, as a fact based on experience, that we must accept the above listed functions, and that we can handle the system to accomplish them efficiently. Then, and only then, does the lithographic process realize its full potential of quality and quantity of production.

THE THREE MAIN SECTIONS OF THE INKING SYSTEM

For convenience, we can consider the inking system of the lithographic offset press as having three distinct sections: (1) The ink fountain or reservoir section; (2) The distribution section; and (3) The form roller section. Each of these three sections is individually discussed in the following.

The Ink Fountain Section. The ink fountain is a reservoir for the ink supply. Its peculiar shape and position — a "V," lying on its side — is not accidental. One leg of the "V," the upper one, is actually a steel roller and is called the fountain roller or fountain ball. The other leg of the "V" is a blade, set to have one edge very close to the fountain roller and capable of having the space between blade and roller adjustable. The fountain roller is rotated intermittently against the blade and draws ink with it through the gap set between the roller and the blade.

When the fountain roller rotates, a resilient ductor roller is held against it and picks up a supply of the ink drawn through the fountain. The amount of fountain roller rotation and the gap set between roller and fountain blade combine to give control of the amount of ink which the ductor roller picks up and carries to the distribution section. Changing the amount of roller rotation governs the supply of ink across the entire roller train. Changing the gap between fountain roller and fountain blade can be accomplished in order to control the amount of ink flow within a specific area along the horizontal dimension of the plate.

The Ink Distribution Section. The distribution section usually comprises metal drums, (sometimes called storage rolls) and a series of resilient rollers in conjunction with metal. Some of the smaller sized presses, especially those of the duplicator type, use hard-rubber or Bakelite instead of metal rollers. Many modern presses use copper-plated metal rollers since copper is one of the most ink-receptive metals. Where a press is not equipped with copper-plated roller, the pressman may chemically copper-plate them periodically. Examination of a roller train will show that there is always a resilient roller (composition, vulcanized oil, or soft rubber) between any two hard rollers (metal, rubber, or Bakelite). The train itself is driven through gears or chains which connect the driven drums to the main drive of the press. The design of the drive is such that the "surface" speed of the rollers is exactly that of the lithographic plate when it is packed to proper printing height. All the resilient rollers are driven through friction contact, directly or indirectly derived from the drums. It is extremely important to know, and remember this point. Under no circumstance should a condition be permitted to exist where the form rollers are driven as a result of friction between them and the plate. These rollers must be driven through friction between them and the press-driven metal-drums.

The distribution section is so designed that between fountain and form rollers the ink is "worked" considerably. The form rollers, consequently, receive a constant and pro-rated supply of properly conditioned ink for each impression which the press makes.

In the designing of the inking unit, attention has been paid to the number of separate rollers required. This number is important because the number of times the ink-film is split when transferring from one roller to another roller is a factor in conditioning the ink. Another design feature that should be noticed is that the driven drums oscillate sideways. This motion assists in working the ink because it is an action similar to grinding. This oscillation helps prevent "ridging" of the ink by accomplishing lateral distribution. The circumferential distribution is accomplished by the use of drums and rollers of different diameters. Last, but not least, if you trace the flow of ink from the ductor roller to the form rollers, you will note the effort made to feed ink to all form rollers in such a way as to produce a uniform film of ink around all the form rollers and on the plate in the around-the-cylinder direction. Thus far, it has been impossible to attain an ideal condition of complete uniformity. The press manufacturers, however, have always striven and still are striving to achieve such a system.

The Form-Roller Section. The form-roller section consists of two to four form rollers, depending on the press size. Some of the presses, with four form-rollers, have, in addition, one intermediate hard roller, sometimes self-oscillating, between the two pairs of form rollers. This arrangement is another attempt to achieve an ink-film of prorated thickness on all form rollers at all times. The form rollers are sometimes more resilient by comparison to those used in the distribution system and are made of vulcanized oil, rubber or synthetic composition. Each form roller is driven by one of the smaller metal drums and is, of course, so set that it makes proper contact with the lithographic plate when the press is running. The form rollers are, as previously explained, not driven by the plate but through the drums, if they are set properly.

In general, the form rollers are of near uniform diameter. It has been established that uniform form-roller diameter leads to "ghosting" problems, especially when light tints are being run. For this reason, in recent years, the inking system has been so designed as to accommodate form rollers of different diameters. Sometimes all four form rollers are slightly different (about one-sixteenth inch difference between each roller); in other cases, the first and last roller have one size while the in-between rollers are each of a smaller size. Where a pressman is operating a press not supplied with form rollers ground to different sizes, he may have them changed, provided the press design permits accommodation of a roller size different from the manufacturer's original specifications.

The inking system is here described in more detail than might be expected. But the author feels that a thorough knowledge of the subject, particularly of the design features, is a necessity for understanding the discussion on handling the inking system which follows the presentation of the dampening unit, our next topic. It is understood, of course, that this discussion of the inking system, like all others in this chapter, is general in nature. Each manufacturer has expended large sums in research, engineering and development. It is imperative that the pressman who is running the press follow the manufacturer's instruction manual for the mechanical details of handling its specific inking system.

THE DAMPENING SYSTEM

Of all the printing processes only lithography requires a plate-treating system in conjunction with inking. It is easy to understand the reason for this if one keeps in mind the peculiar nature of the lithographic plate. It is planographic, meaning, as we know, that the image areas are in the same plane as the non-image areas. The image areas are hydrophobic, which means they are not receptive to water. They do, of course, accept greasy ink. The non-image areas are hydrophylic, which means they are receptive to water but resist greasy ink. It must, however, be understood at the outset that both image and non-image areas must be continually treated during running to retain their individual properties.

It is true of course that the ink-receptive properties of the lithographic plate are quite difficult to destroy — if the plate is properly made. However, the water-receptive characteristics of the non-image areas can be destroyed within a matter of seconds if, during running, the dampening rollers are kept from contacting the plate. A well made plate,

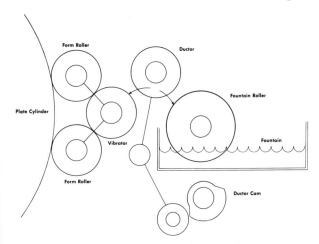

Schematic of a Conventional Dampening System.

running on a properly operated press, will print a strong sharp image while retaining perfectly clean non-printing areas for extremely long runs. This is true even in the infinitesimally small, clear spaces between dots of a 300-line halftone plate.

The Main Components of the Conventional Dampening System. The dampening system of the lithographic offset press consists of three basic components: (1) The water fountain; (2) A vibrating distributor roller; and (3) The form dampeners. The water fountain, generally called pan, is a reservoir for the dampening solution which is applied to the plate. In it is a roller that may be either of brass, chrome plated, or cloth covered. In rotating, this roller lifts some solution out of the pan. Another roller, the ductor, rests intermittently against the water-pan roller. The ductor roller is generally covered with a fairly thick, absorbent cloth, known as molleton; it soaks up so-

lution from the water roller. The ductor oscillates between the pan roller and a metal distributing roller. When the ductor roller contacts the metal distributor roller, some of the surplus water is transferred. The distributor roller, in turn, spreads this solution evenly over the entire surface of two form-dampening rollers with which it is in constant contact. These are also covered. The dampening rollers deposit solution in the non-printing areas of the plates just before the plate passes the inking form rollers.

This description makes the dampening system appear to be a rather simple device. This is admittedly true. However, the tremendous improvements in lithographic plate-making techniques made in recent years seem to justify the feeling that the dampening system was not the cause of many of our troubles in the past. The basic fault was poorly made plates resulting in unduly severe demands on the dampening system.

In recent years we have not only learned to make better plates but also learned a lot about the chemistry of dampening. In addition to research on dampening itself, much work is being done to find another and better method of dampening for keeping the non-printing areas of the plate absolutely clean during extended periods of running.

The reader must always keep in mind that just as the inking form rollers contact both the image and non-image areas of the plate, so do the dampening form rollers. While the form rollers of the inking system *tend* to resist water, especially because they are covered with greasy ink, they will pick up some dampening solution, especially if an excessive amount is being supplied to the plate. The dampening rollers, even though wet with a solution which is generally about 99.984 percent water, are not too well protected because of the very slight amount of solution carried by them. Therefore, they are easily greased by the ink on the plate unless both the inking and dampening systems are very carefully handled. A greasy dampening system will not function with even the slightest degree of efficiency and consistency.

New Dampening Systems. Most of what has been written here is oriented to conventional dampening, that is, a system employing a water pan (the fountain), water pan rollers, ductor roller, vibrator, and dampening form rollers. This is, by far, the widest used system. Over the years, much work has been done in three directions: (1) To improve the materials used in the system; (2) To improve the system by modifying designs; (3) To change, entirely, the dampening method. (Technically, there is even a fourth — to eliminate dampening completely. But this is still a dream for the future).

The most important recent change in materials is the development of paper covers for the dampening form rollers. This is discussed more fully in the section on handling the dampening system. Recent modifications in the system have been aimed at improving the feeding of water to the vibrator. In one method a constantly revolving brush replaces the ductor and, through contact with the pan roller, flicks water to the vibrator. The speed of the motor-driven pan roller, and the pressure of the rotating brush against the pan roller are variable for control of amount of water distributed to the dampener form rollers. Another technique for feeding water uses a rotating shaft on which flaps of leather or molleton are mounted. This assembly replaces both the ductor and pan roller. As the shaft rotates, the flappers pick up moisture from the pan and wipe the moisture on the vibrator rollers.

Over the years only two really new systems reached a stage where they become operable. The "Diffusor" system deposits a heavy film of water on the plate without actual contact. The plate then passes under an "air knife" which cuts away the surplus moisture. The system showed great promise, but is not in wide use because of its cost, the power consumed by the air knife, the need for constant maintenance to keep the system absolutely clean and free of dirt and solids, and its high level of noise.

Within the last five years the Dahlgren dampening system has gained acceptance which is increasing rapidly. The basic principle of the system is not new. It is based on using the inking system to carry the required moisture to the plate, as well as the ink. But until Harold Dahlgren, a press engineer, tackled the problem, the basic principle was used only in the offset duplicator field. The Dahlgren dampener retains the familiar water pan with its water pan roller. However, this roller, which is rubber, contacts a steel roller also running in the pan. The rubber roller meters the water film which the steel roller lifts out of the pan. The steel roller runs against another special Dahlgren roller, which serves also as the first form roller. The direction of rotating of the plate cylinder in relation to the form roller is such that water deposited on the ink roller contacts the plate first, rather than being carried up into the ink train. Control of water supply is attained through speed control of the pan roller as well as the adjustable squeeze between the rubber pan roller and the intermediate steel roller.

Our description of the inking and dampening units is now completed, and we can turn to the handling and operating of both systems.

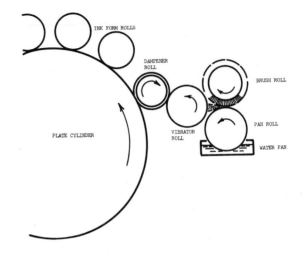

Continuous Brush Water Feed

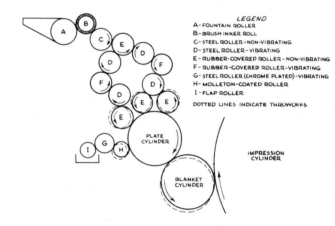

LEGEND
A - FOUNTAIN ROLLER
B - BRUSH INKER ROLL
C - STEEL ROLLER - NON-VIBRATING
D - STEEL ROLLER - VIBRATING
E - RUBBER-COVERED ROLLER - NON-VIBRATING
F - RUBBER-COVERED ROLLER - VIBRATING
G - STEEL ROLLER (CHROME PLATED) - VIBRATING
H - MOLLETON-COATED ROLLER
I - FLAP ROLLER

DOTTED LINES INDICATE THROWOFFS

Flap Feeding System

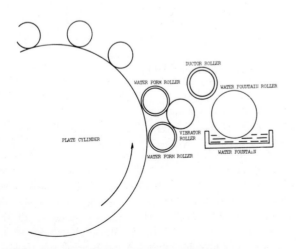

Conventional Dampening System

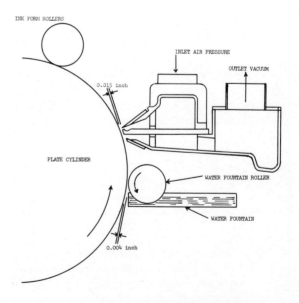

Mullen Dampening System

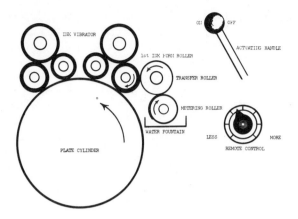

Dahlgren Dampening System

HANDLING THE INKING SYSTEM

The general characteristics and functions of the inking system were described in the previous section. Insofar as selection and principles of handling rollers are concerned, the problems here are similar to those discussed in connection with the offset blanket. The "soft" rollers (all those other than steel, hard rubber, and Bakelite) are available in different materials: (1) Natural rubber; (2) Synthetic rubber; (3) A combination of natural and synthetic rubber; (4) Vulcanized oil; and (5) Various plastics. All of these materials have special properties and will very satisfactorily do the job for which they were designed, provided they are selected intelligently and handled properly. The best advice is, again, to pay heed to the press manufacturer, the roller maker, the ink maker, and your supplier of solvents and similar materials. Follow their advice and instructions; then, and only then, may you hold them responsible for results. If the system is adjusted to the press manufacturers' specifications, if it is kept clean, and if the proper kind of rollers are used with the particular kind of ink, the system will perform. It is assumed, of course, that ink and water are in proper balance and that the dampening solution is compatible with the plate and ink being run.

Replacing the Fountain Blade.

Our discussion of the subject is divided into the following seven points: (1 Keeping the fountain clean; (2) Setting the fountain blade; (3) Regulating the ink flow; (4) Adjusting and setting of rollers; (5) Wash-up procedures; (6) Steel drums and rollers; and (7) Storage of rollers. Each of these points is now discussed.

Keeping the Fountain Clean. As simple as the fountain is, it is very often seriously damaged because of improper handling. There is no excuse for this because — as has been stated previously — it does not take any longer to handle it properly than improperly. A fountain in good condition is actually not only a timesaver, but a back saver. The need for cleanliness is not difficult to understand when we think of following a job printed in black ink with a process yellow ink for a four-color process job. But a sloppy washup can result in an aggravating amount of trouble caused by dirty fountain keys, a buckled fountain blade, or

Checking Aperture between Fountain Blade and Fountain Roller With Feeler Gage.

a scored fountain roller. When a fountain is cleaned it is important to see that *all* parts of the fountain are clean. The keys should be clean of ink and solvent. The base of the fountain and such rods or bars as may be located under the fountain should also be clean and dry. Periodically, all keys should be taken out, and both keys and keyholes should be carefully cleaned. Where grease is allowed for, to prevent ink from drying in the side blocks, it should be used as directed.

Setting the Fountain Blade. After cleaning, the blade is put back in the fountain. Some presses have fountain blades which are not removed from the press. The blade is so mounted that it drops back and down, away from the fountain roller. However, after cleaning, the blade is swung back to its operating position and then handled as described here. The pressman makes certain that it is seated in accordance with the manufacturer's instructions. Now, all keys are started in their respective holes. Turn up the center key until it just touches the blade and starts to push the blade towards the fountain roller. Do the same with all other keys — *working from the center out*. Now you start gradually closing the gap between blade and roller to the desired aperture, always working from the center out

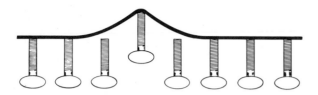

Schematic Showing how a Buckle May Be Developed in the Fountain Blade

to both ends. Judgment, developed through experience, is the only real guide for this operation. However, a good start is often possible by setting the blade to a feeler gage of .005 inch thickness. From this original setting you come up again gradually, always working from the center to either end. If the gap between blade and roller appears to change at some other point than at the particular key that you are actually setting, it signifies that the blade is buckled. In this case the blade should be replaced since these buckles cannot be overcome by setting the keys.

Final Setting of the Fountain

After the initial setting you put ink in the fountain and you turn the roller continuously. Now, the amount of ink flow can be further adjusted for the job on hand. Where overall adjustment is required, you *work again from the center out when you are closing the gap* and you *work from the ends to the center when you are opening it*. Following this rule will go a long way toward preventing buckles in the blade. One thing should never be done when setting the fountain blade; that is to set any part of the blade so tight that it actually scrapes the roller clean. In this case you may score the roller and you will definitely grind the blade because there is no lubricating action by the ink. Regardless of how little the required ink flow may be in a particular area, you can always get it without ever scraping the ball clean.

Regulating the Ink Flow. The amount of ink flow from the fountain is governed by two things: (1) The

amount of ink passing between the blade and fountain roller; and (2) The distance through which the roller turns during the time when the ductor dwells against the fountain roller. This distance is adjustable by a ratchet or some other device at one end of the fountain. You should set the fountain in such a way that the device is set at about three-quarters of the full swing — the bigger the swing the better! In other words, a *thin film of fresh ink deposited around one-third of the ductor-roller surface is better than a thick film deposited around one-sixth of the ductor-roller surface.* The reason why you should not attempt to set the fountain feed for the full swing is easy to see; if it is necessary to increase the overall ink flow you would have no adjustment left at the fountain ratchet and would be forced to make the adjustment at the keys. The key adjustment is, of course, far more troublesome and timeconsuming.

When an extremely light flow of ink is desired over the entire plate, a spiral may be cut out of a spare ductor roller. This roller can be kept in roller storage for use whenever needed. If you cut a spiral out of the ductor, a smaller area is left for contacting the fountain ball. Then you can still set the fountain ratchet for a good swing of the roller and not feed too much ink. Finally, you must not forget that the ductor roller must be checked for parallelism with the fountain as well as the ink train. The fountain is usually so mounted that it can be shifted slightly to be made parallel with the ductor roller after the ductor roller has been paralleled to the ink train.

Adjusting and Setting of Rollers. On the lithographic offset press, rollers are usually adjustable in at least one direction. In some cases they may ride free and depend on their own weight for proper contact. The manufacturers' manuals give clear instructions on this point. In this Manual we concentrate on general problems, and try here to provide you with some practical hints on the handling and setting of rollers.

Checking for Minimum Flow of Ink between Fountain Blade and Fountain Roller.

The universally accepted method of setting the rollers in the inking system is by inserting a set of thin paper strips. This set is made of two strips about two inches wide and a third strip about one inch to one and one-half inches wide.

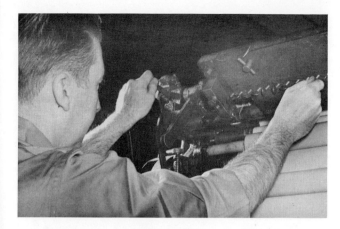

Setting Fountain Ratchet and Fountain Key.

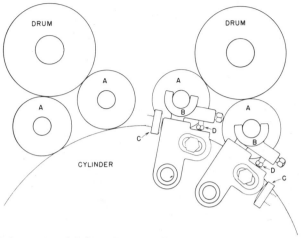

Schematic of Inking Form Rollers. C — Adjustment to drum; D — Adjustment to plate.

This narrower strip is sandwiched between the two wider strips. These three strips are inserted between the rollers to be adjusted, or between roller and plate. A set of strips is inserted near each end of the rollers being tested. By pulling on the center, a fairly accurate and even setting can be made. What amount of tension on this center strip is required for a good setting is learned by experience. Size and hardness of the rollers are two factors which determine the pressure required. When rollers are changed in the press, this adjustment system should be used before any attempt is made to ink up the system. Every time after making these adjustments you should check their accuracy by taking a "picture" on the plate.

After the fountain is set and the rollers are adjusted in the manner specified by the manufacturer, you are ready for the inking of the system. Spread a thin film of ink with a spatula on the uppermost roller in the train (the "top-on" roller if there is one), and make sure that the ink film is even. Now you start the press with this film and the ink-feed from the fountain. Let the press run until there is just about the normal amount of ink on the roller train and then stop the fountain feed. Now you stop the press in such a position that the plate is under the form inking

rollers. You must reach this position without inching the press.

When we finished putting the plate on the press we had rolled it up solid, as you recall, to test the blanket. You also remember that we then washed off the ink with a solvent and replaced the asphaltum. Now you lower the inking mechanism to the plate, carefully and without bouncing. Leave the inking mechanism down for a few seconds and then lift it up. Next you inch the press to a point where the form roller marks are easily visible; each form roller should have left an even print across the plate. The width of the line depends on the hardness of the roller and its size. One-eighth inch is a good average "bite." The last roller over the plate, usually called the #1 roller, should have the lightest bite. The first roller over the plate, the one nearest the dampening system, should have the heaviest bite.

The form rollers must be adjusted to the plate and to the ink drum. On some presses the sequence of adjustment is first to the plate and then to the form; on other presses this sequence is reversed. The manufacturer's manual tells you the sequence of a particular press. If you do not follow

A Spiral-Cut Ink Ductor Roller.

Preparing for Picture Test.

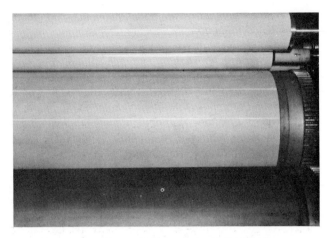

Picture on Plate of Two of the Form Rollers.

Picture of Form Roller-to-Drum Bite.

these instructions you will have to readjust again because whichever adjustment you make first, out of proper sequence, will be upset by the second adjustment and, consequently, require doing over. In all cases the picture method should be used as a final check on the adjustment of the form rollers.

The adjustment of the rollers to the press plate is tested by an impression of the rollers against the plate, whereas the adjustment of the rollers to the ink drum or vibrators is tested by an impression of all soft rollers on either ink drum or vibrators. To get a picture of the setting between soft and hard rollers is a bit more difficult than getting a picture of the roller setting to the plate. Run the press for several revolutions and stop it. Let the press stand for several seconds and then inch it just once, *and sharply,* in the direction away from the nip which is being checked. You will see a bead on both rollers. The width of this bead represents a fair picture of the bite between the two rollers depending on type of ink and rollers. Where a roller contacts two other rollers, the bite at both nips should be

the same. On the inking form rollers the bite between the form rollers and the vibrator drums must be a little greater than the bite between roller and plate. This is necessary to assure firm driving of the rollers by the inking system rather than by the plate.

It is advisable to use this system periodically to check the roller settings. It only takes a few moments but assures you that if trouble develops the inking system is not contributing to it. GATF's Press Department Memo No. 4 describes a very handy device and simple technique for setting both ink and dampening rollers. As a further measure against trouble due to the inking system, it is essential to maintain the system clean and to keep the rollers in good condition. Their desirable operating condition is similar to that of the offset blanket.

Wash-Up Procedures. Modern wash-up materials and techniques considerably reduce the need for pulling rollers out of the press for hand cleaning. Nor do they require washing with harsh solvents, scraping and as used to be sometimes the case, even grinding. The newer materials dissolve all gum as well as ink, varnish, resin, etc., off the

Comparing Roller Bite on Plate With That on Drum.

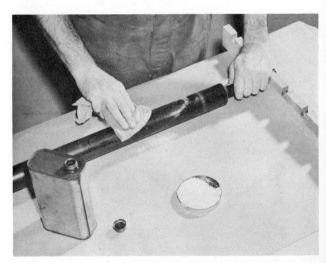

Pumicing an Inking Roller.

Washing-up the Inking System. Note that only one-half at a time is done.

Chemically Copper-Plating the Steel Rollers.

rollers. In fact, they do such a perfect job that old rollers often only held together by dried gum, ink and varnish, practically disintegrate when cleaned by these methods. But such rollers should not be in the press anyway! Again, rely on your supplier for the proper materials and follow his instructions. Then you may hold him responsible for the results, or you may switch to another material.

These newer wash-up materials generally require a two- or three-stage wash-up procedure. To really clean the rollers in an ink train, requires more than a single solution or a one-stage procedure, since getting dried gum out of the ink rollers presents an entirely different problem than cleansing the train of ink. These multi-stage materials, as a general rule, are not used for routine wash-ups. If used once a week they will keep the system really clean and the rollers in good condition, thereby eliminating an important cause of hickies and roller stripping. These materials will also prevent excessive emulsification, to some extent at least. This doesn't, however, permanently eliminate the

need for periodic hand-cleaning of rollers removed from the press.

Steel Drums and Rollers. Another important factor in good inking is the nature of the storage drums and of the metal rollers in the train. These are usually steel, sometimes copper-plated. Steel has quite an affinity for water, and after a time, gum from the fountain solution begins to dry on steel rollers. This is especially true if too much acid or gum is used in the fountain solution. Another source of this trouble is the bad habit of permitting the strong acids from the plate etches to get into the ink train. This happens if the plate etches are not washed off the plate thoroughly when starting the press.

When this happens steel rollers lose their affinity for ink. To prevent the loss of ink affinity of steel rollers some plants send these rollers out for copper plating. Copper is one of our most ink receptive and at the same time most water repellent metals. Electroplating these rollers with copper is expensive, although the most effective method. GATF has developed a method of chemically copper-plating these rollers during the wash-up operation. This method is much less expensive and the plating lasts quite a while, except on the roller which contacts the scraper blade of the washing machine. However, chemical plating is done so easily and the materials are so inexpensive, that this single disadvantage is very inconsequential.

Storage of Rollers. Spare form rollers, whether new or old, should never be stored without first being thoroughly cleaned and conditioned. This condition should be similar to that of a restored blanket. If proper, modern wash-up techniques are not being used, this conditioning operation may be a lengthy and vigorous one. If the inking system is handled properly, all that may be required is to powder the roller and stand it in the roller locker. If harsher methods must be used, follow the advice of the supplier of the rollers.

Rollers should never be stored by hanging in a horizontal rack. They should always be in an upright position. When handling them, care must be taken not to bounce them on

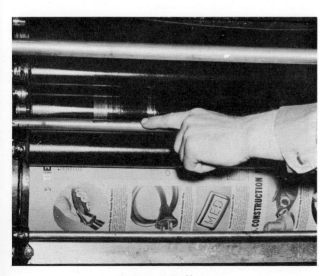

Stripped Rollers.

an end or drop them. A large roller especially, can be easily bent and the slightest bend will make proper setting in the press impossible.

Rollers should be stored in a locker which can be kept closed. If this is not possible, the roller rack should be in a dark, cool area. Never permit sunlight to fall, for any length of time, on "soft" rollers. When a roller is put into storage its surface should be protected. Whether to use only powder or vaseline, or similar products should be determined by discussion with the roller manufacturer.

HANDLING THE DAMPENING SYSTEM

The conventional dampening system is essentially the same as that used since the times of stone lithography, despite the fact that it is one area of press design which has received considerable attention in order to find a better way of dampening the plate. Before we consider the problems of handling the system, we pause for a general discussion of dampening, its purpose and problems. Then we will present the following specific points: (1) The water fountain; (2) The dampener vibrator; (3) Care and adjustment of dampening form-rollers; (4) Dampener covers; (5) Breaking in new dampening form-rollers; and (6) The starting of the dampening system. Each of the above mentioned points is now individually discussed.

The Purpose and Problem of Dampening. When originally describing the function of the inking system, earlier in this section, it was mentioned that a certain amount of dampening solution is picked up by the inking system. There it was pointed out that picking up solution by the inking system was not harmful within certain limits. In fact, some people believe that if this didn't happen we couldn't print lithographically with any high degree of satisfaction. However, the dampening system — different from the inking system — has just one, and really only one function. This function is to dampen the non-image area

Courtesy Jomac, Inc.

A Dampener Roller Washing Machine for Molleton-Covered Rollers.

of the plate. While the dampening system contacts the image area, it must definitely resist picking up any ink.

In actual practice, this is virtually impossible. But if the fountain solution is compatible with plate, paper and ink used on a specific job, if the inking and dampening systems are properly adjusted, if the correct amounts of ink and water are fed to the plate, then there should not be too much trouble with dampeners becoming dirty and greasy too quickly.

If and when they do, the dampening rollers should be pulled out of the press and cleaned immediately. For this reason a spare set of dampeners should be available at all times for each press. The changeover does not take too long, and the dirty set can be washed away from the press.

In recent years, dampener washing machines have been developed which do an excellent job of cleaning, provided that ink has not been permitted to dry on the molleton with which the dampening rollers are sometimes covered. These washing machines are also excellent for "running-in" a freshly covered dampener, if molleton is being used as the cover. They save time and trouble on the press by removing the lint, fuzz, and loose fibers from freshly covered dampeners, preventing them from reaching the ink train or the plate. Once a dampener has been used, it must always be put back in the press without turning it end for end. If it is put in wrong, the twist of the covering, caused by its original use, will be reversed and the whole cover becomes loose and baggy.

Many of the press troubles in the past have been blamed on the need for, and the method of dampening the lithographic plate. However, our problems have decreased, although it is hard to tell how much of this decrease is due to improved plates. But work is constantly going on to improve dampening methods. One simple improvement, the use of paper or cloth dampener covers to replace the molleton, is mentioned further down in this presentation.

The Design and Functioning of the Water Fountain. The fountain of the dampening system has the same function as the ink fountain. However, because of the nature of the fountain solution — which consists of over 99 percent water — existing local controls across the plate are lacking by comparison to the controls we have at our disposal when handling the ink fountain. As stated above, however, work is constantly being done to improve the operation of dampening.

The fountain roller, in most presses, revolves constantly, and part of its surface is always immersed in the fountain solution. The fountain roller is a metal roller, sometimes used bare and sometimes covered with cloth. A ductor roller, covered usually with a molleton sleeve, oscillates between the fountain roller and the dampening vibrator-roller which is also a metal roller. The length of time which the ductor roller "dwells" against the fountain roller governs the amount of water that will be fed to the vibrator periodically. Like ink, fountain solutions are not always fed with each revolution of the press. On some presses the fountain roller is driven by its own motor. This arrangement gives additional control over the amount of fountain solution

Courtesy American Type Founders

Typical Dampening System. Note bare pan roller and molleton-covered ductor and plate-dampening roller, water pan.

Several Types of Pan Roller Motor Drives.

fed to the system since with it we have an infinitely variable-speed drive.

The Dampener Vibrator. The vibrator roller is always gear-driven through the main drive of the press, and its surface speed is identical to that of the cylinders. This roller does two jobs: (1) It drives the dampening form rollers; and (2) It equalizes the water feed across the dampening system through a considerable sideways oscillation. The two dampening form rollers are generally covered with molleton and, while driven by the vibrator, contact the plate with just enough pressure to dampen it. They must not miss any part of the plate, nor should they squeegee the plate because of excessive pressure.

Care and Adjustment of Dampening Form Rollers. Improper care and handling of the dampening form rollers is the most important cause of dampening troubles. When they are molleton covered, a perfectly true, even and level surface is impossible to attain on these rollers. Therefore, and particularly if we wish to achieve a light and even roller pressure on the plate, every serious unevenness of the molleton-covered roller will immediately show up as a point of too much or too little pressure. Reasonable care when covering the rollers with molleton can help prevent these troubles. At the time when the covers were still sewn on, a great deal of skill was required to make a really good roller. Now, however, the dampener covers can be bought as pre-sewn or pre-woven sleeves. This, of course, simplifies the task but does not eliminate the need for good care.

Roller adjustments, as we have said repeatedly, should be checked periodically to make sure they have held their original setting. The manner of adjustment is generally similar to that of the inking form rollers.

Courtesy Harris-Intertype Corp.

Another Dampening System. Note water stops and cloth-covered pan roller.

Setting Dampening Form Roller to Plate.

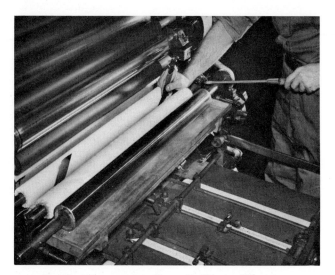

Setting Dampening Form Roller to Vibrator.

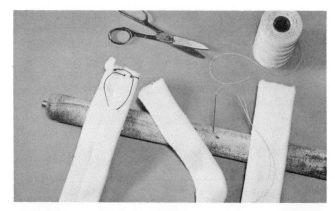

Paper Covered Dampeners. In recent years the use of special parchment paper strips for covering dampener form-rollers has gained very wide popularity. This specially made paper is wound, spirally, around a roller whose circumference is large enough to fit properly into the dampening system with just the thin paper covering. This roller also has a specially formulated rubber to give proper resiliency.

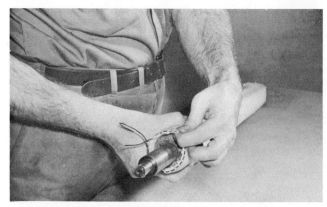

This paper covering is generally considered to have numerous advantages over cloth covered dampening form rollers. The paper is considerably less costly than molleton or other cloth covering materials despite the fact that a paper cover does not last as long. Wrapping a fresh paper cover is done very much faster than putting on a cloth cover, even the sleeve-type covers. Because the pa-

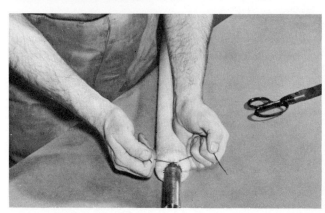

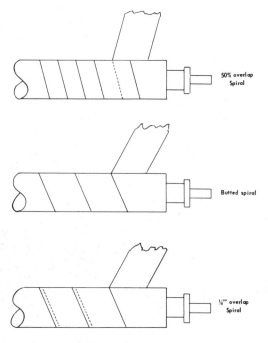

50% overlap
Spiral

Butted spiral

1/4" overlap
Spiral

Three Methods of Wrapping Paper Covers

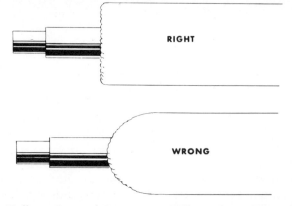

RIGHT

WRONG

Molleton-Covered Dampening Rollers. Top — Tying the end of the sleeve-type molleton; Bottom — Comparison of good and bad roller ends when using molleton type sleeves.

per is not costly and because it is so easily replaced, there is no tendency to run a cover too long. Whenever a newly covered cloth dampener form roller is installed the roller must be set for proper contact with plate and vibrator. These adjustments may have to be changed during the life of the cover because there is some decrease in overall roller diameter. This is not the case with a paper covered dampener. With the smooth plates so widely used, the paper-covered dampener is able to lay down a more controllable thin film of water which such plates require. With just reasonable care, these covers will not become greasy.

Experience has shown that best results are obtained with these paper covers when only one of the dampener form rollers is so covered. This roller should be run in the low position in the dampening system. A conventional cloth covered dampener form roller is used in the upper position. However, this roller is so set that it touches the vibrator but not the plate. It performs the function of a storage roller. By putting it in the upper position, with the paper covered roller in the lower position, the bead of water fed by the ductor roller is spread out before the vibrator feeds to the paper-covered form roller.

Work is now in progress to develop this paper covering material in a sleeve form. Such a sleeve would eliminate one of the drawbacks to the use of paper strips. The spiral winding, especially if in a single layer, may create a ghosting pattern of the spiral when running large solids of tint colors. This can be eliminated almost completely by double wrapping.

Thin Cloth Sleeves. Thin cloth covers come as prewoven sleeves which are pulled over specially rubber-covered or cloth damper base material. What's aimed at, by these materials, is a combination of the advantages of the paper and conventional molleton-type covers. Sleeves of this type, however, are not available for larger presses.

Some General Observations on Dampening. Some general comment is in order on this business of dampener covers. The author does not presume to be an all-knowing expert. And even if he were he would not flatly state a preference. What is said *emphatically* is that management as well as the man-on-the-bench should always be alert to new methods, materials and equipment. Coupled to this alertness should be a really open-mindedness toward claims for new things. They should be tried, and in all fairness to everyone concerned, the trial should be an accurate one as well as one of sufficient duration. Those who introduce or try to sell us these "new" things should not be considered as peddlers, rather they should be looked on as technical advisors or ambassadors representing the best that supplier research and development have to offer us.

Breaking-In a New Molleton-Covered Dampening Form Roller. A newly covered dampener should be thoroughly soaked with water, then the excess should be squeezed out, and the roller rolled out on a clean sheet of uncoated paper which has no alum content. This helps to get rid of some loose fibers and lint and also tends to condition the undercover — if one is used. As soon as the rollers are put in the press they should be adjusted according to the manufacturer's instructions. Then the press

should be idled, off the impression, until no more lint appears on the dampener vibrator. Lint, if it gets on the plate or up in the inking system, causes a defective printing-image on the sheet, just as will a hickey stemming from any cause.

Starting the Dampening System. When starting the press, it is best to give the dampening system a priming by squeezing fountain solution from a sponge across the dampener vibrator-roller while feeding from the fountain with the press idling. At this point note carefully whether the film of water on the vibrator (always a metal roller) is a continuous one. If the film is broken, it means the roller has a greasy area. Such an area must be cleaned immediately. How this is done depends on the metal used for this roller. Follow the manufacturer's instruction for cleaning. If this roller is not chrome covered, it can be plated with a "porous" chrome plating. Chrome, under the proper condition (porous) is naturally water-receptive and resists becoming greasy. If the fountain roller is one that runs without a cloth cover, it should be treated like the vibrator roller. If it is cloth-covered, watch it for any tendency to develop a broken film of water. When this happens, recover it.

Auxiliary Dampening Systems Aids. While much time and effort has gone into attempts at radical changes in the dampening system, there has been developed and put into use a number of devices to improve the performance of the conventional dampening system. Among the oldest of these devices are those aimed at selectively changing amounts of water fed across the length of the water-pan roller. For many years, pressmen attempted to do this with simple techniques using materials usually at hand — pieces of blanket, etc. But then, engineered devices were introduced such as squeeze rollers, metal scraper fingers, squeegies, etc.

It has long been known that level of water in the water-pan should be kept constant as one of the necessary procedures to help maintain consistent dampening. This meant constant attention and frequent addition of fountain solution to the pan. Simple devices to do this automatically were developed rather early in the introduction of

Courtesy of Baldwin-Gegenheimer Corp.

Variable Control Water Stops

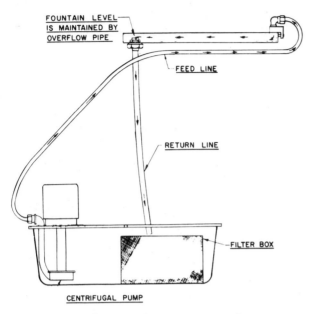

FOUNTAIN LEVEL
IS MAINTAINED BY
OVERFLOW PIPE

FEED LINE

RETURN LINE

FILTER BOX

CENTRIFUGAL PUMP

Baldwin Circulating Water Level

small offset duplicators. The success of these led to the development of fountain water level devices for larger

presses. Today, it is rare to see any press not so equipped.

Since the earliest days of the lithographic process, its craftsmen have applied their ingenuity to improving every phase of the process. Lacking technical training, or help from technically trained people, these craftsmen nevertheless stumbled on many techniques and materials which improved quality. The fountain solution certainly received more than its share of doctoring. Even as the chemistry of the lithographic process began to be better understood as a result of scientific investigation, many excellent suggestions developed outside the laboratories. One of these is the use of alcohol in place of some of the water used in the fountain solution. It is believed that the first general use of alcohol was suggested as being of great value with the Dahlgren Dampening System. The use of alcohol did pose one problem, how to maintain a constant proportion of alcohol since it evaporates so much faster than water. Since the Dahlgren requires a re-circulation system, the idea of re-circulation through dampening-solution storage tanks of larger capacity than the conventional water pan suggested itself. In such a system, control of the proportions of all the materials used is made practical. While all Dahlgren installations have a re-circulating system as an integral part, the same principle is being applied to conventional systems, with excellent results.

Section Seven: The Delivery

All sheet-fed lithographic offset presses deliver the printed sheet by finally transferring it to a set of grippers moving on a continuous chain. The transfer may be direct from the impression cylinder to the delivery grippers or through intermediate transfer cylinders. But in general, behind and slightly below the impression cylinder (the last one on a multicolor press) is a so-called "skeleton" or delivery cylinder. Actually, the delivery cylinder is not a cylinder but a pair of sprockets for driving the delivery chains, with segments and special devices for preventing the sheet from rubbing, whipping or waving, spaced between the sprockets. The travel of the sheet is so designed that it comes to the delivery pile face-up and gripper edge toward the front of the press. The chains carry delivery gripper bars. These are so spaced that one of them is always in taking position for each impression.

On smaller presses the delivery pile itself is an integral part of the press. This, therefore, limits the number of printed sheets which can be piled on the delivery dolly without changing dollies. On larger presses, the delivery is built as an extension to the press permitting the delivery pile to generally be the same height as the feed pile.

Two-pile deliveries can be quite useful in some classes of work. They make possible alternate delivery of sheets to one pile and then the other. This allows greater ink-setting time between delivered sheets. Such a delivery set-up also permits removing a printed skid load without breaking the run. Two drawbacks to a two-pile delivery setup are (1) The space required for the second delivery;

and (2) The cost of the extra delivery. In recent years, the press manufacturers have developed simple and inexpensive devices which make it possible to remove a load from the delivery without stopping. These devices are quite similar to those used for continuous feeding in pile feeders, and were described in the feeder section of this chapter.

Some of the medium sized, and even smaller presses, can be equipped with extension pile deliveries on special order.

DELIVERY GRIPPERS

Delivery grippers have the same problems as discussed in Section Four. But delivery-cylinder grippers have an additional and most critical problem: that of perfect timing with the impression-cylinder grippers. If any appreciable gap exists between the closing of the delivery grippers and the opening of the impression-cylinder grippers, the sheet will be pulled away by its tendency to stick to the blanket. This leads to battered blankets, and is the cause of ripped paper in the inking train. All makes of lithographic presses are provided with means for adjusting the delivery-gripper timing, especially on such presses where the impression cylinder is adjustable. The necessity of this adjustment is the fact that blanket-to-impression-cylinder pressure must be adjustable in order to accommodate paper of a wide variety of calipers. In those cases where the impression cylinder is the press member which is so adjusted, adjusting the impression cylinder for change of paper thickness causes a

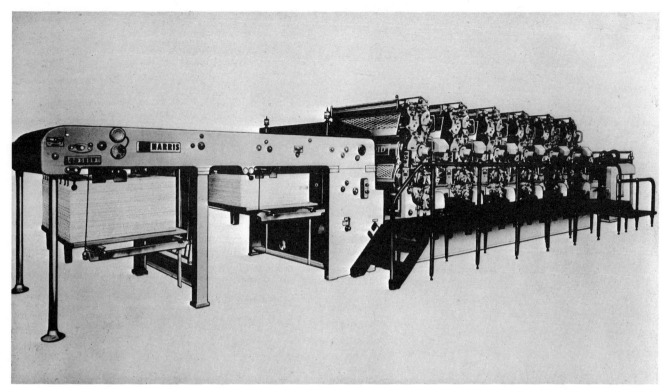

Courtesy of Harris-Seybold Co.

Two-Pile Delivery

change in the sheet transfer point. Where the change is a radical one it becomes necessary to check transfer timing in order to assure good delivery transfer.

From watching the operation of the delivery, it may appear that the setting of delivery grippers presents about the same problem as the setting of grippers on a swing or transfer device. This is not true. The bite of delivery grippers must be as firm as the bite of the impression-cylinder grippers. This is so because at the time the sheet is transferred from impression cylinder to the delivery the tail end of the sheet may still be in the nip or trying to follow the blanket. Any tendency to pull out may lead to damaged sheet gripper-edge or faulty delivery.

Because of differences in design the manufacturer's instructions should be followed explicitly for setting delivery grippers and timing the delivery gripper-bars.

SETTING THE DELIVERY

When setting the delivery we want to accomplish two things: We want to jog the sheets as perfectly as possible and we want to float the printed sheets onto the pile in such a way as to prevent smudging, smearing or set-off. The adjustable joggers, usually on three sides of the sheet, should be so set that the sheet falls exactly between them when it drops down. Then the sheet requires a minimum

Sheet Just Taken from Impression Cylinder and in Delivery Grippers.

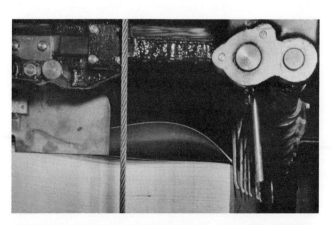

Delivering the Sheet. Control of this curl is essential for good jogging.

of movement to be jogged straight with the pile. But this is often more easily said than done.

If static is present, the sheets may tend to drag at the back end and therefore drop some distance from the front gate. In this case the sheet must slide forward because of the action of the rear joggers (where they jog) and some smudging may result. Static can cause the sheet to "jump" to the pile rather than to float down on it, and this will cause set-off.

Normally, static will not cause trouble in a properly conditioned plant. But in the dry atmosphere of a heated, but not humidified pressroom, static can be a constant source of trouble during that period of the year when heat is required. There are several palliatives against static, but at best they are temporary and makeshift. For example, running the sheet over or under Christmas tinsel (but in contact with it) tends to bleed off the static. (Specially made tinsel woven on copper wire instead of twine is available

for this purpose.) Anti-static chemicals are also available. About the only known cure for static, other than air-conditioning, is to equip the press with electrical or radioactive neutralizing bars. In extremely bad conditions such bars may be required at both the feed ramp and the delivery. Sheet heaters are also useful in fighting static, but they can cause other problems which outweigh their usefulness.

Another most important factor is sheet-curl or tail-end hook. This trouble is caused by the peeling action when the sheet is pulled away from the blanket. There are any number of auxiliary devices to help overcome these delivery problems. The pressman, left to his own devices, can do very little about them. One simple trick at his command is to place stock wedges in judiciously chosen spots. These wedges tend to guide the sheet without causing it to move unnecessarily. For example, if a bad tail-curl is present, a wedge under each rear corner of the pile will tend to overcome the trouble caused by this curl during jogging.

Section Eight: Running the Press

In the preceding sections of this chapter we have discussed the handling of the main press units with emphasis on preparing them to perform their functions in running. This section on running the press is really an extension of these preceding discussions because running is the culmination of all those operations.

The problem of running is to see to it that all press units perform as they should. The ink fountain must deliver, consistently, the set amount of ink; the inker must unfailingly deliver for each impression the proper charge of ink. The dampening system must do the same with the fountain solution. From the very end of the feeder to the very front of the delivery, everything must function perfectly. Nor may we overlook the human element. The performance of the press must be supervised by a human being. Supplying paper at the right time and in the proper condition for feeding is up to the press crew, which is also seeing to it that the water and ink fountain are properly charged.

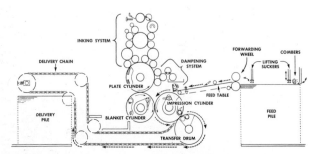

Schematic of the Lithographic Offset Press.

Our discussion of running centers, first, on three preparatory steps: the checking of paper, the preparing of the plate for running, and the getting of lay and fit. Thereafter we turn to running itself, which we will discuss in terms of maintaining the preparatory settings and the required quality

throughout the total run, or for the complete production of a job.

CHECKING THE PAPER FOR RUNNING

We must assume here that the requirements concerning paper (as discussed in the "Ink and Paper" chapter) are met by the paper we want to use for running. This implies that the grade, size and quantity of the paper are correct. We also assume that paper conditioning, so far as moisture content is concerned, has been taken care of within the limitations of the plant. Under the worst conditions the paper has, at least, been in the pressroom long enough to reach a temperature balance. This is especially important in areas where winter temperatures are low enough to require heating of the plant. Even though the subject of paper is outside of our chapter, we must, nevertheless, discuss four points very important for our subject of running. These are: (1) Protecting paper before running; (2) Paper moisture-content; (3) Protecting paper during running; (4) Lithographic quality control and paper testing.

Protecting Paper Before Running. The paper should be in moisture-proof sealed wrappings. If the stock, as originally received, must be cut before going to press, it must be kept in its wrapping up to the moment of cutting and then re-sealed. This is not as difficult as it seems. Plastic covers, which are designed for this specific purpose, are available in a variety of sizes. They come in two parts: (1) A bottom sheet which is put down on the skid or platform; and (2) A top envelope section. The paper is piled on the bottom sheet; the top envelope is brought down over the pile; the edges of the bottom sheet are brought up around the envelope and sealed with a pressure-sensitive adhesive tape. Thereby the edges of the piled paper are exposed to the atmosphere for as short a time as is possible.

This precaution can appreciably decrease the amount of press trouble due to tight- or wavy-edged paper.

Skids of paper which are going to run "as-delivered-by-the-mill" are easily protected between passes through the press or between final printing and subsequent processing. If the skid wrapper is carefully removed, it can be used as a skid cover. Slit the tape which fastens the upper wrapper to the base sheet and lift it off. When the printed pile is removed from the delivery, the upper wrapper is pulled over the skid and, if desired, can be taped to the original base sheet or a new one placed on the skid when it was placed in the delivery.

Paper Moisture-Content. It is assumed that the paper has been tested for moisture balance with the pressroom atmosphere. A particular plant may not be equipped to do anything about attaining a proper moisture-balance between paper and the pressroom atmosphere. However, if the pressman knows which way and how far the paper is out of balance with the pressroom atmosphere, he can take some steps to minimize the subsequent problems. For example, if a sheet is entirely too dry in comparison with the pressroom atmosphere, and if it is going to pass through the press several times, an experienced pressman knows that at least the edges will pick up moisture very rapidly and may become extremely wavy. (He also knows that the entire sheet will pick up some moisture, up to a point, with each printing.) While picking up more moisture may tend to flatten out the wavy edges, this benefit is derived at the cost of overall stretch of the sheet, in the across-the-grain direction especially. In this case the pressman will have a problem of fit on subsequent printings. He can perhaps meet this condition by printing as "short" as is possible without reaching the point at which good quality suffers. Short, as used here, is a relative term. "Printing short" implies that we have packed the plate and blanket cylinders in such a manner as to counteract the tendency of an offset press to produce an image on the paper, which is longer than the image on the plate, as measured on the plate *before* it was put on the press.

Protecting Paper During Running. All these factors are covered in detail in our "Ink and Paper" chapter. Now, that the paper is on the press, it must be controlled whatever its condition may be. An important factor is the length of time the paper will be exposed to the atmosphere between printings. In an air-conditioned pressroom, with pre-conditioned paper, this is not a problem. But in the average pressroom, steps must be taken to reduce the time of this exposure. The same covers as recommended previously for covering the paper between cutting and putting it to press can be used between runs too. Every pile of printed sheets must be sealed between printings, assuming that there is more than one pass through the press.

Lithographic Quality Control and Paper Testing. Paper testing must be an integral part of any quality control program. Much of the information required for paper testing is covered in the following chapter on *Paper and Ink.* Here we will be concerned only in introducing the basic concept as part of *Running the Press.*

Paper usually represents the largest single item of "out-

Wet Washing the Plate. First the plate is sponged with water, then the image is washed out with solvent; the plate is then rinsed thoroughly to remove all trace of solvent, and finally the image is rolled up.

side purchases" in a piece of printing. Paper which is un-suited to the job, or not properly handled, can represent not only a costly waste in cash dollars but, also, in lost press time which can be even more costly when total costs of producing a piece of printing are determined.

There are a number of tests which can be made in the plant without the need for large investments in sophisti-cated and elaborate equipment. These are discussed in the following chapter. Any plant desiring to institute such a program should have a qualified person attend the GATF seminar on *Paper and Ink Relationships.* Here, all the tests are discussed and demonstrated. The plant can, with such information at its disposal, organize a program best suited to its needs.

PREPARING THE PLATE FOR RUNNING

At this point of our discussion we assume that the plate is already on the press and that it was under gum and asphaltum. As we know the plate was rolled up solid in order to test the evenness of the blanket; then it was washed with an ink solvent and placed under asphaltum. We also used the packed plate for setting the inking form rollers, as well as to develop the proper squeeze pressure.

Bringing the Plate to Running Condition. In actual practice, after the plate is mounted the pressman washes it with water and a sponge. The water dissolves the gum (even if asphaltum was applied over it), and lifts off the asphaltum from the non-image areas. The pressman wipes the plate with a squeezed out sponge to remove excess water, starts the press and drops the inker for one or two revolutions. Then the inker is lifted, the press stopped and the plate examined. First, the image is examined care-fully to see whether all of it has picked up a charge of ink. The entire plate is examined to determine whether the amount of ink on the inking system appears to be about right for the job at hand.

Dampen the plate with a squeezed-out sponge, start the press and drop the dampeners. Watch the plate carefully to see that sufficient dampening is being done. Do not feed additional water at this time unless needed. Drop the inker and again watch the plate to see that there is no tendency to "catch up." Catching up is the term commonly used to describe the condition where ink sticks to the non-printing areas of the plate. If water and ink appear to be right but the plate starts to catch up, you stop the press (after lifting inkers and dampeners) and "wet-wash" the plate.

Wet-Washing the Plate. First you wet the plate down with water, wash it with the regular ink solvent on a rag, and quickly rinse it with water to remove the ink solvent. Then you wipe the plate with a squeezed-out sponge, start the press again, and drop the inkers for one or two revolutions. Now you lift the inkers, stop the press and examine the plate carefully; the image should be well inked and the background should be absolutely clean.

Dust the plate carefully with a wad of cotton dipped in a half and half mixture of talc and powdered rosin. Dampen the plate with a squeezed-out water sponge and etch it with the regular plate etch. Do this carefully and

rub the etch down smooth and dry. Roll the the press and fan the plate if necessary. If you are working on a large plate, you repeat the etching operation. When the etch is *dry,* you wash the plate with the water sponge, wipe off the excess moisture, and you make sure that the dampeners have enough water in them. Finally, you start the press, drop the dampeners and inkers, and now the plate should stay clean.

The above procedure is in general suitable for most jobs. Several points, however, should be made with respect to special cases. Developing ink is always black. If the plate is going to run with black ink and the plate has not been waiting for any appreciable time between platemaking and going to press, the procedures previously suggested hold sway. If the plate is not freshly made, the developing ink should be washed out. The best procedure is to wash the plate with a solvent to remove the ink. Then rub a smooth, thin, and even film of asphaltum down. Now wash the plate with water. This will dissolve the gum and lift the asphaltum except where it is on the image. Run the press and drop the inkers for a few revolutions. Lift the inkers and stop the press. Examine the image carefully for any faults.

If the plate is to run with a color, and even though it may come to press under asphaltum, it is advisable to wash it out completely and rub-up or roll-up the image with the press ink. Put the plate on the press, wash off the asphaltum (for a color job the platemaker has in all probability re-placed the developing ink with asphaltum) with solvent, rinse off the solvent and then rub-up the plate with some press ink. An alternate method is to follow the solvent wash with water to remove the gum and then roll-up the plate by running the press and dropping the ink rollers.

An important point to remember is that press ink should be removed, after the plate is gummed, and replaced with asphaltum if the plate is to stand for any length of time, especially overnight. Once press ink dries on the image it may be impossible to wash out, and it is not grease-receptive. When gumming the plate on the press use a gum solution of about 8° Baumé. Using a 14° Baumé solution (usual stock solution) may easily lead to a poorly rubbed down film and blinding.

GETTING LAY AND FIT

In getting lay and fit you should keep in mind many of the factors previously mentioned in this chapter. Make certain that the gripper-bite is correct, that sheet is separat-ing, advancing and forwarding at the correct time and to correct position for registering. Keep in mind that the lay may vary with the speed of the press on a press having a simple three-point register system (without an insertion device). In other words, that lay sheets pulled at idling speed may not register with sheets pulled at full running speed.

Plate Shifting. In Section Six we discussed handling of the plate to the point of mounting it on the cylinder. At that time it was mentioned that cooperation among strippers, platemakers and pressmen would result in short down time for obtaining proper lay. But plate shifting does sometimes have to be done due to no fault of the men involved with preparing the job or putting it on the press.

If the plate is reasonably close to its proper sideways position, setting the side guide for proper positioning of the sheet involves no trouble and very little time. So far as front-to-back position is concerned, there are several means available to do this. Shifting the plate cylinder by changing the position of the cap-screws which fasten the plate cylinder to the plate-cylinder gear takes care of gross shifts. Coupled to this feature on practically all plate cylinders is some type of vernier adjustment for fine movements. In this case we still move the cylinder with respect to the gear but the plate cylinder locking cap-screw remains in the same hole. Both of these shifts move the plate image forward or back, but in a straight line.

A third method available to the pressman for shifting the plate is to slide the plate around the cylinder by use of the space between the plate clamps and the plate-cylinder body. Shifting at the clamps makes possible "cocking" or "twisting" of the plate, as well as side shifting if for some reason the side guide cannot be adjusted for side margin.

The matter of cocking or twisting a plate calls for some special comment. Many operators do not visualize what is happening to a plate when it is being cocked. They develop the bad habit of trying to bring into proper position an isolated area of the plate, and fail to realize that this area is inseparably tied into the entire plate.

A simple trick in visualization handles this problem. One need only remember that a plate can be twisted around the cylinder in one of two ways: (1) By imagining that the plate is fastened to the cylinder at the exact center of the plate, and when twisting the *entire* plate revolves around this center point; and (2) By imagining that the plate is fastened to the cylinder at one corner, and that when the plate is being cocked it is pivoting at that corner.

The important thing to bear in mind is that when twisting a lithographic plate the *entire* plate must be cocked in order to guarantee that it will continue to hug the cylinder

smoothly when the clamps are pulled up tight after the shift is made.

Also keep in mind that radical shifts in packing may require rechecking of the inking- and dampening-roller settings. Such shifts should always be compensated for by the necessary change in the squeeze applied at the back cylinder. If the new job is on a paper that varies considerably in caliper from that of the previous job, check to see that transfer between impression-cylinder grippers and delivery grippers is still properly timed. If you are working on a first color, or first-time-through on a back-up job, or on a once-through-the-press critical register job, you must check for exact fit by using a Register Rule on the printed image, and by checking these measurements against those that were taken off the plate *before* it went to press.

Always remember that if the first color or first-side-down isn't to correct size, getting fit of subsequent printings will be very difficult if not impossible. If the manipulations required to get subsequent fit are too radical, the quality of the printed image must suffer, and sometimes the plate life itself can be seriously affected.

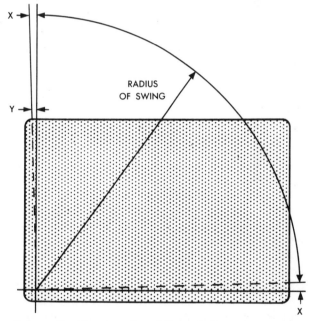

Schematic Showing One Way of Considering Plate Cocking. Note that here one corner is considered as being anchored and is the pivot point.

Waste Sheets. Obtaining lay should be done with waste sheets, if they are available. Sheets pulled for lay, fit, color okay, etc., on the first time through the press, should be saved for use as waste sheets on the succeeding passes through the press. When getting ready for the next pass, make "books" out of waste sheets and good sheets by taking four or five waste sheets and then two good ones, etc. Pile these in the feeder on top of the pile and put in an adequate flag to separate the books from the pile. Each time you pull a book, you run the set of waste sheets followed by the good ones and followed by one more waste sheet. In this way waste is cut down and by the time you

Shifting the Plate Cylinder.

have lay and fit okays, enough sheets have been run to indicate how well ink and dampening fountains are functioning for this job.

Start the feeder and print one book. While one good sheet is being checked for proper lay, you examine the other for quality of print. Permitting the ink fountain and water fountain to feed only while pulling sheets during the positioning stages is a check on the accuracy of their setting. One precaution may be indicated at this point. If the press stands for an appreciable length of time it may be necessary to apply extra water to the dampeners because of water loss due to evaporation. Do this carefully. When the press is stopped, while you are getting lay or you are waiting for position okay, make certain that the plate-cylinder gap is opposite the dampeners. If the down time is likely to be of appreciable length (over fifteen minutes), gum the plate. If the down time goes to an hour or more, put the plate under asphaltum.

RUNNING THE PRESS

The time has come when the job is ready for running or final production. Our main concern during running is fast, trouble-free, quality production. All units are set for this purpose, and in running we want to keep them at their original setting. For this reason we discuss running with the main idea of maintaining the predetermined setting of our five press units. The topics covered under running the press are therefore: (1) Handling the feeder; (2) Handling the dampener; (3) Handling the inker; (4) Handling the printing unit; and (5) Handling the delivery.

HANDLING THE FEEDER

At the time the feeder was set for this job, the pile should have been checked for its "contour." It was stated then, that the pile should be flat and level. This is not always possible, especially on a pile which has passed through the press previously.

Pile Contour and Its Problems. On a job with a very heavy ink lay across the back end, there is bound to be a decided curl. All the sheets, of course, will be curled the same way, fortunately, and therefore can be uniformly treated. One method is to roll out the curl while the pile is loaded in the press or on the skid. This technique may produce a reasonably flat pile at the back end of the sheet, but the whole back end may be higher than the front of the pile. If the difference is not too great the rear of the pile can be permitted to come higher than normal in order to get the front of the pile to the proper height for good control of the sheet advancing cycle.

However, it should be borne in mind that, as the pile gets smaller, the front of the pile will reach a level higher than the recommended height. Therefore, constant attention should be given to the feeder when running a pile which has been *manipulated* into proper contour. If wedges are used to get the top of the pile, or some part of the pile (corners especially) to correct height, the position of the wedges and the depth of their insertion will have to be

adjusted constantly while the press is running, to prevent mis-feeds. Also, when wedges are used, they should be watched constantly to prevent their getting into the press as a result of working loose or reaching the top of the pile as the run proceeds. On presses which are so equipped that the skid or platform can be manipulated to bring the gripper edge of the pile to the recommended height, the adjustment itself will have to be changed as the pile runs down.

Checking the Forwarding Mechanism. Forwarding devices will have to be checked constantly to make sure that the original position has not been altered. Some jockey-

Stream Feeder, Showing Tail-End Wheels and Brushes

ing of these devices may be required if the sheets are not perfectly trimmed or there is considerable curl or wave present. Watch the action of the side guide. What happens here is a good signal of the adequacy of the sheet's control. Watch the gripper and tail ends of the sheet very closely for any evidence of sheet buckling or bouncing. Pay special attention to the position of tail brushes, drive-up wheels, and balls, if they are being used.

Gripper-Edge Register. The best way to check register is to have adequate register marks print on the sheet. Near the gripper edge there should be marks running off the sheet at both sides. They must not appear within the work area, of course. Everytime a sheet is pulled for inspection, the position of these marks should be compared with those on the okay sheet. If the pile is jogging properly, this mark can be watched for alignment as a signal against inconsistent register.

Side-Guide Register. Side-guide register can be better watched if a small mark is permitted to print half off the sheet. Any slight variation of this will be noticeable. This mark should be put on the plate at exactly that point where the side-guide edge of the sheet touches the side-guide face-plate. If the mark is placed at this point it will always appear the same, even if the sheets are out-of-square. An elongated wedge-shaped mark at the side-guide edge makes checking even easier for both side and up-and-down register.

HANDLING THE DAMPENER

Following the sheet through the press, checking the mechanical controls of the sheet for satisfactory functioning, we arrive at the printing unit. Here it isn't possible to isolate every point completely. Everything is so interlocked and interdependent in the printing unit that, with few exceptions, we can never talk about one point concerning the actual running, without also including some others. For convenience we start at the dampening system. Assuming that all adjustments have been properly made and are holding their setting, we are concerned with the three following items: (1) Composition of the fountain solution; (2) Its level in the water pan; and (3) Its reaction with ink, plate and paper.

The Composition of the Fountain Solution. The composition of the fountain solution is determined by experience, whether it is a proprietary product or a formula made up in the plant. In formulating a specific fountain solution, the kind of plate to be run and the composition of the ink is, of course, considered. Both of these factors can be eliminated as troublesome if the pressroom is cooperating with the plateroom and with the suppliers of both plate-making materials and inks. Regardless of what solution is used, once a solution has been standardized in a particular plant, there must be no deviation except by deliberate design, due perhaps to the need for accommodating a new ink or paper.

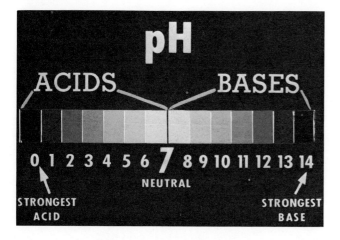

Schematic of the pH Scale.

The control technique available for fountain solution is the measurement of pH. pH is the term used to describe the acidity or alkalinity of a solution. pH is represented by a scale which measures from .1 to 14.0. 7.0 is the neutral point. Theoretically, pure distilled water which has not been exposed to the atmosphere has a pH of 7.0.

Measuring pH. There are several ways of measuring pH. The simplest is by the use of indicator papers whose color is changed on immersion in the solution being tested.

Various indicator papers are available for a range of pH readings depending on the class of solutions being controlled. These papers are simple and fairly accurate but their use is limited to the testing of solutions whose color doesn't mask that of the dyes in the indicators. Bichromate solutions, unfortunately, usually have this effect.

Color comparators are another device for measuring pH. But they, too, may be affected by solutions which can act to mask the color of standard solutions used in the test. In addition to this limitation, the color comparator is somewhat cumbersome to use. In recent years reasonably priced, and yet accurate, electrically operated pH meters have become available. Any plant preparing its own solutions should have one in the chemicals-mixing room. One such device, which is operated by a self-contained battery is most convenient for use at the press on fountain solutions.

Testing pH of Fountain Solution with Battery-Operated pH Meter.

Need for Constant pH Control. The question may arise, why test proprietary solutions or solutions prepared in a well run chemicals-mixing room. The answer is that fountain solutions may change on the press during the run. If printing trouble develops, the easiest step is to find out whether the pH of the fountain solution is correct; doing this first can save time otherwise spent in looking for their causes. The people responsible for your fountain solution formula, or the manufacturer of a proprietary solution will indicate the pH to be maintained. It is worth repeating that the *formula* as well as its pH must be compatible with the ink, plates and paper being run; especially the inks.

The Level of the Fountain Solution in the Pan. It is important that the solution be maintained at a consistent level in the pan during operation of the press. This is now best done automatically by installation of a water leveling device on the press. This is simply an auxiliary tank which keeps the solution in the pan at a predetermined level. The capacity of the tank is generally sufficient to run for quite a length of time. The tank can be kept full without

Courtesy Wm. Gegenheimer Co., Inc.
Fountain Level Device Installed on Two-Color Press.

stopping the press or disturbing the level of solution in the pan.

The unique design of the Dahlgren dampening system, with its use of alcohol in the fountain solution and metering system for feeding solution to the #1 inking form roller, introduced the concept of re-circulating the fountain solution. This has now been adapted to the conventional dampening system. A re-circulating system makes it possible to easily maintain consistency in pH of the fountain solution, proper water level in the water pan, a generally cleaner system. In addition, the old bugaboo of too-warm a solution during hot weather in a non-air-conditioned plant can also be eliminated.

Ink-Water Balance. One of the basic problems in handling the lithographic press is that of ink-water balance. The attainment of maximum print quality in tonal reproduction depends on running the thinnest possible film of ink. This latter statement, as it stands, is largely theoretical. It presumes use of the strongest inks that can be manufactured and a perfectly smooth surface on which the ink is to be applied. Practical considerations make both of these conditions virtually impossible to achieve. But, the theoretic basis can be modified by adding to the statement "under the conditions imposed by the particular job."

Theory aside, getting the "proper" ink film to the lithographic plate depends not only on the ink and how it is handled, but on the dampening solution and how it is handled. The key to this is just the right amount of water depending on the ink used, the amount of ink required for the plate and paper being run, and the area of ink coverage required by the particular design of the printed piece. To accomplish this requires a high degree of craft skill usually acquired only as a result of long experience.

Many years ago GATF designed the Bench Inkometer. This is the standard instrument used by ink-makers to determine and control ink tack. In recent years, GATF's Research Department has adapted the principle of the

Bench Inkometer to develop a Press Inkometer. This device makes it possible to measure ink-water balance as a deviation from the desired balance established by the pressman when he finally completes his makeready and has his color set. Watching a meter connected to the Press Inkometer, warns the pressman when the balance is being lost. The device is so sensitive as to show this even before the printed sheets reflect the changed condition.

Efforts are now being made to establish automatic control of the ink-water balance as an adjunct to the Inkometer. Once the pressman has attained proper color and dampening, the device could be set to increase or decrease water-feed as the inkometer registers a need for such change.

The problem of ink-water balance is discussed a bit further at the end of the sub-section "Handling the Printing Unit," which follows this sub-section.

HANDLING THE INKER

Ink Agitation. The condition of the ink in the ink fountain also requires some attention. Since lithographic ink is more like a plastic than a liquid, it will not flow without being worked. Sometimes it is necessary to work it on a slab before putting the ink in the fountain. Generally the action of putting the ink in the fountain and spreading it with the spatula while turning the fountain roller accomplishes this. Working the ink is further accomplished by periodic agitation with the ink spatula while the press is running. This serves also to break up any skinning tend-

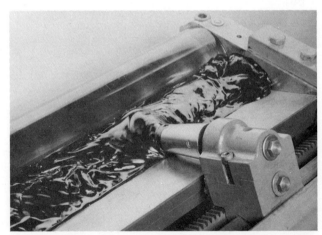

Courtesy Wm. Gegenheimer Co., Inc.
One Type of Ink Agitator.

ency as well as to keep the ink up against the fountain roller. An ink fountain should never be permitted to run nearly dry. This can be a great source of hickies on the press. Agitation can also be accomplished automatically and continuously by installation and use of ink agitators.

Oscillation of the Drums and Vibrators. As we go down the ink train we come across another source of possible trouble, at least on certain types of jobs. This source is the oscillating ink drums. The amount of trouble due to the axial oscillating action of these drums is very limited on modern presses if the inking system is kept in good condition and all rollers properly adjusted. It may be necessary to time the oscillation, if this is permitted by press design, to change direction at the point where the form rollers are over the plate cylinder gap.

It may also be necessary, at times, to control the amount of oscillation if a split fountain is used. One other trouble caused by metal rollers in the inking system was covered previously. This trouble appears on presses using steel rollers which have not been copper-plated, or otherwise treated. Another possible cause of trouble here is end play of the form rollers. This *must* be prevented. The best way to reduce the likelihood of developing such end play is to make certain that the pressure between form rollers and drums is not excessive, and to be certain that the roller spindles and sockets are properly lubricated.

Ink Skin and Other Foreign Matter. A general precaution with respect to running the inking system is that of maintaining absolute cleanliness. The cleanliness referred to in this paragraph is not the aspect discussed under the washing of the inking system. Here, cleanliness refers to freedom of the ink from any trace of skin, foreign particles, or abrasive materials. The possibility that abrasive materials may be present as a result of ink formulation is remote if you are dealing with reputable suppliers. But skin will be found around the top edge of almost any can of ink. When emptying a can of ink into the fountain, the operator must be absolutely certain that no skin passes his scrutiny. Another possible source of ink skin is in the fountain itself. If the press runs any length of time, some ink may dry at the back end of the blade or on the faces of the side blocks. When agitating the fountain by hand, the operator should be careful *not* to scrape any of this dried ink into the ink supply.

Water-in-Ink Emulsification. At several points in this chapter we have mentioned emulsification. Emulsification can take place in two ways: (1) Water may be emulsified into the ink; (2) Ink may be emulsified into the water. As has been previously stated, a certain amount of water emulsified into the ink will not cause trouble. But too much emulsification of water in the ink will waterlog the ink and produce a poor print. Too much of such emulsification prevents the ink from properly transferring between rollers

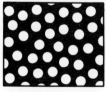
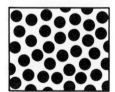

WATER–IN–INK
EMULSION

INK–IN–WATER
EMULSION

Schematic of Two Ways in which Emulsification May Take Place.

and plate, between plate and blanket, and between blanket and paper. Once the ink becomes waterlogged, the press must be washed up, and the ink in the fountain thrown away. This should not happen if a minimum amount of water is being fed to the plate. The proper amount of water

is just barely enough to keep the plate from scumming, but not more. One of the dangers with water-in-ink emulsification is that this type of emulsification may not be noticed for some time. If the print begins to gray most pressmen automatically increase the ink flow. If the print begins to look fat and mushy most pressmen automatically increase the water flow. Each of these changes only serves to compound the original fault; a perfectly good plate image may be irreparably damaged before the basic cause — *emulsification* or waterlogging — is noticed.

Ink-in-Water Emulsification. Ink-in-water emulsification is also a tricky thing. The cause here is usually a poor match of ink type and fountain solution formula. Ordinarily one would expect such a condition to show up immediately as ink on the dampeners. This is not so. When dampeners show signs of greasing or accepting ink, it means faulty handling of the dampening system or flooding of the plate by ink. An ink-in-water emulsification may be recognized by the appearance of tinting on the plate. Sometimes this tinting is mistaken for a scumming and the flow of water increased. Such a mistake only aggravates the condition.

Tinting and Scumming. Tinting and scumming are easily recognized conditions. Scumming results when the non-image areas of the plate accept ink from the inkers. Tinting is a deposit of water into which ink has been emulsified, or ink pigment has deposited itself as a result of the action of the fountain solution on the ink. This condition may be caused, also, by surface-active materials in the paper.

A simple test will indicate whether the trouble is scum or tint. If a plate is tinting, the tint can be wiped off from any area of the plate by a light touch of the finger or sponge. But one single revolution of the press *with the dampeners on* re-tints this same area. Scum cannot be wiped off the plate easily, and when it is wiped off will not come back again immediately unless a dry plate is contacted by the inkers.

When tinting occurs, the three covered rollers should be removed and thoroughly rinsed in clear water. The water pan should be emptied and rinsed, and the oscillating roller also rinsed and treated in the manner recommended by the manufacturer. Then the pressman starts up again, with a different fountain solution. If the tinting soon comes back the paper should be tested for presence of any surface-active material which tends to combine with the dampening solution and to break down the ink. This subject is discussed in detail in the "Ink and Paper" chapter.

Automatic Ink Fountain Control. The inking system of the lithographic offset press leaves much to be desired, from engineering and theoretical points-of-view. A great deal of time, effort, and money have gone into attempts to devise more efficient inking systems, and controls.

The most that has been accomplished, to date, is the adaptation to the ink fountain of automatic overall control. This is, in a sense, not much different than the kind of control being developed for the dampening system. The pressman attains the desired color and, with it, the desired ink-water balance. This is usually done by use of a densitometer which measures, by reflection, the density of the ink film on a reference block of the solid color printed in the trim area of the sheet. A scanning device is attached to the press which, through a photo-electric cell similar to that in the pressman's densitometer, reads the density of a target block as the block passes under the scanning head while the press is running. The device "compares" the readings on the printed sheets with the desired reading established by the pressman when the run started. Through the hook-up to the fountain mechanisms, the overall amount of ink being fed from the fountain is increased or decreased automatically.

HANDLING THE PRINTING UNIT

Watching the Run. Watching the run on a lithographic offset press involves more than maintaining specific settings and adjustments. The problems concerning specific segments of the press have been discussed in the preceding paragraphs of this section. We concern ourselves now with maintaining the appearance and quality of the print as produced on the press. It is assumed, of course, that for purposes of this discussion the mechanical aspects of running the press have been attended to: feeder is functioning properly; the sheet is registering; we have good fit; the color is okay; and the printed sheets are delivering and jogging in a satisfactory manner. Watching the run then involves seeing to it that no hickies or spots appear on the print, and that the proper amount of ink is being deposited on the sheet.

Hickies and Spots.* Under magnification, they look somewhat like doughnuts in reverse, although they are not always around. Once they appear, they repeat on sheet after sheet in the same places and increase in number as the run progresses. They are caused by solid, more or less ink-receptive particles that are stuck to the blanket or plate, and which are not transferred to the paper or dislodged by the form rollers. It takes a wash-up to get rid of them but, unless their source is removed, they start coming back as

soon as the run is resumed. The figure gives a rough idea as to why hickies print the way they do.

White or light spots in the work can, like hickies, be caused by particles or fibers stuck to the blanket or plate. The only difference is that, instead of being ink-receptive, these particles are water-receptive. In fact, some particles start out printing as hickies, but as they become saturated with water the solid center spot tends to fade out and disappear.

It is interesting to select a particular spot or hicky and thumb down through the pile of printed sheets till you find the sheet on which it first appeared. Doing this, and examining the spot under a glass or microscope will generally give a clue as to source of the hickies or spots, or both, that are ruining the quality of the job.

The main sources of particles that cause hickies and spots are ink and paper. But a dirty press, a dirty ceiling, or bad rollers can also supply particles of foreign matter.

Ink Particles.* More hickies are probably caused by ink skin (dried ink) than by anything else. This was discussed in this section under the heading "Handling the Inker."

Hickies caused by dried ink or skin can usually be recognized by their shape and appearance. The figure shows one very much enlarged. Notice that the spot inside the white ring has an irregular shape and sharp edges. The edges are also slightly denser than the center.

If you select a particular hicky of this type and thumb down through the pile until you find the first sheet on which it appeared, you will notice that there has been practically no change in its appearance.

If you locate the particle on the blanket or plate, you can pick it off and examine it under a microscope. By feeling

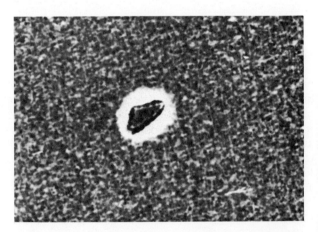

Greatly enlarged photo of a typical hicky caused by a particle of ink skin.

it with a needle you will find it soft and pliable, with no fibers present.

These things are characteristic of ink skin or dried particles. And once the particles are identified, the only thing

Greatly enlarged diagram showing how a solid particle like a wad of paper fibres, piece of ink skin, or dirt on the blanket produces a hicky on the printed sheet.

* From GATF *Research Progress*, No. 35.

* From GATF *Research Progress*, No. 35.

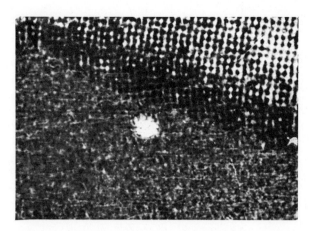

Greatly enlarged photo of a typical hicky caused by a loose particle of paper several sheets after it first appeared.

to do is wash up the press, discard the ink, and load the fountain with a fresh, skin-free batch of ink.

Paper Particles. * Despite all the precautions taken by the mills, paper is second to ink as a source of hickies. It can produce hickies as well as several kinds of spots. More knowledge and experience are necessary to identify the defects in paper that cause them. These defects are as follows:

PAPER DUST. When paper is slit and cut to sheet size in the mill, there is a certain amount of dust formed. Some of this dust is likely to get between the sheets and remain there. In most mills, some attempt is made to get rid of this dust by means of compressed air or vacuum, but they are not always completely successful. And if only one or two particles remain on each sheet, printing a thousand sheets can produce a lot of hickies and spots.

PICKING OF THE PAPER SURFACE. Small areas of surface fibers or coating are sometimes picked, generally in the solid areas. These stick to the blanket or plate and produce hickies or spots that repeat sheet after sheet.

LINT, FUZZ, OR WHISKERS. Slitting and sheeting of paper sometimes sets free individual fibers that get trapped between the sheets. Lint, however, is usually due to fibers being loosely bonded in the paper surface. It is usually worse on the wire side than on the felt side. These fibers are pulled out of the sheet by the ink, but they quickly become saturated with water, refuse to take fresh ink, and leave white images of themselves in the printed work. They are, of course, most apparent in solids.

HOLES IN THE PAPER SURFACE. These are holes resulting from air bubbles in the fiber finish when the paper is made or bubbles in the coating mix when the paper is coated. They are deep enough to prevent the blanket from depositing ink in them. Spots due to such holes occur on only one sheet and do not repeat. In other words, the distribution of spots on each sheet will be different.

Spots caused by slitter and cutter dust can be any shape from that of individual fibers to that of slivers. If you thumb down through the printed sheets to where a spot

first appeared, the original spot will be white and show no evidence of picking. On succeeding sheets, the spot will be a hicky, but the center spot will be gray or a tint, not a solid. It will tend to get lighter on succeeding sheets. This, and the absence of a sharp edge around the center spot will distinguish paper dust from ink skin. The figure shows how a hicky of this type looks several sheets after its first appearance.

Spots due to picking of the paper surface of coating can be any shape. If you locate the sheet where the spot first appeared and examine it under a glass, you will see that the surface was picked. Hickies will appear on succeeding sheets, but their center spot will lack the sharp edge of an ink-skin hicky, and may print lighter on succeeding sheets as the fibers become water-soaked. One figure shows a spot in a solid on the surface of the sheet that picked. The other figure shows how such a spot may appear on sheets that follow the picked sheet and after a number of them have been printed.

Particles From Other Sources. * Hickies can also be produced by particles of dust or dirt falling from a dirty ceiling or dislodged from a dirty press or disintegrating rollers. Ceilings should therefore be cleaned and painted at

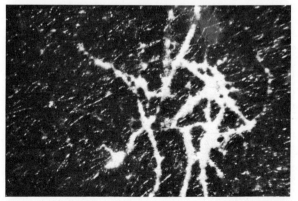

Greatly enlarged photos. Top shows a picked spot on a coated sheet. The coating and some fibres stuck to the blanket leaving a crater in the paper. Bottom shows a typical spot in a printed solid on sheets following the one that was picked.

* From GATF *Research Progress,* No. 35.

* From GATF *Research Progress,* No. 35.

regular intervals. Press members should be cleaned at least once a week. They must be kept free from oil or grease that can accumulate dust and non-offset spray or powder.

Fiber-shaped spots can be caused by shedding dampener covers. These have the same appearance as spots caused by lint or fuzz, but are generally much longer, since the dampener fibers are cotton. Newly covered dampeners can cause them if they were not thoroughly washed before they were installed on the press. Old dampener covers may become rotten and shed fibers.

Maintaining Proper Color. Depositing the proper amount of ink on the sheet is a complicated problem involving considerable judgment as well as experience. To the assumptions listed previously, we will now add one more: that the plate has been well made. This implies desensitization by the most modern techniques as recommended by the Graphic Arts Technical Foundation, Inc., and includes a wet-wash, as described previously. This procedure produced a clean, sharp image and a really tough non-printing area. When we say a "sharp image" we mean an image on the plate which is a faithful reproduction of the flat from which the plate was made. We do not mean an image which has been "sharpened" as a result of improper handling by the pressman. Such a plate is printing less than the full image produced by the platemaker.

One of the first items to consider here is the "color strength" of the ink. If the color is weak it may be necessary to run an excessive amount of ink to produce the desired color on the sheet. This "crowding" may lead to several problems. In the first place the print produced on the sheet will begin to appear heavier than that which was originally produced on the plate. The entire job will look too "full." At first the job may look fine. But as the run progresses the appearance will gradually change from a nice full print to a "squashed out" print. When this happens the plate has been damaged to the point where usually it cannot be brought back to its original degree of sharpness. If this is a full-color process job, the finished product will show up as a finished piece with the particular color run too full. But even on a black-and-white type job, running this way will show up as a poorly reproduced version of the original type style and, in all probability, an entire book printed this way will show variation from page to page as the binder gathers the first sheets from one signature with later sheets of other signatures.

Another problem that must be faced when we try to crowd a plate is the difficulty of running clean. In the attempt to meet this problem, the amount of water being run is increased or the pH of the fountain solution is lowered. While either or both of these steps may lick the symptoms, the basic fault still remains and all that is accomplished is a compounding of several faults.

The only real cure is to prevent the need for crowding. This can be done by running an ink of the same color but with stronger color or better covering qualities. The ink man can solve this problem quite easily.

When we run with too strong a color, the job will also suffer. First, the pressman tries to run his ink "spare." That

is he runs with too little ink. As a result the plate begins to sharpen. Then, in an effort to produce a full print, ink and water flow are increased. Too much water and too little ink may damage the image as a result of insufficient protection to the image afforded by a proper charge of ink. Running excess water for any length of time must also lead to waterlogging.

Again, the symptoms can be eliminated, but only temporarily. The only real cure, here, is to cut down the strength of the ink. In this case, judicious addition of laketine, or some other approved reducer, to the ink can cure the original fault. However, the ink man should first be consulted. It may be better in this particular case to have the ink man formulate a new batch of ink for this job.

The adaption, in recent years, of instrumented techniques to attain and maintain desired color is one of the most significant developments of recent years. Photography as an instrumentally controlled process, is quite old. By the end of the 1940's, GATF had succeeded in bringing lithographic platemaking to the point where a properly made plate was no longer a "by-guess-and-by-gosh" operation. But, only within the past ten years have we reached the point where instruments and highly-developed technical concepts were made available to the pressman.

A well-run pressroom, especially where color is critical, no longer depends entirely on the craftsman's eyes to assure that a near-perfect match of the color O.K. sheet is being maintained. Color blocks, various target and tint patterns have been designed for inclusion somewhere in the trim margins of the sheet. When the color has been O.K.'d for running, certain of these blocks or tints are "read" with a reflection densitometer. As the job is running, sheets pulled from the press are read with the instrument and checked against the recorded readings of the O.K. sheet. Some of the target and tint patterns are so designed that print quality factors, other than ink-film thickness, can be either measured instrumentally or easily judged by eye if they drift from the established O.K. sheet.

GATF's Star Target

The Ink-and-Water Balance. Earlier in this discussion we mentioned the need for judgment and experience. It is extremely difficult to describe in words, or show by examples, what is meant by proper ink-and-water balance. In an effort to discuss this, let us add one other assumption to the long list already made in this sub-section on "Watching the Run." We will now assume also that the ink on the press does have the proper color strength and covering power.

We know that in order to print we must dampen the non-image area of the plate and ink the image areas. We have discussed what may happen when running too much ink or too little ink. In both cases it was pointed out what may happen when we try to cure the symptoms by changing the amount of water being fed to the plate. With the proper ink the trick to be learned is that of "balancing" the amounts of ink and water being fed to the plate.

The basic rule is to run sufficient ink to give full color to the job and as little water as possible to keep the plate clean. Watching the plate and the printed sheets carefully, at the start of the job, will facilitate reaching the ideal balance on the job. The important point to remember is that when you change either the ink flow or the water flow, make sure that the reason for the change *is* the needs of the plate. Do not make a change to meet a poor condition in one or the other of the inking or dampening systems.

The matter of plate needs requires that the pressman keep in mind the demands of different types of plates. A coarse grained plate will require more water than a finely grained plate, assuming all other conditions remain the same. A smooth plate, such as the bimetallic or pre-sensitized plates, runs best with a *very* small amount of water. If the pressman notices water collecting at the back end of the plate and/or blanket, it is a sure sign of too much water.

In order to cure a symptom of insufficient dampening, the tendency to increase the fountain acidity (lower the pH) much be avoided. Unless there is absolute proof that the job demands a pH of less than 5.0, you should maintain the pH at somewhere between 5.0 and 6.0. Too low a pH will retard drying of the ink on the paper. It may also damage the image, especially on surface plates. Actually we know that the *primary* reason for acid and gum in the fountain solution is to help keep the dampeners clean.

HANDLING THE DELIVERY

If it is assumed that the press is now running and printing properly, our last point of concern is the delivered sheets. Jogging has been previously discussed, but set-off was merely mentioned and needs further comment. Set-off may occur not because of poor pressmanship, but because a particular job on the press is taxing the capacity of the press to deliver a smooth, uniform but thin film of ink. It must be borne in mind that the offset method itself contributes to the inability of the lithographic process to lay down a thick film of ink. This is a principal reason why a lithographic ink must be formulated with strong color and covering power. This situation is aggravated when overprinting two or more colors. The best way to overcome set-off is by the installation of anti-offset devcies.

Anti-Offset Sprays. A variety of anti-offset sprays are on the market to choose from. There are two dangers to watch out for in the use of these sprays. Too many pressmen rely on anti-offset sprays almost completely and acquire the habit of running too much ink, in their dependence on the spray to prevent set-off. Another bad habit is that of running too much spray to the detriment of the equipment.

A Well-Jogged Lift.

Actually, if the pressman runs so much spray that it is clearly visible as it comes out of the nozzle, too much spray is being used. A barely visible spray, properly directed, and from the proper height (depending on area to be covered by the gun) will do just as effective a job of set-off prevention as an excessive amount of spray. Spray guns that use a liquid spray should be carefully controlled to prevent any of the liquid itself from reaching the sheets and thereby causing them to stick together.

Piling the Delivery. Regardless of how carefully a job is run, and despite anti-static devices, spray guns, etc., some jobs cannot be piled too high. This is especially true with varnishes, metallic inks and, very often, high gloss inks. Experience will dictate how high the lifts should be. Such lifts must be constantly winded, while drying, in order to prevent their sticking together. In a similar vein, certain inks will permit piling a delivery to full capacity but will still require winding shortly after coming off the press. Experience and your ink maker can tell you which inks to watch. What happens is that during drying certain inks generate considerable heat. This process may cause sheets to stick or have the equally dangerous result that the inks change color. This can be prevented only by constant winding during the drying period. It is obvious, of course, that all such winding must be done with care to prevent set-off and/or smudging.

Jogging. It has been previously mentioned that jogging of the sheets in the delivery should be accomplished in a manner preventing set-off. This task directly concerns the pressman. He should also be concerned that jogging may not cause damaged sheet edges, especially if the sheet has to be put through the press again. Also, he owes it to the finishers (diecutters, binders, etc.) of the job to deliver a well-jogged pile to make their work easy.

Before permitting a job to leave the pressroom, it should be properly flagged and identified in accordance with whatever system has been installed for this purpose.

Section Nine: Multicolor Presses

It is generally accepted that the ultimate in full-color (process) printing is attained by running the colors "dry." This is true in all printing processes. However, the advances made in recent years through research in techniques, materials and equipment have brought the lithographic process to a point where it can employ "wet" printing techniques and equal, at the very least, the very finest of "dry" printing in the other printing processes.

Dry Printing and Wet Printing. "Dry" printing means that each color is printed and permitted to dry on the sheet before the succeeding color is run. "Wet" printing means that two or more colors are printed with a single pass through the press with no appreciable drying time between color lays. It is possible, of course, to intermingle the two methods. For example, if a four-color process job is run on a two-color press, then the first two colors are being done wet and the last two are being done wet. But the last two colors are printed on the first two *after* the first two have had the opportunity to dry.

In web offset operation the possible combinations of wet and/or dry printing are limited only by the press design, especially the placement of drying units between the printing units in the press. If the drying is done *only* after all the printing is completed, then a totally wet method is being used.

There are four basic problems in multicolor press operation which are common to all processes. These problems are: (1) Register; (2) Fit; (3) Trapping; and (4) Color contamination. The manner in which color contamination appears in lithography is commonly referred to as "counter-etching." This subject is, therefore, in our Manual, discussed under the heading of "Counter-etching" rather than color contamination.

REGISTER

The problem of register is not different on multicolor work — wet or dry — from on black-and-white work; but register is here more critical and has, in most cases, a much smaller tolerance of variation. A properly handled press always registers, and it may be taken for granted that all presses should be properly handled be they used for single-color or for multicolor work. In some ways the multicolor press is easier to handle with regard to attaining and maintaining register; in other ways it is more difficult.

An important way in which wet multicolor operation simplifies matters is that the sheet is inserted into the press a lesser number of times. It is obvious that the more times a sheet is handled the greater the likelihood of mutilated gripper edges. It is equally obvious that the more times a sheet goes through the press, the less likely it is that the pile in the feeder will retain a nice flat contour. On the other hand, transferring a sheet from unit to unit increases the points at which trouble with register may be encountered. And, by the very nature of the beast, it should be obvious that it is much more difficult to build and synchro-

nize a press with two or more units, each of which must register perfectly, than it is to build a single unit which registers perfectly. The fact that our presses achieve such fine results is something for which we must praise our engineers and manufacturers without stint.

FIT

The problem of fit is considerably affected by multicolor printing. It has been said repeatedly — in this and in other chapters in this Manual — that sheet distortion due to change in moisture content of the sheet is one of lithography's most difficult problems. Ways and means of controlling the moisture content have been described. One great contribution to alleviating this problem is the ability of a multicolor press to put down two or more colors within so short a space of time that the sheet has no opportunity to give up or take up any appreciable amount of moisture. If the stock is kept in moisture-proof wrappings up to the very time it is put on the press, even unconditioned stock running in a non-conditioned plant will hold size satisfactorily. Of course, if the sheet is going through the press more than once, it is essential that the stock be protected between printings. The best method for doing this has been described previously.

In multicolor work, dry or wet, it is imperative that the first-color-down be in register and fit perfectly. The easiest way to check fit of the first color is by comparing the image size on the first plate with the printed image size on the sheet. This is best done by using GATF's Register Rule, as described previously. The GATF Rule will show the amount of error, and the nature of the error usually indicates its cause. Between the remedies at the pressman's disposal — shifting of packing, bowing of stops, or deforming the sheet contour on the feedboard — good fit within narrow limits will be attained. If the sheet is too wavy, or too tight-edged, little or nothing can be done — short of conditioning the stock.

There is another precautionary step that should be taken when preparing to run a multicolor job. The temperature and moisture balance of the pile should be tested — *before the wrappings are removed.* Details of this have been discussed in the chapter on "Ink and Paper."

TRAPPING

Trapping is an important item to consider whether running wet or dry multicolor work. It is essential, here, that the lithographer work closely with the ink maker because the ink man does have at his disposal the materials and knowledge to cope successfully with the problems of trapping. Trapping, on the press, describes the phenomenon of a printed film of ink accepting a subsequently applied ink film. Two prime factors generally affect trapping. They are the absorbing characteristics of the paper, and the relative tack of the inks being superimposed on each other.

If the ink maker has adequate samples of the stock to be run, he can match his ink vehicle to it. GATF's Inkometer which most ink houses have, makes possible accurate determination of ink tack before it goes to press. In this respect it is important to assume, on principle, that the ink maker knows his business. The lithographer should never dope an ink unless the ink man has approved the materials used, the quantity to be used, and the circumstances of its use. In general, each succeeding color has less tack than the preceding one.

COUNTER-ETCHING

A fourth problem which all processes have in common is the contamination of succeeding colors by those previously run. This problem applies almost entirely to wet multicolor printing. The way in which the problem of color contamination affects the actual printing operation is, however, quite different in lithography. Let us hold fresh in our minds that we are handling a planographic plate, a plate where both image and non-image areas are on the same plane. We also recall that the inking and dampening form rollers contact both the image and non-image areas. Now let us add another item. The blanket, when receiving the inked image from the plate, also contacts image and non-image areas of the plate. Let us add still another, and last, item. The paper also contacts the image and non-image areas of the blanket.

Now we are ready to follow a fresh, unprinted sheet through the press. For the sake of simplicity we have selected a two-color press. The press is running, and both blankets have been charged with their respective images. The sheet goes into the first unit where the first image is transferred from the blanket to the paper. Then the sheet passes to the second unit where it is again pressed in contact with a blanket. *But now the sheet is not blank anymore.* Now it has an inked image from the first unit. We know, of course, that the image elements of a full-color process job do not always completely superimpose on each other. Therefore, part of the first image is pressed against areas of the blanket which correspond to non-image areas of the second plate. The blanket, of course, is ink-receptive. It must be so in order to be usable as a blanket at all. Some ink, and be it only the slightest amount, *always transfers from the paper to the blanket.* When this second blanket contacts its plate for a fresh transfer of the image, the ink from the preceding impression that was pulled from the sheet is now pressed against non-image areas of the second plate.

The immediate reaction is to say: "So what? Are the ink rollers not always contacting the non-image areas of the plate?" But the effects of the blanket and the ink rollers on the plate are vastly different. The inking form rollers *roll* against the plate, and they do so without too much pressure. The blanket cylinder, on the contrary, is squeezed against the plate with tremendous pressure. This factor would be troublesome enough by itself; but we must also consider compression. The plate compresses the blanket. This may bring about a change in surface speed.

Because we are working with materials that cannot be fabricated as accurately as optical mirrors, or Johannsen gage blocks, we have an even greater possible variation in surface speeds between the plate and blanket surfaces. This speed difference causes a rubbing action. Even if the rubbing action be comparatively slight, it has a great effect on the plate; the ink transferred from the first impression is literally *ground* into the second plate. On presses with more than two color units the problem is further compounded by the time we reach the last frame. If the second plate begins to hold the ink from the first image, it is said to be "counter-etched" by the first image. What has happened is that the water-receptive layer on the non-image area of the plate has been broken down to the point where it becomes "sensitive" or ink receptive and prints a scum of the second color on the first.

There are three mitigating factors that make good reproduction possible under what appear to be impossible conditions. The first is a contribution by the ink maker. He has been able to contribute immeasurably by formulating inks that — when laid on the paper, or over previously printed inks — want to stay there rather than lift off. *These inks have trapped perfectly.* Therefore, the author advises, even at the risk of being repetitive, that the pressman must not interfere with the ink, but rather should use materials and techniques as prescribed.

Another, and possibly equally important, factor is plate research. Plate research has made plates possible whose non-image areas just won't break down. The pressman should make all changes under the guidance of the supplier of the materials and techniques.

A third factor which makes it possible to produce full color printing on multicolor equipment is our advanced knowledge of the dampening procedure and the means to better adapt the composition of the solution, as well as its pH, to the particular ink, paper, and plate being run.

Planning the Production of a Color Job. Regardless of whether a full-color job is to be printed dry (on a single-color press), or wet (on a multicolor press), or by a combination of the two methods, it is imperative to understand that the press can, at best, only reproduce what is on the plate, and in the color which is on the press. It is true that some manipulation on the press is possible. We can run the plate sharp or full. We can run the ink spare or heavy. We can also change the ink in the fountain. But either or all of these steps should not be resorted to as a *planned* procedure of operation. Either or both of the first two procedures leads to early deterioration of the image or non-image areas of the plate, or both. Efforts by the pressman to prolong the life of the plate, under these conditions, lead to a variation in tone and color throughout the run.

Techniques have been developed whereby the exact reproducible results obtainable on the press can be known in advance. Then all the preparatory steps should be planned around this knowledge. The ink should not be manipulated to change tone or color which was photographed in the original color separation negative. Rather the negative should be so shot as to produce the desired tones and colors as can be derived from the ink to be run. This is exactly the opposite of what is done in most cases, but all evidence to date indicates that this is the correct method.

Simple tests run on the presses in the plant will tell the photographer, artist, and platemaker exactly what a particular press and its crew will produce. Such tests will show what a single-color press will produce, in the way of tones, as compared to a multicolor press. It will also show what to plan for if a four-color process job is to be run on a two-color press, where we are combining wet-and-dry printing. And the preparatory departments can prepare their part of the job to meet these standards. Not only can they do this, they *must* if the full advantages of the lithographic process are to accrue to the benefit of the plant.

Section Ten: The Lithographic Offset Web Press

At the beginning of this chapter it was pointed out that reference to specific presses or types of presses would not be made within this chapter. However, this section is included because of the tremendous interest — an ever increasing one — in the specific area of rollfed lithographic offset presses.

Generally speaking the operation of such equipment is little different from that of sheet-fed presses. The general principles and practices of cylinder pressures, plate handling, blankets, inking, dampening, etc., are practically identical. A transition from sheet-fed into roll-fed is not as staggering a change as it may sound. Roll-fed operation is not new. Therefore, the lithographer who is planning to go into web printing has a tremendous body of existing knowledge from which to borrow and receive assistance. Even roll-fed lithographic offset operation is not new. It dates back to at least 1916. In this field, too, a large volume of knowledge has been developed, but not too much has come to the fore despite the fact that very little of it is really "secret."

WEB PRESSES ARE SPECIALIZED

The transition to web offset poses much less of a problem on the pressroom level than on the management level. The main consideration need not be whether the plant can operate the equipment, but whether the sales force can sell the production facilities offered by such equipment. In this respect management must recognize that the factors that determine the purchase of a web-fed press are quite different from the factors on which the selection of sheet-fed equipment is based. A sheet-fed press, single or multicolor, can be selected on the basis of its ability to handle the widest range of jobs actually produced by a plant, or on the kind of work that the sales department thinks it can sell.

But a web-fed press is by nature a piece of specialty equipment. It is designed and purchased to handle a specific job or type of job. While it is true that width of the roll can be any size up to the maximum of the particular press, the around-the-cylinder direction cannot be changed except on still higher specialized equipment, that is on *specially designed* specialty presses. In other words a web-fed press rated as a 22¾" x 35" press can print any width up to 35 inches, but can only deliver a 22¾ inch unit in the around-the-cylinder direction. Smaller jobs can, of course, be printed too, but the difference in size up to 22¾ inches is wasted paper, unless the 22¾ inch cutoff length is an exact multiple of the smaller size or sizes. "Ganging" is, of course, possible on web-fed equipment just as it is in sheet-fed, but the flexibility still isn't too great. All of these conditions point up the fact that web-fed presses are primarily built to order.

STANDARD SIZE WEB PRESSES

As a result of experience, especially in the last ten years, a few "standard" sizes have been developed. As of the moment these are 17" x 26", 22" x 26", 22¾" x 35", 35" x 39". Because such presses are purchased to do a particular job, a magazine for example, or a type of work such as business forms of standardized sizes, these presses can be designed to do much more than merely print. In addition to this is the fact that some manufacturers build standard-sized printing units and assemble them to meet the customer's requirements.

In the case of publication or book work, the web can be fed into a folder followed by a saddle-stitching attachment. From there on, all possibilities are open. Nobody has as yet exhausted them. Some day, soon, we may see the printed web go from the folder into a gatherer if necessary, be bound, trimmed, packed, labeled and mailed — all in one continuous operation. In the case of specialties such as folding boxes, an in-line set-up can be devised producing completely folded and glued cartons in one continuous operation. In the case of business forms, the web can be numbered, punched, perforated, slit, collated with other webs, pasted, stitched, accordion folded, and so *ad infinitum;* again in one continuous operation. The key to the selection of a web press, or to entering the field of web-offset, is, therefore, management's ability to sell its productive capacity in competition with those already in the field, as well as in competition with the other printing processes.

RECENT PROGRESS IN WEB PRINTING

It is worthy of asking why at this time, we find such an increased interest in web-offset? The answer is the tremendous growth of lithography in general, as compared with the growth of the other printing processes. The reasons for this growth of web-offset lithography are still more improved materials, techniques, and equipment. To make this even more clear, consider the plate cylinder gap of a sheet-fed press.

The Plates. On a sheet-fed press the cylinder gap takes up about one-fifth of the total surface area of the cylinder, and measures many inches. But the corresponding gap on web-fed equipment is not more than a fraction of an inch on any size press. The narrowness of the gap on web presses posed a serious problem because the then existing plate metals were not suitable for the necessary sharp bend. On a sheet-fed press, especially when we get over 17 inches, the plates are not very sharply bent for mounting, and yet plates still do break at the clamps. But on the web-fed press the plates are bent at an angle over 90° and then "jammed" into the gap. It is obvious why, for this reason alone, web-fed lithographic offset would not develop until we had plate metals capable of withstanding such extreme demands. This problem is no longer a serious one; not only are improved plate metals available, but excellently engineered plate bending devices and cylinder plate locks make it possible to wrap a plate snugly around the cylinder and the cylinder gap edges. Eliminating the possibility of the plate flexing as the edges of the gap contact the blanket, has greatly reduced the incidence of cracked plates.

Let us consider the plates themselves. We need go back only a few years when 100,000 impressions on a "good" deep-etch plate was considered a wonderful figure. The web-fed press is by its very nature long run equipment; what good would such equipment be, if the plates would not stand up? There are now cases on record where the image outlasted the ability of a *steel-based* plate to withstand the hammering at the gap: several millions of impressions. An incidental, but important benefit of steel-based plates is, that like any bimetallic plate, they produce excellent dot structure not obtainable on grained aluminum or zinc. This should not be interpreted to mean that only steel plates can be used successfully on web-offset presses.

Paper. Let us next consider paper costs. Two comparable grades of paper, one offset and one letterpress, sell for a difference of about 13 percent, with the offset paper being the more costly. Now, considering the fact that lithographic plates *may* be cheaper than letterpress plates, and that the makeready on a lithographic offset press *may* cost a fraction of the makeready on letterpress, the question is, how long must a run be before offset begins to cost more because of the differential in paper costs. To cut down this paper cost differential, or eliminate it, has been the aim of all interested in offset lithography. Better made letterpress papers and less costly lithographic papers are becoming more and more available. Another improvement of the paper situation is connected with the plate. The modern lithographic plate requires very little water to run clean. This reduces the high water-resistance requirement of paper for the lithographic process. Improvements in litho inks have also helped to reduce this requirement, and so have improved blankets. In consequence of all these accomplishments by the industry and its suppliers, lithography has not merely retained its quality superiority, it has actually increased it. All this becomes still clearer if we consider the basic reason for choosing gravure in large volume catalog — news supplement and magazine production. In gravure, good pictorial reproduction is possible on very low cost paper. The paper cost can be decisive, if the runs are long enough to more than absorb the phenomenally high original cost of gravure cylinders.

THE FOUR BASIC TYPES OF WEB-PRESSES

There are four basic types of web-fed lithographic offset presses, as follows: (1) Blanket-to-blanket unit type; (2) Drum type; (3) Unit type; and (4) Single-plate job press. The latter is used for high-speed production of small handbills, throw-aways, etc., printed on one side, and of standard size such as 8½ x 11 inches. All the others are usually perfecting presses and print at least two colors on both sides. Such presses permit many kinds of combinations; there are even presses which print the inside and the covers of a magazine, and bind it in one continuous operation.

Blanket-to-Blanket Type. At the date of this writing the blanket-to-blanket press is most common. Each blanket cylinder acts as the impression cylinder for its mate in the pair. The paper passes between the two blanket cylinders and is perfected simultaneously. In a press of this type the paper generally passes from roll stand to delivery in a straight line. Register is maintained by tension control of the web in both the lateral direction as well as in the running direction. These controls can be installed at the infeeding point, between units, and at the delivery. Some of this is controlled by graduating the cylinder pressures — the first unit is designed for the lowest pressure and the last unit for the highest. The difference between units is very slight — on the order of .0005 inch to .00075 inch. This difference is just enough to prevent the web from trying to follow the blanket, as the paper does on sheet-fed offset presses. The cylinders on these presses are laterally adjustable while running, to maintain register to accommodate any weaving motion of the web. The cylinders can also be advanced or retarded, as on a sheet-fed press, in order to get original register and to help maintain it during the run without down time. Both of these shifts are limited. Therefore, when originally started, all cylinders should be set at the center

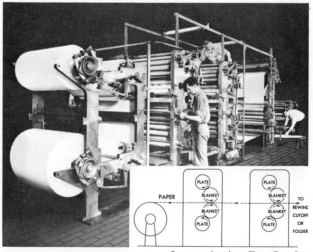

Courtesy American Type Founders

Blanket-to-Blanket Type press. Schematic shows web threaded for running two colors on both sides of a web. A four-over-four press of this design could run one color on both sides of four different webs, four colors on both sides of a single web, two colors on both sides of two webs, etc. The photo shows two webs being perfected.

point of the adjustment. At the roll-end of the press, any one of a number of tension devices are available for control of register. To compensate for action of the tension device at the in-feed end of the press, there may be a device between the last unit and the folder, sheeter, or re-winder, whichever happens to be installed on the particular press. Where both of these devices exist they must be handled together if register is to be maintained and web breaks prevented. While the blanket-to-blanket type of press is referred to as a "unit" type it should not be confused with the true unit type of press described later in this section.

Drum Type. The drum type press is an attempt to obtain better web control than is theoretically possible with the blanket-to-blanket unit type of press. In the drum-type press the web is wrapped almost completely around a large impression cylinder (the "drum"). Mounted around the drum are individual printing units each consisting of a plate cylinder, blanket cylinder, inking system, and dampening system. The fact that the paper is wrapped around the drum under tension, resists the tendency of the web to follow the blanket. On some presses of this type, additional control is attained by graduated cylinder pressures. And as in all web presses, tension devices at the in-feeding and delivery points are available. The one problem on this type of press, and largely a theoretical one, is that large-sized cylinders, or drums, produce a wide printing nip. It is held by many authorities, that the narrower the nip the sharper the print with resultant gain in quality. On the usual drum-type press the web is completely printed on one side, is threaded through a drying unit and is fed to a second drum

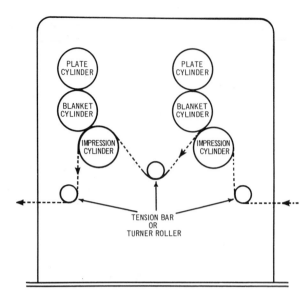

Schematic of a Unit-Type Press. This shows a single web running two colors on one side. If web is turned between units it would be printed both sides in one color. Or, two webs could be run printing one color on one side. The double-ender principle can also be utilized.

to be perfected, or it may go over the same drum or "double-ended."

The Unit Type. The unit type of press is essentially the same as the blanket-to-blanket type except that the web is perfected in a different unit. It is generally differentiated from the blanket-to-blanket type of unit press by referring to it as an "open" unit type. The word "open" signifies that each completely individual plate-printing unit can be handled separately from every other plate-printing unit. In the blanket-to-blanket unit, a pair of plate-printing units have to be handled together. Theoretically, a steel impression cylinder for each blanket improves printing quality. Steel impression cylinders also produce sharper printing because of the narrower nips that are possible. With today's knowledge, positive register control on unit-type presses is possible by the use of electronic devices which include photoelectric cells driving control mechanisms. One advantage of this type of operation is that the units can be so arranged as to cut down the amount of "wet" printing. Theoretically, each color on each side could be dried on a unit-type press before the following color is laid down. Another advantage to such a press is that a most compact assembly of all units can be made. It is also more versatile in that combinations of webs are more easily handled with this design.

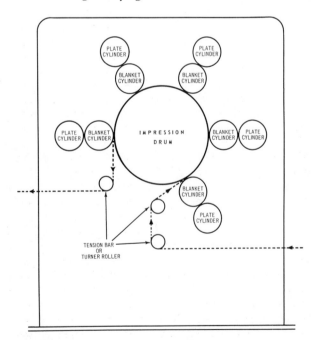

Schematic of a Drum-Type Press. This shows five colors being printed on one side of the web. The web could then be turned and passed into a second similar unit for perfecting. Or, using the "double-ender" principle, a half-width web could be perfected in five colors on this one unit.

INKS FOR WEB OFFSET

In addition to the problems mentioned above, there is one which is universal with all web printing. This is the problem of ink drying. It should be realized that we are trying to completely dry the ink at high speeds and within a limited distance of web travel. This creates a tremendous problem for the ink maker, the paper manufacturer, and the press engineers. Inks must be formulated that can be dried quickly without changing color while still being workable in the lithographic process. Paper must be manufactured that meets the requirement of the offset method and yet will withstand the harsh action of an efficient drying system. To date, heat-set inks are used almost exclusively in web-offset. Until some new technique for drying the printed ink film proves feasible, the web-offset method will require drying ovens, or tunnels, through which the printed web travels between the last printing couple and the folder. Today's ovens make use of several techniques to accomplish drying; sometimes techniques are combined. The most common drying technique utilizes open gas flame. Another popular method utilizes the impingement, on the web, of super-heated air forced against the paper at high velocity. Some ovens combine open flame heat and super-heated air. Electric heater coils are sometimes utilized in oven design. But all the work in this area requires close cooperation between ink maker and oven engineer. As long as high heat is required for ink-drying, some device for chilling the web before folding is essential. Unless the web is sufficiently cooled, breaking at the folds cannot be prevented.

A great deal of work is going on in the area of ink handling on the press. A comparatively minor item is that of pumping ink to the inking system. This is, actually, not new, since the technique has been used in other printing processes and methods for many years. Of greater importance, and the subject of much debate as well as investigation, is the control of temperature in the ink system. The fact that a conventional inking system on a high-speed press will develop heat has long been known. What needs to be known is, just how much heat (or lack of heat) is beneficial. Most of the work to date has been in the direction of cooling the ink system. This is accomplished by building into the ink-drums provision for circulating cool water. Some lithographers are firmly convinced this is helpful, others are skeptical, and some are firm in their belief that reducing the heat generated during operation is unnecessary.

PAPER FOR WEB OFFSET

While paper in rolls costs less than sheet paper, the economics of purchasing in rolls quickly are lost in an inefficient operation. This is most readily grasped if the reported figures on paper-waste are examined. The best available information shows a range of about 5% up to 25% for spoilage. 3% is generally accepted as the irreducible minimum and covers core weight, waste at core, wrapper weight and waste at outer layers of a roll. With a possible savings of up to a maximum of 13%, there isn't too much margin for paper spoilage.

Some explanation of the 5% to 25% spoilage experience is in order. A simple throwaway in a long run can very well be accomplished with very little more than the basic 3% waste. With low quality demands many pieces, which would not be acceptable for some runs, can be used. The web-press operation in a plant which produces a product for its own use (a comic book publisher, for ex-

ample), can set minimum standards for its class of publication and thereby prevent gross waste from going above 5%. However, an experienced web-offset plant doing a high quality advertising brochure or magazine insert in full-color, may easily experience a waste above the 13% cost-savings of rolls over sheets. The savings to the customer are not found in lower cost of paper but in production economics possible with a web-offset press. Profits, of course, can go way above industry average where the fine-quality web-offset plant succeeds in holding waste down to a point close to the irreducible minimum of 3%.

A skillfully operated web-offset press can run papers which cost less than true lithographic grades of equivalent quality. This is due to the fact that it is possible to maintain closer dampening control and run with less water on a web-press, where the cylinder gap is virtually non-existent. This characteristic of the web-offset press offers another opportunity for reduced costs without sacrifice of paper quality. In the past decade, the paper industry has contributed enormously by developing papers which are suitable for web-offset at little if any increase in cost over an equivalent letterpress paper. This is true in all grades, from newsprint to the finest uncoated texts and coated book papers.

Where a plant must use so-called letterpress papers, the troubles which may arise are not always costly. For example, a letterpress-coated paper will produce some piling of dissolved coating on the blankets. If the press is not equipped with a flying paster, the time during which the next white roll is being loaded can be used to wash the blankets, thereby preventing the coating piling from reaching a point where quality of print drops below the required standard. If a press is equipped with a flying paster, then it is generally required that paper which will cause minimum down-time be purchased.

Of the more serious problems associated with paper in web-offset operation are shut-downs due to linting, surface dust and dirt, slitter dust, and similar paper characteristics. There is a considerable amount of give-and-take between paper mills and web-offset operators, as to how best this group of problems can be handled. It's not possible, as yet, to make perfect paper. More and more printers are recognizing this fact and assuming part of the responsibility. The most common technique is to pass the web of paper through a pre-conditioning phase between in-feed and the first unit. Generally, a pre-conditioner is a simple oven where open flame is utilized to burn off loose paper materials. Another approach is to pass the web through a set of cleaners which brush the sheet lightly and then, by use of vacuum, draw off the materials loosened by the brushes. The oven-type pre-conditioner is the more popular. Many printers believe that there are several other benefits gained by the warming of the web before it passes into the printing unit. This is a subject of some controversy, and considerable research is now being devoted to learning the true facts about pre-conditioning with heat.

In the following chapter there is information on ordering paper in rolls, handling roll stock, and record keeping.

Section Eleven: Safety in the Pressroom

Every person who operates a press must learn that it can be done safely. The *right way* of doing a job is the *safe way*. If one starts out by always doing a job the right way, doing it the right way will become a habit. Accidents are the result of doing a job the wrong way. A smart operator recognizes that it is just as important to follow the safe practices and procedures already developed for a particular operation, as it is important to follow the mechanical details of that operation.

First aid should be obtained for all injuries, no matter how small. This serves as a guard against infection and prevents delay in healing.

HOUSEKEEPING

Poor housekeeping in and around the press contributes to many accidents, especially trips and falls. For carrying out the personal responsibility for your own safety, and those who work in the pressroom, a check of the press area should be made for the following points:

1. Are the oil drip pans emptied periodically?
2. Do you have safety containers for solvents?
3. Are metal containers for cleaning rags available?
4. Are waste containers for paper provided?
5. Are there no ink cans on floor or platforms?
6. Are no tools left on walkways?
7. Is no wearing apparel hanging on control boxes or on press frames?
8. Are rollers properly racked so they cannot be accidentally knocked from their positions?
9. Are the floor, platform, and steps free of grease and oils?
10. Are there any empty skids standing on edge or leaning against equipment, walls, or columns?
11. Are the air hoses in reels or racks?
12. Are all aisles free of trucks and empty skids?

And do not forget that men assigned to empty the disposal containers should wear gloves and safety goggles.

FIRE PROTECTION

There are safety factors pertaining to the hazards of smoking and the handling of solvents. Fire prevention emphasizes the importance of good housekeeping and the safe handling of flammable chemicals. The personnel of a lithographic pressroom should also know what fire protection measures exist. Everyone should be familiar with the following:

1. How to report a fire.
2. What to look for in making a fire prevention inspection in your immediate work area. In the event you are called upon to make a fire prevention inspection in the department or plant, a Safety Instruction Card is helpful.*
3. How to use the fire equipment that is available.
4. How to evacuate the building.

HANDLING OF MATERIALS

Dollies and lift trucks are often used at a press to put loads in and to take them out. Injuries can be avoided in this work by wearing safety-toe shoes, and by observing the following precautions pertaining to the trucks themselves.

1. Keep trucks and their handles out of aisles and walking areas.
2. Return trucks to a designated area when not in use.
3. Do not ride on these trucks nor stand on them at any time.
4. Do not use a truck unless you have learned how to operate it and have been authorized to do so.
5. Report any operating difficulties you might notice. Leaky cylinders on a hydraulic pump type truck, for example, may cause handles to fly up and to injure the operator. Latches and catches on the ratchet type truck should be in good condition to prevent loads from dropping suddenly.
6. Make sure that all the wheels on trucks are always in good condition.

Piling stock often requires handling of skids or lifts of sheets. The following practices should be observed in lifting:

1. Keep load close to body.
2. Get good footing and solid grip on object.
3. Bend knees and keep back straight.
4. Lift with leg muscles.
5. Get help for heavy or awkward loads and lift as a team.

The following practices should be observed in handling skids:

1. Do not lean skids against the press.
2. Do not leave skids standing on edge.
3. All skids should have a definite place and should not extend into aisleways or gangways.
4. Empties should be transported on dollies whenever possible.
5. Empties should be stacked one up and one down, so that the pile is stable. Pile should not be more than five feet high.
6. Obtain help in handling large skids.
7. Do not drop skids. The noise is distracting and may be the cause of injury at the press. Dropping also may cause wood to splinter and create the additional hazard of slivers.
8. In loading skids, make sure the load will not topple or slide when bumped accidentally.
9. Steel strapping on skids of paper should be removed in such a way that the strapping will not spring when cut and possibly penetrate an eye or the operator's flesh. Claw-hammers, crowbars, or similar tools should not be used to apply leverage for breaking the steel strap. Use the steel

---

* See "Safety Manual for the Graphic Arts," published by the National Safety Council and the Education Council of the Graphic Arts Industry.

strapping cutters with extension handles. These cut in such a way that it is impossible to get sharp ends. The device illustrated can be used to place over steel strapping to keep it from springing after being cut. This is an L-shaped piece of sheet metal (16-gage or lighter steel), six inches wide, with a handle riveted on the 12-inch section. The top extension measures seven inches long.

10. Make sure that proper disposal is made of the scrap metal as it is cut off. Curved or bent pieces are tripping hazards when left on the floor.

In hanging sheets at paper-conditioning machine, watch finger clearance and head clearance so as to avoid bumping against the frame of the machine.

OCCUPATIONAL DERMATITIS

In the preface of the Graphic Arts Technical Foundation's Technical Bulletin No. 6, *Prevention of Occupational Dermatitis in Lithography,* Robert F. Reed states: "The health hazards in lithography are very few, relatively. However, chemical dermatitis, generally referred to in the trade as "chromic poisoning," still does exist among a small percentage of lithographic workers. It is now known to be caused not only by chromium compounds, but also by solvents and certain ink ingredients. . . ." The bulletin suggests these main principles for protection of skin:

1. Try to avoid unnecessary contact of skin surface with irritants and sensitizers.

2. Keep workrooms as clean as possible.

3. Keep skin soft and clean, avoiding dryness, cracking, or splitting.

4. Be careful when mixing or pouring materials.

5. Use funnels or any other apparatus which will help prevent spilling.

6. See that the outside of the bottles and other containers are not splattered over with materials, especially chromates.

7. Wear neoprene gloves whenever handling or using solvents. Never spill anything over the cuffs into the gloves. Do not use gloves with cracks or leaks. When materials such as the bichromates get inside the gloves, the gloves are even more dangerous than none at all. Be sure your hands are clean before you use gloves. Inspect the gloves regularly because even contaminated dust from the workroom may get into them. When you are wearing gloves do not touch other parts of your skin with the soiled gloves. Do not contaminate objects with gloves which you later may have to touch with your bare hands. Cleanse the gloves frequently.

If you protect your skin as a daily routine and follow the routine faithfully, there is little chance of skin irritations resulting from the fluids or chemicals you handle in the lithographic pressroom.

SAFETY IN PRESS OPERATION

Safe press operation means that the press is always operated in the correct way. Personal safety factors, as well as mechanical and general shop conditions should be con-

sidered. Check your procedures to see that you observe the following practices:

1. Nothing that can catch in the moving machinery, or that can trip the wearer, should be worn in the plant. Short sleeves, tucked-in shirts with no tie, cuffless trousers and safety-toe shoes are recommended. If an apron is needed, it should be snug fitting and fastened lightly enough to be torn off quickly if caught in the press. Wear protective gloves and eyewear when required.

2. Jewelry, especially watches and rings, should not be worn when working around the press. The desire to keep one's hands intact should take precedence over any sentiment.

3. Use hand-holds and hand-rails in going up and down the press.

4. Don't jump from one elevation to another, or from press to press.

5. Watch eye clearance when removing printed sheets for inspection.

6. Do not lean against press or rest hands where there is any chance of getting them caught in moving parts. Use hand-holds whenever they are provided, particularly when working at the ink fountain. Get in the habit of keeping hands on hand-hold bar whenever walking between units.

7. Place knives in sheaths when not using them for cutting, packing or other pressroom operations. If razor blades are used, they should have holders on them.

8. Avoid carrying tools in pockets to prevent the possibility of dropping them into the press or hazardous locations.

9. Use proper size tools when making adjustments. Keep wrenches and other hand tools in good condition.

10. Unauthorized operation of a press that you have never run before is dangerous and should not be attempted.

11. Watch finger clearance when handling rollers in and out of the press and at similar operations. Inspect edges of plate before handling it on press, especially if it has been cut down from a larger size to a smaller. Rough edges should be filed smooth to avoid cutting fingers or hands.

12. Oiling the press should not be attempted unless the press is standing. Wipe up oil from floors and platforms to reduce slipping hazards.

13. Do not reach into press while it is running. Stop machine to clear jams, to oil, to set and to make adjustments, to make repairs, or to clean. No attempt should be made to scrape ink off drums while the press is running. Stop the press and sheet-off the ink. The same is true in picking-off hickies. Stop the press before picking-off the hickies.

14. All guards should be in place before press is started.

GUARDS

Lithographic presses are equipped with adequate mechanical safeguards when they are shipped by the manufacturer. However, in the process of transferring equipment from one owner to another, the guards may become misplaced or lost. Also, through experience and use, the operator may find additional areas which may need mechanical protection. The wise pressroom worker will learn what kind of mechanical protection his machine provides, noting especially such points as:

1. In-running cylinders and rollers.
2. Between the blanket cylinder and the plate cylinder.
3. Gears at edge of plate and blanket cylinder; near the bearers.
4. At the foot-board; rear of the blanket and plate cylinder.
5. At feeder end over insertion devices.
6. Chain delivery.
7. Cam that controls height of pile in feeder.

PRESS CONTROLS

Whatever the control system, the operator should thoroughly acquaint himself with it before attempting to operate it. Know where the master switch, the fuse box, and the speed control are located.

Before pressing the "run" button, make sure everyone is in the clear. Anyone who is working on a press should make sure that he is protected against accidental starting of the press. This means having the safe button in before starting any work such as makeready, cleaning, etc.

Gumming the plate requires teamwork and coordination for safety not only to the operator but his helper as well. If the press is small, the person doing the gumming should inch his own press while he is performing the operation. He should make sure that he presses the "inch" button and not the "run" button.

On larger presses when two men are gumming up the plate, the person controlling the inch button should make sure that he does not press the wrong button through error, for not only is his own welfare at stake but that of his co-worker as well. Multicolor presses should be equipped with approved signal systems thoroughly understood by all press crews.

Coordination has been established to such preciseness that some pressrooms are able to have one man at the control station inching the press while he and a crew gum up plates on more than one unit simultaneously. This shows the extent to which teamwork can be developed and still provide safety for all concerned.

Putting on plates and blankets requires teamwork when two men are doing this work. The press should be inched slowly so that the men have control especially when nearing the back clamps or blanket reel.

In backing up the press to take the blanket off, make sure you hit the "reverse" button and not the inch or run, otherwise fingers may get pulled in. Control stations which conform to the Safety Code, previously mentioned, will have the reverse button equipped with a guard, if this button is adjacent to the inch button. You will find that in some pressrooms, these guards on the reverse button are in the form of swing plates which have to be pushed aside before the button can be pressed. This makes it difficult to press the button by mistake. Other pressrooms have made the

reverse button inoperative on the control station and, instead, have an arrangement whereby the reverse button is on a pendant attached to a reel. The reel makes it possible to move the pendant control from one unit to the other. When this particular work is being done, it is, therefore, the only button being used. The press should be backed up slowly.

FEEDERS

The space between the points where the press ends and where the feeder begins should be covered to prevent the possibly of the foot slipping through. In some pressrooms protection has been provided by extending the guard over the feeder.

The length of large offset presses, especially web and multicolor, introduces the need for additional safe buttons on both sides of the feeder. Learn where these are located, if they are provided, so that you can reach them readily when necessary.

When loading feeders of large presses, take the following precautions:

1. Chains and cables should be free of kinks.
2. They should be properly positioned in their drum pulleys.
3. They should be securely fastened to the bars.
4. The rods should be in place and secure.
5. The platform should be in proper position for lifting.

When raising and lowering loads, watch fingers on feeder or delivery elevators which must be turned manually. Do not get under loads either at feeder or delivery elevators.

WASHING OPERATIONS

These may include cleaning blankets, plates, rollers, or parts of the press such as the ink fountain, and require the following precautions:

1. Do not smoke while using solvents.
2. Take only small amounts of solvent to the press and then only in approved safety cans.
3. Avoid spilling flammable liquids — vapors may flow long distances along floor or ground before they are ignited and flash back.
4. Do not pour used solvents down drain or sewer. They should be transported in a closed container to a safe dump or open area where they will not contaminate streams or drinking water supplies, or be accessible to children. Then they should be dumped in small quantities and burned, with someone standing by until the solvents are all burned out.
5. Observe health measures such as protection against inhalation of fumes, do not use solvents on the body, and always use neoprene gloves when handling solvents.
6. Place rags and materials used with solvents into self-closing approved safety containers.

Finally, two last points. For removing sheets stuck to the blanket use water with the sponge and then the solvent with a rag. Make sure that the power is turned off before you begin. On fountain (dampening) solutions, operators using bichromate fountain solutions should report promptly any skin irritations noticed. Non-bichromate fountain solutions, suggested by the Graphic Arts Technical Foundation for use with zinc or aluminum plates, are helpful to those pressmen who are sensitive to bichromate.

CHAPTER THIRTEEN

Ink and Paper for Lithography ─────────────

Section One: Lithographic Ink Fundamentals

Ink of one kind or another is essential to every kind of mechanical printing. In every printing process the printing form must lay a film of ink on a surface where it must remain and dry. Therefore, the ink must be a fluid during printing, and afterwards the printed film must dry to a solid. Just how fluid the ink must be and how it dries varies widely and depends on the printing process, the material being printed, and the press speed.

The Main Ingredients of Litho Inks. Basically, the composition of a litho ink is simple. The principal ingredients are a pigment, a liquid varnish called the vehicle, and a drier. The pigment provides color and hiding power. The varnish vehicle not only carries the pigment, but eventually dries and binds the pigment to the printed surface. The drier regulates the drying speed of the varnish. Pigments and vehicles are discussed in greater detail in the next section of this chapter.

Many Factors Influence the Printing Performance of an Ink. But the ability of ink to *print well* depends also on how well its body and working properties are adjusted to the press, the speed, the surface being printed. Generally, this requires a careful selection of the pigment, varnish, and drier, and often the addition of other materials, called modifiers.

Litho Inks Must Work with Water. From a practical point of view it is not easy to make a good ink. The formula for a good working ink may contain 12 to 15 different ingredients and is developed only after many experiments. The principal thing about lithographic ink that makes it different from other inks is that the litho ink must work in contact with water.

The ink maker must therefore select materials that perfer to be wet by greasy varnish rather than water. The pigments in a litho ink should not dissolve in water. In other words, water should not be able to separate the pigment from the varnish vehicle. Likewise, the varnish should not emulsify or break up and mix into the water. Further, the combination of pigment and varnish must not emulsify or mix excessively with the water.

Two Types of Emulsification. A water-in-ink emulsion, that is, a small amount of water mixing into the ink during printing does little harm. But, excessive amounts of ink mixing into the dampening water produces a disastrous overall tint on the printed surface. To keep an ink-in-water emulsion in equilibrium, the ink must definitely be "greasy," but still not too greasy.

If the ink is too greasy, the non-image areas of the printing plate will become ink-receptive and grease or scum. The greasiness of an ink is determined mainly by the greasiness of the ink vehicle. Some pigments, compounds, and driers also affect the greasiness of the ink. These must all be carefully controlled by the ink maker.

WATER-IN-INK
EMULSION

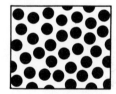
INK-IN-WATER
EMULSION

Two ways in which water and ink may emulsify on the press.

Inks and Plates. There must be nothing in a litho ink that can react chemically with the plate. Undesirable chemical reactions between the ink ingredients and the plate may cause scum, discolor the plate, or even destroy the grain. Finally, there should be no grit in a litho ink. Grit can wear the plate, damage the image, and cause scum. (See Section Five of "Platemaking" Chapter.)

How Inks are Manufactured. The actual process of making an ink is relatively simple. The varnish, and the pigment or mixture known as "dry color," are weighed and stirred together in a tub until the pigment is thorougly mixed with the varnish. The mixture is then ground on a roller mill, where it passes between the rollers as a thin film.

As you can see by the diagram the rollers turn at different speeds and thus severely rub the ink film between them. This breaks down the pigment into microscopic particles so that each particle becomes completely surrounded and wet

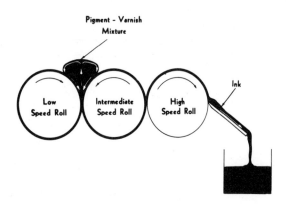

Grinding action on a three-roll ink mill.

by the varnish. The ground ink is taken off the high-speed roll at the right by a doctor blade. A thorough job of grinding may require at least three passes over the mill, depending on whether the pigment is soft or hard, and on how easily it is wet by the varnish.

The Flushing Process. Another way of making ink is called the "flushing" process. Most pigments are made by mixing two or more chemical solutions. These solutions react and form tiny solid particles of pigment which are then filtered out. While still water-wet, this pigment paste is mixed with varnish in a machine like the one shown.

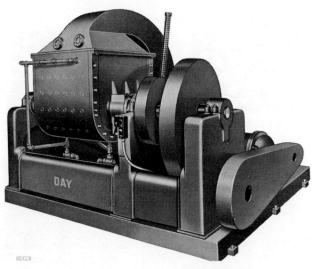

Courtesy of J. H. Day Co.

A machine for making ink by the "flushing" process.

While in this machine, the pigment transfers to the varnish and water separates or "flushes" out and is drained off. The flushed ink is then dried further by vacuum and needs very little grinding.

Ink Driers and Drying. When should the drier be added? That depends on the particular circumstances. Many lithographers carry stocks of inks and prefer that they contain little or no drier, because the same ink used on different papers may require different amounts of different kinds of drier. This makes it best to add drier to each batch of ink as it is mixed for the press.

Also, stock inks that contain drier tend to skin after the can has been opened and this results in waste. Still another reason for omitting drier in manufacture is that in some colors the drier gradually loses its drying power if the ink is stored. In some cases, drying power is lost altogether after a few days or weeks.

The ease with which an ink dries, and therefore the amount of drier it requires, depends largely on the pigment. Some pigments are good driers to start with and inks containing them don't need much drier. Other pigments dry poorly and their inks need much more drier. Knowing this, some ink makers add a little drier to inks made with poor-drying pigments. This makes it possible for the pressman to dry all colors by adding approximately the same amount of drier. When inks are custom-built for a job, and will be used within a short time, the ink maker should be permitted to add all the drier needed. He will also test the ink for drying on the paper to be printed. In recent years the trend has been more and more toward the use of press-ready inks.

Ink Pigments Vary Greatly. In addition to *how* they dry, ink pigments vary widely in other ways. Specific gravity, particle size, wettability and opacity or transparency, as well as color and tinting strength, are different for each one. Different colors of inks, therefore, cannot be built on any one standard formula. Each pigment has its own characteristics and its ink must be formulated to accommodate them.

Important Ink Properties. The three most important properties of an ink are color, body, and ability to dry. The color properties of an ink depend on the pigment. These properties are mass-tone, undertone, and tinting strength.

Mass-tone, Undertone, Tinting Strength. Mass-tone is the hue or color of a thick mass of the ink. It is the color of light reflected by the ink pigment. Undertone is the hue or color of a thin, transparent or translucent film of the ink. It is the color of light reflected by the paper and transmitted through the ink film. Tinting strength is

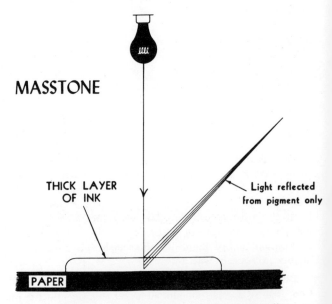

A schematic representation of "masstone."

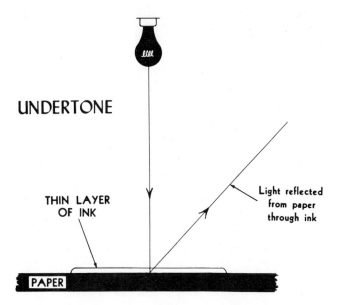

UNDERTONE

THIN LAYER OF INK

Light reflected from paper through ink

PAPER

A schematic representation of "undertone."

coloring power, or the amount that an ink can be reduced or diluted with a white ink to produce a tint of a given strength.

All three of these properties affect the appearance of a print. No printed ink film is completely opaque or completely transparent. As a result, what we see on a printed sheet is a combination of light reflected in different ways. Part of the light is reflected by the ink, and part is reflected by the paper through the ink. Therefore, if you are after an exact ink match, mass-tone, undertone, and tinting strength must all be matched. How to determine the mass-tone, undertone, and tinting strength is discussed in the following section under "Making a Drawdown."

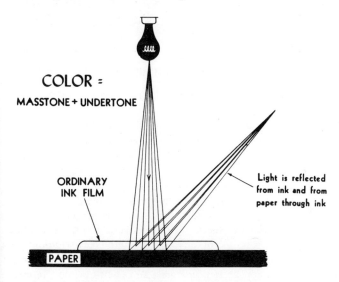

COLOR = MASSTONE + UNDERTONE

ORDINARY INK FILM

Light is reflected from ink and from paper through ink

PAPER

How masstone and undertone affect what we see.

Body, Tack and Length. The body of an ink refers to its consistency. Litho inks are thixotropic, meaning that their consistency or body changes a great deal according to how much they are worked. Because of this characteristic,

the precise measurement of ink body is a highly technical process. For practical purposes the ink maker and printer consider body as a combination of two things, tack and length.

Tack is stickiness, or the resistance of a thin film of the ink to being split. Tack is sometimes estimated by a tap-out test with the finger, usually in comparison with another ink that you want to match. An ink that is not tacky enough may not print clean and sharp and may lack finish. An ink with too much tack will pick, blister, and split the paper.

Length is the ability of an ink to flow. This is indicated by its ability to form a string when pulled out by the finger. A certain degree of length is necessary to make an ink feed properly to the fountain roller and transfer without piling. Too much length may cause an ink to fly or mist. Both the apparent tack and length of an ink change when the ink is worked either with a knife or on the ink rollers.

Viscosity. In the can, ink may set up until it is practically a solid. But when it is worked with the knife, it quickly becomes softer and more fluid. In matching inks for body it is important to match both tack and length in order to get the same printing qualities. The finger tests for tack and length must always be comparison tests made against inks that are known to work properly.

If you want to keep records, you need an accurate instrument that gives numerical values. There are two such instruments available. The Rotational Viscometer measures the viscosity of varnishes and the more fluid inks. The Inkometer, which measures the tack of ink on rollers at printing speeds, is more suitable for the stiffer inks used in lithography. (See the "Testing of Lithographic Inks" in Section Two of this Chapter.)

How Litho Inks Dry. On paper and board, regular litho inks dry in two stages. The first stage of drying is setting or absorption. Some of the ink vehicle is absorbed by the paper, leaving a stiffened film of ink on the surface.

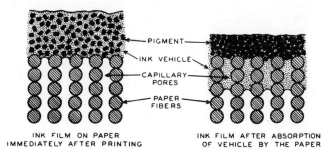

PIGMENT
INK VEHICLE
CAPILLARY PORES
PAPER FIBERS

INK FILM ON PAPER IMMEDIATELY AFTER PRINTING

INK FILM AFTER ABSORPTION OF VEHICLE BY THE PAPER

How drying by absorption takes place.

The ink must be adjusted to the absorbency of the paper so that the setting is fast enough to avoid set-off in the delivery pile. But setting must not be too fast; otherwise, the pigment on the surface of the paper may be drained too dry and the ink may powder or chalk. Special quick-set inks are designed to avoid this trouble.

The second stage of drying is oxidation. This is a chemical reaction that hardens the ink vehicle and makes the film of ink reasonably rub-proof. Oxidation usually requires from four to twelve hours and is controlled by the amount and kind of drier, and the vehicle formulation. But you can only go so far. Excess drier does not speed up drying and often causes scumming. (See the "Testing of Lithographic Inks" in Section Two of this Chapter.)

Ordinarily, 1 to 1½-ounce of drier per pound of ink is enough. In fact, only under unusual conditions is it ever necessary to use as much as 1½-ounces.

Being a chemical reaction, drying is greatly affected by temperature. Heat speeds it up and cold slows it down. Ink dries about twice as fast at 85 to 90 degrees F. as it does at 70 degrees F. if the relative humidity is the same.

Moisture Affects Ink Drying. Relative humidity is another thing that affects ink drying. High humidity really slows it down. Therefore, when the humidity is above 50 percent, use more drier, or still better, use the same amount of a stronger drier. High humidity retards ink drying mainly because there is more moisture in the paper. By the same token, running too much moisture on the press will also slow the drying. GATF's new methods of platemaking make it possible to run a plate with very little moisture. This helps ink drying considerably.

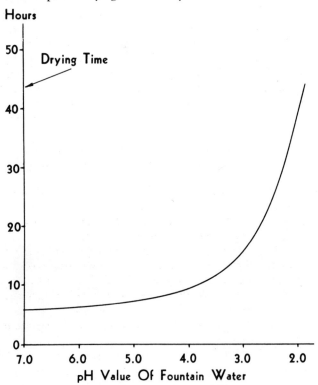

The effect of pH of the fountain solution on ink drying.

Still another factor that affects drying is the amount of acid used in the press fountain water. This curve for a typical offset paper shows that ink will dry in 9 hours if the fountain pH is 4. It would take 37 hours to dry—4 times as long—if the fountain pH were 2. In some cases, too much acid kills the drying altogether. With well desensitized plates you can run with a pH of 5.0 or 6.0 and drying will not be slowed down at all by acid.

The printing paper itself can also affect the drying of ink. Ink dries fastest on absorbent paper and slowest on hard, non-absorbent papers. Acid or alkali in the paper also affects drying. Inks dry normally on uncoated papers having their pH values above 4.5. If the pH of the paper is much below 4.8 drying will be slowed down, especially in humid weather.

Coated litho papers have pH values between 6.5 and 8.5. The higher the coating pH, the better the ink will dry. The effect of pH is not very important when the relative humidity is low, but when the relative humidity rises above 60 percent, ink will dry very slowly on clay coatings if their pH is below 7. However, if the pH of the paper were 8 to 8.5, the same ink would dry almost normally.

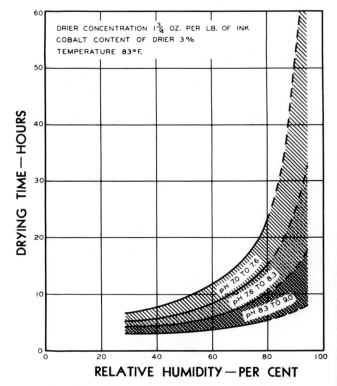

The effect of paper-coating pH on ink drying.

Our illustration shows approximately the relation between the coating pH and drying time of ink. The higher the pH, the faster the drying. The lower the pH, the slower the drying. Alkaline coatings give much less drying trouble during the summer months.

Lack of oxygen can slow down the drying of ink. If you are running heavy solids, there may not be enough air in and between the sheets on the delivery pile to supply the oxygen necessary for drying. Hanging or winding the printed sheets will help. With some colors, especially certain blues and greens, this must be done to prevent heating and chemical reactions that change or burn out the color.

Heat-Set Inks. The newer heat-set inks dry mostly by absorption and evaporation. They require little drier and are used principally on web presses where the printed web is passed between heating units or over hot cylinders that drive off the ink solvent. Since oxidation is not an important factor in the initial drying, the drying of heat-set inks is little affected by relative humidity, press moisture, the pH of the fountain, or the characteristics of the paper.

In printing on metal, there is naturally no absorption of the ink vehicle. With regular litho inks, therefore, drying takes place entirely by oxidation which is speeded up by dryng ovens. Heat-reactive inks do a good job in metal decorating and their use is widespread and increasing. Printing on plastics and decalcomania papers is like metal decorating in that there is no absorption of ink vehicle, and the sheets must be racked singly until the ink dries.

Ink Troubles on the Press. Now let's look at some of the most common ink troubles on the press. They are seven in number: Offsetting, chalking, smudging, crystallization, tinting, scumming, and piling. Each of these seven ink troubles is discussed in the following:

Offsetting results when too much ink is run, or when the ink is too stiff for the paper and does not set quickly enough. To avoid offset, make the ink strong in color and run it as spare as possible. If this does not correct the trouble or give the desired finish, try adding a compound or using an affective non-offset spray properly.

Chalking, where the dried ink powders off, occurs on coated papers if the ink varnish is too thin or improperly formulated for the paper, or if, for some reason, drying is delayed so long that the paper absorbs too much of the varnish. To prevent it, the ink can be stiffened with a long-varnish, body-gum, or synthetic varnish. Before you can do this though, be sure there is not too much acid in the fountain water or in the paper. If the relative humidity is unusually high, use more drier or a stronger drier. Unfortunately, chalking is often not noticed until the job is off the press, and the only remedy is to overprint it with a transparent size or varnish.

Smudging can be caused by not enough drier, or too much non-drying compound in the ink. If the ink doesn't contain enough drier, the sheets may be overprinted, or sprayed with a drying compound. If the smudging is caused by too much non-drying compound, so that the ink dries but does not dry hard, there is no remedy. Drying will not be uniform if the drier is not mixed thoroughly into the ink. Also, large, heavy solids may dry only around the edges because of insufficient oxygen at the center of the sheet. Jobs carrying heavy solids should be winded to provide more oxygen for drying.

Crystallization occurs when an ink dries so that succeeding colors will not adhere properly. To prevent this, avoid straight cobalt or manganese drier except in the final color, and do not allow the sheets to stand too long between printings. Also avoid wax compounds in all colors but the final one.

Tinting is caused by the ink emulsifying excessively in the plate moisture. It can be caused by an ink that is too soft or that does not resist water. The usual remedy is to run a different ink. It is also possible to stiffen the ink with body gum or magnesia carbonate powder. If at all possible, it is best to mix a new batch of ink. Wetting agent in the fountain water or in the paper coating can also cause tinting. Fresh fountain water will eliminate the first type of tint, but if the paper is at fault, there is nothing you can do except get a different paper.

Scumming can be caused by ink that is too greasy. But scumming is far more likely to result from dirty dampeners, improperly set form rollers, too much pressure between the blanket and plate, a poorly desensitized plate, or an unsuitable paper. Slight greasiness of the ink can sometimes be corrected by adding a little body gum or magnesium carbonate powder. But if the greasiness is caused by too much compound, it is best to mix a new batch of ink. (See the "Testing of Lithographic Inks" in Section Two of this chapter.)

Piling of ink on the blanket, plate, and rollers results when the ink is not thoroughly ground or is over-pigmented. Piling can also occur if the ink is too short to start with or becomes too short due to running excessive moisture. Ink that does not resist water will waterlog, become short, and pile. A possible remedy is to make the ink longer and more water-resistant by adding varnish or alumina hydrate. Yet on the other hand, making the ink more water-compatible may be the solution. If the ink is not well ground it should be rejected.

Summary. Ink is a complex mixture of pigment, varnish vehicle, modifiers, and drier. Its important properties are color, strength, opacity or transparency, body or working properties, and drying properties. Color, strength, and opacity or transparency must be selected to suit the particular job. All lithographic inks must have good body, work well on the press, and, in addition, must fit the paper.

Drying is affected by temperature, moisture, acidity of the fountain water, absorbency of the paper, and the pH of the paper.

All kinds of troubles are often blamed on ink when the real cause is poor plates, dirty dampeners, or improperly set rollers. But ink can be made or adjusted to suit almost any paper, so long as the paper meets the normal requirements of pH and pick-resistance, and is free from lint and dust.

Good lithography requires good plates, good press conditions, good paper, and good ink. Cheap inks may be a false economy. It is best to deal with a reliable supplier and depend on him for help if you have trouble. It doesn't take much productive press-time to pay the difference in price for good ink.

Much of this section has been written around pressroom practices as they exist. This accounts for so much mention of compounds which may be added by the pressman. Sometimes they help; sometimes they do harm; sometimes its just plain wasteful. The best all-around rule in this respect is to have inks formulated by the ink-maker, for the job, and "press-ready." If it is believed that some doctoring must be done, it should be done *only* on the ink-makers specific advice. Where "stock" inks must be used, compounds for doctoring these should be recommended by the manufacturer of the specific ink.

Section Two: Lithographic Printing Inks

A lithographic ink is made from a pigment or from a blend of pigments dispersed in a viscous liquid called the vehicle. White extenders such as alumina hydrate serve to reduce the color strength; if necessary opaque whites can also be used as a part of the pigment portion. Small amounts of additives, such as driers and wax compounds, are incorporated in the ink to improve its performance.

A lithographic ink should have sufficient flowing properties so that it will travel from one roller to the other roller as it passes from the ink fountain to the rubber blanket and thence to the paper. It must also have the ability to stick to the printing areas and not to the non-printing areas, which have been first made wet by the fountain solution. The ink vehicle must have the ability to form a hard film either by oxidation of the drying-oil varnish, or by evaporation of the solvent — leaving in this case the binder behind — or even by both methods at the same time.

Our study of lithographic inks is divided into three general subjects: (1) Study of pigments; (2) Study of vehicles; and (3) Testing of inks. Each of these is discussed in detail in the following pages.

PIGMENTS FOR LITHOGRAPHIC INKS

Our discussion of pigments is divided into the following twenty-five points: (1) Ink transfer percentage; (2) Color strength; (3) Bleeding in the fountain solution; (4) Effect of pH on bleeding; (5) Non-bleeding pigments; (6) Sensitivity of pigments to acids; (7) Effect of heat on different pigments; (8) Subliming of pigments; (9) Subliming in tints; (10) Fading of pigments; (11) The effect of sulphonic acid groups; (12) Pigments not inclined to sublimation; (13) Light-fastness; (14) Light-fastness in tints; (15) Darkening of pigments; (16) Darkening and fading; (17) Outdoor exposure; (18) Pigments affected by the rain; (19) Differences in outdoor and indoor light-fastness; (20) Change of light-fastness in tints; (21) Permanency ratings of pigments; (22) Brillance; (23) Flocculation; (24) Ink Stripping; and (25) Ink tack. Each of these points is briefly discussed in the following.

Ink Transfer Percentage. The offset method is in our times the dominant method of lithography and therewith also for the use of lithographic inks. Here the ink is transferred from the lithographic plate to a rubber blanket and then to the paper or to a metal plate. If a 50 percent transfer occurs at each operation, then about 25 percent of the original ink film is transferred to the surface to be printed. If as much as a 60 percent transfer occurs at each operation, then 36 percent of the original ink is transferred. In order that the lithographic ink may be of a suitable color strength after printing, it is necessary to start with pigments of high color strength considering that the final printed ink film is very thin.

Color Strength. A pigment of low color strength, such as ultramarine blue, does not have enough coloring power to yield the color intensity necessary in the offset lithographic process. The addition of alkali blue, which has a very high color strength, to the ultramarine blue can bring up the color strength of the latter to a suitable color level.

Bleeding in the Fountain Solution. A pigment to be used in lithographic ink should not bleed in the fountain solution, although there are some exceptions to this. If it does, color is imparted to the non-printing areas of the plate and from there to the paper in areas where no such color must appear. It has been observed, for example, that barium eriglaucine lake, commonly called the fugitive peacock blue, bleeds somewhat in the fountain solution. This fact must be kept in mind by the ink formulator.

Effect of pH in Bleeding. When the fountain solution is rendered more acid, or has a lower pH, the bleeding of this blue lake is increased in intensity. Other pigments, too, react in a similar way to more acid fountain solutions. There is a similar increase of bleeding with calcium lithol rubine toner, calcium permanent red 2B toner, calcium pigment scarlet toner and other red lake pigments. A large increase in the acidity, a low pH, has even more severe consequences. It causes chrome yellows to break up chemically, and produces yellow bleeding in the fountain solution.

Photograph by F. S. Lincoln

Finger tapout and bleeding tests.

Non-Bleeding Pigments Replace Bleeding Pigments. It has been observed that phthalocyanine peacock blue is non-bleeding in the fountain solution and, therefore, is gradually replacing the barium erioglaucine lake in lithographic inks. Besides being non-bleeding in the acid solution, it is also higher in color strength and is much more resistant to light.

Sensitivity of Pigments to Acids. Pigments that are sensitive to acids, such as ultramarine blue, may lose some of their color strength or may even shift in their color hue, due to the chemical action of the acid in the fountain solution. Background tints printed with inks containing such sensitive pigments can become unsatisfactory because of the relatively large shifts in color that occur at the low concentration of the pigments in tints. Uncoated papers are particularly dangerous in this respect. They are acidic and this acid content may act to fade the sensitive tints.

Effect of Heat on Different Pigments. When lithographic inks dry by oxidation, and most of them do, heat is generated during drying in the pile of the printed sheets. The chemical reaction — scientifically called exothermic — between the drying oil and the oxygen in the air gives off heat.

Subliming of Pigments or "Ghosting" of Inks. Pigments that possess vapor pressure (and there is a series of such pigments) can sublime with heat and thus travel in the form of a gas from one sheet to the next. There they

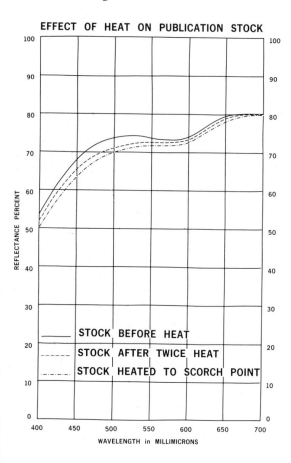

EFFECT OF HEAT ON PUBLICATION STOCK

REFLECTANCE PERCENT

WAVELENGTH in MILLIMICRONS

_____ STOCK BEFORE HEAT

- - - - - STOCK AFTER TWICE HEAT

— · — · STOCK HEATED TO SCORCH POINT

may re-deposit themselves on the non-printing areas. This can yield a color staining, sometimes called a color "ghosting," in undesirable areas.

There is no known remedy to prevent this form of ghosting dependent upon the vapor pressure of certain pigments. The only recourse open to a manufacturer of printing ink is to replace the coloring matter that has caused the ghosting by pigments having much lower pres-

sures or by using pigments that are incapable of subliming.

Subliming in Tints. Weak tints made from pigments that are able to sublime can cause unpleasant surprises. They can actually evaporate during drying in the pile, so that the color strength of the printed tint is greatly reduced or entirely lost.

When an ink used in printing tints is made up of several pigments, it is possible that one component pigment evaporates or sublimes almost completely, causing a loss of color strength and a hue shift at the same time.

Fading of Pigments Because of High Temperature. At still higher temperatures, such as are used in the drying of metal-decorating inks, the vapor pressure increases greatly. In metal decorating, varnishing is customary and the pigment may travel into the overcoating varnish layer. Tints have also been known in metal lithography to fade because of the evaporation of the pigment at these high temperatures.

In heat-set inks the high heat is needed to evaporate the ink solvents. Here, too, occur color changes and loss of color due, again, to the increased vapor pressure of certain pigments. These color changes are — as already mentioned — most noticeable in blends, for example, where a yellow pigment and a red pigment are used for an orange. It may happen that the yellow pigment leaves and that that the red pigment remains on the paper or *vice versa*.

The Sulphonic Acid Group and its Bearing on Sublimation. Pigments and dyestuffs that are liable to sublime do not contain the sulphonic acid grouping in their chemical structure. The introduction of the sulphonic acid group by a chemical treatment with concentrated sulphuric acid or with oleum, changing the molecular structure, reduces the vapor pressure to practically zero. The following pigments show varying but definite amounts of vapor pressure: paranitraniline red, toluidine red, chlor-para-nitraniline red, benzidine yellow, hansa yellow, and indigo blue.

Pigments Not Inclined to Sublimation. On the other hand, the following pigments show no perceptible vapor pressure, having a sulphonic acid group somewhere in their molecular structure: barium red lake C, calcium lithol red, calcium permanent red 2B, alkali blue, and calcium pigment scarlet. But the introduced sulphonic acid group increases the tendency to bleed in the water which is, as generally acknowledged, a most undesirable feature in lithographic ink. Fortunately, it was found that this tendency can be reduced by combining the new products with metallic compounds. This explains why many of the lithographic ink pigments are combinations with calcium, or with barium or even with aluminum.

You Can See How Complex Pigment Problems Are. First we sulphonate dyestuffs to stop the tendency to sublime. Then we must combine the new product with a suitable metal in order to reduce the increased water-bleed.

Light-Fastness. Many applications of lithographic inks require that the printed ink film be resistant to light. Of course, the degree of light-fastness needed depends upon each individual application. The effect of light, be it now sunlight or electric light, is a function of the concentration of the pigment in the ink film and to the intensity of the light. Thus, tints where the pigment concentration is low tend to fade rapidly, whereas inks where the same pigment is present in a high concentration are but slightly affected.

Light-Fastness in Tints. Only very permanent pigments can be used in tints where even moderate light-fastness is needed. Toluidine red is used commercially at high concentrations in many applications involving light-resistance, but when this red is reduced to tints it fades rather easily.

Most pigments of dyestuff origin fade in principle as does the toluidine red. But they differ among themselves as to the amount of fading; some pigments are rather fugitive and others are quite permanent.

Some Pigments Darken Under the Influence of Light. When light induces a chemical change in the pigment itself, causing a darkening or a color shift, it is to be expected that high-strength lithographic inks, containing a high concentration of such pigment, are more affected than the corresponding tints. Such is the case with chrome (lead chromate) yellows. They darken where used at high strength; but the darkening is barely noticeable in tints which contain a low concentration of the same pigment.

Some Pigments Darken and Fade as Well Under Light. Barium erioglaucine lake is used in lithographic process-blue ink. When this pigment is exposed to light, it fails both by darkening and by fading. Lakes of other triphenyl methane dyestuffs such as methyl violet, victoria blue, malachite green, rhodamine red, brilliant green, and setoglaucine blue fail with light similar to the erioglaucine lake. The degree to which they fail depends, of course, upon the individual pigment.

Effects of Outdoor Exposure. When lithographic inks are exposed outdoors, they encounter both light and rain. It has been observed that a number of pigments laked by metals, can be un-laked by the rain, yielding back their original dyestuffs. As these dyestuffs are quite soluble in water, they are removed by the rain with the detrimental result of leaving the poster ink without its proper color. Consequently, we must consider fading and discoloration by light as well as un-laking by rain as possible failures of lithographic poster and sign inks.

Examples of Pigments Which Are De-Laked By Rain. Calcium lithol rubine, for example, is de-laked by the rain. This cold red pigment shows a good resistance to light indoors but is rapidly un-laked outdoors. Other examples are barium anthosine red, calcium permanent red 2B red, calcium lithol red, and barium red lake C; all of them are un-laked by the rain. Non-laked pigments such as toluidine red, chlorinated paranitraniline red, hansa yellow, and dinitro orange are, of course, not capable of being un-laked and are but slightly attacked by rain. They are, however, subject to attack by light when used outdoors.

Some Pigments Are Light-Resistant Indoors But Not Outdoors. Cadmium yellows and cadmium oranges are very resistant to light indoors but are not permanent outdoors. Evidently, these pigments are attacked by rain and oxygen and probably oxidized to cadmium sulphate. Cadmium sulphate, on its part, is soluble in water and is washed away by the rain. Regardless of its mechanism, the failure of cadmium yellows and oranges is different from a failure by the attack by light alone.

Pigments Matched at High Concentrations Vary in Their Light-Fastness in Tints. It is also known that pigments having the same light-fastness at the high-strength level may differ in permanency when brought down to the level of tints. In other words, the curves representing light-fastness can have different slopes.

If a pigment is used in small amounts in an ink, be it now in combination with opaque whites, white extenders, or with other colored pigments, the pigment used in a small amount generally acts as though the other pigments were absent. In blends of pigments the ink formulator has, therefore, a difficult time in choosing pigments. He must see to it that the resultant pigment blend will only weaken by fading, without having the objectionable shifting of color hue in ink.

Permanency Ratings Are Important Pigment Characteristics. The majority of lithographic pigments are affected by light in some manner. This makes it imperative to know the amount of permanency required for each application, and also the permanency rating of each pigment at different color concentration levels.

Among the pigments with excellent resistance toward light, both indoors and outdoors, are: carbon black, lampblack, phthalocyanine blues, phthalocyanine green, and many iron oxides.

Brilliance and Hue of Pigments. Lithographic pigments vary in brilliance and in hue. Few inorganic pigments — meaning pigments that are not derived from dyestuffs — have acceptable brilliance, and these few occur in but a limited hue selection. Inorganic pigments are generally low in color strength and are therefore often blended with organic pigments — meaning pigments that are derived from dyestuffs — to bring up their color strength. Organic pigments, different from the inorganic ones, are very numerous, quite brilliant, and occur in all of the colored hue range. By a combination of their useful properties they have gained very wide usage in lithographic inks.

Flocculation. Because lithographic inks are affected by their steady contact with the mildly acid fountain solution, it is important that they do not absorb too much of this solution. Cases are known where the ink changed from a flowing state to that of a very short paste, which change prevented the required distribution on the rollers and resulted in a failure to print with the full tone. This phenomenon is frequently explained as flocculation of the pigment particles. (Flocculation is a technical term; expressed in non-technical language and applied to our case, it means that the pigment particles leave their required positions in the ink vehicle and bunch together into flocks or clusters of an unstable nature.) Regardless of the explanation, such an ink is definitely unsuited for lithographic printing.

However, an ink that is on the borderline of flocculation may still print properly if the ink flow on the press is rapid; for instance, when printing solid areas. But if the ink flow is slow, then the ink may change to a paste and thereby fail to print. This explains why it is possible that different and often contradictory reports are made on the same ink.

The Stripping of Ink. It is essential that a lithographic ink absorb fountain solution to a moderate degree so that the ink will not go off the rollers leaving them to be wet by the fountain water solution. This phenomenon is called *stripping*. Some inks can absorb as much as 30 percent of their weight of fountain solution and still have enough length to travel from one roller to the next and finally to the plate.

Ink Tack. As fountain solution is absorbed by an ink, the tack of the ink goes down. Thus, the quantity of the fountain solution fed along with the ink must be controlled, so as not to lower the tack too far. Here is where the press inkometer is needed because it can measure the change in tack.

While the behavior changes of the ink by the fountain solution may be due in part to the vehicle used in a lithographic ink, these behavior changes are more often due to the pigment portion of the lithographic ink. They are therefore mentioned here under the heading of pigments.

VEHICLES FOR LITHOGRAPHIC INKS

Our discussion of vehicles is divided into the following seventeen points: (1) The viscosity of ink vehicles; (2) The vehicle in its relation to drying; (3) The functions of dryer; (4) The influences of acidity on drying; (5) The three basic types of lithographic ink vehicles; (6) Drying-oil vehicles and blankets; (7) Solvents for resin solvent-type vehicles; (8) Drying-oil heat-set vehicle blends; (9) The effect of aging on drying-oil ink films; (10) The effect of light on drying-oil ink films; (11) Livering of lithographic inks; (12) False bodies; (13) Relation between gloss and vehicle type; (14) The effect of aging on lithographic inks; (15) Drying by oxidation; (16) Anti-skinning agents; (17) Waxes and non-rubbing inks. Each of these points is briefly discussed in the following.

The Viscosity of Ink Vehicles. In order that the vehicle shall not mix too readily (mechanically) with the fountain solution, the viscosity of the two should be far apart. That is why a lithographic vehicle should be quite viscous in nature and quite insoluble in the fountain solution. A good vehicle for lithographic ink must produce an ink that will not tend to emulsify excessively in the fountain solution. When water is mixed with ink, it should be a water-in-oil emulsion and not an oil-in-water emulsion.

In the case of four-color process printing, there is a sequence of descending viscosity (tack) from ink to ink, so that the last-down ink actually has considerably less viscosity than the first-down ink. It is advisable though, not to go too low in viscosity, for then the ink mixes mechanically too readily with the fountain solution.

The Vehicle in Its Relation to Ink Drying. Besides carrying the coloring matter from the ink fountain to the paper, the vehicle serves another important function, that of binding down the ink film. Drying can be accomplished either by oxidation of the drying oils and — to a lesser degree — by the oxidation of certain resins, or by the

evaporation of the solvent present, or by both oxidation and evaporation at the same time. Along with the oxidation of drying oils there can occur varying amounts of polymerization, especially when heat is used in the drying of inks.

The Functions of Driers. In order to control and to accelerate drying by oxidation, it is necessary to add metallic driers, which act as catalysts. The most potent of these are made from cobalt, followed in power by those made from manganese, lead, iron, and zirconium. Generally speaking, the driers are soluble in the ink vehicle and are prepared as linoleates, resinates, soyates, and naphthanates of the above mentioned metals.

The Influence of Acidity on Drying. The uncoated papers are acidic in nature because aluminum sulphate (alum) is added just prior to the formation of the paper on the paper machine. The alum behaves as an acid in a water solution. The fountain solution must also be acidic. This is necessary to prevent the formation of ink-receptive plate-metal oxides (such as zinc and aluminum oxide) whose presence would upset the distribution between the printing and the non-printing areas of the plate. On damp days, and when considerable amounts of fountain solution are used, delayed drying, or even complete failure to dry, can occur. Then, the acid from both sources — the paper and the fountain solution — can attack the oil-soluble metallic drier, therewith converting it chemically to a state where it loses most of its effectiveness as a drier.

Whereas excess moisture merely retards the rate of drying, excess acid needs counteracting. To combat its adverse result upon drying, the use of a drier in the fountain solution is needed. This drier is a water-soluble cobalt catalyst that stimulates drying. The more fountain solution is run on the plate, the more of the undiluted acid is present, and the more of the counteracting catalyst is needed and is actually added.

The Three Basic Types of Lithographic Ink Vehicles. There are three general vehicle types for lithographic inks: (1) A straight drying-oil vehicle, (2) A resin solvent vehicle, also known as heat-set vehicle; and (3) A combination of a drying-oil vehicle with a resin-solvent-type vehicle. The popular drying oil is linseed oil or a modification thereof; the popular solvent is a low solvency petroleum solvent; but the resin varies according to purpose. It may be a member of the pentaerythrytol-resin series, or a member of the phenolformaldehyde series, or even a member of the maleic resin series.

Drying-Oil Vehicles Affect Rubber Blankets. While the drying-oil vehicle has a tendency to attack and swell some rubber blankets, it has been possible to make lithographic blankets that show very little, if any effects of attack by drying-oil vehicles. This improvement in blankets has been possible by the use of new types of synthetic rubber.

Solvents For Resin Solvent-Type Vehicles. As solvent in the resin solvent-type vehicle, generally a petroleum solvent of high boiling range, is selected because it possesses the necessary slow-evaporation rate on the press rollers and the plate. The ink maker has at his disposal a number of these solvents, which differ mainly in the boiling range and in the rate of evaporation on the rollers at room temperature.

In order that the solvent used in the resin solvent inks should attack the new rubber blanket as little as possible, it is necessary to select a low solvency petroleum solvent. It has also been observed that this type of a petroleum solvent shows better performance in heat-set inks than a corresponding high-solvency petroleum solvent. Some believe if the two types of solvents are matched in boiling range, it has been observed that the low-solvency solvent will evaporate less from the rollers than will the high-solvency solvent. Also, the former has less color and odor than the latter solvent. Of course, the solvency must not be too low, for then it is difficult to find a suitable resin that can be dissolved in it in order to make a heat-set vehicle. Finally, it is mentioned that heat-set ink must be dried by the application of heat, as its name indicates.

Drying-Oil Blend With Heat-Set Vehicle. A blend of the drying-oil vehicle and of the heat-set vehicle can yield useful ink properties. Less oxygen is needed to dry the ink by oxidation, proportional to the amount of the drying-oil vehicle used. Because of the resin present, a higher finish is generally obtained which makes the printed matter appear more snappy. If wax is omitted from the ink formula, the dried ink film can be overprinted successfully at any time.

A new type of a rubber blanket must be used with this ink vehicle and with the heat-set ink vehicle, to minimize the penetration of the petroleum solvent into the blanket. The tack of the ink rises when the solvent leaves the ink and goes into the blanket. In this case it can easily happen that the ink picks the surface of the paper, or that the ink even fails to print.

The Effect of Aging On Drying-Oil Ink Films. Weak lithographic tints containing drying-oil varnishes can acquire a tan color upon aging in the dark. Thus, so-called standard tints are not reliable in color after they have aged in the dark. A light blue tint, such as an ultramarine blue tint, can change considerably in the dark. Light blue is a complementary color to tan, and that is why this color shows such a prominent color shift.

The Effect of Light on Drying-Oil Ink Films. Because the pigment in a weak tint may fade with light, the keeping of such a dried tint in the presence of light can make the tint-standard unreliable. In order to make sure that the freshly printed tint is correct in color, it is wise to use a spectro-photometer to chart the wave length curve and to compare it with the curve made of a freshly printed standard tint. This spectro-photometer can also be used with high-strength inks, for it is not restricted to tints.

Livering of Lithographic Inks. Certain lithographic inks are subject to livering, which really is a very great increase in body, resulting from hot milling or aging in combination with high (fatty) acid vehicles, and pigments with high moisture content and/or high relative amounts of acidic residual electrolytes. Livering is due to a chemical reaction occuring between the pigment and a vehicle containing some reactive fatty acid. The product of this reaction is a metallic soap, which is very short and buttery, and eventually causes the ink to set up as a livery mass. If and when this product is reclaimed by adding rosin or oleic acid plus soft linseed varnishes or solvents, the color strength of the ink goes down and the ink is likely to be unfit for lithographic usage.

False Bodies. A false body, which may look like livering, can occur when inks are stored for some time. But if the thickened ink batches are worked with a spatula or run through a three-roller ink mill, and they revert nearly to their original ink flow and body, then the phenomenon is not livering but false body or, scientifically speaking, thixotropic setup. The inking rollers on a printing press are able to break down thixotropic setup as well as thixotropy encountered during ink aging.

Relation Between Gloss and Vehicle Type. Ink vehicles differ greatly as regards the gloss produced. Because paper is the most important factor in the printing of gloss inks, it must be very carefully selected. Due to the thin film printed by the offset lithographic process, the gloss may not turn out as expected; it may either become a moderate or a high finish. It is the resin component rather than the oil or solvent in the lithographic ink that furnishes the gloss. However, the pigment also has an influence upon the resultant gloss. Therefore, the ink maker has to study the pigments and the resins to be able to compound a good lithographic gloss ink.

The Effect of Aging On Lithographic Inks. When the pigment is dispersed in a lithographic vehicle by milling, a portion of the pigment surface is wet by the viscous vehicle. As the ink ages, more of the pigment surface is wet by the vehicle. A lithographic ink should therefore neither be tested nor used for printing until it is at least one day old. Continued aging allows more of the surface to be wet by the vehicle. It is well known that aged halftone black inks in the letterpress field print better than freshly ground halftone black inks. The same reasoning applies here, too. Also, it is intended in ink making to cover the pigment surface so well with vehicle that the fountain solution cannot attach itself to the surface of the pigment, but must act as a water-in-oil emulsion.

Drying By Oxidation. When a linseed-oil vehicle oxidizes to linoxyn, the solubility characteristics of the vehicle change from easily soluble in greases, fats, waxes, oils, and many solvents to become insoluble in the same materials. It has been found that the drying of linseed-oil vehicles occurs in stages. The ink film can be already dry to moderate rubbing but it may not yet have reached the satisfactory drying stage, namely, that of insolubility to the aforementioned materials.

Tung-oil vehicles dry harder and become more insoluble than do linseed-oil vehicles. Tung-oil vehicles are also more alkali-resistant than vehicles made from linseed or other drying oils.

It is true that the resins used in lithographic inks harden further by oxidation, but the further change in their solubility characteristics is indeed relatively small. Hence, heat-set lithographic inks are not recommended for butter, lard, and bacon wrappers, because the printed ink film does not acquire the needed insolubility.

Anti-Skinning Agents. Anti-skinning agents are useful in lithographic inks because they have a tendency to reduce the skinning and the drying of the ink while it is still in the fountain and on the press rollers. If a volatile anti-skinning agent is selected, the drying of the ink on the paper is but moderately affected, since the bulk of the anti-skinning agent leaves the film by evaporation.

Waxes and Non-Rubbing Inks. Waxes are added to drying-oil vehicles in order to impart slipperiness to the dried ink films. Regardless of whether or not the wax is soluble at the outset, the wax will not function properly as a slip-agent unless it is insoluble in the final dried ink film and can be squeezed out of it. A petroleum drying oil also tends to keep the wax in solution after drying by oxidation, and that results in an ink of unsatisfactory rub-proof characteristic.

In heat-set lithographic inks, the wax will not serve well for the purpose of imparting non-rub properties, because the heat needed for the drying of this ink also melts the wax. By heating, the wax becomes very thin and penetrates the paper readily. It is therewith lost as a lubricant on top of the ink film, where it is needed for making the ink rub-proof. Recent developments with still higher melting waxes have shown some improvement.

THE TESTING OF LITHOGRAPHIC INKS

This part of our study covers two different groups of tests. First we discuss the testing of ink for its operational functions, then we present the test made on the litho-graphed sheet in conjunction with its end use. In the first group you find the following six points discussed: (1) Making a drawdown; (2) Determining the tinting power; (3) The GATF Inkometer, (4) Applying pick tests to the testing of inks; (5) The mortar test of bleeding; (6) Scumming of lithographic inks.

In the second group you find fourteen end-use tests: (1) The rub test; (2) Light-fastness; (3) Outdoor exposure; (4) Water-bleeding; (5) Testing for solvent resistance; (6) Testing for bleeding in spirit varnish; (7) Testing for resistance to fats; (8) Testing for protein foods; (9) Testing for acid resistance; (10) Testing for waxing; (11) Testing for hot-iron sealing; (12) Testing for alkali-resistance; (13) Testing for wet soaps; (14) Testing of soap and detergent cartons. Each of these points is discussed in the following.

Making a Drawdown. Lithographic inks are examined for color characteristics by making drawdowns on a moderately soft white paper. If you want to make a drawdown, proceed as follows: Place a small lump, half an inch wide, of the standard or an acceptable batch, of ink on the upper right hand corner of the white paper. Next to it, at the left, you place a similar lump of the ink to be tested. Then you draw a wide steel blade across the pair of inks and you draw down in one swoop first a thick film one inch long and then a thin film for the balance of the drawdown. The thick film represents the mass-tone, and the thin film represents the print-tone. Holding the drawdown up in

front of a light and looking through the thin film shows us the color of the undertone. The two inks being compared should match closely in mass-tone, print-tone, and undertone.

Determining The Tinting Power. The tinting power of each ink is obtained by adding to the test sample an opaque white ink, usually a zinc oxide ink, in sufficient amount to yield a relatively weak tint. The two tints should match in color and also match in the drawdown test. The average lithographic printed matter lies in its color appearance between the mass-tone and the tint-tone, usually closer to the tint-tone because of the thin film layed down in lithography.

The GATF Inkometer. The GATF Inkometer is useful for testing the ink body to help make sure that the ink has the proper viscosity for the press operation. Because there are many variables, such as the speed of the press, the pick test of the paper, the use of multicolor inks in sequence, it is not feasible to assign a specific value for a given lithographic ink. The inkometer is used for setting comparative standards. After the pressman has noted the best performance of an ink, or inks, on the press, the inkometer can now be used to insure uniformity of the ink bodies for that specific press and its operation.

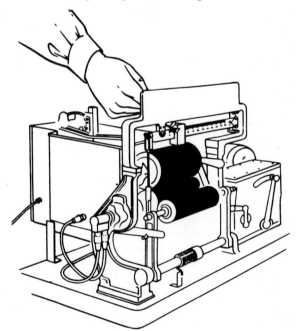

The GATF Inkometer.

Applying Pick Tests To the Testing of Ink. Because lithographic inks are made from viscous vehicles, the inks may be too viscous in nature and can therefore pick the surface of a given paper. A static test, such as the Dennison wax test, for evaluating the pick resistance of paper is much less reliable than a pick test involving motion. Accordingly, the Graphic Arts Technical Foundation and others have developed pick tests for examining paper while the ink on the paper is in motion. (See the "Paper Properties and Testing" section of this chapter.) These pick tests can be reversed to evaluate lithographic inks by using a standard paper and varying the inks to be tested.

The Mortar Test Of Bleeding. Because lithographic inks are on the press in intimate contact with the fountain solution, it is important to know how inks are affected by the fountain solutions. The bleed test is made in a mortar. The fountain solution should be colorless; the colorless phosphoric acid is therefore used instead of the colored chromic acid. Instructions for making the mortar bleeding test follow:

Add to the hydrant water enough 1 percent phosphoric acid so that the bromphenol indicator just changes from purple to a pale green. This indicator must be used as an outside indicator. To 1000 parts of the acidified hydrant water, add one part of gum arabic previously dissolved in three parts of hydrant water. The approximate pH of the finished fountain solution is about 4.3.

Place sufficient lithographic ink in the bottom of the mortar to cover well the bottom after rubbing with the pestle. Then add about an equal volume of the above discussed fountain solution. Rub the ink and the solution well for five minutes. Pour the remaining solution into a filter paper, which has been placed in a funnel. Note the amount and color of the filtrate. The bleeding should be in the region of small amounts, such as traces.

Collect the treated ink with a spatula and free it from adhering water by rubbing on absorbent paper. Note if the ink has now sufficient length to transfer from one roller to the next. If not, it is considered unsatisfactory. Also, note whether the tack has dropped little or much during the mortar treatment by comparing it with the tack of an untreated ink. An ink that has dropped very far in tack is to be regarded with suspicion.

The Scumming of Lithographic Inks. Sometimes an ink will 'grease' the printing plate, in the non-image areas of the plate. That is, the plate becomes 'scummy.' This is a reaction between the ink and the plate, so sometimes the plate is at fault and sometimes the ink is the offender.

The non-image areas of the plate usually are water-receptive because they are covered with a thick absorbed film of a hydrophilic gum, such as gum arabic, or cellulose gum. Such gums usually contain a carboxyl group (-COOH) in their molecules, and it is believed that this group is oriented toward the metal surface to provide the absorption bond between the gum and the metal surface. The rest of the molecule sticks out into the air from the plate, and contains groups, such as -OH groups, which make the molecule accept water rather than ink.

Dr. Paul Hartsuch, in GATF Text #401 *Chemistry of Lithography,* wrote:

"Now suppose there are molecules in the ink which contain groups, such as carboxyl groups, that are also capable of forming an absorption bond to the metal plate. Suppose, further, that the other end of these molecules is ink-receptive, instead of water-receptive. Then it may be possible for such molecules to displace the gum molecules, become attached to the metal themselves, and thus make the metal ink-receptive in that area. For example, oleic acid is known by pressmen to be a very 'greasy' material. This is because it fulfills the above require-

ments. It has a carboxyl group on one end of the molecule, and the rest of the molecule consists of a long chain of carbon and hydrogen atoms which is ink-receptive. In fact, oleic acid will displace gum molecules so easily that it must be used very sparingly or it will grease the whole printing plate.

"It is possible that certain pigments and vehicles may behave in a manner similar to that of oleic acid. Some pigments have a greater tendency to grease a printing plate than other pigments. In certain cases, a pigment which tends to go greasy will work satisfactorily if it is mixed with the proper vehicle. The chemistry of this is very complicated and is not well understood.

Most things which can be added to an ink, such as a wax compound, or 00 varnish, will increase the tendency of the ink to grease. Recently, however, the ink companies have developed special varnishes which will reduce the body of a litho ink, and at the same time make it less greasy. This is something which the litho pressman has needed for a long time.

This discussion of scumming concludes the first part of our ink testing presentation. In the second part we will discuss ink tests pertaining to the end use of the printed sheet. It is essential in all these tests that the ink film be fully dry before the tests are made.

The Rub Test. The dried ink films are often given a rub test. This can be done by using the Sutherland Rub Tester, which is an instrument designed for rubbing dried ink films. The details of the operation of this machine are available from the Sutherland Paper Company. Other manufacturers too make rub-test machines, all of which are in-

Courtesy of Atlas Electric Devices

The Fadeometer.

tended to minimize the personal factors involved in testing. Frequently, 25 rubs on the Sutherland Machine are sufficient, but a number of companies require 50 or even 100 rubs.

Light-Fastness. One of the important tests for printed matter is testing of light-fastness. The amount of light-fastness needed varies with the nature of the job. The fadeometer is used for accelerated testing of indoor light-fastness. Because of the heat of the fadeometer, the pigments having vapor pressure are faded by both heat and light and not by light alone. The non-subliming pigments are attacked by light alone.

A more accurate test is to expose the prints, a foot inside the south window, during the months of May, June, July, and August. If the prints are pasted on the window, it is possible that condensed moisture will attack the pigments and yield results resembling outdoor exposures. That is why the printed matter should be at least a foot inside the window. Because of the time involved and because of its restriction to certain months, the indoor light test is not popular.

Outdoor Exposure. The Weatherometer is used to test printed matter for an accelerated exposure outdoor test. A more accurate test is to expose the prints on an inclined poster board during the months of May, June, July, and August. This test is not popular because of the time involved and the restriction to certain months. Again, the pigments that can sublime show a more rapid failure in the weatherometer, due to a combination of both light and heat than when inks made with them are exposed on the actual billboard.

Water-Bleeding. Water-bleeding is a frequent problem with printing inks, especially those containing pigments derived from water-soluble dyestuffs. There are two tests used for evaluating the bleeding of ink films in water.

In one test two test strips cut from the dried printed matter (customer's paper) are placed back-to-back in a test tube containing distilled water. The convenient size for these test strips is $2'' \times \frac{3}{8}''$. After 24 hours, the test strips are removed and the resultant bleeding, if any, is compared with another test tube containing distilled water and serving as a blank. The degree and the hue of the bleeding are noted.

The other test is more severe. A number of pigments that do not bleed in the above described test, may show bleeding in the following test: Place four unprinted sheets of the customer's paper on a piece of glass. A convenient size of these sheets is $2\frac{1}{2}'' \times 2\frac{1}{2}''$. Wet these well with distilled water. Then place over them the printed matter to be tested, which has now been cut to the size $2'' \times 2''$. Over this print are placed four more pieces of the customer's paper cut to $2\frac{1}{2}'' \times 2\frac{1}{2}''$. Wet these well with distilled water. Next, drain off the excess of the distilled water and place another glass plate on the very top of the pile. To insure excellent contact, a pound-weight can be placed on top of the glass plate.

After two hours, save the printed piece and the paper sheet touching the print. Discard the other sheets, which merely served to keep the assembly wet. Allow the printed piece and the touching paper to air-dry. Note the amount

and the hue of the staining of the paper. (In the absence of the customer's paper, one can use a low acid-type of filter paper.)

Testing For Solvent- And Oil-Resistance. Printed matter is frequently required to withstand some type of solvent or oil. A beer label, for example, must withstand the action of beer, which may be spilled on the labelled bottle; a vinegar label is required to withstand the action of the vinegar, which too can easily be spilled on the label, and so forth.

In order to examine the lithographed printed matter for its proofness to solvents or oils, you may proceed as follows: Place two test strips ($2'' \times \frac{3}{8}''$) back to back in a test tube containing the solvent or oil in question and make sure that the test tubes are fully covered. After 24 hours, remove the test strips and note any fading or discoloration of the inks, any bleeding in the liquid, or even any staining of the unprinted paper areas.

Another test, which is quite severe but more cumbersome, is to place the lithographed printed matter between eight sheets of paper, four above and four below, all wet with the oil or the solvent under study. The details of this test have been given under the water-staining test, previously described. Note any fading or discoloration of the inks and any staining of the touching paper sheet. For relatively fast-evaporating solvents a period of two hours is acceptable, but for relatively slow-evaporating solvents and for oils a 24 hour period is recommended.

Testing For Bleeding In Spirit Varnish. When the lithographed prints are coated with spirit varnish, there is a tendency for certain pigments to bleed in the solvents present in the spirit varnish. Denatured alcohol is the main solvent in the type of coating varnish that is applied over the printed matter by means of large coating rollers. The time of drying, which is the time of evaporation of the solvent or solvents, determines the relative amount of bleeding of the pigments contained in the ink films.

There are borderline pigments that show bleeding in solvents during two hours, but do not bleed appreciably in ten seconds, the approximate time required for evaporation of the denatured alcohol in the spirit-varnish coating. Even though barium red lake C and calcium lithol red do bleed considerably in alcohol during a period of two hours, their bleeding during the ten-second period is nevertheless so slight that inks containing these pigments can be spirit-varnished. However, there are pigments that bleed very rapidly in alcohol such as alkali blue and rhodamine toner. These are not recommended for use where lithographic ink films are to be spirit-varnished.

When the printed matter is to be spot-varnished, there is generally little or no problem encountered, since the oils and solvents present do not cause bleeding, even during the time required for oxidation of the oils present.

Testing For Resistance To Fats. There are two types of greasy and fatty products, those not containing water at all, and those containing water in an emulsified form. Hydrogenated cottonseed oil, such as Crisco or Spry, as an example of the first kind, can be packaged in cans or jars quite warm or even hot, while in thin liquid form, because there is no water present. On the other hand, butter and oleomargarine contain water in emulsified form and must therefore be packaged near or below room temperature in order not to break their emulsion. Therefore, tests applied to lithographed printed matter must be based on different temperatures for the two groups of greases and fats.

Thus, the test for fats not containing water can be made at 200°F for one hour using two test strips ($2'' \times \frac{3}{8}''$) back to back in a test tube containing the fat to be packaged. Remove the test strips and note any bleeding or any discoloration of the ink film. Gently rub the ink film with a greasy finger and observe any attack on the ink vehicle.

The test for fats containing water can be made either at room temperature for three days or at 35°F for one week. A test strip $2'' \times \frac{3}{4}''$ is placed ink side toward the butter or oleomargarine. At the end of the test period, remove the test strip and note any staining of the food product. Rub the ink film gently with a greasy finger and observe any attack on the ink vehicle.

Testing For Protein Foods. Bacon and meats have protein areas as well as fatty areas. For this reason bacon is frequently used for testing lithographed labels for protein foods. Place a test strip $2'' \times \frac{3}{4}''$ of the printed matter ink side toward the bacon, and cover with another slice of bacon. Place the entire sandwich between two glass plates and transfer it to an automatic electric oven, held at 100°F. A pound-weight on top of the glass plate will insure full contact. After an overnight period, remove the bacon strips and note the staining, if any, in both the protein and the fatty areas. Watch out also for fading or discoloration of the printed matter. Rub the ink films again gently with a greasy finger to observe any attack on the ink vehicle.

A refrigerator test is similar to the test just described, except that the temperature is 35°F and the time is one or even two weeks.

Testing For Acid Resistance. Occasionally, lithographed prints are used as labels for products that are acid in nature (having a pH reading below 7). Vinegar, pickles, fertilizer bags, and auto batteries are representatives of these products, which vary greatly in the intensity of the acids present. Thus, several tests are recommended for testing printed matter, differing in the intensity of the acid (pH value).

A severe test is obtained by using 2 percent hydrochloric acid for two hours. This acid is able to remove the chrome yellow from a chrome-green label and causes the ink film to turn blue because the iron-blue component of the chrome-green pigment mixture is not affected by this acid.

A milder test is made by using 5 percent acetic acid for two hours. This is approximately the amount of acetic acid present in commercial vinegar. Moderate and high strength chrome-green ink films are unaffected by this acid. A noticeable shift in color can, however, occur in weak chrome-green tints.

Uncoated paper is acidic in nature and can fade tints containing ultramarine blue, which is very sensitive to even weak acids. The fading occurs when the paper is wet, for example on a billboard or outdoor poster.

Because lithographic fountain solution is acid in nature, an attack on certain pigments can occur. However, the great majority of pigments are not affected by the acid in the fountain solution. More pigments are affected by moderately strong alkalies than by moderately strong acids.

Testing for Waxing. Many food labels, such as bread wrappers, are waxed. Here, then, are needed two tests, one for the waxing process and the other for the hot-iron sealing process. Because of the addition of low-polymer polyethylene to the paraffin wax, a higher waxing temperature is needed. Thus, the following test has been devised to examine the possible bleeding of the pigment contained in the dried ink film, in the compounded wax. Place two test strips ($2'' \times \frac{3}{8}''$) back to back in a test tube containing the paraffin wax blend. Hold at 230° F. for 15 minutes. Remove the test strips and note any bleeding in the wax. Pigments that bleed more than a trace are not recommended.

Testing for Hot-Iron Sealing. The hot-iron sealing process requires a higher temperature for testing the bleeding of the pigment in the compounded wax. Accordingly, an electric iron held at 425° F. is pushed back and forth over the waxed print for five complete cycles. Each time forward, push the iron a bit further in order to produce a piled layer of wax on the sides of the iron. Examine the wax layer for any color staining, which originates from the pigment. It is possible to find pigments that pass the previously described test (waxing test) and do not pass the hot-iron test. The big factor involved here is the temperature difference.

Testing for Alkali Resistance. As stated before, there are more lithographic pigments (in ink films) that are attacked by moderately strong alkalies than by the corresponding acids. There are varying types of alkaline products, and this necessitates several tests differing in intensity (pH value).

A severe test, which simulates the requirements put on labels for lye-bottles is performed as follows: Soak two test strips ($2'' \times \frac{3}{8}''$) back to back in a test tube containing 2 percent caustic soda. After a half hour, remove gently the test strips and allow them to air-dry without washing. Note any color changes and any bleeding in the solution. By rubbing gently with a wet finger, it is possible to examine any attack on the ink vehicle. This test is much too alkaline for testing soap wrapper labels, soap cartons, and detergents.

Testing for Wet Soaps. There are two types of wet soaps: One like Ivory Soap, which has no added alkaline material but has pure soap and water; The other like laundry soap, which has alkaline materials added to it. A product test involving the wet soap to be wrapped is very useful for testing the printed label. In order to accelerate the test, a temperature of 120° F. for three days is quite satisfactory. Slice the wet soap bar in half using a fine wire. Place the printed matter, ink side toward the soap surface, inside the two halves, making a print-sandwich. When the test period is over, open up the print-sandwich and examine any staining of the soap and any color change of the label. Also, rub gently with a wet soapy finger to examine any attack on the ink vehicle. It has been observed that there

Courtesy of IPI

Testing for the effect of soap on ink.

are vehicles that pass the toilet soap test, but not the laundry soap test because of the presence of the added alkali in the latter.

Testing of Soap and Detergent Cartons. The following test can be used for soap cartons and detergent cartons. Rub the dried ink on a carton with fingers covered with a creamy paste, made from the product in the carton, mixed with water. Note any bleeding during one minute of rubbing. This test indicates whether or not the pigments in the ink film can be transferred to white clothes by handling the carton with wet hands.

Rub the dried ink on a carton with fingers covered with a creamy paste made from the product in the carton mixed with water. Note any bleeding during one minute of rubbing. This test indicates whether or not the pigments in the ink film can be transferred to white clothes by handling the carton with wet hands.

To examine the vehicle in the lithographed ink on the cartons, rub gently back and forth twenty-five complete cycles with fingers wet with a 10 percent solution of the product inside of the carton. Note any disintegration of the vehicle.

There are many tests applied to lithographed prints that have not been described in this study. Different companies have variations of the described tests as well as additional tests tailored for their particular products. But the end use is always important in the selecting of tests to be applied to lithographic printing.

Section Three: Facts About Paper Ingredients and Paper Making*

Our presentation of paper ingredients and papermaking is divided into the following twelve subjects: (1) Pulps, (2) Beating and hydration, (3) The reaction of pulps in beating, (4) Refining, (5) Uses of various pulps, (6) Tearing strength and poke-through strength, (7) Sizing, loading, and coating, (8) Loading of uncoated papers, (9) Forming uncoated papers, (10) Pigmented papers, (11) Coating materials, and (12) Applying the coating. Each of these subjects is presented in the following.

PULPS

The origin of papermaking is a subject of controversy, but it is known that the Chinese made paper in an early period and Marco Polo is credited by some for the introduction of the Chinese secret into Europe.

Historical Pulpmaking Materials. The Chinese made paper from a pulp compounded from mulberry bark. Since then paper has been made from grass, cornstalks, trees, rags and numerous other vegetable substances, and scientists have demonstrated that any fibrous vegetation can be made into paper of one quality or another. However, the modern papermaker depends principally upon trees as the source of fibers for paper pulps, because the forests represent a constant and uniform supply the year around.

The Main Classes of Pulp. The character of the fibers in different woods varies considerably and the treatment of these fibers in pulpmaking varies also. Trees of the same species from different parts of the country will

deliver fibers that are different in character and consequently it is difficult to classify and describe all of the various fiber differences that may occur in pulp. However, there are certain general classes of pulps in common use and these can be defined as follows: (1) Mechanical Wood Pulp (Ground Wood), (2) Old Paper Pulp, (3) Chemical Wood Pulp, (4) Rag Pulp.

Mechanical Wood Pulp (Ground Wood). The name "Ground Wood" comes from the mechanical method of converting wood logs into pulp. In this process the logs are ground until reduced to tiny particles. These fine particles are mixed with water and flowed into the screen of the paper machine, where they form into a web of paper.

The Ground-Wood Process Is Simple and Inexpensive. The simplicity of the ground-wood process makes it relatively inexpensive. The whole of the wood log (with the exception of the bark) is used without perceptible shrinkage or waste, and therefore the cost of pulping is low. This type of pulp is necessary for the making of paper for use in newspapers and mass circulation magazines which require a constant and rapid flow of tonnage at a very low price, for a brief service.

The Disadvantages of the Ground-Wood Process. The disadvantage of the mechanical or ground-wood method lies in the fact that the whole log is converted into pulp with the result that the pulp contains all the substance that are invariably present in trees. When the pulp is made into paper, some of these substances cause discoloration and weakening.

* Illustrations courtesy S. D. Warren Co.

Wood chips being conveyed to the top of a tower from which they will be measured into the digestors.

Old Paper Pulp. This kind of pulp is made from paper that has already been used. This used paper is gathered together and cooked in chemicals (lye) which dissolve the printing ink off the paper and reduce the paper back to pulp again. It may also be bleached to whiten it.

The Two Classes of Old Paper Pulps. Old paper pulps must be divided into two classes to be fairly discussed. Some of the old paper pulping processes deliver an inferior pulp with a poor color. Yet some mills develop old papers into excellent pulp. Old paper pulps of the inferior group are used in papers made for sale in the cheaper price brackets and for boxboard, but those of the better class can be made into well-appearing papers with good formation and good printing qualities.

Chemical Wood Pulp. The name "Chemical Wood Pulp" indicates that the wood has been cooked in chemicals for the purpose of removing lignin, gums, resins, and similar materials, so that the pulp is nearly all pure fiber. In the process almost fifty percent of the weight of the log is lost. The chemical process, therefore, delivers only about half as much pulp as the ground-wood process would deliver from the same logs.

Papers Made by the Chemical Process are Regarded as Permanent. Because the chemical processing develops a pulp that is nearly all pure fiber, it is believed that papers made from chemical pulps may be regarded as "permanent."

The Four Main Types of Chemical Wood Pulp. There are several types of chemical wood pulp generally used in papermaking, and each type has certain characteristics of its own. These different pulps are classified as (a) Sulphite Pulp; (b) Sulphate Pulp; (c) Alpha Cellulose; (d) Neutral Sulfite semi-chemical pulp.

Sulphite Pulp. The long fibers required for papermaking are obtained from coniferous woods, which are woods of the evergreen group, such as spruce, pine and hemlock.

The bark is removed, the logs are cut into chips and the chips are cooked in a liquor made from lime and sulphurous acid, which frees the impurities so that they may be washed away after bleaching. Only the pure fibers remain as pulp.

Sulphate Pulp. This pulp is produced by cooking broadleaf or coniferous woods by the sulphate process, i.e. with caustic soda and sulphur. The sulphate process has been used commonly to develop Kraft pulp for grocery bags, etc. However, more and more in recent years bleached sulphate pulp is being used in fine book paper manufacturing.

Sulphate Pulp Makes Papers with a High Tear Test. Sulfate pulp makes paper with a high tear test. Sulfate Pulps produce, in paper, strength in all respects, particularly pop and tensile strength. The pulping process is simple and flexible. As a result of this, the sulphate process has reduced the use of the soda process of producing pulp from hardwoods. Fibers prepared by the sulphate process are being used with great success in almost every type of paper.

Alpha Cellulose. Sulphite fibers are composed of three kinds of cellulose which are known as Alpha, Beta, and Gamma. Of these three the Alpha is the choice cellulose. The Alpha cellulose contained in coniferous woods is segregated by cooking and bleaching the wood successively and severely in different chemical liquors — first in sulphurous acid and then in caustic soda.

The Features of Paper Made from Alpha Pulp. The Alpha pulp thus developed is strong, yet soft and flexible, and consequently it will form into a paper that will show a high tear test and will fold well. It is extremely bright in color and therefore contributes brightness to paper. Alpha cellulose is used in some bonds and in some fine text papers.

Lower portion of a digestor.

Neutral Sulphite Semi-Chemical Pulp. This pulp is made from hardwoods cooked in a liquor of caustic soda and sulphur dioxide. This liquor is nearly neutral as far as acidity and alkilinity are concerned. This process yields a somewhat greater quality than results when making hardwood Kraft pulp. The pulp is a bit stronger than Kraft and more dense. These characteristics produce a paper with more rattle or "character" than does Kraft pulp. Neutral sulphite semi-chemical pulps yield an inherently less opaque paper. This pulping process is used predominantly in locations where the odor of the Kraft process cannot be tolerated, or where other considerations make it particularly desirable.

Soda Pulp. This pulping process must be mentioned even though it is no longer considered one of the main types of chemical wood pulps. The woods used for soda pulp are broadleaf or hardwood, beech, birch, maple, oak, and poplar. The bark is removed, and the logs are cut into chips and cooked in caustic soda. Caustic soda is used in the cooking in order to remove the unwanted substances. The fibers are bleached after cooking in order to whiten them.

Features of Papers made from Soda Pulp. Soda fibers are short. They can be formed into a smooth, fine printing paper with an excellent formation, or they may be formed into a high-bulking paper with a high opacity. But because of the shortness of the fibers a paper made entirely of soda would be extremely weak, so in the manufacture of book papers, soda pulps are mixed with sulphite or sulphate pulps in varying proportions. In body stock for coated papers, still less soda and more sulphate would be used, because longer fibers are required to secure the necessary strength.

Rag Pulp. The term "Rag Pulp" may mean a great deal or very little, because there are all kinds of rag pulps — some excellent and some not very good.

Pulps Made from New Rags. New cotton rags that have never been artificially colored, used, or laundered become a superior pulp with the characteristics of Alpha pulp. Such a pulp would make a very strong paper that would fold well.

Pulps Made from Used Rags. Rags that have been used and subjected to wear and laundering will not make an equally good pulp. The quality will depend on the degree of wear and upon the destructive nature of cleansing chemicals to which the rags have been subjected.

Colored rags that have been worn and laundered make an inferior pulp. Natural wear and cleansing processes weaken the fibers and the chemical treatment for removing colorings further impairs the fibers.

The Superiority of Pulp Made from New Rags. There is no finer pulp for permanence and strength than pulp made from new white No. 1 rags, though there is some basis for believing that Alpha pulp is equally good. Pulp made from used colored rags may not be considered in the same terms and may easily be inferior to sulphite pulps.

Rag pulps are used principally in the manufacture of bond papers and in decorative antique book and cover papers.

BEATING AND HYDRATION

We have defined the different types of chemical wood pulp in common use in the manufacture of book paper and we have listed the distinctive characteristics which identify each pulp, yet we have only partly explained them. Paper pulps are like people in that they react differently to different treatments. And, like people, no two pulps react in exactly the same way. Consequently, a description of pulps is not complete without an explanation of their performance in processing and of their nature after being processed.

The final character of pulp is developed in the beating process and therefore beating is a vitally important factor in paper making.

Pulp being beaten.

The Beater. There are several mechanisms for beating pulp, but the "common" beater is an oval tub, designed like a race track, and the fluid pulp moves around the oval beater much as the horses move around the track. On the long side of the oval tub a cylindrical drum fits down into the track and extends its full width. Each time the watery pulp comes around, it must pass under this drum, which presses the pulp down and rubs it against the bed plate on the bottom of the beater. The cylindrical drum is called the beater roll; it can be raised to let the pulp pass with little disturbance, and it can be lowered until it beats the pulp fibers severely.

Fibrillation and Hydration. Three things happen to the pulp fibers while they are in the beaters: (a) They are fibrillated, (b) They are hydrated; (c) They are shortened. Fibrillation and hydration are, in one respect, independent of each other, yet they are related. The fibrillation process roughens the fibers by fraying and flattening them. The hydration process is difficult to explain because scientists do not agree about it, but it might be described as a reaction which causes the wet fibers to become more adhesive, or more plastic (deformable). The ability to become more adhesive is inherent in the pulp; beating does not "produce" the adhesiveness, but only brings it out.

The combined purpose of beating and hydration is to "plasticize" the fibers so that they will cling to each other. The shortening of the fibers, when desired during the beating process, is done to help produce better formation when the furnish goes over the paper-making machine.

Effect of Beating and Hydration. The effect of beating varies with the severity of the beating. If the beater roll is set down close to the bed plate it will cut the pulp fibers short and the effect of this, on paper formed from this pulp, would be a low Elmendorf or tear test. If the beater roll is raised so that the fibers are not cut, the pulp can be formed into paper with a higher Elmendorf.

In either case if the beating is carried on for a short time the pulp will hydrate or gelatinize only slightly and will form a sheet with a low Mullen or "poke through." If the beating time is increased, hydration will progress further and as the degree of hydration increases, the degree of gelatinization will increase. This well-hydrated pulp would form a paper with a high Mullen.

Unbeaten pulps tend to be high in tearing strength and very low to low in tensile properties such as Mullen, fold and tensile strength. Paper made from them is bulky, weak and poorly consolidated, tending to fluff or lint. The primary desired effect of beating is to increase the tensile strength properties of the sheet. Beating is always accompanied by a decrease in the bulk or the softness of the sheet and is usually accompanied, particularly after it has been carried out for a certain period of time, by a decrease in the tearing strength of the sheet. Any reasonable beating device will increase the Mullen, tensile strength, fold and Gurley. Beating always decreases the brightness and opacity of the sheet.

Bulky, soft grades of papers such as antiques require only a small amount of beating whereas others like bonds, which need rattle or character, are given considerably more beating. Transparent papers such as tracing or glassine are beaten for very, very long periods.

REACTION OF PULPS IN BEATING

Some pulps hydrate speedily yet will remain long and strong through severe beating. Other pulps will break down too rapidly to maintain fiber length after extreme hydration. So if a strong but soft paper is required, the pulp selected will be one that is long-fibered and strong but that hydrates slowly. If a strong, hard sheet is required, the pulp used will be one that is long-fibered and strong, but that hydrates rapidly. The general reaction of chemical wood pulps to beating and hydration is as follows:

"Hardwood kraft is significantly stronger than soda pulp at any level of beating, and develops strength and sheet density to a greater degree than soda pulp. Hardwood kraft fibers do not cut upon beating, and develop a minimum amount of fibrillation and debris. Therefore, for soft bulky grades hardwood kraft can be used with relatively little beating; but if a dense and strong sheet is required, it can be obtained by extensive beating of the hardwood kraft fibers."

The Reaction of Soda Pulp in Beating. The short fibers cut up easily and hydrate most rapidly. Soda beaten gently and quickly so that fiber length is preserved and so that hydration (and consequent gelatinization) occurs only

to a small extent will form into a loose, high-bulking, soft antique sheet. Soda beaten longer but not severely can be formed into a soft, smooth, English Finish paper with an excellent printing surface. Because soda pulp hydrates quickly it can be developed into a hard sheet with a high Mullen in a reasonably short beating time. However, the Elmendorf or tear test will be low in each instance because soda fibers are short.

The Reaction of Sulphite Pulp in Beating. Sulphite pulp hydrates relatively quickly. If beaten gently, long enough to cause normal hydration, but not enough to shorten fibers, sulphite can be formed ino a soft, strong paper. A lengthening of beating time will cause a greater degree of hydration and some breakdown of fibers and deliver a pulp that will make a harder sheet with a higher Mullen. Such a sheet will have the characteristics of a bond paper.

The Reaction of Alpha Pulp in Beating. Alpha fibers are very long and very soft. They are also very tough and therefore will not break down even though beaten for a long time. Alpha pulp hydrates very slowly and consequently may be beaten a long time without gelatinizing enough to harden. Thus, the advantage of Alpha pulp is due not only to the natural length of fibers but also to the fact that those fibers retain their length and softness after beating.

The Reaction of Sulphate Pulp in Softwood Beating. Sulphate fibers are very long and very tough. Sulphate fibers will retain their length even after a long and severe beating and consequently may be formed into papers that possess great strength.

Sulphate pulp hydrates quickly; therefore, it must be beaten quickly if it is to be kept soft enough to be used in forming book papers. If beaten for a long time, extreme hydration will occur and the pulp will form into a very hard sheet. Such a sheet will have an extremely high Mullen reading. This paper will also show a high Elmendorf reading because of the peculiar and unusual toughness of sulphate fibers which permits them to withstand prolonged beating without breaking down or suffering a loss of length.

REFINING OF PULP

In recent years, as paper technology improved, it became apparent that the "Hollander" type beater could not perform all the desirable functions of pulping, wet beating, cutting and fibrillating. This was true even though the Hollanders were modified so that each beater, or section of a multi-stage beater was used for a specific function. It became obvious that to perform each function best required completely different types of equipment. There were developed over the years a variety of pulp refining equipment to meet these needs.

In mills where dried pulp is to be re-suspended, a pulper is used. This is essentially an open tank which is loaded with the bales of pulp, waste paper, and other raw materials required in the preparation of a specific stock. High-speed, revolving elements serve to create a sufficient swirling movement to break up the fibrous materials and thoroughly mix the fibers with the other raw materials.

From the pulper, the stock is passed through one or more refining engines (Jordans, Claflins, etc.) depending on the fiber treatment desired. Essentially, a refining engine is a conical rotor (plug) with metal bars attached along its length, and which revolves inside a conical shell lined with bars. The stock to be treated enters the small end and is forced through to the opposite end passing between the opposing rows of bars. The clearance between the bars on the plug and those in the shell is set to cut, burnish, or bruise the fibers. Which function is chosen depends on the original nature of the stock and the required needs in the paper which will be formed by that stock.

USES OF VARIOUS PULPS

Because of the different character of these pulps and because of their different reactions in beating, the paper-maker will use these pulps in combinations in order to secure certain advantages from each, and the proportions of each will be determined by the result desired. Some idea of the uses of these various pulps is indicated in the following list:

For Blotting. Soda or hardwood kraft pulp for bulk. Just touched in the beaters. Only silghtly hydrated. (Some manufacturers combine soda pulp and cotton linters for blottings.)

High Bulking Antiques. Mostly all soda or hardwood kraft for bulk with a small proportion of sulphate or sulphite to hold the sheet together. Beaten very little and only slightly hydrated.

Ordinary Antiques. Slightly less soda or hardwood kraft and more sulphate or sulphite. Beaten a little harder than High Bulking Antiques and hydrated a little more.

English Finish. More sulphate or sulphite than Ordinary Antiques to secure body strength. Beaten more and hydrated more than Ordinary Antiques to secure formation smoothness and firmness.

Litho E. F. Sulphate or sulphite content greater than English Finish and hydrated more to make a more cohesive sheet.

Bond. All sulphite or hardwood kraft beaten well and hydrated well to deliver a crackle and a high Mullen.

Coated Body Stock. A high percentage of soda or hardwood kraft pulp to make for smoothness, and enough strong sulphate to make strong paper.

TEARING STRENGTH AND "TENSILE" STRENGTH

The foregoing discussion of beating and hydration indicates that two distinctly different kinds of strength can be introduced into paper and that ordinarily one is achieved at the expense of the other: (1) The strength contributed by fiber length; and (2) The strength resulting from gelatinization.

Fiber Length. Fiber length makes for tearing strength, which is a desirable quality in book and cover papers. Fiber length makes it possible for papers to stand the severe strain of mechanical folding without tearing at the folds. Strength resulting from fiber length is measured with the Elmendorf tester.

Gelatinization. Strength created by gelatinization resulting from hydration is measured with the Mullen tester and may be described as "poke through" strength or the strength of fiber cohesion. Gelatinous strength, in its varying degrees, is the strength that makes a litho paper hold together when subjected to the pull of a rubber blanket; gelatinous strength is the cause of the crackle in bond papers.

Extreme Fiber Strength and Extreme Gelatinization are Mutually Exclusive. Extreme fiber strength and extreme gelatinous strength are rarely captured together. Extreme gelatinous strength is achieved only by beating for a long period to stimulate a maximum of hydration, and long beating breaks down fibers so that their strength-giving character is impaired. Consequently a paper that will show an extremely strong Elmendorf tear test may ordinarily be expected to show a low Mullen or "poke through."

SIZING, LOADING AND COATING

The beating of pulp roughens and frays the minute fibers so that they have a tendency to cling to each other. The gelatine-like substance that is stimulated by hydration serves as an adhesive agent that helps the fibers to cling together. With proper beating and the correct degree of hydration, fibers can be made so cohesive that they can be formed into printable and usable paper.

The Purpose of Sizing. Sizing is not required to hold fibers together, but it is used principally in book papers to make paper somewhat repellent to water so that watery fluids will not cause the paper to wrinkle.

The Importance of Sizing for Offset Papers. Sizing materials are mixed with the pulp while it is in the beaters and varying quantities of sizing are used to achieve different results. Pulps for Litho Supers, Litho English Finish, and Offset papers receive generous quantities of sizing materials which protect the fiber structure from the softening effect of moisture and thus prevent the fibers being pulled apart when the paper is subjected to the pull of the blanket on an offset press.

Sizing for Papers That Will be Stained on Their Edges. For papers that are to go into bound volumes with stained edges, considerable sizing is introduced into the pulp so that the finished paper will be relatively non-absorbent and will not soak up the staining fluids.

The Sizing of Bond Papers. Bond paper pulps are sized highly so that the finished paper will not be too absorbent and so that it may be written upon without danger of the writing ink feathering or blurring.

Surface Sizing of Bond and Offset Papers. Bond papers may also be treated with a surface sizing which is applied to the surface of the finished paper. Surface sizing may also be applied to Wove Offset papers and to Litho E. F. and Super papers. The purpose of surface sizing on Offset papers is to provide an outside binder that will hold fibers down and prevent fuzz and that will, at the same time, hold the offset ink upon the surface of the paper so that the colors may retain density and brilliance.

Sizing Materials. The sizings generally used for uncoated papers are: (a) For beater sizing — Rosin; (b) For surface sizing — Starch.

LOADING OF UNCOATED PAPERS

An English Finish or Super paper made entirely of Soda Pulp will print fairly well but it will be likely to tear in printing or in folding. Therefore it is necessary to use some sulphate or sulphite pulp to secure a reasonable degree of strength.

The Purpose of Loading. Paper made entirely of sulphite and soda fibers is a bit too uneven for good halftone printing and does not have a good affinity for ink. It is also transparent and lacking in brightness. Therefore, papermakers use loading materials (also called fillers) to smooth up the surface of paper, to provide a better affinity for ink, to brighten color and to increase opacity.

Loading Materials. The most generally used loader is clay, which is a natural earth product that is susceptible to refinement to a smooth powder form similar to talcum powder. This refined clay is mixed with the pulp in the beaters. Clay loader fills in the irregularities in the formed paper, makes for a smoother printing surface, and has an excellent affinity for printing ink. Clay loader improves opacity.

Another type of loader is calcium carbonate. Calcium carbonate has a lower specific gravity than clay and consequently will not wash through the screen on the paper machines as readily as clay; and so more of it is retained in the formed paper. Therefore calcium carbonate used as a loader in the English Finish and Super papers makes improvements over clay in printing quality, brightness and opacity. It is mixed with the pulp in the beaters.

Other available loading materials are Titanox, Titanium Oxide and Zinc Sulphide. They contribute brightness and a high degree of opacity.

FORMING UNCOATED PAPERS

English Finish and Antique papers derive their character from the nature of pulps used and the proportion of each; from the degree of beating and hydration administered to the fibers; from the amount and the nature of sizings and loadings that are introduced while the pulp is in the beaters. (Coloring materials are also added in the beaters.)

The Stuff Chest. When the beating process is concluded, the mixture of water, cellulose fiber and loader is flowed into a huge vat on the paper machine. The vat, called a stuff chest, is located on the feed end (known as the "wet end") of the machine. From this stuff chest the milky fluid (called "stuff") is permitted to flow onto the paper machine wire which is shaken rapidly from side to side while traveling forward at high speeds. The amount of stuff that is permitted to flow onto the wire is regulated to make the weight of paper required.

Several Items Influence the Quality of Paper Formation. The excellence of the formation of a web of

"Wet" end of a Fourdrinier Paper Machine.

paper depends principally on the kind of pulp used and the nature of its treatment during beating, but the formation is also affected somewhat by the speed of the wire movement and by the degree of shake. If the machine is run too fast or if the shake is improperly adjusted formation will be impaired.

How the Web of Paper is Formed. As the stuff is carried forward on the forming wire the fibers are shaken together until they cohere and the water drains off through the wire mesh until the wire delivers a formed (but very moist) web of paper.

The Dandy Roll. If the paper is to carry a laid mark or a watermark the pattern is impressed onto the wet sheet, while it is on the wire, by a metal roll bearing the engraved design and called a "dandy roll."

Wire and Felt. In the process of transforming fluid "stuff" into paper a large amount of water must be extracted and the speed of extraction must be properly controlled, so suction devices are used to help draw the water off. The wire delivers the formed web of paper onto a traveling felt which conveys it through presses and drying rolls. The presses squeeze out water and smooth the paper. The heated drying rolls cause the evaporation of excess moisture still remaining.

Paper of Various Finishes is Handled in Various Ways. As the web of paper comes off of the dry end of

Super Calendering Stacks.

the paper machine it is wound on rolls. If the paper is an Antique or English Finish grade the manufacture is considered completed at this point. If calendered paper is required the English Finish is run through another series of rolls which are called "calendar rolls." These iron and polish the paper and give it its smooth finish. This polishing is done on both sides at the same time. When supercalendering is required this is generally done as a separate operation, one side at a time.

PIGMENTED PAPER

Pigmented papers contain more pigment (clay or calcium carbonate) than can be contained in English Finish or wove offset papers. The increase of pigment content is attained by employing machine coating facilities to apply a layer of coating on both sides of a web of paper.

Therefore, true pigmented papers are machine-coated papers; but because the method is an impregnation, pigmented papers do not have an enameled appearance. Instead, pigmented papers have the appearance of English Finish or of wove offset.

Many papers are surface-sized. This means that after the sheet is formed and dried its surface is treated before final drying and winding. A variety of materials may be used depending on the end-use characteristics desired. The most commonly-used sizing material is starch. Casein is also used. Quite frequently, optical brightness and pigments are included. Some insist that when a surface size is heavily loaded with pigment that the resultant sheet is pigmented. Others simply say it is pigment sized. This tends to avoid confusion with papers that are actually coated, but so lightly as to be characterized as "wash-coated paper."

Where Pigment is Used. Pigment is used as a loader in English Finish and wove offset papers. The pigment is introduced in the beaters and is mixed with the pulp fibers.

Similarly, pigment is used as loading in pigmented papers and, in addition, a heavy layer of pigment is placed on the surface.

Thus, the pigmenting method increases the amount of pigment in the paper and places a great percentage of it on the surface where it can be most beneficial in printing or lithographing.

COATING MATERIALS

The quality of body stock for coated paper is determined by the choice of pulps, by the nature of beating and by the degree of hydration.

Coating Materials. Coated two-side paper was originally developed by S. D. Warren Company for use in the printing of fine wood engravings. The purpose of coating today is, of course, to create a surface better suited for the printing of fine screen halftones.

The Five Requirements of Coated Papers. The requirements of a coated surface are (1) that it be uniformly smooth but firm so that it will contact all of the dots in a halftone; (2) that it have an affinity for ink; (3)

that it hold the ink pigment on the surface while permitting penetration, absorption and drying of varnish; (4) that it have a bright color; (5) that it flex reasonably well when folded.

Coating Materials Are Used in Many Combinations. A variety of materials may be used for the coating of paper, but only a careful combination of them, in proper proportions, will deliver a proper coated surface.

Clays. A natural produce of variable particle size serving as the basis for all coatings. It might be considered as the foundation of coating much as flour is the foundation for bread.

Blanc Fixe. A chemically precipitated product technically known as Barium Sulphate. Blanc Fixe has a splendid affinity for ink, a fine bright color, and good opacity. Blanc Fixe will not produce a high finish and therefore is usable only in dull coated paper.

Calcium Carbonate. A chemically produced calcium carbonate product contributes brightness and opacity. The particle size of the carbonate used for coating is much finer than the particle size of the carbonate used for loading. The fine particle carbonate is used in combination with superior clay for coating; and these two pigments combine to produce a coating that is flexible, that will pack well to make a smooth surface with a remarkable affinity for ink, and a bright color. This coating will finish up with a shine but it will not become slippery or brittle.

Titanium Dioxide. A chemically produced product with a splendid affinity for ink, an outstanding brilliance of color, and a high opacity. Makes for a low finish.

Casein. Dehydrated milk that is used as an adhesive for binding pigment particles to each other and to body stocks. Casein used to be largely imported and of greatly varying quality. It is now produced mostly from soya protein (soy bean product); some is produced as a phospho-protein precipitated from skimmed milk.

Starch. Extracted from corn by American manufacturers, who maintain a uniformity of quality. Starch is the major coating adhesive of the paper industry.

Latex. A synthetic rubber that is a good adhesive for the binding of coating pigments.

Coating Formulas Pose Many Problems. The papermaker must use these materials in varying combinations and in varying proportions to secure the different surface characteristics required for different grades of glossy coated papers and dull coated papers. The problem is complicated because of the fact that coating formulae must be altered for different body stocks.

APPLYING THE COATING

Six mechanical methods are in use for applying coatings to printing papers. These are: (1) The machine coating method; (2) The roller coating method; (3) The air blade method; (4) The double coating method; (5) The Trailing Blade method; (6) The fusing or casting method.

Machine Coating. The web of paper is formed on the wire and transferred to the felts which carry it through squeeze presses and heated drying drums which remove excess water. Then the web passes through coating stations which apply coating to both sides (to to one side if CIS is desired). Then the coated web is carried through another series of heated drying drums. In a subsequent and separate operation, the paper is passed through calender stacks which iron it and give it an enamel-like surface.

The machine coating method is the most economical method for applying coatings.

Air Blade Coater.

Roller Coating Machine.

Roller Coating. Where this method is employed, the web of paper is formed on the paper machine, then conveyed to a separate coating mill where coating is applied in an independent operation. After coating and drying, the paper is passed through calender stacks which polish the surface and give it gloss.

The application of coating in an independent operation is more costly than the machine coating method, but it permits more precise control and allows the use of desirable materials that cannot be used in machine coating.

Air Blade Coating. This is an independent coating operation. A generous quantity of coating is applied to the web of body stock and a razor-like blade of air shaves the surplus and thereby creates a uniformly even surface. This method allows the use of all desirable materials for coating.

It is an efficient method for producing superior quality CIS papers.

Double Coating. Double coated papers receive two coatings in two separate operations. First, the web of paper is coated on both sides on the paper machine. (CIS is coated only on one side.) This first coating or prime coat creates an uncommonly smooth-surfaced body stock which then is conveyed to a coating machine which employs rollers to apply a second coating which merges with the first.

The double coating method permits the use of the most desirable materials in the most effective combinations; it allows more precise controls; and it delivers a thicker and smoother layer of coating.

Trailing Blade Coating. Trailing blade coating is a very recent addition to paper coating techniques. By this technique, it is possible to lay extremely uniform thin films of coating on light-weight sheets. As the web of paper passses under a doctor blade it scrapes to a thin uniform film the coating material which is riding on the paper web, but behind the blade.

Section Four: How Certain Paper Characteristics Are Achieved*

In this section we present some of the processes whereby the papermaker achieves certain paper characteristics. The subject is divided into the following seven units: (1) Achieving good formation in book paper; (2) Making paper opaque; (3) Bulk and its relation to other characteristics of paper; (4) Giving paper a bright white color; (5) Building stiffness and hardness into paper; (6) Building a good printing and folding book paper; (7) Finishing. Each of these is presented in the following.

ACHIEVING GOOD FORMATION IN BOOK PAPER

For reasons with which we are all familiar, fine quality coated or plain book paper should be compactly and evenly

formed. The "look through" should reveal a uniformly woven structure free from streaks, pinholes and blotches.

In practice, however, perfect formation cannot always be achieved because the characteristics that must be built into some papers necessitate the use of materials and processes that will not permit of perfect formation.

The Four Most Important Factors Affecting Paper Formation. Formation is affected by a combination of factors, most important of which are: (1) Fiber length; (2) Beating and hydration; (3) Loading; and (4) The adjustment of speed and shake of the wire on the Fourdrinier. Each of these factors has an effect on formation and, also, all of these factors have a definite influence on each other so that it is impossible to measure accurately the effect of any single one of them.

* Illustrations courtesy S. D. Warren Co.

Therefore, the following study of the individual factors that affect formation deals only with the inherent qualities of each factor.

How Fiber Length Affects Paper Formation. Short fibers form best. Consequently the short-fibered hardwood, chemical or groundwood pulp may be expected to deliver superior formation. The longer sulphate or sulphite fibers will not form as well as shorter fibers. Therefore, short and long fibers must be used in measured combinations.

How Beating and Hydration Affect Paper Formation. Long lumpy fibers do not form as well as short fibers, so for superior formation long fibers must be shortened by beating.

Fibers that are only slightly hydrated will pile loosely and form poorly, so for superior formation the hydration of pulps must be carried to the point at which proper cohesiveness is developed. Yet, if hydration is carried beyond that point, a gelatinous hardness results, which makes paper too transparent for printing.

Therefore, *for maximum of excellence in formation, a delicate balance must be established between fiber length and hydration,* but because the various pulps respond differently to the beating process, certain pulps may be processed to the proper point of balance more readily than others.

Sulphite is longer fibered than soda. If sulphite is beaten gently, it may be hydrated properly without appreciable loss of fiber length. In this case the strength-giving quality of sulphite is preserved, but the forming quality is not good. If sulphite fibers are processed to develop a maximum of excellence in formation, they must be deliberately cut by severe beating so that they become short within the time required for proper hydration — in which case the inherent strength-giving character of sulphite fibers is distinctly impaired.

Therefore, sulphite pulps must either be processed for superior forming quality at the expense of strength or for strength-giving quality at the expense of formation.

How Alpha Cellulose Affects Paper Formation. Alpha cellulose possesses a peculiar combination of characteristics: (a) It hydrates very slowly and consequently permits of some liberty in processing; (b) It retains strength-giving qualities.

Because Alpha pulp hydrates very slowly, it may be beaten long and severely and the beating may be continued after the proper degree of hydration is developed without risk of producing hardness.

Because Alpha pulp retains strength-giving qualities when shortened, it may be beaten short to produce an excellently formed paper that will possess the strength required in body stock for coated papers.

How Softwood Sulphate Fibers Affect Paper Formation. Sulphate fibers are long and they give strength to paper, but a paper formed of softwood sulphate fibers exclusively would be lumpy and would not print well. So these fibers are used in combination with hardwood pulp and loading to make papers that possess a proper balance of strength and printing quality. Sulphate fibers supply the structural strength for double-coated papers.

How Loading Affects Paper Formation. Proper loaders improve formation. Their presence in the "stuff" permits of closer packing during the forming on the wire and this results in a closed or closely knit formation.

How Adjustment of Speed and Shake of Screen Affect Paper Formation. Machine speed and the degree of shake should really not be included among the factors that affect formation. It should be assumed that in good mill operation proper mechanical adjustments are made at all times. However, any tampering with proper adjustments as, for example, an increase in speed to achieve abnormal production, will impair good formation. However, any changing of proper adjustments, once made for a particular run, will affect formation. This is true whether it is the shake or speed of the wire which is being changed.

Summary and Conclusions. The foregoing comments may be summed up into several conclusions, i.e.: (1) That the maximum in good formation is generally achieved in papers that have a low tear strength (a low Elmendorf rating) ; (2) That papers made of Alpha cellulose are exceptional in that they may possess superior formation and yet retain a good tear strength; (3) That extremely strong papers composed of long uncut Alpha or sulphate fibers will not ordinarily develop superior formation; (4) That papers with extreme Mullen or "poke through" strength (which is secured through extreme hydration) should not be expected to develop superior formation.

MAKING PAPER OPAQUE

There are numerous devices available to a papermaker for developing a high degree of opacity in paper. A close even formation will give a paper greater opacity than can be secured with a loose uneven formation of the same pulp. Yet a loosely formed high-bulk paper will gain opacity from its bulk or thickness. High bulks, however, cannot be considered for halftone printing purposes so a study of opacity should begin with normal bulking Machine Finish and English Finish papers.

Factors Influencing Paper Opacity. In the manufacture of these papers various degrees of opacity may be secured by: (a) Varying the pulp; (b) Varying the beating and hydrating processes; (c) Using loaders. Each of these possibilities is discussed in the paragraphs that follow.

Pulps and Their Relative Opacity. A well-formed M.F. paper made entirely of unloaded pure chemical wood pulps cut short in beating and properly hydrated (bulking about 500 pages to the inch in the 60 lb. weight) will be translucent. Such a paper may be low in color and offer a rough surface unless preparation of the furnish is so formulated as to counteract this.

Hardwood, soda, or sulphate pulps are the most opaque fibers followed by softwood sulphate, softwood sulphite and then neutral sulphite semi-chemical hardwood pulps. Groundwood pulp is an enirely different pulp and is the most opaque of all fibers available to us. Wood from the **northeastern United States tends to have the highest** opacity for any chemical cooking process followed by west coast fibers, and lastly by fibers out of the southern part of the United States which tends to be the most translucent.

A well-formed M.F. paper made from unloaded old paper pulps that have been properly processed will be slightly more opaque because of the darkening effect of a carbon residue remaining in old papers after de-inking.

An M.F. paper containing unbleached pulps, ground wood, or old papers that have not been properly de-inked will be slightly more opaque because of the beneficial effect of reusing a pulp that has been dried several times and because of the beneficial effect of the cooking liquors used to de-ink the waste paper.

The Effect of Beating and Hydration on Opacity. Pulp fibers are more opaque than the gelatinous matter that is produced by hydration. Consequently, any degree of hydration of pulp fibers will increase the transparency of the paper made from these fibers. This is because beating or hydration increases the bonding capacity of the pulp fiber, the caliper of the sheet is decreased and the scattering surfaces which are responsible for opacity are lost as hydration is increased.

Loading Pigments and Their Effect on Opacity. M.F. papers made entirely of pulp fibers are not suitable for present-day requirements for good halftone printing for several reasons, one of which is the transparency of these papers. This transparency can be overcome through the use of loading pigments which change an M.F. paper into an English Finish. The most common of these loading pigments is clay.

Clay. The clay used for loading is the same substance that is used for coating (but generally of an inferior quality). When used as a loader for uncoated papers clay is mixed with the pulp in the beaters. When the "stuff," consisting of water, pulp, loader and sizing, flows onto the screen of the paper machine, some of the clay washes through the screen and the remainder merges with the fibers. This wedding of fiber and loader makes for smoothness of surface. The whiteness of the clay makes the paper brighter, and because clay is more opaque than pulp fibers, the clay-loaded paper is more opaque than paper made entirely of pulp fiber.

Calcium Carbonate. Calcium Carbonate is a superior loader. In its refined condition it looks like clay though it is more uniform in texture. Calcium Carbonate does not wash through the Fourdrinier screen as readily as clay and therefore more of it is retained in the formed paper. Consequently a carbonate-loaded sheet is more opaque and brighter than a clay-loaded sheet.

Other Loaders. Excellent opacity can be secured by loading with titanium oxide, titanox, or zinc sulphide, and each of these products develops brilliant color. Other opacity producing loaders are available but these are darkening pigments which dim the brightness of the paper.

Opacity of Coated Paper. The opacity of coated paper is controlled to a considerable extent in the manufacture of the body stock and the factors that affect the opacity of English Finish papers affect the opacity of body stock in exactly the same way. However, coating materials have their effect on the transparency or opacity of a coated paper. A coating containing considerable carbonate is more opaque than either clay or satin white.

BULK AND ITS RELATION TO OTHER CHARACTERISTICS OF PAPER

Uncoated Papers. The maximum of bulk that might be introduced into a sheet of book paper would be achieved by using pulp agitated in water for a very brief period, piling it as high as possible to form a sheet within a specified weight limit, and carrying it across the paper machine felts with the minimum of roll pressure. Such a paper would be coarse, fuzzy, weak and too rough for book paper use.

Minimum Beating Makes for Maximum Bulk. The maximum of bulk, therefore, is secured with a minimum of beating, and a minimum of hydration of pulp, and a minimum of calendering — with a resultant sacrifice of printing quality in the formed paper.

Printing Quality Requires Processing Making for Bulk Reduction. Inversely, the development of printing quality in a book paper requires that pulps be beaten more and hydrated more and that the paper receive more calendering — all of which brings a reduction of bulk in the formed paper.

Comparison of Different Papers for Bulk. A practical demonstration of these facts is found in a comparison of three Warren standard grades, as follows (the bulk figures given are for 60-lb. paper):

	Pages to Inch
Bulking Antique	320
Normal Antique	392
English Finish	554

Bulking Antique is made of pulps that have been beaten gently and hydrated slightly. This paper has a rough surface that is suitable only for the printing of type and line drawings. Pulps used in making a Normal Antique are beaten more and hydrated more and the paper is suitable for the printing of fine line drawings. Pulps used in English Finish are beaten severely, hydrated more thoroughly, loaded more heavily and calendered more firmly. This paper is suitable for halftone lithography.

Maximum Halftone Printing Quality and Maximum Bulk are Mutually Exclusive. The above comparison reveals one of the many irreconcilable conditions in papermaking. Maximum halftone printing quality and maximum bulk cannot be combined together, so the papermaker must arrive at the most acceptable balance of the two characteristics as indicated by the requirements of printers and buyers of printing.

The Bulk Problem in Coated Paper. Coated papers are expected to print extremely well, to be opaque, to have a bright color, to fold without body fractures, and with a minimum of flaking of coating at folds.

This combination of characteristics necessitates that body stock be made of a mixture of fibers which provide, primarily, strength, flexibility and firmness without hardness.

The secondary necessity is that the body stock be properly loaded to make the paper bright in color and opaque. The combination of materials that must be used to produce these qualities develops a given bulk and, as in the case of English Finish papers, there is little opportunity to manipulate this bulk in body stock save at the sacrifice of one or more of the primary or secondary qualities. The possibilities are as follows:

POSSIBILITY #1. Bulk of body stock can be increased by omitting or reducing the amount of loading in a furnish, but this reduction or omission of loading would reduce opacity and gray the color of the paper.

POSSIBILITY #2. Bulk of body stock may be increased by shortening the time for beating and hydrating. The sheet so produced will be lacking in cohesion and have a rough surface. It will have a tendency to split when lithographed.

Possibility #3. Bulk of body stock may be made high by using a furnish all of hardwood pulp. Such a short-fibered paper would form well, but it will split and tear easily in handling or in folding.

POSSIBILITY #4. Bulk of coated paper may be made high by making the body stock a greater proportion of the substance weight and reducing the amount of coating. The paper thus produced will deliver an inferior printed result, because the thin coating will not completely equalize the irregularities in the surface of the body stock.

POSSIBILITY #5. Bulk of coated paper may be increased by reducing roll pressure on the body stock and by easing the calendering of the finished paper. Either or both of these manipulations will deliver bulk at the expense of levelness but the resulting unevenness of surface will impair printing quality.

Summary. Therefore, if and when greater bulk is desired in a particular paper, there should be a clear comprehension of the means available for securing bulk and of the effect that such means may have on other qualities in the paper.

GIVING PAPER A BRIGHT WHITE COLOR

"Whiteness" and brightness are phenomena of light reflection. "Whiteness" is the measure of the purity of color. Brightness results from a combination of purity of color and directness of light reflection.

Whiteness. The only thing in the world that is pure white is sunlight. Yet, peculiarly, if a ray of sunlight is broken up for examination, it will be found to contain all the colors of the rainbow. In fact, sunlight is pure white only because it does contain all of the colors of the rainbow. If one of these colors were missing, sunlight wouldn't be pure white.

White Light Is a Balanced Mixture of Colored Lights. The sun's rays are of different wavelengths. Some are long and some are short and each different length of ray is a different color. When these rays are separated they are discernible as red, orange, yellow, green, blue and violet. When the rays are re-combined they merge together to make pure white light.

The Color of an Object is Determined by the Light in Which It Is Viewed and by the Reflectance of the Object. All color comes from these colored rays because no object actually contains color within itself. An object appears to be colored because it reflects some of the colored rays contained in light. If an object doesn't reflect any of these rays then it is considered colorless — or black.

How Different Papers Absorb and Reflect. A black cover paper is not really black in itself. It is black because it absorbs all of the colored rays in light and reflects none of them. A blue cover appears blue only because it reflects the blue rays in light while absorbing the others. Grass absorbs all of the colored light rays except the green rays which are reflected to the eye and cause the grass to appear green.

The Reflectance Requirements of a Pure White Paper. A paper that would reflect the complete combination of colors as they are contained in sunlight would be a white paper. Therefore, in order to make a paper that is a pure white the papermaker must find materials that are chemically and physically constituted so that they will reflect all of the colors that are contained in light. Up to date no papermaker has been able to do this. Any combination of known materials will either reflect a surplus of blue rays and cause the paper to appear blue-white, or it will reflect a surplus of the orange rays, in which case the paper will appear cream-white in color.

However, in the past few years some progress has been made in the use of colorings with the result that the color of white papers has been brought nearer to the true pure white.

Brightness. The degree of brightness that can be captured in paper is proportionate to: (1) "Whiteness;" and (2) Directness of reflection.

Pure white light reflections are brightest, therefore as the papermaker approaches nearer to pure white color he improves the brightness of paper.

Directness of reflection preserves brightness. If a pigment bounces the white light rays directly back to the eye, brightness is retained. If a pigment is so constituted that the light rays skid along its surface or reflect off to one side, there is a loss of brightness.

The Refractive Index and Its Importance for Materials. Scientists measure the reflecting qualities of different materials and give each a rating which is called the "refractive index." A material that bounces the reflection back to the eye and thus preserves brightness is given a high index. A material that bends the reflection to one side causing a loss of brightness is given a low index.

The refractive indices of pulp fibers and most coating materials or loading materials are about the same. Titanium dioxide and zinc pigments are exceptions.

Carbonate has a better color and a higher reflecting quality than clay and these are maintained through manufacture so that carbonate used as a loader in uncoated paper or as a coating pigment produces a brighter white color than clay. Fine particle carbonate, zinc sulfide, and titanium dioxide are all whiter than clay and have a higher reflecting rating than clay, and therefore produce bright color when used as loaders or as coating materials.

Cream and Blue Shades. For many years paper men have held different opinions regarding the advantages of blue-white or cream-white papers.

In papers for halftone reproduction cream-whites and blue-whites are both undesirable because they are evidence of the papermaker's inability to achieve the pure white shade that would produce a greater degree of brightness which would add sparkle to halftone illustrations.

Lacking the opportunity to attain pure whiteness, the manufacturers of printing papers have pressed to attain a high measure of brightness and, over a period of years, printing papers have been brightened progressively. In pressing for improvements in brightness, manufacturers have been impelled by a physical law to move away from blue to cream.

Complementary Colors. Artists, physicists, and experienced users of colors describe opposite colors with the word complementary. They know that when complementary or opposite colors are combined the resulting color will be grayed — its brightness will be reduced.

When a papermaker tries to make a blue-white paper he reduces brightness and achieves a graying. That happens because paper pulps and loading pigments and coating pigments are yellowish or creamy. Blue is a near opposite to cream and when blue and cream are combined a graying follows invariably.

Why Cream-White Papers are Preferred for Process-Color Work. The chemists of the paper mills are well aware of the physical laws of color. They know that pulps and pigments will be brightest when they are kept in the yellow or cream shade. Consequently, almost all of the printing papers that now are offered for sale are in the cream-white scale.

The Subject of Paper Color Is Controversial with Many People. One can get a lot of arguments about the accuracy of these paragraphs. For, although almost all good printing papers are cream white, some are less creamy than others. And when two sheets of unprinted paper are compared, the sheet that is less creamy will appear to be a blue-white.

True measurements will demonstrate that the appearance of blueness is accompanied by a lowered brightness — an inferior reflection of sunlight which promises a proportionate reduction in the brilliance of printed colors and a proportionate compromise of contrast in black halftones.

The Relation of Brightness and Opacity. High reflecting quality (a high refractive index) makes for opacity. Thus pulps or pigments, which bounce light rays back to the eye, develop opacity because the light rays are reflected and not transmitted through the paper. Therefore, pigments such as carbonate, titanox and zinc sulphide make for opacity because they possess high reflecting qualities which are combined with a high degree of basic "whiteness.'

Opacity and Purity of Colors. There are pigments, however, that have high reflecting qualities but inferior color. Carbon, for example, has a high refractive index and therefore it reduces light transmission and makes for opacity in paper though at the same time dimming or dirtying the color. Old paper pulps that have been improperly de-inked are opaque because they contain a residue of carbon ink pigment. Yet because of the carbon residue these papers cannot have bright color.

So, peculiarly, the highest degree of opacity can be secured with the two extremes in brightness, i.e., the maximum of brightness when carbonate, titanox, or zinc sulphide are used for loading and the minimum of brightness with pulps that contain carbon and similar pigments which lack purity of color or "whiteness."

BUILDING STIFFNESS AND HARDNESS INTO PAPER

There is an erroneous belief that a paper can be made stiff, rigid, hard and snappy by hard sizing. But these characteristics are not secured with sizing.

Increased Gelatinization Contributes Increased Stiffness and Hardness. Stiffness and hardness are secured by increasing the degree of hydration and thereby increasing gelatinization of the fibers. The fiber gelatine is the ingredient which gives stiffness, rigidity and snap to paper. A high fiber gelatine content makes paper hard and gives it a high cohesive strength which will produce a high Mullen test.

How Different Pulps Influence Paper Hardness and Stiffness. Obviously, stiffness and hardness can be achieved more readily with some pulps than with others. Soda pulp is not particularly useful in creating stiffness because the relatively long beating necessary to develop an extreme degree of hydration reduces the short soda fibers to a pulverized form. Alpha pulp is not ordinarily used in the making of hard papers because Alpha fibers are very soft, gelatinize very slowly and do not harden readily. Sulphite pulp can be hydrated to the point of hardness before the fibers are entirely broken down, consequently sulphite is useful in making stiff, hard papers. Sulphate pulp hydrates quickly, the fibers are tough and will withstand a long period of beating and as a result sulphate can be hydrated to an extreme degree and can be formed into an unusually hard paper.

Hard and rigid papers are not susceptible to good letterpress printing though satisfactory for offset printing.

The Purpose of Sizing Materials. Sizing materials are introduced in paper to minimize absorption so that writing ink, moisture and staining fluids will not be soaked up or absorbed. Sizing materials will not make a paper stiff and snappy.

BUILDING A GOOD PRINTING AND FOLDING BOOK PAPER

Spongy packing on a letterpress press will give under-impression and become indented, thus creating a matrix that will wear type and halftones. Therefore, the packing around a letterpress cylinder or on a tympan should not be spongy, but needs to be firm because good printing is done with firm impression.

Firmness and Hardness. Coated and uncoated papers for good letterpress printing must also be firm. Yet they must present a printing cushion and consequently they may not be "hard." Papers for lithography must be made more cohesive and consequently are harder.

The Surface Characteristics of Paper. Good halftone reproduction also requires papers that are level or even surfaced, and free from irregular or lumpy variations that meet halftones unevenly and thereby fail to contact all of the minute halftone dots.

The Ink Receptivity of Paper. And good halftone reproduction requires papers that have affinity for ink — papers that will take the ink from a halftone dot in a precise manner without repelling it and without absorbing it unduly.

Pulps, Coating and Loading Materials for Good Printing Papers. Therefore, the manufacture of papers that will serve best for good reproduction necessitates the processing of materials and the combining of those materials so that they will form paper that is level and even surfaced; that is, paper that is firm, and that has affinity for printing ink. The available *pulps* are: Groundwood, Soda, Old Papers, Sulphite, Sulphate, Alpha.

The Coating and Loading Pigments: Clay, Carbonate, Satin White, Blanc Fixe, Titanium Dioxide, Titanox, Zinc Sulphide.

The six pulps listed are not equally firm though they can be equalized in processing. The coating and loading pigments may be accepted as equally firm.

The six pulps are not naturally constructed to provide the same degree of levelness, though some equalization can be made in processing. The various coating and loading materials do not possess the same size particles and therefore do not produce equal levelness.

The pulps listed may be assumed to have equal affinity for ink in their normal condition though that affinity may change in processing. The coating and loading pigments do not provide equal affinity for ink.

These materials with dissimilar characteristics are the best materials available for the making of good quality printing papers. They must be used in favorable combinations to make paper that possesses qualities which no single one of these materials can develop.

Making Paper Spongy, Firm or Hard. The firmness of a paper is established in the beating of the pulp. The pulp may be sloshed around in the beater for a very brief period and formed into paper. This paper will be spongy. The same pulp hydrated to an extreme will form a paper that is too hard for good halftone printing. Development of the desired firmness is a matter of proper hydration; insufficient hydration of pulp results in sponginess; extreme hydration produces a crystalline hardness. Firmness lies between these, but the desired middle point is not the same for every pulp.

The normal hydration point, which develops the correct degree of gelatinization necessary for firmness, arrives

quickly in the beating of soda pulp and old paper pulp. Sulphite requires more hydration to develop firmness. Thus, by manipulation in beating, pulps may be brought to a desired state of firmness.

FINISHING

Calendering. Antique book paper, English **Finish** papers, and body stock for coated papers come off the paper machine in their final form. Coated papers must be super-calendered after coating. Papers which are smooth-surface on the paper machine are calendered by passing through the nip of two steel rollers. The number of such nips will determine how smooth the end result. At its best, on the machine calendering will not produce a result anything like super-calendering.

The calendering device is called a calender stack. It is a series of rolls supported in a frame — one roll on top of another. Every other roll is made of steel. The alternate rolls are the bearing rolls. In the super-calender stacks the bearing rolls are compressed paper. The bearing rolls in the Coated calender stacks are compressed cotton.

Super-Calendering a roll of paper is much like the process of pressing a pair of pants. The pants are laid on a padded ironing board, covered with a damp cloth to soften and to prevent burning, and pressed or ironed with a hot iron. In the calendering of paper the bearing rolls serve as the ironing board, the steel roll serves as the iron, and steam is sometimes used to soften the paper.

Description of a Roll Calender Stack. A seven-roll calender stack with the web of paper threaded through the rolls. The bottom roll is a geared drive roll, but all other rolls run free and are rotated only by the force of friction, with the result that there is some slippage. The slippage corresponds to the movement of a tailor's iron in the pants pressing process. The slippage, therefore, is the cause of calendering.

In some cases, only one side of the paper is calendered in one operation. This side comes in contact with the revolving steel roll, which irons the surface. After one side of the roll of paper has been calendered, the roll is reversed and the other side receives the same treatment.

The Hazards of Calendering. Calenders require skillful manipulation because insufficient calendering causes underfinished paper and too much calendering "burns" the paper, dimming its bright color and giving it a speckled appearance.

Sheeting. (Cutting from Rolls.) Finished rolls of Coated and Uncoated paper are cut into sheets by a machine called a rotary cutter. This machine is somewhat similar to a web-fed cylinder press. A steel cutting edge is fastened along the length of a cylinder (see our diagram). The web of paper is fed to the cylinder. Each time the cylinder makes a revolution, the cutting edge chops a sheet of paper off the roll (see our diagram). Our next diagram shows three rolls being fed into the cutter, which in such a case would chop through three thicknesses of paper and cut three sheets at one time.

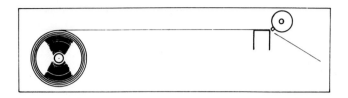

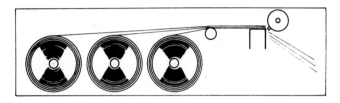

Multiple- and single-roll sheeting.

Machine-Trimmed Paper. Rotary cut paper is generally referred to as "machine-trimmed" paper and it is cut accurately enough for the requirements of most booklet jobs that are to be printed work-and-turn and folded as a full sheet. Consequently it is the common practice of the paper industry to deliver uncoated papers "machine trimmed" and to charge extra for trimming.

For jobs that are to be printed in the full sheet but cut apart for bindery operations, "machine-trimmed" paper will not always serve. Broadsides, folders, labels and similar jobs must have accurately trimmed edges and require guillotine trimmed paper. Uncoated paper intended for such usage should be ordered guillotine trimmed. Coated paper are guillotine trimmed as a regular practice.

Work-and-Tumble Jobs Should Not Be Printed on Machine-Trimmed Papers. Paper that is to be printed as a "tumble sheet" requires special cutting and the mill should be so instructed. No extra charge will be made on making orders for coated paper. Regular trimming charges will apply on grades that are ordinarily "machine trimmed."

Trimming. The guillotine cutters are giant modern machines, equipped with magnifying lenses on the cutting gages, so that gage settings may be accurate. Trimming is done by skilled operators who have been trained to exercise great care. Cutting knives are kept sharp at all times. Paper that is guillotine trimmed at the mill will be more accurately trimmed on the average than paper trimmed in a printing plant.

Sorting. Sorters are expected to inspect sheeted paper and to discover and reject sheets containing visible defects. A sorter must watch for seventy-two different kinds of defects which are causes of rejection.

Section Five: The Properties and Testing of Paper*

The properties of a paper are the characteristic qualities which enable us to differentiate a specific paper from other materials and from other papers. When we can measure the individual properties of paper and when we can assign values to these measurements, we have a language for usefully talking about paper. With this language we can describe the requirements a paper must have for a particular use, we can describe the level at which a particular property must be maintained for continued good behavior of the paper, and we can, finally, describe the level to which a given property must be raised in order to eliminate the bad behavior of this specific paper.

If we consider all properties that are of importance in some grades and in some uses of paper — though not necessarily in every individual type — these paper properties probably total more than one hundred. Some properties are relatively easy to define and to measure, for example, the tensile strength of paper. Other properties are complex, difficult to define and difficult to measure, for example, printability.

In the frame set for this study it is neither possible for the author, nor desirable for the reader, to go into a detailed discussion of each of these many paper properties and their testing methods. For the purposes of *The Lithographers Manual,* the author has set himself a rather different aim. He wants first to acquaint the reader with this vast field

of paper properties and paper testing, then he wants to familiarize the reader with existing sources of information, and finally he wants to discuss some of the generally more important but still too little understood characteristics of paper.

To this effect our study is divided into the following ten subjects: (1) Recognizing and balancing paper properties; (2) Objective and arbitrary paper tests; (3) Sources of information on paper testing; (4) The moisture content of paper; (5) Paper formation; (6) Paper grain and sides; (7) Paper stretch and strength; (8) Paper smoothness; (9) Pick resistance; and (10) Miscellaneous paper properties. The author reiterates the introductory nature of the following discussion which precludes the otherwise customary but here much too burdensome scientific apparatus of references, etc.

RECOGNIZING AND BALANCING PAPER PROPERTIES

Some paper properties are easily recognized and defined, as already mentioned, whereas other properties are rather difficult to describe and define. A property that is not cleanly and clearly defined is, of course, very difficult to measure or to test for.

The Complexity of Printability. Printability is generally conceded to be complex because it is thought to involve a number of paper properties. To a lithographer,

---

* Illustrations courtesy The Institute of Paper Chemistry.

printability involves such paper properties and characteristics as lintiness and dustiness, flatness, pick resistance,
moisture resistance, moisture aborbency, curling tendency,
ink absorbency, ink-drying characteristics, and chemical
inertness. It is, of course, not certain that this list includes
all of the components of printability. Nor are the methods
currently available for measuring some of these properties
entirely adequate.

End-Use Paper Properties. Printing of paper may
be the main concern of the lithographer but it is not its
end use. The printed sheet may be folded and creased,
stitched, stapled or glued; it may be laminated to another
material, and it may even require additional conversion
before it can serve its final purpose. Hence, the sum total
of the required characteristics is greater than those required
for good printing.

The sheet must have adequate stiffness, tearing strength,
and resistance to penetration of adhesive, proper scoring
and folding characteristics, rub resistance, and so on. In
each case, the characteristics of the paper must be appropriate to the marriage of paper and ink and also to the
subsequent life of the printed product.

Balancing Essential Paper Properties. It is not
possible to make paper which has the maximum value of
every property that might be desired. For example, a maximum pick resistance may be obtained only at some loss in
ink absorbency and at some increase in curling tendency.
In general, the papermaker must arrive at a compromise
among the many properties required of his product.

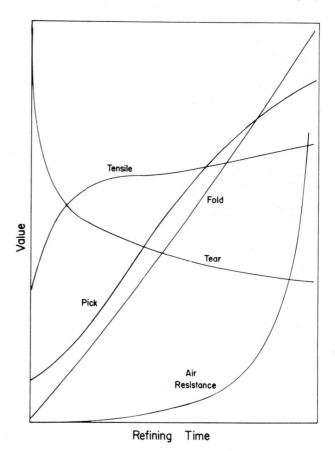

Variation of physical properties of paper with degree of
refining given the papermaking stock.

OBJECTIVE AND ARBITRARY PAPER TESTS

Paper properties may be classified in several groups: as
structural properties, such as thickness, formation, and
porosity; and *strength* properties, such as tensile strength
and tearing strength; as *optical* properties, such as color,
brightness, opacity, gloss; as *surface* properties, such as
fuzziness, smoothness; as *physio-chemical* properties, such
as dimensional stability, moisture content, and degree of
sizing; and finally, as *chemical* properties, such as acidity
or alkalinity, and wettability.

Objective and Arbitrary Tests. Corresponding to
the large number of properties and characteristics of paper
of interest to a lithographer are a large number of testing
methods. Whenever possible paper properties are measured by instrumental or objective means so as to eliminate
personal judgments to the greatest possible extent. But for
some properties and characteristics of paper, there are as
yet no generally accepted test methods. Lintiness or dustiness of paper are examples.

When objective methods of testing are not available, it
is necessary to resort to comparative testing where a set
of arbitrary "standards" may be established, representing
arbitrary steps or levels in the values of a specific paper
property. Papers may be compared with these arbitrary
standards and be assigned a rank on the basis of subjective
judgment.

It is desirable to use objective testing methods and
standards that are as absolute as possible. The drifting of

the scale of measurement is then eliminated, or at least
minimized, and it becomes much easier to obtain agreement between measurements made at different times in
different laboratories by different operators.

SOURCES OF INFORMATION ON PAPER TESTING

Standardized methods of testing paper are developed
and maintained by the Technical Association of the Pulp
and Paper Industry (TAPPI), the American Society of
Testing Materials (ASTM), and the Packaging Institute.
TAPPI has established nearly a hundred for paper testing
and ASTM established approximately seventy-three methods for paper testing. Descriptions of these testing
methods may be obtained from the Technical Association
of the Pulp and Paper Industry, 155 East 44th Street, New
York 17, New York; from the American Society for Testing Materials, 1916 Race Street, Philadelphia 3, Pennsylvania; and from the packaging Institute, 342 Madison
Avenue, New York 17, New York.

Readers not well-acquainted with the properties of paper
and the methods for testing paper will find it helpful to
read ASTM special technical publication No. 60A, "Paper
and Paperboard — Characteristics, Nomenclature, and Significance of Tests." This publication (dated October 1951)

briefly describes the characteristics, nomenclature, and the significance of tests of paper, but it does not describe the testing methods themselves.

Sampling Paper for Testing. Whether the testing is done by the manufacturer for control purposes during the manufacture of paper, or by a customer for the purpose of determining whether the paper meets his requirements, it is essential in either case that the paper sample used for testing be truly representative of the paper being manufactured, or of the shipment of paper received by the customer. TAPPI Method T-400 and ASTM Method D-585 describe appropriate methods for sampling paper.

THE MOISTURE CONTENT OF PAPER

Many of the properties of paper are dependent on its moisture. For example, tensile strength, pick resistance, and the dimensions of paper are sensitive to moisture. TAPPI Method T-412 and ASTM D-644 describe procedures for determining the moisture content of paper and paper products by what is called the oven-drying method.

The Cambridge "Sword" Hygrometer, the Hart Moisture Indicator, and the Sabre-Champ are instruments useful to the lithographer. Proper use of such tools can help in determining whether a shipment of paper is in relative humidity balance with the pressroom atmosphere. Knowledge of whether the paper is too dry or too wet makes it possible to determine what precautions should be taken if paper which is out of balance should be run.

As paper is manufactured on the paper machine, its moisture content depends upon the drying conditions at the machine. Consequently, the moisture content of the paper tends to vary with the relative humidity and — to a lesser extent — with the temperature of the atmosphere in which it is stored or used.

The Equilibrium Moisture Content. If paper is stored in a space maintained at constant temperature and constant relative humidity until the moisture content of the paper no longer changes, it is said to be in moisture equilibrium with the atmosphere and the moisture content of the paper is said to be the equilibrium moisture content. If the temperature is maintained at a constant value and the relative humidity is increased and maintained at a higher value, the moisture content of the sheet will increase to a new equilibrium value; or, if the relative humidity of the space is decreased to a lower value with the temperature held constant, the moisture content of the paper will decrease to another equilibrium moisture content. *Thus the equilibrium moisture content of the paper decreases as the relative humidity decreases, and increases as the relative humidity increases.*

If the equilibrium moisture content of a paper at constant temperature is plotted against the relative humidity, the resulting curve is called a moisture equilibrium curve or a moisture adsorption isotherm. If the equilibrium moisture contents of the paper at various relative humidities are determined at a higher temperature, the resulting curve will be slightly lower than the first one. Correspondingly, if the experiment is repeated at a lower temperature, the third moisture equilibrium curve will be

slightly above the first one. *At constant relative humidity, the equilibrium moisture content of paper tends to increase somewhat as the temperature is decreased and tends to decrease slightly as the temperature is increased.*

However, it is the relative humidity that is the main conrolling factor in the moisture content of the paper. Actually the equilibrium moisture content of a paper is slightly higher when that equilibrium condition is approached from a higher moisture content than when the equilibrium is approached from a lower moisture content. This lagging effect — scientifically called hysteresis — in moisture content is seldom in itself of practical importance, but the extent to which some of the moisture sensitive properties of paper show a corresponding dependence upon the direction from which an equilibrium condition is approached may often be of practical importance.

How Increased Humidity Affects the Paper. When a sheet of paper is exposed to a higher relative humidity than the one corresponding to its equilibrium

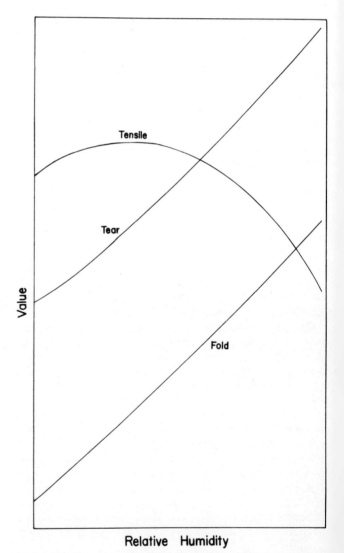

Variation of physical properties of paper with relative humidity.

moisture content, the absolute moisture content of the paper increases. The individual cellulose fibers in the sheet adsorb moisture from the atmosphere and individually increases in weight. When the fibers absorb moisture they swell or expand principally in width and thickness rather than in length. As the fibers expand, they push away the neighboring fibers, and cause the sheet to expand in length, width, and thickness. At the same time the bond of one fiber to another is reduced, and such properties as tensile strength, stiffness, and pick resistance decrease as the moisture content increases.

Conversely, if the relative humidity of the space in which the sheet is placed is reduced and the moisture content of the sheet decreases, the fibers shrink and the sheet contracts in length, width, and thickness. Other properties change correspondingly.

Paper Tests Must be Made at Standardized Temperature and Relative Humidity. Because of this dependence of many properties upon moisture content and therefore upon relative humidity and temperature, it is essential in most cases that paper testing be performed at constant temperature and relative humidity. In the United States the standard condition for testing paper is 73° F. and 50 percent RH. TAPPI Method T-402 and ASTM Method D-685 describe the conditioning of paper and paper products for testing and the tolerances of the temperature and relative humidity conditions.

PAPER FORMATION

By formation of paper one refers to the uniformity with which the fibers and other solid components are distributed in the sheet. Formation is judged visually by transmitted light.

Poor or Wild and Good Paper Formation. A paper is said to have poor or wild formation when the fibers are so unevenly distributed that a blotchy, mottled, or streaked appearance is observed when the sheet is viewed

against the light. The formation is good when the sheet appears to be uniformly translucent. The formation of paper is dependent upon the extent to which fibers clump in the stock suspension before they are deposited on the forming wire of the paper machine. In some papers a wild formation is desirable. In printing paper good formation is desirable.

The Effects of Wild Paper Formation on Ink-Receptivity. In a wildly formed sheet, the clumps of fibers (the dark areas when the sheet is viewed by transmitted light) usually correspond to thick areas in the sheet, and these areas receive more vigorous treatment in the calender stack and become denser than surrounding areas. The dense, clumped areas are less porous and less ink-receptive and less absorbent of ink vehicle, leading to non-uniformities in ink transfer and setting of the ink.

Photograph of paper by transmitted light — Example of poor formation.

How Paper Formation is Judged. Formation is frequently judged on a relative basis by comparison with an arbitrary set of formation standards ranging from well-formed to wildly formed sheets. An instrument for measuring the formation of paper is described by Davis, Roehr and Malmstrom: "An Instrument for Formation Measurements." Paper Trade Journal, 101 No. 4:31-36 (July 25, 1935). In this instrument the paper specimen is rotated, like a phonograph record, and a light source on one side and a photocell on the other side of the paper permit measurement of the fluctuations in the intensity of the transmitted light.

A formation number is calculated from the instrument reading, and it has been found that the correlation between visual rating of formation and the readings of the instrument is good — Institute of Paper Chemistry. "Instrumentation Studies IV." Paper Trade Journal 104, No. 1:39-41 (January 7, 1937). Other formation testers have been made available recently.

Photograph of paper by transmitted light — Example of intermediate formation.

Photograph of paper by transmitted light — Example of good formation.

PAPER GRAIN AND SIDES

There are two characteristic directions in a sheet of paper. The machine direction or grain direction is the direction of the paper parallel to its movement on the paper machine. The cross direction or cross-grain direction is the direction in the paper at right angles to the machine direction.

Why Grain Direction is Important. This distinction between directions in the sheet of paper is necessary because of the marked differences in properties in the two directions. The fibers in a sheet of paper are not completely oriented at random in the plane of the sheet. There is a tendency for fiber orientation parallel to the machine direction. Because of the tension in the machine direction of the paper web as it passes over the paper machine, there usually are pronounced differences of paper properties in the two principal directions of the sheet.

Methods for Determining Paper Grain. Methods of determining the machine direction or grain direction of paper are described in TAPPI Method T-409 and ASTM Method D-528. Of the several methods included in the standard procedure, the simplest one for most printing papers is probably the method involving the direction of curl. A piece approximately two inches square is cut from the sheet to be tested and a line is drawn with pencil parallel to one of the edges of the original sheet. This small square is floated on water and the direction of the axis of curl is noted. The axis of curl is the machine direction of the piece.

Wire Side and Felt Side. Except in a few special cases, paper is two-sided in that the two sides of a sheet of paper appear and behave differently. The wire side of a sheet is that side which was in contact with the wire of the paper machine during manufacture. The opposite side is called the felt side. Sometimes the designation bottom and top side is used instead of the wire and felt side. The wire side receives an impression of the pattern of the wire

on which the web was formed on the paper machine. Subsequent treatment in the paper machine and in the calender stack tends to smooth out the wire marks and to make the two surfaces more nearly alike. In addition to the wire mark, the two sides of the sheet differ for structural reasons as well.

Differences Between Wire Side and Felt Side. The tendency for preferred orientation of fibers parallel to the machine direction is greater on the wire side of the sheet than on the felt side. Furthermore, the distribution of fiber fines and filler pigments is not uniform through the thickness of the sheet. There is a definite tendency for greater concentration of fiber fines and fillers on the felt side of the sheet compared with the wire side. Thus, the wire side of the sheet has a somewhat more open structure than the felt side.

Methods for Distinguishing Wire and Felt Side. Methods for distinguishing between the wire and felt sides of paper are given in TAPPI Method T-455 and in ASTM Method D-725. The differentiation of one side from another is sometimes very difficult and it may be necessary to use several methods before the determination of side is made with certainty. The simplest procedure which is effective in many situations is to fold a sheet of the paper and to observe the relative smoothness of the two sides. The pattern of diamond-shaped impressions of the machine wire can frequently be seen, thus identifying the wire side. This observation is most conveniently made when the light strikes the sheet at an angle of about 45° and when the light reflected to the eye also makes an angle of about 45° with the surface of the paper.

The Dipping Method. If the simplest procedure does not yield a distinction between the two sides, it is frequently helpful to dip a piece of the paper in water or in a dilute sodium hydroxide solution and then to drain off the excess liquid and to allow the piece of paper to stand for a few minutes. This treatment swells the fibers of the sheet to some extent and tends to restore the surface texture that the paper had before calendering and thus makes the identification of the wire pattern easier.

The Tear Test. The following method is also frequently helpful when the simpler method does not yield the desired distinction. It should be used, however, only after practice with sheets of known wire and felt sides. Lay the sheet on a table and hold it with one hand, pull upward with the other hand to start a tear along the machine direction and then gradually guide the tear so that it moves across the grain toward the edge of the sheet, thus producing a tear line in a curved path. Then turn the sheet over so that the opposite side is uppermost and make a similar tear.

Observe the degree of feathering caused by the splitting of the sheet at the edges of the two tears. Usually one of these tears will show a more distinct feather edge than the other, especially in the curved part of the line of tear as it departs from the machine direction. The tear having the more feathered edge is the one that was made when the wire side of the sheet was upward and when the felt side of the sheet was against the table.

The Heat Test. Another method is to cut a specimen from a paper approximately one inch wide and two inches long with the long dimension in the cross direction of the paper. This specimen is placed in a drying oven maintained at a temperature of approximately 100°C. or 212°F. or in a desiccator over a drying agent such as anhydrous calcium chloride. It is important that both sides of the specimen be equally exposed to the air in the oven or in the desiccator. As drying proceeds, the specimen will curl; any pronounced curl of the specimen will be toward the wire side with the axis of curl parallel to the machine direction.

PAPER STRETCH AND STRENGTH

The tensile strength, stretch, and the more general load-elongation characteristics of paper are considered to be important characterizations of the serviceability of paper in many uses. In the case of printing paper in particular, these characteristics indicate the resistance to breaking in web-fed presses.

Definition of Tensile Strength. The tensile strength of paper is defined as the force parallel to the plane of a specimen required to break a specimen of specified width and length. Frequently the tensile strength is expressed in pounds per inch, and this value indicates the force in pounds required to break a strip one inch wide. The standard procedures for measuring tensile strength are described in TAPPI Method T-404 and in ASTM Method D-828.

Paper Stretch. The stretch of paper is considered to be important whenever a web is handled under tension. Together with tensile strength the stretch is related to initial tearing strength. Initial tearing strength is the resistance to the start of the tear. Stretch is involved in the ability of a sheet to fold well and to resist the concentration of local stress. Stretch is defined as the percentage elongation of a strip of paper at the time of rupture under tension. Procedures for the measurement of stretch are described under TAPPI Method T-457 and under ASTM Method D-987.

The Load-Elongation Curve. The most complete information on the behavior of paper under tension is given by the load-elongation curve. The most direct way of obtaining a load-elongation curve is by means of a load-elongation tester which automatically plots the force (or load) applied to the tested strip against the increase in length or elongation of the specimen. The maximum load — that is the load at the time of failure of the strip — corresponds to the tensile strength as measured by the usual tensile strength tester. The elongation at failure divided by the length of the strip and multiplied by 100 yields the stretch of the paper. From the load-elongation curve one may therefore obtain not only the tensile strength and stretch in the usual sense, but also the load-elongation relationship at all loads less than that required to produce failure of the strip.

Tearing Strength. The tearing strength of paper is the force required to tear a specimen under standardized conditions after the tear has been started. It is sometimes

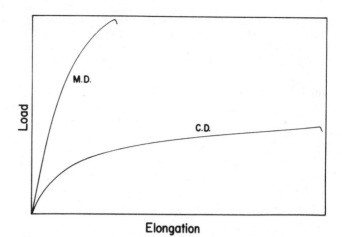

Load elongation curve for machine direction (MD) and for cross direction (CD) of a ledger paper.

called internal tearing strength. Procedures for measuring this internal tearing strength are described in TAPPI Method T-414 and in ASTM Method D-689. In a very general way one can say that the treatments of stock and paper which tend to increase tensile strength and bursting strength tend to decrease the tearing strength.

Tensile strength and tearing strength are good examples of properties between which compromises must be made in papermaking. It is not possible to treat a stock so as to obtain a sheet having simultaneously maximum tensile strength and maximum tearing strength.

SMOOTHNESS

Traditionally, paper smoothness has been thought of strictly as a measure of the uniformity of a paper's surface in terms of minute high and low areas. For example; an "antique" finish is less smooth than "English" finish paper; an English finish is less smooth than a "machine" finish; a machine-calendered paper is less smooth than a super-calendered one. But, of equal importance to the lithographer is the "printing" smoothness which may be produced on a particular sheet.

Paper Smoothness. The smoothness of paper relates to the deviations of the actual paper surface from an ideal plane surface. Because of the compressible deformable nature of paper, the smoothness of the sheet as it lies on a table is not the effective smoothness at the actual time of ink transfer in printing. It is believed that smoothness in the sense of printing smoothness is most important in rotogravure printing, somewhat less important for letterpress printing and least important but not completely unimportant in offset printing.

Measuring Paper Smoothness. The older and more commonly used methods of measuring smoothness of paper are the so-called air-leak methods which involve the rate at which air can leak between the paper surface and a polished reference surface pressed against the paper, or the rate at which air can leak through the space between two paper surfaces when pressed together. Three of these air-leak methods are described in TAPPI Method T-479 and in the ASTM Proposed Methods of test for smoothness of paper.

The Chapman Test of Paper Smoothness. A quite different method of measuring printing smoothness was developed by Chapman. The later modifications of this method of measuring smoothness are described in a series of three papers in TAPPI 38, 2:90-114 (February, 1955). In the Chapman test the paper is pressed against the polished face of a glass prism under any desired pressure between 0 and 700-1000 pounds per square inch, and the percentage of the paper surface that is in optical contact with the polished glass face is measured and called the Chapman printing smoothness.

Thus the degree to which the paper surface can be made to conform to the polished prism face can be measured at different pressures and with different backing materials behind the paper. The results of this type of test are considered to be more important in connection with rotogravure and letterpress printing than in the case of offset.

Photograph of surface of coated book paper — 25x magnification.

and/or means for controlling ink film thickness and ink transfer to the paper being tested.

PICK RESISTANCE

The pick resistance of paper is particularly important in offset printing. The tackiness of inks and the thin ink films used in offset printing lead to greater forces tending to disrupt the paper surface as the sheet is separated from the blanket cylinder in the offset press. Consequently, there is a high requirement on pick resistance for offset papers.

Definition of Paper Picking. Paper is said to pick when the coating, fibers, or small bits of the paper itself are separated from the sheet as it is printed. Several methods of measuring the pick resistance of paper are currently in use. At the present time, only the Dennison wax test is recognized by TAPPI or ASTM. This wax test for the surface strength of paper is described in TAPPI Method T-459 and in the ASTM Proposed Method of wax pick-test for surface strength of paper, published in June, 1948.

The Dennison Wax Test of Paper Picking. The Dennison waxes consist of a series of hard resin waxes. Numbered from two up, each wax in the series is progressively more adhesive than the next lower one. The test specimen is placed on a stack of eight or ten sheets of paper which rest on a table top. A stick of wax is selected and heated at its end in an alcohol flame by rotating slowly until several drops of melted wax have fallen from the end of the stick. The melted end of the wax is then quickly placed on the paper surface and pressed firmly against the paper with the stick in a vertical position.

The wax is allowed to cool for fifteen minutes. A wooden block having a hole larger than the stick of wax is placed over the wax and on the paper. This block is held firmly against the paper, and the wax stick is pulled away from the sheet with a quick jerk at right angles to the paper surface.

The tip of the wax stick and the specimen are examined for evidence of removal of any coating particles, fibers or bits of paper. The test is repeated using waxes in ascending numerical order until a wax is found which removes either

Photograph of surface of uncoated book paper — 25x magnification.

Other methods of comparing smoothnesses of papers involve printing with thin ink films and judging the relative smoothness of the papers on the basis of the relative uniformity of the resulting solid prints. There are also profile-tracing procedures in which the profile of the paper surface is obtained by drawing over the surface a needle whose vertical displacement is amplified and automatically recorded as a trace.

Printing Smoothness. Recent years have witnessed considerable efforts to develop bench tests which could reliably predict how well a paper surface will accept a printed impression. In many cases, paper smoothness and printing smoothness are quite interdependant. Some of the printability instruments and the tests devised attempt to measure these attributes with one test. Some of the tests have been designed around the use of letterpress precision proof presses, conventional and specially adapted for this type of testing. In these cases, much of the test development evolves around specially designed printing blocks coating particles or fiber, and blisters the paper surface or splits the paper. The pick resistance of the paper is indicated by the number of the wax of highest numerical designation *that does not disturb the surface of the paper*. This number is called the critical wax number.

There are now a number of instrumental methods of measuring pick resistance and they seem to possess some advantages over the wax test.

The GATF Pick Tester. The GATF pick test is made with the pick tester developed by the Graphic Arts Technical Foundation. The test inks used are the series of tack-graded inks supplied by the Printing Ink Division of the Interchemical Corporation. An ink film of controlled thickness is applied to the surface of an offset blanket mounted on an impression element. The paper specimen is mounted on a specimen holder, and the inked impression element strikes the paper and rebounds from it. The paper specimen is inspected for signs of picking. If no picking occurred, the test is repeated using ink of the next higher tack level. The number of the softest ink that causes picking or rupture of any kind is taken as the pick number of the paper.

Pick Testers Employing Rolling Contact. The Hercules-Brookfield print tester, the Waldron pick tester, and the I.G.T. printability tester, all employ a rolling contact between the ink-bearing surface and the paper surface. The use of this principle permits differentiation between the pick resistance of paper for the machine direction and the cross direction — corresponding to the picking conditions in a web-fed press or a sheet-fed press with the conventional *grain long* sheets.

The Hercules-Brookfield Tester. In the case of the Hercules-Brookfield tester the strip of paper is cut in the desired direction and mounted on a cylindrical surface. The desired thickness of ink is applied to the surface of a disk which can be run against the paper to be tested by printing an ink-film on it. The ink used as the test liquid may be one of the tack-graded series of inks or some other tacky test liquid. The print is made at constant speed, and the specimen examined for signs of picking. If no picking is found, either another print is made at a higher speed or a tackier ink is used for printing at the same speed. The pick resistance of the paper is determined by the number of the tack-graded ink that produces picking or by the printing speed at which picking occurs with a particular ink.

The Waldron Pick Tester. In the Waldron pick test the paper specimen is cut in a strip in the desired direction, and this is mounted on a cylindrical surface. The ink is applied in a film of desired thickness to a flat plate. The ink may be one of the tack-graded series. A print is made with rolling contact between the paper specimen on the cylinder and the inked plate. The pick resistance may be measured in terms of the number of the tack-graded ink which causes picking when the print is made at constant speed, or the pick resistance may be measured by the speed at which picking occurs when a print is made with a particular ink.

The I.G.T. Pick Tester. In the I.G.T. pick tester the paper specimen is cut as a strip in the desired direction and is mounted on a cylindrical surface. An ink film of desired thickness is applied to the surface of a disk which rolls against the paper specimen. The two disks or cylinders are driven in such a way as to execute an accelerated motion whereby the speed of printing varies from zero at the beginning of the print to approximately 300 feet per minute at the end of the print.

Some users of this instrument use the tack-graded series of inks and express the pick resistance of the paper in terms of the number of the tack-graded ink which just picks the surface of the paper. Others describe a pick resistance in terms of the speed at which picking occurs with a particular ink. Still others use an unpigmented test liquid and express the pick resistance of the paper in terms of the product of the speed at which picking occurs and the viscosity of the particular test liquid used. Use of these rotary types of pick testers commonly shows less pick resistance in the cross grain direction than in the machine direction of tested papers.

The Grindometer. The use of a modification of the National Printing Ink Research Institute Grindometer in combination with a proof press for measuring the pick resistance of paper is described by Connell "The Printing Gage" TAPPI 38, No. 8: 460-467 (August 1955). This modification of the grindometer consists of a type-high metal block with two 6 x 1 inch grooves machined into its top surface. These grooves vary in depth from 0 to 0.001 inch. One of the tack-graded inks is applied to one of the grooves in the block by doctor-blade coating with a steel bar. This inked block is placed on the bed of the Vandercook No. 4 proof press and a print is made on this test specimen. The picking force varies with the thickness of the ink film; the force being greater for the thinner portions of the ink film.

Pick tests are also sometimes made with a proof press and a solid plate using the tack-graded series of inks as test inks. The pick resistance of paper may be compared by determining which of the tack-graded inks causes picking when the print is made at constant speed.

MISCELLANEOUS PAPER PROPERTIES

Here we mention merely a few of the more interesting remaining paper properties. These are: (1) Basis weight, (2) Paper caliper and bulking thickness, (3) Bursting strength, (4) Folding endurance, (5) Air permeability, and finally (6) Vehicle absorbency. Each of these is now individually discussed, if ever so briefly.

Basis Weight. The measurement of the basis weight of paper is described in TAPPI Method T-410 and ASTM Method D-646. In these procedures sheets of known area are conditioned under standard conditions and then weighed. From the weight and area of the sheet the equivalent ream weight is calculated for the basic size sheet as commonly used by the paper trade.

Paper Caliper and Bulking Thickness. The standard procedures for determining thickness or caliper of paper are described in TAPPI Method T-411 and ASTM Method D-645. The thickness of paper or paperboard is the thickness in thousandths of an inch of a single sheet of paper or board. Thickness is determined by calipering individual sheets of paper or board after conditioning. A calipering device having standardized jaw areas and exerting a standardized pressure upon the test specimen is used for this purpose.

Bulking thickness must not be confused with the calipered paper thickness. Bulking thickness refers to the average thickness of paper in a pile, in books and magazines for example. The standard procedure for determining bulking thickness of paper is described in TAPPI Method T-426 and in ASTM Method D-527.

For this measurement, the thickness of a pack of conditioned sheets is determined. This thickness is divided by the number of sheets in the pack to obtain the average thickness of the individual sheets. The bulking thickness of paper is usually somewhat lower than the single-sheet thickness. Because the thickness of the paper pack is sensitive to pressure of the micrometer whereby the thickness is measured, the micrometer jaw pressure is standardized.

Bursting Strength. The bursting strength test is an entirely empirical one intended to define the utility of a paper when resistance to bursting is a use requirement. Although widely used, its principal value is probably in the paper mill as a control test. Bursting strength of paper is defined as the hydrostatic pressure required to produce rupture of the material under specified conditions. Procedures for determining bursting strength of paper are given in TAPPI Method T-403 and in ASTM Method D-774.

Folding Endurance. Folding endurance of paper, as its name implies, describes the ability of the paper to withstand repeated folding. Folding endurance is defined as the number of folds under specified conditions which a specimen will withstand before failure. The standard procedures for carrying out the two most common folding endurance tests, the Schopper folding endurance test and the M.I.T.

folding endurance test, are described in TAPPI Method T-423 and in ASTM Method D-643.

Air Permeability. Air permeability, or resistance to the passage of air, is related to the structure of paper and depends on the number, size, shape, and distribution of the pores or air spaces in the paper. The air permeability, which is often called porosity, is usually measured as the resistance to air flow in terms of the time required for a given volume of air to pass through the paper under specified conditions.

The Gurley Densometer method of measuring air permeability of paper is described in TAPPI Method T-460 and in ASTM Method D-726. The resistance to passage of air can sometimes be used to estimate the resistance to passage of some other fluids, such as oils and organic liquids. This type of estimate is most valid in the case of relatively homogenous sheets such as uncoated papers.

Vehicle Absorbency. Vehicle absorbency of the paper is an important factor in the ink receptivity of the paper. The rate at which a vehicle leaves the ink film and penetrates into the paper determines or influences three factors. These are: (1) the percentage of ink transferred from the printing surface to the paper; (2) the setting time of the ink, or the tendency of the ink to offset; and (3) the "drying time" of absorption drying inks.

There have been efforts to simplify the situation from the point of view of laboratory testing, and to use oils or vehicles rather than inks in testing for vehicle absorbency of papers. The oldest such test which is commonly found among the standard methods is the castor oil test.

Under the title of "Printing Ink Permeation of Paper," this method is described in TAPPI Method T-462 and in ASTM Method D-780. The test involves dropping castor oil on the paper surface and recording the time elapsed when the spot reaches a uniform and maximum translucency. Other methods too are known, but their discussion is beyond the scope of our presentation.

Section Six: Paper Requirements for Offset

Offset lithography is more versatile than either letterpress or gravure since it is able to produce quality printing on a wider variety of papers. These include bond, machine finish, super, vellum, parchment, coated, and various paperboards, as well as embossed and special finish papers. Because its printing element is a resilient rubber blanket that can conform to the surface being printed, offset is the only high-speed process that can print high-quality fine halftones on both smooth and rough-surfaced paper and board.

Printing experience over the years has shown that for best results, both in quality and efficiency, paper must be designed to meet the special requirements of the printing process to be used. Papermakers have responded to this demand by producing lines of letterpress, gravure, and offset papers, each with special characteristics. And these developments have been important factors in enabling presses to run trouble-free at higher and higher speeds, while at the same time meeting increasing demands for high-quality printing. There are, of course, some types of

paper that can be printed equally well by two, or all three processes. But, when ordering paper or board, much trouble can be avoided if the papermaker is informed as to the printing process in which it will be used.

The term "Offset Paper" commonly used in the trade refers to a Machine Finish Book paper, usually surface-sized, originally designed especially for offset. Nowadays, practically all printing papers and boards are supplied in offset grades.

There are four ways in which the offset press impression differs from that of either or both of the other processes. These are:

1. The impression is a uniform squeeze over the entire sheet or web. There are no gutters or routed-out areas where slack due to lack of perfect flatness can be taken up.

2. The lithographic plate is one single unit. Individual cuts or pages can't be shifted to improve register.

3. Offset printing applies a thinner film of tackier ink

to paper than letterpress, so the pull of the ink on the printed surface is greater.

4. The lithographic plate carries moisture on both its printing and non-printing areas. Part of this moisture is transferred to the offset blanket, and thence to the surface of the paper or board.

It is mainly because of these characteristics of the impression that papers for offset must have properties somewhat different or better than papers designed only for letterpress or gravure printing. The presence of surface lint and dust is equally detrimental in all printing processes, and while freedom from these defects is important, it can't be called a special requirement for offset papers.

FLATNESS

Because of the uniform squeeze of the offset impression, paper or board that is not perfectly flat will be distorted in printing. Lack of flatness is mainly due to non-uniform moisture distribution.

Wavy-edged and tight-edged paper.

If a skid of sheet paper is exposed to a damp atmosphere, the edges of the sheets absorb moisture, expand, and become wavy. On the other hand, if the atmosphere is very dry, the edges lose moisture and contract, producing baggy or tight-edged sheets. Either condition, if bad enough, can cause wrinkles in printing. But even though there is no wrinkling, either condition will cause serious register trouble in multicolor printing. Their effects are discussed under "Register Troubles" in Section Seven of this chapter.

Paper and board in rolls are also affected by atmospheric moisture. But the effects are not as great since the exposed edges are *with the grain,* and their expansion or contraction for any given change in moisture content is much less than for *cross-the-grain* edges of sheets. Nevertheless, wrinkling and misregister frequently occur on web presses due to lack of paper flatness.

The papermaker is responsible for packaging offset papers in a flat condition. If properly wrapped in moisture-proof Asphalt-Liner Kraft paper and sealed with gummed tape, the paper will be flat when received in the lithographic shop. At this point the lithographer becomes responsible. What he should do to keep the paper flat is discussed under the heading "Paper-Conditioning Schedule."

Paperboard for offset is a special problem. At the present time it is not general practice to wrap skids and rolls of board for shipment. This is, no doubt, because of its bulkiness, relatively low price per pound, and less stringent requirements for register. But, as more and more board is being printed by offset, and as higher quality multicolor printing is being demanded, the practice of wrapping skids and rolls of board may become necessary to protect them from moisture changes during transit.

GRAIN DIRECTION

The direction of the grain in sheet papers should preferably be the long way of the sheets (grain-long) for two reasons:

1. For any given change in moisture content, paper expands or contracts far more across the grain than with the grain. It is only common sense, therefore, to have the direction of greater percentage dimensional change the short way of the sheets.

2. The lithographer can easily change the length of his impression to maintain register in the round-the-cylinder direction by shifting packing sheets from plate to blanket cylinders, or vice versa. But, since his plate is a single unit, he has no way of changing impression length parallel to the cylinder axis. This makes it important to have the direction of less dimensional change the long way of the sheets.

In general, the only cases where grain-short paper can safely be used are jobs where economy of layout requires it, and then only where a single printing is involved. The paper, of course, must be flat enough to print without wrinkling. Multicolor work requiring close register or more than one printing should not be attempted.

PICK RESISTANCE

Since offset inks are generally tackier than letterpress inks and are printed in a thinner film, papers and board for offset should have somewhat greater pick resistance than letterpress papers. Otherwise, surface picking, blistering, splitting and tearing will occur, particularly in solid printed areas. Such damage is most likely to appear in solids near the back edge of the sheets. When it does occur, the pressman's main recourse is to reduce the tack of his ink, a remedy that often results in loss of print quality. An alternative is to cut down the press speed, provided the job can stand the increased cost.

Adequate pick resistance of papers for offset is the papermaker's responsibility. But a bad lot of paper can cause expensive delays and the lithographer should be able to spot papers and boards with low pick resistance before they go to press. Methods of measuring and comparing the pick resistance of stocks are discussed in the section "Practical Paper Testing."

MOISTURE RESISTANCE

Since the offset impression brings paper and board into close contact with the moist blanket, offset stocks must have some degree of moisture resistance. And for wet multicolor printing, where there are two or more contacts with the moist blankets in quick succession, the paper needs somewhat more moisture resistance than for single-color printing.

Insufficient moisture resistance can cause trouble with both uncoated and coated papers. Uncoated offset papers are mostly surface-sized with starch to reduce their ink absorbency and improve the bonding of surface fibers and mineral filler. But if the original fiber bonding is too weak, the press moisture softens the starch so the fibers can be lifted by the pull of the ink. This usually happens on the second, third, or fourth unit of a multicolor press, when the moisture from one or more units has had time to soften the starch sizing. As a result, fibers are lifted so that the printing looks and feels rough, and some fibers are transferred to the blanket, plate, and ink rollers.

In coated offset stocks, the coating adhesive is principally a protein material such as casein, soybean protein, or a mixture. It may contain some starch and latex, but should be moisture-resistant enough to run on a four-color press without any coating pigment being transferred to the offset blankets. In letterpress coated papers and boards, the coating adhesive is usually starch alone. Many lithographers have run letterpress coateds successfully on single-color presses, but, on two- and four-color presses, the coating pigment tends to transfer and "pile" on the blankets, making frequent wash-ups necessary. However, some letterpress coateds run very well on multicolor web offset presses.

MOISTURE ABSORBENCY

The surface of paper and board for offset printing should be highly moisture-absorbent. The reason for this is that the ink image on the offset blanket carries on its surface myriads of minute water droplets that must be absorbed into the paper surface before the ink can take hold or trap. Otherwise, these water droplets act as barriers to the ink, preventing complete transfer. As a result, the ink impression, particularly in solids, appears gray or weak. Through a glass, it is seen to be full of light spots commonly referred to as snowflakes.

Lack of moisture absorbency can be caused by greasy or waxy materials in the paper surface. It is usually more troublesome with coated than with uncoated stocks. Unfortunately there is no simple way as yet to measure or compare stocks for moisture absorbency.

MINIMUM CURLING TENDENCY

To be handled efficiently by the press feeder on any type of press, sheet stocks must be reasonably flat and free from curl. And to be delivered and jogged properly, the printed sheets should not develop any appreciable curl as a result of printing. Both letterpress and offset can cause sheets to curl at the back edge (tail-end hook) if extensive solids are printed close to the back edge of sheets. But offset sometimes causes a peculiar type of curl due to the moisture applied to sheets by the rubber blanket.

The first effect of press moisture is to swell the surface fibers and make sheets curl "with the grain" and away from the printed side. With some lightweight papers the sheets have been known to roll up on the delivery like mailing tubes. This curl is only temporary. When the sheets dry there is a reversal of this initial curl, the final curl being toward the printed side. This final curl is permanent and may be either with or against the grain. It is due to relaxation of stresses in the surface fibers by the moisture, followed by drying and shrinkage to a closer formation than the original one. In other words, the printed surface of each sheet shrinks.

Moisture curl in offset is negligible in the case of boards and the heavier weight papers, but it can be troublesome at times with papers lighter than about 60 pound basis weight. It is less troublesome than formerly because modern offset plates require less moisture than they once did.

This curling tendency of paper seems to be greater the more the fibers are hydrated and the more heavily the paper is calendered. And while there is no simple way to measure curling tendency, there are ways of comparing different papers in this respect.

INK ABSORBENCY

The rate of setting of ink is not a criterion of good offset paper. It is possible and practical to "tailor" or adjust ink to print on a wide variety of surfaces from highly absorptive to non-absorptive. What is important is uniformity of ink absorbency (1) over the surface of a paper, (2) from sheet to sheet in a given lot of paper, and (3) from lot to lot of paper of the same brand and finish. Only with this assurance can the lithograper operate efficiently with assurance of uniform quality and freedom from set-off and chalking troubles.

At the present time there are no good methods of measuring the ink absorbency of paper directly. But there are simple ways to compare different papers for this property. They are discussed in the section "Practical Paper Testing."

GOOD INK DRYING

Temperature, relative humidity, the amount of press moisture, and the acidity of the press moisture all affect the rate at which ink dries on a given paper. This applies, of course, to inks that dry by air-oxidation and polymerization. It doesn't apply to inks of the heat-set type. Proper composition and adjustment of the ink and control of printing conditions are the responsibility of the lithographer.

Paper can also affect ink drying. In the case of uncoated papers the main retarder of drying is acidity. This can be measured fairly simply in terms of pH. Papers having pH values between 4.5 and 6.0 rarely give trouble. But below 4.5 serious trouble can result, especially in humid weather.

In coated papers, the acidity of the base stock has little if any effect. It is the coating that determines how fast inks will dry. Most offset coatings are neutral or alkaline, and the more alkaline a coating is made, the faster ink will dry on it. But coating pH isn't the only factor. Ink can dry differently on papers of the same coating pH from different mills, and the reason is not yet known.

The important thing is, of course, that the lithographer should be able to depend on paper having good ink-drying properties, and this is the papermaker's responsibility.

CHEMICAL INERTNESS

Good lithography depends on the ability of ink and water to perform their functions without one interfering with the function of the other. Water can and does become emulsified in the ink, but it mustn't interfere with the ability of the ink to transfer and print. But ink can't become emulsified in the plate moisture without causing tinting or "toning" in the areas that should remain white. The workable balance between ink and water can be upset by the presence of certain chemicals in paper.

In the early days of photolithographic plates, scumming was a common occurence. It was often thought to be due to chemicals in the paper, particularly aluminum sulfate. But with modern methods of plate desensitization, and pH control in papermaking, scumming is almost a relic of the past.

There still remains the recurring problem of tinting. It is seldom if ever seen in printing uncoated papers, and when it does occur it is probably due to an unsatisfactory ink.

Occasionally a coated paper causes tinting. That the paper is at fault is proved by the fact that another similar coated stock runs clean with the same plate, ink and fountain water. Studies indicate that the tinting is due to some surface-active chemical in the paper coating that causes ink-in-water emulsification. Paper and board coatings should be free from harmful amounts of such chemicals. These can be detected by laboratory methods, but there is no simple, dependable test that the average lithographic shop can use.

Section Seven: Paper Storage and Conditioning

When paper is received in the lithographic shop, it should be in exactly the same condition as when it left the mill except for its temperature. In winter it may be colder, and in summer warmer than the pressroom, depending on outdoor weather conditions. If its wrappings are intact, it will be unchanged in moisture content and just as flat as it was when originally packed for shipment.

At this point the responsibility of the papermaker ends and that of the lithographer begins. And the first thing the lithographer should do is to inspect the skids or rolls for damage. Torn wrappings should be repaired immediately and reported to the mill and the carrier in writing, just in case damage to the paper shows up later on.

Paper storage practice varies somewhat from shop to shop. Some store all paper in the pressroom. Others have a separate storage room for wrapped skids, cartons and roll paper. Shops that do important amounts of color process work have paper-conditioning equipment either in the paper storage room or pressroom, and many of them are air-conditioned. Whatever the facilities, the objective is to get paper to the press in good condition so that printing will be trouble-free and of the desired quality. This requires a good knowledge of paper's behavior, in addition to having proper facilities, and intelligent handling.

TEMPERATURE CONDITIONING

During the winter months when the shop is artificially heated, the paper may be quite cold when received. If it is unwrapped immediately in the warm pressroom it will quickly become wavy-edged. This is because the cold paper cools the surrounding air and raises its relative humidity. It is even possible for the air to be cooled below its dew point so that moisture condenses on the paper in the same way as dew forms on a glass of ice water. Paper that has developed wavy edges in this way is permanently damaged and can't be returned to its original flat condition by any practical method.

During the summer months it is possible for paper to be warmer than the pressroom when received. If unwrapped immediately, it will warm and reduce the relative humidity of the surrounding air. The edges of the paper will thus become tight. However, this is far less likely to happen, and is not nearly as serious a problem as wavy edges due to cold paper.

Avoiding these effects is far more practical than correcting them after they have occurred. It is simply a matter of storing the wrapped paper for a few days at pressroom temperature before removing the wrappings and exposing it to the atmosphere.

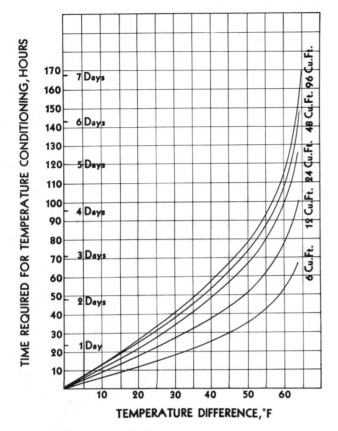

Graph for temperature-conditioning of paper.

This means, of course, that storage of wrapped paper must be in the pressroom, or in a separate storage area at the same temperature and preferably at the same relative humidity as the pressroom. Paper should never be stored in unheated areas in winter.

The time required for temperature adjustment depends on the size of the package and the difference between the paper's temperature and that of the pressroom. This is shown graphically in the temperature-conditioning chart. But if paper is stored a week or more before use, there should be no trouble. Even the largest skids will become

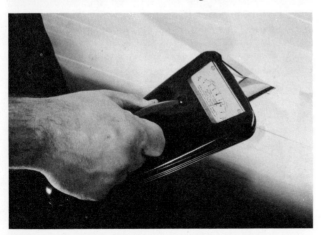

Using the GATF Sword Hygroscope to check for the
moisture balance of a pile of paper.

adjusted in that length of time regardless of their temperature.

TESTING PAPER FOR MOISTURE BALANCE

Once the paper has been brought to the pressroom temperature, the lithographer is concerned only with whether its moisture content is in proper balance with his pressroom atmosphere. If his pressroom is air-conditioned this problem is somewhat simplified. He can specify to the papermaker that the paper's moisture content must be in balance with the relative humidity maintained in his pressroom. If the pressroom is not air-conditioned, the best the papermaker can do is to try to meet the average relative humidity existing in such pressrooms, which, of course, varies with the seasons.

Testing of paper to determine its moisture balance is a simple matter of using the Paper Hygroscope or sword hygrometer. This instrument is first adjusted by swinging its blade in the air as close to the paper to be tested as is possible. It is advisable that this be done while the paper is in the pressroom. When the pointer of the sword stops moving, it means the sword itself is in balance with the RH of the area. The pointer should now be set at "zero" and the blade inserted into the pile about 6" down from the top. The sword is left in the pile until the needle moves less than 1% in one minute. The pointer will now show whether the pile of paper has a higher or lower RH than the surrounding atmosphere, and how great is the deviation. This exact information serves as a guide as to the paper's suitability for running, at least so far as wrinkling or register problems are concerned.

Whether or not the paper needs to be moisture-conditioned before printing depends not only on its moisture balance, but also on the nature of the job to be run, the size of the sheets, and whether one or more than one printing is involved. In most cases, the schedule on the following page can safely be used in deciding whether or not to condition paper.

Testing paper for moisture balance should be done as soon as the paper is in temperature equilibrium with the area in which it is to be tested (preferably, the area in which it is to be used.) The wrapper should be punctured where the sword is to be inserted. If this testing is done early enough, corrective measures, if needed, can be taken before the paper is required for the press.

It can be seen, from the foregoing, that the sword hygroscope is readily useful in only a limited way. In can also be used to check moisture balance of paper when the paper is not in temperature balance. This involves use of a thermometer suitable for measuring the temperature of the pile, and converting the sword reading by reference to psychometric tables. A similar situation is involved when checking RH of paper in an area other than the one in which the paper will be unwrapped and used. In this case, it is necessary to determine the RH of the atmosphere in which the sword is being zeroed, by use of a sling psychrometer and from this reading determining the suitability of the paper for exposure in a different atmospheric environment.

PAPER-CONDITIONING SCHEDULE

Type of Job	Paper Hygroscope Reading	Decision
No register — danger of wrinkles only	12 percent dry to 8 percent moist	Safe to print
	More than 12 percent dry or more than 8 percent moist	Condition paper
Commercial Register — single printing on 2- or 4- color press	8 percent dry to 8 percent moist	Safe to print
	More than 12 percent dry or more than 8 percent moist	Condition paper
	8 percent dry to 12 percent dry	Use judgment
Close Register — single printing on 2- or 4- color press	5 percent dry to 8 percent moist	Safe to print
	More than 10 percent dry or more than 8 percent moist	Condition paper
	5 percent dry to 10 percent dry	Use judgment
Commercial Register — two or more printings	4 percent dry to 8 percent moist	Safe to print
	More than 8 percent dry to more than 8 percent moist	Condition paper
	4 percent dry to 8 percent dry	Use judgment
Close Register — two or more printings	0 (balance) to 8 percent moist	Safe to print
	More than 4 percent dry or more than 8 percent moist	Condition paper
	0 (balance) to 4 percent dry	Use judgment

This schedule is based on data obtained in a survey of practice in 30 lithographic shops. (Hammer and Greenwood: *PAPER MOISTURE BALANCE IN LITHOGRAPHY*, Proceedings of the Sixth Annual TAGA Meeting, 1954.) It applies principally to large sheets. If the sheets are smaller than 23″ x 35″, there is somewhat more leeway.

MOISTURE CONDITIONING OF PAPER

The purpose of moisture conditioning is to bring the paper's moisture content uniformly to balance with the pressroom atmosphere so it will have no tendency to expand or shrink or to develop wavy or tight edges. To accomplish this, the sheets must be exposed to the air individually. Diffusion of moisture through paper is so slow

A cabinet type of paper-conditioning machine.

that paper in piles and rolls becomes adjusted at its exposed edges only, even after months of exposure.

Modern paper-conditioning equipment consists of hangers from which small lifts of sheets are suspended. Blowers force air upward between the sheets. The hung sheets are enclosed in some sort of cabinet that prevents too much of the air from by-passing them. The best practice is to hang the sheets from one edge for half the conditioning time, then reverse the sheets, hanging them from the opposite edge for the second half. Also, the best practice is to hang the sheets with the grain direction vertical. Lightweight papers, especially coated papers, sometimes develop a sag if hung with the grain horizontal.

The conditioning time depends on the type of paper and the amount of effective air circulation. Dense, heavyweight papers take longer than porous and lightweight papers.

The amount of air contacting the sheets is highly important. Air is the medium by which moisture is added to, or taken from the paper. The rate of moisture transfer depends on the difference in relative humidity between the air and the paper. And, since this difference decreases continually during the conditioning, the rate of moisture transfer becomes slower and slower. Actually, complete moisture balance is never reached, but in a reasonable time it comes close enough for practical purposes.

In any case, moisture conditioning of paper should be controlled. The conditioning should be continued until a few lifts taken down and checked with the Paper Hygroscope show a difference in RH of not more than about 2 percent. With papers of 60 to 80 pounds basis weight, this should not take more than about four hours — two hours hanging from each end.

To speed up paper conditioning, some paper conditioners are so constructed that water can be sprayed into the circulated air. This also enables conditioning the paper to a slightly higher relative humidity than the pressroom atmosphere, which is highly desirable when close register must be obtained with two or more printings.

In non-air-conditioned shops, piles of conditioned paper should be protected by means of moisture-proof covers. Also, when multicolor jobs require more than one printing, the sheets should likewise be covered between printings. Otherwise the continual variations in relative humidity in such shops will make close register work a hit-or-miss proposition.

Exact moisture balance is not as important in roll as in sheet papers, because there is never more than one printing.

Paperboard is seldom if ever moisture-conditioned in the

lithographic shop. This is because (1) it would require excessive time and conditioning capacity, and the added expense wouldn't be justified, (2) multicolor work on board is usually printed in one operation, and (3) the register requirements on board are usually not as severe as on fine papers.

Section Eight: Offset Printing Problems

Long experience and a high degree of skill are required to make a good offset pressman. But even the best pressman has to contend with many variables over which he has little or no control. These include plates, blankets, form and dampening rollers, inks, paper, and atmospheric conditions. Fortunately, air-conditioning effectively removes the atmospheric variable, but there are plenty more. Here we will discuss briefly some of the more common problems with paper and ink.

SELECTING PAPER AND INK

Most offset pressmen must work with a wide variety of papers. Sometimes they are chosen by the lithographer with knowledge of offset paper requirements. But sometimes they are chosen by a customer who likes the color, feel or finish, but who has little knowledge of offset. In a few cases the pressman works with one type of paper, such as label paper, and here there is the best chance of standardization of both paper and ink.

Usually it is pressman's job to select and adjust the ink to the paper at hand. The ink must print well and dry well without set-off, have the desired finish, and the printed job must meet the requirements of end use. These requirements may be light-fastness; fastness to alkali, alcohol, spirit varnish or lacquer; rub-proofness or scuff-proofness. Unless the shop has an ink expert to make the necessary advance tests, the pressman must rely on an ink maker for advice and help.

The past 20 years has seen great improvements in lithographic ink. In addition to the conventional and time-honored linseed base inks we now have synthetic base inks, quick-set inks, and heat-set inks to select from. Oldstyle conventional inks are still used and are satisfactory for commercial jobs where set-off, rubbing and scuffing are not a problem. Synthetic base inks are available in semi-gloss and gloss types and are better than conventional inks for rub- and scuff-proofness. Quick-set inks are best for coated papers where set-off is a problem, and can sometimes be printed without the use of anti-offset spray. Heat-set inks dry by evaporation with the aid of heat and are suitable for web-press work, but lack rub- and scuff-proofness. All types are available in all colors, both fugitive and light-fast. But for inks to resist alkalies, alcohol, varnish and lacquer, the ink maker should be consulted.

Because of the wide variety of papers to which an ink must be adapted, various compounds, reducers, and driers are needed. It is only for the standardized job that press-ready inks can be supplied. For new and untried papers and inks, the ink maker should be consulted as to the proper inks, compounds and driers to use.

REGISTER TROUBLES

As was mentioned before, lack of perfect flatness in paper and board is the main cause of register trouble. If the sheet is wavy- or tight-edged, it is distorted in printing and the impression doesn't have the same dimensions as the plate image. A wavy sheet will be "fanned in" by the impression and the print along its back edge will be longer than the plate image. If such a sheet requires two or more printings, the "fan in" will never be the same and register is impossible. The reverse is true for tight-edged sheets. These "fan out" in the impression and the print is short along the back edge. Where two or more printings are necessary, the cause of misregister is therefore due to distortion in the first printing. It is not usually discovered till the second printing when the color or colors fail to fit. Fortunately, the four-color press can handle moderately wavy- and tight-edged sheets quite well, since press moisture and atmospheric conditions haven't time enough to change the condition of the sheets between printings.

When two or more printings are required, register should be checked at the start of the first printing. This is done by measuring the length of the impression along the back edge of the sheets and comparing this with the corresponding length of the plate image. The Graphic Arts Technical Foundation has developed a special Register Rule for this purpose. If the impression is longer, the sheet was wavy;

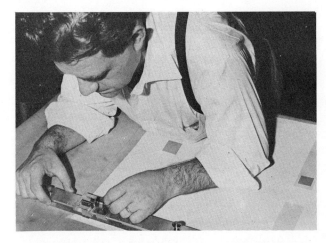

Using the Register Rule to check printed-image size.

if shorter, the sheet was tight-edged. To print under these conditions would be asking for trouble.

A long impression due to wavy-edged paper is by far the more common experience. When it occurs, there is a choice of four things to do to overcome it:

1. Recondition the paper by hanging. If the waviness is bad, this is the thing to do. In fact, the waviness should have been prevented by checking the paper's moisture balance and conditioning it before going to the press.

2. Use heat lamps or electric strip heaters on the sides of the feeder pile. Heating the cross-grain edges of the sheets drives out moisture and shrinks them. This remedy is best when waviness is relatively slight, and must be applied with caution and frequent checking of impression length.

3. Cut the blanket packing along the side edges wherever possible. This relieves the pressure and reduces distortion by permitting the edges of the paper to slip in the impression.

4. Shorten the gripper edge of the sheets by putting a slight kink in them at the front guides. This is an old trick. It is done with a "bustle," either purchased or homemade. This remedy is also best when the sheets are only slightly wavy.

A short impression due to a tight-edge condition is much less common and troublesome. It is also harder to combat. The best method is to recondition the paper by hanging.

In printing lightweight papers there is sometimes the serious problem of sheet-to-sheet misregister. This can occur on any press, whether one-, two-, or four-color. It is caused by the paper having been sheeted from several rolls (multiple sheeting) where the paper from the different rolls varied in stretchability across the grain. The rolling pressure of the offset impression stretches the sheets toward the back edge, but some sheets stretch more than others. There is no remedy for this type of misregister except to reduce the ink tack and the back-cylinder pressure as much as possible. If this doesn't do the trick, nothing will.

Register trouble is very likely to occur in printing embossed, pebbled, and cockle finish papers. Embossing and pebbling operations rupture some of the fiber bonds and weaken the sheet, making it more susceptible to mechanical stretch in printing. Also the raised areas are flattened by the squeeze impression causing more stretch than with level-surfaced papers. Accurate register jobs should not be attempted on heavily pebbled, embossed, or cockle finish papers.

LINTY AND DUSTY PAPERS

In printing some uncoated papers, the inked areas of the blanket pick up surface fibers. These quickly work their way throughout the inking system and foul it up. White, fiber-shaped spots show up in the printed solids, halftones become grainy, and frequent wash-ups are necessary. This condition is variously called lint, fuzz, fluff or whiskers.

Linty paper is the result of insecure bonding of surface fibers. Reducing the tack of the ink is seldom a help. To avoid trouble, the paper should be checked for lintiness before going to press and rejected if unsatisfactory. However, if the lithographer is desperate for paper, he can generally reduce or prevent linting by press sizing the paper with Laketine or alumina hydrate ink before printing it.

Paper, surface-sized with starch, is not always the answer to linting. It generally works satisfactorily on a single-color press, but the repeated applications of moisture on a multi-color press can soften the starch so that lint can be picked up. Sizing with Laketine or hydrate ink also improves this condition. But testing the paper for wet-rub resistance before printing will save time and money.

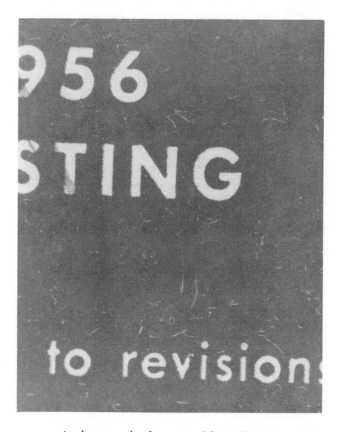

A photograph of a printed linty sheet.

Dust in paper means the presence of loose particles on the sheets. Usually it is slitter or cutter dust. It can occur with both uncoated and coated papers. Dust particles differ from lint in that most of them are clumps of fibers or chips of coating, and they show up in the printing as spots that are not fiber-shaped. They are not picked particles, since the surface of the sheets is not ruptured.

PICKING OR PLUCKING OF PAPER

Picking occurs when the paper surface is ruptured by the pull of a tacky ink. It occurs in different forms such as coating pick, base stock pick, blistering, and even splitting and tearing of the sheets. It occurs mainly in solids, seldom in halftones unless the paper is very weak. It is most prevalent in solid areas near the back edge of sheets.

Almost any paper will be picked if the ink is sufficiently tacky. But there is a limit beyond which the pressman can't go in softening the ink without loss of print quality. Offset papers should therefore have enough surface strength for inks of normal tack. Testing the paper for pick resistance before it goes to press is the only insurance against trouble, and pick-testing methods are discussed later on.

Set-Off. All types of offset ink except heat-set inks dry in two stages. The first stage is physical, in which part of the ink vehicle is absorbed into the paper. The second stage is chemical, in which air oxidation and growth of molecules (polymerization) combine to solidify the ink vehicle.

The first stage, called setting, should take place in a matter of seconds, so that the ink will not set-off in the delivery pile. The second stage, true drying, requires about four hours or longer, depending on the type of ink, the amount of drier used, the temperature, the humidity, and the amount of air available in the pile of printed sheets.

Set-off can occur under five conditions:

1. When setting of the ink is too slow. This may be due to lack of absorbency of the paper, or to ink vehicle that penetrates too slowly.

2. When heavy paper or board is printed and pressure in the delivery pile builds up rapidly.

3. When gloss inks are printed.

4. When static electricity draws the sheets together in the delivery pile.

5. When embossed or cockled paper is printed, or when the printing causes embossing of solid areas. Under these conditions the air cushion is not effective in holding the printed sheets apart until setting is complete.

Proper setting of ink is primarily a matter of proper adjustment of ink to the paper. This is best done by submitting samples of the paper to the ink-maker. For short runs, this procedure is not practical since most lithographers

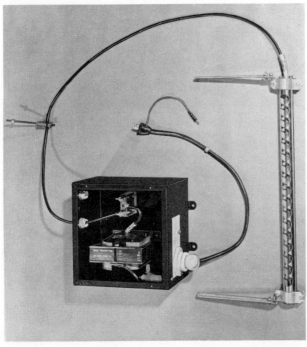

Courtesy of The Simco Co.

A static eliminator.

keep "all-purpose" inks handy for this kind of work. Where some ink adjusting is required, the ink-maker can make available to the pressman, compounds which are compatible with his inks, and which can be safely used if the ink-maker's instructions are followed.

In printing heavyweight papers and boards, anti-offset spray is often necessary to prevent set-off and blocking (sticking together of the printed sheets).

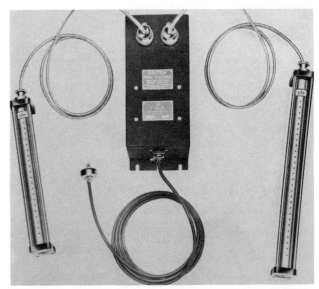

Courtesy of Takk Corp.

A static eliminator.

Static electricity is generally not a problem in lithographic operation because of the water present in the process. However, if the relative humidity of the pressroom falls below 35%, and/or the temperature falls below 70°, static may be induced in the paper with its ensuing feeding and delivery problems. Humidifying the pressroom atmosphere effectively prevents static, and such humidifying is done easily and at little cost. When it is not practical to do this, then static neutralizers on the press are helpful.

The printing of embossed or cockled papers often requires an anti-offset spray. The same is true when lightweight papers are embossed in printing, although this embossing can sometimes be reduced by lowering the tack of the ink.

Set-off is aggravated when two or more colors are superimposed, either wet or dry, so most multicolor presses are equipped with sprays for use when needed.

Quick-set inks have been a great help in preventing set-off, especially in the printing of coated papers and boards.

NON-DRYING AND CHALKING OF INKS

Ink is dry when the chemical part of the drying is complete. But the printing of additional colors and backing up can often be done before the down ink is completely dry. However, finishing operations, such as cutting, folding, binding, and the forming of boxes or cartons, require that the drying be complete. The dried ink must also be hard enough to resist being marred or scuffed, and must not transfer to or smudge adjacent sheets. The right type of ink for the job is important.

Four things affect the rate of drying of inks:

1. Amount of Drier Used. There must be enough drier, but not too much. Too much drier may prevent ink from drying hard enough to resist finishing operations.

2. Temperature. Like all chemical reactions ink drying is slower at low temperatures and faster at high temperatures. In practice a pressroom temperature of 75° F to 80° F gives the best results.

3. Relative Humidity. Chemical drying of inks is faster at low humidities and slower at high humidities. Excessive moisture in the paper due either to high humidity or to excessive press moisture can lengthen the drying time considerably.

4. Acids or Alkalies (pH Value). Chemical drying is retarded or prevented altogether by acids, depending on the amount present. Slow drying is encountered on uncoated papers having pH values much lower than 4.5. On coated papers, drying is generally faster the higher the pH value of the coating. Drying is also retarded by excessive acid in the press fountain water. Generally there is no trouble if the fountain water has a pH of 4.5 or above.

Chalking of inks on coated papers is closely related to ink-drying rate. Paper coatings can be highly porous and have a very high capillary suction. If drying is too slow, the coating may drain too much vehicle out of the ink film, leaving insufficient binder for the pigment. So it is important that inks on coated papers dry on schedule. The best method of assuring this is to make some test prints or tap-outs of the ink on the paper to be used, and check their drying time, before the job goes to press.

Methods of testing papers for pH value and ink-drying time are discussed in the section *Practical Paper Testing*.

SPOTS AND HICKIES

Visible white spots in printing are usually due to slitter or cutter dust on the paper, or to particles picked out of the paper surface by the tacky inks. These adhere to the blanket or plate, become saturated with moisture, and refuse to transfer ink.

Hickies are visible spots with a solid center area surrounded by a white ring. In most cases they are caused by particles of dried ink (ink skin). These can be formed when ink dries in the can or kit and all the skin is not

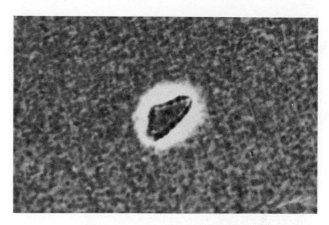

Photomicrograph of a hickey.

removed. Ink can also dry in the press fountain or on the rollers. Prevention of such hickies requires scrupulous care in handling ink and cleaning the press. Other sources of hickies can be chips of paint from the ceiling, or particles of any foreign material that is ink-receptive in the presence of moisture.

SNOWFLAKY SOLIDS

As was said before, press moisture becomes emulsified in the ink during printing. Also, the ink image on the blanket carries myriads of minute water droplets on its surface. If there is excessive water, or if the paper lacks moisture absorbency, these water droplets act as barriers, preventing ink from transferring uniformly to the paper. Solids, particularly, appear gray or weak. Seen under a glass, they are full of minute light spots or snowflakes. When the pressman sees this condition he may think that more ink is

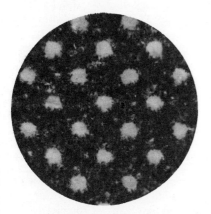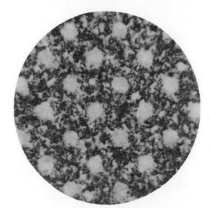

Photomicrographs of a 133-line halftone on enameled stock show, left to right, (1) slight piling, (2) moderate piling, and (3) severe piling.

 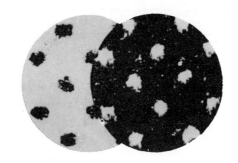 

a	b	c
Shadow and highlight dots printed with correct back-cylinder pressure — 100x magnification.	Dots printed with excessive pressure. Note that highlight dots do not slur — 100x magnification.	Greatly slurred shadow dots. Slurring to this extent is not common but does occur — 100x magnificaion.

needed. But, instead of increasing the ink, he should try cutting down the water.

Sometimes snowflaky solids appear in the second, third or fourth color on a multicolor press. This can be due to either:

1. Too much moisture in the ink involved, or
2. Too much plate moisture on the first or previous unit. In the second case, cutting down the moisture on the previous unit is indicated. But if this doesn't help, the addition of a little wetting agent to the fountain water on the previous unit may do the trick.

SLURRING AND DOUBLING

Slurred halftones occur almost exclusively in printing coated papers. Slurring is first evident in the shadow tones which appear to fill in. Sometimes the back edges of solids appear slurred. At the same time the highlight dots print clean and sharp. Slurring usually occurs over the entire sheet, but it may also appear in areas where the offset blanket is embossed. The pressman often thinks the plate is scumming or filling in, and adds more acid to the fountain water. This is not the remedy.

Slurring can be due to either too much impression pressure, or too much ink. Excessive pressure causes slippage of the blanket against the paper just before the impression. This slippage can take place only if there is enough ink coverage for the ink to act as a lubricant, so it occurs only in solids and halftone shadows. The remedy is to first reduce the back-cylinder pressure as much as possible, then cut down the amount of ink. If necessary, strengthen the ink color and run less ink.

Doubling of halftones increases all tone values. Not only are the shadow tones filled in, but two highlight dots appear where there should only be one. Doubling occurs on either uncoated or coated papers, and sometimes only in certain areas.

Doubling can occur on a single-color press when the paper ripples and contacts the blanket prematurely. It may be seen in some areas and not in others when the ripple is due to distortion of a wavy- or tight-edged sheet. One possible remedy is to tighten the hold-down brush. If the paper is not flat, it should be reconditioned.

Doubling occurs on a multicolor press when the ink from dots printed on one unit is picked up by the blanket on the following unit, but not printed back in register. This can be due to paper distortion, or slippage of paper in the grippers. It can also be due to failure of the blanket, impression or transfer cylinders to track because of either end play or too much backlash. When doubling occurs on flat paper, a check-up of cylinder gears, bearings, and grippers is called for.

PILING

The cause of piling is lack of sufficient moisture resistance of paper coatings. This was previously discussed under the heading, "Moisture Resistance" in the section "Paper Requirements for Offset."

Piling can occur on either the non-printing or printing areas of the blanket. A little transfer of coating pigment to the non-printing areas seems to do no harm. But if it accumulates, it causes imperfect transfer of ink, and halftones become broken or sandy. Piling of this type should not occur. It necessitates frequent stops and washing of the blanket with water.

Piling on the printing areas of the blanket shows up first in the middle halftones. It occurs only on multicolor presses, never on the first unit but only on later units. It seems to be due to moisture from the first unit softening the coating so that it can be lifted by the tacky inks on later units. Here the coating seems to amalgamate with ink, forming a putty-like mixture that piles on the blanket. It sometimes builds up in the form of embossed blobs that slur the halftones in peculiar patterns.

This type of piling is also the fault of the coating. In the lithographic shop, it can be prevented only by sizing the sheets with Laketine or hydrate ink prior to printing.

TINTING

The cause of tinting in printing coated papers was previously discussed under the heading "Chemical Inertness." While it can be due to ink that is lacking in water-resistance, it seems usually to be caused by excessive surface-active material in the paper coating.

Coated papers for offset should be free from any tinting tendency. If not, the paper supplier should be consulted.

Section Nine: Practical Paper Testing

Some of the larger lithographic plants have found it profitable to maintain research and testing laboratories. To meet the constant demand by customers for higher and more uniform quality in printing without increasing prices, these lithographers have introduced statistical quality control. This involves systematic testing of both raw materials and finished product. As far as paper and ink are concerned it is aimed at doing away with the time-honored custom of trying to solve paper and ink problems after the job is on the press. The expense of unproductive press time, inefficient press operation, and upset production schedules can no longer be afforded.

By far the majority of litho shops have no laboratories nor any means of evaluating paper and ink except the experienced judgment of skilled operators. To a large extent, they depend on the ink maker and papermaker to solve problems for them. No doubt this will always be the case with the smaller shops.

Statistical quality control in printing is still in its infancy. What is holding it back is a lack of sufficient dependable testing methods. Both paper and ink are very complex materials, and there is still much to be learned about their properties, especially those properties that contribute to their printability. Ink makers, papermakers, some lithographers, and the Graphic Arts Technical Foundation are concentrating their research on printability testing, and expect in time to solve its problems.

In the meantime there are a number of practical tests that are helpful. Some of these require laboratory equipment and trained personnel. Others can be made by lithographers with an understanding of their purpose, and good judgment. The tests outlined here, if properly used, would make it possible to avoid many expensive delays, and to produce a higher percentage of acceptable quality printing. Unfortunately, space is too limited to give complete working descriptions of these tests, but they are described in detail in GATF's Bulletin No. 308, *What the Lithographer Should Know About Paper*.

When paper testing is done regularly and the results recorded for future reference, it should be done under standard conditions of temperature and relative humidity. Most papermakers do this and maintain testing rooms at 73°F and 50 percent relative humidity (TAPPI Standard) for this purpose. All paper samples are conditioned in this atmosphere before the tests are made. This is necessary since paper's properties vary with its moisture content. Inks and oils used in testing vary in their viscosity with temperature.

However, when tests are made on two or more papers at the same time and purely for the purpose of comparing them, standard atmospheric conditions aren't necessary. All that is required is that the paper samples being compared are in balance with the existing atmosphere, regardless of its temperature and RH.

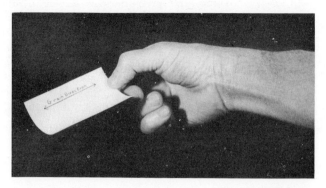

Determining grain direction by moisture method.

GRAIN DIRECTION

As stated previously under "Paper Requirements for Offset," sheet paper for multicolor work should be *grain-long*. A simple test will show whether or not this is the case and may prevent an expensive mistake.

Method. Cut a small piece of the paper (about 2 x 3 inches), moisten one side of it, and observe the direction of the curl. The curl will always be parallel to the grain direction (with the grain).

FELT AND WIRE SIDES

All papers and boards are two-sided. With most boards this is obvious since they are made to be printed on one side only. The same is true of coated 1-side papers. With uncoated papers designed for printing on both sides, the felt side is usually the better printing side, and such papers are usually packed with the felt-side up. To be sure of this the following test can be used.

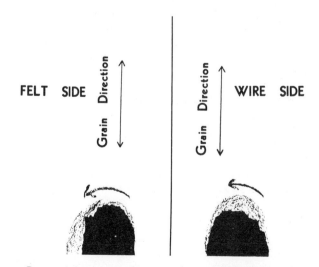

Determining grain direction by tear test method.

Method. First find the grain direction. Then lay a sheet of the paper on a flat surface and make a semi-circular tear in its cross-grain edge. Then turn the paper over, and repeat the tear on its opposite side. In most cases the paper will "feather" as it is torn. If the principal "feather" occurs during the first half of the tear, the wire side is up. If it occurs during the second half, the felt side is up.

With some thin, dense papers this test is not conclusive. In this case, cut a small square (about 3 x 4 inches), being careful not to introduce any mechanical curl, and hang it by one corner in an oven at about 220°F (105°C). The sheet should curl as it dries out, and the curl will be toward its wire side.

PICK RESISTANCE

As mentioned before, pick resistance of paper is its ability to withstand the pull of tacky inks in printing without surface rupture of any kind. Various methods of measuring pick resistance and of comparing the pick resistance of different papers are in use.

The Dennison Wax Test. This test requires a set of numbered waxes with different degrees of adhesiveness. A stick of the wax is softened by heat and impressed on the

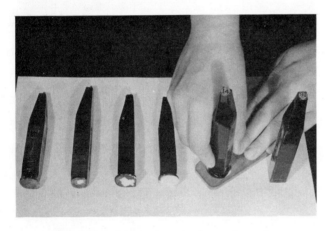

Using the Dennison waxes for pick testing.

paper. When cool, it is separated by a vertical pull, and the paper and wax examined for signs of picking. This is repeated with different waxes until one is found that just picks the paper. The number of this wax is used to designate the paper's pick strength.

The wax pick-test is valuable to the papermaker as a quick means of controlling pick strength of any given paper in production. But it is unsatisfactory for use by the printer in comparing the pick strengths of different types or brands of paper.

The GATF Pick Test. This test uses a series of tack-graded inks. It applies these inks, one at a time, to the paper in a manner that closely simulates the offset printing impression. The inks are numbered, and the number of the ink that just picks the paper is used to designate its pick strength. The results of many tests and practical experience show that the GATF pick test tells accurately how

The GATF Pick Tester.

well different papers will resist picking on the offset press.

Equipment for the GATF pick test is supplied by The Welch Scientific Company, 1515 Sedgwick Street, Chicago 10, Illinois.

Courtesy of IGT Industries

The IGT Printability Tester.

The I.G.T. Pick Test. This test can use a tack-graded ink or a press ink. It applies ink to the paper sample by accelerated rolling contact with an inked metal cylinder. As the speed increases, the pull of the ink increases, and the length of the impression before picking occurs is a relative measure of the paper's pick resistance.

Equipment for the I.G.T. pick test is available from Saunders Agencies, 141-30 Pershing Crescent 1A, Jamaica, Briarwood 35, Long Island, New York. It was designed primarily to measure picking tendency in letterpress printing.

The Hercules-Brookfield Pick Test. In this test also the ink is applied to the paper by rolling contact with an inked cylinder, but at constant speed. To change the picking force, the speed can be increased or decreased. Either tack-graded or press inks can be used.

Courtesy of Brookfield Engineering Laboratories
The Brookfield Pick Tester.

The Hercules-Brookfield pick testing equipment is available from Brookfield Engineering Laboratories, Stoughton, Massachusetts.

The Waldron Pick Test. In this method, four samples of paper can be tested at a time. The paper strips are held on a cylinder and backed by a rubber blanket. The ink is applied from flat plates at known temperature.

Courtesy of John Waldron Corp.
The Waldron Pick Tester.

In any test the speed is constant, but can be changed to increase or decrease the pull of the ink. A tack-graded ink is used, and the pick resistance is measured by the speed at which picking begins to occur.

The Waldron Pick Tester is supplied by the John Waldron Corporation, P. O. Box 791, New Brunswick, New Jersey.

The Proof Press Test. Papers can be compared for pick resistance by means of a letterpress proof press, but this method doesn't give numerical values. A solid plate is inked, preferably by means of mechanically driven form rollers. Two pieces of paper to be compared are placed on the cylinder, and pulled through at as nearly constant speed as possible. Either the speed or the ink can be changed until one or both of the samples are picked.

Courtesy of Kimberly-Clark
The Proof Press Test for Picking.

Summary. Methods of pick testing paper are still in the investigation stage. None has been adopted as standard, but studies and tests in this direction are in progress. The problem is to determine which of the above tests most accurately predicts the relative behavior of all types of paper on the offset press.

MOISTURE RESISTANCE OF PAPER

For many years lithographers have used the "wet-thumb" test on coated papers to see how well the coating pigment was bonded. This test has some value, but is generally too severe.

A better method for coated papers is to place two or three drops of tap water on the coating, gently massage the moistened area with the fingertip for one or two seconds, then slide the moisture off the coating and onto a piece of black paper. Any coating pigment removed will plainly show on the black surface. The method is not absolute. A paper may show a slight removal of coating pigment, and yet run all right on the press, particularly in single-color printing. But if much coating pigment is loosened, there is likely to be piling trouble.

For uncoated papers, the method is also a wet-rub test. But, in this case, the rubbing is continued for four or five seconds, and the result is judged by the feel of the paper surface. If the fibers are loosened they will roll up under the finger and give the paper a rough or sandy feel. Such paper may print all right on a single-color press, but on a multicolor press the fibers may be picked up by the blankets on the second, third, or fourth units, and make frequent wash-ups necessary. Also, the printed areas will look and feel rough.

CURLING TENDENCY

While there is no simple way to measure the curling tendency of paper, different stocks can be compared rather simply.

Method. Apply a thin uniform film of moisture to a clean grained metal plate or to a clean glass plate, using a cellulose sponge. Place a sheet of the paper (about 10 x 12 inch) on the moist plate, and press it firmly into contact, preferably by means of a hand roller. Set the moistened sheet aside to dry. Repeat this procedure with the comparison paper. When the sheets have dried they will curl toward their moistened sides and their degree of curl can be compared. Three or four sheets of each paper should be compared before drawing conclusions.

LINTINESS OF UNCOATED PAPER

There is no way of measuring the linting tendency of paper. It can only be judged by observation.

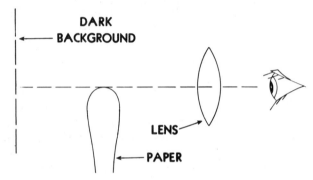

Checking for lintiness.

Method. Bend a sheet of paper as in the illustration. Then, holding it under a bright light, examine the profile of the bend with a magnifier against a dark background. Any lint or whiskers will be seen to stand up from the paper's surface. Paper is more likely to show lint on the wire than on the felt side.

INK ABSORBENCY OF PAPER

The ink absorbency of paper determines its ability to absorb or hold out the printed ink film. It is important to the control both of offsetting and of finish and gloss of the dried ink. Ink absorbency is not the same as porosity. It is primarily a surface characteristic, depending on the degree of surface sizing or on the nature of coatings. It can be measured by the rate at which a film of viscous oil loses gloss after being applied to the surface, but this requires special laboratory equipment.

Vanceometer Method. Immediately after a film of oil is spread on paper, its surface has a high reflectance as gloss. As the oil is absorbed by the paper surface this gloss decreases, but only to the gloss value of the paper itself. Timing the rate of gloss decrease gives a measure of the paper's absorbency. The Vanceometer is an instrument designed specifically for this test. It is made by the Hillside Laboratory, 333 N. Michigan Avenue, Chicago 1, Illinois.

The oil-absorbency test can also be made using the Bausch and Lomb Gloss Meter or the Ingersol Glarimeter. But the

Courtesy of Hillside Laboratory

The Vanceometer Absorbency Tester.

oil must be spread on the paper sample by a hand operation and its film thickness and the timing are not as easy to control.

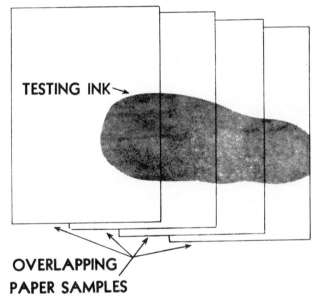

Diagram for making absorbency test by use of the K & N inks.

K & N Ink Absorbency Test. This test is made with an ink that has an oil-soluble dye in its vehicle. The ink is spread in a thick film on the paper surface and allowed to act for two minutes. It is then wiped off as completely as possible. The depth of color of the remaining stain is proportional to the paper's absorbency.

The K & N test is best on coated and smooth-surface papers. It is useful in comparing two or more papers for absorbency. The K & N Ink is supplied by he K & N Laboratories, 1985 Anson Avenue, Melrose Park, Illinois.

Printing Test for Absorbency. On coated papers, ink absorbency can also be measured by using a proof press to pull an impression on the paper in soft letterpress ink. The impression at first is glossy but becomes dull and dry looking rather suddenly when the ink sets. Timing this change gives a measure of the paper's absorbency.

pH OF PAPER

The degree of acidity or alkalinity of paper is found by pH measurement. It is important because it affects the drying rate of inks.

Method for Uncoated Papers. A 1.0-gram sample of the paper is allowed to soak in 70 cc of cold, distilled water for one hour. The water is then poured off and tested with an electric, glass electrode pH meter.

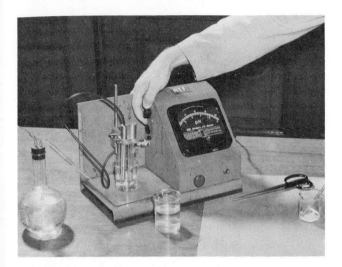

Determining the pH of paper.

Method for Coated Paper. The coating is scraped off the paper until an 0.12-gram sample is accumulated. As small an area as possible is used, removing as much of the coating as possible. The coating powder is soaked in 50 cc of cold, distilled water for one hour. The mixture is then stirred and tested with the electric, glass electrode pH meter.

There are a number of satisfactory electric pH meters available from lithographic and scientific supply houses.

DRYING OF INK

While the pH test will indicate any tendency of the paper to retard ink drying, it can't guarantee that the printed job will dry in a certain time. This depends also on the type of ink and the amount of drier used. To be sure there will be no drying or chalking trouble when the job is printed, a drying test should be made before the run is started.

Method. Take some of the ink and mix in the exact amount of drier you think is needed. Pull some impressions on the paper planned for the job. This should be done on a letterpress proof press with mechanical inking, and the amount of ink printed should be as nearly as possible the same as required on the production job. Place the proofs in a telephone book or between glass plates and check them every hour, noting the time required to dry. You can expect drying of the printed job to take half again or twice as long as the proofs because, in offset, the press moisture and fountain acid will retard drying somewhat.

A simpler but cruder method is to make tap-outs of the ink on the paper to be tested, and check them for drying time.

CONCLUSION

During the past 30 years, offset lithography has grown more than twice as fast as letterpress printing. From about 10 percent of the commercial printing done in 1925, it rose to about 25 percent in 1955. Many developments have contributed to the economies and improvements that made this growth possible, and not the least of these have been improvements in papers and inks. These have been brought about mainly through research and the dissemination of knowledge. Long ago it was said that papermakers knew too little about the offset process and its requirements, and the lithographer knew too little about paper. But this situation has greatly improved. Papermakers have installed offset presses for use in testing and research to improve their products. Many lithographers have air-conditioned their plants and some have installed testing and quality control laboratories. Much of the information gained has been published and is available to all concerned.

In spite of these gains, there is still much to be done. As long as research is continued and the lithographic industry remains open-minded to technical changes, there will be growth and progress. Many avenues for research are open, but the most immediate and crying need is for improved testing methods by which the offset printing properties of papers and inks can be precisely measured. The lithographic industry is fortunate in having well-established research laboratories and technical associations working toward this end.

Section Ten: Ordering Paper for Lithography

Our presentation of ordering paper for lithography is divided into the following four units: (1) Kinds and brands of paper; (2) A paper sampling program; (3) Ordering paper in sheets; and (4) Ordering paper in rolls. Each of these is discussed in the following.

KINDS AND BRANDS OF PAPER

You are invited to study the information collected in our table of "Millbrand papers for offset lithography." This table is most essential for the subject under discussion.

BOND-1

Atlantic	Northwest
Eatonian	Nekoosa
Hamilton	Quality
Hammermill	Tanonka
Howard	Ward
Mead	Wausau
Monadnock	

BOND-2

Adirondack	Monoplane
Caslon	Navajo
John Edwards	Volume
Management	Wytek
Maxwell	

BOND-4

Ardor	Pennsylvania
Ariel	Pressman's
Carleton	Snowland
Clear Spring	Westwood
Manifest	Whippet
Moistrite	Workwell
Montgomery	

GLOSSY COATED 1-SIDE LABEL

All Purpose	Richgloss
Appleton	Sebago Label
Catskill	Sterling
Kromekote	Tenor
Lithogloss	Uniflex
Maineflex Enamel	Varnoset
Monarch	Waretone
Overprint Label	Warren's Offset Enamel

GLOSSY COLORED COATED 1-SIDE LABEL

Brilliantone	Lithotints	Permacolor

PRINTING BRISTOLS
Antique & Plate

Brewster (A)	Mobile (A)
Carolina (A)	Mohawk (A)
Chateau (A)	Olympic (A) (P)
Chester (A)	Pericles (A)
Coronado (A)	Poseiden (A)
Direct Mail (P)	Quality (A)
Eatonian (A)	Queen (A) (P)
Fairfield (A) (P)	Radar (A)
Fibrefold (P)	Rogers Folding (P)
Franklin (A)	Rollstone (P)
Greenbrier (A)	Saturn (A)
Hamilton (A)	Shenandoah (A)
Husky (A)	Sorg Plate (P)
James River (A)	Springhill (A)
Jersey (A) (P)	Starwhite (A)
Innovation (A)	Superfine (A) (P)
Lees Bright White (A)	Twentieth Century (P)
Linetone (A) (P)	Vicksburg (A) (P)
Louvaine (A)	Winsted (A)

COVER
Coated 2-Sides

Apco Hi-Fold	Printflex
Cameo Gloss	Richgloss
Cameo Dull	Scott
Cellugloss	Springhill
Dilcol Translucent	Super-Cover
Herculite	Supertuff
Herculite Dull	Tourist
Imperial	*Waretone
*Kromekote	Warren's
*Lusterkote	Zenagloss
Maineflex	Holcote
Mark I	

*With matching post card thicknesses

Coated 1-Side

Carolina	Husky
Franklin	Springhill

Colored Coated 2-Sides for Cover Use

Esopus Postcard
Mellochrome Postcard (Dull)
Woodbine Cover
Woodbine Duplex Bristol

Uncoated

Ariel	Kimberly
Atlantic	Navajo
Beckett	Orchid
Bermuda Duplex	Peninsular Duplex
Buckeye	Potomac
Buckeye Duplex	Potomac Duplex
Carnival	Quality
Coat-of-Arms	Rhododendron
Daily Sales	Rogers
Economy	Skywove
Hammermill	Strathmore
International	Sulgrave
Interwoven	Tuscan
Jersey	Wolverine

Every effort has been made to make the tabulations on this and the following three pages as complete and up-to-date as is possible.

TEXT AND TEXT COVER
Plate

Alexandra Japan	Linweave Text

Extra Smooth Antique

Alamo	Pastelle
Colophon	Permalife
Coronado	Sheffield
Courier	Strathmore Impress
Everest	Strathmore Opaque
Navajo	Superfine
	Vicksburg

Smooth Antique

Alexandra Japan	Linweave Text
Beckett	Old Stratford Book
Beckett 184	Old Style
Brighter	Shasta
Buckeye	Strathmore
Carrara	Suede
Corinthian	Sulgrave
Corsican	Sunray
Curtis Rag	Ticonderoga
Eatonian	Town Crier
Everest	Snoweave
Flooro Antique	Victorian
HiWine	Wausau
Kilmory	

Laid Antique

Beckett	Old Style
Buckeye	Strathmore
Curtis Rag	Suede
Eatonian	Sulgrave
Everest	Tanglewood
Garamond	Ticonderoga
Greenbrier	Town Crier
Kilmory	Victorian
Linweave Text	Wausau
Old Stratford Book	

Light Felt Finish

Blue Ridge	L'Aiglon
Bouquet	Pastelle
Cortlea	Shalimar
Double Deckle	Stoneridge
Diana	Teton
Fiesta	Tweed
Kismet	
Krestweave	

Heavy Felt Finish

Andorra	Gainsborough
Artemis	Grandee
Carousel	Milano
Chroma	Spectra
Corsican Text	Weycroft Text
Early American Text	

Extra Heavy Felt Finish

Beau Brilliant	Tweedweave

There you can linger over more than two hundred grades of paper by name, in classifications you are most concerned with.

If you're "old hand" at purchasing and production you'll recognize these papers by given names, with recollections of experiences and comparative values. If you're new to this wonderful business, you'll recognize instantly the great breadth of papers that can be lithographed successfully.

It's important that newcomers know only a few kinds of paper *can't* be lithographed.

Examine our table of "Millbrand papers for offset lithography" line-by-line to understand the significance of the statement — "only a few kinds of paper *can't* be lithographed." And believe at the outset that this presentation represents 96.75 percent of papers you'll be called on to select or purchase; meaning, classifications.

See the long list of papers captioned "Uncoated Offset Papers." The term "Offset Paper" is trade nomenclature for smooth, wove, machine-finish paper that is surface-sized during manufacture to guarantee against lint and loose fibers. "Offset Papers" look very much like bond papers — papers used for business correspondence and forms. "Offset Papers" are like bond papers because they are sized extra-hard to be "almost waterproof." You can write on bond and offset papers with pen and ink without blur, blot, or scratch.

Impregnated Offset Papers. *"Impregnated" Offset Papers New.* See the names of papers under the heading "Impregnated Offset Papers." Here are shown a few mill brands in a special classification At no advance in price, incidentally.

These grades, during manufacture, receive a film coating — coating that is more or less invisible. One manufacturer calls this process "pigmentizing." Claims for these papers are worth noting. *One,* surface of the paper is more uniformly smooth. *Two,* reproduction values are improved, because ink is deposited on the coated film, a superior background for pictures, type and color. *Three,* dimensional stability — resistance to stretching and shrinking — is improved measurably.

This "impregnating" development helps substantiate claims that, some time in the not-too-distant-future, most papers will, in some way, be coated.

Embossed or "Fancy Finish" Offset Papers. *Embossed Offset Papers Are Decorative.* See, too, that many of these offset papers are listed under the heading reading "Embossed (Fancy Finish) Offset Papers." After offset papers are made they can be embossed with attractive fancy finishes — handmade, linen, leather patterns, woodgrains; dozens of different surfaces to make papers interesting. Lithographed illustrations benefit from the interest created by these fancy designs as background. Matter of fact, black inks take on unusual glossy appearance when lithographed on fancy finish offset papers. Colors are livelier, too.

Coated Papers. *Coated Papers in Demand.* See the next main heading on the chart: "Coated Offset Papers." Great strides are made in the manufacture of glossy coated and dull coated papers to be run on lithographic presses. Time was, when lithographers shuddered at the thought of working with coated papers. But that's not true any more. Papermakers, ink makers, and lithographers teamed to whip most of the old problems of putting ink on enamel surfaces. Before long, all these problems will represent so much history. Reproduction qualities can reveal only benefits.

Coated papers are today standard equipment with lithographers. Just as letterpress printers consider coated papers desirable for utmost fidelity of halftone reproductions, truest colors and jet-est blacks, so, too, do lithographers recognize the value of the coated printing surface.

Cast-Coated Papers. *Cast-Coated Papers Win Friends.* Consider the almost unbelievable demand for papers like cast-coated *Kromekote* and *Lusterkote.* These patent-leather-like papers no longer worry lithographers. They take *Kromekote* and *Lusterkote* in stride, and, each year process greater tonnage of these strictly "premium" printing surfaces. Reproduction values are proof enough of the high store lithographers place in these papers.

It's worth knowing that much of the success enjoyed by papers like *Kromekote* and *Lusterkote* is traceable directly to lithographers' enthusiasm for them. Their development offered opportunities to expand the lithographic art deeper into commercial and specialty printing. As a "bonus," color

lithography has blossomed to almost unbelievable proportions and new uses for color lithography have been created.

Kromekote and *Lusterkote* have grown to the status "staple" on the shelves of paper merchants. So it is proper to add that these deluxe printing surfaces are available as "top side" of blotting papers, gummed papers; of blanks, folding box boards and match-pack stock. Demand for cast-coated papers' high-gloss is growing in all directions; for box wraps and gift wraps. Further, that fancy cover paper known as *Crystallon* Cover — a mother-of-pearl pattern, incidentally — uses cast-coated paper as the base for the interesting design.

It's smart to keep your eye on the future of cast-coated papers. New uses spring up regularly.

The list of coated papers for lithography is long. Biggest suppliers of these papers provide more than one grade, indicating the depth of advancement in the industry. Today colored coated papers are also manufactured with lithographers in mind, because color in paper grows daily in popularity with designers.

Dull Coated Papers. Pay special attention to the sub-section headed "Dull Coated Papers." Three brands identified as Consolith Opaque, Prentice Velvet, and Fontana represent new developments in coating. To "eye" and "fingertips" these grades do not appear to be coated. There is no evidence of coating on the surface. But these papers are coated, with as much coating materials as "enamel" papers. Only "polish" has been omitted.

Premium Papers. *Trend to "Premium" Papers.* It's a fact, most standard offset papers have been improved until they represent a far, far cry from qualities known only a few short years ago. Papers are brighter; they're whiter, optically; they're more opaque — that is, they enjoy a higher opacity-to-weight ratio. As an example, today's 20 x 38 — 50-pound offset papers are as opaque as 25 x 38 — 60-pound papers used to be. Papers are cleaner. Altogether nicer to look at before printing.

Pressworthiness. Pressworthiness of papers also benefits from papermakers' improvement programs. Lithographers now enjoy the fruits of papers' greater resistance to linting, fuzzing, picking and wet-rubbing. These old bug-a-boos of lithographers are gradually being eliminated. Resistance to expansion and contraction is being accomplished. Control over moisture content represents advanced engineering practice.

Result, reproduction qualities improve demonstrably, and press performance reveals greater economies.

Modern Paper Advancements Are Appreciated by Lithographers and by Their Clientele. These advancements are appreciated by lithographers and their clientele. To this point: that lithographers process almost as much tonnage of "premium" quality papers as standard wove offset papers. Even though improvements in standard wove offset papers make history, lithographers' customers are willing to pay for the plus-values of "premium" papers — superior opacity, whiteness and brightness.

That's why papers shown on your chart in the sub-section marked "Vellum and Opaque" grow daily in importance. These papers resemble typical offset papers and greet-

UNCOATED OFFSET

Standard Wove Offset Papers

Adena	Nekoosa
Alpena Hibulk	Northland
Atlantic	Northlite
Ausable	Old Forge
Beckett	Penn-Brite
Bennington	Pinehurst
Brentwood	Pinnacle
Brittany	Printone Lithoplate
Cherokee	Profile
Clear Spring	Ranger
Custom	Rangley
Finch	Ruskin
Glatex Bulking	Silkote
Hamilton	Snowline
Hammermill	Solar
Hillcourt	South Shore
Hopper	Spring Grove
Inspiration	Standard
International Feedwell	Test
Kedswick	Thor Offset
Kimberly	Volunteer
Lithobulk	Warren's Water Resisting
Maxwell	Text
Metro	Wausau
Moistrite	Wedgwood
Mohawk	Wescar
Monadnock	Zenith
Mountie	

Colored Wove Offset Papers

Atlantic Pastel	Kimberly Colors
Beckett Offset	Moistrite Offset
Britehue Tints	Nekoosa Offset
Carnival	Profile
De & Ce Tints	Rainbow Tints
Hamilton Offset	Sulgrave Plate
Howard Pastelle	

Embossed Offset Papers (Fancy Finish)

Adena	Maxwell
Beckett	Moistrite
Hamilton	Silkote
Hammermill	Standard
Hopper	Wedgwood

Impregnated Offset Papers

Adena	Nekoosa
Hamilton	Silkote
Moraine	Wescar Satin Plate

COATED OFFSET

Glossy Coated-2-Sides Offset Papers

Art Gloss	Litho Gloss
Black & White	Lusterkote
Cameo Brilliant	Lustro
Carlton	Maineflex
Casco	Masterfold
Catskill	Polar
Cellufold	Prentice
Cellugloss	Printflex
Consolith Gloss	Productolith
Duoset	Rex
Empress	Richgloss
Excelgloss	Shorewood
Facility	St. Lawrence
Foldette	Snowtone
Fotolith	Sterling
Glacier	Sunlite
Glossette	Templar
Herculite	Tenor
Highbrite	Velour
Hi-Sette	Velvo
Horizon	Warren's Water Resisting
Imperial	Warren's Offset Enamel
Javelin	Wedgwood
Kromekote	Zenagloss
Lithofect	

Dull Coated-2-Sides Offset Papers

Black & White Dull	Polar Dull
Cameo Brilliant Dull	Prentice Velvet
Consolith Opaque	Warren's Offset Enamel Dull
Fontana	Woodbine Dull
Herculite Dull	

Glossy Coated Colored 2-Sides Offset Papers

Brilliantone Duplex	Miami Tints
Brilliantone Enamel	Miami Duplex
Comet Enamel	Rainbow Tints
Esopus Tints	Woodbine Enamel
Impact	Woodbine Duplex Enamel

Dull Colored Coated 2-Sides Offset Papers

Polychrome Dull

Plastic Coated Offset Papers

Tensalex	Texoprint

VELLUM & OPAQUE Opaque Papers

Smooth & Vellum

Astrolite	Mead Opaque
Atlantic	Mohawk
Beckett Brilliant	Nekoosa
Beckett Hi White	Panchroma
Brightex	Pinnacle
Brokaw	Sapphire
Chalice	Skylark
Chillopaque	Sonata
Eatonian	Standard
Fantasy	Sunray
Fenwick	Tiopake
Fra-Opaque	Velopaque
Hammermill	White Velvet
Kimberly	Winsted
Maxopaque	Wonderwhite
Meadbrite	

Vellum with Matching Cover

Alamo	Louvaine
Astrolite	Luminescent
Astropaque	Mohawk
Atlantic	Pericles
Beckett Brilliant	Shenandoah
Chalice	Skylark
Cumulus	Standard
Eatonian	Starwhite
Eatonian Sparkling White	Sunray
Fairfield	Vicksburg
Hamilton	Winsted
Hi-White	Winsted Glo-brite
Kimberly	

Wedding Vellum

Alamo	*Hamilton
*Atlantic	#Hi-White
*Beckett	Louvain Supreme
Brewster	#Luminescent
Bridal	*Mohawk
Brokaw	Navajo
#Linweave Brilliant	Pericles
Carrara	#Poseidon
Chateau	Quality
Chester	Shenandoah
#Eatonian	#Starwhite
#Eatonian Sparkling White	*Sunray
Fairfield	#Superwhite Opaque
Fantasy	*Tintex
Garamond	Vicksburg
*Halfmoon	Wedgwood
	Winsted

*Full range of colors
#Fluorescent-dyed

---

ing card papers in appearance. They enjoy high favor in the field of advertising printing. These are standard grades on paper merchants' shelves. Lithographers use them for small as well as large orders. Premium qualities of opacity, brightness and all 'round rich appearance contribute "eye appeal" to these papers. Colors of ink sparkle more brilliantly. Blacks are jet. Type is said to increase in legibility.

Notice that some of these grades are made with matching cover weights. That's an essential "design" element in advertising printing. Designers like whites of covers and texts to be identical. Some of these grades are made in arrays of delightful pastel tints.

Prediction is you will hear more, rather than less about these "premium" papers.

Text Papers. *Text Papers Are Functional and Beautiful.* Remember this, lithographers can reproduce halftones and screens on *both rough and smooth* paper surfaces. Smoothest surfaces — coated, for example — represent most desirable backgrounds for pictures and tones. Nevertheless, good quality pictures and screens also are lithographed on antique surfaces that vary from "offset paper" smoothness to "turkish towel" roughness. (Surfaces of some text papers resemble turkish towels and terry cloth.)

Lithographers trade on their ability to produce halftones on rough papers. Letterpress printers, on the other hand, can print satisfactory halftones only on smooth surfaces — coated, uncoated and impregnated English finish, and plate surfaces.

REGULAR SIZES AND WEIGHTS OF BOOK PAPERS

COATED 2 SIDES BOOK PAPER

Letterpress and Offset
Standard 25 x 38 — Ream Weights

25 x 38	*50	*55	60	70	80	100	120
Sizes	Equivalent Weights per 1000 Sheets						
†17½ x 22½	---	---	---	58	66	83	99
19 x 25	50	55	60	70	80	100	120
†23 x 29	---	---	84	98	112	140	169
22½ x 35	83	91	99	116	133	166	199
23 x 35	---	---	---	102	118	136	---
24 x 36	90	100	110	128	146	182	208
25 x 38	100	110	120	140	160	200	240
26 x 40	110	120	132	154	176	218	262
28 x 42	124	136	148	174	198	248	298
28 x 44	130	142	156	182	208	260	312
32 x 44	148	164	178	208	238	296	356
35 x 45	166	182	198	232	266	332	398
36 x 48	182	200	218	254	292	364	436
38 x 50	200	220	240	280	320	400	480
41 x 54	234	---	308	326	372	466	560

* Machine coated only.   † Not standard in machine coated papers.

UNCOATED BOOK PAPER

English Finish, Supercalendared, Antique
Standard 25 x 38 — Ream Weights

25 x 38	30	35	40	45	50	60	70
Sizes	Equivalent Weights per 1000 Sheets						
22½ x 35	50	58	66	75	83	99	116
24 x 36	54	64	72	82	90	110	128
25 x 38	60	70	80	90	100	120	140
28 x 42	74	86	100	112	124	148	174
28 x 44	78	90	104	116	130	156	182
30½ x 41	78	92	106	118	132	158	184
32 x 44	88	104	118	134	148	178	208
33 x 44	92	106	122	138	152	184	214
35 x 45	100	116	132	150	166	198	232
36 x 48	110	128	146	164	182	218	254
38 x 50	120	140	160	180	200	240	280

UNCOATED OFFSET

Standard 25 x 38 — Ream Weights

25 x 38	50	60	70	80	100	120	150
Sizes	Equivalent Weights per 1000 Sheets						
17½ x 22½	41	50	58	66	83	99	---
22½ x 29	68	82	96	110	137	---	---
23 x 29	70	84	98	112	140	---	---
22½ x 35	83	99	116	133	166	199	---
23 x 35	84	102	118	136	168	---	---
25 x 38	100	120	140	160	200	240	300
28 x 42	124	148	174	198	248	298	---
28 x 44	130	156	182	208	260	312	---
32 x 44	148	178	208	238	296	356	---
35 x 45	166	198	232	266	332	398	498
36 x 48	180	218	254	292	364	436	---
38 x 50	200	240	280	320	400	480	600
38 x 52	208	250	292	332	416	500	---
41 x 54	234	280	326	372	466	560	---
42 x 58	256	308	358	410	512	---	---
44 x 64	296	356	416	476	592	712	---

REGULAR SIZES AND WEIGHTS OF LABEL PAPERS

COATED 1 SIDE LABEL PAPER

Letterpress and Offset
Standard 25 x 38 — Ream Weights

25 x 38	*50	60	70
Sizes	Equivalent Weights per 1000 Sheets		
20 x 26	55	66	79
25 x 38	100	120	140
26 x 40	110	132	154
28 x 42	124	148	174
28 x 44	130	156	182
32 x 44	148	178	208
35 x 45	166	198	232
36 x 48	182	220	256
38 x 50	200	240	280
41 x 54	234	280	326

* Machine coated.

REGULAR SIZES AND WEIGHTS OF COVER PAPERS

COATED COVER

Standard 20 x 26 — Ream Weights

20 x 26	50	60	80	100
Sizes	Equivalent Weights per 1000 Sheets			
20 x 26	100	120	160	200
23 x 35	155	186	248	310
26 x 40	200	240	320	400
35 x 46	310	392	496	620

UNCOATED COVER

Standard 20 x 26 — Ream Weights

20 x 26	25	35	40	50	65	80	90	100	130
Sizes	Equivalent Weights per 1000 Sheets								
20 x 26	50	70	80	100	130	160	180	200	260
23 x 35	78	108	124	155	201	248	279	310	402
26 x 40	100	140	160	200	260	320	360	400	520

So — the exciting market for text and matching cover papers opens wide for advertising designers working in the litho media. To help you picture these papers, see sub-section "Text and Text-Covers" on your chart. See how the grades are segregated by finish: *plate, extra smooth, antique, smooth antique, laid antique, light felt finish, heavy felt finish and extra heavy felt finish.* The last three classifications include papers with eye-appealing surface char-acteristics. Lithographers use these surfaces as design elements for distinguished advertising literature.

Cover Papers. *Cover Papers Enjoy Prosperity.* Designers of booklets, annual reports, catalogs, recipe books, and instruction manuals create attractive and functional covers. Longer useful life is built into books by the addition of strong and serviceable covers.

Consequently, cover paper business is big business. Subsection reading "Cover Papers" presents both coated and uncoated cover papers in popular use. Most of the coated cover papers match whiteness and surface character of coated-2-sides book papers. See *Kromekote, Lusterkote, Warren's Offset Enamel, Mead's Printflex, Oxford's Maineflex, Allied's Cellugloss,* to name a few grades. They're listed under both headings — "coated-2-sides book paper" and "coated cover paper." Designers, to repeat, like this "matching" quality of papers they select for cover and text pages of booklets.

Under the heading "coated cover papers" note the asterisk. It identifies grades that are made with matching postcard thicknesses. Postcard thicknesses often serve as cover papers. For instance, heaviest coated cover papers are the equivalent of 20 x 26-100-pound weight; 10 points thick-

REGULAR SIZES AND WEIGHTS OF BRISTOLS

PRINTING BRISTOL

Standard 22½ x 28½ — Ream Weights

22½ x 28½	---	67	80	90	100	120	140	160	180	200	220

Sizes	Equivalent Weights per 1000 Sheets										
22½ x 28½	---	134	160	180	200	240	280	320	360	400	440
22½ x 35	----	164	---	---	250	300	350	400	---	---	---
26 x 40	----	---	---	---	330	396	---	---	---	---	---

INDEX BRISTOL

Standard 25½ x 30½ — Ream Weights

25½ x 30½	-------	90	110	140	170

Sizes	Equivalent Weights per 1000 Sheets			
20½ x 24¾	-------	117	144	182	222
22½ x 28½	-------	148	182	230	280
22½ x 35	-------	182	222	284	
25½ x 30½	-------	180	220	280	340

COATED BRISTOL AND POSTCARD

Standard Thicknesses

22½ x 28½	-------	.008	.010	.011	.012

UNCOATED POSTCARD

Letterpress and Offset

Standard Thickness

Sizes	Equivalent Weights per 1000 Sheets
22½ x 28½	94 (.009)
22½ x 28½	188
28½ x 45	376

REGULAR SIZES AND WEIGHTS OF WRITING PAPER

BOND, LEDGER, MIMEOGRAPH, DUPLICATOR, VELLUM

Standard 17 x 22 — Ream Weights

17 x 22	----------	13	16	20	24	28	32	36	40	44

Standard Sizes of Bonds, Writings, and Mimeograph

17 x 22	17½ x 22½	17 x 28	19 x 24	22 x 34	22½ x 35	24 x 38	28 x 34	34 x 44	35 x 45

Standard Sizes for Ledgers

16 x 21	17 x 28	18 x 46	19 x 48	21 x 32	23 x 36	28 x 34
17 x 22	18 x 23	19 x 24	20 x 28	22 x 34	24 x 38	---

Standard 17 x 22 — Ream Weights

Basis 17 x 22	Equivalent Weights per 1000 Sheets						
	13	16	20	24	28	32	36
8½ x 11	6.5	8	10	12	14	16	18
8½ x 14	8.25	10.25	12.75	15.25	17.75	20.50	23
16 x 21	23	29	36	43	50	57	65
16 x 42	46	58	72	86	100	114	130
17 x 22	26	32	40	48	56	64	72
17 x 26	31	38	47	57	66	76	85
17 x 28	33	41	51	61	71	81	92
17 x 56	66	82	102	122	142	162	184
17½ x 22½	27	33	42	51	59	67	76
18 x 23	29	35	44	53	62	71	80
18 x 46	58	70	88	106	124	142	160
19 x 24	32	39	49	59	68	78	88
19 x 26	34	42	53	63	74	85	95
19 x 28	37	46	57	68	80	91	102
19 x 30	40	49	61	73	88	98	110
19 x 48	64	78	98	118	136	156	176
19½ x 24½	33	41	51	61	72	82	92
20 x 28	39	48	60	72	84	96	108
21 x 32	46	58	72	87	101	116	130
22 x 34	52	64	80	96	112	128	144
22½ x 22½	35	43	54	65	76	87	97
22½ x 28½	45	55	79	82	96	110	123
22½ x 34½	54	66	83	99	116	133	149
22½ x 35	56	68	84	101	118	135	152
23 x 36	58	70	88	106	124	142	160
24 x 38	64	78	98	118	136	156	176
24½ x 24½	42	51	64	77	90	103	116
24½ x 28½	49	60	75	90	105	119	134
24½ x 39	66	82	102	122	144	164	184
26 x 34	62	76	94	114	132	152	170
27 x 40	75	92	116	139	162	185	208
28 x 34	66	82	102	122	142	162	182
28 x 38	74	92	114	136	160	182	204
34 x 44	104	128	160	192	224	256	288
35 x 45	112	136	168	202	236	270	304

ness. Postcard stock may be obtained 12 points thick. Designers frequently prefer the extra bulk for their covers. Our table of "Equivalent Weights" shows the equivalent weights of all paper listed in our table of "Millbrand papers for offset lithography."

Some mills include cover papers and postcards in a single line. For instance, S. D. Warren Company lists *Lusterkote Cover-Bristol.* Cover and postcard weights are companions.

Colored Coated Cover Papers. Colored coated cover papers are not numerous. That's why designers use colored coated postcard as cover papers. That's why sub-section "Colored Coated-2-Sides for Cover Use" is included in your chart. Appleton Coated Paper Company's *Woodbine Coated Cover* is listed with three colored postcard stocks, each representing satisfactory cover paper. One of these three grades is duplex in nature, colors are in pleasing side-to-side combinations. Designers have a "field day" with a paper like *Woodbine Duplex.*

Uncoated Paper. *Uncoated papers are functional and decorative.* Uncoated covers — principally antique finish, a finish resembling the wove, smoothness of typical offset papers — are favorites of lithographers. Grades shown in your chart are standard, made in pleasing, modern, bright whiteness, and array of colors. Each grade boasts a distinctive color range — white to black and all 'way stations including brilliant reds, oranges, purples.

Many of these same grades are available in embossed patterns, leather, linen, handmade, for instance. Other covers,

not listed, but in frequent demand by lithographers are pyroxilyn coated, leather embossed papers of great serviceability and rich appearance. Most are moisture-proof and alcohol-proof. They may be cleaned for extra service, such as papers like *Marco Cover, Chameleon Cover, D'Artagnan Cover.*

Plastic Topped Papers. Some cover papers are plastic-topped. *Plasticolor* and *Colorfilm* are two such grades. Hammermill Paper Company's *Dura Glo* is plastic-coated favoring the dull side instead of high gloss. All are hardy and durable.

Covers With a "Novel" Appeal. Other covers are "novel" in appeal, with special designs printed over-all, or with special embossing patterns providing decorative treatments. Some familiar names are these: *Woodgrain Cover, Twiltex Cover, Spotlight Cover, Leatheright Cover* and *Highlight Cover.*

Equivalent Weights

Knowing which weights of offset paper, for instance, are comparable (equivalent to) to bond papers, vellum papers, cover papers, is good business because using one for the other often represents the difference between saving and losing an order.

Equivalent weights of various types of paper in reams of 500 sheets

Equivalents for	Offset 25 x 38	Bond 17 x 22	Cover 20 x 26	Bristol 22½ x 25	Index 20½ x 24¾
Offset	50	20	27	41	27
	55	22	30	46	29
	60	24	33	50	32
	65	26	36	54	35
	70	28	38	58	37
	75	30	41	62	40
	80	31	44	66	43
	90	35	49	75	48
	100	39	55	83	53
	120	47	66	99	64
Bond	33	13	18	27	18
	41	16	22	34	22
	51	20	28	42	27
Vellum & Opaque	61	24	33	51	33
	71	28	39	59	38
	81	32	45	67	43
	91	36	50	76	49
	102	40	56	89	54
Cover	91	36	50	76	49
	100	40	55	83	54
	110	43	60	91	59
	119	47	65	98	63
	146	58	80	121	78
	164	65	90	136	88
	183	72	100	151	98
Bristol	133	52	73	110	71
	151	59	83	125	81
	181	71	99	150	97
	211	83	116	175	113
	241	95	132	200	129
	271	107	149	225	145
Index	110	43	60	91	58½
	135	53	74	112	72
	170	67	93	141	91
	208	82	114	172	111

The above table shows standard basis weights and indicates what those weights become when translated from one basis to another basis. For example, a reference to Bond shows that 24-pound is the equivalent of a 60-pound offset paper, a 33-pound Cover and a 33-pound Index paper.

Metallic Covers. There are metallic covers — gold, silver, bronze; plain and embossed; one-side and two-side. Other cover papers are made with a suede flocking as the printing surface. *Potomac Velour* is an example.

The heavy weights of most text papers present cover-paper opportunities. These lovely patterns offer designers unique backgrounds, colorful deckle edges, interesting duplex treatments and just, plain, old-fashioned, rich-looking antique surfaces of great character.

When designers require "something different" in cover papers they need never be lost for inspiration.

Printing Bristols. As postcard stocks are used sometimes for cover papers when coated surfaces are required, printing bristols are often used as heavyweight cover papers — antique and plate finish. Sub-section "Printing Bristols — Antique and Plate" is important for closer examination with the aid of samples. Further along in this "short course" in paper buying a practical sampling program is recommended for your guidance. This reference medium can present printing bristols in their truest light, because comparative characteristics of printing bristols and cover papers are quickly distinguished.

Litho Coated-1-Side Papers. With lithographers rapidly becoming important producers of package wraps and labels, litho coated-1-side papers are processed through litho shops in increasingly large tonnage. Sub-section "Glossy Coated-1-Side Label" presents available white papers, and a selection of three colored lines of label papers.

Bond Papers. High on the list of papers processed through litho plants in great tonnage is bond — sulphite variety. Sulphite bond, to repeat, is not unlike typical, wove offset paper in appearance. Grades, in what are generally known as Number 1 and Number 2 classifications, are watermarked. They're good quality, well-advertised papers used for business correspondence. The grade commonly called "plain bond," or "Number 4 bond," is unwatermarked and is used for form work, principally one-color; for long-run direct mail letters and bulletins.

Some Other Papers You Should Know About: True, papers already mentioned here represent, in tonnage, better than 95 percent of all the papers you'll be concerned with. Nevertheless, it's good business to brush-up on information about papers you will encounter from time to time.

Mimeograph and Duplicator Papers. Much paper in these business paper classifications is lithographed before processing through stencil or spirit duplicating machines. Bulletin heads, letterheads, special forms, special notices are first lithographed.

Translucent Papers. Papers in this classification are new. They're used as "masters" for copy to be reproduced on Ozalid and Bruning Machines, "white print" machines. Translucent papers are often lithographed as letterheads, forms, statements and reports to be filled in further by pen and ink or typewriter before copies are made.

Safety Paper. Safety Paper, invented and patented by George La Monte in 1871, is designed to prevent attempted alteration of any writing applied to it. Though the largest proportion of the safety paper produced is used for checks, drafts, and other negotiable instruments or documents, the product has a multitude of other uses. Receipts, notes, business forms, licenses, permits, transportation tickets and many other legal forms requiring protection against fraudulent alteration and counterfeiting are commonly produced on safety paper.

Manifold and Onion Skin. These lightweight "copy" papers are used frequently for special forms, air mail stationery, lightweight reports and catalogs. (Incidentally, order manifold and onion skin made with grain direction short dimension of press sheet, rather than customary long dimension.)

Ledger Paper and Index Bristol. These business papers are grouped as one because index represents heavy weights of ledger papers. Both are used in accounting forms — sometimes in ledger books, sometimes in stand-up files. Heaviest weights are used when forms must stand up in trays.

Rag Bond Papers. Principally used for business stationery, rag bond papers are also used for insurance policies, certificates, important documents when longevity is an important factor. Lithographers prefer machine-dried rag papers rather than air-dried rag papers. The former are free from cockle and less susceptible to vagaries of the weather.

Tag. Strong stocks, jute, rope and sulphate tags are used when extra service is expected from paper selected.

Blanks. These are heavyweight stocks that range from 15 points to 48 points in thickness. Some grades are coated, some uncoated. Some grades are made in colors. Principal use is for displays. Four-Ply and Five-Ply thicknesses of coated blanks are used for carcards. This is substantial business for lithographers.

Blotting Papers. Blotter advertising still represents considerable annual volume. Special "tops" are made for lithographing. Most manufacturers provide coated and uncoated grades for lithographing.

Gummed Papers and Heat-Seal Papers. In limited areas, gummed paper tonnage runs into substantial quantities. Merchandise labels; tip-ins for books; merchandise stamps and direct mail premiums open wide the market for gummed papers. Heat seal labels are important in mass-merchandising, phonograph records and all sorts of heretofore undreamed-of uses.

Poster Paper. These papers are used by the billboard and outdoor advertising trades, by specialists among lithographers.

Parchment Papers. These papers are used for wrapping foods. Use of special inks is essential when printing these papers.

Diploma Papers. These papers are used for certificates, warranties and diplomas. Some brands are 100 percent rag content; others are vegetable parchment papers that resemble real parchment papers.

A PAPER SAMPLING PROGRAM

Seasoned buyers of papers maintain almost "fool-proof" sampling of grades in principal use. Quality changes and competitive advantages are watched with the vigilance of a Hawkshaw. "Professional" buyers recognize trends, sense superiorities, and capitalize on them. This technique of professional buying pays off handsomely. It is highly recommended.

"Professional" sampling is a step in the right direction. *How, though, are lithographers expected to learn about changes? And, after they learn about changes how are they going to "store" the knowledge? How can they use it?*

Answer to question 1 — How are lithographers expected to learn about changes? — First, by indicating to suppliers a principal interest in printing papers — coated book, offset, cover, or any other classification or classifications. Ask for a complete review, samples and manufacturing data, covering latest developments mill-by-mill. Second, ask for a continuous flow of such information.

Answer to question 2 — After lithographers learn about changes, how can they store the knowledge? How can they use it? — First, by developing a workable sample system, based on standards — highest qualities, characteristic-by-characteristic, for grades. Second, by cataloging the information in useful format.

This practical sampling method is suggested, together with a series of checklists and rating charts. It must be recognized — this point is worth repeating — lithographers, however seasoned as paper buyers, aren't expected to be paper technicians and researchers. Therefore, their methods of "keeping tab" on changes in paper qualities, must of necessity be based on personal preferences — *whiteness, surface characteristics,* and other *optical values* — until evidence of *press-worthiness* or *end-usage* supplements opinions. Then this "shop" information should be included.

A Suggested Method of Sampling Changes in Paper Qualities: First, throw away all samples of white printing papers you now have. Start afresh to build a file of up-to-date whites. Then, decide upon a form of sampling best suited to your needs. You could follow or adapt this plan:

STEP ONE. File your whites by classification, coated book, offset, vellum and opaque, cover, text, bristol and bond.

STEP TWO. Select a 9" x 12", 3-ring binder as your container. Fill the various sections — by paper groups named above — with the single-sheet samples, the largest of which should be 8½" x 11". Then swatch all other papers in the section in widths 8¼", 8", 7¾", 7½", etc. You can see at a glance the varying whiteness of different brands. Selection of whiteness from a file like this is easy.

STEP THREE. Ask your paper suppliers to furnish the samples you require. Have them cut to size 8½" x 11". Be sure you insert them in your sample book felt-side up. You could ask your paper supplier to punch the samples with three standard round holes to fit your binder. Be sure "felt" sides are identified.

STEP FOUR. Ask your suppliers to accept responsibility for keeping your files up to date. Quality and appearance changes occur frequently enough so that constant patrol of your samples is necessary.

STEP FIVE. Identify each paper along the stepped-off end of the sample and indicate the date you inserted the sample.

STEP SIX. Make this sample file in duplicate so that sales and production departments have copies and can talk identical paper language.

Instructions for Making the Sampler. Instruction for making the samplers is simple. The cost of making the container is slight. A five-and-dime-store, 3-ring binder is file enough for samples. Dividers can be cut from heavyweight cover paper or strong bristol. Index tabs can be cut out by hand. Tabs can easily be labeled and protected by acetate.

Desire to "keep tab" on quality changes is the only requisite for a successful and effective sampler.

Keeping score is more difficult, yet a very fascinating chore. It's not likely to be abandoned once started.

Remember, keep score around a set of standards — qualities and characteristics — preferences of top-notch values for the grade or grades.

Choice of Standards. Choice of standards may be based on nothing more than personal opinions of special values — eye tests and fingertip tests — for grades in given price brackets. Or, choice of standards may be based on laboratory reports paper suppliers provide. Printers fortunate enough to obtain such information to help them establish their standards, will discover their score-keeping will be more accurate and more effective than eye and fingertip testing. However, for printers' practical purposes, personal or plant preferences offer strong basis for the adoption of standards.

Our two forms "Suggested checklist to help keep tab on offset papers" and "Suggested checklist to help keep tab on cover papers" can be used as guides for the serious study of paper-quality changes and for the development of score cards.

Examples shown present the kind of information to seek when reporting on offset papers and cover papers, two papers used in large tonnage by lithographers.

A Few Remarks on Using the Quality Checklists. The checklists are self-explanatory, but some reference to them could be helpful.

Each paper grade — offset papers and cover papers — provides its own quality points; special benefits to the printers. As each of the points is recognized for its superiority, that point becomes the standard all other papers are measured by. In offset papers, for instance, superiority points to look for are *brightness of white, smoothness, opacity, finish, bulk,* and *tearing-strength.*

SUGGESTED CHECK-LIST TO HELP KEEP TAB ON OFFSET PAPERS

(1, 2 and 3 indicate standing in relation to standard you select as first choice.)

Grade:

Manufacturer:

Merchants:

Ream Weights, 25 x 38: _____

Whiteness: ☐ Cream; ☐ Blue ☐ 1 ☐ 2 ☐ 3

Brightness: ☐ 1 ☐ 2 ☐ 3

Finish:
☐ Smooth ☐ Smooth-Vellum
☐ Vellum ☐ Antique

Pigmentized: ☐ Yes ☐ No

Bulk: ☐ Single Sheet ·——— ; ☐ 2 Sheets ·——— ; ☐ 4 Sheets ·———

Opacity: ☐ 1 ☐ 2 ☐ 3

Dimensional Stability: ☐ 1 ☐ 2 ☐ 3

Likesidedness: ☐ 1 ☐ 2 ☐ 3

Foldability: ☐ 1 ☐ 2 ☐ 3

Stiffness: ☐ 1 ☐ 2 ☐ 3

Fibre Content:
☐ With Sulphate ☐ Without Sulphate
☐ With Titanium Oxide ☐ Without Titanium Oxide
☐ With old papers ☐ Without old papers
☐ Groundwood ☐ Other Fibres

SUGGESTED CHECK-LIST TO HELP KEEP TAB ON COVER PAPERS

(1, 2 and 3 indicate standing in relation to standard you select as first choice.)

Grade:

Manufacturer:

Merchants:

Ream Weight, 20 x 26: _____

Whiteness: ☐ Cream; ☐ Blue ☐ 1 ☐ 2 ☐ 3

Brightness: ☐ 1 ☐ 2 ☐ 3

Color:

Finish:
☐ Smooth Antique ☐ Light Felt Finish
☐ Vellum Antique ☐ Heavy Felt Finish
☐ Rough Antique ☐ Extra Heavy Felt Finish
☐ Extra Rough Antique ☐ Laid Antique
☐ Coated ☐ Duplex ☐ Embossed

Likesidedness:
☐ Finish: ☐ 1 ☐ 2 ☐ 3
☐ Color: ☐ 1 ☐ 2 ☐ 3

Foldability: ☐ 1 ☐ 2 ☐ 3

Strength: ☐ 1 ☐ 2 ☐ 3

Caliper Thickness: ._____ ☐ 1 ☐ 2 ☐ 3

For instance, "H" OFFSET listed on an accompanying score card is *more bulky* than other grades tested; consequently it has a *low finish.* It is *supple, good-folding, high* in brightness; rates "excellent" in *likesideness* and *opacity.* It is not "impregnated." Each measured value is reported. As a matter of fact, "H" OFFSET represents the standard by which the other offset papers in the report were measured. *Smoothness,* so important a consideration in today's market for offset papers, obviously doesn't contribute to *high bulk;* nor strongly to exceptional *opacity.* Smoothness offers other plus values in combination — *superior detailed halftone illustrations; brighter colors, sharper blacks, more defined middle tones* — each "plus" measured by pressworthiness rather than by eye and fingertip.

Two Scoring Methods. Two methods of scoring are presented for consideration. Both are basic interpretations of all the facts that are assembled about brands within grades.

The Value of "Keeping Tab" on Paper Quality Changes. Competitive advantage is one good and principal reason for continuously studying the paper market for changes in qualities and characteristics. (Papermakers never stop "scouting" competitive products.) Awareness of *benefits just waiting to be capitalized* is a strong point enjoyed by the studious paper buyer or paper user. Knowing the *existence of superior points-of-difference* and exploiting them marks seasoned printers. Working with the sampling and study methods presented here can only stimulate interest in personal study, and can only pay off in competitive advantages and improved quality production.

Suggested Grade-by-Grade Rating Chart of Offset Papers

Characteristics	Mill A Grade 1	Mill B Grade 1	Mill C Grade 1
Whiteness	Cream	Blue	Cream
Brightness	1	2	2
Finish	Vellum	Smooth	Impregnated
Opacity	1	3	2
Dimensional Stability	1	1	1
Caliper—1 sheet	60# .004	60# .00325	60# .0035
2 sheets	.0875	.0070	.0080
3 sheets	.0190	.0150	.0017
Likesidedness	1	2	1
Foldability	1	1	1
Stiffness	3	2	3
Fibre and Filler Content	with Titanium	with Titanium	with Titanium
	without Titanium	without Titanium	without Titanium
	Sulphate	Sulphate	Sulphate
	Sulphite	Sulphite	Sulphite
	high "ash"	high "ash"	high "ash"

Mills are listed by capital letters, grades by numerals.
"Standard" samples—swatches at a given date—are grades 1, 2, or 3; good, better, or best.

ORDERING PAPER IN SHEETS

Our "Inquiry and order form for paper and board" presents a "foolproof" inquiry and order form for writing specifications of paper in sheets. Followed to the "letter," paper suppliers, merchant and manufacturer are provided with all the information they need to deliver satisfactory paper at competitive price, to the assigned destination at the proper time.

In the itemized list of specifications that follows, the importance of clear inquiry-and-order-writing is painstakingly spelled out.

Quantity. Don't write so many cases, so many cartons, so many skids. Specify number of sheets with number of pounds in parentheses. Like this — 175,000 sheets (62,300 lbs).

Size and Weight. Specify dimensions and weight per 1,000 sheets. To prevent misunderstanding show ream-weight in parentheses. Like this — 44 x 64 — 356M (25 x 38 — 60).

Grade and Color. Specify by brand names, not by number or letter; identify color in correct mill terminology. Don't write "white" when you know the paper you are ordering is made cream-white and blue-white. Don't write "blue," when you know two blues are in the line.

Finish. Identify by name when there is any possibility of misunderstanding. For instance — Laurel finish is a

A Lithographer Uses This Form to Rate Offset Paper He Uses

Standard Quality Uncoated Offset Papers	Comparative Bulk-to-Weight		Surface Finish		Feel		Bright Whiteness			Likesidedness	Opacity	Pigmented Surface
	Superior	Standard	High	Low	Stiff	Supple	High	Med.	Low			
Ream Weight 25 x 38												
Key: A Offset _____	X			X		X		X		Fair	Excel.	
B " _____		X		X		X		X		Fair	Good	
C " _____		X		X		X		X		Good	Good	X
D " _____		X	X			X			X	Poor	Excel.	
E " _____		X	X			X	X			Good	Good	
F " _____		X		X		X		X		Fair	Good	
G " _____		X	X			X	X			Good	Good	X
H " _____	X			X		X	X			Excel.	Excel.	
I " _____		X	X	X				X		Fair	Good	
J " _____		X	X			X		X		Good	Good	
K " _____		X	X			X	X			Good	Good	
L " _____	X			X	X				X	Poor	Good	
M " _____		X	X			X	X			Excel.	Good	X
N " _____	X			X	X			X		Good	Good	
O " _____	X			X		X		X		Good	Good	
P " _____		X		X		X	X			Good	Good	X

handmade-like finish in one grade of offset. Write Laurel finish, to be sure. No two handmade-finished are identical in texture or character.

When finish is a design, identify it by name or number. When paper is safety check, indicate direction of the chain line. When paper is text or text-cover, indicate dimension of grain, chain line and deckle. Don't leave anything to conjecture.

Mention Intended Varnishing, Laminating or Other Finishing on Your Inquiry. When paper will be varnished, lacquered, laminated, embossed or "finished" after printing in any other manner, be sure to say so. Many standard papers are not suited to varnishing or lacquering. Specially treated, they're perfectly satisfactory. Spell out your exact requirements. Failure to mention additional properties necessary for effective production will lead directly to certain grief.

Make Sure Paper Is Suitable for Special Inks. When you know paper will be printed with metallic inks, high-gloss inks, heat-set inks or other special kinds of inks,

INQUIRY-AND-ORDER FORM FOR PAPER AND BOARD

Salesman   Order No.

Customer   Date

Address   Purchasing Agent

Ship to

Address

Quantity: .... Sheets. .... Pounds. Size & Weight ....

Basic Size & Weight .... Grain: ☐ Long ☐ Short ☐ Optional

Color .... Grade .... Finish .... Design ....

Bulk .... Caliper: Thickness ......; .... pages to inch. Watermark ....

Trimming: ☐ 4 sides ☐ 1 side & 1 end ☐ untrimmed

Design Deckle or Pattern Direction: ☐ long ☐ short ☐ optional ☐ deckle edge

Packing: ☐ sealed packages ☐ cases ☐ single-tier skids ☐ felt-side up
☐ unsealed ☐ bundles ☐ double-tier skids ☐ wire-side up
☐ junior cartons ☐ pallets ☐ uncoated side up ☐ coated side up
☐ standard cartons

Desirable Skid Specifications: ☐ standard ☐ short way ☐ long way
☐ 4-way entry ☐ legs flush ☐ legs recessed

Skid Runners:
  Distance between runners ...... inches. Clearance skid to floor ...... inches.
  Skid height: ...... inches maximum; ...... inches minimum.
  Skid weight: .... lbs. maximum; .... lbs. minimum.
  Skid wrapping: ☐ single wrappers; ☐ double wrappers; ☐ protected corners.
  ☐ mark skid number and contents on wrappers and runners

Production: ☐ one-color offset ☐ two-color offset ☐ multi-color offset
  and   ☐ wet ☐ dry   ☐ wet ☐ dry
Finishing: ☐ pen and ink ☐ metallic inks ☐ liquid laminating
           ☐ varnishing ☐ high gloss inks ☐ acetate laminating
           ☐ lacquering ☐ embossing

Shipping: ☐ Siding on .... RR. ☐ No Railroad Siding
           ☐ Plant has receiving platform ☐ No platform
           ☐ Can accommodate trailer trucks: platform height ....
                            depth of bay ....
           ☐ Cannot accommodate trailer trucks
           ☐ Maximum elevator load ....
           ☐ Maximum elevator skid dimensions ....

Delivery date wanted ....

Most satisfactory delivery hour: ☐ early A.M. ☐ late A.M. ☐ early P.M. ☐ receiving closed 12-1 P.M.
                            ☐ late P.M.

Plant humidity requirements: .... **Special markings:**

be sure the paper manufacturer knows the facts. You'll take further precautions in cases like these when you identify the ink maker and the ink by number.

Grain. Specify exact direction of grain — long or short dimension. When grain direction is not important, specify "grain optional."

Trimming. Specify squared-four-sides when you mean just that. While many grades of paper are standard trimmed-four-sides, don't take it for granted. You may need E. F. Litho book paper trimmed-four-sides. Not to say so will most certainly cause trouble later. Paper will be automatically delivered to you machine-trimmed because that's standard practice in the trade.

When you know paper trimmed one side and one end is perfectly satisfactory for your production purposes, say so.

When you need text paper with plain edge, be sure to say so. Fail to mention it and you'll receive paper with a lovely feathery deckle edge. Ornamental, no doubt, but not useful.

Packing. Identify exact packing required — in cartons, standard size, or junior size (contains 10 reams of cut sizes 8½" x 11" or 8½" x 14"); in cases, on skids. Whatever the packing, be sure to specify whether paper is to be sealed in packages or unsealed (marked).

Be sure to underscore weight limitations, if any. When so many printing and lithographing shops are situated in loft buildings, weight and size limitations are bound to arise. Skid-loads of anything less than standard 3,000-lb. weight should be so identified. When you know that elevator capacity and width of elevator or plant doors make it necessary to pack paper on single-tier skids, say so in cap letters.

When you know skids must be double-tiered for practical reasons, say so. When you know you want skids double-wrapped to seal-in mill-made moisture content, make the point clear. When relative humidity of your plant is known be sure to specify RH maximum and minimum for the time of year.

Delivery. Be specific about delivery date. Specify most desirable delivery time — early morning, mid-morning, early afternoon, late afternoon. When you know the receiving department is closed during the usual 12 to 1 lunch hour, say so.

Shipping. When your plant has a *railroad siding,* say so. Identify the railroad. When your plant has a *receiving platform,* be sure to indicate whether or not truck trailers can be accommodated. When your plant has *no receiving platform,* be sure to say skid loads must be delivered by winch truck. When you know the paper is being shipped into a *warehouse,* be sure to identify it. If it is situated on a railroad siding, say so.

Special Requirements. When adherence to certain scientific manufacturing requirements is important, itemize your order property-by-property, characteristic-by-characteristic. When strength is the factor, emphasize by measured reading the folding strength, the tearing strength, the Mullen, whichever property is essential to the job. When you know the opacity reading of paper considered acceptable, be sure to make it clearly part of the order. When you know the caliper thickness desired, write it out. When

you know how many pages you need to-the-inch, **write it** out so your supplier will be fully informed.

The more complete the specifications you write, fewer **the** chances of mistakes and awful consequences.

ORDERING PAPER IN ROLLS

Production processes to which roll paper are exposed are as obviously different from sheet-fed operations as day is from night. Buyers and specifiers of paper for sheet-fed presses are thoroughly acquainted with trade customs, practices and nomenclature. Merchant pricelists tell complete stories of grades, sizes, weights, finishes, packing, handling. All this information is common knowledge. People in graphic arts plants are weaned on it.

Why No Simple Rules Can Be Laid Down for Ordering Paper in Rolls. For three obvious reasons no simple rules can be laid down for ordering paper in rolls. One, there are no established standards for paper in rolls; Two, every order for paper in rolls is tailor-made; Three, because operators of web-rotary presses make most profitable use of their machinery's facilities, width and accessories.

A veteran manufacturer of web-rotary presses, talking about paper requirements for them said, "Paper must be fitted to the job. Selection of paper should be determined by speed of the press, by number of after-printing operations paper must endure, kinds of ink, number of colors to be applied one over the other, area of coverage, whether printing one or two sides of the sheet, and quality of results desired."

The job-determines-the-paper theory, therefore, is an important consideration when selecting paper you know will be processed on web rotaries.

Web Strength is Vital. Remember this — paper runs off a reel and delivers in sheets or in rolls for slitting later. Running at extremely high speed, paper's strength and printing qualities are tried severely, particularly on web-rotary presses that print on both sides of web in one operation.

Remember, too, that it's not unusual for paper in process on some web-rotary presses to pass through several operations after printing. For instance, in addition to usual lithography — up to four colors — paper is punched for all sorts of business systems, numbered, perforated — lengthwise and crosswise, rewound, slitted and folded. That kind of single-flow processing represents an unsparing ordeal for any paper.

This valuable advice of another highly experienced press manufacturer is also worth driving home. "It's a fact," he said. "Rolls that might be entirely satisfactory for letterpress printing will not get by on precision lithographic presses. Be sure the paper manufacturer knows what process of reproduction will be used and on what particular press the paper will be run. While all rolls should be wound accurately and trimmed accurately, it's especially important that rolls for high-speed offset presses be handled with extra care and precision."

Here, though, is a bright note. Now, papers used on web-rotary presses are chiefly limited to a few classifications: book papers — coated, super, English finish, antique; bible;

coated-on-side label; bond, writing, ledger and thin papers. There's no reason why bristols, index, tags and boards that are pliable enough to go around the feed roller and the turning bars can't be lithographed. There is call for these grades. Several specialists in the production of merchandise tags print .010 coated-bristol satisfactorily. Still others run regularly three-ply tough check, 150-pound tag stock and 91-pound index.

The Trend toward Webs. It's only a matter of time before more and more heavier weight papers, and a greater variety of papers, are lithographed on web rotaries. For the present, and because scarcely more than a handful of lithographers are seasoned buyers of paper in rolls, we are treating the subject in a-b-c fashion. However complete

---

SOME TIMELY TIPS WHEN WRITING ORDERS FOR PAPER IN ROLLS

Indicate clearly
- [ ] speed of press
- [ ] exact roll width
- [ ] minimum & maximum diameter
- [ ] machine roll   [ ] rewound roll
- [ ] wire side out   [ ] felt side out
- [ ] coated side out   [ ] uncoated side out
- [ ] one color   [ ] two colors
- [ ] three colors   [ ] four colors
- [ ] one side of sheet   [ ] both sides of sheet
- [ ] directional arrows on wrappers of large rolls

Core specifications
- [ ] inside diameter
- [ ] fibre   [ ] metal
- [ ] returnable   [ ] non-returnable
- [ ] slotted   [ ] not slotted
- [ ] width of slots
- [ ] slots in juxtaposition

Be sure to insist upon high quality hard rolls
- [ ] tight wound   [ ] even wound
- [ ] free from slitter dust
- [ ] load on side   [ ] on end
- [ ] on skids   [ ] on pallets
- [ ] minimum of splices — indicate acceptable number of splices-per-roll
- [ ] flag splices

Be sure to indicate weight of paper as maximum — not to do so cheats you of yardage.

Caution — remember weight of roll includes outside wrapper and non-returnable core.

Remember, you are billed for gross weight of roll — paper, wrapping and non-returnable core. Weight of returnable core is not charged.

When estimating, be sure to allow for spoilage. Most operators say 5% covers loss of paper weight.

Be sure to instruct supplier to number and show weight of each roll on outside wrapper and on shipping and billing papers.

Be sure to indicate when printing is to be produced with heat-set or other special inks. Extreme care is given the "pick" factor, and splices are properly treated for processing.

---

a list of do's and don't's we compile, circumstances will be encountered that aren't "in the book." Erect a fairly solid shield of information. To help soften some of the blows, draw on personal experiences of paper men and lithographers.

SOME FIRST-HAND EXPERIENCES

NUMBER ONE. *It's important to order rolls made to maximum diameter.* Why? Because, press operators say, the fewer roll changes in a run, the fewer the press adjustments, the more profitable the operation.

NUMBER TWO. *It's important to limit the number of splices to rolls.* Why? Because the greater the number of splices encountered, the greater the number of press adjustments, the more press time lost, the greater the loss of paper yardage. More important, there is a possibility of running into splices that aren't flagged and suffering the consequences of broken blankets, smashed plates, even damaged presses.

NUMBER THREE. *It's important to "flag" all splices.* Why? Because, as just pointed out, unflagged splices raise havoc on presses. Broken blankets are a certainty; battered plates, and worse, lost machine time. An operator tells how one of his major producing machines was out of operation an entire week because a splice on a roll was not flagged. The over-all loss to the operator mounted into thousands of dollars.

NUMBER FOUR. *It's important to specify the maximum basis weight required.* Why? Because the operator buys yardage, not pounds of paper. When ordering 17" x 22" — 20 pound bond paper without stipulating "not heavier than," buyers may receive 21-pound, 22-pound, or even 23-pound paper. Consequently, yardage is cut down, yielding fewer forms, letterheads, envelopes than figured.

NUMBER FIVE. *It's important to allow for at least 5 to 7% spoilage when estimating.* Why? Because the weight of the roll always includes the outside wrapper and the core; also because in unwrapping the roll, the paper is invariably damaged in some degree. In transit, rolls might be dropped on their edge or otherwise knicked. Almost always — depending on the weight of paper — the last ten to fifty pounds of paper nearest the core are worthless. Paper is curled beyond value.

NUMBER SIX. *It does no harm to specify "free from slitter dust."* Why? Because slitter dust causes all sorts of trouble when the job is being produced, shows large solid areas of black or color. Dust piles up on the blanket of offset presses. Result—spoilage; lost time for wash-ups.

(Note: Most mills wind satisfactory rolls. They've overcome the "slitter dust" trouble by installing special vacuum cleaning units on papermaking and slitting machines.

NUMBER SEVEN. *It's important to stipulate "tight-wound rolls."* Why? Because soft, unevenly wound rolls are useless. They are likely to telescope in transit. When rolls are slightly uneven — high on one side — the paper can be run, but only with care; and at great loss of time.

NUMBER EIGHT. *It's important to provide the proper "core" information.* Why? Because there are no standard-size cores. Weights of paper and board dictate diameter and style. Three-inch cores are in most general use. Some operators want non-returnable cores; others want returnable cores. Some want slotted cores. Others don't.

NUMBER NINE. *It's important to stipulate "rewound" when rolls are narrow width.* Why? Because narrow gage equipment is high precision equipment. Slitting must be exact. Winding must be hard and firm.

NUMBER TEN. *It's important to estimate carefully. Don't take anything for granted.* Why? Because allowances — differentials between standard-packed sheets and rolls — are not standard with all paper manufacturers. Until buyers establish an expert working knowledge of mill practices, it's wise to investigate each inquiry. For instance, some mills deduct $2.30 a hundredweight from prices for paper packed in cartons to arrive at cost of roll merchandise. Other mills deduct $2.05, $2.20 and $2.25. Some mills make no additional charge for winding rolls larger than 11 inches. Other mills charge an additional sum for rolls between 17" and 12" in width. Still another charge is added for rolls narrower than 11" Weight-per-roll also determines pricing. Some mills price rolls of 250 pounds higher than 500 pound rolls. It is, therefore, best to check when ordering. Take nothing for granted.

NUMBER ELEVEN. *Specify "wire side out" or "felt side out."* Since most of your paper will be coated-two-sides, this specification is probably unimportant. However, when selecting your paper be sure your mill-source will wind your rolls "wire side out." Some will, but they'll charge extra for it. Get the facts.

NUMBER TWELVE. *Specify "directional arrows to appear on wrappers."* This detail is important.

NUMBER THIRTEEN. *Be sure to give handling instructions for shippers.* Stipulate "load on side" or "load on end," whichever way you prefer. But, be sure to identify your wishes.

NUMBER FOURTEEN. *Specify "for four-color letterpress printing on 4-color Miehle feeding from web-feed device."* Here again, this instruction seems, unnecessary, but, as in all good order-writing you can't take anything for granted. Also, paper manufacturers do like to know what presses their rolls are being printed on.

NUMBER FIFTEEN. *Be sure to stipulate "number all rolls, and show roll-weights on wrappers."* Since no two rolls you order will be identical in weight, be sure to instruct your paper manufacturers to number rolls and mark prominently the weight of each roll. Then as you receive, inventory, and select rolls for press, you can easily identify them and easily fit their contents into each job requirement.

NUMBER SIXTEEN. *Be sure to ask your paper manufacturers for shipping papers that number your rolls and their weights.* Your shipping, stock, and accounting departments can use this information handily.

NUMBER SEVENTEEN. *On the side of each roll, near the core, mark lot number, roll number, roll weight and manufacturers' code.* All big buyers of paper in rolls follow this procedure.

A Few Points to Remember. Remember, weight of roll includes outside wrapper and non-returnable core. Remember, you are billed for gross weight of roll — paper, wrapping and non-returnable core. Weight of returnable core is not charged. When estimating, be sure to allow for spoilage. Most operators say 5 percent covers loss of paper weight. Be sure to instruct supplier to number and show weight of each roll on outside wrapper and on shipping and billing papers. Be sure to indicate when printing is to be produced with inks other than those used normally. Extreme care is given the "pick" factor, and splices are properly treated for processing.

Arithmetic Help. Here is the approved method of figuring the approximate weight of paper in rolls:

EXAMPLE: To determine the weight of a roll of bond paper that is 30 inches in diameter and 12 inches wide: Square the diameter, $30 \times 30 = 900$; Multiply by the width, $900 \times 12 - 10,800$; Multiply by the factor .027, $10,800 \times .027 = 291.6$. Answer — 291.6 pounds.

Factors for Determining Approximate Weight of Paper Rolls. These are the factors to use to help you determine the approximate weight of a roll for papers purchased in rolls: antique finish, .018; machine finish, English finish, offset, bond, ledger, writing, manifold, onion skin, .027; super, .030; coated two sides, .034; coated one side, .030; newsprint, .0162. These factors — average among paper manufacturers — apply for all weights.

For any given diameter, lighter weight papers will bulk less. More of it, therefore, will be wound on a roll.

Approved Method of Figuring Approximate Linear Yardage in Paper Rolls. Here is the approved method of figuring approximate linear yardage in a roll of paper:

1. Multiply the weight of the roll by 500, and then multiply that sum by 24.

2. Divide that result by the sum of the roll-width by the basis weight.

EXAMPLE: Weight 100 lbs. $\times$ (factor) $500 \times$ (factor) $24 = 1,200,000$. Width $24 \times$ basis weight $50 = 1,200$. $1,200,000 \div 1,200 = 1,000$ yards.

APPROXIMATE WEIGHT OF ROLLS PER INCH OF WIDTH
(Multiply figure below by roll width to get weight of roll.)

Grade	28" Diam.	30" Diam.	32" Diam.	34" Diam.	36" Diam.	38" Diam.	40" Diam.
Coated 2 sides	26.7	30.6	34.8	39.3	44.0	49.1	54.4
Coated 1 side	23.5	27.0	30.7	34.7	38.9	43.3	48.0
Super	23.5	27.0	30.7	34.7	38.9	43.3	48.0
English Finish	21.2	24.3	27.6	31.2	35.0	39.0	43.2
Antique	14.1	16.2	18.4	20.8	23.3	26.0	28.8
Offset	17.1	19.7	22.5	25.4	28.4	31.6	35.1

Approved Method of Determining the Number of Reams in a Roll of Paper. Here is the approved method of determining the number of reams in a roll of paper: Divide the weight of the ream into the approximate weight of the roll. The result is approximate because the weight of core and plugs isn't considered.

CHAPTER FOURTEEN

Binding

Section One: Pamphlet Binding

Pamphlet binding is that branch of the book binding industry which produces leaflets, folders, booklets and soft covered books. Our presentation of pamphlet binding is divided into the following seven points: (1) General exposition of pamphlet binding; (2) Sheet cutting; (3) Folding; (4) Tipping of end papers, gathering and stripping; (5) Binding; (6) Trimming; and (7) Auxiliary bindery operations. Each of these points is discussed in the following.

GENERAL EXPOSITION OF PAMPHLET BINDING

The products of pamphlet binding are distinguished by their cover and their kind of binding. Folders are the simplest products of pamphlet binding; they have — as the reader knows — neither binding nor cover. Their sequence of pages is determined by the folding; the first page serves in a sense also as the cover. Booklets are bound but not necessarily equipped with a cover. If their cover consists of a different material than their content, the booklet is considered to be bound with a cover; if the outside pages of the booklet are produced on the same paper as the content, the term self-cover is employed.

In the course of our presentation you will find a description of saddle wired and side wired books, smyth and singer sewed books and of perfect bound books as well as their various kinds of covers.

In addition to binding itself, pamphlet binderies very often perform many auxiliary operations such as round-cornering, punching, drilling, numbering, collating, and padding. These operations are often designated as manifold binding operations. Some pamphlet binderies supplement the above mentioned list of services by such operations as diecutting, eyeleting, riveting, and indexing. Banding, packing, and the making of drop shipments conclude this long list of services rendered by modern, well-equipped pamphlet binderies.

The subject of impositions is extensively discussed in the Stripping and Photocomposing chapter, section eight, of this manual. But a few words must be also said on imposition in the context of our subject. Jobs are usually printed on large size sheets on which are found many pages or multiples of leaflets, folders and so on. There are several methods of combining pages or other printed units such as folders. Here we distinguish four: (1) Sheetwise impositions, (2) Work-and-turn impositions, (3) Work-and-tumble impositions, and (4) Work-and-twist impositions.

Sheetwise Impositions. Sheetwise impositions can be defined as the method of lockup and printing in which half the required amount of pages that satisfy the need of the sheet are printed on one side and the balance on the reverse side. Two different forms are used in this case.

Work-and-Turn Impositions. Work-and-turn designates the method of lockup and printing in which all the plates that are going to be printed on one sheet are locked up in one form in such a manner that when the sheet is folded or flipped over and the same gripper edge is used, one-half of the sheet automatically backs up the other half of the sheet. The gripper is kept constant, and the side guide of the press is moved from one side to the other when backing up is performed, which in effect keeps the same edge of the sheet as the side guide edge. When the sheet is cut in half — parallel to the side guide — two identical sheets are produced.

Work-and-Tumble Impositions. Work-and-tumble can be defined as the method of lockup and printing in which all the plates that are to be printed on a sheet are so arranged in one form so that after the sheet is run through the press once, the gripper edge is flipped to the back of the sheet and, on backing up, the edge opposite the original gripper is used for the straight side and the side guide is kept constant. When cutting in half — parallel to the gripper — two identical sheets are produced.

Work-and-Twist Impositions. Work-and-twist is a method of producing two identical smaller sheets from one larger sheet by first printing half the larger sheet and then using the two opposite ends as the gripper and side guide and printing again.

Disregarding the kind of imposition selected, a sheet must always be printed in such a manner that the folded product (section or signature) will have the pages in proper order or rotation.

SHEET CUTTING

Some jobs are printed in such a manner that the sheet is ready for folding as it is delivered to the pamphlet bindery; other jobs need sheet cutting before they can be folded. In our following discussion, we must distinguish between two kinds of cutting and folding: cutting and folding for the production of individual leaflets and folders and cutting and folding in order to produce book sections or signatures.

In the sheet cutting department, various models and makes of guillotine cutters are used in various sizes. Here we discuss the following three points: (1) The guillotine or straight cutter, (2) Various kinds of guillotine cutters, and (3) Cutting problems.

The Guillotine or Straight Cutter. The guillotine or straight cutter cuts through a comparatively high pile of sheets at one time making a single cut in the process. The sheets are placed in the cutter in a pile or lift with one straight side against the movable back gage and the other straight side against the rigid side of the machine. A clamp and a beveled knife are put into motion, the clamp seizes the paper while the knife cuts through the lift. Cutting machines are made in sizes that are from as little as several inches wide and long, to sizes that are better than 90 inches wide and long.

The average machine will accommodate a sheet of about 50 inches wide and its back gage can be moved again 50 inches back from the knife. It can be readily seen that a 50 x 72-inch sheet can be split in half into two sheets 36 x 50 inches but cannot be cut parallel to the 72-inch side on a 50-inch machine. For this, a 74-inch or larger cutting machine must be used.

Various Kinds of Guillotine Cutters. Aside from different size cutting machines there are different models. There are the simple type of guillotine cutters with manually operated clamp and back gage; guillotine cutters with automatic clamp and power back gage; and cutters with automatic clamp and automatic spacing power back gage. A special model guillotine cutter is the Brackett Trimmer, which has its movable gage in the front of the cutting blade and the work is moved toward the blade and away from the operator giving an advantage of easier loading for long narrow strips and also regular sheet cutting and books.

Cutting Problems. Where the sheet cuts in half there usually are no great problems with ordinary book papers ranging in weight from 45 to 100 lb stock. Problems in sheet cutting arise with very light and fluffy papers, very hard papers, wavy or curled stock.

When multiple units have to be cut from a sheet, they can be so arranged as to be chopped apart — the cut being the finished edge of the paper. However in the case of bleeds, small pieces, or where great accuracy is required a "cut out" is arranged for. A cut out means that a piece of waste is removed from between units.

All cutters are subject to what is known as "draw." Draw is defined as a slight difference in the size of the sheets on top of the pile or lift to those at the bottom of the pile after cutting.

FOLDING

There are two main types of folders, namely the knife folder and the buckle folder. The knife folder is the original style, the buckle folder the more recent. Knife folders are manufactured by such firms as Dexter Folder Company, Chambers Brothers or Brown Folding Machine Company. Buckle folders are manufactured by such firms as Baum Folding Machine Company and Dexter Folder Company; the Dexter buckle folder has the tradename Cleveland Folding Machine.

The Three Main Models of Knife Folders. The knife folder is made in three main models in a host of sizes from 25" x 38" or even smaller to 50" x 72" and possibly slightly larger. The three main models are known as the Jobber, the Double 16 — Double 32, and the Quad.

The Principle of the Knife Folder. The basic action of the knife folder can be described as follows. A sheet of paper in conveyed into the machine by the use of several canvas tapes about 1 inch wide; this sheet is stopped by a gage and positioned by a mechanical side guide. A knife blade, regulated by a timed cam action, forces the paper between two knurled rollers and the folded product is conveyed to the next fold station by canvas tapes. The process is repeated and repeated again (usually 3 or 4 times) until the desired amount of folds is made. The number of folds possible on a specific folder depends on its construction; so does the sequence of folds and the general pattern of folds producible on it.

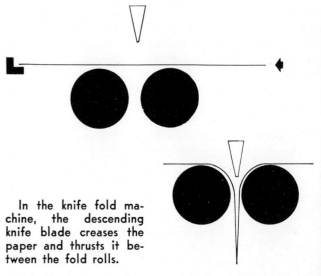

In the knife fold machine, the descending knife blade creases the paper and thrusts it between the fold rolls.

Courtesy John F. Cuneo Company

The Scope of Jobber Models. A Jobber model can be set to make any of the following combinations of folds: Either one fold, or two right-angle folds (the second fold at right angles to first), or three right-angle folds, or four right-angle folds. It is also possible to make two right-angle folds and the third fold parallel to second right-angle, or to make three right-angle folds with the fourth fold parallel to the third right-angle. Folders can have perforating mechanisms that can perforate the head on top of the signature and thereby allow the air to escape to prevent wrinkles. In the case of the last two impositions mentioned above, provisions are made on folders for slitting the section in half. The Jobber is the most popular of the three models of knife folder because of its flexibility in impositions.

The Scope and Purpose of the Double 16 — Double 32 Folder. The double 16 machine is a specialized folding machine designed to produce two 16-page units, either separately or inserted into each other to make one 32-page signature. Its greatest use is for magazine work, heavy stocks where 32 pages are printed on one sheet, or book work. The double 16 folder is flexible only as to size but not as to its products. This folder can only produce two 16- or one 32-page units. The added double 32 section can also produce two separate 32-page signatures.

The Quad Folder. The Quad folder is used mostly in edition binderies but almost never in a pamphlet bindery. The Quad folder is again a specialized folder which produces four 16-page units, separately, or inserted to make two 32-page units. Its main advantage is that it can produce four folded 16-page units from one single sheet and that the 16-page units produced on a Quad folder have what are known as *closed heads.*

The knife principle is also used for a type of folder known as a *Chopper* which is used to put additional folds into an already folded signature.

The Meaning and Purpose of Closed Heads. Closed heads mean that the top of the signature is produced by a fold and that it presents a solid surface when such a signature is opened in its center. This feature is desirable in operations subsequent to folding, namely in sewing and in automatic wire stitching. Signatures made with closed heads can be opened at their center accurately and at great speed for the feeding of the sewing or wire stitching machines.

The Principle of the Buckle Folder. The buckle folder is the more recent machine. The principle it uses to produce a fold is as follows: Two rollers push a sheet of paper between two metal plates. When the paper meets a stop or gage placed in a set position between the two plates, it starts to buckle at the entrance of the plates. A third roller in conjunction with one of the two original rollers seizes the buckle thus produced and puts a fold into the paper.

Various Kinds of Buckle Folders. Buckle folders are usually built with multiple folds in each folding bank. In the smaller machines, there are two or three folds in this first or parallel section and three or four folds in the second or 8-page section. In the medium and larger machines,

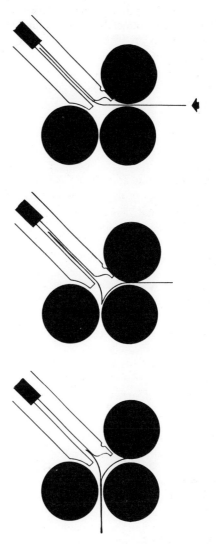

Courtesy John F. Cuneo Company

In the buckle fold machine the sheet passes through drive-up rollers into the fold plate. It buckles and passes through the fold rolls.

there are usually three or four folds in the parallel and 8-page sections, and one to three folds in the 16-page section. In the larger machines a fourth or 32-page section is added that contains one or two plates.

Setting a Buckle Folder. In each section all, one, more than one, or none of the fold plates may or may not be used. The setting is made by simply closing the nose of the plate with what is known as a *deflector,* or by leaving the nose of the plate open and unobstructed for entry of the sheet. Also, only the parallel section may be used; but if the job so requires, more than one of the subsequent fold sections may be used too. From this description it is easy to see that the buckle type folder is an extremely versatile machine. In addition to a multiplicity of folds, buckle folders are capable of pasting, slitting, and perforating.

The Importance of the Bindery Imposition. Due to the large variety of sizes and models of folding machines, the fact that all of them are not necessarily available in a specific bindery, also because grains and weights of paper present different folding problems, and that operations subsequent to folding may need a special type of signature, due to all these factors it is important that the lithographer obtain a bindery imposition before proceeding with stripping. An imposition is a diagram which shows the position of each page as it is to appear on the printed sheet; this diagram also designates side guide and gripper edges. Margins and line-ups are left to the lithographer who must bear in mind that at least ⅛-inch trim is needed top, bottom and front of any page except for the places where two-up or other multiple printing join each other, require no bleeding and are merely chopped apart. In book work so laid out, a ⅛-inch margin is at the head of the upper page; there is no trim between the tail of the upper page and the head of the lower pager and a ⅛-inch margin is used at the tail of the bottom page. Since the binder is usually more familiar with folding machines and necessary trims than the lithographer, particularly when it comes to complicated impositions, it is well for the lithographer to submit a diagram of his intended trims or his blueprint to the binder before stripping.

Grain of Paper and Weight of Paper Must be Considered. As a general rule, folding is performed most accurately in parallel folds, and with the folds being parallel to the grain of the paper. The lithographic press requires grain of paper to be parallel to the length of the cylinder, a requirement that does not always agree with the needs of the binder. Sometimes a change in plans must be made, or a compromise between printing and binding needs must be struck. Book and coated papers of 45 lb. to 60 lb. weight can be folded in 32-page signatures; in the case of many papers even 70 lb. stock can be folded as 32-page units. Lighter papers may be able to be folded as 64-page units, heavier paper should be limited for folding to 16-page sections.

Slitting and Chopping. As previously mentioned, folded signatures can be slit on buckle folders. Slitting can be compared to chopping; there are devices which can even accomplish a double slit or trim comparable to the cutting of bleeding pages on guillotine cutters. With this apparatus, folders or leaflets can be run in multiples of two or more, and trimmed to finished size on the folding machines. Pasting of a booklet of 8 or 12 pages can also be accomplished on buckle folders equipped for this type of work.

TIPPING OF END PAPERS, GATHERING AND STRIPPING

Tipping of end papers is our next subject. At times end papers are required in pamphlet binding; these are usually four pages of blank or printed stock which are tipped to the first and last leaf of the book. The cover of the book is later glued or pasted to the first end leaf at the front of the book and the last end leaf at the end of the book. Again tipping can be accomplished by hand or machine. Tipping is usually performed before gathering.

Gathering. Gathering is used for binding of bodies consisting of several independent signatures. When books become thicker than ¼ inch, it becomes impractical and awkward to fasten the sections together through their center. A method of binding must be resorted to which binds the books with the sections lying flat on top of each other in the proper sequence.

Manual and Mechanical Gathering. Gathering can be done by hand or mechanically. If done mechanically, the machinery can be so arranged to just gather and do subsequent operations later. In the case of side wiring and adhesive binding, the books are fed right into the side wire and covering machines or the perfect binder.

Stripping. Stripping is the name of an operation in which a length of cloth is applied to the edge or center of a piece of paper or is wrapped around the edge of the binding of a book overlapping the front and back cover. Stripping is used for two purposes, for reinforcing and for decoration. In the case of stripping end papers on their edge or down their center, the purpose of stripping is to reinforce the paper against strain of wire stitching or singer sewing.

In the case of stripping books along their backbone, the strip is fastened from the front cover, around the backbone into the back cover.

The Function of Stripping for Side Wired and Singer Sewed Books. For side wired books the strip covers the wire and the backbone and is mostly decorative even though it also reinforces the cover at its flexing line. In the case of saddle singer sewed and side singer sewed books the strip not only serves for decorative purposes but also helps to secure the lock stitch.

BINDING

Our discussion of binding is divided into the following three major points: (1) Saddle wiring, (2) Side wiring, and (3) Smyth sewing. Each of these is now discussed, sometimes under several headings.

Saddle Wiring. Saddle wiring, also known as saddle stitching, is a method of binding that produces books bound from the backbone through the center. The number of wire stitches that are put in a book depends on the nature of the job; three stitches are very often considered sufficient.

Wire Used for Saddle Wiring. The wire used for saddle wiring is usually galvanized, tinned or lacquered metal, from 28 gage up to 25 gage. It comes in five-pound spools. (The higher the gage number the thinner the wire). Heavier wire can be used with specially constructed machinery.

Equipment for Saddle Wiring. Saddle wiring can be done on very diversified machinery. The most simple equipment for saddle wiring is foot-operated; it has a single wiring head and the book is placed by hand on the saddle. On the other end of the equipment side we find completely automatic machines that feed the book sections, open them, reject improperly assembled books, and stitch them automatically. Between these two extremes a variety of saddle wiring equipment is available. A description of this variety is far beyond the frame of this article. It must suffice to mention some of the best known names in the field such as Christensen, Rossback, McCain and Sheridan.

Side Wiring. Side wiring is the name of the operation which describes the binding of books by driving two or more wire stitches through the side of the book, about ⅛″ away from its backbone. Round or flat wire can be used; round wire is employed in gages from 28 to 18, flat wire in sizes 21 x 25, to 18 x 20. The smaller the numbers the thicker the wire.

The Construction of the Wire. It is interesting to note that the flat wire has one dimension thicker than the other. The wider dimension adds strength, the thinner dimension reduces the bulk of the wire and therewith the hazard of forcing the wire through the cover of the book.

Various Procedures in Side Wiring. Side wiring can be accomplished by gathering the book by hand and then feeding it into a wire stitching machine with a single head, which machine is operated by a foot treadle. Books stitched in this manner are usually glued on the backbone and have a cover applied. For larger jobs, however, automatic machines are used. These machines automatically gather the sections and feed the books into a stitching mechanism and onto a covering machine which also automatically applies glue to the backbone and finally the cover. The speeds of these automatic machines range from 2,500 books per hour up to 6,000 and possibly even 8,000 books per hour.

Covering Side Wired Books. The side wired book is the strongest and most economical binding for a square backed book. If the coverstock is light enough and the grain of cover parallel to the binding, it is not necessary to score the covers; however, it is well to check this before proceeding with the cover operation, as scoring may be necessary to produce a good job. An alternate way to cover a book is to use single leaf cover that can be stitched in front and in back of the text together with the stitching of the text. A cloth strip can then be used in this case for covering the stitches as well as the backbone of the book.

The Drawbacks of Side Stitching. Side stitching has several drawbacks, primarily that it does not produce a flat opening book and that the stitches may press through the cover and thereby spoil its attractiveness. Side singer sewing is a little softer and more flexible. Side sewing is done on specially built sewing machines which produce a lock stitch. The books are then usually stripped with cloth as described above.

Smyth Sewing. Smyth sewing is another method of binding the gathered sections together. Sections are fed individually opened to their center in rotation (back section first) into smyth sewing machines. The product of this machine comes out in an endless stream which is cut apart into individual books.

Smashing of Smyth Sewn Books. Smyth sewn books are in a loose, soft shape and must be run through a machine which applies compression known as a smasher — to solidify the books and to give them a firm straight shape. In smashing books that have been printed by offset lithography, it is important that the first book be checked for offsetting of the ink from page to page as some offset inks powder on the surface and transfer this powder under the pressure of smashing.

Covering of Books. After sewing and smashing, the books are either covered by hand or by machine by gluing off the backbone and applying a cover. Many times end leaves are tipped and the covers are not only glued to the backbone but to the front and back end leaf as well. Other times a ribbon of glue about ¼″ wide is applied parallel to the backbone on the first and on the last leaf of the book. The cover is scored with four scores. The two center scores fit the backbone and the first and last score allow the cover to adhere to the extra glue applied and hinge just past this point. This is known as *cover gluing with hinge front and back*. Side wired books can also be hinged which not only gives the cover greater strength but also covers the unsightly stitch.

Smyth Sewing and Side Wiring. Smyth sewing is a more expensive binding than side wiring but is preferred for its flexibility and strength. The flat opening feature of the book so produced is highly desirable.

Adhesive Binding. A type of binding which is becoming very popular due to its economy and flexibility is known as adhesive binding. Adhesive binding can be defined as a method of binding books with adhesive or glue as the only binding medium — no thread or wire is used. The common pad was the forerunner of our present adhesive bound books.

The Origin of Perfect Binding. The Sheridan Machine Company designed and built a machine which bound books in the adhesive method mechanically at high speeds. They named the machine the "Perfect Binder" and the process was called perfect binding. Telephone books were bound in this method for many years. More recently this method has been adopted to the general run of paper backed books.

Points to be Checked When Using Adhesive Binding. For a time only certain book papers could be used but at the present time processes have been devised in which even the impossible coated stocks can be bound either by themselves or in conjunction with book papers. The process today is generally accepted in popular use. However before proceeding with an adhesive bound job it is good practice to check with the firm who is to do the job and see if the book size, type of paper and grain of paper are properly balanced for best results.

TRIMMING

The last major operation in the manufacturing of pamphlet bound books is trimming. By definition, trimming means to trim (or cut) the head, front and bottom of the book to a predetermined size. This produces open single sheets on these three sides and thereby opens the folds and also straightens the irregularities of the folded sheets. There can be other specifications in trimming, such as trim front only, or trim head only, or trim 4 sides — which produces single leaves suitable for mechanical binding or looseleaf binding.

Trimming on Guillotine Cutters. For many years trimming was done exclusively on straight knife guillotine cutters similar to those used for sheet cutting. Of course, the smaller sizes such as a 40-inch cutter, are preferred for this operation because the cutter has less stretching to do from the left side of the machine to its middle and right. Most, if not all guillotine cutters have back gages which can be split or separated in 2 places producing 3 separate gages. The gage at left is usually set to cut off the tail, the middle gage to cut the front, and the right hand gage cuts the head of the book off. Books are usually cut in lifts of 15 to 100 books depending on the trim size and thickness of the books involved.

Specifying the Size of a Book. When specifying trim size the width of the book is mentioned first and the height second. A book 6″ wide and 9″ high would be 6 x 9 and an oblong book 9″ wide and 6″ high would be 9 x 6.

Three Knife Trimmers. To get greater production, a machine was first invented capable of cutting two sides at a time, known as duplex cutters. After the duplex came a machine that could cut three sides at a time — the three knife trimmers. The three knife trimmers have proven very successful. They have been further developed with a view to making their feeding a continuous operation. In modern three knife trimmers, untrimmed books are fed from one side and the trimmed ones are delivered on the other side. The operator merely feeds the untrimmed books; the finished product and the waste trim are removed automatically.

The Single Book Trimmer. In recent years the single book trimmer has been introduced. This is a trimming mechanism that is attached to the stitcher or covering machine that trims the books one at a time or in multiples of two or three depending on the way in which the books are delivered by the binding mechanism.

Packing and Shipping. After trimming, the books must be readied for shipping. Many times the books are merely piled in an interlocking pattern on a wooden skid and banded with steel strapping. At other times the books are bundled in bulk packages of about 30 to 50 pounds. A further method of packaging is to band or bundle the books in small units and then place them into cartons of 30 to 50 pounds for bulk delivery.

Preparing of Catalogs and Periodicals for Mailing. Catalogs or periodicals are usually mailed in wrappers, envelopes or by merely affixing an addressed label. U. S. Postal Laws require sorting, mailing, tying, and placing into mailbags, according to very strict regulations. It is necessary to check these rules carefully at the first mailing of such a job.

AUXILIARY BINDERY OPERATIONS

Many times a pamphlet bindery is called upon to perform a variety of auxiliary operations, for example round cornering, drilling, punching, collating, and padding. These auxiliary operations are also known in the trade as manifold binding operations. In addition to the first group of manifold operations, pamphlet binderies may render such services as silk stitching, eyeleting, staining of edges, and applying of tassels. The most important manifold binding operations are briefly discussed in the following.

Round Cornering. Round cornering is usually done after trimming. It is applied to books which must stand much handling over a long period of time and where the square edge may become excessively dog-eared. There are four types of machines which perform this operation. One type of round cornering machines is foot powered, having a knife that cuts through the paper pile down into a wooden block; there is also a motor-powered machine of the same design. Then, there is a foot-powered machine in which the knife passes through the pile and past a female die which is used instead of the wooden block; the same type of machine is also available with an electric motor.

Round cornering machines do not usually have the same power or produce as neat an edge as a paper cutter. The size of the book determines the size of the radius to be used; larger books usually need a larger corner. Customarily only the top and bottom corner of the page opposite the binding edge are rounded; there are, however, instances — especially in looseleaf work — where all four corners are rounded.

Drilling of Paper. Paper drills make one or more hollow round holes from $\frac{1}{8}$-inch diameter to $\frac{1}{2}$-inch diameter in a lift of paper or a book. Drilling is accomplished by machines, with a single or multiple spindle drill. The number of holes and their spacing is very important. The number of holes, their diameter, and center distance from each hole is all that the binder needs to know. The distance of the hole from the edge or backbone is usually $\frac{1}{8}$-inch to $\frac{3}{16}$-inch. For example three $\frac{1}{4}$-inch holes, $4\frac{1}{4}″$ center to center, is a specification indicating size and distance of three holes as used for the standard $8\frac{1}{2}$ x 11 inch looseleaf binder. For smaller jobs a single spindle drill with multiple gages or a moving gage with multiple stops is sufficient. However, for larger volume work a drill with 3 or more spindles moving through the stock simultaneously is quite necessary.

Paper Punching. Punching is the operation in which a set of male and female dies is used to produce either round, slotted, elongated, or special shape holes in a lift of paper or books. Paper punching is done in special type punch presses designed especially for this purpose. The usual lift for punching is $\frac{1}{8}$ inch to $\frac{3}{8}$ inch; two or more holes are punched simultaneously. For every special shape, a different set of punching dies must be used. Paper punching is needed for making of holes as required in various looseleaf binding devices. Examples for these holes are the specially designed and popular type punched holes such as the *slotted* hole and the *Kalamazoo* hole.

Collating. Collating is the operation in which single sheets or leaves are gathered in sequence. A very frequent collating job consists in putting carbon leaves between printed leaves.

Padding of Paper. In padding, sheets are first counted into lifts of a given number, then a piece of chip board or other stiff divider is placed at the bottom of each lift; thereafter a type of flexible animal or synthetic glue is applied to the binding edge of the stack of materials. The glue or adhesive must be flexible and also release the sheet easily when the user removes a leaf from the rest of the pad. A frequently used padding technique consists in first applying a layer of glue, then a piece of cheesecloth, and then a second layer of glue. Padding is usually accomplished in large or high piles of multiples of two or more pads. The pads are stacked and glued-off. After drying the pads are cut apart by hand with a thin knife and then trimmed to size on the paper cutter.

Summary. Pamphlet binding, as you can easily see, covers a large range of operations which must be skillfully performed at high speeds either by machine or by hand. Although pamphlet binding is one of the last skills to be applied in the producing of a leaflet or book, this type of work entails an even greater responsibility than that of the preceding crafts. It can be said that pamphlet binding is a very responsible finishing operation; if done properly the printed job is finished nicely, and if not done properly the printed job may suffer greatly or even be destroyed. It is wise to consult with the person in charge of pamphlet binding in the planning stages of a lithographic job in order to utilize the various processes to their fullest and to avoid pitfalls that cannot be rectified once they are made.

Section Two: Mechanical and Looseleaf Binding

Our discussion of mechanical binding and looseleaf binding is divided into the following seven points: (1) General exposition of specialty binding, (2) Mechanical binding devices, (3) Looseleaf binding devices, (4) Covers for mechanical and looseleaf bindings, (5) Binding procedures for mechanical and for looseleaf binding, (6) Miscellaneous specialties, (7) The end use and products of mechanical and looseleaf binding. Each of these points is individually taken up in the following.

GENERAL EXPOSITION OF SPECIALTY BINDING

Mechanical binding and looseleaf binding are commonly considered in the graphic arts industry as a field of activity reserved for the "special or specialty" bindery. Few lithographers include mechanical binding and looseleaf binding in their own production activities, even if they maintain their own bindery department. Specialty binderies overlap to some extent with pamphlet binderies and with edition binderies, though less in their products and services than in some of the equipment used. In this section of our bindery chapter we present the multitude of specialty binding devices, procedures and products; pamphlet binding is discussed in the preceding section of this chapter, edition binding in the section following our presentation.

MECHANICAL BINDING AND LOOSELEAF BINDING; CLARIFICATION OF TERMS

Mechanical Binding and Looseleaf Binding are terms applied to both a number of mechanisms or devices for, and their utilization in, the binding of pamphlets and books. "Spiral" binding and "Plastic" binding are probably the first names that come to one's mind as mechanical bindings. Mechanical bindings are for the most part permanent bindings that do not permit ready changing of the bound material. Looseleaf bindings are also permanent but they do permit changing of the bound material, as they can be opened for the insertion or removal of pages. The three-ring binder and the post binder are familiar examples of looseleaf binding.

Division of the Field. Some general trade binderies offer the lithographer one or the other of the many existing mechanical and looseleaf binding types. In some instances, lithographic plants maintain their own specialized mechanical binding departments, but even these rarely have their own looseleaf binding facilities. Our types of binding are essential to the main stream of business, but their use is sporadic rather than continuous or regular. As in other similar cases the rendering of these services has become a specialized business with highly specialized production facilities and equally specialized know-how.

Hand Equipment for Dummy Making. Powered production facilities for mechanical binding are rarely found in lithographic plants other than those producing children's books and stationery items. If mechanical binding equipment is used at all by the average lithographic company, it is of a different kind and for a different purpose. Hand-operated desk-top style punching and inserting equipment for certain plastic devices, designed for office use, are also used in litho plants, for dummy making primarily.

The Purpose of Our Presentation. The variety of services and products for which our types of binding are essential is discussed later on in this section. Here, we merely mention that looseleaf and mechanical bindings are very often used in conjunction with lithography. It is therefore advantageous for the commercial lithographer, his art and sales staff in particular, to be well versed in our subject. Many a lithographic job has been placed and will be placed with the lithographer who is capable of assisting his customer in the planning and selecting of the most suitable kind of specialty binding.

MECHANICAL BINDING DEVICES

Our discussion of mechanical binding devices is divided into the following five points: (1) Definition of mechanical binding devices, (2) Spiral binding devices, (3) Comb plastic binding devices, (4) Closed-ring binding devices, and (5) Individual ring binding devices. Each of these is discussed in the following.

Kamket,

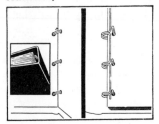

Continuous single wire forms series of equidistant, interconnected rings with open prongs. Wire passes through round holes, paper strip, or other material, not through cover, and is fastened on inside of back cover so that the two covers are integral for flat opening at any page. Pages are removable when prongs are held vertically; prongs are concealed when book is in use. Five sizes, nickel or enameled wire, wholly hidden. Multiple grip features frequency of rings (9- to 11-inch binding length), minimizes lost or torn sheets, binds sheets of different sizes, allows book to double back.

Minimum binding edge......... 3"
Maximum binding edge......... 24"
Maximum book thickness........ 13/16"

Spiralastic

Plastic spiral formed from continuous plastic filament. Available in numerous colors and gauges in exposed, semi-concealed, and concealed styles. Its resistance to breakage and combination of attractive appearance and mechanical strength makes it particularly adaptable to catalogs, manuscripts, portfolios, and easel presentations.

Minimum binding edge............ 1"
Maximum binding edge............ 30"
Maximum book thickness............ 1½"

Cerlox

Rings of colored plastic connected by thin backbone. Loose-leaf slot punching allows insertion of sheets easily. Back-to-back turning at any page. Diameters: 3/16" through ⅝". Used with one-piece (wrap-around) or two-piece covers of flexible or stiff material, cut flush or extended. Full length, dual, or multiple binding styles. Available in a wide variety of striking colors.

Minimum binding edge............ Any
Maximum binding edge............ Any
Maximum book thickness............ 4"

Cercla

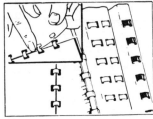

Smooth-edged, colored metal rings connected by flat backbone. Rectangular punch holes for permanent binding, or slot punch holes for loose-leaf use. Twelve standard colors and metal finishes. Diameters: 3/16" through 1". Can be used with wrap-around (one-piece), or two-piece paper, or case-made covers. Dual style, using two short binding elements, permits printing on backbone and adds to visible area of double spreads. With binding through back of one-piece cover (square back style), full backbone imprinting is possible.

Minimum binding edge............. Any
Maximum binding edge............. Any
Maximum book thickness........... Any

Examples of mechanical and loose-leaf bindings. Shown by courtesy of the Ninth Graphic Arts Yearbook; copyright 1950, Colton Press, Inc.

Tauber multi-ring

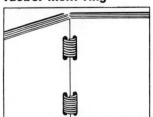

Short, closely wound plastic coils that fit standard Tauber slot holes. Rings are spun into place without machinery. A number of rings may be used; many colors and sizes available. Pages stay in perfect alignment.

Minimum binding edge............. Any
Maximum binding edge............. Any
Maximum book thickness........... 1"

Wire-o

Series of double wire loops formed from single continuous steel or brass wire run through longitudinal slots along back of book. Double-cover type leaves binding exposed; single conceals partly. Binding can be completely concealed by wiring book into lining for paste-down sheet (semi-exposed style), then using as limp or stiff cover, fast-bound, or loose-leaf, through slotted holes. Pages lie flat in perfect alignment, turn back to back. Binding can be omitted at top, bottom or center. Lacquered wire, nine regular, nine metallic shades.

Minimum binding edge............. Any
Maximum binding edge............. Any
Maximum book thickness........... Any

Spiral

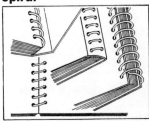

Plated wires in spiral form run through round holes punched along back. Exposed, semi-exposed, and concealed styles available in brass, bronze, copper, aluminum, and other wire. Semi-concealed type uses one-piece cover; in concealed style, wire passes through separate strip of material fastened to inside of back cover, not through cover. Both allow printing on backbone. Books 3 to 4 inches thick are bound by double Spiral, and double and triple interconnected Spiral bindings are used for thicker books.

Minimum binding edge............. 1"
Maximum binding edge............. 30"
Maximum book thickness............ 2"

Mult-o

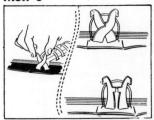

Loose-leaf, multiple metal rings spaced every half inch. Pages lie flat in perfect alignment, can be removed without disturbing other sheets. In opening, rings split in middle by pressing top levers toward each other, close by pressing bottom levers toward each other.

Minimum binding edge............. Any
Maximum binding edge............. Any
Maximum book thickness........... 1"

DEFINITION OF MECHANICAL BINDING DEVICES

A mechanical binding device is a device or mechanism made of wire, flat metal or plastic, and formed into a ring shape. Dozens of mechanical binding devices have appeared on the market since the early 1930's when mechanical binding devices were first used in this country, but only a few of this number have survived the competitive race. In spite of the great variety of existing trade names we distinguish only four basic types of mechanical binding, as presented in the following.

Spiral Binding Devices. The corkscrew or spring coil form, accurately called "spiral" binding, is perhaps the oldest and certainly the most familiar form of all mechanical binding devices. Nickel-plated wire is standard; brass, stainless steel and spirally-coiled plastic filament are minor variations.

Comb Plastic Binding Devices. Most of the bindings known as "plastic" consist of a piece of rigid vinyl plastic sheet, diecut in the shape of a comb or rake. When this device is formed into a ring, the teeth are rolled backwards and tucked under the backbone. Relatively minor design variations in the shape of the diecut are of no great concern, but variations in the spacing of the rings are significant and must be closely observed.

Closed-Ring Binding Devices. "Wire-O" and "Cercla" binding are examples of closed-ring bindings. "Wire-O" has continuously connected parallel wire loops; "Cercla" binding features enameled metal rings connected by a backbone. Both of these devices must be crimped after insertion of sheets. Crimping closes these bindings securely by forming a complete ring and therewith a permanent binding. "KamKet," a variation of this type, is designed to remain partially open with the opening concealed by a flap adhered to the back cover, thus offering a limited looseleaf feature. The sheets in "KamKet" may be inserted or removed as in a post binder. "Slide Ring," discussed under "Plastic Looseleaf" below, has similar attributes.

Individual Ring Binding Devices. Several varieties of individual rings are available. One ring is made of tightly-coiled spiral plastic; another is a self-locking flat plastic band. The "closed-ring" and the "comb" types of rings, conventionally used in full length along the binding edge of the book, may also be used in two- or three-ring sections. Spaced along the binding edge, ring sections provide a usable result at lower cost of material, but require more labor for insertion.

LOOSELEAF BINDING DEVICES

Our presentation of looseleaf binding devices is divided into the following five points: (1) Definition of looseleaf binding devices, (2) Ring binders, (3) Post binders, (4) Plastic looseleaf binding devices, and (5) Miscellaneous looseleaf binding devices. Each of these points is discussed in the following.

Definition of Looseleaf Binding Devices. A looseleaf binding is a device so constructed as to permit the addition or removal of pages. Within this broad definition there is a range of mechanisms from extremely simple rings, posts and brass fasteners at one end of the spectrum to complex metal hardware weighing several pounds at the other.

The relationship of the binding device to its covers is the critical point of difference between mechanical and looseleaf binding devices. For the most part mechanical binding devices are made, sold and used independently of the cover. In looseleaf binding, on the other hand, the cover and the binding are fabricated and sold together, as one unit. A looseleaf device is, almost without exception, riveted or locked into the cover in some way.

Ring Binders. There are many varieties of the basic looseleaf mechanism, which can be described as follows: A metal housing conceals wire rods or steel plates held in tension. Heavy wire rings which open in the center are attached to this housing. The rings open in the center. The binding may therefore be opened at any page for making a change in the bound material without disturbing the sequence of the already bound leaves. Ring binders are available in a variety of opening mechanisms as well as in the shape, finish and spacing of their rings.

Post Binders. Binding posts range in complexity from simple screw posts to heavy-duty compression-expansion type posts. Small screw posts can be used similar to brass fasteners. In such cases they are not permanently attached to a cover but simply inserted into the punch and scored material. The brass "Tang" fasteners too are post binders; they are often riveted permanently into the cover.

Screw posts are often used together with very heavyweight covers — made of several layers of various materials, board, paper and cloth — whereas fasteners, being much lighter than screw posts, are rarely used in heavy covers.

Plastic Looseleaf Binding Devices. The "Slide Binder" is a looseleaf binding device similar in finished appearance to mechanical binding devices. The "Slide Binder" offers some of the advantages of both the heavy-duty looseleaf binding device and the light-weight plastic binding. A colorful backbone provides a track into which slides a separate connected comb of semicircular teeth. Changes in the bound material may be made fairly quickly and easily.

Miscellaneous Looseleaf Binding Devices. Spring-back binders, rod binders, blade binders, lace-and-strap binders, parallel-prong binders are among the many looseleaf binding devices available for specialized purposes. Here the hardware — as the trade calls the binding devices themselves — is so specialized that its description would go way beyond the frame of this study.

Rather than trying to find his way through the thicket of these specialized products, the lithographer will better rely on the advice of an experienced and reputable specialty bindery in solving problems requiring such highly specialized binding devices.

COVERS FOR MECHANICAL AND LOOSELEAF BINDING

The covers used on mechanically bound and looseleaf bound books include every kind of cover material used on

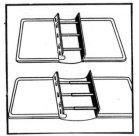

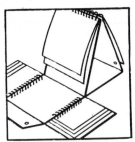

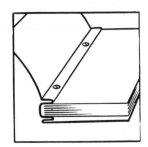

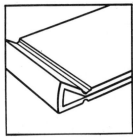

Expansion post. Construction and operation are similar to the quick action angle back, but the cover is all in one piece. Telescoping posts and curved back allow for expansion and removable "L" shaped transfer bar facilitates changing of sheets. Binding mechanism is attached to the back of the book, rather than the covers, eliminating the crease which is found in the covers of many notebooks. Capacity is from 2″ to 3″.

Sales accelerator display unit. This may consist of a combination of single or double vision display binders, on the front edge of which may be hinged one or two data books or sample books that deal with the illustrations on the easel. For instance, the main easel might include pictures of a new automobile while the small books on the front section may contain color chips on one side and upholstery samples on the other.

Tongue, case bound. Consists of a continuous cover having two tongues that are either sewed or glued into the book cover. These tongues in turn are punched and equipped with the fastening devices as described above. Case-bound tongue binders are usually covered in artificial leather, book cloth, or genuine leather. While they are made in capacities up to several inches, they are more practical only up to a capacity of 1″.

Spring back sheet holders. Constructed with a spring style round back that can be sprung apart for inserting sheets between the open jaws, which when released clamp the sheets without the necessity of punching. This style is much used for holding bulletins, magazines, and the like.

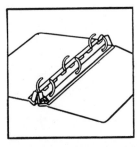

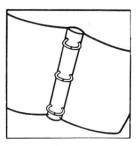

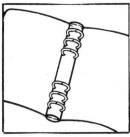

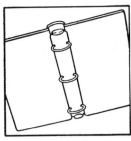

Prong—1″, 1½″, 2″, and 3″. This is the most versatile, as well as the most durable, type of loose-leaf binder, having a multiplicity of half-round arcs or prongs anchored into hinged metal angles of steel. Equipped with a second stage opening for flat writing.

Cut flush ring ½″ to 1¼″. About the least expensive style of loose-leaf binder having two or more rings, with or without a mechanism for springing open the rings. Metal assembly is riveted or fastened with a backplate to a scored cover of material such as cover stock, one-piece artificial or genuine leather, or Lexide cover.

Memo ring. The same as the cut flush or case bound except that the capacities are smaller, running from ¼″ to 1″, and the rings are usually grouped in sets of three at either end of the metal housing.

Case bound ring ½″ to 1¼″. The same general style as in the cut flush ring binder except that the cover material, being of paper, cloth, artificial leather, or genuine leather, is bound over stiff or flexible boards. Backplate that holds metal mechanism is bound into cover, then lined with additional piece of material on the inside.

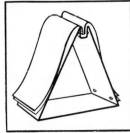

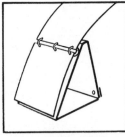

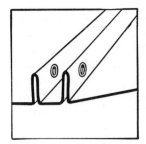

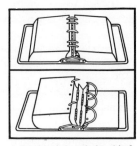

Easel, single vision display. Stands up in triangular form. The visible sheets lie on the top of the triangle while the used sheets flop over the top and lie on the back triangle. This binder folds up neatly and compactly for carrying. It may also have a binding mechanism such as tongues, rings, etc.

Easel, double vision display. General construction is the same as that of the single vision except that a prop supports the sheets one above the other, so that descriptive literature may be displayed on the top sheet while the lower sheet shows photographs, blueprints, etc.

Tongue, one-piece, six score. This is one piece of cover stock or Lexide material with 5, 6, or 7 scores and folded to form tongues. The fastening devices and materials are the same as for Simplex. Tongues or stubs may be stitched or eyeletted together when desired.

Double jointed ring binder. Rings are complete arcs—not jointed in the middle. Sheets are always impaled on two or more prongs. Entire sheet body can be accommodated on either side of rings. Maximum book thickness 3″.

Examples of mechanical and looseleaf bindings. **Shown by courtesy of the** *Ninth Graphic Arts Yearbook;* copyright 1950, Colton Press, Inc.

all conventional bindings and, in addition, some unconventional materials.

Our discussion of covers is divided into the following points: (1) Paper covers for mechanical binding, (2) Board covers for mechanical binding, and (3) Covers for looseleaf binding. Each of these points is now presented.

Paper Covers for Mechanical Binding. A considerable range of cover treatments may be used in connection with mechanical binding. The self-covered style, where cover and inside pages are printed together on the same paper, is perhaps less popular for mechanical binding jobs than the coverstock cover. Coverweight paper is available in a great variety and is very well suited for lithographing.

Coverstock covers can be of two kinds, either "two-piece" covers, or "semi-concealed" covers. Two-piece covers consist of a separate front and back cover; semi-concealed covers are one-piece covers that are scored and slotted or punched for combining with the mechanical binding device forming the backbone of the bound units.

Board Covers for Mechanical Binding. Board covers such as those usually associated with edition binding and with looseleaf binding are also used with mechanical bindings. These covers may be two-piece, semi-concealed or fully concealed; the two-piece and the semi-concealed cover are discussed in the preceding paragraph. In the fully concealed cover, the closed bound book gives no hint of the binding method used.

Paper may be used in various ways on board covers, either mounted to and wrapped over the edges of the board, or in combination with cloth; book cloth, or one of the many types of imitation leather may of course be used over boards. Paper and book cloth are frequently lithographed.

Covers for Looseleaf Binding. Like the heavy-duty covers for mechanical binding described above and the covers of edition bound books, looseleaf binders too, may be made of lithographed coverweight paper covers or of lithographed book cloth. Combinations, such as a cloth backbone with printed paper over board sides, (called "quarter bound") and covers made with cellophane or other films laminated to paper and used over board without cloth reinforcement, represent a growing use of lithographed paper for looseleaf and mechanically bound books.

The quality of reproduction obtainable by lithography on book cloth competes strongly with the conventional gold-stamped leather or imitation leather-covered looseleaf binder. This technique has so far had its greatest volume of application for edition bound books, but it is beginning to make progress in the mechanical and looseleaf binding field.

BINDING PROCEDURES FOR MECHANICAL AND FOR LOOSELEAF BINDING

In this unit the reader finds a description of the most important steps taken in mechanical and looseleaf binding. These steps are more or less the same for both methods up to the point of inserting the material to be bound, where different procedures are used for each of the two. Our presentation is divided into the following seven points: (1) Selecting the binding device, (2) Folding, gathering, collating and trimming, (3) Punching, (4) Combining the material to be bound with the cover, (5) Inserting the mechanical binding into the material, (6) Inserting the material into the looseleaf binding, (7) Miscellaneous subsidiary operations. Each of these points is discussed in the following.

Selecting the Binding Device. Mechanical binding devices are at this time freely sold on the market. Earlier in the development phase of mechanical binding, the devices were only available on a license basis. Three plastic mechanical binding devices are also offered as desk-top or office-style units for limited production.

All mechanical binding devices with the exception of spiral wire are supplied as formed mechanisms to the specialty bindery by the manufacturers of these devices. Spiral wire is customarily turned into its proper size by the bindery from a spool of raw wire of the proper temper by a specially designed wire-forming die assembly.

The variety of available looseleaf binding devices is considerable. The manufacturers of the devices publish detailed catalogues for the information of looseleaf binderies. These, in turn, offer a free consultation to their customers, who are very often lithographers. Such a consultation service is much better suited to the solution of concrete problems than a blanket offering of the whole bewildering and confusing variety of existing looseleaf devices.

Folding, Gathering, Collating and Trimming. Pages for the book must be put into sequence before binding. Conventionally folded signatures are gathered, and trimmed on four sides. One of the great advantages of mechanical binding is a great freedom of the limitations imposed by the folded signature. In mechanical and looseleaf binding one can mix paper stocks, press runs and even page sizes at will by working with individual sheets rather than with folded signatures. Often pages are simply trimmed and collated without previous folding and gathering.

Punching. For all mechanical binding devices, and for all looseleaf devices with two minor exceptions, the sheets to be bound must be punched or drilled with holes. Holes may be round, square or oblong; they may be placed at varying distances from the edge of the sheet, and aligned in various spacings according to the specific requirements of each of the various binding mechanisms.

For all multi-ring devices, it is most efficient to *punch* round holes rather than to drill them. All square and oblong holes must of course be punched. All punching of holes is done with specially engineered punching dies in heavy, power-driven punching machines. For mechanical bindings, each mechanism has its own characteristic hole and thus requires special punching with specially designed dies. There is practically no multiple use possible of punching dies for more than one type of binding mechanism.

Two looseleaf mechanisms operate without punched sheets: (1) the Spring-Back Binder — which tightly clamps individual sheets, and (2) the Magazine Binder whose rods or wires are threaded through folded signatures or side-wire stitched booklets.

Combining the Material to be Bound with the Cover. This stop is a hand operation in mechanical binding. Except in the case of self-covered books, covers frequently require a heavier weight of paper and often are slightly larger — to overhang and thus protect the inside sheets. Consequently, such covers are not collated with the sheets but are combined with them as a separate step immediately before the binding insertion stage.

Inserting the Mechanical Binding into the Material. Each type of the mechanical bindings is inserted into the sheets in a distinct way. The "Slide Ring" and the individual plastic rings are hand-inserted into the punched sheets, and the assembly is then also completed by hand. The closed-ring devices "Cercla" and "Wire-O" are inserted into the sheets by hand but closed mechanically. After inserting, the edge of the book with the still open binding mechanism already in place is put into a closing die which crimps the metal or wire band of rings into its final circular shape.

The plastic rings, Plastico and G.B.C.-Cerlox, are inserted into the punched holes by means of a device which grasps the rolled-up comb and pulls back the teeth to an "open" position. This permits the operator to place the punched sheets in position onto the teeth. Then the binding device is released and it takes its final from.

"Spiral Binding" is inserted into the pre-punched holes like a corkscrew is driven into the cork of a wine bottle. The wire has been previously formed into coils of the proper diameter and pitch and was cut into a length somewhat longer than the binding edge of the book. The spiral coil can be inserted by hand, but in practice two methods are used: (1) The coiled wire is inserted by hand into the book for a distance of two or three inches. Then the book is held against a rapidly revolving rubber roller and the balance of the wire is thereby automatially pulled through. Thereafter the excess wire is trimmed off, and the ends of the coil are turned inward. (2) Automatic insertion machines continuously form wire into the proper diameter and pitch, and may cut it off if desired in lengths of about five or six feet. The operator starts a long length of wire into the inserting machine, places a punched book with its covers into position in the machine, and the machine automatically threads the wire, and trims it, and turns in the ends without waste. The machine is automatic and merely guided by the operator.

Inserting the Material into the Looseleaf Binding. In all cases of looseleaf binding the punched or drilled pages, collated into the proper sequence together with index tab dividers etc., are hand-inserted into the looseleaf binder. In the case of the true looseleaf metal mechanism, a quick opening and closing action permits fast inserting. With the post and fastener looseleaf binding devices things go much more slowly; there a painstaking hand operation is required to insert the pages into the binder.

Miscellaneous Subsidiary Operations. In a well-equipped bindery we find an array of equipment for cutting, tabbing, diecutting, scoring, glueing, tipping, mounting, hinging, stripping, riveting, and eyeletting. These tools and machines as well as a variety of glueing machines, gold-stamping and embossing presses can be found in many a specialty bindery. They are either necessary for, or supplementary to, the production of mechanically or looseleaf bound books.

MISCELLANEOUS SPECIALTIES

By the combined use of this variety of subsidiary equipment and binding mechanisms can be made a further category of products that can not be properly classified as books. These are the "specials" of the specialty bindery.

These "specials" need not only a lot of special equipment but even more special know-how and a fertile imagination on the part of the specialty bindery. Sales kits, salesmen's presentations, sample cases, portfolios that take the form of cases, boxes, easel bindery, flip charts, fold-overs, etc., are among the more common "specials." The lithographer, too, has his part in the making and creating of such specials. Covers, lining and inside matter of "specials" are very often lithographed.

THE END USE AND PRODUCTS OF MECHANICAL AND LOOSELEAF BINDING

The end product of mechanical and looseleaf binding is in most cases the result of printing as well as binding. A discussion of the market for bindery products is necessarily also a discussion of the market for printing and lithography. Our presentation is divided into the following four points: (1) Specialty binding for book publishing, (2) Specialty binding for stationery items, (3) Specialty binding for advertising, sales promotion and sales training, and (4) Specialty binding for packaging. Each of these fields is briefly discussed in the following.

Courtesy Sloves Mechanical Binding Co., Inc.

This illustration of five books shows a variety of applications of plastic ring and spiral wire bindings.

Courtesy Sloves Mechanical Binding Co., Inc.

The photo shows a Cercla bound easel binder at the left and a double spiral wire bound book at the right.

The application of mechanical binding to a fully concealed cover.

Specialty Binding for Book Publishing. Certain kinds of books are typically bound with mechanical and looseleaf bindings, others only occasionally. The following listing does not pretend to be complete but is rather indicative of the great variety and possibilities in the book publishing field for specialty binding: (1) Children's books, particularly the so-called "action books" invloving diecuts, wheels and pop-ups, etc. (2) Cookbooks, for which mechanical bindings are often specified because of their flat opening feature. Looseleaf devices are also often used for cookbooks because they permit the adding of new recipes. (3) "Workbooks" or the manuals that accompany technical courses in high school and college.

Specialty Binding for Stationery Items. This field is very highly specialized. Companies active in it often have their own complete production facilities including printing, lithographing, ruling and binding. Calendars of various types, stenographer's notebooks, record books and bookkeeping systems are some of the most commonly used items in this classification.

Specialty Binding for Advertising, Sales Promotion and Sales Training. For almost every conceivable business function in the advertising and sales promotion field there exists the possibility of application for mechanical and looseleaf binding. Manuals, price lists, catalogs, sales presentations and merchandising portfolios use both types of specialty binding. The only publication that is unlikely to appear in looseleaf form is the annual report.

Specialty Binding for Packaging. Specialty binding finds a growing market in the binding of books whose real function is to serve as a package rather than as a book. The record album is the best known but not the only example of this category. Here the book is designed to do three jobs: storing, protecting and last but not least, selling the packaged product. The combined skill of the lithographer and the specialty binder may result in the making of a powerful visual sales aid in this type of packaging.

Section Three: Case Binding*

Practically all rigidly or semi-rigidly bound books are "case" bound, denoting that the cover of the book has two distinctive characteristics. The cover is made separately from the book, and it consists of rigid or flexible boards covered with leather, leather substitutes, cloth, paper, or other material in such a manner that the covering material surrounds the outside as well as the edges of the board. In the bookbinder's language, this is known as covers turned over boards, and the covers always project beyond the edges of the pages.

Case binding can be conveniently divided into three different branches: (1) Edition binding; (2) Job binding; and (3) Library binding. These divisions consider both

quantity and nature of binding to be provided. Each is identified as follows:

Edition Binding. Edition binding is the manufacturing of new titles, or of reprints, in relatively large quantities. Edition binders handle jobs from 1,500 and up. Smaller runs are, generally speaking, more suitable for job binding. Edition binding uses semi-automatic or fully automatic equipment in preference to handwork.

Job Binding. Quantities that are either too small for edition binding, or that require by their very nature considerable amounts of handwork, are considered job binding. Bibles and prayer books, bound in limp leather, are an example of the kind of work referred to as job binding.

Library Binding. Library binding renders a variety of binding services to libraries, including the re-binding of

---

* Illustrations in this section are from "Plan For A Good Book," courtesy John F. Cuneo Co.

small lots of new books, or of individual books, so as to provide books of superior strength suitable for the wear and tear to which a book is exposed in public libraries. The binding of individual books includes keeping books in repair as well as the binding of magazines and other periodicals.

The following discussion is devoted to edition binding rather than job and library binding, because edition binding is the most interesting branch of case binding for the reader of *The Lithographers Manual*. Lithography plays an increasing role in book manufacturing. The text or illustrations of many books are printed by lithography; for others, lithography supplies the jackets and in some cases even the printing of the cover. Edition binding, with its comparatively large runs, is obviously more important to the lithographer than the other two branches which use lithography but very rarely.

EDITION BINDING

A case bound book consists mainly of the book itself (the printed matter) the case, and the end papers. End papers are four pages each at the beginning and at the end of a book, one leaf of each being solidly pasted against the inside board of each cover.

Head and tail bands are sometimes used to give a more finished look to the book by filling up the gap which normally forms between the spine or backbone of the book and its cover. These bands however, impart no additional strength in edition binding, and are merely glued or pasted onto the back as the book is lined-up.

Many books destined to be sold in bookstores are placed in a printed jacket which serves as a protector as well as an attention-getter. Sets of books, or very valuable tomes, are occasionally boxed in decorated slide boxes of varying design known as "slip" cases, if the book or books are inserted in such a manner that the backbone remains visible.

Edition binding involves a large number of different operations, divided somewhat loosely into five broad groups: (1) Sheetwork; (2) Forwarding; (3) Casemaking and stamping; (4) Casing-in; and (5) Inspecting, jacketing, packing and shipping.

Sheetwork. The term sheetwork is an all embracing title for all work in a bindery from the arrival of printed sheets until the books are sewn and trimmed.

Forwarding. The term forwarding denotes all operations on a book between trimming and covering or casing-in.

Casemaking and Stamping. Casemaking and stamping include all operations involved in the making and decorating of a case or book cover, up to the point where the case is ready for casing in.

The industry's language has not yet caught up with the recently growing trend of decorating covers by means other than flat stamping or embossing, other than to call such products "pre-printed." Such pre-printing of cover materials is being done by lithography, gravure, and silk screen.

Casing-In. Casing-in is the operation whereby the forwarded book and the completed case are assembled into one unit, the completely bound book.

Warehousing and Shipping. These include the variety of steps that must be taken before the bound book can finally be shipped.

Summary. Bookbinding can be compared to a stream that has two feeder rivers. One is sheetwork and forwarding, the other is casemaking. Both join at casing-in where the complete book is formed. In the following, each of the five main phases of bookbinding are presented in more detail.

SHEETWORK

As already mentioned, sheetwork comprises all operations up to and including assembling and joining together the signatures or sections, and trimming the three outer edges. But signatures can be bound in several techniques, and the steps to be taken in sheetwork differ somewhat for each of these different binding techniques.

For the purpose of our discussion, we might as well replace the term binding by a different and somewhat broader designation, and speak of uniting the printed matter into permanent and unchangeable book form. This different expression has become necessary by the technological changes that have taken place in this, as in all other industries, during recent years.

The classical manner of binding is sewing. Books can be sewn in two ways: Either adjacent to the binding edge, called side sewing; or through the center fold of each signature, called Smyth sewing. The term Smyth is derived from the brand name of the machine largely used in the United States for this kind of sewing, the Smyth sewing machine, and is a common term in the binding industry. A parallel term used years ago was Singer sewing, meaning side sewing. But in our times, the designation side sewing and McCain sewing have become current since the advent of the McCain-built machine.

Sewing is reserved for uniting signatures by means of thread; and if wire is used instead of thread, the term "stitching" is more often employed.

Stitching is done in two ways, either as saddle stitching or as side stitching. In saddle stitching, the stitches are made through the center of the folded signatures; but because only very few pages can be secured in such a manner, it is not prevalent in edition binding. In side stitching, the stitches are placed adjacent to the binding edge.

Uniting signature with glue or synthetic adhesives is a relatively modern form of binding, sometimes known as "perfect" binding or under various proprietary names. Each of these different binding techniques uses different equipment and requires certain changes in the sequence of operations.

After this general discussion of sewing, stitching, and uniting with adhesives, we turn to a step-by-step presentation of sheetwork.

The Main Steps of Sheetwork. Sheetwork requires a variety of different steps according to the specific requirements of each job. The most commonly used steps are: (1) Folding; (2) Cutting of large printed sheets containing inserts; (3) Reinforcing or tipping of end papers; (4) Inserting of illustrative material; (5) Gathering; (6) Sewing, stitching, or uniting with adhesive; (7) Nipping or smashing; and (8) Cutting or trimming.

Folding. Folding converts flat printed sheets into signatures, but is also used for end papers and certain kinds of inserts, such as single and multi-fold maps and statistical tables. A detailed discussion of folding machines being beyond the scope of this article, it is here merely stated that edition binding uses automatic, high speed folding machines capable of producing signatures of the desired page numbers. The term signatures is used for designating the sec-

Printed sheets are folded to make 8, 16, or 32 page sections.

tions of the book proper, and the number of pages in a signature depends on the nature of the job and particularly on the kind, weight and finish of the paper employed. Generally speaking, 8-page, 16-page, and 32-page signatures are commonly folded, and occasionally 64-page signatures are folded. The decision on the number of pages per signature is part of the planning of a book and *must* be arrived at in cooperation with the binder before the job is printed. This decision is expressed in the imposition selected for a particular job.

Cutting of Large Sheets Containing Inserts. In letterpress printed books, but also in those printed in lithography, illustrations — particularly color work — are often printed on one or several separate sheets rather than including them on the same sheet with the text pages. Such material is usually cut into single leaves or 4-page units, and combined with the rest of the book in several ways. Cutting these large printed sheets is a step preliminary to the inserting of such material, and is performed on straight or guillotine cutters.

Reinforcing or Tipping End Papers. End papers (sometimes called end linings or end sheets) are composed of 4 pages each at the beginning and end of the book, consisting of paper stock stronger and heavier than the text paper. They are sometimes plain white, and sometimes colored, or printed with maps and drawings characterizing the contents of the book. The first sheet of the front, and last sheet of the back end paper, are solidly pasted to the cover board extending beyond and covering up the raw edges of the turned-over cover material. The remaining sheet protects the first and last pages of the book.

End papers are either attached by tipping to the front

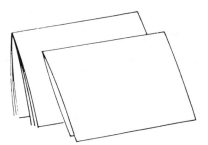

Endsheets of strong paper are tipped to first and last sections of book.

and back of the book, or they are reinforced by a separate strip of cloth or paper which is in turn glued and sewn to the first and last signature. Tipping as well as reinforcing of end papers is done by machine.

Inserting of Illustrative Material. The manner in which illustrative material is combined with the bulk of the book varies in accordance with position and style of binding. Individual leaves or 4-page units are the most common kinds of inserts. They are called "tip-ons" or "outside-tips" if they are attached to the outside of a signature; if they must be inserted into a signature they are known as "tip-ins" or "inside-tips." Outside-tips can be inserted mechanically. Inside-tips require the opening of the signature at the particular page before tipping, and both operations, the opening of the signature as well as the inside tipping, are done by hand.

Tipping is not the only way in which inserts can be bound in a book. Sometimes illustrations are planned for "jacketing." Jacketing in this sense means that a 4-page- or 8-page section is placed inside or over another section and bound without any additional tipping. In the case of side sewing or side stitching, and in that of uniting by means of adhesive, the step of placing the insert in its proper position completes the operation of inserting as these binding techniques obviate the necessity of tipping itself.

The sections are gathered in sequence to make a complete book.

Gathering. Gathering is the operation of assembling the component book sections or signatures into a complete book, and is mechanically executed in edition binding. The signatures of the book are placed in proper sequence into the pockets of the gathering machine, swinging arms remove each singly and drop it onto the advancing pile of a conveyor chain which delivers the completely assembled book into a hopper.

Sewing, Stitching or Uniting with Adhesives.
As already discussed in the introduction to sheetwork, binding distinguishes between Smyth sewing, side sewing, saddle and side stitching, and perfect binding or uniting with

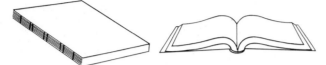

Smyth Sewn Book, open and closed.

adhesives. Smyth sewing is done on machines that operate in the following manner. The gathered signatures are each separately opened through the center, and saddle sewn with thread, using five or six needles. Each signature is not only sewn by itself, but also to each adjacent signature, the thread being continuous. After sewing, the thread is cut between books and the books removed. Smyth sewing machines are either hand-fed, or equipped with automatic feeders.

Side sewing is used on jobs requiring a particularly strong binding, such as grade schoolbooks, for example. In side sewing, the whole book is sewn together as a single complete unit. The stitches are made adjacent to the binding edge and penetrate throughout the whole book. They do not open as flat as Smyth sewn books and need a wider margin than Smyth sewn books, at the binding edge.

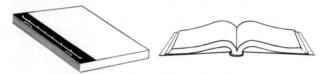

Side Sewn Book, open and closed.

Saddle stitched books are comparatively rare in edition binding, and you find a description of wire saddle stitching in the section on pamphlet binding of this chapter. Side wire stitching when used in edition binding, is primarily useful for hopper feeding books through side sewing machines. Such wire stitchers are usually attached to the end of the gathering machine.

Uniting with adhesives (sometimes called perfect binding) uses a very different technique. Here the back folds of the signatures are cut open, the back of the book is roughed, and an adhesive is applied. All of this is done on fully automatic equipment.

Nipping or Smashing. Nipping and smashing have the same purpose, namely to reduce the swell of the book caused by the thread in sewing. Nipping is done on books

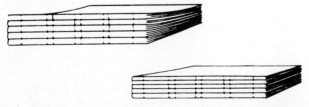

The sewed book is "smashed" to reduce bulk and swelling in the back.

printed on hard surfaced papers, and applies pressure only along the binding edge. Smashing is done on those printed on soft and bulky stock and applies pressure over the entire surface. Nippers and smashers are semi-automatic machines.

Cutting or Trimming. Cutting or trimming are terms used interchangeably, although the trade usually refers to "cutting" as the cutting apart of large flat printed sheets

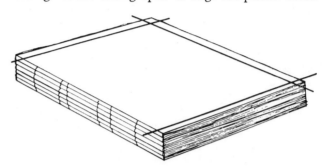

The book is trimmed on three edges in one machine in one continuous operation.

on a guillotine cutter, and "trimming" as the cutting-off of the three rough edges of a book. The smashed books are placed in a three-knife trimmer where they are trimmed to the prescribed size at the head, side, and foot of the book; the excess paper is removed, and the books are ready for forwarding.

FORWARDING

Forwarding is a peculiar term, traditionally used in bookbinding but without self-evident meaning, and refers to a group of operations necessary before the trimmed book can be cased-in. Some of these operations are optional; they do not contribute to the wearability of the binding itself but have the purpose of beautifying. But most of the forwarding operations are very important steps that must be taken for technical reasons.

The trimmed book cannot be cased-in as it is because it is lacking in strength and rigidity, and it must be rounded and jointed along the back with or without hinging material before the cover can be applied. Forwarding consists of the following six operations: (1) Edge treatments; (2) Back gluing; (3) Rounding; (4) Backing; (5) Lining-up; and (6) Head banding. Each of these operations is briefly discussed in the following.

Edge Treatments. Edge treatment is one of the optional operations included under forwarding. Many books are bound without any edge treatments whatsoever, while others are given edge treatments of varying degrees. Some books are stained, others sprinkled or marbled; and in certain cases edges may be gilded, either plain or red-under-gold. Fore-edge painting, a kind of edge treatment that is given to deluxe books of the most demanding variety, has practically faded out of the edition binding field.

Back Gluing. Back gluing is the operation whereby the binding edge is coated with a glue or flexible resin film. The purpose is twofold; to hold the binding edge in a uniform plane, and to insure the retaining of a convex section of the back edge after backing. It can be done by hand or mechanical equipment. In hand gluing the worker applies a coat of glue to a stack of books with a brush; in mechanical gluing the brush is replaced by a roller turning in a reservoir of glue.

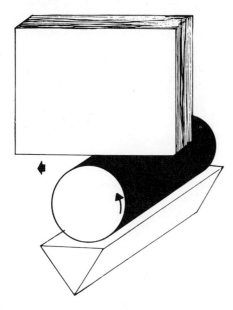

The glue is applied with a roller to the backbone so that it penetrates between the sections.

Rounding. Rounding has the purpose of producing a free-opening action to the book without the fore-edge being pushed out. It is done on fully, or semi-automatic equipment which also provides backing; and it may or may not also perform all of the remaining forwarding operations in addition to rounding and backing.

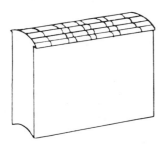

Backbone is rounded and backed to form the shape of the book.

Rounding is produced by passing the book, from the binding to the fore-edge, between two tightly set steel rollers which revolve in opposite directions. This produces a convex curve at the binding edge, and a concave curve at the fore-edge. Both Smyth sewn and adhesive bound books can be rounded if the backs have been previously glued off with an adhesive of suitable flexibility and tenacity.

Side sewn books are not rounded because the threads or wires hold the sheets too tightly; they are either backed or jointed.

Backing. Backing fulfills three important tasks: It insures the permanency of the rounded back; It gives the book greater flexibility on opening; And it provides the necessary joints or ridges against which the covers swing. These effects are obtained by clamping the book on both sides and flaring the back from the center outward, over the clamped edges. It is part of the same machine operation which rounds the book.

Lining-Up. If the book is forwarded on equipment that combines only backing and rounding in one trip through the machine, it must be transferred to another piece of equipment for the remaining forwarding operations. But if the very modern fully automatic forwarding machines are used, this transfer is not required for lining-up and head banding; they are part of the same machine step.

Muslin cloth and lining paper are glued to backbone and headbands are affixed.

Lining-up has the purpose of reinforcing the book by gluing to its back one or two layers of gauze called "crash" or "super" and a strip of strong paper, kraft paper for example. Lining-up joins all signatures together, and by extending the first crash about 1″ beyond each joint, relieves much of the strain born by the front and back end papers and signatures, to which the case is finally attached.

Head Banding. Head banding is again an optional step that does not add to the strength of a book but does impart pleasant decoration. The forwarding machine attaches head and tail bands either separately to the book, or to the paper lining before it is glued to the back.

The forwarded book is now ready for casing-in. But before we can discuss this subject, we want to study the production of the case itself. Our next subject is therefore casemaking.

CASEMAKING AND STAMPING

This is the second feeder river of edition binding comprising all operations necessary for the making and decorating of a book-binding case up to the point of casing-in where it is combined with the forwarded book.

A case consists of two boards, back lining paper, and covering material, all firmly united by means of an adhesive at the stage of casemaking. These materials must be carefully chosen in accordance with the exigencies of each particular job.

The subject is much too broad to be fully discussed within the frame of reference set for this Manual, and before listing the main steps in casemaking we must discuss the printing and decorating of the case because manufacturing procedures vary according to the kind of printing and decorating selected for a job. Broadly speaking, there are two kinds of cover printing and decorating, namely, pre-printed and post-printed cases.

In pre-printed cases, the printing and decorating precedes casemaking; in post-printed cases, printing and decorating follows the casemaking operation. In pre-printing, the covering material is printed in sheets, although more recently, there has been some progress made toward web printing.

In post-printing, the case is decorated after it is made, with specially cut dies, and can be grained, embossed, foil stamped, or ink stamped. In many cases more than one, and occasionally all, of these decorative procedures are involved. One also finds on occasion, cases that have been decorated by the silk screen method.

Decorating covers by pre-printing has increased in recent years, with most of the halftone and color process work done by offset-lithography on rough textured cloth; although one also finds some of the line and type work done by letter-press. In any case, the printer or his customer are advised to make sure before they decide on such a cover that the binder is equipped for the casemaking of pre-printed covers.

There are five main steps in making and decorating the case: (1) Board and paper slitting and cutting; (2) Slitting or cutting of the covering material; (3) Pre-printing of the covering material; (4) Casemaking; (5) Post-printing of the completed case.

Board Slitting and Cutting. Boards are slit on machines designed and built for this purpose. They are known as board cutters, mostly hand fed, but some recent models include automatic feeders. The slitting is done by feeding each board individually through a pair of rotary cutting members that work against each other. The slit board comes through the first cut in long strips, and is then fed through a second cutter which slits the strips into the final size.

The paper, positioned as a liner between the boards and along the backbone, is slit to the proper width, re-wound and, in the casemaker, automatically cut to the proper length and fed into position along with the boards. It is called the "backlining." The purpose of this backlining is to give rigidity to the cover material, and to form a base that will accept and hold the impression received from graining, embossing, stamping or inking.

Slitting and Cutting of Covering Material. All casemaking machines use individual boards already cut to size, but the cloth used by some is in web form (the Sheridan machine) and by others in the form of individually cut units (the Dexter and Smyth machines). The cover material is cut into individual cover blanks for the Dexter and Smyth machines, but slit and re-wound for casemaking on a Sheridan machine.

For pre-printing in sheets, the covering material is sheeted considering both the necessities of casemaking and pre-printing. If a cover is best pre-printed two- or four-up, then the material must be sheeted to the printing size first and then cut to the individual cover blank size as required for casemaking.

Pre-Printing. For pre-printing in sheets, any printing process that can print on the covering material selected in a specific case can be used for pre-printing. Offset-lithography is widely used for this purpose; letterpress, gravure, silk screen and collotype less frequently. Web printing poses severe register problems for casemaking because it is difficult to exactly register the imprint on the backbone or spine of a book using a pre-printed web. For this reason web printing is used mostly for random patterns; and the spine and title of the book are usually not included in the web print, but are post-printed after the case is made.

Casemaking. Casemaking is done on the Smyth, the Dexter, or the Sheridan machine. The Smyth and Dexter casemakers require boards, covering material, and a roll of backlining paper all cut to size. The covering material is automatically glued and moved to a position where the boards and the backlining are mechanically placed on the glued surface; the top and the tail edge of the covering material are then turned in; next the remaining two side edges; and finally the completed cover is pressed and delivered into a hopper.

The web-fed Sheridan casemaker uses boards cut to unit size, a roll of backlining paper of the proper width, and a roll of cloth or other cover material cut to its proper width. The cloth is pulled through a set of rollers which apply a uniform coating of specially formulated adhesive to the back of the cover material. As the web advances through the machine with the freshly applied adhesive-side up, the two boards are first applied to carefully gauged positions, corners are then cut out between each two covers, the back-lining paper is fed out to the proper length, cut, and exactly gauged between the two boards, the edges of the material are then turned over the boards the long way of the machine, a knife cuts each cover apart from the web, and finally the short edges of the material are turned over the boards and the cover delivered between two pressing rollers.

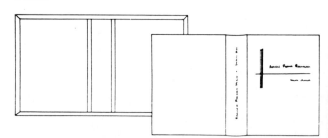

The case is made to fit the book and is stamped with cover and backbone design.

Post-Printing. The term "post-printing" is not actually used in the bookbinding industry, but it is used in this study for the convenience of the reader as a parallel term to pre-printing. Bookbinders speak of "stamping" when they refer to the printing or other decorating of the completed case with either ink, genuine gold, or foil. Inking is done in a heavy platen press with cold dies. Genuine gold, foil, graining and embossing are usually performed in upright machines similar to die presses, using heated heads and dies.

For stamping with ink, brass dies are used in conjunction with a very heavy bookbinders ink.

For genuine gold or foil stamping, the press is often equipped with a roll leaf feeder as well as a heating unit. The brass dies transfer the heat to the releasing agent used on the web which carries the gold or foil. In blind stamping, the impression is made with heat, but without the use of either ink or foil, which results in a plain intaglio image on the cover.

Graining, embossing, and silk screening are other techniques for decorating or post-printing made-up covers.

Having reached the junction of the two rivers that form the stream of bookbinding, the next operation is casing-in, where the forwarded book and the completed case meet and emerge as a finished, bound product.

CASING-IN

In casing-in, the cover and the book are assembled, to be followed by an operation called "building-in." These two operations are sometimes separately discussed, but are here grouped together because they certainly belong together, particularly for the layman who is not concerned with the many peculiarities that are part of bookbinding parlance for historical reasons alone.

Casing-in, according to a standard definition, is the operation of applying paste or glue to the end papers of a book, inserting the book in the cover and building into presses between press boards to dry. Building-in, according to the same authoritative source, consists in placing freshly cased-in books in a press between either smooth or edged boards, shaping backs carefully, and applying sufficient pressure in a press or by clamping devices to hold books firmly while drying. Nowadays casing-in as well as building-in are done on more mechanized equipment, and in many instances, the cased-in book is not pressed for hours, but leaves the building-in machine ready for use within a few minutes after casing in.

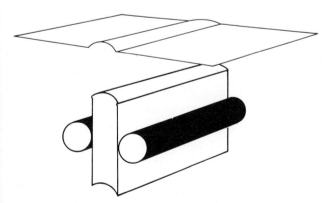

Paste is applied to endsheets and the case falls into place.

Casing-In. Casing-in is performed on hand-fed or semi-automatic equipment, combining the forwarded book, with the completed cover by automatic action. The end papers of the book are coated with paste, the back of the case is placed on the book in register, and the cover drawn tightly around the book, carefully gauged so that all three

edges of "squares" project an equal amount, head, front and tail.

In "loose-back" casing-in, no glue is applied to the backbone of the book itself, thus letting the cover "gape" open when the book is opened. But many books, espcially side sewn books, are cased-in "tight-back," which includes gluing off the backbone of the book and pasting off the end papers.

Building-In. Done by hand, books are placed flat on boards with the joints fitted into the metal or plain edges of the board, layer upon layer to a distance of about five feet. Pressure is then applied to the pile, the pressure locked on the pile with tie rods, and the pile then rolled away to the drying area.

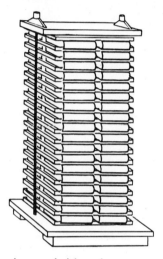

Finished books are held under pressure until dry.

This same process is now mechanically accomplished by conveying single books through jaws which apply both heat and pressure.

Inspecting, Jacketing, Packing and Shipping. These are the final operations of bookbinding, easily identified by the name.

Although inspection points are maintained at several points along the way, the final inspection of the completed book is a most important and effective tool for quality con-

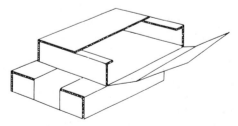

The book is packed according to specifications and shipped.

trol. Jacketing, or the putting of a paper cover — commonly known as a book jacket — over the case, either by hand or machine, is followed in turn by packing and shipping. Here at last this industry becomes very similar to all others!

This short presentation has barely covered the fundamentals of edition binding. The reader can learn more on the subject in the trade press and at technical forums where the latest developments are presented and discussed.

Section Four: Binding Specifications for Litho Production

The Bindery Specifications, with comments, which are listed in this section are the result of a Bindery Panel discussion at one of the member meetings of the Metropolitan Lithographers Association. The Panel was led by representatives of the Bookbinders Guild under chairmanship of Eugene Rieder. The purpose of the discussion was a better understanding and solution of mutual problems.

The Specifications were supplied by the Bookbinders Guild, and the comments were added from notes on the Panel discussions.

Bindery Imposition. Before making flats be sure to get imposition from binder who will do the job. If there is an odd form, be sure to check with binder for layout before printing last form; also for imposition for any miscellaneous material in addition to straight text forms.

Comment: For book work, if there is any indication of an odd form, put this in middle of book rather than as last form. Best to have full form last to take end paper.

Extra 32-Page Forms. When there is an extra 32-page form, most binders prefer this as a double 16-page; however, some want it in form of "half quad" — difficult to fold unless binder has suitable folders. Stripper should secure instructions from binder as to how work should be laid out.

Positioning of Linings and Jackets Printed Together with Text. When linings and jackets are on a form with text, they should be positioned on opposite side from guide. Put identifying mark on front-and-back lining.

Comment: If guide marks are on end, cut off first (linings and jackets, etc.); this leaves no such marks for remaining bindery work.

Ruled Sheets are Needed for Avoiding Mistakes. When form contains a mixture of ad matter, unfolioed pages, end papers, etc., lithographer should provide binder with ruled sheet so binder can see just how job should be handled.

Cutting Layout on Large Sheets. Flat cutter limit is 65" (some binders do not have this maximum size). Larger sheets should be laid out to cut short way first without spoiling work.

Press Slitting. Press slitting is more accurate than a cutter, and should be used when available (to cut large sheets into two or more signatures for folders). Jogging of extra large sheets, and of lightweight stock, is difficult and frequently inaccurate.

Uniform Margins and Trims. Make margins and trim on all sheets uniform. Print guide and gripper indication on each form, outside trim area.

Comment: Trim-cutting equipment set for $\frac{1}{8}$" normally; other trim means changing machines. If any difference in trim margins, call to attention of binder. Avoid using sheet with more than one margin width. Normal $\frac{1}{8}$" trim holds for both edition (one-up) and pamphlet binding.

The Consequences of Inaccurate Margins. Uneven or inaccurate margins are multiplied and increased in the binding. A 96-page booklet (3-32's) can end up with 18 different margins; a $\frac{1}{16}$" inaccuracy can increase to $\frac{1}{4}$" in margin.

Guides and Their Positions. Whether side or center imposition guide should be used depends on individual binder. Consult first. Stripper sometimes does not pay attention to guides and binder has to trim both sides (may end up too short for job). Stripper should not forget to change his guides on back-up of sheet. Check lay-sheet (print proof of form) for fold and line-up.

Oversize Paper. On oversized paper consult binder as to where he wants excess paper placed.

Comment: "Tails" from oversize paper — result is long tail (extra wide trim) from some sheets; binder cannot set for sewing unless all sheets have uniform tails. Find out if binder wants paper cut, then publisher pays. "Tails" are the most frequent complaint of the binder.

Distributing Extra Space on Oversize Sheets. When a larger sheet is used, i.e., 33" x 46" instead of 32" x 45", the extra space is best distributed over the margins. If the job is a reprint and already stripped, the extra paper should be divided between the front and back edges, with the extra inch of length placed opposite the guide. In this way the extra paper may be trimmed off after the sheets have been folded.

Imposition of Low Folios. Check with binder if he wants low folio printed up or down.

Comment: Type of feeder in bindery determines whether low folio should be (face) up or down. A Cross Feeder (used by 80 percent of binders) takes folio face-up; a pile feeder, face-down. Ask binder if he wants low folios top or bottom of skid—binder should not be required to turn entire skid load to get low folio on top (when designated).

Dummies for Unfolioed Books. If book is unfolioed, mark folded dummy should accompany job. Put collating mark on outside of gutter fold.

Marking of Work-and-Turn Sheets. Work-and-turn sheets must always be plainly marked as such.

Comment: Some binders use the center cut for guide, and others use the side press guide and center guide. Ask binder which he wants.

Work-and-Tumble Sheets. Work-and-tumble sheets (forms)—outside pages should go to the gripper edge. Don't forget to allow for bottom gripper margin.

Markers for Breaks. If two or more forms are piled on one skid, markers should be used to show where break occurs, and each form should be clearly identified. A lined-up sheet must accompany every job.

Marking Different Kinds of Paper Stocks. If different kinds of paper stock are used they should be clearly marked, and binder notified before shipment is made.

Bindery Spoilage Allowances. Bindery spoilage allowances should be based on Book Manufacturers' Institute code for spoilage. These spoilage allowances apply to all types of bindery work, as well as to book work, in absence of written agreement to the contrary. (See Spoilage Allowance Schedule.)

Comment: Higher than normal press spoilage sometimes results in insufficient allowance for bindery. For example, when customer changes approved layout and plans in favor of larger sheet to include end papers and jacket. The frequent higher spoilage of end-paper area often results in 10,000 books and 9,000 end papers. Low count on any unit of job determines delivery count.

Skid Delivery and Marking. Protective sheets should be placed both top and bottom of each skid load, and should be marked as waste sheets. Skids should be of adequate size so no paper protrudes over edges with resulting damage in shipment or handling. Skids should be adequately strapped, with a solid top to prevent shifting.

Load Tags of Skids. A load tag should appear on each skid giving the following information: (1) Title (No abbreviations), (2) Publisher or customer, (3) Number of sheets delivered (Press spoilage deducted), and (4) Lithographer.

Marking of Protective Wrapping. If skid has protective wrapping, this information should appear inside wrapping as well as on outside. Delivery receipt covering shipment should be complete with same information as load tag.

Bad Work. Loads not properly marked, sheets not dry, sheets that have offsets, sheets that have bad printing, sheets with marks inside trim area or other bad work should not be delivered to the binder for him to sort out. The binder has made no allowance in his estimate for such extra work which is normally the responsibility of the lithographer.

Folding and Grain of Paper. Book forms should be printed so the grain of the paper will be parallel with the backbone of the book. This applies also to linings, inserts or tips which will be pasted into the book either by machine or hand. This eliminates rippling and insures proper adhesion.

Comment: Try to avoid folding across the grain — 32-up sheets frequently hard to fold satisfactorily, particularly in smaller page sizes. When use of short-grain paper is inadvisable consult with binder in advance to try to work out problem.

Web Press Folding. In web press folding the folds are apt to be uneven, the runs crooked on last fold. Here allow ¼" trim.

Folding for Pamphlet Binding. For pamphlet binding (folders, leaflets, etc.) folding should be with the grain

as far as possible, particularly with the heavier and stiffer stocks. Imposition should be in accordance.

Folding in Multiples. In pamphlet binding it is customary to fold a sheet of multiples, i.e., 2-up or 4-up rather than 1-up as in edition (book) binding, trim and then cut units apart. Imposition should provide for this important bindery economy where possible. Repetition of a 1-up imposition eliminates this opportunity.

Uneconomical Items. Not advisable to take a one-sheet imposition and then cut in half to run on smaller press — increased bindery costs cancel any press economy. With accordian-fold circulars, avoid inside trim if possible. With "bleed" design, however, inside trim may be necessary, and extra sheet size should be provided. If scoring of heavy stock is necessary for folding, this work should be done before sheets go to the binder. Here folding with the grain is particularly important.

Reminder. Always consult ahead of time with binder, not only for imposition, but for other details of the bindery work. Different binders have different types of equipment; also their own methods and "tricks." Don't assume that the instructions of one binder apply to all other binders.

SCHEDULE OF PERCENTAGES OF SPOILAGE ALLOWANCE FOR BINDING

Quantities bound at one time (or completed to sewn or stitched stage)	Binding Allowance (percent)				
	40 lb. & heavier	35 lb.	30 lb.	25 lb.	20 lb.
1,000	6.0	6.5	7.5	8.5	10.0
2,000	4.5	5.0	6.0	7.0	8.5
3,000	4.0	4.5	5.5	6.5	8.0
4,000	3.5	4.0	5.0	6.0	7.5
5,000	3.0	.3.5	4.5	5.5	7.0
10,000	2.5	3.0	4.0	5.0	6.5
15,000	2.5	3.0	4.0	5.0	6.5
20,000	2.5	3.0	4.0	5.0	6.5
25,000 and over.	2.0	2.5	3.5	4.5	6.0

Additional Allowances to Above. For titles having muslin reinforced end signatures (concealed cloth joints) add to bindery spoilage allowances on such two signatures 1.0 percent of all runs.

For printed end papers employed on titles with concealed cloth joints or concealed or visible twill (side thread-stitched) joints, add to bindery spoilage allowances on such end papers 1.0 percent of all runs.

For editions not folded, gathered and sewn (or stitched) as initial operation, bindery spoilage allowances should be increased for each separate folding by full bindery allowances; when initially folded, gathered and sewn (or stitched), but binding done in two or more operations, increase bindery spoilage allowance by 1.0 percent up to 5,000 copies bound at one time and by 0.5 percent for over 5,000 copies bound at one time.

Variations from normal such as dull coated or other special paper, bleed pages or perforating, should take an extra spoilage allowance.

CHAPTER FIFTEEN . .

Various Supplementary Processes

Section One: Bronzing and Varnishing

Varying with the end use of a lithographed product, the sheet is subjected to different operations supplementary to lithographing. In label work these supplementary operations consist of bronzing, varnishing, embossing and die-cutting for example. In this section we present bronzing and embossing. Varnishing and coating of lithographed papers is the subject matter of the following section; die-cutting of labels is presented in section three of this chapter.

BRONZING

Bronzing is the technique whereby metallic powders are applied in the form of a design to a sheet of paper. Even though it is possible to bronze a blank or unprinted sheet, almost all bronzing is done on printed or lithographed sheets. The sequence of operation is such that the sheet is first printed or lithographed and bronzed thereafter. If a sheet is to be bronzed and varnished bronzing always precedes spirit varnishing in some plants; other plants prefer the reverse order. In the case of print varnishing, which is usually done on a lithographic press, the print varnish is either applied before or after bronzing.

Our presentation of bronzing is divided into the following five points: (1) General discussion of bronzing, (2) Bronzes, (3) Applying the adhesive for bronzing, (4) Applying the metallic powder, (5) Burnishing. Each of these points is now discussed.

General Discussion of Bronzing. Bronzing consists of three related operations. First an adhesive known as gold size is applied to the sheet, then the sheet is exposed to the bronze powder in a bronzing machine, finally the bronzed sheet is run through a burnishing machine.

It is possible to obtain effects similar to bronzing by lithographing metallic ink. But bronzing is still the preferred technique for obtaining the effect of gold on a sheet of paper. Bronzing is not restricted to gold, even though most bronzing has this purpose.

Bronzes. Gold bronze takes the place of gold leaf which was used in the past. Gold leaf is much too expensive

and its application much too slow for mass production and has therefore fallen into disuse. Gold bronze is used in its place for label and similar quantity work.

Gold bronze powder consists of fine flakes of brass. Brass is, as the reader may know, an alloy of copper and zinc. Different proportions of the two metals produce bronzes of different colors. The specifications of bronze powders are rather technical; here we merely mention that they include shades or color of the bronze, size of particles, grease content and bulking density.

Applying the Adhesive for Bronzing. Before the adhesive can be applied, care must be taken that all colors printed on the sheet are thoroughly dry. Still wet or tacky inks will have a similar result as the bronzing adhesive. The application of an adhesive is the first step in bronzing. The bronze powder is applied to this adhesive and therewith permanently attached to the sheet. The bronzing adhesive is called *size* or *gold size* by the trade. Gold size is a tacky ink ranging in color from yellow to a dark green according to the color bronze used and the effect desired. Gold size is applied to the sheet on a lithographic press.

Applying the Metallic Powder. The metallic powder is applied to the sheet in a bronzing machine. As the powder must be applied to the still-wet size, the sheet travels immediately after application of the size into the bronzing machine. There bronze is dusted over the entire surface of the sheet; where the sheet is printed with size the bronze adheres; dusting pads dust off the excess bronze before the sheet leaves the bronzing machine. The sheets should be allowed to dry for at least 24 hours and then re-dusted to remove remaining unwanted or unadhered bronze whenever this is the case.

Burnishing. Burnishing has the purpose of endowing the bronzed sheet with extra luster or high sheen. This effect is obtained by flattening and polishing the bronze particles until they form a very smooth surface. Burnishing machines have one or several pairs of calender units. Each of these consists of a steel roller and a composition roller. The steel roller runs faster than the composition roller; friction is caused whereby the bronzed sheet is polished. The pressure between the rollers controls the degree of sheen and smoothness given to a sheet. After burnishing the bronzed sheet is ready for further processing.

EMBOSSING

We can define embossing as an industrial way of creating relief images on printed, lithographed or blank paper or similar material in order to create a beautifying effect. Our presentation of embossing is divided into the following eight points: (1) The two main kinds of embossing, (2) The effect of embossing on the handling of the embossed product, (3) Roller embossing or pebbling, (4) Plate embossing, (5) Embossing dies, (6) Assembly of embossing dies, (7) Makeready for embossing, (8) Presswork for embossing. Each of these points is now described in detail.

The Two Main Kinds of Embossing. There are two types of embossing; they are used for different purposes and executed on different equipment. These two types are roller embossing and plate embossing. Roller embossing is used for all-over patterns, plate embossing for individual unit patterns.

The Effect of Embossing on the Handling of the Embossed Product. Embossing breaks, stretches, and separates the fibres of the paper. It thereby increases the flexibility of the paper and makes it much more easy to apply it to curved surfaces. This is a very important consideration in labeling which is done on high speed machines.

Roller Embossing or Pebbling. Roller embossing is also known as pebbling. It is done on a cylinder machine having two rollers. The embossing roller is an engraved steel roller, its mate a smooth cotton or papier-maché roller. The paper is run between both rollers, their pressure is adjustable and produces the required or desired depth of embossing. Pebbling designs commonly used are known as eggshell, moiré, crash, stucco, skytogen, linen and other patterns.

Plate Embossing. Plate embossing is used for most label work but also for many other purposes. Plate embossing is also called spot embossing. In it such images and designs as medals, heads, reading matter, scrolls, frames and many, many others are produced. The same embossing plate can of course include background pattern or overall designs. Plate embossing is executed in presses having two parallel platens. One of these holds the embossing plate, the other receives the makeready and the paper. For print-

ing, the bottom plate moves up in contact with the top plate holding the embossing plate assembly.

Embossing Dies. Embossing dies are made in a variety of techniques. They are supplied to the lithographer by companies specializing in their making. The technique used depends on the detail of the job. Some dies are hand-engraved, others are made by means of the pantagraph or by etching for example. In many cases various techniques are used in combination.

In label work, where a large number of units is embossed in one operation, duplicate embossing dies are needed. These are made by electrotyping; if the runs are very long, electrotypes can be nickel-surfaced (commonly called steel-surfaced) or chrome-plated.

Assembly of Embossing Dies. The assembly of embossing dies for a large size job is a very exacting task. First each electro is glued to a piece of strawboard in order to give it a base for the later gluing on the main head plate of the embossing press. Then this head plate is removed from the press and prepared for the mounting of the electros which serve as embossing dies. The electros are placed in register with the sheet layout on the head plate. This job must be done with the greatest care.

Once the electros are in position they are glued to the head plate. The assembled electros are inserted (on the head plate to which they are attached) into the head of the embossing press, facing down toward the bottom plate.

Makeready for Embossing. The makeready for embossing produces a male bottom plate corresponding to the female electros. The first step consists in preparing the bottom plate of the press by pasting several layers of strawboard or approximately 60-point Draftboard down to it. A mixture of gum arabic and barium sulfate is used as adhesive. This mixture has the advantage of producing a workable surface when the glued board is wet and a hard surface when the board is dry.

This prepared plate is shaped into a male counter plate of the assembled electros by forcing these into the plate. Once this is done, the male bottom plate is covered with a French folio tissue stock and all unembossed areas of the plate are cut away. After the composition has properly set, the press is ready for embossing.

Presswork for Embossing. Once the press is ready, embossing has fewer problems in presswork than in printing. This does not mean that the pressman and his assistant can be careless. All parts of the press must be maintained in best order just like in any other kind of presswork.

Section Two: Varnishing and Coating of Lithographed Papers

Not all products of lithography require finishing, but in many instances there is a demand for a surface finish that imparts resistance to chemicals, heat, scuffing etc., that provides smoothness and lustre, and thereby enhancement of color values. All these requirements can be met by one or more finishes available to the lithographer today. In the following, some of the major categories of finishes will be discussed.

PRINT VARNISH

It is the oldest and most commonly used finish consisting of drying-oil lithographing varnish, modified with driers, synthetic resins (for instance alkyds), waxes, and compounds to form a slow-drying, protective film printed on the lithographic press.

The Advantages of Print Varnish. Its advantages

are: (1) Easy and speedy application, using little material, often from a solid plate without the use of dampeners; therefore, it is very economical. (2) The possibility of spot varnishing is important in spacing out areas for gumming, stamping etc. (3) Producing the flattest type of labels, due to the absence of a heating operation. (4) Can be run together with colors as a last print on multicolor press. (5) Alcohol resistance.

The Disadvantages of Print Varnish. Its disadvantages are: (1) Tendency to after-yellow within a few months. (2) Thin film, which has the least scuff resistance of all finishes. (3) Requires high-grade coated papers; on absorbent papers it will produce a muddled, dull and ungainly finish.

VARIOUS KINDS OF COATINGS

All the finishing materials discussed on the following pages can best be classified as coatings, i.e. film formers dissolved in solvents, because in contrast to the print varnish, they are applied on a roller-coating machine and dried by forced evaporation of a solvent, leaving a dry film on the face of the lithographed sheet. Limitation of space necessitates that only the major items in this field can be mentioned.

Spirit Varnishes: This group has been an old standby and still proves very valuable in spite of the modern synthetics. It dries by evaporation of alcohol (spirit), and leaves a film on the paper which is shiny and hard, but of course, never resistant to alcohol. They all are imprintable.

Copal Varnishes: The best-known of these spirit varnishes are the so-called Copal varnishes. They consist of a solution of about 40 percent to 50 percent of Copal resin (a fossil and semi-fossil gum, for instance, found in the Philippines) in denatured alcohol. The good grades of this resin have a light color, and deposit a practically colorless film on the paper.

Advantages of Copal Varnishes: The advantages of copal varnishes are: (1) Quick and thorough drying due to fast solvent (alcohol) release, using only moderate heat (approximately 180° F); therefore having good stacking qualities. (2) Good lustre. (3) Good scuff resistance. (4) Light color. (5) Good moisture resistance.

Disadvantages of Copal Varnishes: The disadvantages of copal varnishes are: (1) Has a tendency to be easily marred by scratches on the surface. (2) Very limited chemical resistance (no alkali resistance).

Shellac Solutions. In this group of spirit varnishes belong shellac solutions made of various types of shellacs dissolved in alcohol. This natural resin originates from insects (India), and has been famous for many years for its smooth finishes; lustre from satin finishes to high gloss, slip and scuff resistance. Its high sensitivity to water and to mild alkali solutions have made it rather undesirable compared with other coatings. Other natural resins sometimes used in combination spirit varnishes are Mastic and Sandarac.

Zein-Rosin Solutions. We may also list as spirit varnishes the alcoholic solutions of *ZEIN-ROSIN*, which made

their appearance in large volume during the last war, and which have since kept a definite position in the field of coatings. Zein, the protein of corn, forms a very tough and highly scuff-resistant film which obtains lustre, and some flexibility through the addition of rosin, which in itself is not a film former. This combination is widely used as a finish which gives satisfactory scuff resistance and lustre. It has a certain water sensitivity and thereby resembles shellac. The color of the dried film is slightly on the gray-green side.

Polyamid Resins Solutions. Recently promoted as protective coatings in alcoholic or alcohol-hydrocarbon solution. For good results they have to be modified with other resinous material.

Maleic Ester Solutions. Purely synthetic are the maleic esters which are used in alcoholic solutions for their good lustre, but they have poor water and alkali resistance.

Naphtha Varnishes. They are similar to the spirit varnishes in performance, but their resins are dissolved in low boiling naphtha, instead of alcohol. Typical for such a varnish is a solution of modified rosin (zinc or calcium salt, plus wax as a scuff-resistant binder) in V.M. & P. Naphtha.

The advantages of these types of coatings are, above all, the low price due to inexpensive resinous material, and cheap solvents. They are used where a certain amount of protection is required, at the lowest possible price. They have a good lustre, but their scuff resistance is very limited — in fact, the lowest of all coatings. They resist imprinting.

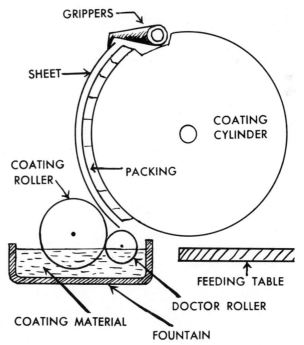

Schematic Cross-Section of a Coating Machine.

Lacquers. This term is foremostly applied to the first synthetic finishes ever made. They consist of solutions of nitro-cellulose (also called pyroxylin) in special solvents (esters, alcohols and hydrocarbons). They are modified with resins and plasticizers and have been widely used as high-quality finishes of good lustre, light color, and good scuff resistance. (Lately, the word "lacquer" is being used in a broader sense for quick-drying high-grade synthetic film formers.) A certain after-yellowing under the influence of light is often observed on these otherwise very useful coatings. Inhibitors can improve this. Their alkali resistance is poor; their heat resistance is good; solvent release is very good. Imprintable.

Ethyl Cellulose Coatings. Other cellulose compounds forming useful lacquers are based on ethyl cellulose (in alcohol-toluene solutions). It forms an alkali-resistant coating of medium lustre and good scuff resistance.

Cellulose Butyrate Coatings. Cellulose Butyrate, a recent development, shows an improved light transmittance and light resistance (no after-yellowing). Colors are being well preserved in their original beauty under this type of lacquer.

Vinyl Coatings. These synthetic film formers have assumed eminent importance in the field of coatings during the last decade. This is due to their light color, good lustre, and high scuff resistance (chemically they are vinyl-chlorides, vinyl-chloride-acetate copolymers dissolved in ketones, and aromatic solvents). They show very good all-around chemical resistance; a certain after-yellowing due to influence of heat and light can be reduced by stabilizers. Their solvent release is good, they can be stacked well and handled easily; they can also be imprinted.

Coatings Made With Acrylic Esters and With Cellulose Acetobutyrate. Coatings which have been used for their specific property of high light transmission and light fastness are based on Acrylic esters and to a lesser degree on Cellulose aceto-butyrate. Their formulation requires careful balancing with other resinous materials.

Coatings Made With Rubber Derivatives. Rubber derivatives such as chlorinated rubber dissolved in toluene blended with lustre-producing resins and plasticizers make useful finishes of good gloss, scuff and chemical resistance. They require protection against after-yellowing and embrittlement due to the influence of light.

Styrenated Alkyds, Vinyl-Compounded Alkyds and Other Film Formers. Recent developments in synthetic film formers comprise styrenated alkyds, vinyl-compounded alkyds and others. They have the desirable property of forming solutions of high concentration without substantial increase in viscosity. Therefore, they can be applied in very heavy films on printed sheets and produce finishes of extreme lustre ("liquid lamination"). Some show good mar and scuff resistance, others do not. The solvent is toluene, which is inexpensive. Care is needed in letting coated sheets "breath" for twenty-four (24) hours, stacked low, or standing in rolls. Some of these coatings can be imprinted.

Coatings Made With Polyesters. Another group of coatings recently developed for quick-drying purposes are known under the name of *"Polyesters."* They consist of a mixture of highly reactive chemicals which, under the influence of heat and a catalyst (a trigger-action material), become polymerized (forming long-chain molecules) or "cured," and produce a heavy film which has a very high lustre, high scuff resistance and high chemical resistance. Even the original solvent, or stronger ones, no longer affect the cured film. These coatings, too, are being used in "liquid lamination." Other chemical compounds called Epoxy resins, react in a similar way and produce similar finishes.

Not all of these new synthetics do what their well-spoken salesmen promise they will. Some, for instance, show after-yellowing, others demand very high heat for curing and therefore are inclined to become brittle. Others do not possess the scuff resistance indicated. It is important to try out these new synthetics — let them age for at least six months — subject them to light, heat, scuff, and chemical tests, and then pick the best one for future use.

Section Three: Diecutting of Labels

Various methods of diecutting are used in the production of fancy outline labels. In this study we discuss two of them, high-diecutting and PMC cutting; this is not to imply that other methods and equipment cannot be used for the diecutting of labels. Our presentation of the subject is divided into the following eight points: (1) General exposition of the label requirements; (2) Straight-cutting; (3) Various kinds of dies; (4) High or hollow dies; (5) The two kinds of presses for high-diecutting; (6) Allowance for trim; (7) Diecutting on descending type presses; and (8) Diecutting on PMC presses. Each of these points is discussed in the following.

General Exposition of Label Requirements. These are very will stated by Robert F. Reed, Senior Research Consultant, GATF, in a study of "Size Variations in Diecut Labels" made by LTF in 1948. We quote from Modern Lithography, June 1948: "Diecut labels usually are applied by means of automatic labeling machines. The labels are stacked face up in a hopper in which they are retained by holding fingers at the bottom. The machine picks the bottom label, coats it with adhesive, and applies it to the package by one of several methods. Unless the labels are reasonably uniform in size, they will either fail to feed to the retaining fingers or drop through them. Dimensional uniformity is of such importance that bottlers have established specifications for maximum allowable variation."

Straight-Cutting. As labels are printed very *manyup* on a sheet, but cut individually though in lifts, the printed and otherwise processed sheets must be straight-cut before high-diecutting. Straight-cutting is done on guillotine cutters, and is in principle not different than described in the Bindery chapter of the Manual.

Various Kinds of Dies. The dies used for the stamping of paper, cardboard and similar sheet material can be divided into two kinds, steel rule dies and high or hollow dies. Steel rule dies are discussed in the following section of this chapter. Here it must suffice to say that steel rule dies are used for very intricate shapes and that the number of sheets that can be cut with them in one operation is very small, rarely more than five to ten sheets; in most cases steel rule dies are used for individual cutting.

High or Hollow Dies. High or hollow dies are made of cold-rolled steel, forged and welded to the required shape. High-dies vary in height; those used on PMC machines must not be higher than $2\frac{3}{8}$ inches and not lower than $1\frac{3}{8}$ inches; they may be as small in area as 1 square inch and as large as 36 square inches. Their inside is parallel for approximately 1-inch height, beyond that height the inside of the die may funnel out. From this description you can see why the term high-die or hollow die is used for them.

The Two Kinds of Presses for High-Diecutting. High-dies can be used on open presses having two flat surfaces. In one kind of press, such as a punch press, the die moves and the stack of paper to be cut is stationary. In the other kind of press, the PMC press, the die is stationary and the paper stack is moved against it. These two kinds of presses are also described as presses with descending cut-

ting member and presses with ascending materials to be cut. Both kinds of presses use, by and large, the same dies. PMC presses, so known by the initials of Printing Machinery Company, their builders, are used where large run and high precision cutting is needed.

Allowance for Trim. In both kinds of diecutting, sufficient space must be allowed between the labels for clean cutting. The trim space allowed is usually between one-eighth and three-sixteenths of an inch.

Diecutting on Descending Type Presses. For diecutting on descending type presses, the sheet is first cut into sections of appropriate size; quarters, for example. A lift of such sections, varying with the job from 25 and up, is placed on the bed of the press which has a wooden base. The high-die is carefully registered manually on this lift by the operator. The down-stroke of the machine causes the die to penetrate the stack of labels. The diecut material as well as the cutting waste is removed and the operation repeated until the required quantity is cut.

Diecutting on PMC Machines. On PMC machines the labels must be accurately square-cut before diecutting. The die is positioned in the head of the machine, the lifts of square-cut labels which may contain as many as 500 units, are fed into the machine, positioned to guides and automatically forwarded into cutting position. The diecut labels come up through the hollow cutting die and are removed by the operator.

Section Four: Steel Rule Diecutting of Cardboard Displays

Diecutting is an intermediate process in cardboard display production. It comes after the mounting of the printed sheet and before the finishing and packing of the display. Diecutting is a stamping process whereby cardboard and many other stocks can be cut, scored and creased and thereby made to assume almost any desired shape.

The most important steps in diecutting are the following three: (1) Diemaking, (2) Presswork, and (3) Stripping. Each of these subjects is discussed in the following.

DIEMAKING

Diemaking is the operation where the tool is made by which the display is shaped. This tool is known as a *steel rule die* and must be custom-made for each job. The steel

rule die combines several functions in a single unit. Cutting, but also the less obvious scoring, creasing and punching can all be performed at the same operation with a steel rule die.

The Composition of Steel Rule Dies. A steel rule die is a cutting tool consisting of three materials, quite dissimilar: steel, rubber and wood; soft and hard, rigid and

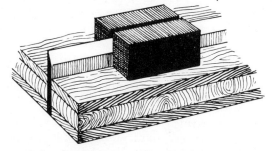

Complete Section of a Steel Rule Die.

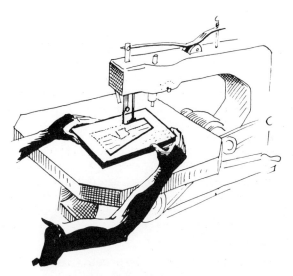

Jigsawing the Dieboard.

resilient. The steel does the cutting, the rubber pushes the cut pieces away from the die, and the wood acts as a base for steel and rubber.

Jigsawing the Dieboard. The plywood base — known as the dieboard — functions like our fist: it grabs the handle of the knife and leaves the cutting edge free to do its work. To this end, the dieboard is jigsawed and the cutting knife inserted in the saw-tracks.

The next question is: what will keep the dieboard in one piece if we make a full circle? The inside of the board will surely fall out! We take this hurdle in a simple manner! The dieboard is kept together by leaving a wooden bridge unsawed.

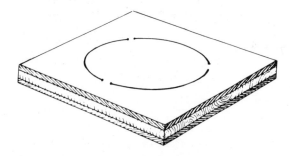

A Bridged Dieboard.

The problem of holding the dieboard together is solved by leaving wooden bridges; the next problem is that of fastening the cutting die where the dieboard is not sawed out. This problem is solved by notching the cutting knife in the corresponding places.

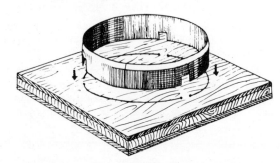

A Notched Cutting Rule for a Bridged Dieboard.

Now we have a technique for making a steel rule die that will cut everywhere and will stay together solidly. Our next topic is the shaping of the cutting knife.

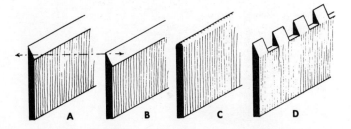

Types of Rule. (A) Cutting; (B) Cut Scores; (C) Creasing; (4) Perforating.

Various Kinds of Rule. The cutting knife, known as rule, is a strip of rather soft steel. Rule is available in many profiles: for cutting, creasing and perforating. Height, width and hardness are all selected to fit the job. Very often, the rule for display jobs is approximately one-inch high and one thirty-second of an inch wide.

Male and Female Die-Sets. The rule is put in shape by bending it between the male and female parts of die-sets which are much harder than the steel rule itself.

Male and Female Die Sets.

The diemaker has several dozen die-sets to choose from. His job requires skill and ingenuity. The die-press, known as bender, is hand operated and permits rapid changes of dies.

Completing a Steel Rule Die. After bending, the rule is inserted right into the saw-tracks of the dieboard. Gluing the rubber on completes the job. The rubber serves to push the cut stock away from the die; the detail of the job governs how much, and what kind of rubber is used.

Inserting Cutting Rule into Saw-Tracks of the Dieboard.

The making of steel rule dies is an art in itself. It requires long experience and considerable skill, like all precision work. The field is very big since steel rule dies are used for the cutting of any number of materials in addition to cardboard. Linoleum, fabric, rubber, felt, cork, plastic, masonite, and rawhide — all are cut with steel rule dies.

PRESSWORK

Several types of presses have been developed for steel rule diecutting. Each of these has its definite place and function. Which press should be selected as the most efficient, cost- and production-wise, depends on the nature of the job in hand.

The Four Types of Diecutting Presses. The most important types of presses are: (1) The open cutter and creaser, (2) The flatbed-cylinder press, (3) The up-and-down press, and (4) The automatic cutter and creaser. Each of these is discussed in the following.

The Open Cutter and Creaser. The open cutter and creaser is a very common type of diecut press for display work. It is a platen press of very rugged construction and it looks very much like a job press stripped of its inking mechanism.

Open cutters and creasers are manufactured in a wide range of sizes. Presses for sheet sizes up to 28 x 42 inches are found in most display finishing houses. Larger presses of this type exist but are much less common. The rate of production depends on many factors; for heavy display work it is between 500 and 1,000 sheets per hour, depending on size and caliper of the stock.

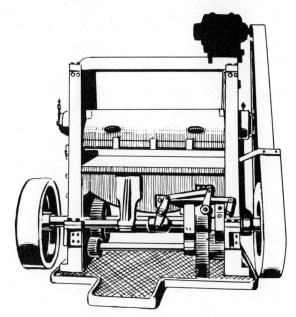

The Vertical-type Cutting and Creasing Press.

The Open-type Cutting and Creasing Press.

The Flatbed-Cylinder Press. Diecutting presses developed very much in the path of printing presses. Here too, the cylinder press came into use after the platen press, and for exactly the same reasons as in printing. Platen presses print by bringing two flat surfaces in overall contact. This principle is practical for small sizes but not for large ones; the pressures required for large sizes are too tremendous.

The cylinder press solved the problem of large size printing by introducing a new principle: line-pressure instead of full area-pressure. In cylinder presses, the type form is carried on a flat surface — the bed of the press — where the stock is wrapped around the circumference of a cylinder which rides over the bed and is called the impression cylinder. The sliding motion of the bed is perfectly timed with the rotary motion of the cylinder, and the necessary pressure is now exerted along a constantly shifting line across the bed. This construction made the printing of large size sheets possible and practical.

Cylinder presses are used in large sizes and primarily for such jobs as cannot be put on flatbed presses. Well-equipped finishing houses have presses that will take sheets up to

44 x 64 inches. but, as cylinder presses are very often rebuilt printing presses, one can find a variety of sizes that defies classification.

The Up-and-Down Press. In this type of press, which is also classified as a vertical diecutting press, display work requiring exceptionally strong pressure is produced.

Up-and-down or vertical presses are manufactured in a variety of sizes, but are not nearly as common in display plants as open presses and flatbed-cylinder presses.

The Automatic Cutter and Creaser. Automatic cutters and creasers are primarily used for folding cartons and other long run jobs. These machines are flatbed-cylinder presses specifically designed for diecutting.

The sheets are automatically fed, cut and creased, and piled after cutting; some makes even have automatic stripping equipment at the delivery end of the press. Makeready is made in a manner similar to that described for cylinder presses. Press sizes range from sheet size 22″ x 28″ up to sheet size $46\frac{1}{4}″$ x $69\frac{1}{2}″$; press speeds vary between 2,000 and 4,000 impressions per hour.

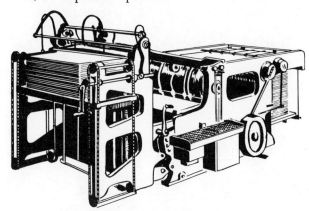

An Automatic Flat-Bed Cylinder Cutting and Creasing Press.

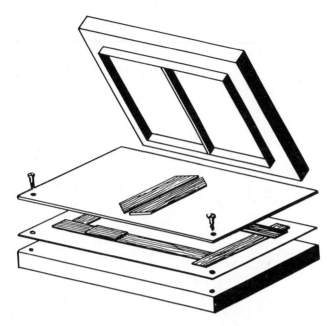

The Die Has Cutting Rule on Four Sides and Creasing Rule in Center. Makeready for Creasing Rule is on Cutting Plate, for Cuts It Is Under the Cutting Plate.

The Three Main Steps in Presswork. Even though each type of press requires a specific technique in operation, all presswork has nevertheless three steps in common. These are: (1) Lock-up, (2) Makeready, and (3) Cutting.

Lock-Up. Lock-up is the first step; it consists in placing and positioning the steel rule die in the press. It is a much simpler job than the following makeready.

Makeready. Makeready is a preparatory act of the greatest importance because it is decisive for the quality of the final result. Makeready is first concerned with register, as the concordance of print and cut is called and also with the quality of the cut itself. But the most difficult part of makeready is posed by creases and scores because they can be very intricate and fragile. This makeready on various kinds of presses is of course done in various ways.

Makeready on Flatbed-Cylinder Presses. In flatbed-cylinder presses the steel rule die is placed on the bed of the press, and the stock is cut by the inter-action of impression cylinder and flatbed. The makeready is made on the cylinder and requires considerable skill and patience.

Underfed and Overfed Flatbed-Cylinder Presses. Feeding of lightweight stocks and of heavyweight stocks on flatbed-cylinder presses is done in different ways. Lightweight stocks that bend around the circumference of

Schematic of the Over-feeding Method.

the cylinder are fed from the feedboard on top of the press. This feeding technique is known as *over-feeding* by the trade.

Heavy boards, such as are used for counter or window displays, cannot be wrapped around the cylinder and are therefore fed directly on top of the steel rule die, or under the cylinder.

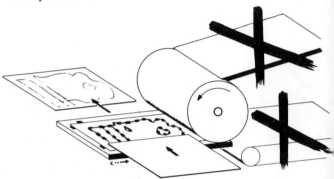

Schematic of the Under-feeding Method.

This technique is called under-feeding by the trade. Underfed flatbed-cylinder presses run intermittently, or stop-and-go. The operator feeds the sheet manually and removes it manually after cutting.

STRIPPING

On presses not equipped with automatic stripping devices, stripping remains to be done after cutting. The cut and scored sheet "is still in the waste" as the trade says. The waste must be removed by stripping. Stripping of display work is mostly done by hand; stripping of folding cartons can be done by one of several mechanized procedures.

Section Five: Mounting and Finishing of Cardboard Displays

The mounting and finishing of displays is here divided into the following three units: (1) Mounting, pasting and easeling, (2) Trimming of cardboard displays, and (3) Display finishing. Each of these is discussed, if ever so briefly, in the following.

MOUNTING, PASTING AND EASELING

The combining of a sheet of paper with a sheet of cardboard is called mounting. If parts of a display are glued to each other, the term pasting is used; if one of these parts is an easel, the word easeling is preferred. These operations differ widely, but nevertheless have one common denominator: They all require an adhesive. The adhesive is, in most cases, a product containing a considerable amount of water, but otherwise specifically formulated for the particular purpose. Adhesives are applied by one of the following five means: (1) By brush, (2) Through a silk screen, (3) With a margin gluer, (4) On a gluing machine, and (5) In a mounting machine.

Applying Glue by Brush. Applying glue by brush is the most primitive technique and nowadays avoided wherever possible. But there are always cases that cannot be fitted into one of the many highly developed and mechanized techniques. Such cases can be tackled more successfully by a hand skilled in the use of brush and glue; nor has the time-honored hand gluing of easels died out completely.

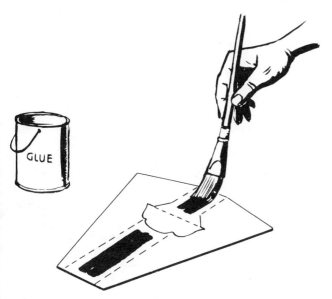

Hand Easeling.

Applying Glue by Silk Screen. Silk screen is another technique of applying the glue by hand — though indirectly. Glue screens are excellently suited wherever ad-

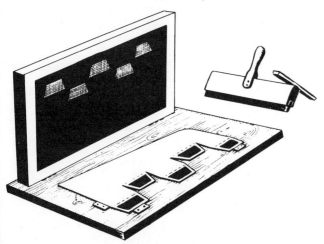

A Glue Screen Set-up Including the Squeegee.

hesives must be applied in irregular shapes or on many small areas. The screen is the same as that customary in silk screen printing, just as the application of the adhesive follows the standard procedures of silk screen printing.

Applying Glue with the Margin Gluer. The margin gluer is a machine for edge gumming and for applying glue to single wing easels. The machine is power driven and applies a glue strip, adjustable in width and thickness, on the easel.

The operator pushes the easel through the machine; a ductor roller transports the adhesive from the enclosed reservoir to the underside of the easel. The wet easel is passed to workers who put it on the back of the display.

A Margin or Easel Gluer.

Hand Mounting. Hand mounting is very economical for small runs — up to several thousand units. It consists of the following three operations: (1) Gluing, (2) Combining, and (3) Pressing.

The Gluing Machine. The gluing machine applies a controlled and uniform film of adhesive to the paper. It has a tank, with or without heating arrangements. A regulator roller determines the thickness of the glue film which the ductor roller transfers from the tank to the underside of the paper. Two pressure rollers force the paper against the ductor, and a series of strippers separate it finally from the machine.

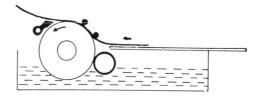

Schematic of Gluing Machine for Paper.

The operator guides the sheet until it is removed from the machine, where it is coated all over, and passes it on to other workers for combining.

Sizes of Gluing Machines. Gluing machines are available in a remarkable variety of makes and sizes. In display mounting plants, 32-inch machines are quite common, but even 46-inch machines, where the largest standard sheet, 44 x 64-inch, can be processed, are frequently seen.

Gluing of Cardboard. Cardboard is glued on a different version of the gluing machine. Now the pressure rollers are much bigger and also in a different position, directly

A Paper Gluing Machine in Operation.

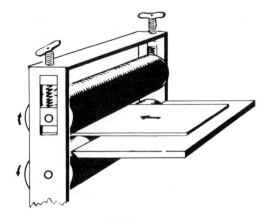

Wringer.

above the ductor roller. Glued paper is moved out of the machine, upwards, at an angle to the table; cardboard, parallel to it.

Because it is obviously easier to handle wet cardboard than wet paper, the glue is applied to the cardboard wherever possible, particularly on large size jobs. Which of the two, cardboard or paper, is glued depends upon the job. Generally speaking, the smaller sheet is glued and the bigger sheet left dry.

The Corner Box. The corner box is a simple gage for maintaining register in mounting. The printed sheet is combined with the board by pushing its guide corner — as that corner of the sheet is called where guide side and gripper side meet — into the corner box. Register must be maintained in mounting, or else! How would it be possible to maintain register in a subsidiary operation, diecutting or trimming, if it were lost in mounting?

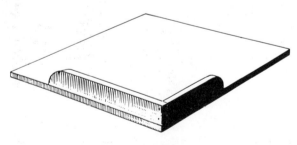

Stock Table.

Pressing. Pressing is the final operation in hand mounting. By pressing, the entire inside area of both combined sheets is firmly bonded. The two most common types of presses are: (1) Rotary presses, and (2) Hydraulic presses.

Rotary or Squeeze Presses. Rotary presses are colloquially known as "squeeze presses" and "wringers."

The press is power driven, and the rollers adjustable for stocks of different thicknesses. The combined sheets are fed through individually and then piled until they are dry. Rotary presses are manufactured in almost as many sizes as gluing machines, up to the very largest.

Hydraulic Presses. Hydraulic presses are capable of developing tremendous pressures; they are also manufac-

tured in large sizes and are therefore very useful in a mounting and finishing plant.

The combined sheets are piled in lifts, several inches high, on the bed of the press. A hydraulically powered cylinder forces the bed and its load against the top plate of the press and holds it there until the motion of the ram is reversed. Even the shortest dwell is sufficient for a thorough pressing of most cardboard displays.

Automatic Mounting Machines. The automatic mounting machine performs automatically in one unit the three operations which are separately executed in hand mounting. It glues the printed sheet, combines it with cardboard, and presses it as well. Our drawing explains the functioning of the machine schematically. The printed sheet enters the machine on one side, the cardboard on the other. The mechanically glued and aligned sheet is combined in register with the cardboard and passes a rotary press before leaving the machine.

The automatic mounting machine is operated by a crew of 3 to 5 men, takes a maximum sheet of 44 x 72 inches and, generally speaking, is not used on runs smaller than several thousand sheets as its set-up is costly.

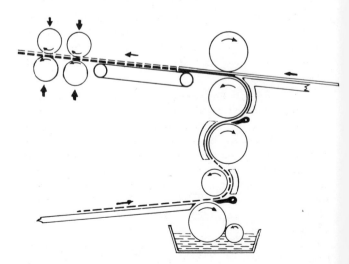

Schematic of Machine Gluing and Mounting.

The Duo-Mounter. The duo-mounter is the most highly developed type of mounting machine, and is used exclusively for very large runs. It combines not only the printed sheet with the cardboard, but also attaches a back liner in the same operation.

TRIMMING OF CARDBOARD DISPLAYS

The printed and mounted display is either trimmed or diecut. If all edges of the finished job are straight and at right angles to each other, the display is trimmed or straight-cut on the guillotine or power cutter.

The Power Cutter. The power cutter has a table equipped with side guide and back gage. The back gage determines the location of the cut and is controlled by the operator from the front where an indicator rule at eye level informs him about its position. The stock is jogged in the corner formed by side guide and back gage, then clamped either manually or automatically and cut when the operator engages the controls which are so arranged, for safety reasons, that he is forced to use both hands in this act. The knife returns automatically and, on the fully automatic

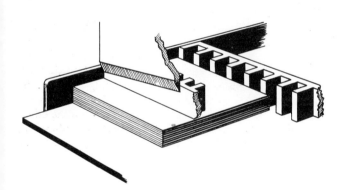

Schematic of a Guillotine Cutter.

models, the clamp must be raised by turning a hand wheel.

Power cutters are all built to square the sheets and come in a wide range of sizes from 34 inches up. Well-equipped display finishing plants have cutters up to to 64 inches; the 85- and 94-inch machines are rarely found outside of paper and board mills.

Trimming or Diecutting? The question whether trimming or diecutting is indicated is asked repeatedly. Whenever a job can be straight-cut, trimming is considered more economical for the following three reasons: (1) In diecutting, the cutting tool is a steel rule die which must be custom-made for each job. In trimming, the cutting knife is a permanent part of the power cutter and is, therewith, the same for every job. (2) The makeready on a diecut press takes much more time and skill than the setting of the power cutter. (3) Cardboard is diecut one piece at a time, but trimmed in lifts of many sheets. On the other hand, in diecutting, all four sides of the sheet are cut in one operation whereas in trimming, each side required a

separate operation. In most cases, trimming is, nevertheless, the cheaper technique of the two.

DISPLAY FINISHING

The term finishing covers a variety of operations of which the following three, as the most important ones, were selected for brief discussion. These are: (1) Varnishing, (2) Laminating, and (3) Stapling, wire-stitching, eyeleting and riveting. Each of them is briefly discussed in the following.

Varnishing. Varnishing and laminating both aim at improving the printed surface by making it shiny and more serviceable. Varnishing, the older of the two processes, consists in coating the sheet with one or several coats of a film-forming liquid. This liquid is known as gum or spirit varnish, lacquer or synthetic, according to its chemical composition.

The varnish can be applied by different means. The most efficient equipment is the varnishing machine which feeds, dusts and varnishes the sheet automatically and delivers a completely dry sheet in one operation. But varnishing is also done directly on printing presses, by roller coaters, and last but not least, by silk screen — the only way for handling heavy boards. The varnishing machine, designed for paper and lightweight stocks, is limited in general to calipers up to 30 thousandths.

Laminating. Laminating consists in applying a sheet of transparent plastic to the printed stock. This application can either utilize adhesives or heat and pressure. Various kinds of plastics are used in laminating according to the nature of the job and equipment available.

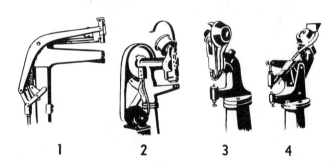

(1) A Stapler; (2) A Wire Stitcher; (3) An Eyeletting Machine; (4) Riveter.

Stapling, Wire-Stitching, Eyeleting and Riveting. Stapling, wire-stitching, eyeleting and riveting are techniques for attaching display parts and protecting holes. The stapling machine utilizes individual staples; the wire-stitcher forms its own out of wire; the eyeleting and riveting machines are provided with automatic feeding mechanisms. The functioning of these machines is self-evident, but one point is frequently neglected. Each of these machines has a throat which limits the distance of the stitch, eyelet or rivet from the edge of the sheet. It is well to remember this little detail in the planning stage; otherwise one can be in very unpleasant trouble where one expects it least.

Section Six: Folding Box Making

"A very large portion of American business rises or falls on the ability of the package to translate billions of dollars' worth of sales effort, advertising, merchandising and promotion into ACTION at the point-of-sale."

That statement by Norman F. Greenway, President of the Folding Paper Box Association of America, at the Seventeenth Annual Packaging Institute Forum significantly points up the situation that today we are in the midst of a tremendous marketing revolution — one which has been accelerating for the past quarter century because of the increasing emphasis on packaging — packaging in cartons, in cans, in tubes, in glass and in film.

The most widely used package is the folding paper box — over 115 billion being produced annually to protect, preserve, carry and help merchandise food, drugs, hardware, beverages, textiles — almost every type of item used in the home, office or factory. They are the end product of that segment of the great paper-converting industry which utilizes bending grades of paperboard as the primary material in their manufacture.

SOME ADVANTAGES OF FOLDING CARTONS

Some of the advantages of folding cartons are enumerated below: (1) They provide the best in printing — producing pictorial results as slick and attractive as any magazine cover. (2) They easily combine various materials — foils, films and other laminants. (3) They provide premiums as cutouts, recipes and directions which are incorporated into the carton design. (4) They provide a variety of styles and constructions — over 200 in common use. (5) They are made with close tolerances for use on high-speed filling machines which require extreme uniformity and dimensional stability. (6) When filled, they ship and handle efficiently and stack well for display purposes. (7) They are the key to new outlets in the traditional service stores and for self-selection super-markets and similar establishments. (8) They are supplied folded, but unopened, to the customer and, therefore, require minimum space for shipping and storing.

Folding Cartons Can Be Manufactured by Use of Lithography. Since the pictorial reproductions and designs on countless millions of folding cartons are striking examples of the lithographic process, a discussion of folding box manufacture seems in order in this Manual.

Other chapters cover in detail the technical phases of the offset process; here attention will be given primarily to those other operations relating to carton production as are essentially different from the production of other products of lithography.

FACTORS TO BE DISCUSSED IN THE MANUFAC-TURING OF FOLDING CARTONS

The satisfactory performance of a folding carton depends upon four factors: (1) The proper choice of the appropriate structural style; (2) The use of a boxboard having the required protective and functional properties; (3) The effectiveness of the design and the suitability of the reproduction process selected; and (4) The quality of manufacture as shown in the end product.

These four factors are discussed under the following headings in our study: (1) Styles of folding boxes; (2) Materials for folding boxes; (3) Design of folding boxes; and (4) Manufacture of folding boxes.

Definition of Folding Cartons. That we may have a common understanding of the nature of the packaging medium called the folding carton, or folding paper box, the following definition will precede our discussion: *The term folding carton designates containers converted from bending grades of paperboard, diecut and creased in a variety of styles and delivered — with or without printing — to their users either in a glued and collapsed form or as flat blanks, ready for mechanical or manual setup and use.*

Folding cartons are distinguished from setup boxes which are supplied in a rigid or erected form with stayed corners, and generally covered with a decorative or printed paper wrapping.

CARTON STYLES

Folding cartons are made in a multitude of one-piece, two-piece telescope, display, and carrier styles. No complete list of carton constructions has ever been compiled as new ones are being continually designed to meet new requirements. Hundreds of patents have been issued; however, there are many carton designs which are merely adaptations or combinations of the elements found in a number of basic constructions. These cartons are commonly designated as follows:

1. Seal end
2. Tuck end (reverse or straight)
3. Brightwood blanks
4. Cracker style
5. Friction end
6. Diagonal infold or outfold
7. Automatic/snap lock bottom
8. Tube and slide
9. Carriers
10. Folders

The Two Primary Concepts of Folding Cartons. The above-listed cartons, and for that matter all carton constructions, have evolved from the two primary concepts of the tube and the tray which are explained as follows: (1) *The tube* — The tube is a diecut sheet of boxboard, folded over and glued along two parallel edges to form a hollow tubular shape, usually rectangular, the ends of which can be sealed, tucked or locked in a variety of ways. (2) *The tray* — The tray is a sheet of diecut boxboard with its edges folded at right angles and locked, stitched or glued together at the corners. One panel can be extended to form the

DIAGRAM FOR "PRINTING BLEEDS" AND PANEL ARRANGEMENT USUALLY USED FOR A REVERSE TUCK-END CARTON

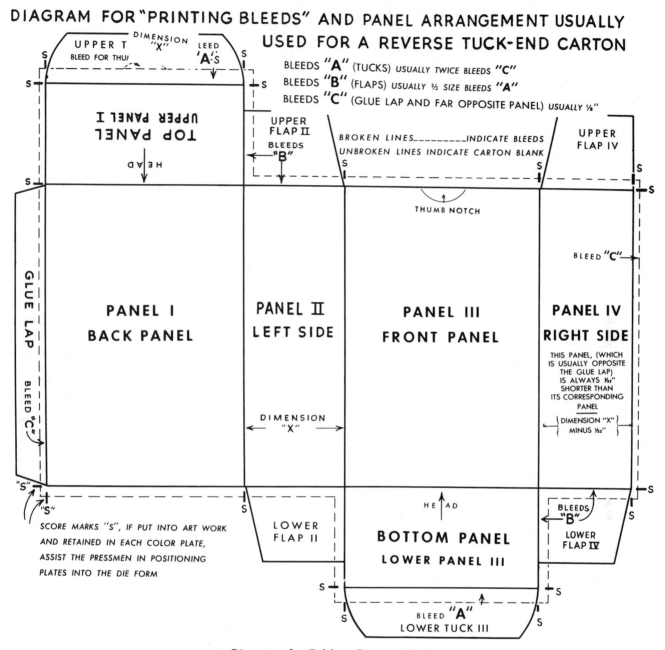

BLEEDS **"A"** (TUCKS) USUALLY TWICE BLEEDS **"C"**
BLEEDS **"B"** (FLAPS) USUALLY ⅓ SIZE BLEEDS **"A"**
BLEEDS **"C"** (GLUE LAP AND FAR OPPOSITE PANEL) USUALLY ⅛"

BROKEN LINES_____INDICATE BLEEDS
UNBROKEN LINES INDICATE CARTON BLANK

UPPER T DIMENSION "X" LEED
BLEED FOR THU

TOP PANEL
UPPER PANEL I
HEAD

UPPER FLAP II
BLEEDS "B"

UPPER FLAP IV

THUMB NOTCH

BLEED "C"

GLUE LAP
BLEED "C"

PANEL I
BACK PANEL

PANEL II
LEFT SIDE

PANEL III
FRONT PANEL

PANEL IV
RIGHT SIDE

THIS PANEL, (WHICH IS USUALLY OPPOSITE THE GLUE LAP) IS ALWAYS ¹⁄₃₂ SHORTER THAN ITS CORRESPONDING PANEL

{ DIMENSION "X" }
MINUS ¹⁄₃₂

DIMENSION "X"

"S"
"S"

SCORE MARKS "S", IF PUT INTO ART WORK
AND RETAINED IN EACH COLOR PLATE,
ASSIST THE PRESSMEN IN POSITIONING
PLATES INTO THE DIE FORM

LOWER FLAP II

HEAD

BOTTOM PANEL
LOWER PANEL III

BLEEDS "B"
LOWER FLAP IV

BLEED "A"
LOWER TUCK III

Diagram of a Folding Carton (Flat).

cover or two trays fitted together to form the top and bottom of a complete box.

The structural complexities of certain styles warrant the designation of a "specialty" classification for folding boxes such as multiple unit carriers and flip-top cigarette boxes.

Folding Cartons are Made for Various Kinds of Loads. With the wide variety of styles available, carton buyers can choose one or have a basic style adapted to suit their individual needs, be they for a non-supporting load or free-flowing product, such as soap powder; a semi-supporting load, such as a tube of tooth paste; or a rigid, full-supporting load, such as a bar of soap.

Specifying Dimensions. The dimensions of a folding carton are given in inches in the following sequence: length, width and depth. In this context *length* is the larger

dimension at the opening of the carton when it is assembled and presented for filling; *width* is the smaller dimension at the opening of the box; *depth,* the remaining dimension, is the distance from the opening to the bottom panel, or the distance between the openings in a carton blank such as a reverse tuck end style.

All dimensions are measured from the center of the score to the center of the adjacent parallel score.

Carton Styles Are Numerous, Their Designation Sometimes Confusing. A certain amount of confusion arises in applying name designations to carton styles other than some of the more basic ones. Even then local designations are given to component parts or members of a carton that are not recognized in other geographical areas. Many patented styles use the inventor's name; some companies have created their own trade labels.

Nomenclature Charts Published by the Folding Paper Box Association. In an attempt to help clear up the situation, the Folding Paper Box Association of America published a series of 18 nomenclature charts for the more common basic constructions, and distributed them widely several years ago. Since then these charts have been reproduced in several books and manuals. They are currently out of print but are being revised; it is expected that they will be available again for distribution late in the fall of 1958.

Federal Specifications for Folding Boxes. Federal specification "PPP-B-566" covering folding paperboard boxes was issued February 14, 1955 for the use of all Federal agencies and is available from the Government Printing Office, Washington, D.C., for 20¢. The diagrams showing ten of the styles covered in the specifications are similar to the drawings for similar constructions, used commercially or in non-governmental business.

Folding Box Constructions for Automatic Machinery. Even with the increasing use of automatic cartoning machines in packers' plants, many basic styles can be handled on the filling equipment that is generally available to load cartons and close or seal the same after filling. There are some special constructions designed to be used only on machines built to handle them. Many are patented and their manufacture is restricted to the patent owners or their licensees. Since a number of packaging lines operate at speeds up to and over 300 per minute, extreme care must be exercised in designing and producing dimensionally uniform cartons.

MATERIALS FOR FOLDING CARTONS

Any consideration of the production of folding cartons should undoubtedly begin with a review of information about the principal material used — folding boxboard. For the most part it is made specifically for each order of cartons so that it may embody the proper characteristics required for the item being packaged.

Description of Boxboard. This material, usually referred to as boxboard, is one of the bending grades of paperboard generally ranging from .012 to .045 inch in thickness and is expected to score, bend or fold without cracking or breaking, in addition to providing a suitable printing surface. Boxboards are obtainable in a wide variety of finishes and are usually made on cylinder board machines, although an increasing amount of tonnage is now being turned out on Fourdrinier machines.

Characteristics Required of a Boxboard. The chief qualities looked for in the grades of board selected for folding cartons are: (1) *Strength* — to protect adequately the products packaged; (2) *Flexibility* — to permit bending up to 180 degrees without cracking or breaking where creased; (3) *Appearance* — to enhance the "eye appeal" of the package; (4) *Printability* — to possess a suitable surface for printing; (5) *Stiffness* — to have rigidity sufficient to hold required shape and to function satisfactorily on automatic

filling machines; (6) *Resistance* to penetration or absorption of moisture, grease, or other specified elements.

Other Materials and Their Properties. In addition, today's packaging requirements frequently necessitate the application of special additives, surface treatments or laminated materials to provide a satisfactory board for the container. A number of other materials such as foil and "polyethelene" are being laminated. Some of these additional functional properties that can be provided include:

1. Moisture-vapor barriers
2. Moisture-water barriers
3. Grease barriers
4. Rust preventatives
5. Tarnish inhibitors
6. Wet strength
7. Insect repellency
8. Mould inhibitors
9. Flame retardancy

Lithographing Method of Printing Must be Indicated When Board is Ordered. When the stock is to be lithographed, that fact must be stated so that the mill can furnish board whose printing surface is suited to lithographic printing.

The bulk of the boxboards used for folding cartons comes within the following grades, each with almost innumerable furnishes and densities:

Bending Chipboard: Bending chipboard is the lowest grade of folding boxboard made principally of reclaimed waste paper. It is usually dark gray in color and unsuitable for multicolor printing.

Single Manila-Lined Board: This is a commercial grade of board having its top liner made of unbleached sulphite and ground wood pulp and the balance composed of news or mixed papers. It is distinguished by its manila color.

Bleached Manila-Lined Board: This board is of a higher grade, produced from the same ingredients but whiter in color. It is extensively used for folding boxes of all kinds and sizes.

White Patent Coated Board: This board is made with a top liner of bleached chemical wood pulp mixed with white shavings, aspen or soda pulp to produce a good white surface suitable for multicolor printing. It is used extensively for high grade carton manufacture. (The name of the board is a misnomer as it is neither a patented nor a coated board.)

Clay-Coated Board: This is a high-grade folding boxboard sheet on which a coating of white clay or other mineral substance is applied to the top liner to produce a hard, smooth, white printing surface.

Solid Board (now more commonly called food board): This is produced entirely from virgin pulp of either bleached or semi-bleached kraft, or sulphite or a mixture of either with ground wood and used extensively for packaging food products.

Board for Folding Cartons Must be Carefully Selected and Exactly Specified. When one considers the wide variety of boxboards available for conversion into folding cartons, it becomes obvious that much thought and care as well as considerable research must go into writing specifications for the mills to use in manufacturing an order. To insure a satisfactory end product requires some real team play between the ultimate user, the converter and the board supplier, with experienced and qualified men in all three positions cooperating to the fullest extent.

Printability, a Most Important Characteristic of Boxboards. Not the least of the requirements are those affecting the printability of the board, whether it's done by letterpress, gravure or offset.

DESIGN OF FOLDING CARTONS

Although the construction or style of a carton is of primary consideration and the board specification is essential, the design factor as it applies to the size, shape, identifying and informative copy, pictorial art and color scheme of the package is certainly of as great importance.

Design Grows in Importance with the Spread of Self-Selection. This is especially true as the trend to self-selection is compelling many consumer goods industries to change their entire merchandising concept. It is imperative that swift and easy identification of a packaged product tie-in with advertising and sales promotional efforts; *the carton on the shelf must be a salesman as well as a container.*

Package Designing, a New Specialty. Out of the need to make packages successful, merchandising has grown a new profession: the package designer. A group of specialists who have acquired considerable proficiency in solving the related problems of their clients are active in this field.

Manufacturers of Folding Cartons Render Design Services. Also, almost all carton manufacturers are qualified and equipped to help their customers to increase the eye-appeal and sales pull of the cartons they make together with recommendations for improved constructions and better functional properties in the board.

Today's beautifully printed food product containers, for example, with tantalizing appetite appeal in their pictorial

realism and color dominance are a far cry from the simple, one-color, product identification labeling that was prevalent a couple of decades ago. Offset lithography in particular lends itself to this kind of carton printing.

Various Printing Processes Used in the Making of Folding Cartons. It is true that the great bulk of folding cartons is still printed by letterpress but an increasing volume is being done by both gravure and offset lithography. Much has already been written and published about the relative merits of these processes. The advantages and disadvantages of each, with respect to the character and quality of their reproductions and the resulting economics from their use, are well known, so there is no need to repeat them here.

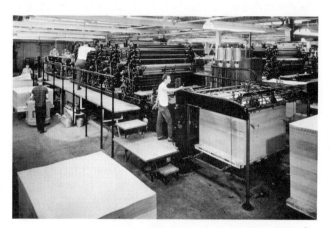

A Multicolor Harris Offset Press Installation at the Rochester Folding Box Company Plant.

Art Preparation for Folding Carton Reproduction. The correct preparation of the artwork and drawings for cartons has long been a problem, regardless of the printing method employed. Artists not experienced in doing carton work, fail to realize that a carton has three dimensions and usually six abutting panels or sides and ends to reckon with. Since most designs extend across two or more of these, allowance for the bend or fold at the corner must be provided according to the caliper of the boxboard used.

A sample carton made to the exact size and of same-caliper stock is essential to preparing correct working drawings. Again close cooperation between the parties involved is necessary to avoid corrections when the design goes into production. This is especially so when offset plates are being supplied through trade sources.

THE MANUFACTURE OF FOLDING CARTONS

The fact that the carton industry is supplying its products at a quality level higher than ever before attests to the better production facilities, improvements in method and the competency of the skilled craftsmen in performing the converting operations involved. Space will not permit a detailed discussion of them; however, some of those peculiar to carton production will be highlighted in the following paragraphs:

Courtesy Ace Carton Co.

A Miehle 76 5-Color with Double Pile Delivery.

Die Making. After the hand-cut sample has been approved, the planning department determines the number and arrangement of the flat blanks to be run on the sheet of stock. Wherever possible the protruding or irregular-shaped members of the carton are interlocked to save material. Because most cartons are generally printed in multiples and then die cut and scored for subsequent processing, the first step is the preparation of a steel rule cutting die.

Two Kind of Dies. There are two types of dies — the unit or block die and a "jigged" die. The unit die consists of the required number of component parts of each carton usually cut from plywood and assembled together in a form or chase with pieces of the steel cutting rule shaped to the contours of the edges of the carton and scoring rule of the desired kind inserted where the attached elements of the carton join. In a jigged die a skilled operator saws a pattern in the die block material in such a way that the die generally remains in one piece and the cutting and creasing rules are inserted in their proper place. The accuracy and uniformity of the work is of the utmost importance because the die cut blanks must be similar and as uniform as possible, especially when the cartons are to be run on automatic filling machines that require close tolerance in their dimensions.

The Rub-Off Sheet. From the assembled dies a rub-off is made on an oiled paper sheet or a vinyl sheet in order to provide a pattern for use in laying out and registering the images of the cartons to be produced. For lithographed work the images on the press plates must be accurately positioned with each other and in register with the creasing die because there is no way to shift them individually later on to register with the die.

Double Knifing. For some types of designs space must be left between the several units in the form, necessitating double knifing. This permits the units in the die form to be shifted into position for the cutting and creasing operation, but it does involve considerable additional stripping to remove the extra scrap thus created. Many carton plants doing lithography successfully use step-and-repeat camera equipment.

Materials Used for Making Cutting Dies. The steel rule cutting dies are generally made from pieces of plywood, but in some instances to insure the utmost accuracy and no distortion with changing climatic conditions, metal, specially impregnated wood composition, or plastic "fill-ins" may be used.

Presswork. As mentioned before, the great bulk of carton printing is done by letterpress, and smaller amounts by gravure and lithography. In this Manual lithographed work is covered.

There has been a tendency for carton plants doing lithography to use the larger sizes of offset presses and in most instances to make four- or five-color installations. Some firms, however, are beginning to use smaller presses for shorter and medium length runs, believing that the higher speed at which they operate and the smaller die forms more than equal the advantages found with the larger presses. The practices followed in setting up and operating lithographic equipment for carton work are quite similar to the

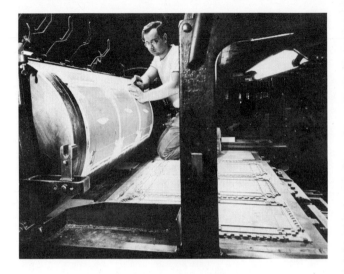

Diecutting Makeready.

steps for label and other lithographic work which are described in other sections of this Manual. Because of the thicker caliper of boxboard, considerable more floor space for work in process is required than for paper.

Cutting and Creasing. This is essentially a finishing operation and, together with the die making is peculiar to this industry. Cutting and creasing equipment, as far as lithographed work is concerned, is operated separately and not in-line as with flexographic or gravure. It is done on platen presses, cylinder type cutters and creasers or reciprocating bed machines using an inverted die. The cutting die is locked in a chase or on the bed of the press and a counter prepared on the impression plate or cylinder which functions as a female pattern to facilitate scoring the paperboard to the desired depth or cutting through the stock along the edges of the carton blank. These presses are either hand or mechanically fed.

Stripping. Small nicks are made in the die form to hold the cut pieces together for delivery from the press. After the work has passed through the machine it is necessary to remove the scrap stock or skeletons from around the

A Folding and Gluing Machine.

outline of the blank, and between the flaps, locks and other elements. This is generally referred to as "stripping" or "picking" and can be done by hand, with the aid of pneumatic or electric hammers or specially built mechanical stripping machines, some of which permit in-line operation with the cutting and creasing press.

Gluing. Some customers buy their cartons in blank form, or die cut and scored but not glued into a tubular or tray shape as their own automatic cartoning equipment will assemble and glue the carton as part of the loading or filling operation. For the most part, however, tube types and many special tray designs have a glue lap or flap on which glue is applied automatically and to which the opposite carton edge is folded and adhered. These machines operate at very high rates of speed and on medium size cartons, it is not unusual to glue upwards of 75,000 units an hour. As the cartons are delivered in collapsed form from this equipment they are inspected, counted and packed in master shipping containers for delivery. The majority of carton constructions require only gluing the overlapping strip to a side panel on straight-line equipment but the more complex styles require right-angle gluing machinery in which the direction movement for the carton is changed in order to glue spots at right angle to the first gluing.

Finishing Operations. A number of special operations may be performed on cartons to increase their utility in addition to the ones mentioned below — metal closures, handles, pouring spouts, etc.

Windowing. In many instances it is desirable to show the product packaged, so cutouts or windows are frequently made in the carton blanks over which there is attached a thin sheet of transparent film — acetate, cellophane, mylar, etc. This is done prior to the gluing operations described above using special high-speed automatic equipment. In cases where very large volume and speed are important, windowing can be done as part of an in-line operation.

Waxing. A protective coating of paraffin wax is frequently applied to carton blanks to give added functional

A Windowing Machine.

properties to the carton. This is done by several methods utilizing hot or cold wax applications.

Varnishing. For appearance as well as protection against rubbing and scratching, many cartons are given a protective coating of spirit or overprint varnish. This is applied in some instances on printing equipment as an extra operation or under some conditions at the same time as printing, but in many plants special varnishing machines with drying equipment have been installed.

CHAPTER SIXTEEN

Lithographic Trade Customs_____

Section One: Court Cases and Their Decisions

A trade custom is an established method of dealing between persons engaged in a particular vocation or trade. Like most legal terms, "customs and usages" uses two words where one would do. "Custom" and "usage" are synonymous terms. Some customs have been in use for so long they have acquired the force of law. However, to vary the ordinary meaning of words used in a contract by proving there is a "usage," it must be well-established that both parties can be presumed to have known the usage. Custom and usage do not spring up overnight but take time to become accepted.

Back in 1843, a usage of carpenters in New York City, to charge a day and a quarter's wages for 12½ hours of work, was held valid.

To establish a custom, it is not enough that an act is frequently done. It must be recognized, so that the parties to the contract must tacitly agree that their rights and responsibilities shall be determined by it.

An individual custom is of no value here, since a custom to be admissible in evidence must be general. Also, a custom, to be admissible in evidence as such, must be uniform. It must also be reasonable.

Of course, a custom which conflicts with an established law is invalid. Evidence of custom is not permitted to accomplish an unfair or immoral construction of a contract.

It is well to be familiar with the custom and usage of a profession or trade, because the law holds that a person is presumed to know the customs and usages of the business in which he is engaged. In order that you may become acquainted with what the courts have said from time to time regarding trade customs in lithography, here are some of the more important decisions, in abridged form.

WHO OWNS LITHO STONES?

Back in the Gay Nineties, one Samuel Knight agreed that the Hatch Lithographing Company would engrave stones from Knight's designs, he to own the engraving, and the Company the stones. The Company afterwards let the stones get into the hands of another company. When Knight found out about this, he offered the value of the stones and demanded delivery. New company said: NO—and a law suit was started, which the Court dismissed, stating that while the original Hatch Company was exposed to a suit for breach of contract, Knight could not follow the stones into the hands of strangers.

This case (*Knight* v. *Sackett & Wilhelms Lithographing Co.*), the report of which is found in 141 New York "Reports" at page 404, contains an interesting opinion by Judge Gray, who argues that the dismissal of the complaint was undoubtedly right because Knight failed to show that he had any right to the possession of these stones. He never had any interest in the stones except under his oral contract with the Hatch Company, which gave him the right to have prints made from them. The contract between Knight and the Hatch Company was one which bound the Company to render services for a fixed compensation. Knight calculated that he had a right based upon a theory that the stones were jointly owned by him and the Company, but he couldn't prove this. All he showed was that the stones belonged to the Hatch Company and that they would not print from them for anyone else. The Judge held that Knight never had any title to, or any right to the possession of these stones and the agreement was one for the performance of services in the making and transferring of lithographic engravings.

PRESS PLATES BELONG TO THE LITHOGRAPHER

In 1949, Mr. Justice Capozzoli decided the first case covering lithographic press plates. Universal Map Co. Inc. had brought suit against the lithographic firm of Lutz & Sheinkman for the value of such plates. In all but one of the orders between the parties, the written quotations contained the statement in writing that no charge is made for the stones, dies or plates on which the work is drawn or engraved and these stones, dies and plates remain the property of Lutz & Sheinkman. Assuming that there was no writing controlling the disposition of the plates, there was offered uncontradicted proof that it is the custom of the trade that the plates belong to the lithographer.

In arriving at his decision dismissing the complaint of the map company against the lithographer (194 misc. 938), the Judge reviewed several decisions in the New York courts, including the Knight case referred to in this article. Another case was that of Colten v. Jacques Marchais, Inc. (61 N.Y. Sup. 2nd 269), decided by Mr. Justice Watson in the New York City Municipal Court in 1946. Colten, a professional photographer, has sued to recover for professional services and the Marchais company counterclaimed for the return of over 400 negatives which, it was orally agreed between the parties, were to be delivered to the customer. The Judge pointed out that the relationship between photographer and customer is that of employee and employer and the customer obtains all proprietary rights in the negative as well as the photographs purchased by him. According to the judge in this case, if the photographer failed to show that he was given the right to have and keep the negatives, he had to surrender them to the customer, to whom belongs the absolute legal ownership.

The photographer claimed there was a custom and usage in the field of commercial photography which gives the photographer the right to own and possess the negative of photographs made for his customer. The Judge said that custom and usage could not be set up to alter a general principle of law and make the legal rights of the parties other than they are fixed by the circumstances of the transaction.

Still another case discussed by Mr. Justice Capozzoli was that of *Hochstadter* v. *H. Tarr* (68 N.Y. Sup. 2nd, 762), in which three Justices of the Supreme Court in New York State decided that where a customer employs a photographer to make pictures of him, the photographer, in the absence of an agreement to the contrary, has the right to retain the negatives. The fact that this determination was made by a higher court than that in which Mr. Justice Watson was sitting, would indicate that, had the Colten case been appealed, a different decision would have been reached. At any rate, the prevailing legal opinion is that, in the absence of an agreement to the contrary, a lithographer's press plates belong to the lithographer and not to the customer.

A case which was decided squarely on trade customs was tried in the Superior Court in New Jersey several years ago. (*Yogg* v. *Reproduction Offset Printing Corporation*). The facts as set forth in the pre-trial statement in that case are as follows:

The customer claims that between April 14, 1947 and Jan. 3, 1952, he engaged the defendant to do certain lithographic printing. It is conceded that defendant conducts a printing plant and lithographic and platemaking shop. It is agreed also that in order for defendant to do plaintiff's work, it was necessary for the lithographer to make certain lithographic plates.

The customer claims that in order for defendant to do the work contracted for, it was necessary for defendant to make lithographic plates, for which the customer paid the defendant the sum of $12,423.34. This figure includes $172 representing the value of one plate which the customer furnished to the defendant. The customer claims that

upon payment to the defendant for the plates and upon delivery of the one valued at $172 the plates became and remained the property of the customer. Upon completion of the work, the customer demanded the return of the plates which the defendant has refused, and the customer therefore seeks a recovery representing the value of the plates. The invoices covering all of the plates involved in this action are marked P-1 for identification.

Defendant admits the engagement to do lithographic work, that it made certain plates in connection with the plaintiff's work, that it received one plate from the plaintiff which it did not make, that it received payment for the plates which it did make; and that it still has in its possession all of the plates either made for the customer or furnished to it by the customer.

Defendant claims that the plates are its property; it claims that although there was no express written or oral agreement with respect to the ownership, the plates became its property by reason of universal custom or practice in the trade, which practice was or should have been known to the customer. Defendant's answer is amended to add as a separate and special defense that the plates in question became its property by reason of the custom or practice in the trade.

The printer has filed a counterclaim seeking recovery for the balance due from the plaintiff for certain printing work. The amount claimed is $932.70 and the customer concedes that this sum is due.

The issues to be determined at the trial are: 1. Ownership of the plates in question; 2. Existence of a custom or practice in the trade with respect to ownership; and 3. Nature of the custom and whether the plaintiff had actual or constructive knowledge of the custom.

The jury heard the testimony of experts on the customs and usages in the trade and found in favor of the defendant printer and lithographer; that by reason of the custom in the trade the plates became the property of the printer.

In the brief submitted for the defendant, its attorney pointed out that in a previous case decided in 1938 in the New Jersey Supreme Court (*Greenberg Publishing Co.* v. *Jersey City Printing Co.*), where, as here, a printer was sued for the value of lithographic plates prepared by the printer for work produced for its customer, the jury decided in the printer's favor after four days of trial. The Court in that case had charged the jury that in the absence of a definite agreement concerning the disposal and ownership of plates on which work has been done, the trade customs would prevail.

REPRODUCTION OF COLOR—HAND-SEPARATION PROCESS

A case which went all the way to the highest court in New York State determined the question of what the customer is entitled to in a color job (Duenewald Printing Corporation v. G. P. Putman's Sons, 301 N.Y. 569). Where the customer's primary concern is not accuracy of reproduction of colors but cheapness of price, he cannot complain of less than perfect results. Where the printer produces a job which is good and acceptable under the process employed, which in this case was the hand-separation process, the customer cannot successfully complain. Where such process is employed, variations in color are to be expected and the final product of the printer is an acceptable standard of such process. Expert testimony in behalf of the printer showed that it had produced a book acceptable in the trade as good in the reproduction of colors as could reasonably be expected in the light of the inexpensive process that the customer had agreed should be employed.

It is significant that this case when tried before the trial justice resulted in judgment for the printer; when it was appealed by the customer, the Appellate Division found in favor of the customer; and when the printer appealed from this reversal to the Court of Appeals, that court rejected the determination of the Appellate Division and upheld the original judgment in favor of the printer.

A Justice of the Appellate Division who dissented in the finding of that Court, said that the ultimate test is whether the result as a color lithographing job by the hand-separation process is as good as could reasonably be expected. Such questions should be determined by the testimony of experts in the craft familiar with lithographic reproduction in colors by the hand-separation process.

WHO IS LIABLE FOR MISTAKES IN OKAYED PROOFS?

Where a printer received from his customer an order "subject to the customer's acceptance of the finished proof" and a proof sent the customer came back to the printer marked "okay" and signed by the customer, the fact that two words were transposed in the proof and had been overlooked by both printer and customer was not the responsibility of the printer.

The Court decided that the printer's contract was to furnish cards according to the finished proof. If there was an error in the sample, the customer was not obliged to accept it, but once okayed, the customer must be considered to have ordered cards corresponding to the sample. (*Gills Lithographic & Liberty Printing Co. v. Chase,* 21 N.E. 765).

If the customer does not okay the proof but merely selects the type, the customer may, according to a legal decision in Illinois, object to the quality of the printing because the appearance of the work depends not only on the style of type but upon the inking and other acts in the printing process. The printer would have to show that he had substantially performed his contract or the customer can rescind the same, and refuse to pay for the order.

A court was asked to define a proof in a case where the customer okayed proofs but asked the printer to rough or emboss the prints to see how they would look. The definition was: "An impression taken from an engraved plate to show its progress during the execution of it." (*Turner v. Osgood Art Colortype Co.* 125 Ill. App. 602).

The author of a famous legal textbook on sales says that as a general rule all the buyer is entitled to in case of a sale or contract to sell by sample is that the goods shall be like the sample. He has no right to have the goods saleable if the sample, which he has inspected, is not (*Williston Sales* (Rev. Ed.) Sec. 257).

New York courts have ruled that a deliberate, intelligent and intentional acceptance of property manufactured under contract after inspection, precludes the customer from claiming damages for any visible or discernible defect in the property sold.

Where the printer invited the inspection of the goods, so as to obtain authority to deliver the goods to the parties who had agreed to print and bind the plates into books, the customer who has actually made the inspection cannot thereafter claim that there was no acceptance of the property sold or to claim damages for defects in the articles so accepted. (*Studer v. Bleistein,* 22 N.E. 243.)

LIMITATIONS ON REJECTION OF GOODS

A printer who delivers stationery and nine months later finds himself suing for payment of goods sold and delivered, which, of course, the customer tries to defend, has the right to a judgment against his customer, even though there was a claim by the customer that the printer was supposed to hold the job until the customer furnished a new address to which he was moving. In his defence the customer claimed the stationery was useless.

The court which decided in favor of the printer said that in view of the fact that the customer had accepted the goods and had never given the printer notice that they were objectionable and not acceptable, but remained silent for six months or until he was sued, by so doing he acquiesced in the quality of the stationery as being according to sample given the printer at the time the order was placed. (*Leigh v. Cornelius,* 15 S.E. 2nd 827.)

In another instance of this character an order for illustrated advertising pamphlets was in part, "Please enter our order for 160,000 copies as per dummy submitted, divided into eight issues of 20,000 per issue. Paper stock subject to okay. Envelopes subject to okay. All artwork, copy, editorials and proofs subject to okay before each issue goes to press." (*Hollidge v. Gussow Kahn & Co.,* 67 Fed. 2nd 459.)

After the first issue of 20,000 leaflets had been delivered the purchaser refused to continue the contract, contending there had been no acceptance of its order and hence no agreement under which it was liable. (*Mason v. Valentine,* 168 N.Y. Sup. 159.)

Said the court, "When the order for 160,000 copies was made," in holding the purchaser liable under this agreement, "and acted upon by the printer, we think it clear that both parties regarded themselves bound." (*Uniform Sales Act,* Secs. 48, 49.)

Late Delivery. In another controversy a printer accepted an order for the manufacture of 63,500 picture postcards for use at a summer resort. Shipment was delayed from three to six weeks. However, the cards were accepted when delivered and retained without objection. In spite of monthly statements the bill remained unpaid for six months when the customer sued the printer claiming damages for failure to deliver the cards on the agreed date.

In its decision the court said: "Retaining the cards without objection and entering upon the sale of them were acts radically inconsistent with the ownership of the seller. Fair dealing and proper regard for the rights of the printer also required the customer, if he had objections on account of any delay in shipment, to notify the printer within a reasonable time of such objection and thus save it from loss in continuing to manufacture and ship cards."

In most of our States, the printer is protected by the Uniform Sales Act. It is the law in the States which have adopted this statute that the customer is deemed to have accepted the goods when he intimates to the seller that he has accepted them or when the goods are delivered to him and he does nothing inconsistent with the ownership of the seller, or when after lapse of a reasonable time he retains the goods without notifying the seller he has rejected them.

In the absence of expressed or implied agreement of the parties, acceptance of the merchandise by the customer shall not discharge the printer from liability for breach of contract. But if, after acceptance of the merchandise the customer fails to notify the printer of the claim of breach of contract within a reasonable time after the customer knows —or ought to know of such breach—the printer shall not be liable.

THE CUSTOMER IN BANKRUPTCY

Trade customs, if set forth in estimates, may preserve the printer's right when a customer goes into bankruptcy and a trustee is appointed. In a case decided in a Federal Court (*Berger* v. *Kingsport Press, Inc.,* 89 F. 2nd 444), a firm had contracted with a printer for a large order of books. The customer delivered to the printer the paper and plates for the printing and the dies for embossing the cover.

When the customer became bankrupt, the printer claimed a lien on all the plates and dies furnished by the bankrupt customer. In the correspondence leading to the order, the printer had given an estimate which referred to Trade Customs set forth on the back of the first page of the letter to the customer. This provision was included in the Trade Customs:

"Manufacturer's lien attaches on all goods in our possession until delivery to customer, notwithstanding the giving of credit or the accepting of notes or guarantee of payment."

The estimate was held to be part of the contract and the Trade Customs governed its terms. A lien therefore was reserved to the printer by express contract.

The court found that the printer was entitled to a lien upon the manufactured goods or materials in its possession at the time the customer was adjudicated a bankrupt.

The importance of this decision is that a printer who takes the precaution to include in his estimate reference to Trade Customs obtains maximum protection in cases where insolvent customers are involved.

BAILMENTS: ELECTROPLATES
DOES THE PRINTER HAVE TO STORE THEM

The Appellate Division of the Supreme Court in New York has ruled that where electroplates are left with a printer under certain conditions and cannot later be found, the printer is not liable to the customer, provided the printer can show that he has made a search for them and has been unable to find them and that he himself did not misappropriate them. (*E. P. Dutton & Co.* v. *Goldman.* 277 App. Div. 556.)

The situation came about in this way. A book publisher delivered to a printer of illustrations some electroplates. The illustrations were printed and delivered to the printer of the book. About three years later, the publisher asked for the electroplates and the printer said they could not be found. He could give no explanation of their disappearance although the printer claimed he used due care in keeping them.

An important part of this case was that both the printer and the publisher introduced testimony that a custom existed covering this situation. The testimony for the printer was that one year was the customary maximum time to keep plates; whereas, the publisher had a witness testify that 27 years was not an unusual length of time to keep such property. Further, the publisher claimed that custom is to retain such plates perpetually and the printer should be regarded as having been obligated to store these plates forever. The Court said assuming there was such a custom, either party could terminate the relationship at any time.

In this case when the work was billed there was a written notice in red ink on the invoice that all plates were held in stock at the owner's risk. This was held to be equivalent to notice to the publisher to come and get the plates and if he did not do so within a reasonable time, the printer would not be responsible for taking care of them any longer.

The Court in this case held that three years was longer than a "reasonable" time.

Although the printer was held to be not liable in this matter, it was necessary for him to account for his failure to produce the plates, at least to the extent of showing that he did not take them himself. When the printer had shown that he did not willfully misappropriate these plates, the claim of the publisher was dismissed.

Section Two: Suggested List of Terms of Sale

The following trade customs have been generally recognized by the courts in interpreting contracts between printer and customer and some of them have been cited in legal decisions. Reference to them is essential to avoid misunderstandings and in some cases litigation between the printer and his customer.

Orders. Regularly entered orders cannot be cancelled except upon terms that will compensate the lithographer against loss.

Experimental Work. Experimental work performed at customer's request, such as sketches, drawings, composition, plates, presswork and materials will be charged for.

Sketches and Dummies. Sketches, copy, dummies and all preparatory work created or furnished by the lithographer, shall remain his exclusive property and no use of same shall be made, nor any ideas obtained therefrom be used, except upon compensation to be determined by the owner.

Drawings, Negatives and Plates. Artwork, drawings, negatives, positives, plates, and other items when supplied by the lithographer shall remain his exclusive property, unless otherwise agreed in writing.

Alterations. Proposals are only for work according to the original specifications. If through customer's error, or change of mind, work has to be done a second time or more, such extra work will carry an additional charge at prevailing rates for work performed.

Approval of Proofs. If proofs are submitted to the customer, corrections, if any, are to be made thereon and the proofs returned to the lithographer marked "okay" or "okay with corrections" and signed with the name or initials of the person duly authorized to pass on same. If revised proofs are desired, request must be made when proof is returned. The lithographer is not responsible for errors if work is completed as per customer's okay.

Press Proofs. An extra charge will be made for press proofs, unless the customer is present when the plate is made ready on the press, so that no press time is lost. Presses standing awaiting okay of customer will be charged for at current rates for the time so consumed.

Color Proofing. Because of the difference in equipment and conditions between the color proofing and the pressroom operations, a reasonable variation in color be-

tween color proofs and the completed job shall constitute an acceptable delivery.

Quantities Delivered. Overruns or underruns not to exceed 10 percent of the amount ordered shall constitute an acceptable delivery and the excess or deficiency shall be charged or credited to the customer proportionately.

Customer's Property. The lithographer shall charge the customer, at prevailing rates, for handling and storing customer's paper stock or customer's lithographed matter held more than thirty (30) days. All customer's property that is stored with a lithographer is at the customer's risk, and the lithographer is not liable for any loss or damage thereto caused by fire, water, leakage, breakage, theft, negligence, insects, rodents, or any other cause beyond the lithographer's control. It is understood that the gratuitous storage of customer's property is solely for the benefit of the customer.

Delivery. Unless otherwise specified, the price quoted is for a single shipment, F.O.B. customer's local place of business. All estimates are based on continuous and uninterrupted delivery of complete order, unless specifications distinctly state otherwise.

Terms. Net cash thirty (30) days, unless otherwise provided in writing. All claims must be made within five days of receipt of goods.

Delays in Delivery. All agreements are made and all orders accepted contingent upon strikes, fires, accidents, wars, floods or other causes beyond the lithographer's control.

Paper Stock Furnished by Customer. Paper stock furnished by the customer shall be properly packed, free from dirt, grit, torn sheets, bad splices, etc., and of proper quality and specifications for the lithographer's requirements. Additional cost due to delays or impaired production on account of improper packing or quality shall be charged to the customer.

Glossary of Lithographic Terms_____

Aberration. General term for various optical errors in photographic lenses which prevent the lens from giving good definition.

Absorption. Optical term for the partial suppression of light in passage through a transparent or translucent medium or material.

Achromatic. Without color. A lens which refracts light of all colors equally is said to be achromatic.

Across the Grain. The direction opposite to that of the paper grain.

Actinic Light. Chemically active light obtained from arc lamps, mercury vapor lamps, photo-flood bulbs (gas filled tungsten filament incandescent lamps) and used to harden light-sensitive plate coating solutions in photographic platemaking techniques.

Affinity. Natural attraction for, as salt for moisture.

Air Eraser. Miniature sand-blasting hand appliance, used for removing superfluous lithographic images from the plate. Also used in erasing art without destroying the texture of the medium.

Albumin. A natural protein soluble in water and most commonly found in the whites of eggs; the colloid used for certain bichromated sensitizers employed in photomechanics.

Albumin Process. That procedure of photomechanics utilizing a coating of bichromated albumin as a sensitized surface, whereon images are made by exposure under a line or halftone negative, followed by subsequent development of the inked image with water.

Alkyd Resin Drying Oils. Synthetic drying oils made from glycerine or glycols by combination with various organic acids.

Aluminum Plate. A thin sheet of aluminum used in lithography for some press plates; image applied photographically; used for both surface-type and deep-etch offset plates.

Ammonium Dichromate. A salt formed by neutralizing chromic acid with ammonia, commonly used in photolithography as a sensitizing agent; also know as *Ammonium Bichromate.*

Angstrom Unit. A unit of measurement of the length of light waves. It is equal to $\frac{1}{10}$ of a millimicron, or one ten-millionth of a millimeter. There are approximately 254,000,000 Angstrom units in an inch.

Anhydrous Plate Wash. An anhydrous alcohol, a water-free alcohol used in lithographic deep-etch platemaking to wash the plate before applying the lacquer image base.

Antihalation. The property of a film or plate, usually with an opaque backing, which prevents halation. *Antihalation Backing,* a coating on the back of a film containing a dye or colored pigment for the purpose of absorbing light rays, thus preventing their reflection from the back surface of the film base.

Aperture. A small opening in a plate or sheet. In cameras, the aperture is usually variable in the form of an iris diaphragm and regulates the amount of light which passes through the lens. *Working Aperture* — diameter of that part of the lens actually used.

Asphaltum. A naturally occurring bituminous mixture of hydrocarbons and complex derivatives thereof, used in various inks and varnishes, and as an acid resist or protectant in photomechanics. In lithography, used to make printing image on press plate permanently ink-receptive.

Autoscreen (Film). A photographic film embodying the halftone screen; exposed to a continuous-tone image, produces a dot pattern automatically just as if a halftone screen had been used in the camera.

Back-Etching. Opening up or lessening of density in a negative. Used extensively in lithographing for color correcting continuous-tone negatives.

Backing-Up. Printing the other side, of a printed sheet.

Back Pressure. The squeeze pressure between the blanket (offset) cylinder and the impression cylinder; sometimes called "impression pressure."

Base Color. A first color used as a background on which other colors are printed.

Baumé Hydrometer. A special hydrometer invented for industrial use by Antoine Baumé and designed for determining the specific gravity of liquids. Of the two types available, the one measuring liquids heavier than water is most generally employed in photomechanics and electro-typing. For lithographic plate-coating solutions, the specific gravity is referred to as density of solution. This varies according to the temperature of the solution.

Bearers. Rings of steel at the ends of the plate cylinder, the blanket cylinder, and sometimes the impression cylinder. On American offset presses the bearers make rolling contact for proper meshing of the driving gears. On all presses, bearers provide a fixed base for determining the packing of plate and blanket.

Ben Day Process. A method of mechanically transferring line, dot or texture patterns to paper, metal or glass by general or local pressure on the back of an inked Ben Day screen (film), the screen bearing the particular pattern in relief on one side of the film. Invented in 1879 by Benjamin Day for introduction of shading effects in line drawings and reproductions therefrom.

Ben Day Tints. A term used for simulated Ben Day screens, applied by the artist by means of stock transparent sheets with printed patterns or screens being pasted on top of artwork, or by using a patented drawing paper with invisible patterns which are developed by artist's application of developing chemical. Also a term erroneously applied to halftone tints which are added to indicated areas by the stripper to give a tone in gray instead of solid.

Bimetal Plates. Lithographic plates in which the printing image base is formed of one metal and the non-printing area of a second metal. Generally, the printing area is formed of copper, while the non-printing areas may be nickel, chromium, or stainless steel. Some plates employ a third metal as a base or backing and could be regarded as trimetallic, multimetallic or polymetallic. Both surface and deep-etch platemaking techniques are used in the making of such plates. With a plating of chromium on copper sheet, the resist stencil of deep-etch method permits etching chromium from image to reach copper for base of lithographic image; with plating of copper on stainless steel base, surface platemaking methods temporarily protect the image while copper is etched away to give stainless steel for non-printing areas of plate.

Bite. A surface characteristic of paper which causes it to accept ink, pencil, or other impressions. (2) An etching operation on metals. (3) Gripper bite, the amount of paper that extends beneath the press gripper, sometimes called *gripper margin*.

Black-and-White. Said of originals and reproductions displayed in monochrome (single-color), as distinguished from polychrome or multicolor.

Black Printer. The black plate made for color reproductions to give proper emphasis to the neutral tones and detail; made frequently by exposure of copy on panchromatic emulsion through a yellow filter (K2 or K3 Wratten).

Blanket. A fabric coated with natural or synthetic rubber which is clamped around the blanket cylinder and which transfers the ink from the press plate to the paper.

Blanket Creep. The slight forward movement of that part of the blanket surface that is in contact with the plate or paper.

Blanket Cylinder. The cylinder where the blanket is mounted. This cylinder receives the inked design from the plate cylinder and "offsets" or transfers it onto the surface to be printed.

Blanket Thickness Gage. A special micrometer for measuring the offset blanket under uniform pressure.

Bleed. An extra amount of tone added to edges and contours of the sketch that is later to be diecut into a conforming shape. Window displays and contour cards are usually cut to shape to make them look more realistic. This "bleed" permits the slight variations that occur when the reproduction is being diecut. (2) Term applied to a lithographic ink pigment which dissolves in the fountain etch and causes tinting.

Blind. A dot on a photographic negative or positive, which lacks density and has become so transparent that any light going through it falsifies the values desired. To be photographically effective all dots must be opaque and all transparent areas must be absolutely clear.

Blind Image. In lithography, an image that has lost its ink-receptivity.

Blocking-Out. The operation of eliminating undesirable backgrounds and portions of negatives by opaquing the image.

Blue Key. A blueprint on glass or a vinyl plastic sheet of a basic design containing all elements with register marks, and used as a guide for stripping a flat of photographic elements of other colors to register. For deep-etch plates, positives are usually stripped to flats made of vinyl plastics.

Blueline. A drafting surface mounted on metal or board, then coated with an iron sensitizer, yielding a non-photographic blue image after contact exposure to a negative and development in water. (2) Some form of blueprint on an offset plate to be used as a guide in applying tusche or crayon handwork. (3) A blue on white print made by exposing sensitized paper to negative in contact.

Blueprint. A photographic print, usually by contact with negative, on paper, glass or metal. Serves as a guide for artist in making "keyed" art for multicolor; also used as a method of securing a copy of unit negatives or of flat for checking layout and imposition. Ozalid prints used for prints from photographic positives.

Brightness. Referring to the light being reflected by the copy to the lens of the process camera. Not to be confused with *illumination* which is the light falling on the copy on the copyboard of camera.

Bronzing. The application of a metallic powder, known as bronze, to the press sheet, usually by a bronzing machine. A sticky base of clear or yellow varnish is applied by the press just before the sheets are fed to the bronzer. There the powder is sifted onto the sheet where it adheres to the sticky image.

Brownprint. A silverprint or photograph of brown color, made of sensitized paper. Not to be confused with a sepia print, or black photograph which has been chemically converted (toned) to a brown color.

Brunak. A treatment for aluminum litho plates, using a solution of ammonium bichromate and hydrofluoric acid, to make them non-oxidizing.

Burn-Out. To overexpose in such a way on a press plate that no tints come up. This is done on deep-etch plates where positives are used. Edges can be sharpened up, while lettering can be obtained in toned areas by burning-out or by double shooting.

Caking. Caking is the collecting of pigment upon plates, rollers or ink table caused primarily by the inability of the vehicle to hold the pigment in suspension.

Camera Back. The back of the camera which holds the photographic material. With a darkroom process camera the camera back holds the plateholder, the ground glass, and the halftone screen. Special purpose camera backs have special equipment such as micrometer adjustment of plateholder for step-and-repeat negatives.

Camera Copyboard. That part of a process camera on which copy to be photographed is placed. Frequently it has a hinged glass cover to hold copy flat, can be tilted to horizontal position for placing copy, and may have a removable section in which a transparency holder can be positioned for back-lighting illumination.

Camera Extension. In photomechanics, the distance between the lens diaphragm and photographic surface in process cameras at any definite scale of reproduction.

Carbros. Reproduction color prints made by superimposition of color pigments transferred from carbon tissues whose differentially hardened image areas were made insoluble in hot water by contact with enlarged photographic bromide prints made from the color-separation negatives. The name is a hybrid of carbon and bromide, distinguishing the process from regular carbon prints which were limited to contact print size of the separations because of the low sensitivity of the bichromate sensitizer used.

Casein. A product of skimmed milk used for sizing and as an adhesive in the manufacture of coated papers. In lithography casein can be used in place of albumin for making surface plate coatings.

Catching Up. A lithographic term used to indicate that the non-image areas of a press plate are beginning to take ink.

Cellulose Gum. A water-soluble gum made from wood fiber cellulose, chemically designated as carboxymethylcellulose. In lithography, a substitute for gum arabic and synthetic gums.

Chalking. A lithographic term referring to the improper drying of ink; in chalking the pigment dusts off due to lack of binding vehicle; caused by too rapid absorption of vehicle into paper.

Chalk Offsets. Impressions on super paper, dusted with red chalk, and pulled over on stone or metal as a key or guide for the artist. This technique is limited in its use to poster hand plates to be run on a direct rotary lithographic press.

Chase (Lithographic). The negative (or positive) frame with glass face scribed with register lines on which photographic film or plates are positioned to register in a photocomposing machine. The frame or chase is attached to the register device, a jig-type fixture which establishes uniform register relationship between all images being photocomposed on offset press plates by the step-and-repeat method.

Chromic Dermatitis. A skin affliction resulting from attack on human tissues by salts of chromium and chromic acid. Commonly termed *chrome poisoning.*

Circular Screen. A circular-shaped halftone screen which enables the camera operator to obtain the proper screen angles for color halftones without disturbing the copy.

Clean Up. An offset plate is cleaned-up when the non-printing areas which have begun to become ink-receptive are made to be ink-repellent again.

Clearing. The operation of applying a very light flat bleaching etch to negatives or positives to remove a fog or scum (slight silver deposit). (2) *Clearing the plate,* the lithographic term for removing the light-hardened gum stencil from the non-image areas of a deep-etch press plate.

Coating. Term applied to the mineral substances such as china clay, blanc fixe, satin white etc., used to cover the surface of paper, thus making the coated surface of enamelled papers. (2) The operation of applying the mineral substance to the surface of the sheet of paper. (3) In photography and photomechanics, application of varnishes and other mixtures to plates and negatives; also application of light-sensitive solutions to plate surfaces, usually by means of a plate whirler.

Cobalt Drier. A type of liquid drier used in lithographic inks; a very strong surface drier.

Cold (Color). A color which is on the bluish side.

Cold Type. A trade term denoting the use of composition methods not involving hot metal type. Most common forms are typewriter composition, paper letters, photocomposition on photo paper and mechanical lettering instruments. Photographic composition on film is a form of cold type composition.

Collotype Printing. A printing process akin to lithography but employing bichromated gelatin images as the printing surface where detail and tone values depend on the degree to which different plate areas have been made water-receptive and ink-repellent. Collotype is capable of printing continuous-tone images; it is mainly executed as a direct printing process and used for fine art reproductions and other pictorial jobs in comparatively short runs. Collotype is known by a number of names; the most familiar American synonym is photogelatin printing.

Color Correction. Any of various methods such as masking, dot-etching, and re-etching, intended to promote improved color rendition. Can be done on screened or continuous-

tone separation negatives, or by corrective work on the halftone printing plates.

Color Filter. A sheet of dyed glass, gelatin, plastic or dyed gelatin cemented between glass plates, used in photography to absorb certain colors and permit better rendition of others. A color filter permits certain wavelengths of light to pass through and absorbs others.

Color Patch. A small pre-printed card showing the inks being used for process color work and attached to the original art when photographed for color separations. An aid to the correction artist when analyzing his tones.

Color Process Work. Also called Process Color. A reproduction of color made by means of photographic separations. Also the method or the copy requiring such operation.

Color Proofs — Progressive. A set of color proofs consists of color proofs of each plate, singly and in combination with other proofs as the job will be printed. For example, yellow by itself; magenta; yellow and magenta; cyan; yellow, magenta, and cyan; black by itself; and all four colors combined.

Color Separation. A photographic negative exposed through one of the tri-color filters and recording only one of the primary colors; in platemaking, manual separation of colors by handwork performed directly on the printing surface. The pre-separation of colors by the artist using separate overlays for each color executed in black or gray tones ready for the camera.

Color-Separation Negative. A photographic negative exposed through a color filter and recording only one of the primary colors in full-color work or one of the two colors in two-color work; in platemaking, manual separation of colors by handwork performed directly on the printing surface. The negative is a gray tonal record of the intensity and the color it is reproducing, being light where the color is strong in the copy, dark where the color is weak in the copy.

Color Swatch. A small, usually square solid print used with the sketch, negative, positive or printing plate to identify it and furnish a sample of the actual ink colors used. A guide in color separation and correction operations.

Color Transparency. A full-color photographic positive on a transparent support. Ektachrome, Flexichrome for example.

Combination Plate. In lithography, the joining of halftones and line negatives or positives in position to appear on the plate as combinations.

Complementary Colors. Any two opposite (or contrasting) light colors which when combined produce white or gray. A mixture of any two primary colors is the complement of the remaining primary. In printing, complementary colors have the power to either neutralize or to accentuate each other; thus to diminish or enhance the attention value of the print.

Contact Print. A photographic same-size copy made by exposure of a sensitized emulsion in contact with the transparency, a negative, or a positive; the exposing light passing through the master image.

Contacts. Same-size negatives made by exposing light-sensitive material in contact with a positive and subsequently developing. (2) Same-size positives made by exposing light-sensitive material in contact with a negative and subsequently developing.

Contact Screen. A photographically made halftone screen having a dot structure of graded density and usually used in vacuum contact with the film or plate.

Continuing Reaction. In an exposed light-sensitive emulsion or coating, the chemical reaction, similar to the light reaction but slower, that occurs in the time between exposure and development.

Continuous Tone. Said of those images (wash drawings, oil paintings, photographic negatives and positives) in which the detail and tone values of the subject are reproduced by a varying deposit (density) of developed silver in the picture. Photogelatin or collotype reproductions duplicate continuous-tone copy without use of a screen and are said to be continuous-tone reproductions. In lithographic color correction, continuous-tone color separation negatives are stained locally by gray dyes to add density, or treated by chemicals to lessen density.

Contrast. Tonal comparison of highlights and shadows in an original or reproduction. The tonal difference in detail, i.e., contrasty copy refers to accentuated detail in both light and dark areas.

Copy. The manuscript or text furnished to printers. Although the term "copy" is widely applied to photographs and different types of artwork submitted for reproduction, a better term for these items is *"original"* because it is from them that the reproduction originates. In photographic platemaking there are two kinds of copy — *line* and *tone,* photographed without and with the halftone screen, respectively. *Line copy* is that in which the design or image of the original is composed of lines or dots of solid color. *Tone copy* is that in which tones or shades of solid color appear.

Copyfitting. Calculations made in order to determine the proper size of type and width of line to fit the copy into a given area of space.

Copy Preparation. In photomechanical processes, the directions as to desired size and other details for illustrations and the arrangement into proper position of the various parts of the page to be photographed for reproduction. Also the work of preparing copy in paste-up form of text and art as a unit, termed a mechanical paste-up. (2) In typesetting, the careful revision of copy to insure a minimum of changes or corrections after type is set.

Core. In lithography and other photomechanical operations, the center portion of the halftone dot. (2) The cylindrical metal bar upon and around which the composition is molded in the making of an ink roller. (3) A cardboard, wood or metal tube on which the rolls of paper are wound.

Counter Etch. The first step in preparing to coat a grained offset metal plate. The purpose is to clean the metal of dirt and oxides without damaging the grain; a weak acid solution is used, such as 1 oz. hydrochloric acid in a gallon of water.

C.P. Abbreviation for "Chemically Pure."

Crayoning. In lithography, the use of a crayon for retouching on direct handmade or on photographic plates.

Creep. Forward movement of the blanket surface during operation of offset press due to improper pressure or stretch of offset blanket.

Cronak Process. The process of treating zinc plates with a mixture of sodium bichromate and sulfuric acid to make them resistant to oxidation.

Crop. To cut off an edge or trim.

Crossline Screen. A standard halftone (glass) screen with the opaque lines crossing each other at right angles, thus forming transparent squares, or "screen apertures."

Crossmarks. Register marks to make possible the accurate positioning of images in composing, double-printing and multicolor printing, and in superimposing overlays onto a base or to each other. Commercially available in a variety of forms, for pasting on copy.

Cross Rail. The horizontal element of the registering mechanism of a photocomposing machine on which the negative carrier travels.

Crowd (ink). A term meaning to ink the plate (offset) heavily in an attempt to print a darker tone; applying too heavy an ink film to plate.

Cutting (of negatives). In lithography, making the density of a negative or positive less by etching. Accomplished in halftone by reducing dot size. Cutting (of Negatives), a term used to refer to the opaquer's work of cleaning up bad negatives by use of needle or scraper.

Cyanide. The short name for sodium or potassium cyanide. It is used to remove the product of the silver bleaching action caused either by ferricyanide or by iodine. It is a much better solvent than hypo but it has a softening effect on gelatin emulsions and is very poisonous. Extreme care must be taken when using it.

Cylinder Gap. The gap or space in the cylinders of offset presses where the mechanism for plate clamps, blanket bar and tightening shaft, and grippers is housed.

Cylinder Guide Marks. Marks on the offset press plate to match corresponding marks on the plate cylinder of the press, so that each plate will be positioned the same on the press.

Dampeners. Cloth-covered rollers that distribute the dampening solution received from the ductor roller of the dampening unit to the lithographic press plate.

Dampening Solution. A solution of water, gum arabic, and various types of etches used for wetting the lithographic press plate (grease-water principle of lithography). Also termed *fountain solution* or *dampening etch.*

Dark Reaction. With light-sensitive plate coatings, the hardening action which takes place without light; this action is greater with high humidity and temperature.

Deep-Etch. An embracive photolithographic term for a process of platemaking, a type of printing plate. Deep-etch plates are made by contact photoprinting of line and halftone positives on grained metal plates sensitized with special solutions, the final printing areas of the plate etched into the sensitized surface to hold the lithographic image. To deep-etch, the application of various etches, depending on metal of plate, to etch the metal (about .0003 inch deep) in order to provide space for the lacquer base of the ink-receptive printing image.

Deep-Etch Pad. A plush-covered wooden block used for applying the deep-etch solution in platemaking. Separate pads used for each operation.

Deep-Etch Stencil. The light-hardened bichromated gum resist which protects the non-printing parts of the plate from the developing and deep-etching solutions.

Densitometer. An electric instrument designed to accurately measure optical density, or tone values, and used in place of the human eye for such purposes. Two general types: visual and photo-electric; transmission densitometers measure the full density range of negatives, and reflection densitometers measure the reflection range of opaque copy. If a photocell "search unit" is provided the instrument can be used as an illumination meter on the ground glass of camera.

Density. A photographic term often confused with "opacity" but correctly applied to the quantity of metallic silver (or dyes) per unit area in negatives and positives.

Dermatitis. A skin disease, characterized by an itching rash, swelling or roughening of the skin, or watery pustules; in lithography, caused by photographic developers, chromium compounds, and solvents.

Desensitize. In lithographic platemaking, to make the non-image areas of a lithographic plate non-receptive to ink through chemical treatment of metal. (2) In photography, a desensitizer is an agent for decreasing the color sensitivity of a photographic emulsion to facilitate development under comparatively bright light. The action is applied after exposure.

Developer, Development. The chemical agent and the process employed to render photographic images visible after exposure to light. (2) In lithographic platemaking, the removal of the unhardened bichromated coating; with a surface-type plate, the non-image areas; with a deep-etch plate, the image areas.

Developing Ink. A greasy liquid applied to plate images in photolithography to protect the image and keep it ink-receptive while the plate is being developed, etched and gummed. For some surface plates the developing ink is relied on to make the image ink-receptive.

Developing Pad. Usually a plush-covered wooden block used for working the developing solution over the surface of a deep-etch lithographic plate to remove the unhardened image areas.

Dimensional Stability. Ability to maintain size; resistance of paper or film to dimensional change with change in moisture content.

Direct Halftone. A halftone negative made by direct exposure of an object through a halftone screen.

Direct Lithogaphy. The method of printing lithographically by direct transfer of the ink from the plate to the paper; the use of a direct rotary press as distinguished from use of an offset press which has an intermediate offset cylinder between the plate and the paper. The rubber (blanket) surface of the offset cylinder picks up the ink and deposits it on the paper or other surface.

Direct Photography. Direct photography designates the making of halftone images by photographing the object to be reproduced rather than by re-photographing a continuous-tone picture of the object. Direct photography is frequently used in the reproduction of jewelry, cutlery, shoes, textiles, etc.

Direct Separation, also Screen Separation. A separation negative made with halftone screen from copy.

Distributing Roller. The rubber-covered roller which conveys the ink from the fountain onto the ink plate of the printing press; its purpose is also to lengthen the path of ink travel, thereby distributing it more evenly; (2) on an offset press, the rollers forming part of a nest of rollers and contacting the vibrating drum roller.

Dope. Water fountain solution; general term applied to litho ink conditioning compounds, reducers and varnishes.

Dot-Etching. Tonal correction of halftone positives or negatives in photolithography by judicious and controlled reduction of dot size through the action of chemical reducers. Tray etching for all-over reduction of dots; local etching done by an artist with a small soft brush.

Double Exposure. In photography and photomechanics, a supplementary exposure given the main image to obtain special effects.

Double Print, Double Printing. The effect and operation of photo-printing different line and halftone negatives in succession and register on the same sensitized surface.

Drag. Register trouble, in lithographic printing, when the dot is enlarged toward the back (non-gripper end) of the sheet. Also called *Draw.* (2) Term for a slur.

Draw-Down. A term used to describe an ink chemist's method of roughly determining color shade by placing a small glob of ink on paper and with a putty knife spatula spreading it by drawing down with edge of spatula to get a thin film of ink on the paper.

Drier. A substance added to inks to hasten their drying. It consists mainly of metallic salts which exert a catalytic effect on the oxidation and polymerization of the oil vehicles employed. Driers are often called *siccatives.*

Dropout Halftone. A halftone reproduction in which highlight effects have been introduced either by treatment of the halftone negative, or by etching the printing plate to eliminate dot formation in the pure highlights. In lithography the dropout is obtained photographically by use of contact halftone screen or manipulation of the camera exposure through cross-line halftone screen.

Drums. Metal inking rollers that furnish power and aid in ink distribution by lateral as well as rotating movement in contact with other rollers of the inking unit.

Dry Brush Drawing. A drawing made with a brush and only slightly moistened with india ink, the aim being to secure a vigorous execution of a character between a bold crayon drawing and pen work. A difficult and highly distinctive technique.

Dry Offset. A process in which a metal plate is etched to a depth of approximately 0.006″, making a "right-reading" relief plate, printed on the offset blanket and then to the paper without the use of water.

Dryplate. A photographic negative material consisting of a glass plate coated with gelatino-silver emulsion and exposed in a dry condition.

Ductor Roller. On an offset press, the roller in both inking and dampening mechanism which alternately contacts fountain roller and vibrating drum roller. Length of contact or "dwell" of ductor can be adjusted.

Dummy. The preliminary drawing or layout showing the position of illustrations and text as they are to appear in the final reproduction. (2) A set of blank pages made up in advance to show the size, shape, form, and general style and plan of a contemplated piece of printing, such as a book, booklet, etc.

Duotone. Term for a two-color halftone reproduction from a monochrome original and requiring two halftone negatives for opposite ends of gray scale at proper screen angles. One plate usually is printed in dark ink, the other in a lighter one.

Dwell. The length of "dwell" or contact between the ductor roller as it alternately contacts fountain roller and vibrating drum of offset press ink and dampening distributing mechanism.

Egg Albumin. The white of a bird's egg often supplied dried. Commercially, the white of a hen or duck egg. Used for making albumin-type surface offset press plate.

Ektachrome. An Eastman Kodak color film now used for commercial color transparencies; produces a positive.

Embossing. Blanket embossing: The swelling of the image on an offset blanket due to its absorbing solvents from the ink is termed embossing. (2) Plate embossing: Offset plate embossing is the result of atmospheric pressure of the vacuum contact in the photocomposing machine causing ridges to appear on the surface of the metal plate.

Emulsion. A mixture of two mutually insoluble liquids in which one liquid is finely dispersed as droplets in the other. (2) Photographic term for a gelatin or collodion solution holding light-sensitive salts of silver in suspension; used as the light-sensitive coating on glass photographic plates, film or metal plates in photomechanical printing processes. (3) High contrast emulsions, which give either completely transparent or opaque areas on exposure, are used for line and halftone photography. Normal contrast emulsions, which have a tonal range of density on exposure, are used for continuous-tone negatives and positives in lithography and in gravure.

Engraved Blanket. A condition that arises when the image area surface has sunk below the rest of the blanket surface as a result of disintegration of the blanket due to ink ingredients.

Etching Operation. The application to the lithographic plate of a solution of various chemicals for the purpose of producing a surface in the non-printing areas capable of being wet by water and not wet by greasy inks. Also in deep-etch platemaking, the application of a solution of acids for the purpose of removing the light-hardened gum stencil from the non-printing areas of the plate.

Excess Pressure. Any squeeze pressure that causes distortion or undue tension, e.g. between plate and offset blanket.

Exposure Chart. In lithographic platemaking, a table or chart of one or more variables which may be used to determine the exposure required under various conditions of temperature and humidity.

Exposure Meter. An instrument which measures light intensity and provides a calculator for determining proper exposure. Calibrated for different emulsion speeds.

Extended Color. The extra area of color necessary for trimming or diecutting when the printed image goes to the very edge, to avoid a white area due to inaccurate cutting of paper.

Fadeometer. An instrument used for determining the light-fastness of inks and other material under predetermined controlled conditions.

Fake-Color Process. Production of halftone color plates from monochrome originals, whereby the color effects are introduced by retouching of photoprints, and by skillful re-etching and finishing of the halftone plates. For lithographic reproduction, the artist pre-separates colors by mechanical overlays, working in gray tones, to provide tone copy for the camera.

Fanning. Expansion of an offset press sheet across the back edge as it goes through press; caused by sheet not being flat due to edges drying and contracting.

Farmer's Reducer. A solution for reducing the density of developed negatives, invented by Howard Farmer, and containing principally potassium ferricyanide and sodium thiosulfate. It tends to increase the contrast of the reduced negative. A strong solution of Farmer's Reducer is used in lithography to dissolve and remove the black silver of negatives from unwanted areas.

Filter Factor. A number indicating, by multiplication, the increased exposure required when a particular color filter is used during the camera exposure.

Fixing. The application of a chemical solution which removes the unexposed silver salts in an emulsion without affecting the metallic silver which has been deposited by the developer. Fixing renders the photographic image permanent.

Flash Exposure. The supplementary exposure given in halftone photography to strengthen the dots in the shadows of negatives. This exposure is made with a small lens stop to a sheet of white paper hung over the original, or to the rays from a flashlamp.

Flat. In lithography, the assembly of photographic negatives or positives on goldenrod paper, glass or vinyl acetate for exposure in vacuum frame in contact with sensitized metal press plate. Equivalent to a typographic form and containing text as well as art.

Flat Etching. The chemical reduction of the silver deposit in a continuous-tone or a halftone plate, brought about by placing it in a tray containing an etching solution. The etching solution is made up of a bleaching chemical and one that removes the product of this bleaching action. The plate is first immersed in water to saturate the emulsion evenly, then it is put into the etching bath. The same effect can be obtained by holding the plate in the hand and flowing the etch over it. The tray method is the more reliable. It is called "flat" because it is an all-over etch.

Fluorescent. Fluorescent tubes sometimes used for illumination or light source in offset platemaking. (2) Fluorescence Process (Eastman Kodak Company) employing special fluorescent watercolor pigments by the artist to simplify separation of water-color art by photographic methods using special lights in the camera color-separation work. (3) Kemart Process uses fluorescent white pigment for artist's use of highlights or for special drawing paper surface; special "flashing" lights used during camera exposure cause pigments to fluoresce and burn-out highlight dots on negative.

Focal Length. A photographic term for the distance between the optical center of a lens and the point at which an object image is in sharp or critical focus. Focal length is usually engraved on the front of the lens barrel by the maker.

Focal Plane. The surface (plane) on which camera images transmitted by a lens are brought to sharpest focus, the surface represented by the light-sensitive film or plate.

Focus. In photography, the point at which rays of light passing through a lens, converge or seem to converge to form a sharp image of the original.

Fog. A photographic defect in which the image is either locally or entirely veiled by a deposit of silver, the defect due either to the action of stray light or to improperly compounded chemical solutions.

Foot-Candle. A unit for measurement of light intensity.

Form Rollers. The ink and dampening rollers which contact the press plate.

Forwarding Mechanism. Conveyor arrangement to carry the sheet from the feeder to the front guide.

Fountain Roller. In the water motion of a lithographic press, a non-ferrous roller which revolves in the fountain. This roller in conjunction with the ductor roller meters the water or fountain solution to the press plate.

Fountain Solution. Commonly called "the water"; a solution of water, gum arabic, and other chemicals used to dampen the lithographic plate, and keep the non-printing areas from accepting ink.

Fountain Stops. Movable riders—rollers or strips of material—sometimes placed to rest on the fountain roller of an offset press dampening system to cut down on the amount of water supplied to the corresponding area of the press plate.

"F" Stops. Fixed sizes at which the aperture of the lens can be set, the values of which are determined by the ratio of the aperture to the focal length of the lens.

Gamma. Photographic term for negative contrast resulting from development and not the contrast of the subject itself; a numerical measure of contrast in the development of a negative.

Gang Negative, Gang Plate. In photomechanics, a negative bearing a number of properly positioned images, and a printing plate made therefrom. A Gang Negative is also known as a *Multiple Negative;* multiple negatives are the method of handling many small images as one unit in the step-and-repeat machine used in lithographic platemaking for making multiple images.

Gear Streaks. Parallel streaks appearing across printed sheet at same interval as gear teeth on cylinder. Caused by improper underpacking or defective press conditions resulting in difference of surface speed between cylinders and pitch diameter of gears.

Glue (Bichromated). Used for the glue deep-etch platemaking process in lithography. Process still used considerably in Europe and the Far East.

Goldenrod Flat. The method of assembling and positioning lithographic negatives (or positives) for exposure in contact with light-sensitized press plate. The goldenrod paper used is translucent enough to see penciled layout on underside, or master layout on separate white paper beneath, so film negatives can be attached in proper position with red scotch tape. The goldenrod paper beneath image areas is cut away before flat is reversed to place emulsion-side of negatives to emulsion on metal plate. Flat is also used for making blueprint of form for checking imposition. Sometimes referred to as a "form." A lithographic flat corresponds to a typographic form.

Grain. The distribution of silver particles in photographic emulsions and images. (2) The roughened or irregular surface of an offset printing plate.

Graining. Subjecting the surface of litho metal plates to the action of abrasive, the operation performed in a special machine for the purpose and imparting greater water-retention to the otherwise non-porous surface.

Graining Machine. A machine used for producing the grain on lithographic plates by oscillating the plate, under wet abrasive and marbles or steel ball-bearings to give weight to abrasive.

Grainy Printing. Printing characterized by unevenness, particularly of halftones.

Gray Scale. A strip of standard gray tones, ranging from white to black, placed at the side of original copy during photography to measure tonal range obtained, and in the case of color-separation negatives for determining color balance or uniformity of the separation negatives. A commercial product available either on paper or on transparent acetate for use with transparencies.

Gripper Bite. The amount of paper that extends beneath the press gripper. Sometimes called *Gripper Margin.*

Gripper Edge. On a sheet, it is that edge of the paper which is fed to the press gripper. With an offset press, image must not extend into gripper edge or margin, about $\frac{3}{8}$ inch.

Gripper Margin. An unprinted area between the edge of the sheet and lead edge of the printing area, allotted for the press grippers to hold the sheet.

Guide Marks. A method of using crossline marks on the offset press plate to indicate trim centering of sheet, centering of plate, etc., as well as press register in multicolor work. Not to be confused with register marks used for stripping elements to register.

Gum Arabic. A gum obtained from either of two species of Acacia trees, used in all branches of the graphic arts. There are a number of different gum arabic varieties which are known in commerce under the various names, Turkey gum, Egyptian gum, etc. Gum arabic solutions are used to desensitize or remove any affinity for ink in the non-printing areas of lithographic plates. Gum arabic also forms a large part of the fountain solutions used on lithographic presses.

Gumming. In lithography, the treating of surfaces with a thin coating of gum arabic as a protection against oxidation and ink-receptive coatings for image, and as an aid to desensitizing the plate.

Gum Stencil. The acid-resistant stencil formed in deep-etch platemaking in non-copy areas of the plate when gum arabic is a constituent of the coating solution. The stencil protects non-image areas while image areas are developed and etched.

Gum Streaks. Streaks, particularly in halftones, produced by the uneven gumming up of plates.

Halation. A photographic term for spreading of light action beyond proper boundaries in negatives, particularly in the highlight areas of the image. The dots on every negative or positive, when shot through the halftone screen, have a soft, fuzzy perimeter known as a halo. This is due to the fact that less light has reached the edge than the center of the dot. The silver deposit on the edge of the dot is therefore weaker and shows a corresponding transparency. It is this halation that permits chemical reduction, as in dot-etching. A blurred effect, resembling a halo, usually occurring around bright objects; caused by reflection of rays of light from the back of the negative material.

Halftone. Any photomechanical printing surface and impression therefrom in which detail and tone values are represented by a series of evenly spaced dots of varying size and shape, the dot areas varying in direct proportion to the intensity of the tones they represent.

Halftone Color Printing. The planographic process of printing depends on the deposit of a greasy ink in the form of dots or lines for its tonal interpretation of the sketch. The eye blends these fine lines or dots with the spaces between them and sees tones that vary with the proportion of dots to spaces between. At first, the greasy ink dots were stippled in with brush and pen; later, mechanical means, known as Ben Day screens, were used. With the introduction of photography and the halftone method, tones were interpreted by photographic dots. Small dots represent the light values; large dots, the stronger values. As individual dots are not easily visible, they appear as continuous tones of color. To achieve the varied color results, three or more colors are used.

Halftone Tint. A solid area of a plate is transformed into a gray tone of any desired density by stripping in a piece of film with uniform halftone density, i.e. 25%—50%, etc.; either negative or positive stock sheets of halftone material are used; avoids necessity for preparing art where uniform tone instead of solid background is wanted.

Halo. The circle or aura of lesser dens-

ity around the core of the halftone dot.

Hand Proof. In offset lithography, a proof of plate made on a hand proof press where operations are manual for inking, dampening and taking the impression.

Hard (Dot). A halftone dot, negative or positive, characterized by a sharp, clean cut edge. Photographically, the term *hard* denotes excessive contrast.

Hickeys. An imperfection in lithographic presswork due to a number of causes such as dirt on press, hardened specks of ink, or any dry hard particle working into the ink or onto the plate or offset blanket.

High Contrast. Refers to the relationship of highlights to shadows on a negative, whether continuous-tone or halftone. In such a negative the highlights are very black and the shadows very open according to the tonal scale.

Highlight. In photomechanics, the lightest or whitest area of an original or reproduction, represented by the densest portion of a continuous-tone negative, and by the smallest dot formation in a halftone negative and printing plate.

Highlight Halftone. A halftone reproduction in which the highlights are devoid of dots for accentuation of contrast.

Hue. That attribute of colors which permits them to be classed as reddish, greenish, bluish, yellowish, etc.

Hydrometer. Generic term for various instruments designed to determine the strength or specific gravity of liquids.

Hydrophilic. Water-loving; preferring to be wet by water rather than by oils; water-receptive.

Hydrophobic. Water-hating; preferring to be wet by oils rather than by water; water-repellent.

Hygrometer. An instrument for measuring atmospheric moisture.

Hypo. An abbreviation for sodium thiosulfate, also named sodium hyposulfite, a chemical used to fix the image on a photographic plate after it has been developed. One of the ingredients in the hardening bath. In reducing or etching solutions such as Farmer's Solution, it is the substance which dissolves and removes the silver ferricyanide formed when the plate is placed in a bleaching bath of potassium ferricyanide.

Imposition. Arranging and fastening negatives or positives to a supporting flat for use in offset lithography platemaking. Multiple imposition—the ex-

posure of the same flat in two or more positions on the press plate.

Impression Cylinder. On an offset press, the cylinder that carries the paper sheet into contact with the blanket.

Indicator. A dye that indicates changes from acidity to alkalinity, or vice versa, by changing its color.

Ink-Dot Scum. On aluminum plates, a type of oxidation scum characterized by scattered pits that print sharp, dense dots.

Ink Drum. A metal drum either solid or cored, a part of an inking mechanism. Used to break down the ink and transfer it to the form rollers; on certain types of proof presses, it is used in lieu of a fountain. The ink is supplied to the drum manually. On an offset press the ink drums are vibrating rollers (move back-and-forth sideways) and aid in ink distribution.

Inking Mechanism. On a printing press, the ink fountain and all the parts used to meter, transfer, breakdown, distribute, cool or heat, and supply the ink to the printing member.

Inkometer. An instrument that measures tack and length of printing and lithographic inks in numerical terms.

Ink-Receptive. Having the property of being wet by greasy ink in preference to water.

Ink-Repellent. Having a surface which will attract water and repel greasy inks.

Inserting. The fitting of one negative into another or the assembling of a number into a definite relationship to each other by the accurate cutting and fitting of the photographic films. Usually films can be thus advantageously handled.

Integrating Light Meter. An instrument which measures intensity of light exposure as well as length of exposure according to predetermined setting.

Intensification. A photographic term for the operation of increasing the density of negatives by chemical treatment of the image after fixation and washing.

Iris Diaphragm. Term applied to the adjustable aperture fitted into the barrel of photographic lenses and so-called because the contraction of the aperture resembles that of the iris (pupil) in the human eye. It consists of a series of thin metal tongues overlapping each other and fastened to a ring on the lens barrel, the aperture made smaller or larger by turning the ring backward or forward.

Kemart. A patented process for use by the artist for highlighting or dropouts, and silhouetting. In the Kemart process a fluorescent white pigment is applied to dropout areas by artist, or a special fluorescent coated illustrator's board is used for silhouetting. When copy is photographed, special flash lights cause the pigment to fluoresce and burn-out the coated areas of copy.

Key. In color art preparation, an image used as a guide for further work as keyline drawing. (2) In photography the emphasis on lighter or darker tones in a negative or print; *high key* indicates prevalence of light tones; *low key* prevalence of darker tones.

Keylining. A technique used in copy preparation by the artist to handle copy for some simple types of color separations, or for indicating reverses or outline of backgrounds. The purpose is to provide copy for the camera which avoids excessive opaquing of photographic negatives or positives.

Kiss Pressure. Kiss pressure is the minimum pressure at which proper ink transfer is possible.

Lacquer. A solution in an organic solvent of a cellulose ester such as nitrate or acetate, or a cellulose ether such as ethyl, benzyl, etc., together with modifying resins and plasticizers. They are used on paper for glossy, decorative and protective effects. In lithography, lacquers are used to form the base for the ink-receptive and water-repellent image in deep-etch platemaking.

Laketine. A colorless reducer (magnesia in linseed oil) used in lithographic inks to reduce color strength.

Lap. The slightly extended areas of printing surfaces in color plates which make for easier registration of color.

Lateral Reversal. Turning of a photographic image as to right and left position, achieved either with optical reversing devices, by "flopping" the negative for stripping, or by placement of the image in a transparency-holder during photography therefrom. Frequently used to get emulsion-to-emulsion in contact printing of lithographic press plates.

Layout. Preliminary sketch or arrangement showing the size, position and colors of illustrations and text matter in advertisements and other printed matter, and also including special in-

structions to platemakers and printers. (2) The lithographic stripper's layout drawn in pencil on goldenrod paper flat for positioning photographic negatives (or positives) of units or pages. Made from original layout or dummy. (3) The printed form used for writing in the instructions for positioning the negative (positive) on a photocomposing machine for exposing each "step" of multiple images.

Lens. A photographic lens made up of several prisms or elements, both negative and positive, and separated in the lens barrel at definite distances by an air space. A negative converging lens element is double concave (resembling two prisms placed apex to apex); a positive lens element is double convex (resembling two prisms placed base to base) which brings the light rays to a focus.

Lifting. The proper adhering of one color (ink) to a previously printed color, or to the sheet in lithography.

Light Integrator. An instrument which measures a predetermined amount of light by taking into consideration both intensity and time of exposure.

Line Copy. Any copy suitable for reproduction without using a screen; copy composed of lines or dots as distinguished from copy composed of continuous tones. Lines or dots may be small and close together so as to simulate tones, but are still regarded as line copy if they can be faithfully reproduced without a screen.

Lines To The Inch. Crossline halftone screens are made up of opaque lines ruled at right angles to each other. Some screens have more or less lines to the inch than others and are accordingly classified. The 120- and 133-line screens are the ones most commonly used. In large size work the screen ruling may be as coarse as 40 lines to the inch; in very fine detail work screens with 250 lines or more to the inch are successfully used. The number of dots to the square inch is the square of the lines to the inch of the screen. A 133-line screen, for example, produces 17,689 dots per square inch.

Litho Crayon. A pencil-shaped stick consisting of soap, tallow, shellac, wax and lamp-black used for execution of crayon sketches on grained paper, also for direct drawing on litho stone and metal plates, and as a

delicate staging medium in halftone relief etching.

Lithographic Artists. Crayon artists who draw on litho stones or plates. Negative retouchers who work on glass or film negatives and positives. Artists or stainers who work on continuous-tone negatives with dyes to adjust density of selected areas as a method of color correction.

Lithographic (Halftone) Conversion. The employment of relief halftone plates or proofs for the photographic production of litho printing plates.

Lithographic Images. An ink-receptive image on the lithographic press plate, either photographic or direct hand or transfer image. The design or drawing on stone or metal plate.

Lithographic Roller. A term that should be properly restricted to leather-covered (nap) rollers for hand rolling (inking) of litho printing surfaces but is also used for various types of rubber and metal inking rollers suitable for lithographic inks.

Lithographic Transfer. A proof of design or type matter pulled with special transfer ink on transfer paper from a lithographic image or a relief image. Such proofs are used to transfer an image to the press plate or stone.

Lithotine. A lithographic solvent developed by LTF to replace turpentine; less toxic and irritating to the skin; its use helps avoid dermatitis.

Livering. An irreversible increase in body of inks as a result of chemical change during storage or hot milling.

Long (Ink). A term used to describe consistency of lithographic inks. Inks are called *"long"* if they stretch out into stringy consistency when tapped between fingers; *"short"* if the ink breaks off short like lard. Both long and short inks can be either stiff or soft.

Magenta Contact Screen. A contact film screen composed of magenta dyed dots of variable density used for making halftone negatives in the camera. Used mostly for lithographic negatives.

Makeovers. A trade term used in lithography meaning the making of various sizes of screened positive separations from a single set of continuous-tone negative separations. A negative is photographed in several different foci to get the positives in different sizes.

Makeready. On an offset press, the adjusting of feeder, grippers, side guide, pressure between plate and offset blanket cylinder, putting plate on press and ink in fountain to be ready to run the press. (2) On a photocomposing machine, the preparatory work of positioning negative in holder, plate on back, and getting ready to start exposures in step-and-repeat operation of platemaking; the "set-up" work.

Makeready Tissue. A tissue paper of standardized caliper, usually 1/1000, 1.5/1000 and 2/1000 inch thickness, used to adjust diameter or plate of offset cylinder by placing under plate or offset blanket in making ready offset press for operation. Used only when necessary to compensate for variables.

Mask (Unsharp or Diffused). In the masking method of color correction used in lithography, an unsharp photographic mask is sometimes made in a printing frame by placing a thin sheet of acetate between the separation negative and the material for the positive, with the illumination placed off-center and the frame whirled during exposure.

Masking (Photographic). Application of a mask to certain areas of orginals to promote better halftone reproduction; use of corrective photographic images on separation negatives for improved color rendition.

Masstone. Color of ink in mass. May differ from the printed color of the same ink.

Mechanical (Paste-Up). A method of assembling all copy elements into a unit for photographic platemaking (copy ready for the camera). May include all copy except text, or be complete with text as well as line and tone copy, proportioned and positioned.

Mechanical Color Separations. The pre-separation of colors for line color or fake-color art by the artist, executing the art for each color in black or gray tones, usually separate overlays of "key" copy, ready for the camera. Either line or tone separations. *"Keylining"* is a method of separating each color area by a line for copy executed in one piece and opaquing areas to ⅛ inch of division line. Color tissue overlay is the color guide for the opaquer who, with duplicate negatives or positives, makes a negative or positive for each color. The width

of the dividing line (common to adjoining color areas) is the overlap of the inks.

Mercury Vapor Lamp. An enclosed light source containing mercury, sometimes used to expose sensitized plates.

Middletone. In halftone, any neutral tone intermediate between the highlights and shadows of an original and reproduction therefrom.

Moiré. Undesirable patterns occurring when reproductions are made from halftone proofs or steel engravings, caused by conflict between the ruling of the halftone screen and the dots or lines of the original; a similar pattern occurring in multicolor halftone reproductions and usually due either to incorrect screen angles or misregister of the color impressions during printing.

Molleton. A thick cotton fabric similar to flannel, having a long nap, and used on damping form rollers.

Montage. A series of related pieces of copy appearing as one to tell a complete story.

Needles. Sharp pointed, needle-like tools, used by lithographic artists for making corrections on plates, glass or film negatives or positives (scraping away, hand-lettering or ruling).

Negative Carrier. That part of the mechanism of a photocomposing machine which holds and positions the photographic image being exposed, and includes the carriage saddle, the register device and the negative frame.

Negative Grouping Machine. A miniature photocomposing machine used for making multiple negatives (positives)

Nesting (forms). Term used for positioning irregular shapes on an offset press plate by means of a photocomposing machine. Nesting is used to avoid waste of stock for diecut forms such as envelope blanks.

Notch Bars. Measuring bars with notches on one-inch centers on both the vertical and horizontal (cross) rails of a photocomposing machine. Registering mechanism is moved and locked into closest notch, and micrometer adjustment positions between notches to 1/1000 inch.

Offset. Wet ink transferred from one sheet to another in a load of freshly printed sheets. (2) Lithographic images printed on an offset press.

Offset Lithography. Lithography produced on an offset lithographic press, the modern commercial printing

method. A right-reading plate is used, and an intermediate rubber-covered offset cylinder transfers the image from the plate cylinder to the paper, metal or other material.

Opaque. Not permitting the passage of light. The opposite of *Transparent.* (2) In photography, a non-transparent pigment applied to certain areas of negatives to prevent passage of light through the particular areas. (3) A water-soluble solution used to cover light pinholes or to alter negatives used for lithography.

Opaquing. Local application of opaque to photographic negatives or positives; blocking-out.

Open Up. To render less opaque so that more light may pass through areas intended to appear more open.

Orthochromatic. Said of photographic surfaces sensitive to ultraviolet, blue, yellow, green and orange rays. Insensitive to red rays.

Outline. A silhouetted piece of copy or reproduction.

Overpacking. Packing the plate or blanket to a level that is excessively above the level of the cylinder bearer.

Overprinting. In lithographic platemaking with surface plates, the exposure of a second negative on an area of the plate previously exposed to a different negative; a method of combining line and halftone image on the plate.

Packing. In lithography, the paper used to underlay a blanket, plate or proof to bring the surface to the desired height, the method of adjusting squeeze pressure. The act of inserting the packing material under the blanket or plate.

Packing Gage. A steel block with a special dial gage mounted on one end. When the block is clamped on plate cylinder of press, and the gage button permitted to rest against the bearer, a pointer indicates the difference in height between the two. This measurement helps in computing the amount of packing needed. The same procedure is used for determining blanket underpacking needed.

Panchromatic. A term applied to photographic materials possessing sensitivity to all visible spectral colors, including red.

Paper-Conditioning. The process of adding moisture to or taking moisture out of paper, to attain proper paper condition for press operation.

Paper Hygroscope. A sword hygrometer instrument for measuring moisture content of a pile of paper relative to humidity of pressroom; an aid in determining whether paper-conditioning is necessary.

Parallax. The displacement of one object to another when viewed from different positions. (2) The difference in position of the images obtained by the finder and the lens in a camera.

Paste Drier. A type of ink drier used in lithographic inks, usually a combination of lead and manganese. Paste drier tends to dry ink throughout with tough surface film but less gloss than cobalt drier. Manganese drier is seldom used alone except for non-scratch inks. Some paste driers are known as "tri-metal" driers, and contain cobalt, manganese and lead.

Paste-Up. The preparation of copy, putting each component element in proper position before photographing. The usual method of assembling copy elements including text for reproduction by offset lithography.

Pen and Ink Keys. A key tracing of the subject made on a transparent plastic sheet with pen and tusche. Sometimes used for transferring key outline of artwork to litho plates for making hand plates for posters.

Pen Drawing. Made by pen and india ink, in lines, dots or stipples, being a copy purely of black-and-white.

pH. A scale used for expressing the acidity or alkalinity of solutions. The degree of acidity or alkalinity present in a solution is determined by its hydrogen ion content: A pH value of 7 is considered neutral; solutions of a lower value are considered acid, while those higher than pH 7 are alkaline in nature. The pH scale ranges from 0 to 14, and determination is made by various electronic and colorimetric devices designed for the purpose.

Photocomposer. A machine for making multiple-image plates or negatives, by step-and repeat action, from one or more negatives or positives. The machine is equipped for vertical and horizontal make-up in accurate spacing and register. Some types of machines are for making multiple negatives only, which in turn are used as the unit positioned in the step-and-repeat platemaking composing machine.

Photographic Proofs. Photographic prints made from negatives or positives. Various forms of blueprints and silver prints are used to check layout and imposition; silver prints approximate quality of halftones; various forms of diazo prints in color are used to approximate quality of process color plates sometimes termed print proofs.

Photolithography. That branch of lithographic printing in which photography is employed for production of the image on the final printing surface. The original printing surface, lithographic stone, has been almost completely displaced by thin and flexible sheets of metal (zinc, aluminum, stainless steel, bimetallic plates, polymetallic plates), bearing a mechanically abraded (grained) surface for retention of moisture on the plate during offset printing therefrom. The oldest photolithographic procedure still in practical use is the albumin process in which light-hardened and inked images of bichromated albumin serve as the actual printing surface. Deep-etch plates are a modern form of photolithographic surface, as are also bimetallic plates and those of the plastic type.

Photomechanical. Generic and broadly applied term for any reproductory process in which photography is employed in the production of a printing surface. The term embraces collotype, photoengraving, photogravure, photolithography, rotogravure, silk screen photostencil printing, etc.

Picking. Removal of part of the surface of paper during printing. Picking occurs when the pulling force of the ink is greater than the surface strength of the paper, whether coated or uncoated.

Pick Tester. An instrument designed to measure the pick resistance of paper through the use of inks with varying standardized tack.

Pigments. Manufactured chemical colors, inorganic or organic; the former generally opaque and produced from basic materials including metals; the latter include coal tar dye lakes formed by precipitation on alumina hydrate and widely used for lithographic transparent inks.

Piling. The sticking or caking of ink pigment on plate or blanket instead of passing on readily to the intended surface.

Pitch Diameter. Rolling diameter of a gear. On offset press, same diameter as cylinder bearers.

Planographic Printing. A generic term used for any and all printing processes in which a flat surface is used—i.e., where the image sections are in substantially the same plane as the non-image sections (such as direct and offset lithography, or collotype). Erroneously, some have tried to apply the term planography in a more restricted sense using it only for the simpler types of photolithography, such as black-and-white line and halftone reproduction.

Plate Cylinder. That cylinder on a rotary press to which the printing plates are attached.

Polish Out. Meaning to erase a design image or unwanted marks on a lithographic plate with a snake stone or similar abrasive.

Polychromatic. Many colors.

Post Treatment. A treatment of the non-image areas of the metal plate after image development. A step in producing maximum desensitization.

Pre-Etching. Applying a thin film of gum on an offset plate before coating it. The purpose of pre-etching is to make it easier to develop the plate in hot, humid weather and to decrease the amount of residual coating, the thin film of coating left in the non-image areas of the plate after developing. The etch used for desensitizing the plate is generally used for preetching.

Press Proofs. Actual press sheets to show image, tone values and colors as well as imposition of form or press plate.

Pre-Treatment. The treatment of the offset-lithographic plate before graining to remove old ink and image substance. Counter-etching, pre-etching, Cronak, and Brunak are pre-treatments in platemaking.

Printing Pressure. The force at the interface of the printing member and the paper which is required to transfer the ink from the printing member to the paper.

Process Colors. Yellow (lemon), magenta (cold red), cyan (blue-green), are the three process colors. They are so selected because when combined they produce black and when used in various strengths and combinations they make it possible to reproduce thousands of different colors with a minimum of photography, platemaking and presswork.

Process Lens. A highly corrected photographic lens for line, halftone and color photography. A camera lens used for photographing flat copy; it is used in lithography for line and halftone photography, continuous-tone and color separation for line; usually not sufficiently color corrected for process-color separation.

Progressive Proofs. Proofs made from the separate plates used in color process work, showing the sequence of the printing and the result after each additional color has been applied. They are furnished to the printer by the engraver.

Projection Printing. A system of lenses and lamps which can be used to project an image upon a sensitized plate. Hence the image may be formed larger (or smaller) than the negative or positive which is projected. Used for large halftone work on some types of lithographed posters.

Proofing. Frequently used instead of "prooving," denoting the operation of pulling proofs of plates for proofreading, revising, trial, approval of illustrations, and other purposes preliminary to production printing. In lithography print proofs (photoprints) are used to check layout and imposition when plates are made from flats and colors.

Proof Press. A printing machine used for making proofs, usually has most of the elements of a production machine but not for automatic sustained production. An offset proof press has provision for transferring printed image to offset blanket and from that to the paper. Hand and power models, single and multicolor, as well as special presses for transparent proofs are available.

Psychrometer. A wet-and-dry bulb type of hygrometer. The two thermometers suitably mounted and with swivel handle are whirled vertically in area for reading. Considered the most accurate of the instruments practical for industrial plant use; for determining relative humidity.

Reducers. Varnishes, solvents, or oily or greasy compounds, employed to bring ink or varnish to a softer consistency for use on the press. (2) In photography, the term refers to chemicals used to reduce the density of negative or positive images or halftone dots.

Refraction. Deviation of a luminous ray of light in passing obliquely from one medium to another, or in traversing a medium of uneven density.

Register. Exact correspondence in the position of pages or other printed matter on both sides of a sheet or in its relation to other matter already ruled or printed on the same side of the sheet. (2) In photo-reproduction and color printing, the correct relative position of two or more colors so that no color is out of its proper position.

Register Marks. Small crosses, guides or patterns placed on originals before reproduction to facilitate registration of plates and printing therefrom.

Register Rule. A metal measuring rule with vernier to measure in $\frac{1}{1000}$ inches; designed by LTF especially for the accurate measurement of image dimensions on the offset press plate and on the printed sheet to avoid misregister difficulties.

Reproduction Ratio. The term used to denote the amount of enlargement of reduction in scaling copy when photographed; defined as any linear distance on the image divided by the corresponding distance on the copy. Same-size copy would be 1.0 expressed decimally, a reduction would be less than one.

Repro Proof. Trade term for reproduction proof, a clear-type proof of superior quality for photographing; used for assembling type elements with photos and art on the mechanical paste-up for photographic plate-making by all processes.

Residual. The very thin film of plate coating always left on the metal of a lithographic plate after development. Post-treatment of the plate with various solutions removes this film and better prepares the non-printing areas of an albumin plate after development.

Resist. In deep-etch offset platemaking, the non-image plate coating hardened by the action of light on bichromated gum or other coating solution; keeps developing solution from contacting metal of these areas; such solutions etch metal of plate slightly.

Restrainer. The ingredient of a developer which prevents too rapid development and chemical fog; usually potassium bromide.

Retouching, Photographic. Corrective treatment of photographic negatives and prints by means of pencils, reducers, transparent shading sheets, airbrush or application of aniline dyes for removal of blemishes and improvement of tone value, detail and photographic quality.

Reverse Plates. Plates which are negative in tone values to copy.

Reversing Prism. An optical prism used in combination with a camera lens to "reverse" the image from right to left, or to make it read "right" when it would read "wrong" with the lens alone. A reversing prism requires that the copyboard be placed at right angles to the plate or film in the camera.

Rider Rollers. Metal or rigid plastic rollers in the inking mechanism which contact one or more soft (glue, glycerine, rubber, etc.) rollers and serve to break down, transfer and distribute the ink. Soft rollers are sometimes used as riders on large metal ink drums and serve to break down the ink.

Roller Stripping. A lithographic term denoting that the ink does not stick to the metal ink rollers on the press.

Rolling Up. In lithography, the inking of the finished plate without taking a proof or impression. Usually done by hand to protect the image or to render inspection easier.

Rub-Proof. Meaning the ink has about reached maximum dryness and the printed surface resists all normal abrasion.

Safelight. In photography, the special darkroom lamp emitting illumination wherewith sensitized materials can be handled without danger of fogging by action of light.

Scale. A rule of graduated dimensions; a device on process cameras for mechanical focusing of images; (2) The ratio of enlargement or reduction of an original to the final reproduction; (3) A table of percentages.

Scanner. An electronic device for scanning color transparencies and separating the colors for photographic separations to be used in the reproduction processes, or in other types of scanners; an electronic device for integrating color separations made in the camera and color correcting them by integrating a color separation with the particular ink to be used for each color.

Screen Angles. In halftone color reproduction, any of the particular angles at which a halftone screen or the original itself is placed for each of the negatives comprising the set of color plates, in order to avoid formation of displeasing dot patterns in the completed color reproduction.

Screen Compensator. A piece of glass positioned in front of the process camera lens when making combination line and halftone negative with two exposures. When halftone screen is removed, the compensator is positioned to allow for the difference in light refraction.

Screen Distance. In halftone photography, the separation or space between the surface of a glass halftone screen of specific ruling and the photographic surface during the halftone camera exposure. This distance permits the rays of light passing through the screen to diffuse before striking the film or plate. Extent of diffusion of rays is in proportion to their intensity which in turn is determined by the reflection of light from the original copy. The variation in diffusion is what produces dots of different sizes on the film or plate.

Screened Photo Prints. A photo print made through the halftone screen giving a screened print instead of a continuous-tone print. Can be photographed as line copy.

Screening. A halftone negative or positive that has a large dot in the highlights and a large white opening in the shadows is said to be "screeny." This is often due to the screen distance being too short or to the use of too small a lens opening.

Scriber. A small hand tool used for drawing lines on the emulsion of an exposed photographic negative, the tool scraping off the black emulsion; the operation is termed "engraving" negatives and is used for fine ruled-form work.

Scumming. A lithographic term referring to the press plate picking up ink in the non-printing areas for a variety of reasons; basically due to spots or areas not remaining desensitized; filling in of halftone dots, spreading of image, streaks are often caused by scumming.

Sensitivity Guide. A narrow, calibrated continuous-tone gray scale with each tone scale numbered. In the plate-making operation the gray scale is exposed on the sensitized press plate along with the rest of the work. The number of steps in the scale showing as solids on the developed plate determine the sensitivity of the plate coating and measure the tone values that were reproduced on the plate.

Sensitizer. Embracive term for the chemical compounds (salts of iron, silver and chromium, also diazo compounds and dyes) utilized to render photographic surfaces sensitive to light and color. With lithography, also used in plate coatings to make them light-sensitive.

Separation. In color photography, the isolation or division of the colors of an original into their primary hues, each record or negative used for the production of a color plate. The act of manually separating or introducing colors in printing plates. In lithography, direct separations are made with the use of the halftone screen; indirect separations involve continuous-tone separation negatives and screened positives made from these.

Setback. In offset platemaking, the distance from the front edge of the press plate to image area to allow for clamping to cylinder and also to allow for gripper margin; this distance varies with different makes and press sizes.

Shading Sheets. Art material, usually patterns or tones on acetate sheets which can be positioned on line artwork in selected areas to avoid tedious hand detail; special drawing paper containing invisible patterns which can be developed to black by chemical on artist's brush. Not to be confused with halftone tints which are only indicated on the art, and inserted by stripping negative.

Shadow. General term for the darker areas of an original, negative and reproduction.

Shadow Stop. The small lens aperture used for the flash exposure in halftone photography.

Sharpen. To decrease in strength, as when halftone dots become smaller; opposite of "thicken."

Sharpness. Photographic term for perfectly defined detail in an original, negative, and reproduction.

Sheet-Wise. The use of a form or offset plate which prints just one side of the sheet when both sides are to be printed; a method of press production.

Short Ink. A descriptive term used to describe quality of lithographic inks; short or buttery-ink when tapped between the fingers, does not draw out into a thread. Inks are described as being "short" or "long," as well as stiff or soft.

Silhouette Halftone. A halftone illustration plate from which the screen surrounding any part of the image has been cut or etched away.

Silhouetting. Opaquing out the background around a subject on a halftone or a continuous-tone negative. On a positive this can be achieved by staging the subject and by flat-etching the background until it is entirely transparent.

Silver Print. Photographic print on paper which has been sensitized with silver chloride salts.

Size (for bronzing). A sticky ink printed as a base to hold bronze powder or flock.

Skeleton Cylinder. A cylindrical framework used in the transfer and delivery mechanism of a printing press, usually having rings of star wheels or similar shape, which contact the printed sheet in the margins.

Smearing. A condition in which the impression is slurred and unclear because too much ink was run or sheets were handled or rubbed before ink was dry. (2) Spreading the ink over areas of the plate where it is not wanted; wiping the ink off the image areas and onto the non-image areas of a plate.

Snakeslip. A stick compounded of pumice powder and flint, used for removing dirt spots or unwanted objects on the lithographic pressplate.

Soft (Ink). Descriptive of consistency of lithographic inks. Inks can be either soft or stiff, as well as long or short.

Soft Dot. When the halation around the edge of the dot is excessive and almost equals in area the dot itself, the dot is called soft. When the amount of halation is so slight as to be barely noticeable and the dot is very sharp, the dot is called hard. Sometimes these terms are used improperly to indicate the ease with which the dots yield to chemical reduction. A contact negative has a harder dot than a negative made in the camera.

Soybean Plate Coating. Soybean, introduced to lithographers about 1949, is a substitute for albumin.

Spectrum. The rainbow-like band of visible colors formed when a ray of light is separated into its constituent colors after undergoing dispersion by a diffracting grating or prism.

Speed of an Emulsion. Degree of sensitivity to light. The time factor in sensitivity of light. The amount of moisture picked up by lithographic plate coating solutions affects their speed of action; a 30° change in humidity can make the speed of a solution twice as fast. For this reason platemaking departments are frequently air-conditioned.

Spotters. Pieces of white or black paper in which small holes have been cut. Used for comparing areas on the sketch with tints on the chart. (2) Term applied to workers doing simple opaquing operations to eliminate defects in negatives.

Staging. Applying a protective coating in selected areas so that these are protected when chemicals are applied to the general area. Normally the staging is removed at a later operation, leaving the protected areas in their original form.

Staining. Corrective treatment or retouching of photographic images with dilute solutions of aniline dyes. Staining negatives lightens tones in printed reproduction. Staining positives produces darker tones in printed reproduction. Dye retouching. In lithographic color correction, the method of adjusting density of local areas on continuous-tone negatives. The use of a gray dye is general practice because the negatives are in gray tones.

Static Neutralizer. A printing press attachment designed to remove the static electricity from the paper to avoid ink offsetting and trouble with the paper.

Stepover. In multiple imposition on a lithographic press plate, the procedure of repeating the exposure of a flat by stepping it along the gripper edge; side-by-side exposure.

Step-Up. In multiple imposition on a lithographic press plate, the procedure of repeating the exposure of a flat by stepping it back from the gripper edge of plate; up-and-down positioning.

Still Development. The development of photographic emulsion in tray without agitation or rocking of tray.

Stipple. Term applied to originals and reproductions in which lights and shades are produced or translated by irregularly spaced dots instead of lines and cross-hatchings. A technique used for getting tone by hand methods on lithographic plates.

Stop. Photographic term for any type of lens aperture or diaphragm. For example, Highlight-, Middletone-, Detail-, Shadow-, Iris-, Waterhouse-Stops.

Stopping Out. In photomechanics, application of opaque to photographic negatives; staging of halftone plates during relief etching; protecting certain areas of deep-etch plates by applying gum solution prior to the application of plate bases, so that no ink attracting medium will be deposited on the protected areas.

Stream Feeder. A type of press feeder which keeps several sheets of paper, overlapping each other, moving toward the grippers.

Stripfilm. A process film for line and halftone photography consisting of a gelatino-silver emulsion coated on a temporary support, which permits stripping or lifting of the negative image from the base support after fixation and washing.

Stripping. The act of positioning or inserting copy elements in negative or positive film to a unit negative; the positioning of photographic negatives or positives on a lithographic flat for form imposition. (2) The condition under which steel rollers fail to take up the ink on lithographic presses, and instead are wet by the fountain solution.

Surface Plate. One of the two basic types of lithographic press plates; a colloid image is formed on the light-sensitized metal plate by the action of actinic light through photographic negatives. The albumin plate is the most common form of surface plate, but there are others, including some of the bimetal or polymetal plates on which the image acts as a resist for the removal by acid of the surface metal to get down to the base metal which tends to resist ink.

Surprint. In photomechanics, a print from a second negative superimposed upon a previously printed image of the first negative, and differing from a double print (q.v.) in that one image is superimposed on the other rather than being photo printed into or around the first image. Surprinting is commonly used to superimpose the print from a line negative on a previously made print from a halftone or other line negative. Line work surprinted will reproduce as solid black and with no screen.

Sword Hygroscope. A special hygrometer invented by the Lithographic Technical Foundation for measuring the interior moisture content of a pile of paper in comparison to that of the air surrounding. An aid in determining whether or not paper-conditioning is necessary.

Tack. The resistance to splitting of an ink film between two separating surfaces, i.e. stickiness. This ink property is of great importance at the moment of printing since it controls picking of the paper and trapping of colors. (2) The quality of adhesion of an offset blanket; when the blanket has been used to a point that the rubber starts to disintegrate, the blanket is said to be tacky.

Thicken. To increase in strength, as when halftone dots become denser and larger; opposite of "sharpen."

Thixotropy. The property of some lithographic inks of becoming fluid when worked and setting to a semisolid state when at rest; the cause of some inks tending to back away from the ink fountain roller.

Tight (negatives). In lithography, a negative so over-exposed that the lighter tones are very dense and will come through very light on the positive. Also, the shadows will come through noticeably lighter than they should.

Tinting. An all-over color tint on the press sheet caused by the ink pigment dissolving in the dampening solution of a lithographic press. Not to be confused with scumming which is more local and due to other reasons.

Tint Laying. The operation of transferring Ben Day tints to plates, drawings or other mediums.

Tints. Various tones (Strengths) of a solid color. For rough work, sometimes handled on the copy by pasting down a piece of stock shading sheet and handled as line copy; or patented drawing board is used by artist and tint areas are developed with chemical. Photographic (halftone) tints are stock developed film (negative and positive) in various strengths of tone (25 percent, 50 percent, etc.) and usually 133-line screen prepared by the camera department and inserted by stripper as indicated on copy.

Tone Density. The optical density of a tone area. With halftones, the over-all density which takes into account both the dots within the tone area and the spaces between them.

Toners. Highly concentrated colors made from "double strength" pigments; both transparent and opaque; used to get greater tinctorial strength in printing inks.

Transfer. A lithographic image transferred from one surface to another;

e.g., from a designer's stone to the printing press plate by means of a proof on transfer paper; a transfer plate has the images transferred to it.

Translucent. Said of materials which transmit light without permitting the objects beyond to be distinctly visible nor clearly seen.

Transparency. A monochrome or full-color photographic positive or picture on a transparent support, the image intended for viewing and reproduction by transmitted light. In photography, also refers to the light-transmitting power of the silver deposit in a negative and is the inverse of opacity. (2) Inexpensive, semi-permanent window posters printed on high grade onionskin paper for application to glass surfaces. (3) The property of an ink which permits light to pass through it. Lack of hiding power.

Trapping. The ability of an already printed ink film to accept a succeeding or overprinted ink film.

Trimetallic Plates. A type of lithographic press plate, consisting of a base metal of stainless steel, aluminum or other metal on which other metals are plated, usually copper and then chromium. Lithographic platemaking techniques are used to etch the surface metal of image to reach the copper for image base; surface metal remains for the non-printing areas. The nature of the surface metal with the dampening solution helps in repelling the ink from non-printing areas. Such plates have a long life and no mechanically grained surface.

Tusching. The operation of adding work to the image on a lithographic press plate, correcting lines and lettering and adding solids by means of a liquid greasy substance known as *Tusche.*

Two-Sheet Detector. A device for tripping the press when more than one sheet attempts to enter the press at one time.

Under Asphaltum. The operation in making a deep-etch offset plate consisting in removing the developing ink from the image areas and then coating these areas with asphaltum to make them permanently ink-receptive. With a surface plate the ink of the image is removed and the image put under asphaltum if a plate is to stand more than 24 hours, or if it is to be stored for a rerun.

Undercut. In printing presses, the difference between the radius of the

bearers and the radius of the cylinder body; the allowance for plate or blanket plus a margin for packing adjustment.

U.S.P. Abbreviation for United States Pharmacopoeia, the American Standard for purity and strength of many chemicals.

Vandyke Print. A silverprint or photographic image made on inexpensive photopaper sensitized with a mixture of iron and silver salts; a brownprint. Frequently used by offset lithographers as a proof from a negative to be sent to the customer as a means to check layout or other corrections.

Vari-Typer. A special typewriter with interchangeable type faces used for reproduction work.

Vehicle. The fluid varnish or oil in which pigment is suspended in printing inks.

Velox Print. Name for one of the chloride printing papers made by the Eastman Kodak Co., and sometimes erroneously used as name for similar developing papers.

Vibrator or Vibrating Roller. A metal or hard roller in an inking or dampening system.

Vignette. A relatively small decorative design or illustration of any kind put on or just before the title page, or at the beginning or end of a chapter of a manuscript or book. It is usually a fine, delicate design representing a vine or tendril. (2) An original piece of copy, halftone printing plate or impression in which the background or a portion of the illustration gradually shades off until the lightest tones or extreme edges appear to merge with the paper on which they are printed. A halftone illustration showing a vignetted finish or edge.

Viscosity. Resistance to flow; the opposite of fluidity. A physical characteristic which allows material to be drawn out into threads; viscosity can be coarsely compared for practical purposes by the length of the strings at the time of breaking.

Walk-Off. Failure of part of a lithographic image to adhere to the metal plate; parts of image disappear during press run.

Warm Color. A color on the red or yellow side. Red, yellow and orange are regarded as warm colors.

Wash Drawing. Made by a brush in washes with a single pigment of black or dark color soluble in water, to be reproduced by the halftone.

Washing Out. The removal of an image coating which has been applied to the plate, such as developing ink or asphaltum, by use of turpentine or other solvents.

Wash Off Relief. Photographic sketches made by superimposing three color images. Positives with relief gelatin images are made from separation negatives. The positive absorbs dye in proportion to the amount of gelatin in any area. Dye can be transferred to paper base. All three dyes transferred in register, produce full-color prints. This process has largely been replaced by the *Dye Transfer Process.*

Water Fountain. The metal trough on a lithographic press which holds the dampening solution.

Waterhouse Stop. A diaphragm for photographic lenses devised by John Waterhouse in 1856, the aperture taking the form of a thin sheet of metal or paper bearing circular or irregular openings of a definite size, and intended for insertion in a slot cut into the barrel of a lens.

Water-Resistance. Papers for lithography require a fairly high degree of water-resistance. Writing papers usually are heavily sized to permit the use of aqueous writing inks and to facilitate erasing. For packaging and for maps or posters subject to outdoor use, papers have been developed that do not disintegrate even when exposed to sea water.

Wax Test. A pick test for paper. The use of a series of waxes in stick form which are graded in adhesiveness. To test surface strength of paper (pick) several grades of wax are heated and pressed against paper surface; after cooling the wax sticks are pulled away from paper vertically, the first of the grades of adhesiveness to cause paper surface to adhere to it determines the picking (by number) quality of the paper.

Wet-Plate. A photographic negative or positive produced by wet collodion photography.

Work-and-Turn Imposition. Work-and-turn is a printing imposition, where the form contains the material to be printed on both sides of the sheet. The entire form first prints on one side of the sheet for half the number of impressions desired, then the sheet is turned over sideways from left to right and the run is completed on the reverse side.

Selected List of References_____

For the reader's convenience there is presented here a list of books which is by no means complete, but may be helpful in the further study of lithography and its related fields. The list was prepared by the staff of the Technical Information Division of the Graphic Arts Technical Foundation's E. H. Wadewitz Memorial Library. This library is probably the most comprehensive source of scientific, technical, and educational information on graphic communications and related subjects to be found anywhere in the western hemisphere. Every effort is made to keep the library up-to-date through constant direct contact with publishers, and through the review of the publishers' trade lists.

Allen, Edward Monington, ed. *Harper's Dictionary of the Graphic Arts.* New York, Harper and Row, Publishers, 1963.

Apps, E. A. *Ink Technology for Printers and Students:* Volume I; *Manufacture and Testing.* New York, Chemical Publishing Co., Inc., 1964.

Apps, E. A. *Ink Technology for Printers and Students:* Volume II; *Inks for Major Processes.* New York, Chemical Publishing Co., Inc., 1964.

Apps, E. A. *Ink Technology for Printers and Students:* Volume III; *Special Applications.* New York, Chemical Publishing Co., Inc., 1964.

Arnold, Edmund C. *Functional Newspaper Design.* New York, Harper and Row, Publishers, 1956.

Arnold, Edmund C. *Ink on Paper.* New York, Harper and Row Publishers, 1963.

Baker, Elizabeth Faulkner. *Printers and Technology: A History of the International Printing Pressmen and Assistants' Union.* New York, Columbia University Press, 1957.

Banks, W. H., ed. *Printing Inks and Color:* Volume I; *Advances in Printing Science and Technology.* New York and other places, Pergamon Press, 1961.

Banks, W. H. *Halftone Printing:* Volume III; *Advances in Printing Science and Technology.* New York and other places, Pergamon Press, 1963.

Barnett, Michael P. *Computer Typesetting: Experiments and Prospects.* Cambridge, Mass., The M.I.T. Press, 1965.

Biegeleiser, J. I. *The Complete Book of Silk Screen Printing Production.* New York, Dover Publications, Inc., 1963.

Billmeyer, Fred W., Jr. and Satzman, Max. *Principles of Color Technology.* New York, Interscience Publishers, 1966.

Bragdon, Charles R. *Metal Decorating from Start to Finishes.* Freeport, Me., The Bond Wheelwright Co., 1961.

Brookes, B. C., ed. *Editorial Practices in Libraries.* London, Aslib, 1961.

Burt, Cyril. *A Psychological Study of Typography.* Cambridge, England, The University Press, 1959.

Carroll, John S., ed. *Photo-Lab-Index.* Hastings-on-Hudson, New York, Morgan and Morgan, Inc.; London, The Fountain Press, 1965.

Casey, James P. *Pulp and Paper: Chemistry and Chemical Technology.* 3 vols. New York, Interscience Publishers, Inc., 1960. Volume I. *Pulping and Bleaching;* Volume II. *Papermaking;* Volume III. *Paper Testing and Converting*

Cartwright, H. M. *Ilford Graphic Arts Manual:* Volume I; *Photo-Engraving.* Essex, England, Ilford Limited, 1961.

Cleeton, Glen V., *et al. General Printing.* Bloomington, Illinois, McKnight & McKnight Publishing Company, 1963.

Cogoli, John E., *Photo-Offset Fundamentals.* Bloomington, IL, McKnight & McKnight Publishing Co., 1960.

Computer Information Service. *Glossary of Automated Typesetting and Related Computer Terms.* Los Angeles, Composition Information Services, 1966.

Deller, Jack. *Printer's Rollers: Their Manufacture, Use and Care.* London, Charles Skilton, Ltd., 1959.

Department of the Air Force. *ACIC* (Aeronautical Chart and Information Center) *Ink Specifications.* St. Louis, Mo., Headquarters Aeronautic Chart and Information Center, 1965.

Division of Air Pollution, U.S. Dept. HEW. *Air Pollution Publications: A Selected Bibliography 1963-1966.* Washington, D.C., 1966.

Flexographic Technical Association. *Flexography: Principles and Practices.* New York, 1962.

Gerber, J. *A Selected Bibliography of the Graphic Arts.* Pittsburgh, Pa., Graphic Arts Technical Foundation, 1967.

Government Printing Office. *Theory and Practice of Bookbinding.* Washington, D.C., 1962.

Government Printing Office. *Theory and Practice of Presswork.* Washington, D.C., 1962.

Government Printing Office. *Typography and Design.* Washington, D.C., 1963.

Halpern, Bernard R. *Color Stripping.* Pittsburgh, Pa., Graphic Arts Technical Foundation, 1955.

Halpern, B. R. *Offset Stripping—Black and White.* Pittsburgh, Pa., Graphic Arts Technical Foundation, 1958.

Halpern, Bernard R. *Tone and Color Correcting.* Pittsburgh, Pa.; Graphic Arts Technical Foundation, 1956.

Hartsuch, Paul J. *Chemistry of Lithography.* Pittsburgh, Pa., Graphic Arts Technical Foundation, 1961.

Hattery, Lowell H., and Bush, George P., eds. *Automation and Electronics in Publishing.* Washington and New York, Spartan Books; London, Macmillan and Co., 1965.

Holmes, Raymond G., ed. *Air Pollution Source Testing Manual.* Los Angeles, Los Angeles Air Pollution Control District, 1965.

Hurst, C. A. and Lawrence, F. R. *Letterpress Composition and Machine Work.* London, Ernest Benn Ltd., 1963.

Hutchings, R. S., and Skilton, Charles, eds. *Modern Letterpress Printing: Materials and Methods in the Machine Room.* London, Charles Skilton, Ltd., 1963.

Jaffee, Erwin, *et al. Color Separation Photography with an Introduction to Masking.* Pittsburgh, Pa. Graphic Arts Technical Foundation, 1959.

Jaffee, Erwin. *Contact Printing.* Pittsburgh, Pa., Graphic Arts Technical Foundation, 1964.

Jaffee, Erwin. *Halftone Photography for Offset Lithography.* Pittsburgh, Pa., Graphic Arts Technical Foundation, 1960.

Jaffee, Erwin, and Reed, Robert F. *The Science of Physics.* Pittsburgh, Pa., Graphic Arts Technical Foundation, 1964.

James, T. H., ed. *The Theory of the Photographic Process.* New York. The Macmillan Company; London, Collier-Macmillan Limited, 1966.

Jorgensen, George W., and Bruno, Michael H. *The Sensitivity Guide.* Pittsburgh, Pa., Graphic Arts Technical Foundation, 1959.

Karch, R. Randolph, and Buber, Edward J. *Graphic Arts Procedures: The Offset Processes.* Chicago, American Technical Society, 1967.

Karch, R. Randolph. *How to Recognize Type Faces.* Bloomington, Illinois, McKnight & McKnight, 1952.

Kasloff, Albert. *Photographic Screen Process Printing.* Cincinnati, The Signs of the Times Publishing Co., 1965.

Katz, Irving. *Adhesive Materials: Their Properties and Usages.* Long Beach, California, Foster Publishing Co., 1964.

Kenneison, W. C., and Spilman, A. J. B. *Dictionary of Printing, Papermaking, and Bookbinding.* London, George Newnes Limited, 1963.

Kosar, Jaromir. *Light-Sensitive Systems: Chemistry and Applications of Non-silver Halide Photographic Processes.* New York, John Wiley & Sons, Inc., 1965.

Lasky, Joseph. *Proofreading and Copy-Preparation: A Textbook for the Graphic Arts Industry.* New York, Mentor Press, 1964.

Latham, C. W. *Advanced Pressmanship—Sheetfed Presses.* Pittsburgh, Pa., Graphic Arts Technical Foundation, 1963.

Latham, Charles W. *Offset Lithographic Press Operating—Sheetfed Presses.* Pittsburgh, Pa., Graphic Arts Technical Foundation, 1963.

Latham, Charles W., and White, Jack W. *Photocomposing.* Pittsburgh, Pa., Graphic Arts Technical Foundation, 1964.

MacKay, Robert, and Cartwright, H. M. *Rotogravure: A Survey of European and American Methods.* Lyndon, Kentucky, MacKay Publishing Co., Inc., 1956.

Messner, Richard. *Selling Printing and Direct Advertising.* New York, Fred W. Hoch Associates, 1947.

Miller, C. William. "Benjamin Franklin's Philadelphia Type." *Studies in Bibliography: Papers of the Bibliographical Society of Virginia:* II, 179–206 (1958).

Neblette, C. B., and Murry, Allen E. *Photographic Lenses.* Hastings-on-Hudson, New York, Morgan & Morgan, Inc.; London, The Fountain Press, 1965.

Noemer, Ewald Fred. *The Handbook of Modern Halftone Photography.* Demarest, New Jersey, Perfect Graphic Arts, 1965.

Printing Industries of America. *A Composition Manual.* Washington, D.C. Printing Industries of America, 1953.

Pulp and Paper Research Institute of Canada. *Thesaurus of Pulp and Paper Terms.* Pointe Claire, Quebec, 1965.

Purves, Frederick, *et al. The Focal Encyclopedia of Photography.* New York, The Macmillan Company, 1956.

Radford, R. G. *Letterpress Machine Work,* London, Staple Press Ltd., 1957.

Ratliff, Floyd. *Mach Bands: Quantitative Studies on Neural Networks in the Retina.* San Francisco and other places, Holden-Day, Inc., 1965.

Reed, Robert F. *The GATF Pick Tester for Offset Papers.* Pittsburgh, Pa., Graphic Arts Technical Foundation, 1953.

Reed, Robert F. *Instruments for Quality Control.* Pittsburgh, Pa., Graphic Arts Technical Foundation, 1963.

Reed, Robert F. *Offset Lithographic Platemaking.* Pittsburgh, Pa., Graphic Arts Technical Foundation, 1967.

Reed, Robert F. *Offset Press Troubles—Sheetfed Presses.* Pittsburgh, Pa., Graphic Arts Technical Foundation, 1962.

Reed, Robert, F. *Web Offset Press Troubles.* Pittsburgh, Pa., Graphic Arts Technical Foundation, 1966.

Reed, Robert F. *What the Lithographer Should Know About Ink.* Pittsburgh, Pa., Graphic Arts Technical Foundation, 1960.

Reed, Robert F. *What the Lithographer Should Know About Paper.* Pittsburgh, Pa., Graphic Arts Technical Foundation, 1959.

Robinson, Karl Davis. *Line Photography for the Lithographic Process.* Pittsburgh, Pa., Graphic Arts Technical Foundation, 1956.

Rodriquez, Cesar, and Humphrey, George H., ed. *Bilingual Dictionary of the Graphic Arts.* (English-Spanish, Spanish-English). Farmingdale, Long Island, New York, George H. Humphrey, 1966.

Roy, Robert H. *Management of Printing Production.* Washington, D.C., Printing Industries of America, 1953.

Senefelder, Alois. *The Invention of Lithography,* trans. J. W. Muller. London, Fuchs & Lang Manufacturing Co., 1961.

Steffens, Robert N. *Engraved Stationery Handbook.* New York, The Cronite Press, 1950.

Strauss, Victor. *The Printing Industry.* Washington, D.C., Printing Industries of America, 1967.

Teddington, Eng. *Visual Problems of Color: Symposium.* Volume II. New York, Chemical Publishing Co., Inc., 1961.

Tinker, Miles A. *Legibility of Print.* Ames, Iowa, Iowa State University Press, 1963.

Updike, Daniel Berkely. *Printing Types:* *Their History, Forms, and Use: A Study in Survivals.* Cambridge, Mass., Harvard University Press, 1963. 2 vols.

Weiner, Jack, and Wroth, Lillian, *Institute of Paper Chemistry: Bibliographic Series, No. 164, Paper and its Relation to Printing.* Appleton, Wisconsin, 1962.

Wright, W. D. *The Measurement of* *Colour.* New York, D. Van Nostrand and Company, Inc., 1964.

Wroth, Lawrence. *The Colonial Printer.* Charlottesville, Virginia. The University Press of Virginia, 1938.

Yule, J. A. C. *Principles of Color Reproduction.* New York, John Wiley & Sons, Inc., 1967.

Selected List of Abstracted Periodicals

The E. H. Wadewitz Memorial Library receives over 400 periodicals. Each of these periodicals is examined for articles of interest which are then summarized, or "abstracted" for ready reference. These abstracts are classified and filed as an index to the information contained in the articles. This file is probably unexcelled anywhere; entries now number over 70,000, and over 3,500 per year are added.

A selection of these abstracts—the most significant ones —is assembled and published under the title *Graphic Arts* *Abstracts.* This is sent directly to GATF members each month. Non-members of the Foundation may subscribe to this publication. On request, the published abstracts are made available to the trade press. Interested readers, if they cannot get the periodical directly, may write to GATF to obtain a photocopy of any article that interests them. A "break-even" charge is made for the photocopy service.

The following periodicals are some of those abstracted by GATF's E. H. Wadewitz Memorial Library staff.

Abstract Bulletin of the Institute of Paper Chemistry. Institute of Paper Chemistry, Appleton, WI.

Abstracts of Photographic Science and Engineering Literature, 345 E. 47th St., New York, NY 10017

Administrative Management. Andrew Geyer-McAllister, Inc., 212 Fifth Ave., New York, NY 10010

Advertising Age. Advertising Publications, Inc., 740 Rush St., Chicago, IL 60611

Advertising and Sales Promotion. Advertising Publications, Inc., 740 Rush St., Chicago, IL 60611

Air and Water News. McGraw-Hill, Inc., 330 W. 42nd St., New York, NY 10036

Air Engineering, 450 W. Fort St., Detroit, MI 48226

American Ink Maker. MacNair-Dorland Co., 254 W. 31st St., New York, NY 10001

American Paper Industry. Paper Industry Management Association, 2570 Devon Ave., Des Plaines, IL 60018

American Press. Michael and Ginsberg Publishing House, 1215 Wilmette Ave., Wilmette, IL 60018

American Pressman. International Printing Pressmen and Assistants' Union of North America, Pressmen's Home, TN 37850

American Vocational Journal. American Vocational Association, Inc., 1025 15th St., N.W., Washington, DC 20005

ANPA/RI Bulletin. ANPA Research Institute, Inc., 750 Third Ave., New York, NY 10017

APCA Abstracts. Air Pollution Control Association, 4400 Fifth Ave. Pittsburgh, PA 15213

Applied Graphics. Newfield Publication Ltd., P.O. Box 157, Agincourt, Ontario, Canada

Applied Optics. Optical Society of America, Inc., 20th and Northampton Sts., Easton, PA 18042

Applied Photography. Eastman Kodak Co., 343 State St., Rochester, NY 14650

Art Direction. Advertising Trade Publications, Inc., 19 W. 44th St., New York, NY 10036

Asian Printer. Insatsu Gakkai Shuppanbu, No. 4, Ginza-5, Chuoku, Tokyo, Japan

Australasian Printer. Lawson Publications Pty. Ltd., 49 Clarence Street, Sidney, N.S.W., Australia

Australian Lithographer. Alfred Stern, 170 Kurraba Road, Neutral Bay, N.S.W., Australia

Battelle Technical Review. Battelle Memorial Institute, 505 King Ave., Columbus, OH 43201

BDSA: Marketing Information Guide. *U.S. Department of Commerce/Business and Defense Services Administration.* Superintendent of Documents, U.S. Government Printing Office, Washington, DC 20402

BDSA: Quarterly Industry Report: Printing and Publishing. U.S. Department of Commerce/Business and Defense Services Administration, Superintendent of Documents, U.S. Government Printing Office, Washington, DC 20402

Book Production Industry: Penton Publishing Co., 1276 W. Third St., Cleveland, OH 44113

Boxboard Containers. Maclean-Hunter Publishing Corp., 300 W. Adams St., Chicago, IL 60606

British Ink Maker. Batiste Publications Ltd., Drummond House, 203-9 Gower Street, London, NW1, England

British Printer. Maclean-Hunter Ltd. 30 Old Burlington St., London, W1, England

Bulletin of the Technical Association of Graphic Arts of Japan. Nippon Insatsu Gakkai, No. 23, Shintomicho-2, Chuo-ku, Tokyo, Japan

Business Graphics. Graphic Arts Publishing Co., 7373 N. Lincoln Ave., Chicago, IL 60646

CA. Coyne and Blanchard, Inc., 809 San Antonio Rd., Palo Alto, CA

CAC News. The Chicago Advertising Club, 365 Wabash Ave., Chicago, IL 60603

Canadian Printer and Publisher. Maclean-Hunter Publishing Co., Ltd., 481 University Ave., Toronto 2, Canada

Carbon Black Abstracts. Cabot Corporation, 125 High St., Boston, MA 02110

Carnegie Magazine. Carnegie Institute, 4400 Forbes Ave., Pittsburgh, PA 15213

Chambon Review. Chambon Ltd., Riverside Works, Standish Road, Hammersmith, London W6, England

Chronicle of Higher Education. Editorial Projects for Education, 3301 N. Charles St., Baltimore, MD 21218

Color Engineering. Chromatic Publishing Co., Inc., 18 John St., New York, NY 10038

Converter. Factory Publications Ltd., Hermes House, 89 Blackfriars Road, London, SE 1 England

DA (Direct Advertising). Paper Makers Advertising Association, 77 N. Washington St., Boston 14, MA 02114

Dot Zero. Dot Zero, Inc., 410 East 62nd St., New York, NY 10021

Dow Diamond. Dow Chemical Co., Midland, MI 48640

Editor and Publisher. Editor and Publisher, Co., 850 Third Ave., New York, NY 10022

Electroplating and Metal Finishing. Robert Draper, Ltd., 85 Udney Park Road, Teddington, Middlesex, England

Environmental Science and Technology. 1155 16th St., N.W., Washington, DC, 20036

Export Polygraph International. Polygraph Verlag GmbH, Frankfurt-am-main, Schaumainkai 85, W. Germany

Fast Announcement. U.S. Department of Commerce Clearinghouse for Federal Scientific and Technical Information, Springfield, VA 22151

Flexogram. Interchemical Corporation, Printing Ink Division, 67 W. 44th St., New York, NY 10036

Flexography. Graphic Magazines Inc., 61 Hilton Ave., Garden City, NY 11530

Focus. Bausch & Lomb Optical Co., Rochester, NY 14602

Graphic Journal. National Graphical Association, Radlett House, West Hill Aspley Guise, Nr Bletchley, Bucks, England

Graphic Arts Bulletin. The Printing and Allied Trades Employers' Federation of Australia, 136 Jolimont Road, East Melbourne, C2 Australia

Graphic Arts Buyer. Angus J. Ray Publishing Co., 2 North Riverside Plaza, Chicago, IL 60606

Graphic Arts Japan. Japan Printers Association, 23, 2-chome, Shintomicho, Chuo-ku, Tokyo, Japan

Graphic Arts Monthly. Graphic Arts Publishing Co., 7373 N. Lincoln Ave., Chicago, IL 60646

Graphic Arts Progress. Graphic Arts Research Center, RIT, Box 3409, Rochester, NY 14614

Graphic Arts Register. Photo Products Department, E.I. du Pont de Nemours & Co. Inc., 2424-D Nemours Building, Wilmington, DE 19898

Graphic Arts Unionist. 233 W. 49th St., New York, NY 10019

Graphic Communications Weekly. Information Services, Inc., 1605 N. Cahuenga Boulevard, Los Angeles, CA 90028

Graphic News. Graphic News Co. 2617 E. Hennepin, Minneapolis, MN 55413

Graphicus. via del Carmine 14, Turin, Italy

Gravure. Graphic Magazines, Inc. 61 Hilton Ave., Garden City, NY 11530

Gravure Technical Association Bulletin. Gravure Technical Association, Inc., 60 E. 42nd St., New York, NY 10017

Greeting Card Magazine. Mackay Publishing Corp., 95 Madison Ave., New York, NY 10016

GRI Newsletter. Gravure Research Institute, Inc., 22 Manhasset Ave., Port Washington, NY 11050

Heidelberg News. Heidelberg Printing Machinery Co., Ltd., Eyot Gardens, Hammersmith, London W6, England

Industrial Arts and Vocational Education. The Bruce Publishing Co., 400 N. Broadway, Milwaukee, WI 53201

IBM Journal of Research and Development. IBM Corporation, Armonk, NY 10504

INCA Monthly. Washingtonplatz 1, 61 Darmstadt, West Germany

Index of Federal Specifications and Standards. Superintendent of Documents, Government Printing Office, Washington, DC 20402

Industrial Art Methods. Syndicate Magazines, Inc., 25 W. 45th St., New York, NY 10036

Industrial Bulletin. Arthur D. Little, Inc., Acorn Park, Cambridge, MA 02140

Industrial Bulletin. NY State Dept. of Labor, State Campus, Albany, NY 12226

Inland Printer/American Lithographer. Maclean-Hunter Publishing Corp., 300 W. Adams Street, Chicago, IL 60606

In-Plant Printer. United Business Publications, 200 Madison Ave., New York, NY 10016

Institute of Printing Bulletin. The Institute of Printing Ltd., 44 Bedford Row, London, WC 1, England

Interchemical Literature Abstract Bulletin. Interchemical Corp., 1255 Broad St., Clifton, NJ 07015

Interchemical Patent Abstract Bulletin. Interchemical Corp. Central Research Laboratories, 1255 Broad St., Clifton NJ 07015

International Bulletin for the Printing and Allied Trades. 9 Railway Street, London, N 1, England

Inter-Society Color Council Newsletter. Inter-Society Color Council, Inc., Photographic Technology Division, Bldg. 65, Eastman Kodak Co., Rochester, NY 14650

Journal of the Air Pollution Control Assn., Air Pollution Control Assn., 4400 Fifth Av., Pittsburgh, PA 15213

Journal of the American Institute of Graphic Arts. 1059 Third Ave., New York, NY 10021

Journal of Industrial Arts Education. American Industrial Arts Assn., 1201 16th St., N.W., Washington, DC 20036

Journal of the Oil and Color Chemists' Assn. Wax Chandlers' Hall, Gresham Street, London, EC 2, England

Journal of Paint Technology. Federation of Societies for Paint Technology, 121 S. Broad St., Philadelphia, PA 19107

Journal of Photographic Science. Royal Photographic Society of Great Britain, 16 Princess Gate, London, S.W. 7

Journal of the Society of Dyers and Colourists. Dean House, 19 Piccadilly, Bradford 1, York, England

Journal of Typographic Research. Press of Western Reserve Univ., 2029 Adelbert Road, Cleveland, OH 44106

Kodak Bulletin for the Graphic Arts. Graphic Arts Publications, Eastman Kodak Co., Rochester, NY 14650

Lithographer, The. Senefelder House, 137 Dickenson Road, Rushalme, Manchester 14, England

Lithopinion. Local 1, Amalgamated Lithographers of America, 113 University Place, New York, NY 10003

Litho-Printer, The. Gillow House, 5 Winsley Street, Oxford Circus W 1, England

Lubrication. Texaco, Inc., 135 East 42nd St., New York, NY 10017

Marketing Communications. Decker Communications, Inc. 501 Madison Ave., New York, NY 10022

Metal Finishing. Metals and Plastics Publications, Inc. 99 Kinderkamach Rd., Westwood, NJ 07675

MGD Graphic News. 3100 S. Central Ave., Chicago, IL 60650

Mid-Atlantic Graphic Arts Review. North American Publishing Co., 134 N. 13th St., Philadelphia, PA 19107

Modern Converter. Ojibway Press, Inc., Ojibway Building, Duluth, MN 55802

Modern Lithography. Industry Publications, Inc., Box 31, Caldwell, NJ 07006

Modern Packaging. McGraw-Hill, Inc., 330 W. 42nd St., N.Y., NY 10036

Modern Photography. Billboard Publications, Inc., 165 W. 46th St., New York, NY 10036

Monthly Catalog of U.S. Government Publications. Superintendent of Documents, U.S. Government Printing Office, Washington, DC 20402

National Printing Ink Research Institute Monthly Literature Review. Lehigh University, Bethlehem, PA

New England Printer and Lithographer. Editor and Printer Publishing Co., 470 Atlantic Ave., Boston 10, MA 02210

Occupational Outlook Quarterly. Superintendent of Documents, Washington, DC 20402

Packaging Abstracts. PIRA Randalls Road, Leatherhead, Surrey, England

Packaging Progress. Southam Business Publications Ltd., 1450 Don Mills Rd., Don Mills, Ontario, Canada

Paint and Varnish Production. Powell Magazines, Inc., 855 Avenue of the Americas, New York, NY 10001

Paper Trade Journal. Lockwood Trade Journal Co., Inc., 49 W. 45th St., New York, NY 10036

Par-Lance. Printing Industries of America, 20 Chevy Chase Circle, N.W., Washington, DC 20015

Patent Abstracts Section: Official Gazette. Superintendent of Documents, Washington, DC 20402

Penrose Annual. Percy Lund, Humphries & Co. Ltd., 12 Bedford Square, London, WC 1, England

Photo Typesetting. Society Publications Ltd., 7 West Halkin St., Belgrave Square, London, SW 1, England

Photoengravers Bulletin. American Photoengravers Assoc., 166 W. Van Buren St., Chicago, IL 60604

Photographic Abstracts. Royal Photographic Society of Great Britain, 16 Princess Gate, London, SW 7, England

Photographic Journal. Royal Photographic Society of Great Britain, 16 Princess Gate, London, SW 7, England

Photographic Science and Engineering. Society of Photographic Scientists & Engineers, Box 1609, Main Post Office, Washington, DC 20013

PIRA Journal. PIRA, Randalls Road, Leatherhead, Surrey, England

PIRA News. PIRA, Randalls Road, Leatherhead, Surrey, England

PMI Photo Methods for Industry. Gellert-Wolfman Publications, 33 W. 60 St., New York, NY 10023

Print. RC Publications, Inc., 1028 Connecticut Ave., N.W., Washington, DC 20036

Print-Equip News. 135 S. Maryland, Glendale, CA 91205

Print in Britain. Gillow House, 5 Winsley Street, Oxford Circus, London W 1, England

Printers' Digest. Standard Service Corp., 2335 Central Ave., Minneapolis, MN 55318

Printers' News. Federation of Master Printers of New Zealand, Inc., Box 1422, GPO, Wellington, New Zealand

Printindia. Amurtha Publications, 111-C Arcot Road, Kodambakkam, Madras-24, S. India

Printing Abstracts. PIRA, Randalls Road, Leatherhead, Surrey, England

Printing Impressions. North American Publishing Co., 134 N. 13th St., Philadelphia, PA 19107

Printing Magazine/National Lithographer. Walden, Sons & Mott, Inc., 466 Kinderkamack Rd., Oradell, NJ 07675

Printing News. 468 Park Ave., New York, NY 10016

Printing Plates Magazine. International Assoc. of Electrotypers & Stereotypers, Inc., 758 Leader Bldg., Cleveland, OH 44114

Printing Production. Penton Publishing Co., 1276 W. Third St., Cleveland, OH 44113

Printing Review. Jonathan Publications Ltd., 146 Bates Road, Montreal 26, Canada

Printing Technology. Institute of Printing Ltd., 44 Bedford Row, London, WC 1, England

Printing Trades Journal. Benn Brothers Ltd., Bouverie House, Fleet St., London, EC 4, England

Printing Views. Midwest Publishing, 740 N. Rush St., Chicago, IL 60611

Printing World. Stonhill & Gillis Ltd., Lincoln House, 296–302 High Holborn, London, WC 1, England

Printink. Rainbow-Printing Inks, 133 C, Vakola, Santacruz East, Bombay-55, India

Pulp and Paper. Miller Freeman Publications, 370 Lexington Ave., New York, NY 10017

Pulp and Paper Magazine of Canada. National Business Publications Ltd., Gardenvale, Quebec, Canada

Quality Progress. American Society for Quality Control, 161 West Wisconsin Ave., Milwaukee, WI 53203

Reproduction Engineer. 18307 James Couzens Highway, Detroit, MI 48235

Reproduction Methods for Business and Industry. 33 W. 60 St., N.Y., NY 10023

Reproductions Review. Geyer-McAllister Publications Inc., 51 Madison Ave., New York, NY 10010

Research in Education. U.S. Dept. of Health, Education and Welfare, Superintendent of Documents, Washington, DC 20402

Research Management. Interscience Publishers, a Division of John Wiley & Sons, Inc., 605 Third Ave., New York, NY 10016

Rheology Bulletin. American Institute of Physics, 335 E. 45th St., New York, NY 10017

Roland News. Roland Offsetmaschinenfabrik, Faber & Schleicher Ag, Offenbach/Main, Germany

School Shop. Box 623, 416 Lonshore Drive, Ann Arbor, MI 48107

Science and Technology. International Communications Inc., 205 E. 42nd St., New York, NY 10017

Screen Printing and Point of Sale News. Batiste Publications Ltd., 203–209 Gower Street, London N.W. 1, England

Screen Printing Magazine. 407 Gilbert Avenue, Cincinnati, OH 45202

Share Your Knowledge Review. 7599 Kenwood Road, Cincinnati, OH 45236

Small Offset (Supplement to Print in Britain and Litho-Printer). Gillow House, 5 Winsley Street, Oxford Circus, London W 1, England

Small Offset User. Corbett Cope Limited, 54 Welbeck Street, London W. 1, England

Southern Printer and Lithographer. Ernest H. Abernethy Publishing Co., Inc., 75 Third St, N.W., Atlanta, GA 30308

Southern Pulp and Paper Manufacturer. Ernest H. Abernethy Publishing Co. Inc., 75 Third St., N.W., Atlanta, GA 30308

SPSE News. Society of Photographic Scientists and Engineers, Inc., 1330 Massachusetts Ave., N.W., Washington, DC 20005

SRI Journal. Stanford Research Institute, Menlo Park, CA 94025

Summaries of Articles from the French Technical Press. Economic Section to the French Embassy, 1301 Avenue of the Americas, New York, NY 10019

TAGA Proceedings. Technical Association of the Graphic Arts, P.O. Box 3064, Federal Station, Rochester, NY 14614

Tappi. Technical Association of the Pulp & Paper Industry, 360 Lexington Ave., New York, NY 10017

Tappi Technical Information Sheets. Technical Association of the Pulp & Paper Industry, 360 Lexington Ave., New York, NY 10017

Technical Communications. Technical Communications, Inc., 647 N. Sepulveda Blvd., Los Angeles, CA 90049

Technical Education and Industrial Training. Evans Brothers Ltd., Montague House, Russell Square, London, W.C. 1, England

Tin Printer and Box Maker. Canning Publications, Peninsular House, 28–34 Monument St., London, EC 3, England

Training and Development Journal. American Society for Training & Development, P.O. Box 5307, Madison, WI 53705

Transactions of the Society of Rheology. Interscience Publishers, 605 Third Ave., New York, NY 10016

Typographic. Edwin H. Stuart, Inc., 422 First Ave., Pittsburgh, PA 15219

Typographical Journal. International Typographical Union, 301 S. Union Blvd., Colorado Springs, CO 80901

Visual. Pergamon Press, Inc., 44–01 21st St., Long Island City, NY 11101

Visual Communications Journal. International Graphic Arts Education Association, 1025 15th St., N.W., Washington DC 20005

Vocational Guidance Quarterly. National Vocation Guidance Association, 1605 New Hampshire Ave., N.W., Washington, DC 20009

Water Pollution Abstracts. H. M. Stationery Office, P.O. Box 569, London, S.E. 1, England

Web Printer. Boise Cascade Papers, 1718 S.W. 4th Ave., Portland, OR 97201

West German Photo Notes. Camera Industries of West Germany, 17 E. 45th St., New York, NY 10017

Westerner. Western Printing and Lithographing Co., 1220 Mound Ave., Racine WI 53404

INDEX

Appendix

Research Progress Reports Sixty, Sixty-seven, Seventy-six, summarize the more recent (through February, 1968) color research developments from the Graphic Arts Technical Foundation laboratories. They are included in the appendix to the fourth edition of *The Lithographers Manual* because of progress made since the chapters on Color Reproduction were written.

Research Progress Reports Sixty-nine, Seventy-one, and Seventy-five are also included in the appendix because of their significance to lithographic print quality, a most important factor in the production of full-color work.

Special attention is called to the Foundation's Research Progress Reports. These are issued as soon as a research project is completed and the results of the research have been demonstrated as being immediately applicable in every-day lithographic production. During the latter part of 1968 and early 1969, no less than three such reports will be issued. Members, of course, receive Research Progress Reports automatically, as soon as they are published.

RESEARCH GATF PROGRESS

NUMBER   SIXTY

GRAPHIC ARTS TECHNICAL FOUNDATION

GENERAL MEMO NO. 8

A NEW METHOD OF RATING THE EFFICIENCY OF PAPER FOR COLOR REPRODUCTIONS

By FRANK M. PREUCIL

IN BRIEF

Our studies of the factors that affect process color reproductions are continuous. A recent investigation was made to see why the color of the same ink looks different on different papers and to try to find a way to predict if this will happen. The study included six basic ink colors printed on eighteen different papers.

It was found that differences in the gloss and absorptivity of paper are major factors in the variations of printed ink color. Differences in them can (1) shift the hue or grayness of the primary inks (cyan, magenta, and yellow), (2) cause a reverse hue shift of secondary overprinted colors (red, green, and blue), and (3) require changes in the amount of

color correction needed. The work has produced a new trial factor for Paper Surface Efficiency that predicts these color changes fairly closely.

Although the study was directly concerned with process inks, the new factor is useful in any type of color printing.

INTRODUCTION

Under truly standard printing conditions process color reproduction may be close to an exact science. In commercial practice, however, it sometimes ranges between intuitive art and guesswork that is full of surprises. Some failures to match important colors and disappointments in the quality of pictures have been due to unknown and often unsuspected differences in the paper stocks.

This report shows that the control and standardization of process inks is only part of the answer to these problems. The reliability of photomechanical processes and our ability to print standard colors will not be possible until we can control the influence of the paper.

In Research Progress No. 51[1], we reported on the effect of paper color on color reproductions. The differences in the appearance of color tints printed on high bright and other near white papers can be surprisingly large. The study reported here has been concerned with the physical properties of the surface of the paper and their influence on the appearance of solid color areas that are printed on them.

Figure 1. *Variety of appearance of the same cyan ink printed on different paper.*

RESEARCH PROGRESS

Published by
GRAPHIC ARTS TECHNICAL FOUNDATION
Research Department
4615 Forbes Avenue
Number 60, May, 1963
©Lithographic Technical Foundation, Inc., 1962
Lithographed in U.S.A.
Written and Edited by JACK W. WHITE

Printing papers are widely different in their physical characteristics of gloss, texture, absorptivity, opacity, brightness, and color neutrality. When printed on a variety of papers, the color of the same ink becomes so widely different that you'd think different pigments had been used. (See Figure 1.) Often, you may not be able to see any differences in the papers on which the same ink looks different. And, equally surprising, the color of an ink may look the same when it is printed on papers that appear different to the eye.

The problem goes beyond papers that are intentionally different. Failures to match trademark colors, for example, have occurred on different mill lots of the same paper. Even opposite sides of the same paper have been different enough to cause mismatches of tints on facing wire and felt side pages.

A method of rating papers that would permit us to predict possible differences in the color of inks to be printed on them should be of great value. Such an index would help to select papers that are suitable for the best possible color printing. It could also serve as a guide for the manufacture of even better papers for the highest quality of color printing.

PRELIMINARY INVESTIGATION

The two most important variables that affect the color of inks printed on different papers are the gloss of the paper and the extent to which the paper absorbs the ink. Our first work was done to see how differences in these two factors would shift the hue of magenta and cyan. Data on single-color solids were collected from samples of the same magenta and cyan inks printed on eighteen papers that had widely different glosses and absorptivities. Differences in the two-color solids (red, green, and blue) were studied later. The data for these studies were obtained from overlaps of the primary colors as they appear in the GATF Color Chart. The Chart was printed with the same set of balanced inks on sixteen different papers.

The color differences of the various inks and papers were measured with a Welch Densichron through red (Wratten 25), green (Wratten 58), and blue (Wratten 47) filters. These density values were then converted to number values for hue, grayness, and efficiency. The exact procedure for doing this is described in GATF's Research Progress #38[2].

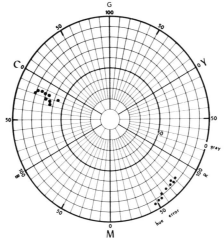

Figure 2. The differences in the hue and grayness of a cyan and magenta ink printed on nine different papers.

In addition, the color differences of the printed inks were studied in several other relationships. To do this, the factors were plotted on the GATF Color Circle, Subtractive Triangle, and Hexagon. The use of these diagrams is described in Research Progress Nos. 38 and 53[3].

Figure 2 shows the colors as they plot on an GATF Color Circle. Plots that are closest to the center of the circle have the least purity or are grayed the most. Again, the grayness of the cyan on the different papers varied widely. The extreme was a difference of 25 per cent between a bond paper and a double coated paper. The extreme magenta hue shift on these papers was a surprisingly

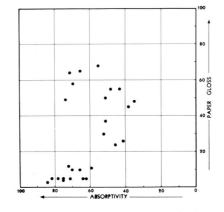

Figure 3. Differences in the gloss and absorptivity of the papers on which the magenta and cyan inks were printed.

large 35 per cent of the entire hue range between ideal primary magenta and red.

Figure 3 shows the differences in the gloss and absorptivity of the papers on which magenta and cyan inks were printed. As expected, the papers fell into two broad groups, coated and uncoated. The glosses of the coated papers ranged between 20 and 70 per cent. The glosses of the uncoated papers were all below 15 per cent. Notice that the absorptivity of some of the coated and uncoated papers overlap. Some papers having the highest gloss were as absorptive as the average of the uncoated papers.

It is common and to be expected that some colors will look weaker, less saturated, and shifted in purity when they are printed on uncoated papers. The surprising thing was that these cyan and magenta color shifts were two or three times greater than ordinarily seen.

There were two reasons for this. First, the papers used in the tests had a wider range of surface properties than those used in most plants. Second, the inks used were the slower drying linseed type. Similar test printings using gloss and quick-set types of inks have shown color shifts in the same direction but not as much. This would be expected since the faster set of these inks would counteract the effect of paper absorbency and tend to increase the hold-out and gloss of the ink.

These differences in ink color occurred on papers that were deliberately chosen for different surface properties. However,

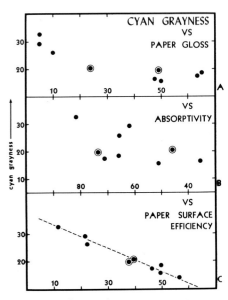

Figure 4. Relation of cyan grayness to paper gloss, paper absorptivity, and the PSE factor.

similar mismatches of color have occurred in commercial production when it was believed that the printing was being done on the same paper.

THE PSE FACTOR

In our efforts to develop some index that would predict changes in the color of the same ink on different stocks, we first tried to correlate the color shifts of printed magenta and cyan inks directly with paper gloss alone and then with paper absorptivity alone. This didn't work as is shown in Figure 4. In the top section of this figure, marked A, cyan grayness measurements are plotted against paper gloss measurements. In the middle section, marked B, they are plotted against paper absorptivity. You will notice how the plotted points are scattered and do not follow a straight line in either case. Notice especially the two plots in each section with the circles around them. These represent two papers that had widely different gloss and absorptivity but on which the printed colors looked the same.

In Section "C" at the bottom of the figure, we have plotted cyan grayness against the new Paper Surface Efficiency (PSE) factor. This factor represents the combination of a paper's gloss and absorptivity. In this case, the plotted points fall very close to a straight line indicating a direct and predictable relationship. Notice also that the two circled dots calculated to almost the same number and are brought closer together as they should be.

As a combination of gloss and absorptivity, the PSE factor takes into account, for example, a paper that has high absorptivity which is compensated for by a high gloss. Or, a paper that has low gloss which is compensated for by low absorptivity.

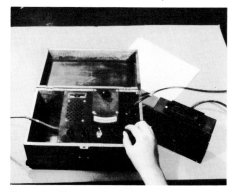

Figure 5. Photovolt Model 660-P Glossmeter used in the studies.

By determining the surface efficiency of different papers, you can predict whether the color of a given ink will look the same when it is printed on the different papers.

Figure 6. Applying K & N test ink to a number of paper samples.

HOW TO DETERMINE A PAPER'S SURFACE EFFICIENCY

Since the PSE factor is a combination of a paper's gloss and absorptivity, these two characteristics must be measured. Here are the procedures to follow:

Paper Gloss: The gloss of the paper is measured with a glossmeter such as the Photovolt Model 660-P. In this model, light is reflected from an angle of 75°. (See Figure 5.) Before the paper is measured, the instrument is calibrated or "zeroed" with a black mirror slab. The amount of light reflected from this mirror is the reference standard and is considered to be 100%. When the meter is adjusted so that it reads 100%, the black mirror is removed. The paper is then placed over the aperture and its per cent gloss is recorded. Usually, five different areas or five consecutive sheets are measured and the gloss readings are averaged.

Measuring Paper Absorptivity: The absorptivity of the paper is found using a simple procedure with K & N Test Ink°. An excess of this ink is applied to one or more samples of the paper as shown in Figure 6. The ink is allowed to stand on the paper for two minutes and is then thoroughly wiped off. The intensity of the ink stain that remains in the sample is then measured with a reflection densitometer as shown in Figure 7. No filter is

---
*K & N Test Ink is available from the K & N Laboratories, 1985 Anson Avenue, Melrose Park, Ill.

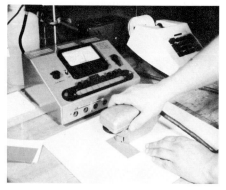

Figure 7. Measuring the intensity of the K & N test ink stain with a densitometer.

used on the densitometer head. The darker the stain, the greater the paper's absorptivity. For consistent results, this test should be made at a standard temperature and humidity since these could affect the viscosity and rate of penetration of the K & N Ink vehicle.

K & N Ink stain intensities can be read either as per cent reflectance or as reflection density. Either of these values can be used in the Paper Factors Conversion Chart (Figure 8) for conversion to absorptivity. Any reflection meter or densitometer will give this measurement if it illuminates the sample at 45° and views it at 90°. Reflection meters read directly in per cent reflectance. Some densitometers read only reflection density. Others have two scales and will read either density or per cent reflectance.

No calculations are needed to convert readings of the K & N ink stain to Absorptivity per cent. The procedure is quite easy when the conversion chart shown in Figure 8 is used. This new chart was developed by Zenon Elyjiw, a member of the GATF photographic staff. If you have the stain value in per cent reflectance, find it on the bottom scale. If this figure is 70%, for example, follow the 70% line vertically from the base of the chart up to the diagonal line. From this point, follow the horizontal line to the left hand scale which shows Absorptivity percentages. In this example, the 70% K & N reading converts to 40% Absorptivity.

If you have the stain value as reflection density, locate the density reading on the diagonal line. From this point, follow the horizontal line to the left hand scale and read the Absorptivity percentage. For example, a density of .15 converts to an Absorptivity of 39%.

You will notice that the lowest per cent reflectance shown on the chart is 25. The reason for this is that when a

PAPER FACTORS CONVERSION CHART

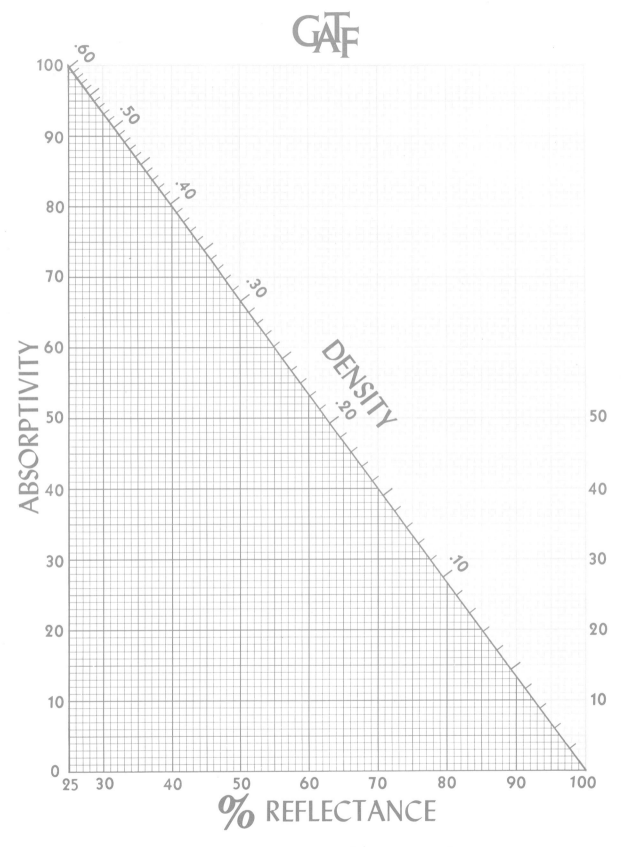

PAPER ABSORPTIVITY $= 1\frac{1}{3}(100 - K \& N \%)$

Figure 8. Chart for converting density or reflectance values to absorptivity.

GATF PAPER SURFACE EFFICIENCY CHART

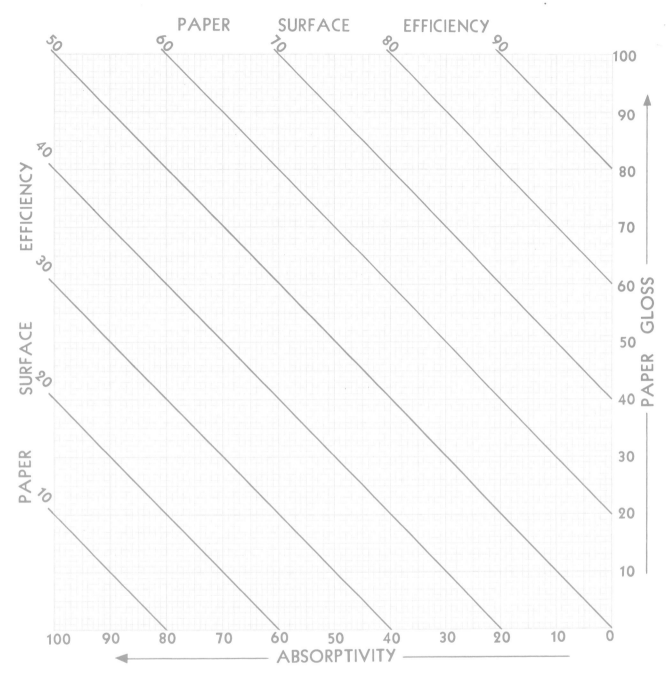

PAPER   SURFACE   EFFICIENCY

EFFICIENCY

SURFACE

PAPER

ABSORPTIVITY

PAPER GLOSS

PAPER	K & N %	ABSORPTIVITY	PAPER GLOSS	PAPER SURFACE EFFICIENCY	% REFLECTANCE			AVERAGE COLOR BRIGHTNESS	EXCESS COLOR	
					R	G	B		%	COLOR

Figure 9.   Paper Surface Efficiency conversion chart. See text for details on its use.

paper has absorbed a maximum amount of the test ink, it still has a reflectance of 25%. This 25% value therefore corresponds to an absorptivity of 100%.

Determining the PSE Factor: We now have the gloss and absorptivity percentage values necessary to determine the PSE percentage. Here again, the use of a conversion chart as shown in Figure 9 makes this quick and easy to do with no need for computations°.

For example, let's say that the Gloss of the paper is 60% and its Absorptivity is 40%. On the right hand scale of the chart, go up the Paper Gloss percentages to the 60% value. Then follow this 60% line horizontally to the left. On the bottom scale of the chart, locate the 40% Absorptivity percentage. Follow this line vertically until it crosses the horizontal Gloss line. From this point of intersection, follow the diagonal line toward the upper left or top of the chart. In this example, 60% Gloss and 40% Absorptivity intersect exactly on the diagonal that shows a PSE of 60%. If the Gloss were 70% and the Absorptivity is 40%, the PSE would be 65%.

USE OF THE PSE FACTOR

The PSE factor can be quite helpful when used with other basic measurements. One example would be to check the suitability of a paper for a rerun. In this application, you would first determine the PSE and whiteness of the paper used for the first printing. The paper selected for the rerun should then have values for these properties that are very close to the paper used originally. We assume here, of course, that the quality of the original job was completely satisfactory and your only aim is to duplicate it.

The PSE factor and chart will be most useful in comparing different papers within the same class of papers and different lots of the same papers to be sure that allowable tolerances are not exceeded. The chart can also be very helpful in learning the basic differences between different types of papers and how

---

°This conversion chart is based on the trial equation:

$$PSE = \frac{(100-A)+PG}{2}$$

in which equal importance is given to Paper Gloss (PG) and Paper Absorptivity (A). In these studies, other trial equations assigning different weights to gloss and/or absorptivity did not correlate as well with the color differences that were observed.

these differences influence the color of inks printed on them.

As you work with the PSE factor, it is easily possible to develop enough information to upgrade and standardize the average quality level of all the plant's production.

New lots of paper should be checked on both the felt and wire sides. In addition, six or eight consecutive sheets within a ream can be checked to see if the PSE is uniform. Sheets of paper that have been cut from a number of different rolls at the mill can vary widely in their surface characteristics.

RECORDING INFORMATION

The form at the bottom of the PSE Chart offers a convenient way to record information on different papers. Places are provided to identify the paper and record its K & N per cent, absorption, gloss, and PSE. The "% Reflectance" spaces are used for recording readings made through the red, green, and blue filters. In each case, the meter should first be set to zero density or 100% reflectance with the head on a block of magnesium carbonate.

If the densitometer doesn't have a per cent reflectance scale, these values can easily be found on the conversion chart (Figure 8) by following down the vertical lines from the density scale to the reflectance scale.

The "Average Color Brightness" is an average of the three readings made through the filters. It represents an overall brightness rating for different papers.

The "Excess Color" spaces are used to see if any color tint of a paper is likely to cause trouble. To use it, subtract the lowest filter reading from the highest filter reading and record the difference in the "%" column. If this per cent excess color figure is 5 per cent or higher and if halftone color tints are to be printed on the stock, a change in the photographic positives is indicated. The halftone dot sizes in the positive for the complementary color should be bigger. For example, if the paper shows 10 per cent excess blue, the dots in the yellow printer should be made larger. A job calling for a critical color match on a paper that has different excess color values than the stock run before, should be regarded with suspicion. Proving the job before it goes to press would be wise.

COLOR CORRECTION

In addition to the visual differences in printed ink color caused by differences in the surface of the paper, other important color reproduction factors are

also affected and now become equally predictable. The first of these is the color correction masking factor.

If you have a new job that will be printed on a strange paper, the best procedure is to print color samples of the inks that will be used on these papers and then determine the necessary mask factors directly from these samples.

If this is not practical or possible, the next best procedure is an application of the PSE factor. The method involves the preparation of graphs using data from previously printed samples or jobs.

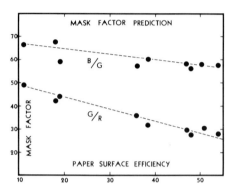

Figure 10. Mask factor prediction chart.

The mask factor prediction chart shown in Figure 10 is an example. The points plotted here represent the different mask factors used for jobs printed on a wide variety of papers having different PSE factors. In its simplest form, this graph can be based on just two papers that have widely different PSE factors. The use of more data from a wider variety of papers as was done here, tends to make the position of the straight line drawn through the points more accurate.

The mask factor percentages are derived as follows: The top B/G line represents the mask factor percentages needed for yellow printers. Samples of magenta ink printings are measured with a densitometer using filters. The blue (47) filter reading is divided by the green (58) filter reading to determine the per cent of masking needed to correct the blue filter separation (yellow printer).

The G/R line is based on mask factor percentages derived from densitometer readings of samples of cyan printings. Here, the green (58) filter reading is divided by the red (25) filter reading. This gives the per cent masking needed for the green filter separation in preparing the magenta printer.

When these mask factor percentages are plotted against the PSE values of the different papers, a graph like that shown in the figure is produced. Once such a graph is available, it becomes very easy to determine the mask factor percentages that will be required for a particular paper. One need only determine the PSE value of the paper. From this value on the horizontal graph line, move vertically to the diagonal line and then horizontally to the left side of the chart. Here, the mask factor percentages required for the paper can be read directly.

INK FACTOR GRAPHS

Another useful tool can also be based on the PSE factors of different papers. These are graphs that can be prepared to see how different PSE values will affect the standard inks that are used in the plant.

From previously or especially prepared printed samples, the grayness of the cyan inks and the hue of the magenta inks can be plotted against the PSE factors of the papers. When such graphs are available, it then becomes possible to estimate what will happen to the color of an ink when printed on papers having different PSE values.

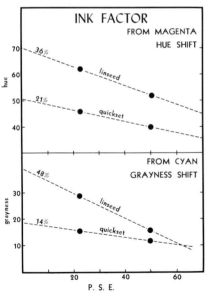

Figure 11. Ink Factor graphs showing effect of different PSE factors on printed ink colors.

These graphs can be as detailed or as simple as the variety of inks used in the plant. Figure 11 is an example. Here, we have curves for two standard magenta and cyan inks, linseed oil and quick-set, printed on a number of papers having different PSE factors. The bottom half plots the cyan grayness per cent against the PSE factors of two widely different papers. The upper half plots the magenta hue shift against the PSE values of different papers.

Each of these curves is based on two widely different papers. Greater accuracy can be obtained by use of additional data from a greater number of different papers. Once such curves are available, it is easy to check what effect the PSE of a strange paper will have on the colors of the standard inks used in the plant.

Color differences between different types of inks, as shown in this example, are normal and should be expected. The faster set of the quick-set inks would counteract the effect of paper absorptivity and tend to increase the hold-out and gloss of the ink.

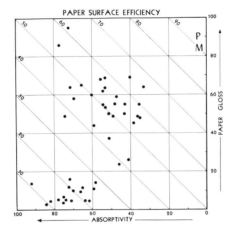

Figure 12. Plottings of the surface efficiency of various papers.

ADDITIONAL INFORMATION

The plottings in Figure 12 shows that a high gloss paper may not have as high a PSE factor as another paper with half this gloss and less absorptivity. Another important fact shown in this figure is that the best papers available today are still only about 65 per cent efficient. The possible range for improvement is up to half again better than the best now being used.

We had a chance to verify this prediction in a study of non-absorbent white coated metal sheets used by metal decorators and a new plastic coated paper. These two surfaces, indicated by "M" and "P" on Figure 12 have very low absorptivity and much higher gloss than regular printing papers. Their surface efficiencies are over 90 per cent.

Figure 13 compares the color differences of a magenta and cyan process ink as printed on the white coated metal (m), plastic coated papers (p), two coated papers (c), and an offset sheet (o). The surface efficiency of the offset paper was 19 per cent, the coated papers were 56 per cent, and the metal and plastic were over 90 per cent. This should predict that on the metal and plastic surfaces the magenta would be bluer and

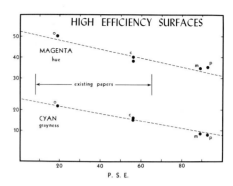

Figure 13. Showing the high surface efficiency of white, non-absorbent metal and plastic.

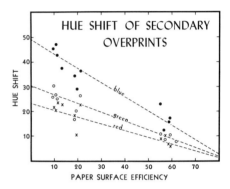

Figure 14. Hue shift of two color overprints.

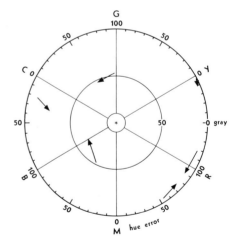

Figure 15. Direction of secondary color shifts on different papers.

the cyan would be purer. Results from the press test agreed with the prediction within one to two per cent.

HUE SHIFT OF SECONDARY COLORS

The extent of the shift in the hue of two-color overlaps of red, green, and blue on papers that have different surface efficiencies is shown in Figure 14. Figure 15 shows that these secondary color shifts

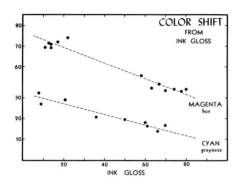

Figure 16. Relationship of magenta hue and cyan grayness to their own gloss.

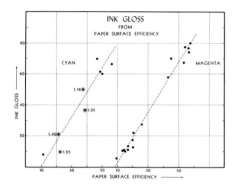

Figure 17. Predictions of printed ink gloss from the PSE factor.

on different papers are opposite in direction to those of the top primary colors on these same papers.

When such large color shifts were found in the first GATF Color Survey[4], we thought they were caused by differences in trapping or the use of inks that were partially opaque. We have now learned that the major cause is the scatter of light on the surface. Also, the differences in the color of inks on different papers are related to and can be predicted from the printed gloss of these inks.

Figure 16 shows that the differences in magenta hue and cyan grayness are directly related to their own ink gloss. This varied from 8 to 80 per cent on the different papers.

Figure 17 shows that the 8 to 80 per cent differences in magenta ink gloss were closely related to differences in PSE of from 10 to 60 per cent[5]. The PSE factor did not predict the gloss of the cyan ink as closely as did the magenta glosses. This could be expected because of variations in the thickness of the cyan ink film which varied the degree of gloss. This is shown by the four circled cyan dots. The red filter density values of these dots are also shown. Where the printed strength

of the cyan ink is below normal, the printed gloss was also below the predicted gloss.

The shifts of the hue and grayness of the magenta, cyan, and yellow inks that are related to their own ink glosses seem to be due to light scatter from the surface of the ink. Hue shifts of the primary inks are toward the nearest secondary color.

Consider also the condition in which the magenta and cyan prints on a paper having a low PSE and also prints on yellow ink on the same paper. Compared to the paper, the yellow ink surface is less absorptive. This, plus the increase in gloss of both the yellow ink and the overprinted ink, seems to compensate for some of the hue shift of the magenta and cyan.

INK STRENGTH

Neither the grayness nor hue of yellow and red ink change much when printed on coated or uncoated papers. Visually, however, the colors definitely do change because of a loss of color strength or color saturation. While such changes cannot be shown on a Color Circle or Triangle, they can be seen on the CIE diagram or the GATF Color Hexagon.

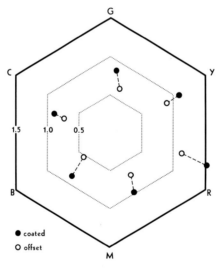

Figure 18. Loss of strength and saturation of the six basic colors.

Figure 18 shows the six basic colors plotted on the GATF Hexagon. Compared to the prints on coated paper, all colors are shown to lose saturation or strength when printed on uncoated paper. Even with the same ink film thickness, we would expect colors to appear less saturated when the ink and paper surfaces scatter the wavelengths of light that they would normally absorb.

AVAILABILITY OF DIAGRAMS

Like the GATF Color Circle, Triangle, Hexagon, and Data Sheets, new GATF Paper Surface Efficiency Charts are available to GATF members for $3.00 per hundred plus postage. Five Paper Factors Conversion Charts will be included with each order for PSE charts. Send orders to the GATF Research Department, 4615 Forbes Ave., Pittsburgh, Pa. 15213.

CONCLUSION

Differences in paper cause greater differences in color reproductions than the average variations in pigments and inks. A prediction of the effect of a paper surface on the color of an ink to be printed on it can now be made using a Paper Surface Efficiency factor. This factor is based on the combined measurements of the gloss and absorptivity of the paper. It gives a basic index to reasonably predict and understand some of the variables of color reproduction that were previously uncertain and unexplained. Still more accurate predictions may be possible if other factors such as ink film thickness or printed strength are included. (Conversely, one paper manufacturer has suggested that the PSE factor may not predict properly the color effects produced by combinations of some unusual types of paper coatings and inks that were not included in this basic study of most commonly used papers and inks.)

This principle of rating papers before printing in terms of their Surface Efficiency may be useful in insuring color reliability and quality. It may also lead to the manufacture of better papers for the highest quality of color reproduction.

REFERENCES

1. Preucil, F. M., "How to Test the Effect of Paper Color on Process Color Reproductions", *GATF Research Progress* #51.
2. Preucil, F. M., "The Evaluation of Process Inks", *GATF Research Progress* #38.
3. Preucil, F. M., "GATF's New Color Diagrams", *GATF Research Progress* #53.
4. Preucil, F. M., "The GATF Color Survey", *GATF Research Progress* #40.
5. Borchers, C. H., "The Effect of Paper Gloss on Ink Gloss", *GATF Research Progress* #50.

RESEARCH GATF PROGRESS

NUMBER   SIXTY-SEVEN

GRAPHIC ARTS TECHNICAL FOUNDATION

PHOTOGRAPHIC DEPARTMENT MEMO NO. 4

THE NEW GATF COLOR REPRODUCTION GUIDE

BY ZENON ELYJIW AND FRANK PREUCIL

IN BRIEF

A new color separation guide has been created with a number of advantages. It is supplied as a set of negatives or positives that are printed in the individual plant. The new guide permits masking and screening of subjects to compensate for the individual plant's ink, paper, and printing variables in process color reproduction.

INTRODUCTION

Photographic masking is an accepted method of color correction and many plants are using it with excellent results. Some plants, however, don't seem to benefit from these correction methods as much as they should. A frequent question is "Why does masking work in some plants but not in others?"

The reason is the many factors that are involved in process color reproduction —factors that are different from one plant to the next and even vary from one job to the next in the same plant.

There are three sources of these vari-

ables. First, are the process inks that are used. These vary in color, pigment concentration, printed densities, tack, and trapping[1, 5]. Paper is next. It can vary in its hue or color cast, brightness, opacity, and in its gloss and ink absorptivity. These last two factors we now combine in the term "Paper Surface Efficiency"[2]. The third important variable is possible change in the size or area of halftone dots that occur when making film contacts, during platemaking, and when the plate is run on the press.

To be successful, a masking system must be designed so that all of these variables are taken into account. Also, it should be obvious that one cannot calculate the masking and screening requirements for one set of variables and then try to use them successfully with different ink, different papers, and different press conditions. But this is exactly what is done in many plants.

The color guides and color control patches used in most plants for the evaluation of masking are printed and distributed by the manufacturers of

photographic materials and printing inks. They can be excellent control guides but only if the ink, paper, and press variables in the user's plant are the same as those in the plant where the guides were printed. It is rare for this to be the case.

One fact brought out by GATF's Color Surveys of the industry is the great extent by which the most important color reproduction factors vary from plant to plant. It follows then, that the usefulness of color guides printed in other plants is quite limited. The most important step in the successful control of color reproduction is the printing of color guides which incorporate the variables of the individual plant.

THE "CUSTOM MADE" COLOR GUIDE

One result of this line of thinking is the GATF Color Chart. It has been available in the form of standardized sets of negatives or positives for a number of years. Some plants have printed a number of sets of Color Charts on each of their color presses and using different

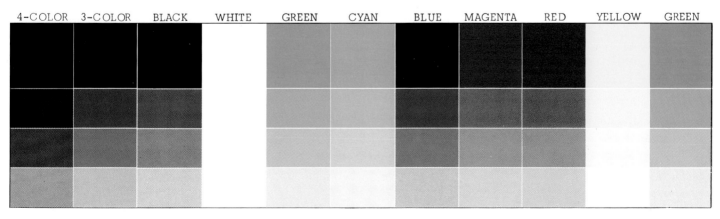

Figure 1. A typical printing of the GATF Color Reproduction Guide.

RESEARCH PROGRESS

Published by
GRAPHIC ARTS TECHNICAL FOUNDATION
Research Department
4615 Forbes Avenue, Pittsburgh, Pa. 15213
Number 67, November, 1964
©Graphic Arts Technical Foundation, 1964
Lithographed in U.S.A.
Edited by JACK W. WHITE

combinations of papers and inks. The men in these plants feel that the improvements in their control of color which is made possible by these Charts, more than justifies the work and effort to print them.

The GATF Color Reproduction Guide was designed around the same basic idea. It is also supplied in the form of standardized sets of positives or negatives. When printed under specific conditions in an individual plant, the Guide will incorporate the ink, paper, plate, and press variables that are unique in that plant. And, of course, the Guide will represent these variables in the color separation process much more faithfully than color guides printed under different circumstances.

As you can see in Figure 1, the GATF Color Reproduction Guide is composed of four rows of ten color blocks plus white. The top row of blocks from left to right are solids. The narrower rows of color blocks below are ¾, ½, and ¼ tints of the same colors. The screen ruling is 150 lines per inch.

PRINTING THE GUIDE

Make a set of plates from the negatives or positives of the Color Reproduction Guide. Use the same type of plates and follow the same procedures that you ordinarily employ.

Print the Guide with your standard set of process inks on coated paper. If you regularly use different sets of process inks or different papers, print the Guide with as many of these combinations as is practical. You may wish also, to print a four color process picture that represents your standard for color strength and quality. This will give you a visual reference for judgments of general color quality such as color strength and color balance.

Detailed records of platemaking and printing conditions may prove very useful in future work.

If you print the Guide for the purpose of setting up new optimum standards, print the yellow ink first to a reflection density of 1.00 if you are using a good bluish magenta. If your magenta ink is reddish (such as a litho rubine) it already has some yellow in it. In such a case, print the yellow to a density of .80.

Make the measurements with a densi-

tometer through a Wratten #47 blue filter. Put the densitometer head with the filter in place on an area of the unprinted white paper and zero the instrument before you measure the density of the ink. Also, correct the measurements to compensate for dry-back or use a polarizing densitometer.*

To measure the proper density for printing the magenta ink, you will need densitometer readings of the red (magenta over yellow) patch through the #47 filter and the green #58 filter. As before, zero the densitometer on the white, unprinted paper with each filter before you measure the red color block. The magenta will be running at proper strength when the density reading of red through the green filter is 85 to 100% of the density reading through the blue filter. Example values might be similar to these:

$$\frac{\#58 \text{ green filter density}}{\#47 \text{ blue filter density}} = \frac{1.25}{1.42} = 88\%$$

To determine the proper strength for running the cyan ink, measure the green (cyan on yellow) patch with the red #25 filter and the blue #47 filter in the densitometer. As before, zero the densitometer with each filter on white paper before you make the two measurements of the green color block. The cyan will be running at correct strength when the density measurement made through the red filter is 90 to 110% of the measurement made through the blue filter. Example values might be:

$$\frac{\#25 \text{ red filter density}}{\#47 \text{ blue filter density}} = \frac{1.09}{1.16} = 94\%$$

USING THE GUIDE

Lets say now that you have printed the Guides with your standard process inks on several types of paper. When a color job comes in for color separation, the order will call for a certain set of inks on a particular paper. The photographer then selects the Guide that was printed with these same inks and on the same paper as specified for the job.

He places the Guide next to the color copy and makes the color separations so that each negative includes the image of the Guide. For work with transparent copy, the printed Guides can be photographed on color film, preferably the same kind that was used for shooting the color transparency. This color transparency can then be used alongside the transparent copy that is to be color separated.

*Hull, Harry H., "The Polarizing Reflection Densitometer," GATF *Research Progress* No. 66.

USE OF THE SOLID INK PATCHES

As with other color control guides, the solid ink patches of the GATF Color Reproduction Guide can be used to (1) measure the solid ink densities, (2) evaluate ink trapping, and (3) calculate mask percentages. Complete details on these procedures can be found in GATF's Bulletin No. 509, *Color Separation Photography.*

In the separation negatives or positives, the appearance of the Guide's solid ink patches indicate the degree of color correction by the "Rule of Three". When this rule is satisfied, each separation (except black) is properly corrected when three of the six basic colors in the Guide are equally dense and black, and the other three colors are as light as white.

The blue filter, yellow printer separation, for example, is properly corrected when the red, yellow, and green patches are equally dense and black and the cyan, blue, and magenta patches are as light as the white patch.

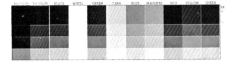

Figure 2. Uncorrected blue filter separation.

Figure 3. Properly corrected blue filter separation. The red, yellow, and green patches are equally strong and all values in the cyan, blue, and magenta patches have been eliminated.

In a properly corrected green filter separation for the magenta printer, the blue, magenta, and red patches are equally dense and the cyan, yellow, and green patches are as light as the white patch.

Figure 4. Uncorrected green filter separation.

Figure 5. Properly corrected green filter separation. The blue, magenta, and red patches are equally strong. All values in the green, cyan, and yellow patches have been eliminated.

Finally, when the red filter separation negative for the cyan printer is properly corrected, the magenta, red, and yellow patches are as light as white, and the cyan, blue, and green patches are equally dense and black.

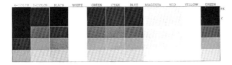

Figure 6. A typical uncorrected red filter separation (cyan printer). A small dot of cyan is printing in magenta and red and there is less saturation in cyan than in black.

Figure 7. Properly corrected red filter separation. The green, cyan, and blue patches are equally strong. All values in the magenta, red, and yellow patches have been eliminated.

The "rule of three" does not apply to the black printer. Ideal black separations have no values in any of the pure color areas. Practically this can not be obtained with any correction system. However, masking or scanning followed by skeleton type screening can produce good practical black printers. The figures which follow are typical examples.

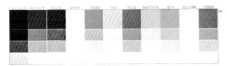

Figure 8. Uncorrected black printer separation.

Figure 9. Black separation corrected with the GATF "X" filter mask. (See Research Progress No. 48 "A Better Color Corrected Black Printer" for details on the use of this mask.) The residual errors are minimized by skeleton type screening.

Figure 10. The same separation shown in Figure 9 screened to eliminate the residual errors.

In making color measurements with the densitometer, it is often convenient to have the three wanted colors side-by-side. With usual color guides this is provided only in the yellow and magenta separations. In the new GATF Guide, a duplicate green patch has been added between the cyan and white patches so that the three wanted colors are kept together in the cyan printer also.

USE OF THE TINT PATCHES

Vertically under each of the solid patches in the top row of the GATF Color Reproduction Guide, there are ¾, ½, and ¼ tints of 150 lines per inch. These tints represent the dark, medium, and light portions of the halftone scale. One use of these patches is to show the amount of dot gain that develops at each stage of reproduction. The procedure for doing this is covered in GATF's *Research Progress* No. 64, "How To Measure Dot Gain or Loss."

Another use of the tint patches is to calculate proportionality failure. Proportionality failure makes the hue and grayness of lighter tints worse (further from ideal) than the hue and grayness of a solid of the ink. To correct for this, the curves for the masks can not be straight lines. In negative masks, the highlights must have a higher slope than the middletones and shadows. Conversely, positive masks must have a flatter slope in their higher densities. The tint patches help to predict the correct mask curves.

In color separations, they will indicate if proper mask curves have been used and show if the proportionality failure has been corrected.

MOIRÉ PATTERNS

The rescreening of any tint or halftone may, under some conditions, produce an objectionable moiré pattern. In some cases, this may happen in the tint patches of the GATF Color Reproduction Guide. To avoid this difficulty, the angle of each color of the GATF Guide is rotated 30 degrees away from the color's customary position.

When the GATF Guide is shot at the usual screen angles, the tint blocks in it will show only a minimum pattern which is seen through a magnifier as a slight irregularity in dot formation.

The use of these adjusted screen angles still may not prevent the appearance of moiré in some tints. This may happen if the separations are not fully corrected and a tint appears where no tint of this color was present on the original of the Color Guide. A similar situation exists with tints of black. In the original, the solid and tints of black are printed only with black ink. When the color separations are made, however, the black patches will be reproduced in each one. This makes it impossible to avoid moiré in the black patches that show in each color separation and it will be seen in some of them. However, the black printer is not important for color balance and the appearance of moiré in color in these black patch areas does no harm. In addition, much of the pattern will be covered

by the black printer which has no pattern.

Most of the moiré problems that might be encountered can be eliminated when the copy and the Guide are reduced.

EVALUATING THE REPRODUCTION

As mentioned before, in the evaluation of the final reproduction of all colors, you should attempt to reproduce the original negatives or positives of the GATF Color Reproduction Guide. Measure the densities of the tints in the final halftoned separations made from the printed Guide and compare them to the densities of corresponding areas in the set of original negatives or positives of the Guide. The extent of differences in these measurements will permit you to judge how well your masking and screening system performs, whether adjustments are necessary, and where they are needed.

In the yellow printer, for example, if there is a dot of yellow that will print in magenta, cyan, or blue, the mask should be made stronger. If there is a yellow dot in the cyan but not in the magenta, an extra exposure through the red filter is needed in making the mask.

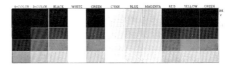

Figure 11. Under-corrected yellow printer. A dot of yellow is printing in the cyan, blue, and magenta patches.

In the magenta printer, if there is a dot of magenta that will print in the cyan, green, and yellow, the mask should be made stronger. If there is no dot in the cyan, but there is in the yellow, an extra exposure through the blue filter is needed in making the mask.

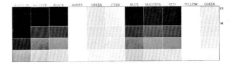

Figure 12. Under-corrected magenta printer. A dot of magenta is printing in the green and cyan patches.

Figure 13. Over-corrected magenta printer. The green and cyan patches are whiter than the white paper.

In the cyan printer, the correct mask takes the cyan dot out of reds and magentas. It also increases the saturation of cyan. (See Figures 6 and 7).

If the yellow and magenta printers are corrected properly in the solid areas of the unwanted colors but there is a tint printing in the middletones of these unwanted colors, the curve shape of the mask should be changed. Such a condition indicates the need for more toe in negative masks or more shoulder in positive masks. (See Figures 14 and 15.)

Obviously, the contrast of the reproduced set of positives or negatives should match the contrast of the original set.

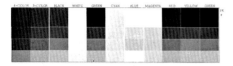

Figure 14. This yellow printer is (1) properly corrected in the solid areas of the unwanted blue and magenta colors but is under-corrected in the tints of these colors and (2) the amount of yellow in red is weakened. Both of these errors can be caused by a positive mask that has a toe shaped curve. Error (2) can also be caused by using narrow band filters, under-exposed separation negatives, or lens flare.

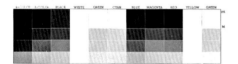

Figure 15. Improperly corrected magenta printer. The solid green, cyan, and yellow patches are properly corrected but the tints of green and cyan are under-corrected. The shape of the curve for the positive mask was toed and should have been shouldered.

GRAY BALANCE

One of the basic requirements of the color reproduction process is to reproduce a gray scale with the three colored process inks. When this is attempted by overprinting three tints that have equal dot sizes, brown and not gray is produced. To appear gray, the dot sizes of the gray scale produced by the three color printers should be properly unbalanced—that is, the dots should not be of equal size. In all cases, the dots in the cyan printer should be larger than the dots of yellow and magenta. Just how much unbalance is needed, depends on the inks, paper, and press variables.

There are several ways to compute the gray balance requirements of process color work. One method was described in a report from the Graphic College of Denmark.[4]

The system involves numerous computations and plottings on the GATF Color Hexagon diagram. While it is simpler than other systems, it is still too involved for general use in the average plant. The GATF Color Reproduction Guide however, offers another and much less complicated way to determine the requirements for gray balance.

The concept of the use of the Color Reproduction Guide is that one of your press prints of the Guide is photographed along with the color copy supplied for the job. The final screened separations of the Guide and the color copy are then produced in exactly the same way that the Guide was reproduced.

Consequently, to achieve a facsimile reproduction, the final halftone negatives or positives made from the print of the Color Reproduction Guide should be identical with the original set of negatives or positives of the Guide. This permits us to use a simple rule. All three separations must be screened to produce equal dot sizes in the 3-color overprint tint blocks. The reason for this follows.

In the original negatives or positives of the Reproduction Guide, equal dot sizes of each color were used to produce the three rows of tints. It is important to keep in mind that the three color overprints which are used to determine gray balance originated from color dots of equal size.

We mentioned before that if the color separations were screened so that equal dot sizes were produced in the black and gray blocks, a printing of these equal dot sizes would produce brown and not gray.

To produce gray, the dot sizes of the 3-color gray scale should be unbalanced. This unbalance in the gray scale is achieved by screening the separations so that equal dot sizes are produced in the *brown* 3-color blocks. This amount of unbalance will be what is required for a satisfactory reproduction of a gray scale with 3 colors.

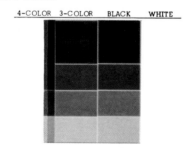

Figure 16. Three color gray balance in the single color black gray scale obtained by simply screening the original 3-color tone scale to equal dot sizes.

HOW TO GET THE GUIDE

GATF Color Reproduction Guides are carefully made by an outside source to the lab's specifications. The Guides are on dimensionally stable film exposed from masters furnished by the GATF Research Department.

The sets of negatives or positives can be obtained directly from GATF, 4615 Forbes Avenue, Pittsburgh, Pennsylvania 15213. The price per set is $8.00 to members (includes handling and postage), and $15.50 to non-members (includes handling and postage). Members may request billing, non-members must enclose remittance with their order.

In placing orders, be sure to specify whether you want positives or negatives. Each set of black and color images is on a single 10 x 12 inch film.

SUMMARY

The new GATF Color Reproduction Guide is now available in the form of standardized sets of positives or negatives. When printed in individual plants, it incorporates the effects of ink, paper, and press variables peculiar to that plant.

In the control of process color printing, the custom-made GATF Color Reproduction Guide is much more useful than commonly used color patches. Such patches are printed under conditions which do not necessarily represent the variables in an individual plant. The tint patches which are included in the Guide provide a check for changes in dot size, the correction of proportionality failure, assurance of proper gray balance, and serve as a guide for screening requirements.

The Guide has been designed primarily for use in the camera department. It is also excellent for studies and control of press conditions if there is room for it. In most cases, however, the use of the narrow GATF Color Test Strip is more practical for use on press sheets.

REFERENCES

1. Preucil, Frank M., "The Evaluation of Process Inks", GATF *Research Progress* No. 38.
2. Preucil, Frank M., "A New Method of Rating the Efficiency of Paper for Color Reproduction", GATF *Research Progress* No. 60.
3. Elyjiw, Zenon, "How To Measure Dot Gain or Loss", GATF *Research Progress* No. 64.
4. Wulff, A., and Jorgensen, H.O., "An Analysis of the Controllability of the Separational Stages in Multi-Color Production", The Graphic College of Denmark, Copenhagen, July, 1964.
5. Preucil, Frank M., "The LTF Color Survey", GATF *Research Progress* No. 40.
6. Hensel, Roy, Private Communication.

RESEARCH GATF PROGRESS

NUMBER   SEVENTY-NINE

G R A P H I C   A R T S   T E C H N I C A L   F O U N D A T I O N

GATF COMPACT COLOR TEST STRIP

By ZENON ELYJIW

IN BRIEF

The GATF Compact Color Test Strip was developed for checking color and printing factors during running of production work on the press. Since the trim margin in production work is usually limited, it was necessary to keep the dimensions of such a strip to a minimum. The GATF Compact Color Test Strip is only ¼" wide, but can be trimmed down to ⅛" if the available margin space on a sheet is less than ¼". In spite of its small dimension, this control strip is designed to check the hues and densities of printed inks, hues of secondary colors, trapping, uniformity of inking across the sheet, dot gain or loss, slur, and dot doubling.

INTRODUCTION

The reproduction of color by offset lithography is a succession of three major phases of reproduction: photography, platemaking, and printing. Each of these phases involves a number of variables, and each variable has some effect on final color reproduction. A properly color-corrected, and properly screened set of color separation negatives or positives, is only one step in the direction of a successful job of full-color printing. In the following step, each halftone must be exposed on a lithographic plate and developed without excessive changes in the area of the halftone dots. Finally, the color reproduction must be printed with correct ink hues and densities, correct dot area, correct trapping and other printing factors.

To check these variable printing factors on the press, some kind of quality control device must be printed with each form on each printed sheet.

COLOR AND PRINTING FACTORS ON THE PRESS

The simplest color control strip is a set of solid bars printed in each process color and running parallel to the gripper across the entire length of the printed sheet. Solid bars show the hues and densities of process inks. They also indicate the necessary adjustments of the ink fountain keys to attain uniform inking across the sheet.

The solid bars are sometimes used in proofing. Their use on the press is limited because the margin space available in production runs is usually too narrow to accommodate four solid bars. To reduce the required margin space, solid patches are used rather than solid bars. These patches are duplicated periodically across the entire width of the printing form, in a sequence. In this manner, all four colors can be accommodated in the same amount of space which a single solid color bar would require.

The information provided by printed solid bars or solid patches is useful, but this information is limited because most printed color pictures are overprints of halftone images made up of halftone dots. During the reproduction process, the halftone dots change. They are not the same on the printed sheet as in the halftone negative or halftone positive. Dot area may be enlarged or reduced in platemaking, or may gain in printing. The dots may be deformed by slur or dot doubling on the press. Since none

of these conditions is indicated by the solid ink patches, a good control strip must also include some halftone tints in each color.

Other important color reproduction factors that should be shown in a color control strip are the hues of secondary colors: red (yellow + magenta); green (yellow + cyan); and blue (magenta + cyan). The hues of these two-color overprints shift with changes in the ink densities of the primary colors. For example, a strong yellow and a weak cyan will produce a yellowish green. A stronger cyan will shift the hue of green toward blue. The hues of the secondary colors will also shift with the trapping and degree of the transparency of the top color.

In color printing, we usually assume that in an overprint of two or more colors the same amount of the top ink is printed on the first-down ink as on the surface of paper. But this assumption is not always true. In some cases the surface of the first-down ink accepts less or more of the second ink than the surface of unprinted paper. This phenomenon is called undertrapping or overtrapping.

To check the trapping, and to show the hues of the secondary colors, the two-color overprints of primary colors should also be included in a test strip.

RESEARCH PROGRESS

Published by
GRAPHIC ARTS TECHNICAL FOUNDATION
4615 Forbes Avenue, Pittsburgh, Pa. 15213
©Graphic Arts Technical Foundation, Inc., 1968
Number 79, August, 1968
Edited by Charles Shapiro
Litho in U.S.A.

CRITERIA FOR A GOOD COLOR CONTROL STRIP

To sum up, a good color test and control strip should indicate the following color and printing factors:

1. Hues and densities of printed process inks;
2. Hues of the secondary colors, trapping, and ink transparency;
3. Dot gain or loss;
4. Deformation of halftone dots, such as may be caused by slur or doubling.

In designing a color test strip for use in production printing, two important points must be taken into consideration. The strip must include an adequate number of various color patches to indicate the most important color and printing factors in each color. On the other hand, to fit in the available margin space, which is often very limited, the dimensions of the strip must be kept small.

Since these two requirements work in the opposite directions, most color test strips available to the pressman today either provide only limited information or take too much space to be practical for use on most production runs.

THE GATF COMPACT COLOR TEST STRIP

The color test strip described in this report was designed specifically for quality control of color work in production printing on lithographic offset presses. This strip incorporates the following features:

1. Small dimensions. The strip is ¼" wide but can be trimmed down to a narrower width, if necessary.

2. In spite of its small dimensions, the strip permits evaluation and measurement of the following color and printing factors:

   a. Densities of printed inks.
   b. Hue, grayness, saturation and efficiency of process colors[1].
   c. Trapping and transparency of process inks in two- and three-color overprints.
   d. Dot gain or loss, slur, and doubling.
   e. Excessive departures from normal gray-balance conditions caused by unequal dot gain in various process colors, or by poor trapping.

3. The solid patches of primary process colors are spaced not more than 2½" apart and thus can be used to adjust the ink fountain for a uniform inking across the entire printing form.

4. For precise evaluation of the printed sheet, the density of each solid or tint patch can be measured on a densitometer.

5. Most printing factors can also be judged visually, without the use of a densitometer.

DIMENSIONS OF THE GATF COMPACT COLOR TEST STRIP

To keep the size of the test strip small, the dimensions of the individual patches were reduced to the smallest size that still allows for making instrumental measurements of density and gloss.

In its final form the strip is approximately 20" long and ¼" deep (Figure 1). It is composed of four identical, 5" units. Each unit is a complete color test strip which can be used alone in a limited space when this is necessary. On larger printed sheets the basic unit is usually repeated, parallel to the gripper edge, as many times as necessary to show any variation in densities and other printing factors across the sheet.

Each basic unit of the GATF Compact Color Test Strip consists of 26 color patches ³⁄₁₆" x ¼". This size was chosen, because it is the smallest area that can be measured on a GATF Small Spot Glossmeter.[2]

Measurement of the gloss of printed inks, though usually not essential in evaluation of printed color, may occasionally be required because gloss is an important factor affecting the maximum possible density of printed colors and their saturation.

To evaluate printed sheets we usually measure the densities of control patches. Since most reflection densitometers found in the pressroom can measure the density of a disc of ³⁄₁₆" diameter, or even ⅛" diameter, the measurement of densities

1 2 3 4 5 6 7 8 9 10 11 12 13 14 15 16 17 18 19 20 21 22 23 24 25 26

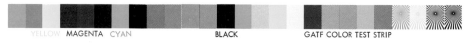

Figure 2. Basic Unit of the GATF Compact Color Test Strip.

Patches 1 thru 7 — Solids of single colors and 2-color overprints.

Patch 8 — 3-color overprint of solid yellow, magenta, and cyan.

Patch 9 — 3-color overprint of 40% tints of yellow, magenta, and cyan.

Patch 10 — Gray balance patch composed of 40% cyan, 30% yellow, and 30% magenta tints. This overprint should appear approximately gray when printed with a set of process inks having a reddish, rubine-type magenta.

Patch 11 — 40% tint of black.

Patch 12 — Another gray balance patch which should appear approximately neutral gray when printed with a set of inks which includes a better, bluish, rhodamine-type magenta. The composition of this patch is 40% cyan, 30% yellow, and 20% magenta.

Patch 13 — Solid black.

Patches 14 thru 19 — Solids and tints of primary colors.

Patches 20 thru 22 — Two-color overprints of 40% tints.

Patches 23 thru 26 — GATF Star Targets.

HOW TO OBTAIN
COMPACT COLOR TEST STRIPS

The GATF Compact Color Test Strips can be obtained from:

Graphic Arts Technical Foundation
4615 Forbes Avenue
Pittsburgh, Pa. 15213

They are carefully made to laboratory specifications and supplied as film negatives or film positives. The price to members is $12.80 per set including postage and handling; to non-members $25.50 per set including postage and handling. All colors are on one sheet of film. It is necessary to specify whether negatives or positives are wanted.

WARNING

The negatives and positives of the Compact Color Test Strip, as sold by GATF, are made for stripping into negative or positive flats for making offset plates. They should not be used for making duplicate negatives or positives by contact printing. Each set of negatives or positives includes 16 Star Targets which are sensitive quality control devices. If contact prints are made from them, either negative to positive or positive to negative, the center of the Star Target will be distorted. The contacted Star Targets will be different from the originals and will therefore loose their ability to indicate dot gain, slur, and dot doubling. To obtain correct indication of all color and press variables, make sure that *original* negatives or *original*

positives of the GATF Compact Color Test Strip are used.

ACKNOWLEDGEMENT

I wish to thank Frank Preucil for his valuable suggestions in designing this Color Test Strip.

REFERENCES

1. Frank Preucil: "Evaluation of Process Inks", GATF Research Progress No. 38.
2. Roy Hensel: "GATF Small Spot Glossmeter, GATF "Reports of Progress During 1966" (1967)
3. Frank Preucil: "GATF's New Color Diagrams", GATF Research Progress No. 53.

QUALITY CONTROL

As a result of GATF research, many testing instruments and quality control devices have been developed. Most of these are simple charts or photographic prints which relate, in visual terms, conditions of the press, ink or paper. For the most part, they can be either printed directly on the press sheet, or completed with press sheet readings. A few are strictly mechanical tests or demonstration instruments which approximate or reproduce actual press results. These devices have proven reliable if properly used. Appropriate **Research Progress Reports** accompany press controls, devices, etc., ordered from GATF.

GATF Color Reproduction Guide. (See RP 67)
8¹/₂ x 11″ sheet of film, negative or positive
$8.00 GATF members • $15.50 non-members
Four rows of ten color blocks plus white. Each row ¼ tint value of higher row—100%, 75%, 50% and 25%. Screen ruling of 150 lines per inch.

GATF Quality Control Strip. (See RP 71)
21 x ³/₃₂″ strip, negative or positive
$8.00 GATF members • $15.50 non-members
A 3″ repeat pattern quality control strip printed in the trim areas. Gives an immediate visual check on the four process colors.

GATF Sensitivity Guide. (See Txb 502/4)
Order direct from Stouffer Graphic Arts Equipment Co.
311 N. Niles Avenue
South Bend, Indiana 46617
A continuous gray scale on film to give a uniform scale of light transmission for measuring plate exposures.

GATF Star Target. (See RP 52)
6 x 10″ sheet of 12, negative or positive
$5.50 GATF members • $10.50 non-members
Provides a quick and effective visual indication of any dot spread, slur, or doubling on the press run.

GATF Vernier Target. (See RP 75)
8 x 10″ sheet of 10, negative or positive
$15.50 GATF members • $30.50 non-members
Measures variations in the length and width of successive color images put down by a multicolor press.

GATF Offset Color Control Bar. (See RP 76)
10³/₁₆″ x 1³/₁₆″, negative or positive
$8.00 GATF members • $15.50 non-members
Composite series of offset color control bars to be used by platemakers and/or printers in standardizing the proofing of color work for offset magazine publishing or as a production press control (trim area permitting). Composite can be used in whole or in part, according to the needs of the platemaker or printer.

GATF Gray Balance Chart.
6 x 7¹/₂″, negative or positive
$15.50 GATF members • $30.50 non-members
Used to determine the percentage of yellow, magenta and cyan needed to produce neutral for given ink, paper and press conditions.

GATF Compact Color Test Strip. (See RP 79)
Four units — 4 x ¼″ each, negative or positive
$12.80 GATF members • $25.50 non-members
Designed for use in production runs to check color and printing factors on the press. Dimensions of the strip are held to a minimum since trim space in production is often

limited. Strip can be trimmed to ¹/₈″. Despite small dimensions, strip can be used to check densities of printing inks, trapping, ink transparency, gray balance, dot gain or loss, slur and dot doubling.

GATF Print Test Image.
Negative only
$20.50 GATF members • $50.50 non-members
Combination of various scales designed to define print quality primarily for letterpress, but can be used for other processes as well.

GATF Dot Gain Scale And Slur Gauge. (See RP 69)
6 x 10″ sheet of 20, negative or positive
$8.00 GATF members • $15.50 non-members
A visual device indicating dot area changes, and indicating directional slur under restricted conditions.

GATF Color Triangle Tablet. (See RP 81)
$3.25 per 100 sheets—GATF members
$5.25 non-members
Plots on this diagram show the gamut of pure color that is possible with a given set of process inks, under or over-trapping, changes in gloss, and prediction of ideal overprint colors.

GATF Color Hexagon Tablet. (See RP 81)
$3.25 per 100 sheets — GATF members
$5.25 non-members
Plots on this diagram show color strength and hue differences, control of the separate primaries and overprint hues.

GATF Paper Factors Conversion Chart. (See RP 60)
$3.25 per 100 sheets — GATF members
$5.25 non-members
A chart which converts density or reflectance values to absorptivity percentages.

GATF Paper Surface Efficiency Chart. (See RP 60)
$3.25 per 100 sheets—GATF members
$5.25 non-members
Plots absorptivity of paper against paper gloss to indicate the printing quality of the paper.

GATF Color and Printing Factors Data Sheets.
$3.25 per 100 sheets — GATF members
$5.25 non-members
Used for the tabulation of the color densities and the color and printing factors in a printed sheet.

GATF Color Circle Tablet. (See RP 81)
$3.25 per 100 sheets — GATF members
$5.25 non-members
An easy visual method to check hue error and grayness of process inks.

GATF Lens Flare Test Chart. (See Txb. 508, 509)
$3.25 per 100 sheets — GATF members
$5.25 non-members
Used for rating optical efficiency of a process lens by evaluating lens flare and other variables of imagery.
Replaced by Cady Model DWL Bench Micrometer. Measures blanket thickness.

GATF Contact Printing Lamp.
Order direct from Colwell Litho Products, Inc.
316 Chicago Avenue
Minneapolis, Minnesota 55415
Provides a point light source to prevent undercutting of dots and lines in contact printing.

GATF Color and Printing Factors Computer.
$3.00 GATF members • $6.00 non-members
A circular slide rule useful in computing ratios for GATF's Color Circle, Color Triangle and Paper Surface Efficiency Chart. Also used for computing efficiency of secondary colors, ink trapping, effective ink transparency, additivity and equivalent dot area of film tints.

GATF Register Rule. (See RP 54)
$225.00 — 46″ $285.00 — 70″
$250.00 — 58″ $310.00 — 79″
Prices applicable to members and non-members.
A high precision metal rule for measuring all forms of mis-register.

GATF Pick Tester.
Order directly from Stouffer Graphic Arts Equipment Co.
311 N. Niles Avenue
South Bend, Indiana 46617
Simulates paper and ink contact for picking.

GATF Thickness Gauge.
Order direct from E. J. Cady Co.
1715 33rd Avenue
Melrose Park, Illinois 60161

GATF Paper Hygroscope
Indicates the moisture or dryness of paper in a pile as the percent relative humidity difference between the paper and the pressroom atmosphere.
The GATF "Sword" is no longer manufactured. There are available several new instruments designed for the original purpose. Some are completely different in principle; some utilize the original principles on which the GATF instrument was based, but utilize more modern sensing devices and engineering. There are also available instruments which will indicate RH of paper in rolls, and give some readings in terms of percent moisture content.
GATF's Instructions book, Txb #321, describes and lists the sources of these instruments.

unsymmetrically, with their centers raised above the centers of the rectangular patches of the strip. This has been done to provide for the trimming of this strip to a narrower width than ¼″. If the margin space on the sheet is limited, the strip can be trimmed by 1/16″, or even 1/8″, and still retain the centers of the Star Targets to indicate dot gain, slur, or dot doubling (Figure 3).

The GATF Star Target is described in more detail in GATF Research Progress No. 52.

VISUAL EVALUATION OF A PRINTED COMPACT COLOR TEST STRIP

For an accurate evaluation of printed densities of inks, and other printing factors, we depend on the use of a reflection densitometer. Quite frequently, however, densitometric measurements of a number of control patches during the press run may not appear practical to the pressman, because he is too busy keeping his eyes on paper feed, ink-water balance, register and other details of press operation. In such cases, quality control strips, which can be evaluated by a quick visual check, are more practical.

For full evaluation of color and printing factors, the color densities of the GATF Compact Color Test Strip are usually measured on a reflection densitometer. But this strip was also designed to make possible a quick visual check of most important variables of color on the press.

The solid patches of process colors and two-color overprints are arranged to permit visual judgment of *trapping*, as described above. The *hues* of two-color overprints can be judged by eye. The shifts in these hues indicate the changes in *densities of printed inks*, or improper trapping. The shifts in hues of gray-balance patches indicate the unbalanced, *unequal dot gain conditions* between separate primary colors. And, finally, Star Targets are visual control devices which indicate *dot gain, slur, and dot doubling*.

A simple and convenient way to visually evaluate color and printing factors using the printed Color Test Strip is to cut from an approved sheet a single unit of this device. The white margin at the top edge of this sample is trimmed off. This sample unit is compared side-by-side with a printed sheet. In this way, all 26 patches of the strip can be evaluated at one glance. This method is fast, convenient, and fairly accurate because the normal human eye is quite sensitive to small changes in color if two samples can be compared side-by-side (Figure 4).

SUMMARY

The GATF Compact Color Test Strip for evaluation and control of printed color and offset press variables was designed to provide "maximum information within a minimum of space." The ¼″ wide strip consists of solids and tints of process colors, and their overprints. The strip also includes gray-balance patches and rectangular versions of the GATF Star Target.

The size of individual color patches in the strip is 3/16″ x ¼″. This size was chosen to make possible the measurement of gloss of printed inks on the newly developed GATF Small Spot Glossmeter which can measure the gloss of area of this small size. If the measurements of gloss are not required, and the margin space in printed sheets is limited, the strip can be trimmed down to a width of 3/16″ or even 1/8″ and still provide the full information on color factors and press variables.

The basic strip is only 5″ long. In its final form, the strip measures 20″ in length, with the basic design repeated four times.

Figure 4. A Simple and Fast Method to Check Color and Print Quality on a Printed Sheet Without the Use of a Densitometer.

By this method, all 26 patches of the printed compact color test strip can be compared to an approved sample at a glance.

Figure 1. The Final Version of the GATF Compact Color Test Strip, With the Basic Design Repeated Four Times.

of individual patches of the strip should not present any problems.*

COMPONENTS OF THE
GATF COMPACT COLOR TEST STRIP

The GATF Compact Color Test Strip is composed of solids, tints, and GATF Star Targets in a rectangular version (Figure 2).

The solid patches indicate the densities of printed inks. In the Compact Color Test Strip the solids of yellow, magenta, and cyan are repeated at least twice in each 5″ strip and thus are spaced not more than 2½″ apart. Closely spaced solid patches indicate the distribution of ink across the sheet, and help the pressman to adjust the ink fountain keys. The solid patches also indicate the hue, grayness, saturation and efficiency of process inks.

The two-color overprints of yellow, magenta, and cyan solids indicate the hues of the secondary colors, and trapping. Trapping of printed inks can be calculated from color densities of two-color overprints and densities of the single colors which produce these secondaries. This method is described in GATF Textbook No. 509 "Color Separation Photography".

Trapping can also be judged visually through suitable color filters. For visual evaluation of trapping, the solids of single process colors should be properly arranged. The two-color overprints must be printed next to solids of their components. This means that red must be printed between yellow and magenta, green between yellow and cyan, and blue between magenta and cyan. The three-color overprint also can be used to check the trapping of the top color on the two-color overprint.

The tint patches show changes in area of the printed halftone dots. Dot gain or loss may be judged visually from

changes in the densities of these tints. The Equivalent Dot Area (EDA) of printed dots may be calculated from densities of tints and solids as described in GATF Research Progress No. 64, "How to Measure Dot Gain or Loss". To avoid possible inaccuracies in EDA measurements due to uneven ink distribution on the press, the measurements of densities of tints and solids should be made in the same area of the printed sheet. In the GATF Compact Color Test Strip, accuracy of EDA readings is improved by printing solids and tints of yellow, magenta, and cyan side-by-side. The solid and the tint of black is separated by one of the two "gray-balance" patches, described below. The two-color overprints of tints are added for evaluating the saturation of printed tints of secondary colors by use of the GATF Color Hexagon.[3] The ruling of all tints in the test strip is 150 lines per inch.

The gray balance patches are the 3-color overprints of unequal tints of yellow, magenta, and cyan. The dot areas of these tints have been chosen to give approximately neutral gray overprints when printed with a correct set of process inks, and no excessive changes in dot area.

The tenth patch from the left edge of the strip is an overprint of 40% cyan, 30% yellow, and 30% magenta tints. This overprint should appear approximately gray when the job is printed with a set of process inks having a reddish, rubine-type magenta similar to the magenta in the AAAA/MPA Standard 4-color Offset Proofing Inks. The twelfth patch from the left edge of the strip should look neutral when printed with one of the better, bluish, rhodamine-type

magenta inks. This patch is composed of 40% cyan, 30% yellow, and 20% magenta tints.

The gray balance patches are designed for visual judgment. When printed without excessive dot area changes, in one or two primary colors, one of these gray-balance patches should look approximately gray. A significant shift in hue of the gray-balance patches indicates that the dot gain is out of control in one or more colors. The human eye, with normal color vision, is quite sensitive to shifts in hue of near-gray colors. For quick and convenient gray reference, both gray-balance patches are printed next to the 40% tint of black.

For an additional visual check of deformation of halftone dots, the GATF Compact Color Test Strip also includes a rectangular version of the GATF Star Target, in each process color.

The GATF Star Targets indicate the dot gain, and also discriminate between conventional non-directional dot gain, and slur or dot doubling. Various kinds of dot gain are indicated by different shapes of the dark spot which will appear in the center of the Star Target. A round, dark spot indicates conventional dot gain. An elliptical spot indicates slur. A spot in the shape of figure "8" indicates dot doubling. Occasionally, the center of the Star Target may reproduce lighter than the areas closer to the edge. This condition (hollow center) usually indicates an excessive sharpening of dots. It may also indicate that the Compact Color Test Strip, used to make the plate, is not an original but, rather, a contact print form an original.

In the GATF Compact Color Test Strip, the Star Targets have been trimmed

---

*Some densitometers can be focused to make it convenient to measure ⅛″ patches.

Figure 3. Basic Unit of GATF Compact Color Test Strip Trimmed to ⅛″.

This miniature version of the strip may be used on printed sheets with limited margin space. It is capable of providing the full information on color factors and press variables, because each of these trimmed patches can be measured on some well adjusted color densitometers that are available to the industry.

RESEARCH PROGRESS

This bulletin was formerly known as the Research Progress, which began publication in 1947. It was changed to the Research Report in 1970. The bulletin reports on the progress of individual research projects as significant developments occur. Issued on an occasional basis, averaging five to six reports per year.

The following listing indicates the depth and variety of GATF's research activities. For the most part, information previous to Research Report #46 (issued in 1959) has been incorporated with the more recent information and newer GATF reports, textbooks, bulletins and other materials.

RP 46   An Interesting Study of Corrosion

Corrosion factors due to electro-galvanic currents at the junctions of metals of bi- or tri-metal plates.

RP 47   Sharpness of Halftone Images on Paper

Correlation of subjective impression with micro-densitometer measurements across black and white halftone dots, and correlation of light scattering coefficients with the sharpness of uncoated papers.

RP 48   A Better Color Corrected Black Printer

Single masking for black printer correction with interference and gelatin filter combination.

RP 49   How to Make the New Fine Wipe-On Plates

Development of tub graining to produce fine brush grains on zinc. Development of new Ink Developer that inks and develops at the same time.

RP 50   The Effect of Paper Gloss on Ink Gloss

Relationship of ink gloss and ink absorptivity of paper, and ink gloss to ink film.

RP 51   How to Test the Effect of Paper Color on Process Color Reproductions

Use of a color spinner to accentuate latent color tinting caused by paper. Suggestions for avoiding and predicting process color problems.

RP 52   The GATF Star Target: For Ink Spread and Resolution Measurements

A simple quality control device for quick detection of dot spread, slur, and doubling.

RP 54   GATF's New Register Rule

A precision metal rule with vernier scale suitable for analysis and correction of misregister.

RP 55   Some Ideas for the Pressman

Direction for making an automatic waste oil pick-up device. How to position a side register mark on the plate.

RP 56   A Method of Determining the Amount of Water in Ink

Vacuum evaporation of water in printing ink samples to determine per cent of emulsification.

RP 57   More Ideas for the Pressroom

More speed in setting rollers, avoiding dampening roller streaks, standardization of the fountain solution level.

RP 58   The GATF Press Inkometer and the Automatic Control of Press Dampening

Measurement of surface tack as an indication of ink-water balance. Development of an automatic measuring, sensing and correcting mechanism.

RP 59   Paper, Relative Humidity, and Color Register

Brief review of correct paper handling in plants.

RP 60   A New Method of Rating the Efficiency of Paper for Color Reproduction

Introduction of the Paper Surface Efficiency (PSE) factor to predict and compare ink performance on papers.

RP 61   All for the Want of a Tissue

Small initial correcting of plate-to-blanket packing pressure leads to unnecessary major press adjustments.

RP 62   Lithographic Image Definition

Resolving power and sharpness in image definition and measurements based on sine and square wave targets.

RP 63   Color Separating Line Copy

Methods for individually separating yellow, magenta, cyan, red, green, blue, and brown from colored line copy.

RP 64   How to Measure Dot Gain or Loss

Development of the Tint Density to Dot Area Conversion Chart and the Equivalent Dot Area conversion factor.

RP 65   Classification for a Library of Printing

Modification and extension of the Dewey Decimal System for greater detailed coverage of printing subdivisions.

RP 66   The Polarizing Reflection Densitometer

Use of polarizing filters to eliminate gloss interference on ink amount and ink trapping densitometer readings.

RP 67   The New GATF Color Reproduction Guide

Printed with the plant's own process inks and papers to illustrate actual variables which limit desired results. More realistic than common color patches.

RP 69   The GATF Dot Gain Scale

A visual device which indicates the dot area changes by displacement of an "invisible number" to a higher or lower value.

RP 70   The New Color Survey of 1963-1964

Results from an industry-wide survey of the state of process color reproduction.

RP 71   The GATF "QC" Strip

A simple tint pattern placed on the trim area to help pressmen control quality.

RP 72   Gloss Ghosting and Other Strange Effects

Theory and study of the nature and cause of gloss ghosting, ink chalking, yellow stain, and other strange paper and ink problems.

RP 73   The Rendition of Fine Detail in Lithography

A study to determine the minimum printable area and the information storage capacity of lithography.

RP 74   Automated Press Data Recording System

Describes an electronic system for measuring and recording press variables during a press run. Handles both analog and digital signals and has numerical printed output.

RP 75   The GATF Vernier Target

Describes a vernier scale used for measuring the relative print size of successive images printed in register. This small target can be used to study distortions between images, fanout, etc.

RP 76   GATF Standard Offset Color Control Bars

Developed in cooperation with AAAA, MPA, and NAPIM for web offset proofing. Describes the use and importance of standardized offset color control bars and process inks in four-color proofing.

RP 77   First Survey of Blanket Piling in Web Offset Printing On Coated Papers

A report of the survey conducted by GATF; includes a summary and discussion of the findings. Proposed definitions for types of piling are included.

RP 78   Packing Gauge Improves Accuracy

How to check for exact relationship between heights of plate and blanket, and their respective bearers. The importance of exact transfer squeeze between plate and blanket cylinder as well as between blanket and paper, for fine printing and long plate life, is discussed.

RP 79   GATF Compact Color Test Strip

Discusses test strip designed to check hues and densities of printed inks, hues of secondary colors, trapping, uniformity of inking across the sheet, dot gain or loss, slur, and dot doubling. Although 1/4" wide, strip can be trimmed down to 1/8" in width.

RP 80   Index

Lists subjects covered in RP's published from 1955-1968, numbers 34-79.

RP 81   GATF Color Diagrams

Instruction in the use of the GATF Color Hexagon, Subtractive Triangle, and Color Circle.

RP 82   Press Interactions Chart

Presents and describes charts showing the high degrees of interdependence of the press outputs on the numerous press inputs.

RP 83   GATF Gray Balance Chart

Establishes empirically determined tone correction for gray balance in color production.

RP 84   Gradation Control for Halftones Prepared using the Contact Screen

Describes a graphical method for evaluating halftone negatives produced from black and white originals, and for halftone positives prepared from separation negatives. Once the desired tone scale is derived, the graphical method provides a convenient way to relate specifications for halftone gradation.

RESEARCH GATF PROGRESS

NUMBER

(REVISED EDITION)

EIGHTY-ONE

GRAPHIC ARTS TECHNICAL FOUNDATION

THE GATF COLOR DIAGRAMS

By F. L. COX

ABSTRACT

The Foundation has developed a systematic approach to full-color reproduction utilizing three diagrams, plotting charts, data forms, and a specially designed computer. The recommended procedures should make possible improved color reproduction planning as well as more accurate prediction of results. These production aids were designed so that the variable effects of paper, ink, plates, and presswork could be predicted and measured. Predicting and measuring these variable effects makes it possible to plan pre-press procedures which should result in optimum quality with any given combination of paper, ink, plates, and press; with minimum makeovers, makeready time, and waste.

The GATF COLOR CIRCLE was first described in Research Progress No. 38, published in April, 1957. The GATF COLOR HEXAGON and COLOR TRIANGLE were described, and their use explained, in RESEARCH PROGRESS NO. 53 issued in September 1961.

All three of GATF's color diagrams have been modified and improved to make them more useful in visualizing, solving, and controlling color reproduction problems. (A sample sheet of each diagram is enclosed with this Research Progress Report.) The GATF COLOR AND PRINTING FACTORS COMPUTER is described in this report. Use of this computer facilitates many of the arithmetical calculations.

This issue of Research Progress supercedes Research Progress No. 53, and includes much of the immediately applicable information in those issues of Research Progress which are concerned with full-color reproduction.

INTRODUCTION

GATF has developed three color diagrams for use by the graphic arts industry — the *Color Hexagon*, the *Color Circle*, and the *Subtractive Color Triangle*. All three were developed from other color notation systems, and adapted to the needs of color reproduction and printing.

The special problems of modifying color systems, for application to the reproduction requirements of full-color copy, result from the fact that color mixtures in the graphic arts are principally subtractive. For example, yellow ink on paper looks yellow because it **absorbs,** or subtracts the blue component from white light. The remaining red and green components of the white light are reflected from the paper and appear yellow.

GATF's diagrams were developed to show graphically the concepts of subtractive color mixtures, and make possible more efficient planning for pre-press procedures. The diagrams are **not** intended to act as **new color notation systems.**

Data for plotting color information on the diagrams are obtained by taking densitometer readings of the solid printed-ink colors. The data are obtained by measuring ink swatches through each of three Wratten filters – red #25, blue #47, and green #58. These are identical with the filters used in color separation of opaque copy, and are the only filters* which will provide proper data for the

*Filters from other manufacturers may be used. But it will be necessary for the user to determine equivalent spectral characteristics.

diagrams. Each GATF diagram provides space for tabulating the data from the densitometer readings.* The letters "R", "G", and "B" are the readings from the red, green, and blue filters, respectively. The letters "L", "M", and "H" designate the low, medium, and high densitometer readings.

Different models of densitometers may give dissimilar readings for the same color swatch because of variation in spectro-photometric responses. The color temperature of the illumination source, and variation in the spectral sensitivity of the photo-multiplier tube, can contribute to these differences. If one densitometer is used for all density determinations, the reading error may be compensated for by using a "mask correction factor". The value of the mask correction factor is determined by the ratio of actual mask percentage to the theoretical mask percentage. The mask correction factor value is introduced to compensate for the color temperature differences existing between the light source used in photography and the light source used in the densitometer.**

*A separate *Printing Factors Data Sheet* is also available. Data from all the diagrams, as well as other factors, can be entered on this all-inclusive form.

**See GATF's Txb #509, "Color Separation Photography," for further details.

RESEARCH PROGRESS

Published by
GRAPHIC ARTS TECHNICAL FOUNDATION, Inc.
4615 Forbes Avenue, Pittsburgh, Pa. 15213
©Graphic Arts Technical Foundation, Inc., 1969
Number 81, September, 1969
(revised April, 1970)
Edited by Charles Shapiro
Litho in U.S.A.

The hue error and grayness co-ordinates, used to plot the colors on the *Color Circle* and the *Color Triangle,* are **computed** from the densitometer readings. Plots on the *Color Hexagon* are **derived directly** from the densitometer readings.

GATF also has available the GATF *Color and Printing Factors Computer.* The computer dial face lists the formulas for calculating a number of properties of printed color, and includes a circular slide rule to make the computation rapidly. A scale is also provided on the calculator for finding the equivalent dot areas of film and printed tints for the lithographic process.

GATF's color diagrams have been under constant review since their introduction, and have been carefully revised to their present form. The most recent improvements should increase the usefulness of the diagrams in solving many of the problems in color reproduction and printing.

MEASURING THE FACTORS WHICH INFLUENCE PRINTED COLORS

Some of the techniques for analyzing color reproduction and color printing, which GATF has proposed to the industry, are adaptations or modifications of developments by other researchers; some have been originated by the Foundation's research staff. The significant point is that all of the techniques are based on densitometric measurements utilizing commercially available instruments which have broad application throughout the plant.

Correctly made densitometric measurements, utilizing appropriate and simple formulas or diagrams, make it possible to:

1. Evaluate process-color inks;[1]
2. Predict the effect of the color of paper on process printing;[2]
3. Measure the effect of paper surface gloss and absorbency on the color of process inks (PSE);[3]
4. Determine color-correction mask densities;[4]
5. Determine the effective dot area necessary to achieve gray-balance;[5]
6. Control color on the press.

The most frequently used densitometric measurements are the readings made on printed solid color patches – on the individual colors as well as on their 2-color overprints and the 3-color overprint. These measurements are made through the red #25, green #58, and blue #47 filters. Each patch is measured through the three filters, and the readings are entered in the appropriate data table (see Figure 1). The formulas for handling these measurements are given and explained in detail in the separate discussion of each diagram, within this *Research Progress.* Although each color diagram has space for logging the measurements, the *GATF Color and Printing Factors Data Sheet* has been designed for those instances where it is desirable to have a complete summary of all the data involved in a particular job.

COLOR	FILTER DENSITIES			HEXAGON H–L and M–L			CIRCLE and TRIANGLE	
	R	G	B	R	G	B	HUE	GRAY
YELLOW	.02	.06	1.04					
MAGENTA	.08	1.14	.45					
CYAN	1.02	.30	.08					
BLACK								
RED								
GREEN								
BLUE								
3 – COLOR								

Figure 1. Density value of paper is cancelled out by setting the indicator needle to 0.0 with the probe on the paper, before reading R, G, and B filter density values.

For illustrating the applications of the *Hexagon, Circle,* and *Triangle,* refer to the density values entered in Figure 1. The pertinent density values are read **after** checking the calibration for each filter, and adjusting the scale setting to 0.0, with the filter head on the paper surface.

THE GATF COLOR HEXAGON
(Ink Hue and Saturation Chart)

The GATF *Color Hexagon* was developed to satisfy the need for a simple way of charting color variations during a press run. The Hexagon was adapted from the "trilinear plot" described by Evans, Hanson, and Brewer in their *Principles of Color Photography.* No mathematical calculations are necessary; color points are positioned on the diagram directly from the densitometer readings. Plotting lines on the *Hexagon* correspond to .02 increments of density, thus permitting an extremely high degree of plotting accuracy.

A single densitometer reading is sufficient to detect a change in the strength of any one process ink when printed alone. In full-color process reproduction, however, practically all of the colors are created by overprints of two or more inks. The fidelity and consistency of the overprinting colors is therefore of prime

importance. Changes in trapping, or other press conditions, may seriously shift the hues of the overprinted colors even though the single inks are still printing without change. Although densitometer readings made through two different filters are sufficient to detect a **shift in the hue** of an overprint color; readings from all three filters are required to determine the exact **nature of any change.** All three filter readings are necessary in order to plot a color on the Hexagon.

Plotting Color Measurements On The Hexagon

Plots on the GATF *Color Hexagon* show saturation and hue error. After the data for Figure 1 are recorded, subtract the lowest (L) density reading from the medium (M) and high (H) readings and enter the values into the "HEXAGON" table (see Figure 2). For the density values opposite yellow, the low value is .02. The entries in the HEXAGON table are, therefore, .06 — .02 = .04(G) and 1.04 — .02 = 1.02(B).

COLOR	FILTER DENSITIES			HEXAGON H–L and M–L			CIRCLE and TRIANGLE	
	R	G	B	R	G	B	HUE	GRAY
YELLOW	.02	.06	1.04	–0–	.04	1.02		
MAGENTA	.08	1.14	.45	–0–	1.06	.37		
CYAN	1.02	.30	.08	.94	.22	–0–		
BLACK								
RED	.11	1.20	1.54	–0–	1.09	1.43		
GREEN	.99	.37	1.12	.62	–0–	.75		
BLUE	1.06	1.42	.50	.56	.92	–0–		
3 – COLOR	1.08	1.43	1.55					

Figure 2. The gray or neutral component of the ink is cancelled by subtracting the lowest density from the mid- and high-density values.

Complete the table by similar procedure. The lowest filter density reading will become –0– in the HEXAGON table.

The higher density value indicates the strength of the ink; the lower value indicates unwanted color, or hue error.

Plotting the yellow ink data, given in Figure 2, is illustrated in Figure 3.

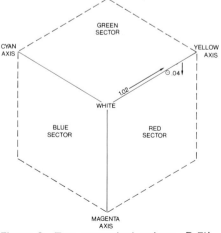

Figure 3. Two numerical values, B-FILTER 1.02 and G-FILTER 0.04, locate a color point in the *Hexagon* space.

1. Locate the strength component on the pigment axis. For the yellow, the value is 1.02 away from the center point – toward yellow.
2. Add hue error by moving .04(G) away from yellow, parallel to the magenta axis. (The green filter value indicates magenta content of yellow pigment.)
3. Locate the strength component 1.06(G) on the magenta axis. (See Figure 4.)
4. Add hue error component by moving 0.37(B) away from magenta, parallel to the yellow axis. (The blue-filter value indicates yellow content of the magenta pigment.)

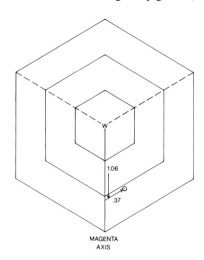

Figure 4. Location of magenta color point in the *Hexagon* space.

5. Locate the strength component 0.94(R) on the cyan axis. (See Figure 5.)
6. Add hue error component by moving 0.22(G) away from cyan, parallel to the magenta axis. (The green filter value indicates magenta content of the cyan pigment.)

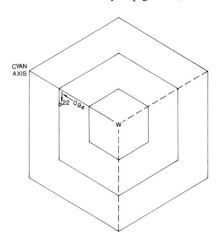

Figure 5. Location of cyan color point in the *Hexagon* space.

Ideal overprints should have equal strength values for two filter readings, and the points plotted should fall on the red, green, or blue axis. Displacement away from the red, green, or blue axis may be considered as **hue error,** while distance away from center may be considered as **strength,** just as for the primary hues.

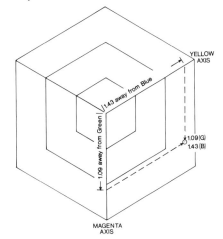

Figure 6. Location of Red color point in the *Hexagon* space.

Figure 6 illustrates how the red, green, and blue values are positioned on the *Hexagon.* The coordinates for "Red" (yellow + magenta) are 1.43(B), 1.09 (G). Starting at the center, the 1.43(B) value may be positioned on the yellow axis, and the 1.09(G) value positioned on the magenta axis. Then, by completing a parallelogram, the "Red" (yellow + magenta) intercept is located. A second method involves starting at center. Locate 1.43(B) on the yellow axis, then step off 1.09(G) parallel to the magenta axis. This procedure is repeated for the "Green" and "Blue" secondary colors. Figure 7 illustrates a completed *Color Hexagon* plot.

The ease and rapidity of plotting colors on the *Hexagon* makes it particularly useful in checking both trapping and printed-ink strength while the press run is in progress. Initial plots from the OK sheet should be made for each of the primary colors and the overprinted secondary colors. Then, as the run progresses, additional plots on the same diagram will show how close the printing is to the OK sheet, at any time during the run.

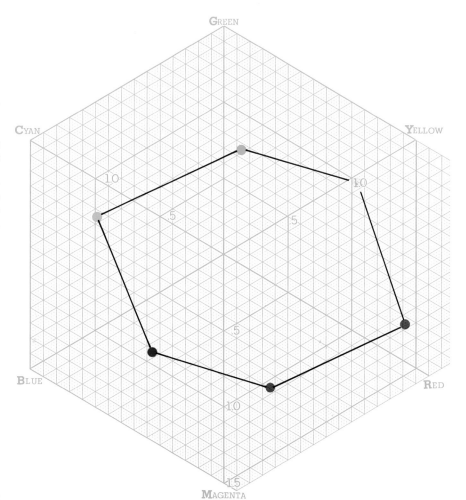

Figure 7. Location of primary and secondary colors in the *Hexagon* space.

Interpreting The Plots On The Hexagon

The position of plots made during the run, relative to the initial plots from the OK sheet, reveals a good deal of information about the cause of any variation. The plots may be interpreted as follows:

1. If the plot for a primary color shifts outward, the printed-ink strength, or density of the color, has increased. A shift toward the center of the *Hexagon* indicates a decrease of printed-ink strength from the OK sheet. In either case, of course, the press ink feed, ink-water balance, cylinder packing, or impression cylinder pressure should be adjusted.

2. When there has been no change in the densities of the primaries, but the plots for the overprint colors have shifted toward one of the primaries, overtrapping or undertrapping is indicated.

3. A change in the printed strength of a primary color will naturally shift the hue of an overprint color produced with this primary. Under these conditions, changes in trapping cannot be detected until the primary ink strength has been readjusted to match the original plot made from the OK sheet.

A normal plot on the GATF *Color Hexagon* shows hue differences around the diagram, and saturation or color strength by the distance of the plot from the center of the diagram. Grayness is in the third dimension and, therefore, does not show.

THE GATF COLOR CIRCLE
(Ink Hue and Purity Chart)

The GATF *Color Circle* makes possible very accurate plotting of close color differences. The line spacing represents .02 density and this makes possible a high degree of plotting accuracy.

The *Color Circle* was the first of GATF's color diagrams introduced. Its continued popularity can be attributed to simplicity and versatility. The *Color Circle* is useful primarily for visualizing the printed characteristics of actual ink colors in comparison with ideal colors.

The *Color Circle* is quite versatile, and a number of different pairs of factors can be plotted on it. In its most common use, the hue differences of inks are plotted around the Circle, and the grayness of the inks is plotted inward toward the center.

Plotting On The Color Circle

The coordinates necessary to plot hue error and grayness are derived from densitometer readings using the following equations:

$$\text{Grayness} = \frac{L}{H}$$

$$\text{Hue Error} = \frac{M\text{-}L}{H\text{-}L}$$

"L", "M", and "H" are the low, medium, and high densitometer readings for each solid printed color made through the three color-separation filters. An example of the use of these formulas for the yellow ink in Figure 8 is:

$$\text{Grayness} = \frac{L}{H} = \frac{.02}{1.04} = .019 \text{ or } 1.9\%$$

COLOR	FILTER DENSITIES			HEXAGON H-L and M-L			CIRCLE and TRIANGLE	
	R	G	B	R	G	B	HUE	GRAY
YELLOW	.02	.06	1.04	-0-	.04	1.02	3.9	1.9
MAGENTA	.08	1.14	.45	-0-	1.06	.37	35	7
CYAN	1.02	.30	.08	.94	.22	-0-	23	7.8
BLACK								
RED	.11	1.20	1.54	-0-	1.09	1.43	76	7.2
GREEN	.99	.37	1.12	.62	-0-	.75	82.5	33
BLUE	1.06	1.42	.50	.56	.92	-0-	61	35
3 - COLOR	1.08	1.43	1.55					

(SOLIDS)

Figure 8. Data used to calculate HUE and GRAYNESS.

The meanings of hue error, grayness, and ink strength may become apparent by referring to the bar chart shown in Figure 9. Density values for the cyan ink in Figure 8 are 1.02(R), 0.30(G), and .08(B).

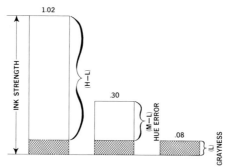

Figure 9. Graphical representation of hue error, grayness, and ink strength for a cyan ink.

The GATF *Color and Printing Factors Computer* simplifies the arithmetical calculation. In using the computer to determine HUE % and GRAY %, ignore the decimal point of all FILTER DENSITIES entries in Figure 8. For yellow grayness, set 2 on scale "C" over 104 on scale "D"; read answer on scale "C" above **100**. For magenta grayness, set 8 on scale "C" over 114 on scale "D;" read 7 on scale "C" directly above **100** on scale "D."

For cyan grayness, set 8 on scale "C" over 102 on scale "D;" read 7.8 on scale "C" over the index **100**

The grayness values for "Red" (yellow + magenta), "Green" (yellow + cyan), and "Blue" (magenta + cyan), are determined in the same manner as the values for the primary colors.

The hue coordinate for *Color Circle* graphs is found by using the formula:

$$\text{Hue Error} = \frac{M\text{-}L}{H\text{-}L}$$

and substituting the (M-L) and (H-L) values entered in the *Hexagon* tabulation shown in Figure 8.

The calculation becomes:

$$\text{Hue} = \frac{\text{smaller}}{\text{larger}} \times 100 = \ldots\ldots\%$$

For the yellow:

$$\text{Hue} = \frac{04}{102} \times 100 = 3.9\%$$

For magenta:

$$\text{Hue} = \frac{37}{106} \times 100 = 35\%$$

For cyan:

$$\text{Hue} = \frac{22}{94} \times 100 = 23\%$$

For "Red":

$$\text{Hue} = \frac{109}{143} \times 100 = 76\%$$

For "Green":

$$\text{Hue} = \frac{62}{75} \times 100 = 82.5\%$$

For "Blue":

$$\text{Hue} = \frac{56}{92} \times 100 = 61\%$$

To position a color point on the *Color Circle,* first locate in which of the three pie-shaped sectors of the *circle* the color should plot. Imagine the *color circle* as being made up of green, red, and blue sectors (see Figure 10A). The coordinates listed under HUE and GRAY will locate a point in the color sector having -0- in the *Hexagon* table of Figure 8. For example, yellow: Hue= 3.9,Gray=1.9 will be located in the red sector. Magenta: Hue=35, Gray=7.0 will be in the red sector. Cyan: Hue=23, Gray=7.8 will be in the blue sector.

It may be convenient to refer to the *Hexagon* data in Figure 8 while positioning the *Color Circle* coordinates. Yellow will fall in the red sector since -0- is in R column (Figure 8). Hue=4% is 2 scale divisions away from the G=0 line which is the same procedure as for plotting yellow on the *Color Hexagon*. Gray=2% is 1 scale division in from circumference of the circle (see Figure 10b). The magenta point will fall in the red sector: Hue=35% is 17½ scale divisions away from B=0 line, and Gray=7% is 3½ scale divisions in from the circumference of the circle. The cyan point will fall in the blue sector; Hue×23% is 11 scale divisions away from G=0 line, Gray=7.8% is 4 scale divisions in from circumference of the circle.

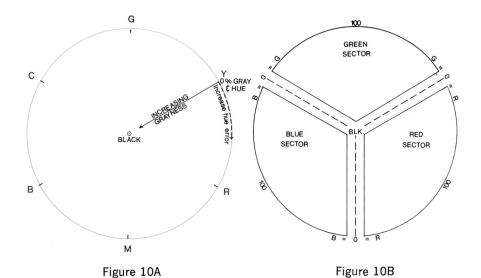

Figure 10A   Figure 10B

Details of plotting on *Color Circle* space

The "Red" (yellow + magenta) value will fall in the red sector; the Hue=76% coordinate is 38 scale divisions away from G=0 line (since lower number in *Hexagon* table appears in the G filter column). The reader should confirm the location of the "Green" (yellow + cyan) and "Blue" (magenta + cyan) coordinates which are plotted in Figure 11.

Interpretation Of The Plots On The Color Circle

The GATF *Color Circle* offers a convenient way to visualize the hue error and grayness of a number of process inks. The six color names printed around the circumference of the circle represent "ideal" colors. The radial lines show relative "grayness" of color. An "ideal"

color (100% purity) would be located on the circumference; a color having 50% grayness would be halfway between the center of the circle and the circumference.

The hue and purity of the same inks on different papers may be determined by plotting on the *Color Circle*. This can be of help in understanding the limits of color gamut, and the potentialities of a set of process inks, trapping conditions, opacity (see Figure 12), and the effect of the surface characteristics of the paper on the color of the printed ink.

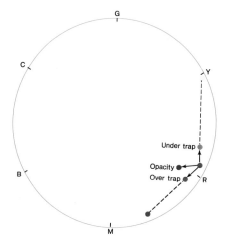

Figure 12. Printing ink properties described by color point on *Color Circle*.

This is done by: (1) predicting the color that should be produced by an overlap of two or three colors; and (2) comparing this with the actual color produced. The color produced by overprinting two inks can be any hue between them. To predict the hue of an overprint, add the red, green, and blue filter densities for each ink. Then compute the predicted hue for the *new* red, green, and blue values using the Hue and Grayness formulas; and plot the predicted values on the chart.

THE COLOR TRIANGLE

The GATF *Subtractive Color Triangle* uses the same data as the *Color Circle* (Figure 9), and presents additional color dimensions graphically. For example, predicted secondary colors formed by overprinting the primaries should fall on straight line drawn between the plots of two primaries. The displacement of the secondary color — above, below, and along the connecting line — is readily interpreted for a particular set of process inks. The *Color Circle* presentation is suitable for evaluation of several sets of process inks by ink makers or printers, while the *Color Triangle* serves to characterize a particular set of process

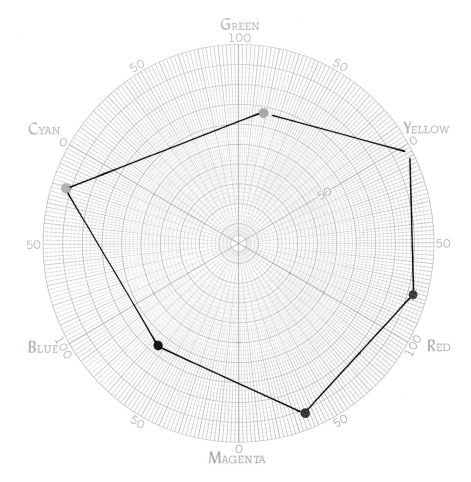

Figure 11. Complete plot on *Color Circle*

20:25

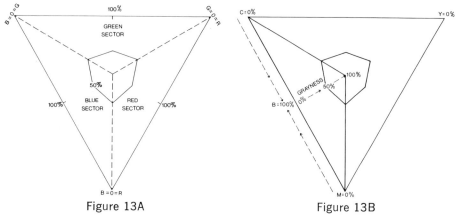

Figure 13A

Figure 13B

Details of plotting on *Color Triangle* space

inks for the pressroom and the color-separation department.

The GATF *Subtractive Color Triangle* originated as a variation of the familiar *Maxwell Triangle*. The *Maxwell Triangle* is not useful for the problems of color reproduction because it describes the effects of additive mixtures of colored light, having red, green, and blue primaries. GATF adapted the *Maxwell Triangle,* to the needs of the graphic arts industry, by substituting the subtractive primaries at the corners of the triangle and inverting it.

The GATF *Subtractive Color Triangle* uses hue-error and grayness co-ordinates in such a way that plots are calculated by the same techniques as for the GATF *Color Circle.*

Plotting Colors On The Triangle

Imagine the *Color Triangle* is made up of green, red, and blue sectors (see Figure 13a. The coordinates listed under HUE and GRAY will locate a color point in the sector having —0— in the *Hexagon Table* (see Figure 8).

Therefore; yellow: Hue=3.9, Gray=1.9 will be located in the red sector; magenta: Hue=35 Gray=7.0 will be located in the red sector; cyan: Hue=23, Gray=7.8 will be in the blue sector. The yellow color will fall in the red sector: Hue=4% or 2 scale units away from G=0 line, and Gray=2% or 1 scale unit in from the edge of the *Triangle.* The magenta point will fall in the red sector: Hue=35% away from B=0 line and Gray=7% or 3½ scale divisions in from edge of triangle. The cyan point will fall in the B sector: Hue=23% away from G=0 line and Gray=7.8% or 4 scale divisions in from edge of triangle. The completed *Color Triangle* is shown in Figure 14.

The color gamut for a particular set of process inks is determined by connecting the yellow, magenta and cyan points to form a triangle.

If the coordinates for "Red" (yellow + magenta), "Green" (yellow + cyan), and "Blue" (magenta + cyan) are typical, they should fall on the connecting lines.

Interpreting Plots On The Color Triangle

A straight line connecting plots of two of the primaries will locate the ideal colors that can be produced by overprinting those colors. When all three primaries are connected to form a triangle, the area enclosed is the gamut of colors that can be produced with the inks plotted. Colors falling outside the lines can be matched in hue, but not in purity.

The total area enclosed on the *Triangle* is not always the most important

factor when considering the gamut of a set of inks. The requirements of a particular job determine the desirable characteristics of the secondary colors.

Almost any set of process inks can produce the desired hues for secondary colors if the strengths are adjusted properly. But different sets of inks will yield different shades of gray. The predicted grayness of a secondary can be found on the *Triangle* by observing where the line connecting the two primaries crosses the 100% hue error line (see Figure 13b). The percentage grayness can be read directly. When this percentage grayness is subtracted from 100, the result is the predicted efficiency of the secondary color.

When the nature of a job dictates that one secondary color satisfy stricter requirements than the others, that secondary color can sometimes be attained by sacrificing purity in the other secondaries.

The *Triangle* can also be used to check two color overprints. Densitometer readings from the actual overprints should be used to plot the overprint colors, following the same method used in plotting the primaries. These plots are than compared to the predictions derived mathematically from the densitometer readings of the printed solids of the primary colors.

The method for deriving the predictions is to add the densitometer readings from the colors which are overprinted. In the case of checking the trapping of

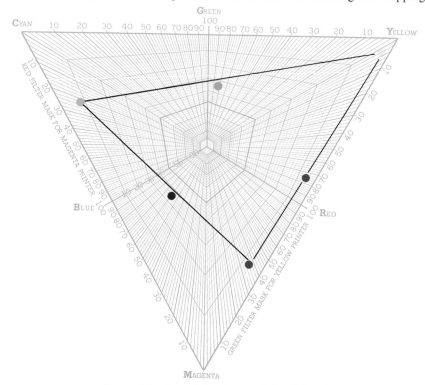

Figure 14. Complete plot on *Color Triangle*

cyan on yellow, the procedure is to add the densitometer readings in Figure 1 for CYAN and YELLOW for *each* filter, and record the sum in the space provided on the *Printing Factors Data Sheet* (see Figure 15). The resulting figures (y + c) are handled in exactly the same way as the primaries to find the hue and grayness co-ordinates. The plot should fall on the line connecting the primaries being mixed by overprinting..

Assuming that yellow is first down: the position of the actual overprint, relative to the ideal prediction, will give the following information:

COLOR	FILTER DENSITIES			HEXAGON H–L and M–L			CIRCLE and TRIANGLE	
	R	G	B	R	G	B	HUE	GRAY
YELLOW	.02	.06	1.04					
MAGENTA								
CYAN	1.02	.30	.08					
Y + M								
Y + C	1.04	.36	1.12	.68	–0–	.76	90	32
M + C								
Y + M + C								
3 – COLOR								

(left margin: PREDICTIONS) SOLIDS)

Figure 15. Extract from printing factors data sheet for trapping predictions.

1. If the actual plot is the same as the ideal prediction, then the printing conditions are ideal (this doesn't happen very often).

2. If the actual plot falls on the segment of the line between yellow and the ideal prediction, then the cyan is undertrapping.

3. If the actual plot falls on the segment of the line between the ideal prediction and the cyan, then the cyan ink is either overtrapping or acting as though it were not fully transparent.

4. If the actual plot falls outside the line (away from Neutral), it indicates an increase or gain in the gloss of the overprinted inks.

5. If the actual plot falls inside the line (toward the center), it indicates a loss of gloss due to possible excess drainage of ink vehicle, or other related causes.

Six masking scales have been printed on the sides of the *Triangle* to simplify finding the masking requirements for a given set of inks. Only a pencil and a straight edge are needed to find the percentage necessary for any mask. The procedure is to draw a straight line from the triangle vertex (the one which is located opposite the masking scale) through the primary color plot to the scale on the opposite side of the *triangle*. For example, the percentage of the, "GREEN FILTER MASK FOR THE YELLOW PRINTER", is found by drawing a line from the cyan vertex through the plotted magenta. The masking percentage is then read at the point where this line crosses the scale. For data given

in Figure 1, the masking percentage "GREEN FILTER MASK FOR YELLOW PRINTER" is 40%; the masking percentage "RED FILTER MASK FOR MAGENTA PRINTER" is 28% (see Figure 16).

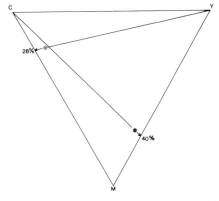

Figure 16. Line connecting apex of *Triangle* with color point, and extended to side opposite, will indicate mask strength required for a specific printing ink.

Theoretically, for perfect color correction, each separation should be masked by images made from two other separations. In most cases, only two main masks are used: red filter mask for the magenta printer; green filter mask for the yellow printer. The scales for these important masks are identified on the diagram by heavy, solid lettering. The errors which can be corrected by other masks are usually too small to cause any serious problems, and are generally ignored. These less important scales are printed on the diagram in light, tinted lettering.

However, the masking percentage shown in Figure 16 by the intersection of the straight line and the masking scale, is correct **only** if the color densities photograph in the separations in the same way as they measure on a color densitometer, i.e. using a tungsten light source.

If pulsed xenon or carbon arc light sources are used, the mask factor for the "GREEN FILTER MASK FOR YELLOW PRINTER" is multiplied by 0.85, and the mask factor "RED FILTER MASK FOR MAGENTA PRINTER" is multiplied by 1.10. The mask percentage values do not give the exact numbers for photographic correction because of differences in the color balance of densitometer light sources, the color balance of the lights used to illuminate the copy, and finally, color balance of the panchromatic films used in separation photography.

The percentage strength for simple single-stage masking may be determined

COLOR	FILTER DENSITIES			MASK FACTORS			
	R	G	B	B/G	G/R	G/B	R/G
YELLOW	.02	.04	1.04			5.5	
MAGENTA	.08	1.14	.45	39 34			7.0
CYAN	1.02	.30	.08	27	30 33		

(left margin: SOLIDS)

Figure 17. Derivation of mask factor values.

from the basic ink matrix data. (See Figure 17). The "GREEN FILTER MASK FOR THE YELLOW PRINTER" is determined by the ratio of the B-filter value to the R-filter value which appear opposite the magenta ink densities.

For tungsten light:

$$\frac{B}{G} \times 100\% = \frac{.45}{1.14} \times 100\% = 39\%$$

For pulsed xenon and carbon arc light sources:

$$39\% \times 0.85 = 34\% \text{ mask strength}$$

These numbers are recorded on the *Printing Factors Data Sheet in the* MASK FACTORS section in the B/G and G/R column. The tungsten value is recorded in the upper left above the diagonal, the pulsed xenon value is recorded below the diagonal (see Figure 17).

The "RED FILTER MASK FOR THE MAGENTA PRINTER" is determined by the ratio of the G-filter value to the R-filter value opposite the cyan ink densities.

For tungsten light:

$$\frac{G}{R} \times 100 = \frac{.30}{1.02} \times 100 = 30\%$$

For pulsed xenon and carbon arc light sources:

$$30\% \times 1.10 = 33\% \text{ mask strength}$$

These numbers are recorded on the *Printing Factors Data Sheet* in the MASK FACTORS, section in the G/R column. Following the same convention as the magenta, cited previously, the tungsten value is recorded in the upper left, above the diagonal; the pulsed xenon value is recorded below the diagonal (see Figure 17).

Some principles of color syntheses can be visualized from plots on the GATF *Color Triangle*. If, for example, a red-shade magenta is substituted for a true magenta: the "GREEN FILTER MASK FOR YELLOW PRINTER" must be increased; the blue (magenta + cyan) will become grayer; the effective color gamut (area enclosed by yellow, magenta, and cyan coordinates) will be reduced.

The reader should confirm how changes in ink hue of a magenta will influence masking and gray attribute of the blue formed by overprinting cyan and magenta.

SUMMARY

All three GATF color diagrams have now been improved to make them more useful.

The GATF *Color Hexagon* is the easiest of the color diagrams to use, since no computations are necessary to plot data. It is best suited for quality control or press control of the separate primaries and overprint hues.

The GATF *Color Circle* is best suited to show the hue and grayness of: (1) actual ink colors in relation to ideal colors; and (2) different sets of process ink. The color gamut for a particular set of process inks is represented by the area enclosed by the six-sided polygon.

The GATF *Color Triangle* likewise uses hue and grayness coordinates. However, it also shows the gamut of colors possible with a given set of inks, and directly predicts ideal overprint colors theoretically attainable with that set of inks. By comparing *Color Triangle* plots of the actual overprints to the "ideal" predictions, shifts in ink gloss and improper trapping can be detected. The masking scales printed on the perimeter of the *Color Triangle* aid in determining color correction.

There are additional dimensions of printing inks and printing papers that may be determined using densitometer readings. *Research Progress Number 60*, "Paper Surface Efficiency (PSE)," describes calculations and applications in detail.

The GATF *Color and Printing Factors Computer* has formulas for calculating printing ink efficiency, ink transparency, trapping, and additivity characteristics. This simplifies the mathematical steps for completing the GATF *Color and Printing Factors Data Sheet*.

Textbook #509, *Color Separation Photography* and *Research Progress No. 67* are useful references for color separation procedures using actual printing inks for corrective masking check points.

The continued improvement of the diagrams depends on their application in color reproduction. Only actual use in plants can determine their usefulness and locate any shortcomings which may still exist. The Foundation welcomes comments concerning the application of these colors diagrams and suggestions for improving the devices.

AVAILABILITY OF DIAGRAMS
and
PRINTING FACTORS CALCULATOR

GATF produces and distributes the diagrams as a service to the graphic arts industry. Each chart is put up in pads of 100 and are priced at $3.25 per pad (non-members $5.25 per pad). The *GATF Color and Printing Factors Data Sheet* is also available at the same price. This form provides for an orderly assembly of the data necessary for easy use of the charts, as well as space for recording pertinent data about press conditions.

The GATF *Color and Printing Factors Computer* is available at $3.00 to members; $6.00 to non-members.

References

1. *Research Progress Number 38,* "The Evaluation of Process Inks"
2. *Research Progress Number 51,* "How To Test The Effect Of Paper Color On Process Color Reproductions"
3. *Research Progress Number 60,* "A New Method Of Rating The Efficiency Of Paper For Color Reproduction"
4. *Txb, # 509,* "Color Separation Photography"
5. *Research Progress Number 83,* "Gray Balance Chart"

GRAPHIC ARTS TECHNICAL FOUNDATION

GATF GRAY BALANCE CHART

By F. L. COX

IN BRIEF

The GATF Gray Balance Chart was developed to equate halftone film dot area to the requirements for gray balance, using process inks for full-color reproduction. The differences in ink, paper, platemaking and printing press operation (including ink rotation) may be resolved by reproducing the GATF Gray Balance Chart under actual production conditions. The Gray Balance Chart films for yellow, magenta, and cyan platemaking are available through GATF in the form of negatives or positives. In addition to the derivation of gray balance requirements for a specific ink, plate, paper, and press combination, the gray balance chart films incorporate several quality control devices created by GATF for visually checking dot gain, slur, doubling and other factors which determine print quality.

INTRODUCTION

A basic requirement for a full-color reproduction process is the correct duplication of a scale of grays when printing the three prime colors: yellow, magenta, and cyan. It is generally recognized that equal dot area relationships of yellow, magenta, and cyan do not produce a neutral result.[1, 2, 3, 4, 7, 8] A quick examination of the gradient scale "3C," shown in Figure 1, illustrates the hue that results when equal halftone dot areas are printed. The "off-neutrality" in this printing is representative of the materials and techniques used in producing *this particular* report. A distinct area interrelationship must exist for dot areas of yellow, magenta, and cyan to print as neutral gray steps.

Two courses of action are followed customarily to produce gray balance: (1) the dot values are adjusted by dot etching the half-tone positive; or (2) the cameraman adjusts the halftone gradation scale by trial and error until the gray scale used in color separation reproduces as neutral. The GATF Gray Balance Chart enables one to select neutral printed areas visually, then relate these selections to the halftoning operation.

It is possible to read the halftone film densities for each color, and then relate these values to continuous-tone density, rather than convert percent area into equivalent halftone density by graphical means.

DISCUSSION

Just as efficient color masking, per se, may not achieve proper gray balance, the accurate reproduction of the neutral scale does not guarantee high quality color reproduction. The proper color masking *and* gray balance tone control must coexist. Color correction by masking may be analysed by known techniques[4], and precedes use of the GATF Gray Balance Chart. The Gray Balance Chart supplements color scale analyses, and provides a method for adjusting the tone scales or gradation for quality color reproduction.

There are many interrelated variables that influence gray balance. These variables include ink strength, spectral characteristic of the pigments, paper surface properties, ink transparency, trapping, ink rotation, platemaking dot-gain (or sharpening)[5], and press characteristics.[6] These variables may be evaluated by one printing of the chart, and the results should be

valid until one or more variables change (e.g. paper, ink, rotation of colors, etc.).

DESCRIPTION

The GATF Gray Balance Chart films have a screen ruling of 150 lines per inch, and the entire chart may be reproduced within a 6″ x 7½″ area. The GATF Gray Balance Chart (Figure 1) consists of five blocks of squares. Each square is composed of a different combination of 150-line tints of yellow, magenta, and cyan. The dot area value of the cyan tint is solid, 75%, 50%, 30% and 15%, respectively, in each of the five blocks. The value of the cyan tint for each block is shown adjacent to the first square of each block (upper left corner). The dot area values of the yellow and magenta tints change in 5% steps in four of the blocks. Below the 15% dot they change in 3% steps. The numbers printed adjacent to each row of yellow and magenta tints indicate the "Equivalent Dot Area" of the respective tints in that row, as measured in the negatives or in the positives of the chart. Additional print quality devices include the GATF Dot Gain and Slur Target, GATF Compact Color Bar, GATF Star Target, and a replica of the GATF Color Reproduction Guide with 10% tint increments. This replica chart

RESEARCH PROGRESS

Published by
GRAPHIC ARTS TECHNICAL FOUNDATION, Inc.
4615 Forbes Avenue, Pittsburgh, Pa. 15213
©Graphic Arts Technical Foundation, Inc., 1969
Number 83, March, 1969
Edited by Charles Shapiro
Litho in U.S.A.

of primary and secondary colors may be used by the camera department for color separation and masking evaluation.

USING THE GATF GRAY BALANCE CHART

The key to gray balance is the cyan printer regardless of ink rotation. The object of the chart evaluation is to locate the tint areas of yellow and magenta which neutralize the tints of cyan ink (the combination of yellow and magenta produces red, the color complementary to cyan). The visual selection of yellow + magenta "squares" may be facilitated by viewing the square through a "window" punched in a gray scale, as demonstrated in Figure 5. The neutral squares selected by visual appraisal may be checked with a reflection densitometer. Equal red, green, and blue filter densitly readings indicate approximate neutrality.[7] If different sets of process inks, or different papers are used in a plant, the Gray Balance Charts should be printed with as many combinations as is practical.

APPLICATION

It is possible to derive empirical equations for gray balance calculation by a mathematical technique called regression analysis.[8] Perhaps a more familiar approach is by graphical presentation. The Kodak *Bulletin for the Graphic Arts*, No. 15, p. 9, illustrates a graphical relationship for cyan, magenta, and yellow halftones for both reflective and transparency copy reproductions. These relationships are valid for a specific ink, paper and printing factors relationship, and are reproduced in abbreviated form

in Figure 2. The graphical relationship in Figure 2 shows that a 30% cyan dot will neutralize a "red" formed by a 20% yellow dot plus a 20% magenta dot. Note that the 80% cyan dot complements a "red" resulting from printing a 68% yellow dot plus a 68% magenta dot.

There may be as many as 24 different ink rotation combinations using yellow, magenta, cyan, and black inks. A common lithographic sequence for 2-color running is magenta and cyan followed by yellow and black. This sequence, i.e. yellow 3rd down, was used to test the gray balance chart at the GATF Laboratories. Analysis of the results of this printing sequence, viewed under a Macbeth Examolite, showed the following percent dot area relationships.

Cyan %	Magenta %	Yellow %
100	75	70
75	50	55
50	30	35
30	15	25
15	6	12

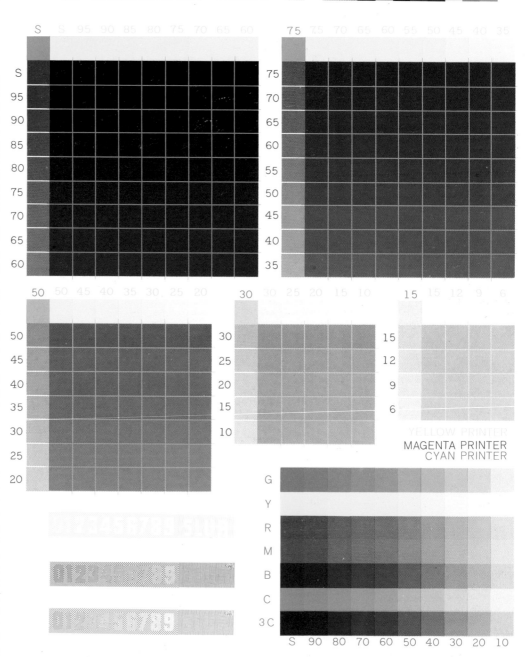

Figure 1. Color Reproduction of the GATF Gray Balance Chart. Note the 3-color scale in the lower right corner (3C) is formed by yellow, magenta, and cyan dot areas which are equal in size.

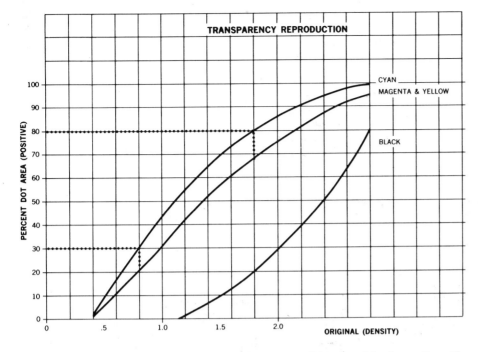

Figure 2. Cyan, Magenta, and Yellow Tone-Scale Relationship for a Specific Ink, Paper, and Printing Combination. Graph 1 in Kodak's Bulletin for the Graphic Arts, No. 15, *shows a method of halftone positive exposure control.*

The results are shown graphically in Figure 3 using a similar cyan "Percent Dot Area (Positive)" versus "Original (Density)" relationship mentioned in the previously cited Kodak *Bulletin for the Graphic Arts.*

The reader may desire to determine the gray balance for the chart shown in Figure 1 of this *Research Progress.* The percentage values for the yellow and magenta tints may be plotted in the space provided in Figure 4. This would illustrate the gray balance for the printing factors inherent in printing *this particular* report.

As with other color control guides, the solid patches of the GATF Gray Balance Chart can be used to: (1) measure the solid ink densities; (2) evaluate ink trapping; and (3) calculate mask percentages. Complete details on these procedures may be found in GATF's Txb No. 509, *Color Separation Photography.*

The green, yellow, red, magenta, blue, and cyan tint blocks at the lower right of the Gray Balance Chart may be "color separated" with reflective copy. Doing this will indicate if proper mask curves have been used, and show if the proportionality failure has been corrected. This evaluation procedure is discussed in GATF's *Research Progress* No. 67, "The New GATF Color Reproduction Guide."

The correct tone scale, or gradation for gray balance requirements, may be arrived at by three photographic techniques. One method involves contrast or tone adjustment at the separation negative step.[9] The shadow or upper-middletone contrast may be adjusted by use of non-image flash techniques. This method permits using a standard halftone positive procedure.

A second method of tone control involves the "Gevarex" system of constant development and varying exposure technique.[10] This system may be adapted for constant machine processing of continuous tone positives for letterpress or gravure, or constant machine processing of offset screened positives. Once the tone-control requirements are specified, the desired tone scale is obtained by the proper balancing of a two-part (hence, variable) exposure system using yellow and blue light exposures. As in the first example, this Gevarex system permits standard halftone screening procedures.

A third method of tone reproduction control involves halftone photography using the magenta contact screen.[11] The desired tone scale can be "shaped" to satisfy the gray balance by proper application of "CC" (color compensating) filters for contrast control, and supplemental exposures for highlight and shadow rendering. It is entirely possible that three halftone curve shapes would be required to satisfy some printing conditions (see Figure 3).

SUMMARY

The GATF Gray Balance Chart establishes empirically determined tone correction for gray balance in color reproduction. Since color correction is the product of color correction masking, and does not necessarily incorporate tone correction, *tone control* techniques are distinct and separate from color correction masking. The information obtained from gray balance evaluation may be used to predict gradation curve shape. This method is applicable to the electronic as well as photographic masking procedures.

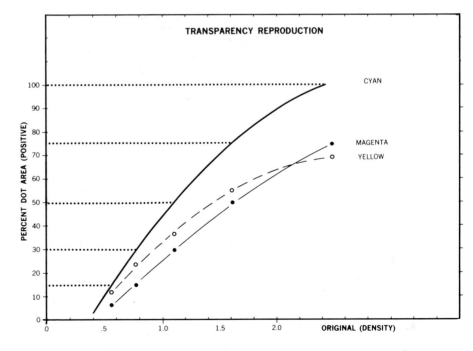

Figure 3. When the cyan tone scale is selected, the yellow and magenta curve shapes may be related to the cyan curve by using the printed chart.

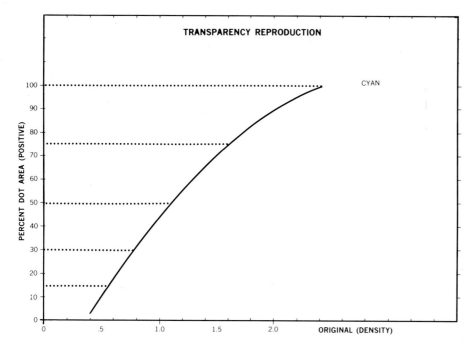

TRANSPARENCY REPRODUCTION

CYAN

Figure 4. This chart may be used to plot yellow and magenta dot-percent values, using the reproduction printed in Figure 1. The three-aim-point method of tone control, using A, M, and B density values, requires positioning of these values on the horizontal scale. (Typical values might be: A = 0.40, M = 1.30, and B = 2.40.) Once the gray balance is determined, the A, M, and B patches may be used for halftoning check points.

WARNING

The negatives and positives of the GATF Gray Balance Chart, as sold by GATF, are made for stripping into flats for making plates. They should not be used for making duplicate negatives or positives by contact printing. If contact films are made from them, the dot value will be distorted. To produce your own Gray Balance Charts, always use *original* negatives or *original* positives of the Gray Balance Chart, as supplied by GATF.

ACKNOWLEDGMENTS

The author wishes to acknowledge the work of former GATF staff members who did much of the original work in developing the GATF Gray Balance Chart. They are Frank Preucil now with RCA, and Zenon Elyjiw now with R.I.T.

HOW TO OBTAIN GRAY BALANCE CHARTS

The GATF Gray Balance Chart can be obtained from:

Graphic Arts Technical Foundation
4615 Forbes Avenue
Pittsburgh, Pennsylvania 15213

They are prepared to laboratory specifications and are supplied as film negatives or positives. The price to members is $15.50 ($30.50 to non-members) per set including postage and handling. It is necessary to specify whether negatives or positives are desired.

REFERENCES

1. Wulff, A., and Jorgensen, H.O., "An Analysis of the Separation Stages in Multi-Colored Production," The Graphic College of Denmark, Copenhagen, July, 1964.
2. Hertz, F. A., and Archer, H. B., "A Method of Direct Screen Exposure & Control," 1968 TAGA Proceedings, pp. 356-363.
3. Preucil, F., "Some Additive Color Principles and the Control of Neutral Group in Process Reproduction," Advances in Printing Science and Technology, Vol. 3, Pergamon Press, London, 1964, p. 76.
4. Elyjiw, Z., and Preucil, F., "The New GATF Color Reproduction Guide," GATF Research Progress No. 67.
5. Preucil, F., Elyjiw, Z., Reed, R., "The GATF Dot Gain Scale," GATF Research Progress No. 69.
6. Jorgensen, G., "The LTF Star Target," LTF Research Progress No. 52.
7. Clapper, F. R., "Balanced Halftone Separations for Process Color," 1959, TAGA Proceedings, p. 184.
8. Pobboravsky, I., "Methods of Computing Ink Amounts to Produce a Scale of Neutral for Photomechanical Reproduction," 1966 TAGA Proceedings, pp. 23-25.
9. "DuPont Process Color Specification and Control System," Photo Products Department, pp. 26-29, E. I. DuPont de Nemours & Company, Wilmington, Delaware 19898.
10. "The Gevarex System," Agfa-Gevaert Inc., 275 North Street, Teterboro, New Jersey 07608.
11. "Halftone Methods for the Graphic Arts," pp. 23-27, KODAK Publication No. Q-3, Eastman Kodak Company, Rochester, New York 14650.

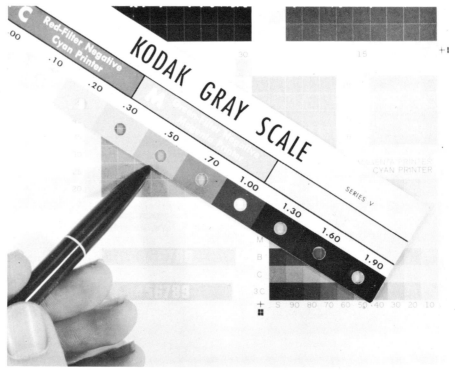

Figure 5. Neutral squares are selected by visual match to a gray scale.